D1201467

TEACHER EDITION

HMH

GO MATH!

Middle School | Grade 8

Edward B. Burger • Juli K. Dixon
Timothy D. Kanold • Matthew R. Larson
Steven J. Leinwand • Martha E. Sandoval-Martinez

© Houghton Mifflin Harcourt Publishing Company
Image Credits: ©TomGrubbe/Flickr/Getty Images

Cover Image Credits: ©Tom Grubbe/Flickr/Getty Images

2018 Edition
Copyright © by Houghton Mifflin Harcourt Publishing Company

All rights reserved. No part of this work may be reproduced or transmitted in any
form or by any means, electronic or mechanical, including photocopying or
recording, or by any information storage or retrieval system, without the prior
written permission of the copyright owner unless such copying is expressly
permitted by federal copyright law. Requests for permission to make copies
of any part of the work should be submitted through our Permissions website at
https://customercare.hmhco.com/contactus/Permissions.html or mailed to
Houghton Mifflin Harcourt Publishing Company, Attn: Intellectual Property Licensing,
9400 Southpark Center Loop, Orlando, Florida 32819-8647.

Printed in the U.S.A.

ISBN 978-1-328-76115-6

1 2 3 4 5 6 7 8 9 10 0607 26 25 24 23 22 21 20 19 18 17

4500658810   A B C D E F G

If you have received these materials as examination copies free of charge,
Houghton Mifflin Harcourt Publishing Company retains title to the materials and
they may not be resold. Resale of examination copies is strictly prohibited.

Possession of this publication in print format does not entitle users to convert this
publication, or any portion of it, into electronic format.

Authors

Edward B. Burger, Ph.D., is the president of Southwestern University, a former Francis Christopher Oakley Third Century Professor of Mathematics at Williams College, and a former vice provost at Baylor University. He has authored or coauthored more than sixty-five articles, books, and video series; delivered over five hundred addresses and workshops throughout the world; and made more than fifty radio and television appearances. He is a Fellow of the American Mathematical Society as well as having earned many national honors, including the Robert Foster Cherry Award for Great Teaching in 2010. In 2012, Microsoft Education named him a "Global Hero in Education."

Juli K. Dixon, Ph.D., is a Professor of Mathematics Education at the University of Central Florida. She has taught mathematics in urban schools at the elementary, middle, secondary, and post-secondary levels. She is an active researcher and speaker with numerous publications and conference presentations. Key areas of focus are deepening teachers' content knowledge and communicating and justifying mathematical ideas. She is a past chair of the NCTM Student Explorations in Mathematics Editorial Panel and member of the Board of Directors for the Association of Mathematics Teacher Educators.

Timothy D. Kanold, Ph.D., is an award-winning international educator, author, and consultant. He is a former superintendent and director of mathematics and science at Adlai E. Stevenson High School District 125 in Lincolnshire, Illinois. He is a past president of the National Council of Supervisors of Mathematics (NCSM) and the Council for the Presidential Awardees of Mathematics (CPAM). He has served on several writing and leadership commissions for NCTM during the past decade. He presents motivational professional development seminars with a focus on developing professional learning communities (PLC's) to improve the teaching, assessing, and learning of students. He has recently authored nationally recognized articles, books, and textbooks for mathematics education and school leadership, including *What Every Principal Needs to Know about the Teaching and Learning of Mathematics*.

Matthew R. Larson, Ph.D., is the K-12 mathematics curriculum specialist for the Lincoln Public Schools and served on the Board of Directors for the National Council of Teachers of Mathematics from 2010-2013. He is a past chair of NCTM's Research Committee and was a member of NCTM's Task Force on Linking Research and Practice. He is the author of several books on implementing the Common Core Standards for Mathematics. He has taught mathematics at the secondary and college levels and held an appointment as an honorary visiting associate professor at Teachers College, Columbia University.

Steven J. Leinwand is a Principal Research Analyst at the American Institutes for Research (AIR) in Washington, D.C., and has over 30 years in leadership positions in mathematics education. He is past president of the National Council of Supervisors of Mathematics and served on the NCTM Board of Directors. He is the author of numerous articles, books, and textbooks and has made countless presentations with topics including student achievement, reasoning, effective assessment, and successful implementation of standards.

Martha E. Sandoval-Martinez is a mathematics instructor at El Camino College in Torrance, California. She was previously a Math Specialist at the University of California at Davis and former instructor at Santa Ana College, Marymount College, and California State University, Long Beach. In her current and former positions, she has worked extensively to improve fundamental pre-algebra and algebra skills in students who have historically struggled with mathematics.

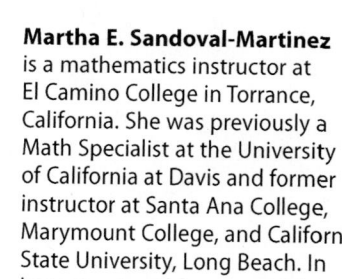

© Houghton Mifflin Harcourt Publishing Company • Image Credits: (Timothy D. Kanold) © Photo courtesy of Tim Kanold; (Juli K. Dixon) © Photo courtesy of Juli Dixon; (Martha E. Sandoval) © Carlos Delgado/AP Images for HMH.

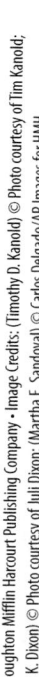

Program Reviewers

Sharon Brown
Instructional Staff Developer
Pinellas County Schools
St. Petersburg, FL

Maureen Carrion
Math Staff Developer
Brentwood UFSD
Brentwood, NY

Jackie Cruse
Math Coach
Ferrell GPA
Tampa, FL

John Esser
Secondary Mathematics
Coordinator
Racine Unified School District
Racine, WI

Donald Hoessler
Math Teacher
Discovery Middle School
Orlando, Florida

Becky (Rebecca) Jones, M.Ed.
NBCT EA-Math
Orange County Public Schools
Orlando, FL

Sheila D.P. Lea, MSA
Ben L. Smith High School
Greensboro, NC

Toni Lwanga
Newell Barney Jr. High
Queen Creek Unified School District
Queen Creek, AZ

Tiffany J. Mack
Charles A. Lindbergh Middle School
Peoria District #150
Peoria, IL

Jean Sterner
Thurgood Marshall Fundamental
Middle School
Pinellas County Schools
St. Petersburg, FL

Mona Toncheff
Math Content Specialist
Phoenix Union High School District
Phoenix, AZ

Kevin Voepel
Mathematics & Professional
Development Coordinator
Ferguson-Florissant School District
Florissant, MO

© Houghton Mifflin Harcourt Publishing Company

MODULE 1 Real Numbers

MODULE 2 Exponents and Scientific Notation

© Houghton Mifflin Harcourt Publishing Company • Image Credits: (t) ©Daniel Hershman/Getty Images; (b) ©Eyebyte/Alamy Images

UNIT 2 Proportional and Nonproportional Relationships and Functions

MODULE 3 Proportional Relationships

MODULE 4 Nonproportional Relationships

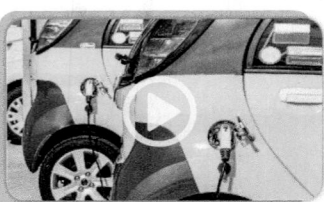

© Houghton Mifflin Harcourt Publishing Company • Image Credits: (t) ©Angelo Giampiccolo/Shutterstock; (b) ©viappy/Shutterstock

 **MODULE 5** # Writing Linear Equations

 **MODULE 6** # Functions

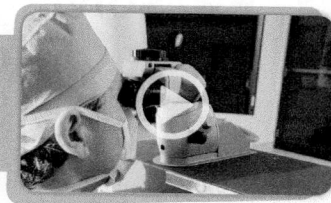

© Houghton Mifflin Harcourt Publishing Company • Image Credits: (t) ©Yellow Dog Productions/Getty Images; (b) ©Huntstock/Getty Images

UNIT 3 Solving Equations and Systems of Equations

MODULE 7 Solving Linear Equations

MODULE 8 Solving Systems of Linear Equations

© Houghton Mifflin Harcourt Publishing Company • Image Credits: (a) ©Image Source/Alamy Images; (b) ©Kenny Ferguson/Alamy Images

UNIT  4 Transformational Geometry

MODULE 9 Transformations and Congruence

MODULE 10 Transformations and Similarity

© Houghton Mifflin Harcourt Publishing Company • Image Credits: (t) ©Gregory K. Scott/Getty Images

UNIT 5 Measurement Geometry

MODULE 11 Angle Relationships in Parallel Lines and Triangles

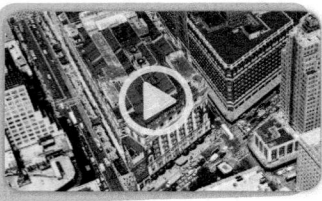

MODULE 12 The Pythagorean Theorem

© Houghton Mifflin Harcourt Publishing Company • Image Credits: (t) ©Nitro Travel Images/Alamy Images; (b) ©Yuri Arcurs/Shutterstock

MODULE 13 Volume

© Houghton Mifflin Harcourt Publishing Company

UNIT 6 Statistics

MODULE 14 Scatter Plots

MODULE 15 Two-Way Tables

© Houghton Mifflin Harcourt Publishing Company • Image Credits: (b) ©John Rowley/Getty Images

Working as a Professional Learning Community

Great teaching materials do not provide great education in and of themselves. Educators who collaborate in Professional Learning Communities can have a profound impact on their students. As a middle school mathematics teacher, your grade-level or course-based collaborative team is the engine that can drive your professional learning and the professional learning community (PLC) process. You and your colleagues hold a critical key to helping *all* students successfully learn the mathematics standards in your middle school. Through your hard work and the work of your collaborative team, effective instruction, assessment, and intervention practices become more coherent and focused.

Coherence implies that the standards in each unit are more than a mere checklist of disconnected content; rather, they are organized into meaningful progressions of content that highlight the unity of the mathematics curriculum at your grade level, and throughout each grade of middle school.

Focus is provided in order to allow *time* for your students to master the intricate complexities of the content progressions across grades. Helping your students to better understand the coherent and focused aspects of the standards becomes one of the major benefits of working closely with your colleagues in a PLC school culture.

The National Board for Professional Teaching Standards states the following:

> Seeing themselves as partners with other teachers, [faculty members] are dedicated to improving the profession. They care about the quality of teaching in their schools, and, to this end, their collaboration with colleagues is continuous and explicit. They recognize that collaborating in a professional learning community contributes to their own professional growth, as well as to the growth of their peers, for the benefit of student learning. Teachers promote the ideal that working collaboratively increases knowledge, reflection, and quality of practice and benefits the instructional program. (*Mathematics Standards for Teachers of Students Ages 11–18+*, ©2010, p. 75)

As a highly accomplished middle school mathematics teacher you understand the value in the practice of effective collaboration with your colleagues. Teacher collaboration is not the icing on top of the proverbial cake of your work. Instead, it is the egg in the batter, holding the cake together.

As your school becomes a learning institution for the adults, it also becomes a learning institution dedicated to preparing all students for the future. The process of your collaboration in a PLC culture capitalizes on the fact that you and your colleagues come together with diverse experiences and knowledge to create a whole that is larger than the sum of the parts. Teacher collaboration is the solution to your sustained professional learning—the ongoing and never-ending process of growth necessary to meet the classroom demands and the unit-by-unit mathematics content described in our series.

—Tim Kanold, Program Author

Program Resources

Plan

Online Teacher Resources

Access a full suite of teaching resources online—plan, present, and manage classes, assignments, and activities.

 **MySmartPlanner** Easily plan your classes, create and view assignments, and access all program resources with your online, customizable planning tool.

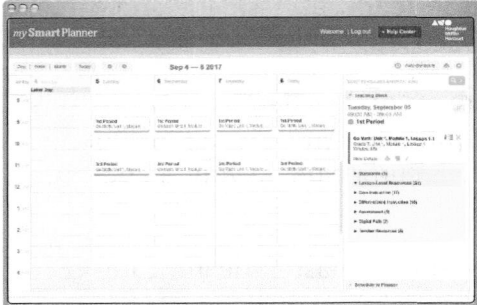

Professional Development Videos

Author Juli Dixon models successful teaching practices and strategies in actual classroom settings.

 **QR Codes** Scan with your smartphone or device to jump directly from your print book to online videos and other resources.

Planning and Pacing Guide

Access pacing suggestions for the course, unit projects for end-of-course review, and end-of-year activities that preview the next course.

Engage and Explore

Real-World Videos Engage students with interesting and relevant applications of the mathematical content of each module.

 **Animated Math** Online interactive simulations, tools, and games help students actively learn and practice key concepts.

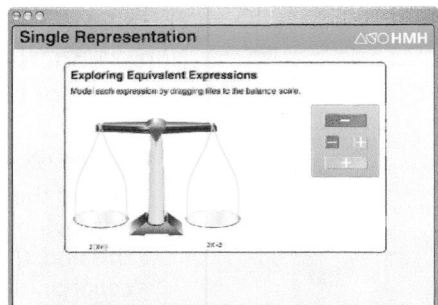

Explore Activities

Students interactively explore new concepts using a variety of tools and approaches.

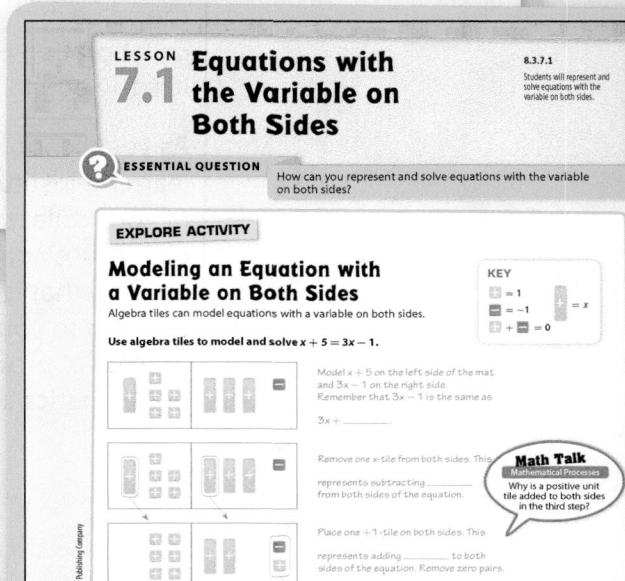

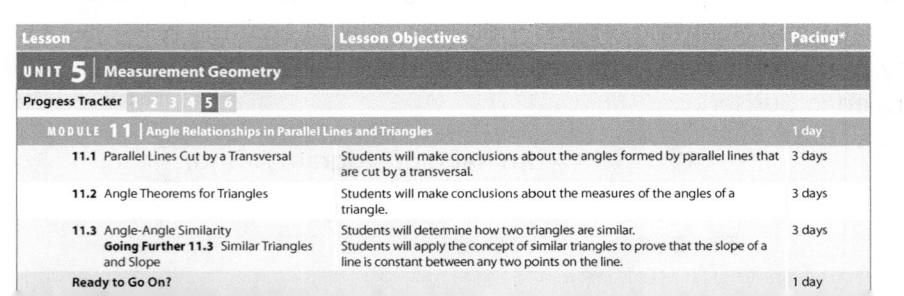

PLANNING AND PACING GUIDE
Instructional Path

UNIT **5**

Lesson	Lesson Objectives	Pacing*
UNIT 5 Measurement Geometry		
Progress Tracker 1 2 3 4 5 6		
MODULE 11 Angle Relationships in Parallel Lines and Triangles		1 day
11.1 Parallel Lines Cut by a Transversal	Students will make conclusions about the angles formed by parallel lines that are cut by a transversal.	3 days
11.2 Angle Theorems for Triangles	Students will make conclusions about the measures of the angles of a triangle.	3 days
11.3 Angle-Angle Similarity **Going Further 11.3** Similar Triangles and Slope	Students will determine how two triangles are similar. Students will apply the concept of similar triangles to prove that the slope of a line is constant between any two points on the line.	3 days
Ready to Go On?		1 day

© Houghton Mifflin Harcourt Publishing Company

⏻ Teach

Teacher's Edition Support students with differentiated leveled questions, teaching tips, additional activities, and more.

Math On the Spot video tutorials, featuring program authors Dr. Edward Burger and Martha Sandoval-Martinez, accompany every example in the textbook and give students step-by-step instructions and explanations of key math concepts.

Present engaging content on a multitude of devices, including tablets and interactive whiteboards.

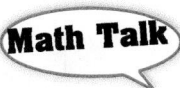

Continually monitor and assess student progress with integrated formative assessment.

Differentiation & Intervention Print Resources

Support all learners with Differentiated Instruction Resources, including

- **Leveled Practice and Problem Solving**
- **Reteach**
- **Reading Strategies**
- **Success for English Learners**
- **Challenge**

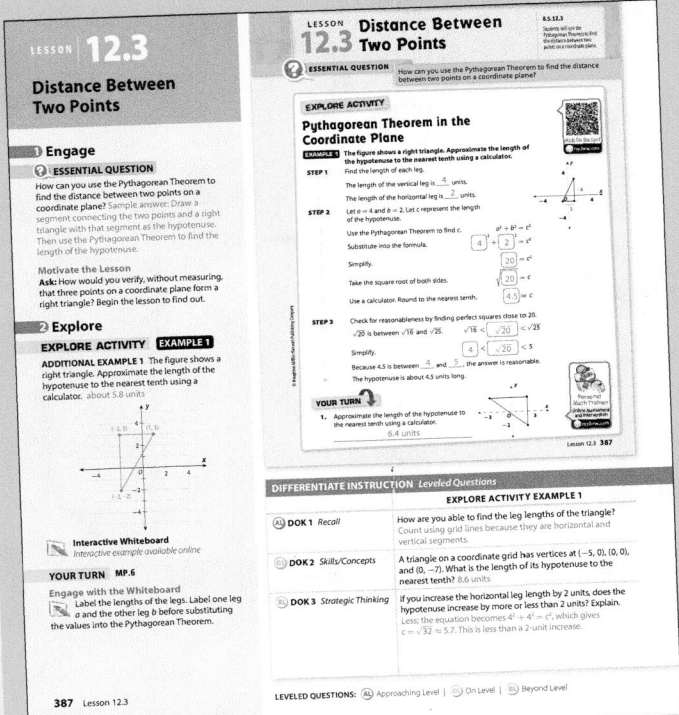

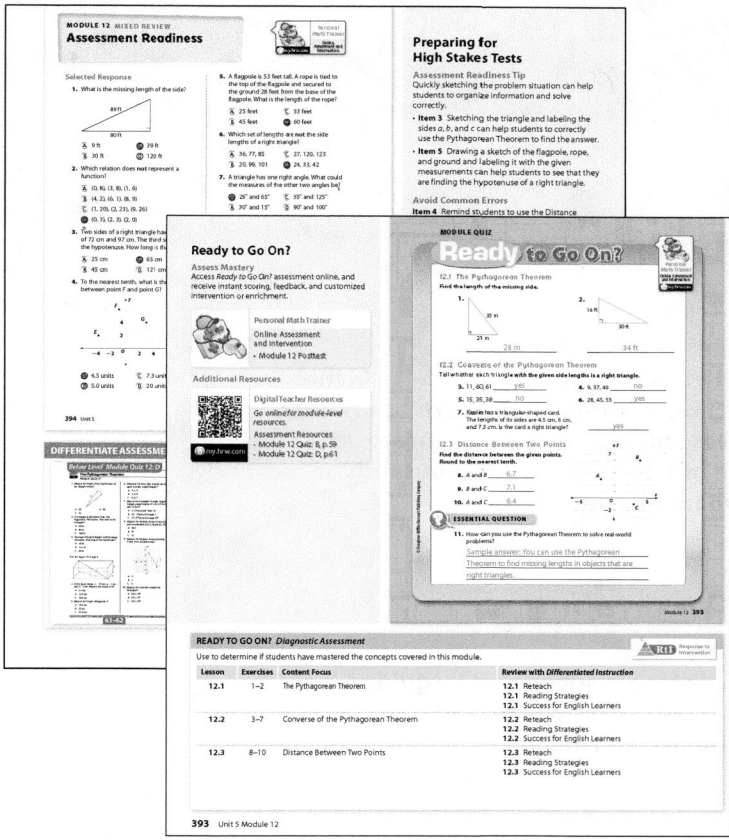

⏻ Assessment

Raise the bar with homework and practice that incorporates higher-order thinking and mathematical processes in every lesson.

Assessment Readiness

Prepare students for success on standardized tests with practice in short-answer and multiple-choice formats at every module and unit.

Assessment Print Resources

Meet diverse needs with these assessment resources

- **Leveled Module Quizzes**
- **Leveled Unit Tests**
- **Unit Performance Tasks**
- **Placement, Diagnostic, and Quarterly Benchmark Tests**

Online Intervention Turn the page for an overview of the Personal Math Trainer online assessment and intervention system.

© Houghton Mifflin Harcourt Publishing Company

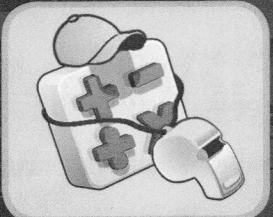

Personal Math Trainer

The Personal Math Trainer provides online practice, homework, assessments, and intervention and allows you to monitor student progress through reports and alerts. You can create and customize assignments aligned to specific lessons.

⏻ Online Assessment and Intervention System

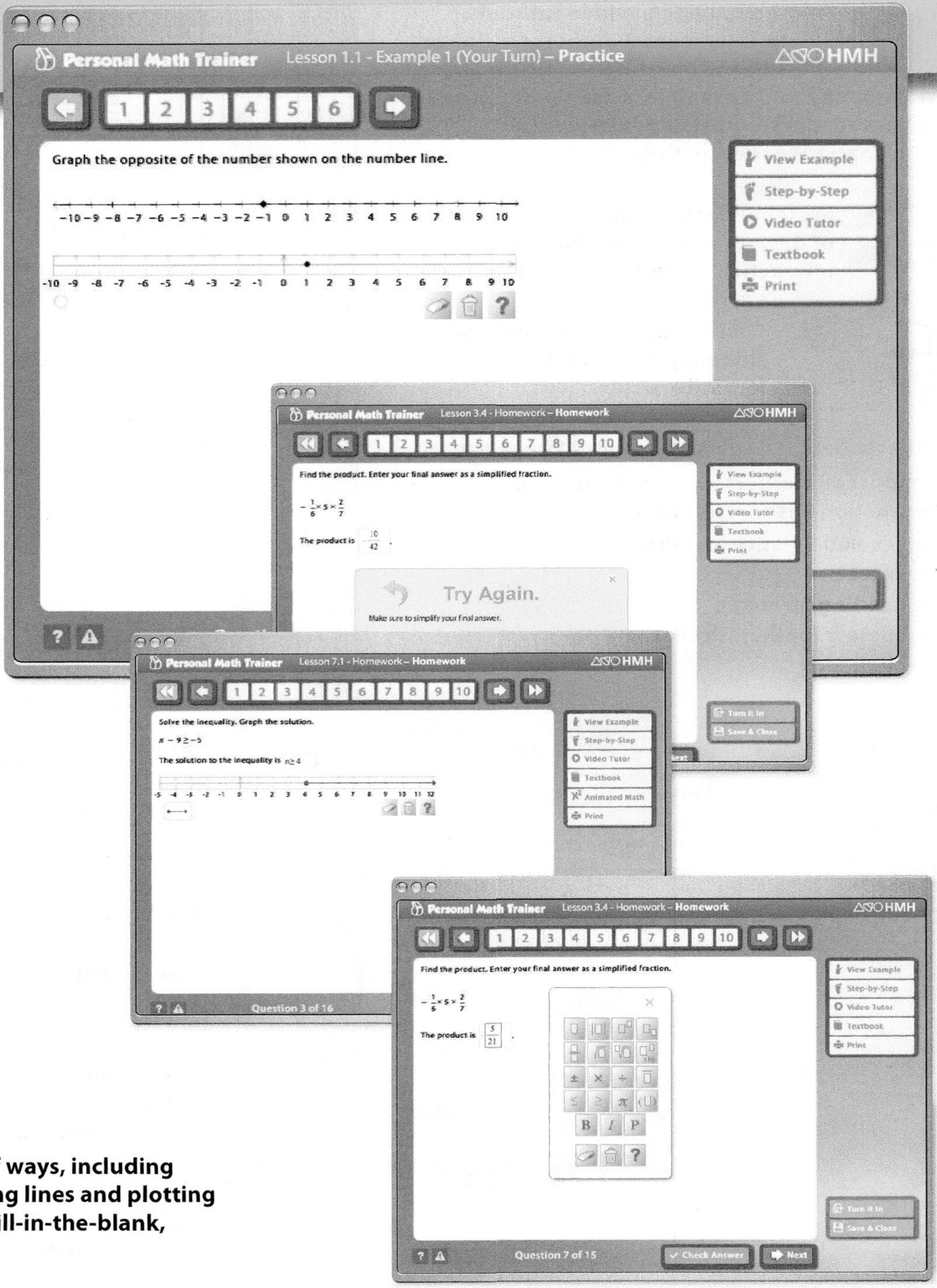

Student Practice

With direct links at point-of-use in the eStudent Edition, Personal Math Trainer gives students access to almost unlimited practice with thousands of dynamic items.

Learning Aids

Students are supported by guided examples, step-by-step solutions, video tutorials, and helpful feedback.

Homework

Personal Math Trainer provides a ready-to-assign homework assignment for every lesson in the course! Let Personal Math Trainer automatically grade homework and generate reports so you can focus where your students need help the most!

Authentic Items

Students can respond to items in a variety of ways, including entering expressions and equations, graphing lines and plotting points, and completing explanations using fill-in-the-blank, short answer, and drop-down menus.

© Houghton Mifflin Harcourt Publishing Company

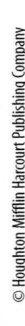

Workflow Editor — Book

HMH

Book | Standard | New Exercise

? | Save

Book:
HMH Go Math Middle School Grade 7

Unit:
Unit 3. Expressions, Equations, and Inequalities

Module:
6. Expressions and Equations

Lesson:
6.A. Are You Ready?

Objective:
N/A

DOK:
All

Exercises: List by
6.A.1 Are You Ready Question
6.A.2 Are You Ready Question
6.A.3 Are You Ready Question
6.A.4 Are You Ready Question
6.A.5 Are You Ready Question
6.A.6 Are You Ready Question
6.A.7 Are You Ready Question

Assignment Title:
Module 6 - Are You Ready?

Assignment Type:
Tests and Quizzes

Assignment Style:
Middle School

14 Exercises in Assignment
6.A.1 Are You Ready Question
6.A.2 Are You Ready Question
6.A.3 Are You Ready Question
6.A.4 Are You Ready Question
6.A.5 Are You Ready Question
6.A.6 Are You Ready Question
6.A.7 Are You Ready Question
6.A.8 Are You Ready Question
6.A.9 Are You Ready Question
6.A.10 Are You Ready Question
6.A.11 Are You Ready Question

View

Edit | Preview

Personal Math Trainer Module 4 - Are You Ready? – Assessment HMH

1 2 3 4 5 6 7 8 9 10

Enter the ordered pair for the point.

Print

The ordered pair for point A is (4 , 1) .

Question 7 of 10

Resource	Action		
Mod 1 Adding and Subtracting Integers - Pretest	View	Assign	Edit
1.1 Adding Integers with the Same Sign - Homework	View	Assign	Edit
1.2 Adding Integers with Different Signs - Homework	View	Assign	Edit
1.3 Subtracting Integers - Homework	View	Assign	Edit
1.4 Applying Addition and Subtraction of Integers - Homework	View	Assign	Edit
Mod 1 Adding and Subtracting Integers - Posttest	View	Assign	Edit
Mod 1 Adding and Subtracting Integers - Assessment Readiness	View	Assign	Edit
	View	Assign	Edit
	View	Assign	Edit
	View	Assign	Edit
	View	Assign	Edit
	View	Assign	Edit
	View	Assign	Edit
	View	Assign	Edit

Personal Math Trainer Intervention HMH

11 12

Divide. Enter the quotient in simplest form.

$4\frac{3}{8} \div 5\frac{3}{5}$

View Example
Step-by-Step
Print

Step 1: ✓

Rewrite the mixed numbers as fractions greater than 1.

$4\frac{3}{8} \div 5\frac{3}{5} = \frac{35}{8} \div \frac{26}{5}$

Step 2 out of 3:

Rewrite the problem as multiplication using the reciprocal of the second fraction.

$\frac{35}{8} \div \frac{28}{5} = \frac{35}{8} \times \frac{5}{28}$

The reciprocal of $\frac{28}{5}$ is $\frac{5}{28}$.

Check | Next

Q.12 of 12 | Try Another | Next

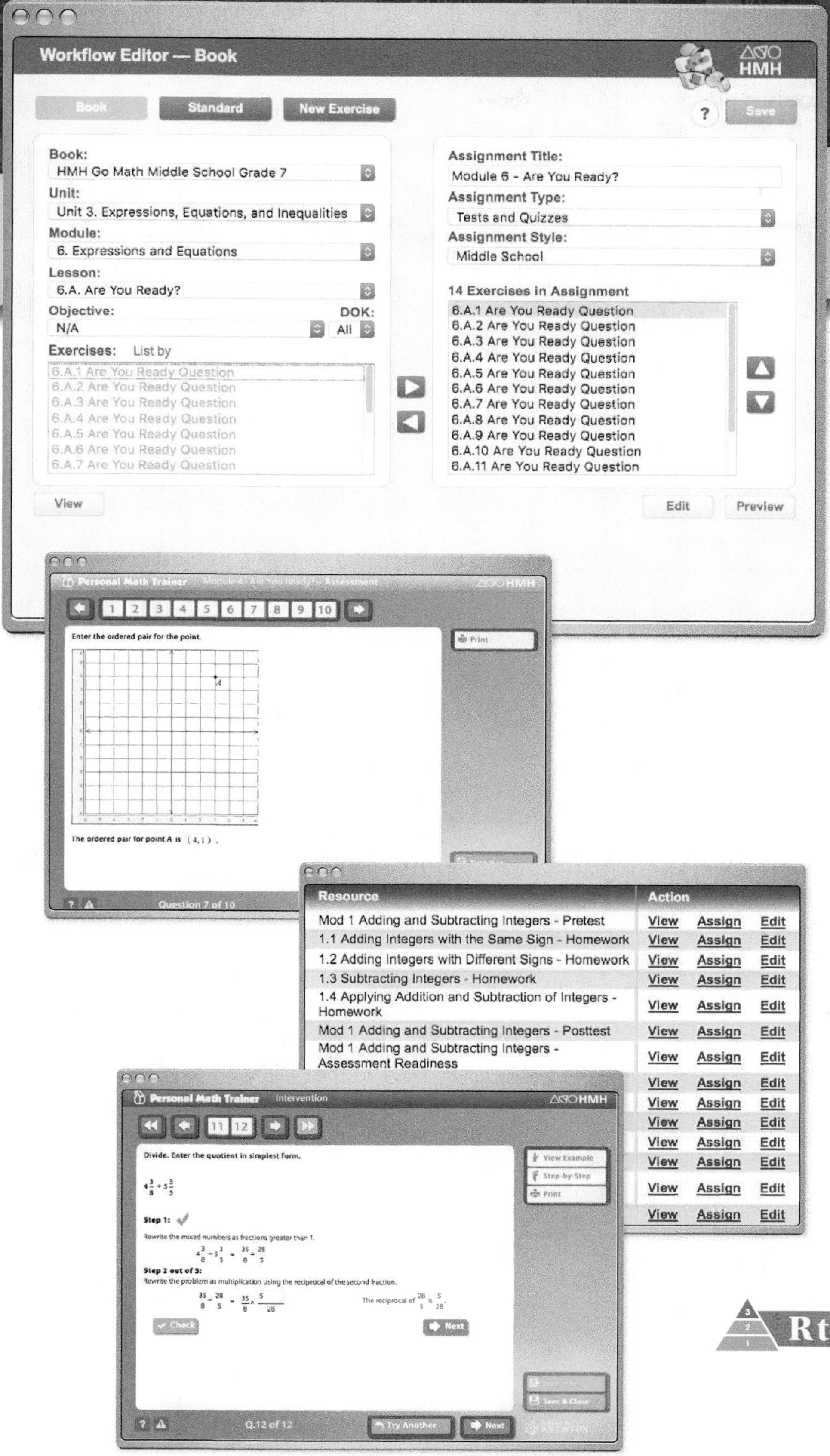

Customization

Build your own assignments from thousands of items, all correlated and searchable by lesson and DOK level.

Assessment

Personal Math Trainer is pre-populated with numerous quizzes and tests aligned to course content. Assessments are automatically scored and reported.

Intervention

Choose a pre-populated intervention assignment for any lesson or module. Based on each student's performance, Personal Math Trainer will automatically create a personal-study-plan assignment targeting each student's individual needs!

RtI for Tier 1, 2, and 3

Personal Math Trainer targets each student's individual needs and provides content support up to 2 grade levels below the current grade!

© Houghton Mifflin Harcourt Publishing Company

Progressions

HMH Go Math is designed to provide coherent and focused progressions across the grades. The table below provides an overview of how important topics within each domain are developed across the grades.

	Grade 6	Grade 7	Grade 8
Ratios and Proportionality	• Understand ratio concepts and use ratio reasoning to solve problems.	• Analyze proportional relationships and use them to solve real-world and mathematical problems.	
The Number System	• Apply and extend previous understandings of multiplication and division to divide fractions. • Compute fluently with multi-digit numbers and find common factors and multiples. • Apply and extend previous understandings of numbers to the system of rational numbers	• Apply and extend previous understandings of operations with fractions to add, subtract, multiply, and divide rational numbers.	• Know that there are numbers that are not rational, and approximate them by using rational numbers.
Expressions and Equations	• Apply and extend previous understandings of arithmetic to algebraic expressions. • Reason about and solve one-variable equations and inequalities. • Represent and analyze quantitative relationships between dependent and independent variables.	• Use properties of operations to generate equivalent expressions. • Solve real-life and mathematical problems using numerical and algebraic expressions and equations.	• Work with radicals and integer exponents. • Understand the connections between proportional relationships, lines, and linear equations. • Analyze and solve linear equations and pairs of simultaneous linear equations.
Geometry	• Solve real-world and mathematical problems involving area, surface area, and volume.	• Draw, construct and describe geometrical figures and describe the relationships between them. • Solve real-life and mathematical problems involving angle measure, area, surface area, and volume.	• Understand congruence and similarity using physical models, transparencies, or geometry software. • Understand and apply the Pythagorean theorem. • Solve real-world and mathematical problems involving volume of cylinders, cones and spheres
Statistics and Probablilty	• Develop understanding of statistical variability. • Summarize and describe distributions.	• Use random sampling to draw inferences about a population. • Draw informal comparative inferences about two populations. • Investigate chance processes and develop, use, and evaluate probability models.	• Investigate patterns of association in bivariate data.
Functions			• Define, evaluate, and compare functions. • Use functions to model relationships between quantities.

Mathematics Objectives
for *HMH Go Math* Grade 8

Objective	Descriptor	Taught & Practiced
Unit 1 Real Numbers, Exponents, and Scientific Notation		
Module 1 Real Numbers		
8.1.1.1	Students will rewrite rational numbers and decimals, take square roots and cube roots, and approximate irrational numbers.	Lesson 1.1: pp. 7–14
8.1.1.2	Students will describe relationships between sets of real numbers.	Lesson 1.2: pp. 15–20
8.1.1.3	Students will order a set of real numbers.	Lesson 1.3: pp. 21–26
Module 2 Exponents and Scientific Notation		
8.1.2.1	Students will develop and use the properties of integer exponents.	Lesson 2.1: pp. 33–38
8.1.2.2	Students will use scientific notation to express very large quantities.	Lesson 2.2: pp. 39–44
8.1.2.3	Students will use scientific notation to express very small quantities.	Lesson 2.3: pp. 45–50
8.1.2.4	Students will add, subtract, multiply, and divide using scientific notation.	Lesson 2.4: pp. 51–56
Unit 2 Proportional and Nonproportional Relationships and Functions		
Module 3 Proportional Relationships		
8.2.3.1	Students will use tables, graphs, and equations to represent proportional situations.	Lesson 3.1: pp. 71–76
8.2.3.2	Students will find a rate of change or a slope.	Lesson 3.2: pp. 77–82
8.2.3.3	Students will interpret the unit rate as slope.	Lesson 3.3: pp. 83–88
Module 4 Nonproportional Relationships		
8.2.4.1	Students will use tables, graphs, and equations to represent linear nonproportional situations.	Lesson 4.1: pp. 95–100
8.2.4.2	Students will determine the slope and the *y*-intercept of a line.	Lesson 4.2: pp. 101–106
8.2.4.3	Students will graph a line using the slope and *y*-intercept.	Lesson 4.3: pp. 107–112
8.2.4.4	Students will distinguish between proportional and nonproportional situations.	Lesson 4.4: pp. 113–120
Module 5 Writing Linear Equations		
8.2.5.1	Students will write an equation to model a linear relationship given a graph or a description.	Lesson 5.1: pp. 127–132
8.2.5.2	Students will write an equation to model a linear relationship given a table.	Lesson 5.2: pp. 133–138
8.2.5.3	Students will contrast linear and nonlinear sets of bivariate data.	Lesson 5.3: pp. 139–146

© Houghton Mifflin Harcourt Publishing Company

Objective	Descriptor	Taught & Practiced
Module 6 Functions		
8.2.6.1	Students will identify and represent functions.	Lesson 6.1: pp. 153–160
8.2.6.2	Students will describe functions.	Lesson 6.2: pp. 161–166
8.2.6.3	Students will use tables, graphs, and equations to compare functions.	Lesson 6.3: pp. 167–172
8.2.6.4	Students will describe a relationship given a graph and sketch a graph given a description.	Lesson 6.4: pp. 173–178
Unit 3 Solving Equations and Systems of Equations		
Module 7 Solving Linear Equations		
8.3.7.1	Students will represent and solve equations with the variable on both sides.	Lesson 7.1: pp. 197–202
8.3.7.2	Students will solve equations with rational number coefficients and constants.	Lesson 7.2: pp. 203–208
8.3.7.3	Students will use the Distributive Property to solve equations.	Lesson 7.3: pp. 209–214
8.3.7.4	Students will give examples of equations with a given number of solutions.	Lesson 7.4: pp. 215–220
Module 8 Solving Systems of Linear Equations		
8.3.8.1	Students will solve a system of equations by graphing.	Lesson 8.1: pp. 227–234
8.3.8.2	Students will use substitution to solve a system of linear equations.	Lesson 8.2: pp. 235–242
8.3.8.3	Students will solve a system of linear equations by adding or subtracting.	Lesson 8.3: pp. 243–250
8.3.8.4	Students will solve a system of linear equations by multiplying.	Lesson 8.4: pp. 251–258
8.3.8.5	Students will solve systems with no solution or infinitely many solutions.	Lesson 8.5: pp. 259–264
Unit 4 Transformational Geometry		
Module 9 Transformations and Congruence		
8.4.9.1	Students will describe the properties of translation and their effect on the congruence and orientation of figures.	Lesson 9.1: pp. 279–284
8.4.9.2	Students will describe the properties of reflection and their effect on the congruence and orientation of figures.	Lesson 9.2: pp. 285–290
8.4.9.3	Students will describe the properties of rotation and their effect on the congruence and orientation of figures.	Lesson 9.3: pp. 291–296
8.4.9.4	Students will describe the effect of a translation, rotation, or reflection on coordinates using an algebraic representation.	Lesson 9.4: pp. 297–302
8.4.9.5	Students will determine the connection between transformations and figures that have the same shape and size.	Lesson 9.5: pp. 303–308

© Houghton Mifflin Harcourt Publishing Company

Module 10 Transformations and Similarity

8.4.10.1	Students will describe the properties of dilations.	Lesson 10.1: pp. 315–320
8.4.10.2	Students will describe the effect of a dilation on coordinates using an algebraic representation.	Lesson 10.2: pp. 321–326
8.4.10.3	Students will determine the connection between transformations and similar figures.	Lesson 10.3: pp. 327–332

Unit 5 Measurement Geometry

Module 11 Angle Relationships in Parallel Lines and Triangles

8.5.11.1	Students will make conclusions about the angles formed by parallel lines that are cut by a transversal.	Lesson 11.1: pp. 347–352
8.5.11.2	Students will make conclusions about the measures of the angles of a triangle.	Lesson 11.2: pp. 353–360
8.5.11.3	Students will determine how two triangles are similar.	Lesson 11.3: pp. 361–368

Module 12 The Pythagorean Theorem

8.5.12.1	Students will use the Pythagorean Theorem to solve problems.	Lesson 12.1: pp. 375–380
8.5.12.2	Students will test the converse of the Pythagorean Theorem and use it to solve problems.	Lesson 12.2: pp. 381–386
8.5.12.3	Students will use the Pythagorean Theorem to find the distance between two points on a coordinate plane.	Lesson 12.3: pp. 387–392

Module 13 Volume

8.5.13.1	Students will find the volume of a cylinder.	Lesson 13.1: pp. 399–404
8.5.13.2	Students will find the volume of a cone.	Lesson 13.2: pp. 405–410
8.5.13.3	Students will find the volume of a sphere.	Lesson 13.3: pp. 411–416

Unit 6 Statistics

Module 14 Scatter Plots

8.6.14.1	Students will construct and interpret scatter plots.	Lesson 14.1: pp. 433–438
8.6.14.2	Students will use a trend line to make a prediction from a scatter plot.	Lesson 14.2: pp. 439–444

Module 15 Two-Way Tables

8.6.15.1	Students will construct and interpret two-way frequency tables.	Lesson 15.1: pp. 451–456
8.6.15.2	Students will organize and analyze categorical data.	Lesson 15.2: pp. 457–464

© Houghton Mifflin Harcourt Publishing Company

Process	Descriptor	Citations
MP Mathematical Processes		*The mathematical processes are integrated throughout the book. See, for example, the citations below.*
MP.1	**Problem Solving** Mathematically proficient students start by explaining to themselves the meaning of a problem and looking for entry points to its solution. They analyze givens, constraints, relationships, and goals. They make conjectures about the form and meaning of the solution and plan a solution pathway, rather than simply jumping into a solution attempt. They consider analogous problems and try special cases and simpler forms of the original problem in order to gain insight into its solution. They monitor and evaluate their progress and change course if necessary. Mathematically proficient students check their answers to problems using a different method, and they continually ask themselves, "Does this make sense?" and "Is my answer reasonable?" They understand the approaches of others to solving complex problems and identify correspondences between different approaches. Mathematically proficient students understand how mathematical ideas interconnect and build on one another to produce a coherent whole.	14, 120, 178, 202, 211, 219, 242, 254–255, 308, 380, 392, 415, 455–456
MP.2	**Abstract and Quantitative Reasoning** Mathematically proficient students make sense of quantities and their relationships in problem situations. They bring two complementary abilities to bear on problems involving quantitative relationships: the ability to decontextualize—to abstract a given situation and represent it symbolically and manipulate the representing symbols as if they have a life of their own, without necessarily attending to their referents—and the ability to contextualize, to pause as needed during the manipulation process in order to probe into the referents for the symbols involved. Quantitative reasoning entails habits of creating a coherent representation of the problem at hand; considering the units involved; attending to the meaning of quantities, not just how to compute them; and knowing and flexibly using different properties of operations and objects.	14, 38, 82, 88, 103, 111, 153–154, 198–202, 214, 254–255, 354–355, 375–376

© Houghton Mifflin Harcourt Publishing Company

© Houghton Mifflin Harcourt Publishing Company

Process	Descriptor	Citations
MP.3	**Use and Evaluate Logical Reasoning** Mathematically proficient students understand and use stated assumptions, definitions, and previously established results in constructing arguments. They make conjectures and build a logical progression of statements to explore the truth of their conjectures. They analyze situations by breaking them into cases and recognize and use counterexamples. They organize their mathematical thinking, justify their conclusions and communicate them to others, and respond to the arguments of others. They reason inductively about data, making plausible arguments that take into account the context from which the data arose. Mathematically proficient students are also able to compare the effectiveness of two plausible arguments, distinguish correct logic or reasoning from that which is flawed, and—if there is a flaw in an argument—explain what it is. They justify whether a given statement is true always, sometimes, or never. Mathematically proficient students participate and collaborate in a mathematics community. They listen to or read the arguments of others, decide whether they make sense, and ask useful questions to clarify or improve the arguments.	20, 100, 146, 208, 258, 302, 352, 410, 444
MP.4	**Mathematical Modeling** Mathematically proficient students apply the mathematics they know to solve problems arising in everyday life, society, and the workplace using a variety of appropriate strategies. They create and use a variety of representations to solve problems and to organize and communicate mathematical ideas. Mathematically proficient students apply what they know and are comfortable making assumptions and approximations to simplify a complicated situation, realizing that these may need revision later. They are able to identify important quantities in a practical situation and map their relationships using such tools as diagrams, two-way tables, graphs, flowcharts and formulas. They analyze those relationships mathematically to draw conclusions. They routinely interpret their mathematical results in the context of the situation and reflect on whether the results make sense, possibly improving the model if it has not served its purpose.	73, 129–130, 204–205, 254–255, 363–364, 413, 457–461

Process	Descriptor	Citations
MP.5	**Use Mathematical Tools** Mathematically proficient students consider the available tools when solving a mathematical problem. These tools might include pencil and paper, models, a ruler, a protractor, a calculator, a spreadsheet, a computer algebra system, a statistical package, or dynamic geometry software. Mathematically proficient students are sufficiently familiar with tools appropriate for their grade or course to make sound decisions about when each of these tools might be helpful, recognizing both the insight to be gained and their limitations. Mathematically proficient students identify relevant external mathematical resources, such as digital content, and use them to pose or solve problems. They use technological tools to explore and deepen their understanding of concepts and to support the development of learning mathematics. They use technology to contribute to concept development, simulation, representation, reasoning, communication and problem solving.	22, 53, 197, 227–231, 285, 315, 347–348, 353, 375, 399
MP.6	**Use Precise Mathematical Language** Mathematically proficient students communicate precisely to others. They use clear definitions, including correct mathematical language, in discussion with others and in their own reasoning. They state the meaning of the symbols they choose, including using the equal sign consistently and appropriately. They express solutions clearly and logically by using the appropriate mathematical terms and notation. They specify units of measure and label axes to clarify the correspondence with quantities in a problem. They calculate accurately and efficiently and check the validity of their results in the context of the problem. They express numerical answers with a degree of precision appropriate for the problem context.	56, 106, 143, 173–178, 214, 234, 250, 352, 404, 437

© Houghton Mifflin Harcourt Publishing Company

Process	Descriptor	Citations
MP.7	**See Structure** Mathematically proficient students look closely to discern a pattern or structure. They step back for an overview and shift perspective. They recognize and use properties of operations and equality. They organize and classify geometric shapes based on their attributes. They see expressions, equations, and geometric figures as single objects or as being composed of several objects.	10–11, 33–35, 45, 133–135, 153–154, 208, 297–300, 381, 434, 439–441
MP.8	**Generalize** Mathematically proficient students notice if calculations are repeated and look for general methods and shortcuts. They notice regularity in mathematical problems and their work to create a rule or formula. Mathematically proficient students maintain oversight of the process, while attending to the details as they solve a problem. They continually evaluate the reasonableness of their intermediate results.	8, 33–35, 45, 107, 197, 235, 243, 251, 297–300, 388, 440

© Houghton Mifflin Harcourt Publishing Company

Succeeding with HMH Go Math

Actively participate in your learning with your write-in Student Edition. Explore concepts, take notes, answer questions, and complete your homework right in your textbook!

Essential Questions ensure that you know exactly what you are learning.

Explore Activities help you develop a deeper understanding of math concepts.

Scan QR codes with your smart phone or device to watch **Math On the Spot** tutorial videos for every example in the book!

Your Turn exercises check your understanding of new concepts.

Play strategy **Games and Activities** with classmates to practice using the concepts you have learned.

LESSON 4.1 Representing Linear Nonproportional Relationships

8.2.4.1

Students will use ta... graphs, and equation... to represent linear nonproportional sit...

ESSENTIAL QUESTION

How can you use tables, graphs, and equations to represent l... nonproportional situations?

EXPLORE ACTIVITY

Representing Linear Relationships Using Tables

You can use an equation to describe the relationship between two quantities in a real-world situation. You can use a table to show some values that make the equation true.

EXAMPLE 1 The equation $y = 3x + 2$ gives the total charge, y, for one person to rent a pair of shoes and bowl x games at Baxter Bowling Lanes based on the prices shown. Make a table of values for this situation.

STEP 1 Choose several values for x that make sense in context. Count by ones.

x (number of games)	1	2		
y (total cost in dollars)				

BAXTE... bowling la...

$3 per game

$2 shoe rental

STEP 2 Use the equation $y = 3x + 2$ to find y for each value of x.

x (number of games)	1	2		
y (total cost in dollars)	5			

Substitute 1 for x
$y = 3(1) + 2 = 5$

YOUR TURN

1. Francisco makes $12 per hour doing part-time work on Saturdays. He spends $4 on transportation to and from work. The equation $y = 12x - 4$ gives his earnings y, after transportation costs, for working x hours. Make a table of values for this situation.

x (number of hours)				
y (earnings in dollars)				

Personal Math Trainer
Online Assessment and intervention
my.hrw.com

Activity 6.2

How Many Squares?

INSTRUCTIONS

STEP 1 How many squares (of all sizes) can you find in the 4 × 4 square grid?
There are four different sizes of squares in the grid.

Count the number of each size square in the 4 × 4 square grid. The table shows you how to find them all.

Size of square	Number of squares	Identification of squares
4 × 4	1	
3 × 3	4	

© Houghton Mifflin Harcourt Publishing Company

© Houghton Mifflin Harcourt Publishing Company

Reading Start-Up

Visualize Vocabulary

Use the ✔ words to complete the diagram. You can put more than one word in each section of the diagram.

(2, 6)	$y = mx + b$
Reviewing Relationships	
m	b

Understand Vocabulary

Complete the sentences using the preview words.

1. A rule that assigns exactly one output to each input

   is a _____.

2. The value that is put into a function is the _____.

3. The result after applying the function machine's rule is

   the _____.

Active Reading

Double-Door Fold Create a double-door fold to help you understand the concepts in this module. Label one flap "Proportional Functions" and the other flap "Non-proportional Functions." As you study each lesson, write important ideas under the appropriate flap. Include any sample problems that will help you remember the concepts when you look back at your notes.

150 Unit 2

Vocabulary

Review Words
- ✔ bivariate data (datos bivariados)
- ✔ linear equation (ecuación lineal)
- nonlinear relationship (relación no lineal)
- ✔ ordered pair (par ordenado)
- proportional relationship (relación proporcional)
- ✔ slope (pendiente)
- ✔ x-coordinate (coordenada x)
- ✔ y-coordinate (coordenada y)
- ✔ y-intercept (intersección con el eje y)

Preview Words
- function (función)
- input (valor de entrada)
- linear function (función lineal)
- output (valor de salida)

Review concepts you will need to know before beginning each module.

Get vocabulary, language, and note-taking support throughout the book.

Are YOU Ready?

Complete these exercises to review skills you will need for this module.

Personal Math Trainer Online Assessment and Intervention my.hrw.com

Integer Operations

EXAMPLE
$$-3 - (-6) = -3 + 6$$
$$= |-3| - |-6|$$
$$= 3$$

To subtract an integer, add its opposite. The signs are different, so find the difference of the absolute values: $6 - 3 = 3$. Use the sign of the number with the greater absolute value.

Find

1.
2. $-6 - 8$
3. $2 - 9$
4. $-10 - (-6)$

5. $3 - (-11)$
6. $12 - 7$
7. $-4 - 11$
8. $0 - (-12)$

Measure Angles

EXAMPLE

$m\angle JKL = 70°$

Place the center point of the protractor on the angle's vertex.
Align one ray with the base of the protractor.
Read the angle measure where the other ray intersects the semicircle.

Use a protractor to measure each angle.

9. F, H, G
10. X, Y, Z
11. R, S, T

Find out if you have mastered the concepts you learned in each module.

MODULE QUIZ

Ready to Go On?

Personal Math Trainer Online Assessment and Intervention my.hrw.com

6.1 Identifying and Representing Functions

Determine whether each relationship is a function.

1.
x	y
2	0
5	1
8	2
	3

2.
Input, x	Output, y
−1	6
3	5
6	5

3. (2, 5), (7, 2), (−3, 4), (2, 9), (1, 1)

6.2 Describing Functions

Determine whether each situation is linear or nonlinear, and proportional or nonproportional.

4. Joanna is paid $14 per hour.

5. Alberto started out bench pressing 50 pounds. He then added 5 pounds every week.

6.3 Comparing Functions

6. Which function is changing more quickly? Explain.

Function 1 (graph)

Function 2
Input, x	Output, y
2	11
3	6.5
4	2

6.4 Analyzing Graphs

7. Describe a graph that shows Sam running at a constant rate.

? ESSENTIAL QUESTION

8. How can you use functions to solve real-world problems?

Module 6 **179**

Apply new skills and concepts to solve real-world problems in Unit Performance Tasks and Careers in Math activities.

Unit 5 Performance Tasks

1. **CAREERS IN MATH** Hydrologist A hydrologist needs to estimate the mass of water in an underground aquifer, which is roughly cylindrical in shape. The diameter of the aquifer is 65 meters, and its depth is 8 meters. One cubic meter of water has a mass of about 1000 kilograms.

   a. The aquifer is completely filled with water. What is the total mass of the water in the aquifer? Explain how you found your answer. Use 3.14 for π and round your answer to the nearest kilogram.

   b. Another cylindrical aquifer has a diameter of 70 meters and a depth of 9 meters. The mass of the water in it is 27×10^7 kilograms. Is the aquifer totally filled with water? Explain your reasoning.

2. From his home, Myles walked his dog north 5 blocks, east 2 blocks, and then stopped at a drinking fountain. He then walked north 3 more blocks and east 4 more blocks. It started to rain so he cut through a field and walked straight home.

   a. Draw a diagram of his path.

   b. How many blocks did Myles walk in all? How much longer was his walk before it started to rain than his walk home?

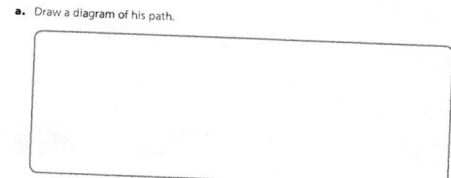

NL9

GO DIGITAL

my.hrw.com

Enhance Your Learning!

Interactive Student Editions provide additional multimedia resources to enhance your learning. You can enter in answers, watch videos, explore concepts with virtual manipulatives, and get homework help!

Real-World Videos show you how specific math topics can be used in all kinds of situations.

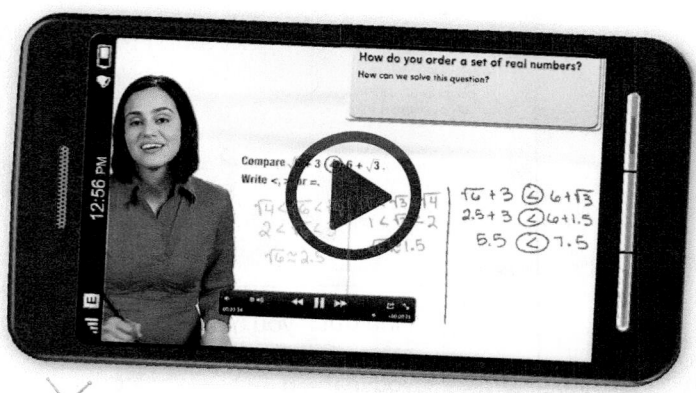

Math On the Spot video tutorials provide step-by-step instruction of the math concepts covered in each example.

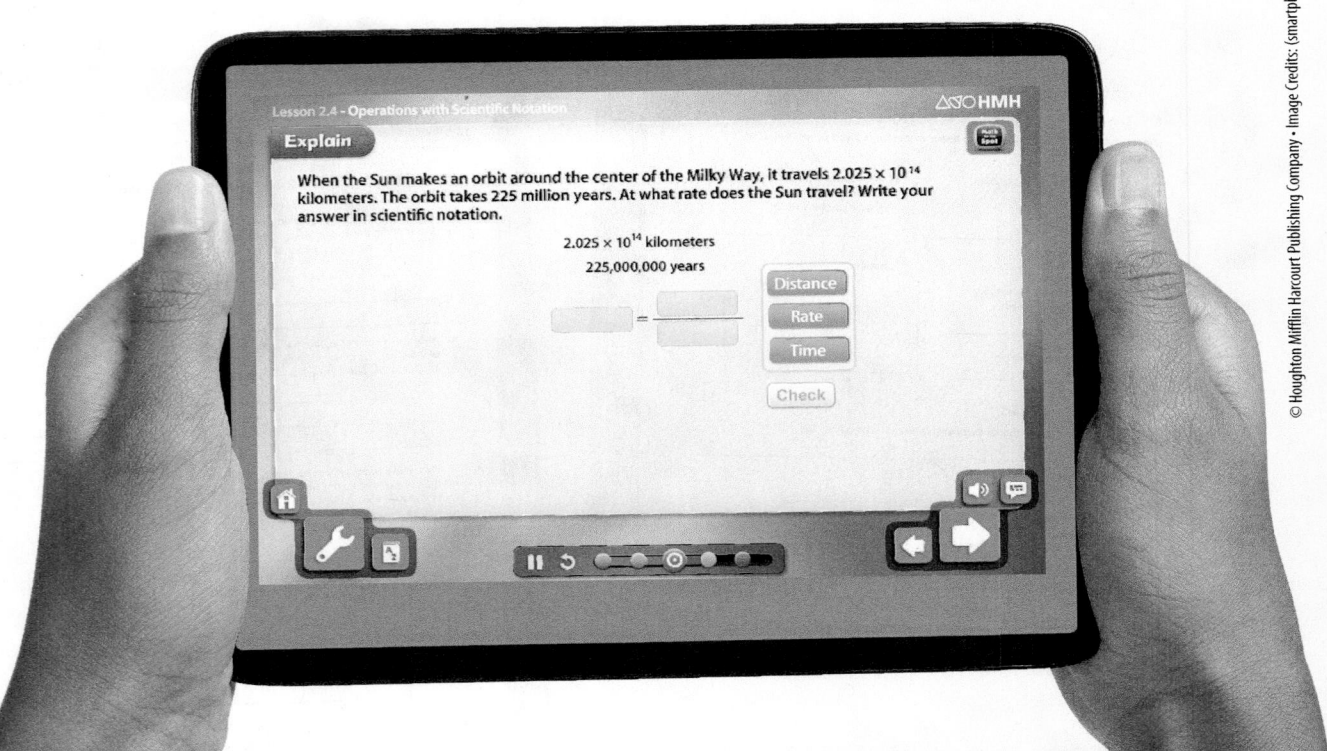

© Houghton Mifflin Harcourt Publishing Company • Image Credits: (smartphone) ©Scanrail/Fotolia.

Personal Math Trainer lets you practice, take quizzes and tests, and get homework help with instant feedback!

Personal Math Trainer provides a variety of learning aids that develop and improve your understanding of math concepts, including videos, guided examples, and step-by-step solutions.

Lesson 4.3 - Homework

Personal Math Trainer

Q.1 of 10 ◄ 1 2 3 4 5 6 7 8 9 10 ►

Graph the equation using the slope and y-intercept.

$$y = \frac{2}{5}x - 2$$

The slope is $\frac{2}{5}$ and the y-intercept is -2

- View Example
- Step-By-Step
- Video Tutor
- Textbook
- Animated Math
- Print

Personal Math Trainer

Online Practice and Help

⏻ my.hrw.com

Multiple Representations △◯ HMH

Exploring Powers of 10

Drag the slider to investigate powers of 10.

10⁰

Giraffe Height
5.0 × 10⁰ meters

Human Height
1.7 × 10⁰ meters

Interior Home Door
2.0 × 10⁰ meters

Animated Math activities and virtual manipulatives let you interactively explore and practice key math concepts and skills.

Geometry Sketcher ?

Tools

Clear Selected Clear All

X²

Animated Math

⏻ my.hrw.com

© Houghton Mifflin Harcourt Publishing Company • Image Credits: (boy using tablet) ©Tetra Images/Corbis.

Mathematical Processes

The topics you study in mathematics will vary from year to year. However, the *way* you learn, study, and think about mathematics will not. The Mathematical Processes described here are skills that you will use in all of your math courses. These pages show some features of your book that will help you gain these skills and use them to master this year's topics.

MP.1 Problem Solving

Solving a problem often involves multiple steps. You must first understand the problem situation, analyze the given information, and identify the goal of the problem. Then you make a plan and implement that plan to solve the problem. Lastly, you check your solution and look back and analyze your solution method.

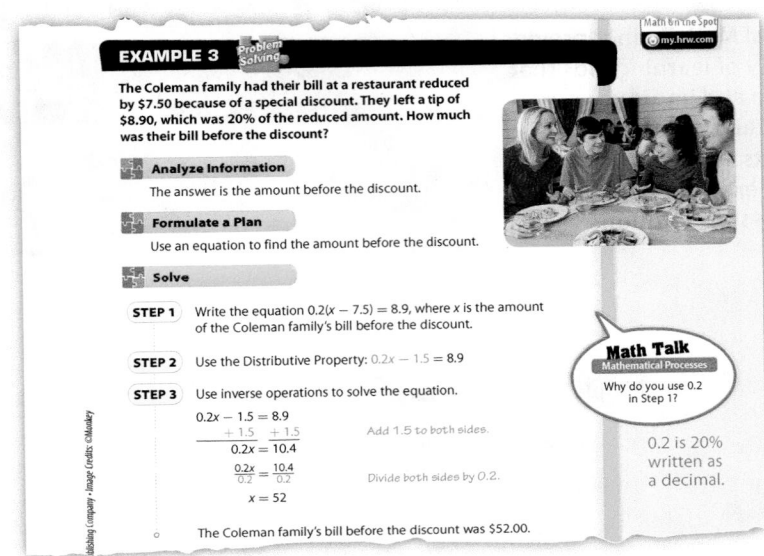

Problem-solving examples and exercises lead you through problem solving steps.

MP.2 Abstract and Quantitative Reasoning

When solving problems, you often need to represent a situation abstractly and work out a solution using a symbolic representation of the problem. At other times, you must refer back to the specific quantities the symbols represent in order to understand the meaning of your results.

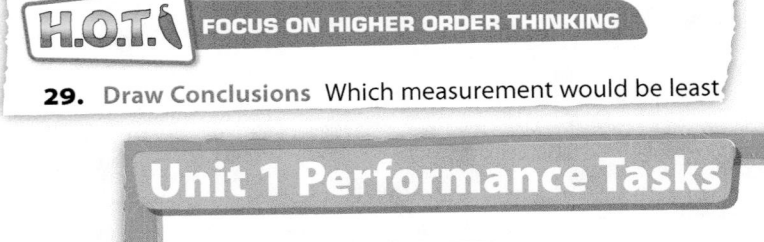

Focus on Higher Order Thinking exercises in every lesson and **Performance Tasks** in every unit require you to use logical reasoning, represent situations symbolically, use mathematical models to solve problems, and state your answers in terms of a problem context.

© Houghton Mifflin Harcourt Publishing Company

MP.3 Use and Evaluate Logical Reasoning

Mathematics provides a unique opportunity to develop your logical reasoning capacities. You can do this by expressing your thoughts and justifying your conclusions. Soon you will recognize and correct flaws in reasoning.

Reflect

2. **Make a Conjecture** Use your results from parts **E**, **H**, and a conjecture about translations.

? ESSENTIAL QUESTION CHECK-IN

Essential Question Check-in and **Reflect** in every lesson ask you to evaluate statements, explain relationships, apply mathematical principles, make conjectures, construct arguments, and justify your reasoning.

MP.4 Mathematical Modeling

You can use mathematics to solve problems in everyday life by learning how to represent real-world situations in mathematical terms.

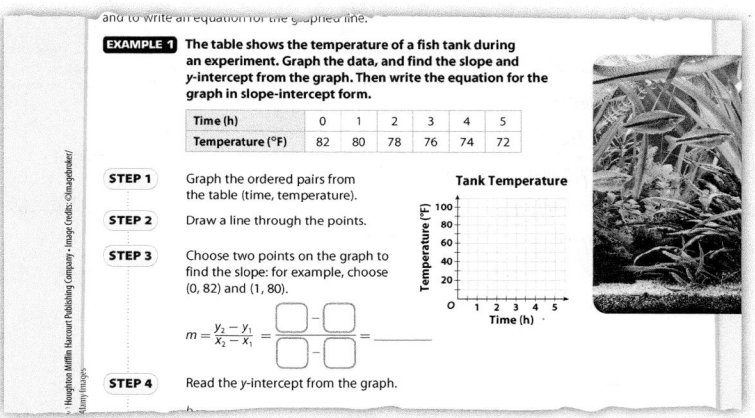

EXAMPLE 1 The table shows the temperature of a fish tank during an experiment. Graph the data, and find the slope and *y*-intercept from the graph. Then write the equation for the graph in slope-intercept form.

Time (h)	0	1	2	3	4	5
Temperature (°F)	82	80	78	76	74	72

STEP 1 Graph the ordered pairs from the table (time, temperature).

STEP 2 Draw a line through the points.

STEP 3 Choose two points on the graph to find the slope: for example, choose (0, 82) and (1, 80).

$$m = \frac{y_2 - y_1}{x_2 - x_1} = \frac{\square - \square}{\square - \square} = \underline{\hspace{1cm}}$$

STEP 4 Read the *y*-intercept from the graph.

Real-world examples and **mathematical modeling** apply mathematics to other disciplines and real-world contexts such as science and business.

MP.5 Use Mathematical Tools

Knowing when and how to use mathematical tools, ranging from rulers and protractors to graphing calculators and computer software, is a valuable skill. Used properly, tools can both simplify problem-solving and give you a deeper understanding of mathematical concepts.

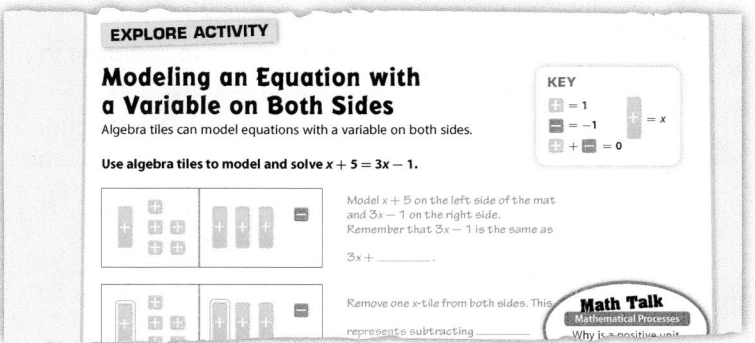

EXPLORE ACTIVITY

Modeling an Equation with a Variable on Both Sides

Algebra tiles can model equations with a variable on both sides.

KEY
+ = 1
− = −1
+ = x
+ − = 0

Use algebra tiles to model and solve $x + 5 = 3x - 1$.

Model $x + 5$ on the left side of the mat and $3x - 1$ on the right side. Remember that $3x - 1$ is the same as

$3x +$ _____

Remove one *x*-tile from both sides. This represents subtracting

Math Talk
Mathematical Processes
Why is a positive unit

Exploration Activities in lessons use concrete and technological tools, such as manipulatives or graphing calculators, to explore mathematical concepts.

© Houghton Mifflin Harcourt Publishing Company

MP.6 Use Precise Mathematical Language

To communicate your reasoning and results to others, you must use mathematical terms, symbols, and units precisely and consistently. Defining terms clearly and labeling diagrams appropriately are essential for writing clear explanations.

19. Communicate Mathematical Ideas Explain how you can fin[d] height of a cylinder if you know the diameter and the volum[e] an example with your explana[tion.]

Key Vocabulary

slope *(pendiente)*
A measure of the steepness of a line on a graph; the rise divided by the run.

Precision refers not only to the correctness of calculations but also to the proper use of mathematical language and symbols. **Communicate Mathematical Ideas** exercises and **Key Vocabulary** highlighted for each module and unit help you learn and use the language of math to communicate mathematics precisely.

MP.7 See Structure

Recognizing patterns and similarities in the structure of varied problems can help you both to solve problems and to understand the underlying mathematical concepts.

Follow the steps to informally prove the Triangle Sum Theorem. You should draw each step on your own paper. The figures below are provided for you to check your work.

A Draw a triangle and label the angles as $\angle 1$, $\angle 2$, and $\angle 3$ as shown.

B Draw line a through the base of the triangle.

C The Parallel Postulate states that through a point not on a line ℓ, there is exactly one line parallel to line ℓ. Draw line b parallel to line a, through the vertex opposite the base of the triangle.

D Extend each of the non-base sides of the triangle to form transversal s and transversal t. Transversals s and t intersect parallel lines a and b.

E Label the angles formed by line b and the transversals as $\angle 4$ and $\angle 5$.

F Because $\angle 4$ and _____ are alternate interior

Throughout the lessons, you will observe regularity in mathematical structures in order to make generalizations and make connections between related problems. For example, you can learn to recognize a linear relationship between two quantities.

MP.8 Generalize

As you do similar calculations repeatedly, you can discover general methods and shortcuts for solving problems.

Use your pattern to complete this equation: $\left(7^2\right)^4 = 7^{\boxed{}}$.

B Describe any patterns you see. Use your pattern to of 1 pencil.

20. Look for a Pattern Describe the pattern in the equation. The[n] equation.

$$0.3x + 0.03x + 0.003x + 0.0003x + \ldots = 3$$

You will look for repeated calculations and mathematical patterns in examples and exercises. Recognizing patterns can help you make generalizations and obtain a better understanding of the underlying mathematics.

© Houghton Mifflin Harcourt Publishing Company

HMH Go Math!

Teachers Edition, Grade 8

Contents in Brief

Teacher Material

Selected Answers are provided at the back of the Student Edition.

Review Test

Personal
Math Trainer
my.hrw.com
Online
Assessment and
Intervention

Selected Response

1. Evaluate $a + b$ for $a = 34$ and $b = -6$.

- (A) 28
- (C) −28
- (B) 40
- (D) −40

2. A triangle has sides with lengths of $5x − 7$, $3x − 4$, and $2x − 6$. What is the perimeter of the triangle?

- (A) $10x − 17$
- (C) $4x − 9$
- (B) $6x − 17$
- (D) $−7x$

3. Which of the following ratios does *not* form a proportion?

- (A) $\frac{28}{49} \stackrel{?}{=} \frac{4}{7}$
- (C) $\frac{4}{7} \stackrel{?}{=} \frac{16}{35}$
- (B) $\frac{4}{7} \stackrel{?}{=} \frac{16}{28}$
- (D) $\frac{4}{7} \stackrel{?}{=} \frac{20}{35}$

4. For a sale, a store decreases its prices on all items by 25%. An item that cost $120 before the sale now costs $120 − 0.25($120). What is another expression for the sale price?

- (A) $120 − 25
- (C) $0.25($120)
- (B) $0.75($120)
- (D) $120 − 75

5. Write an equation that models the situation and find its solution.

It's going to be Lindsay's birthday soon, and her friends Mary, Mikhail, Anne, Kim, Makoto, and Isabel have contributed equal amounts of money to buy her a present. They have $36.00 to spend between them. Determine how much each contributed.

- (A) $6x = 36.00; $x = 108.00
- (C) $6x = 36.00; $x = 216.00
- (B) $7x = 36.00; $x = 5.14
- (D) $6x = 36.00 $x = 6.00

6. Solve $4(a + 4) − 2 = 34$.

- (A) $a = −5$
- (C) $a = 5$
- (B) $a = 8$
- (D) $a = −8$

7. Four sisters bought a present for their father. They received a 10% discount on the original price of the gift. After the discount was taken, each sister paid $9.00. What was the original price of the gift?

- (A) $40.00
- (C) $16.00
- (B) $36.00
- (D) $32.73

8. Justin is redoing his bathroom floor with tiles measuring 6 in. by 13 in. The floor has an area of 8,500 in². What is the least number of tiles he will need?

- (A) 448 tiles
- (C) 109 tiles
- (B) 108.97 tiles
- (D) 108 tiles

9. One winter day, the temperature ranged from a high of 20 °F to a low of −25 °F. By how many degrees did the temperature change?

- (A) −5 °F
- (C) −15 °F
- (B) 55 °F
- (D) 45 °F

10. Terry drove 310 miles in 5 hours at a constant speed. How long would it take him to drive 403 miles at the same speed?

- (A) 3 hours
- (C) 7 hours
- (B) 6.5 hours
- (D) 62 hours

11. 128 is 74% of what number? If necessary, round your answer to the nearest hundredth.

- (A) 0.58
- (C) 1.73
- (B) 94.72
- (D) 172.97

12. Tell whether the data show a direct variation. If so, identify the constant of variation.

Number of Baskets	Cost
5	$15
7	$21
9	$27
13	$39
15	$45

- (A) direct variation; $k = \frac{1}{3}$
- (B) not a direct variation
- (C) direct variation; $k = 3$
- (D) direct variation; $k = 10$

13. The graph shows the distance Jamie walks over time. Does she walk at a constant or variable speed? How fast is Jamie walking?

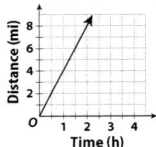

- (A) variable speed; 8 mi/h
- (B) constant speed; 4 mi/h
- (C) constant speed; 2 mi/h
- (D) constant speed; 8 mi/h

14. Darryl is reading a book at the rate of 4.5 pages per minute. What ordered pair on a graph of his reading rate would represent the number of minutes it would take him to read 90 pages?

- (A) (20, 90)
- (B) (4.5, 20)
- (C) (90, 4.5)
- (D) (4.5, 90)

Mini-Tasks

15. The water level in a plastic pool changed by −8 gallons each hour due to a small hole in the bottom. After 6 hours, the pool contained 132 gallons. How much water was in the pool originally?

180 gallons

16. The ratio of adults to children attending a new exhibit at the museum was found to be 8:5. Based on this ratio, if 390 people attended one day, how many would be children?

150

Performance Task

17. The graph shows the relationship between the total cost and the number of pounds of rice purchased.

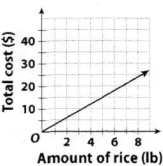

Part A: What does (6, 18) represent?

6 lb will cost $18

Part B: Which point represents the unit price?

(1, 3)

Part C: How many pounds would you have to buy for the total to be $12? Explain how to find the answer.

4 lb; divide $12 by the unit price of $3

Grade 7

Review Test

Use this test to ensure that your students have mastered the concepts from the previous course.

Scoring Guide for Performance Task

A. 1 point for correctly identifying what the *x*-value represents;
1 point for correctly identifying what the *y*-value represents

B. 2 points for correctly identifying the point that represents the unit price

C. 1 point for correctly identifying the number of pounds;
1 point for explaining how to find it

Grade 7 Student Edition

Items	Modules	Items	Modules
1	Module 1	10	Module 4
2	Module 6	11	Modules 3, 5
3	Module 4	12	Module 4
4	Module 5	13	Module 4
5	Module 6	14	Modules 3, 4
6	Modules 2, 6	15	Modules 1, 4
7	Module 5	16	Module 4
8	Modules 7, 9	17	Module 4
9	Module 1		

© Houghton Mifflin Harcourt Publishing Company

Review Test

Personal
Math Trainer

Online
Assessment and
Intervention

my.hrw.com

Selected Response

1. What are the actual dimensions of the Check-out Area?

Floor plan of library

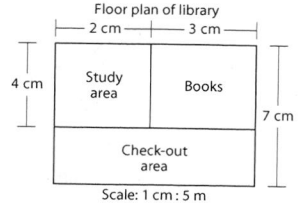

	2 cm	3 cm
4 cm	Study area	Books
	Check-out area	7 cm

Scale: 1 cm : 5 m

- Ⓐ 25 m × 15 m
- Ⓒ 15 m × 35 m
- Ⓑ 15 m × 20 m
- Ⓓ 2 m × 4 m

2. For a history fair, a school is building a circular wooden stage that will stand 2 feet off the ground. Find the area of the stage if the radius of the stage is 19 feet. Use 3.14 for π.

- Ⓐ 1,133.54 ft²
- Ⓒ 2,267.08 ft²
- Ⓑ 119.32 ft²
- Ⓓ 4534.16 ft²

3. Find the area of the circle to the nearest tenth. Use 3.14 for π.

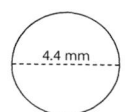

4.4 mm

- Ⓐ 47.7 mm²
- Ⓒ 60.8 mm²
- Ⓑ 15.2 mm²
- Ⓓ 13.8 mm²

4. What is the solution of the inequality $-0.4x - 1.2 > 0.8$?

- Ⓐ $x < -5$
- Ⓒ $x < -0.8$
- Ⓑ $x < -1$
- Ⓓ $x > 5$

5. Find m∠LMN.

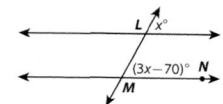

L $x°$

$(3x-70)°$ N

M

- Ⓐ m∠LMN = 40°
- Ⓒ m∠LMN = 35°
- Ⓑ m∠LMN = 45°
- Ⓓ m∠LMN = 50°

6. Ralph is an electrician. He charges an initial fee of $32, plus $33 per hour. If Ralph earned $197 on a job, how long did the job take?

- Ⓐ 5.1 hours
- Ⓒ 5 hours
- Ⓑ 132 hours
- Ⓓ 4 hours

7. Find the volume of the cylinder. Use 3.14 for π. Round your answer to the nearest tenth.

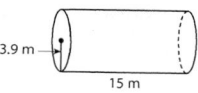

3.9 m

15 m

- Ⓐ 183.7 m³
- Ⓒ 2,865.6 m³
- Ⓑ 716.4 m³
- Ⓓ 2,755.4 m³

8. Which is the least valid way to simulate how many boys and girls are in a random sample of 20 students from a school population that is half boys and half girls?

- Ⓐ Flip a coin 20 times, assigning one outcome to boys and the other to girls.
- Ⓑ Drop 20 coins at once and count the number of each outcome.
- Ⓒ Count how many boys and girls are in your math class and use a proportion.
- Ⓓ Have a calculator generate 20 random integers and count the number of even and odd integers.

9. Roberto plays on the school baseball team. In the last 9 games, Roberto was at bat 32 times and got 11 hits. What is the experimental probability that Roberto will get a hit during his next time at bat? Express your answer as a fraction in simplest form.

- Ⓐ $\frac{32}{11}$
- Ⓒ $\frac{21}{32}$
- Ⓑ $\frac{11}{32}$
- Ⓓ $\frac{11}{21}$

10. A coin-operated machine sells plastic rings. It contains 14 pink rings, 10 green rings, 9 purple rings, and 13 black rings. Sarah puts a coin into the machine. Find the theoretical probability she gets a pink ring. Express your answer as a decimal. If necessary, round your answer to the nearest thousandth.

- Ⓐ 3.286
- Ⓒ 4.6
- Ⓑ 0.304
- Ⓓ 0.217

11. A manufacturer inspects a sample of 400 personal video players and finds that 399 of them have no defects. The manufacturer sent a shipment of 2000 video players to a distributor. Predict the number of players in the shipment that are likely to have no defects.

- Ⓐ 5
- Ⓒ 399
- Ⓑ 1995
- Ⓓ 1950

12. An experiment consists of rolling two fair number cubes. What is the probability that the sum of the two numbers will be 8? Express your answer as a fraction in simplest form.

- Ⓐ $\frac{5}{36}$
- Ⓒ $\frac{36}{5}$
- Ⓑ $\frac{1}{9}$
- Ⓓ $\frac{31}{36}$

Mini-Tasks

13. A map of Australia has a scale of 1 cm : 110 km. If the distance between Darwin and Alice Springs is 1444 kilometers, how far apart are they on the map, to the nearest tenth of a centimeter?

_13.1 cm_

14. The student council president wants to find out the opinion of the students on the issue of school lunch options. The president sends out a survey to a random sample of students in the school. What type of sample is this? Explain.

random sample; the students are
within the population (students
in school) and are randomly
chosen

15. Using the following data, state the errors in the box-and-whisker plot.

33, 27, 6, 34, 31, 59, 26, 1, 30

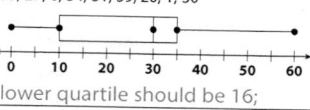

0 10 20 30 40 50 60

lower quartile should be 16;
upper quartile should be 33.5

Performance Task

16. The number of goals scored by a hockey team in each of its first 10 games is 2, 4, 0, 3, 4, 1, 3, 1, 1, and 5.

a. Find the mean number of goals scored.

2.4 goals

b. Find the mean absolute deviation (MAD) of the number of goals scored.

_1.4_

c. A second team in the same division scores a mean of 4.5 goals in its first 10 games, with the same MAD as the team above. Compare the difference in the teams' mean number of goals with the MAD in the number of goals scored.

difference in means is 2.1,
which is 1.5 times MAD

© Houghton Mifflin Harcourt Publishing Company

Grade 7 Student Edition

Items	Modules
1	Module 8
2	Module 9
3	Module 9
4	Modules 3, 7
5	Modules 6, 8
6	Module 6
7	Module 9
8	Module 10

Items	Modules
9	Module 12
10	Module 13
11	Modules 10, 12
12	Module 13
13	Module 8
14	Module 10
15	Module 10
16	Module 11

Scoring Guide for Performance Task

a. 2 points for correctly finding the mean

b. 2 points for correctly finding the mean absolute deviation

c. 2 points for correctly comparing the difference in the means with the MAD

Benchmark Test

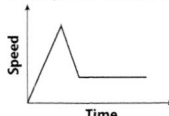

Personal
Math Trainer
Online
Assessment and
Intervention
@my.hrw.com

Selected Response

1. Multiply. Write the product as one power.
$a^8 \cdot a^5$

Ⓐ a^{13} Ⓒ a^{40}

Ⓑ a^3 Ⓓ Cannot combine

2. Simplify $(6^{-4})^6$.

Ⓐ -24^6 Ⓒ 6^2

Ⓑ $\frac{1}{6^{24}}$ Ⓓ $\frac{1}{6^{10}}$

3. A square mosaic is made of small glass squares. If there are 196 small squares in the mosaic, how many are along an edge?

Ⓐ 98 squares Ⓒ 14 squares

Ⓑ 49 squares Ⓓ 16 squares

4. Simplify $2\sqrt{-19 + 44}$.

Ⓐ 13.3 Ⓒ 10

Ⓑ 44 Ⓓ 27

5. A passenger plane travels at about 7.97×10^2 feet per second. The plane takes 1.11×10^4 seconds to reach its destination.

About how far must the plane travel to reach its destination? Write your answer in scientific notation.

Ⓐ 8.85×10^8 feet Ⓒ 8.85×10^6 feet

Ⓑ 9.08×10^6 feet Ⓓ 9.08×10^8 feet

6. Approximate $\sqrt{158}$ to the nearest hundredth.

Ⓐ 12.57 Ⓒ 16.57

Ⓑ 16.62 Ⓓ 8.52

7. Write a rule for the linear function.

x	y
−3	12
−2	10
3	0
5	−4

Ⓐ $y = -2x - 6$ Ⓒ $y = \frac{1}{2}x + 6$

Ⓑ $y = -2x + 6$ Ⓓ $y = \frac{1}{2}x - 6$

8. A remote-control airplane descends at a rate of 2 feet per second. After 3 seconds it is 67 feet above the ground. Write the equation in point-slope form that models the situation. Then, find the height of the plane after 8 seconds.

Ⓐ $y - 67 = -2(x - 3)$; 57 feet

Ⓑ $y - 67 = -3(x - 2)$; 49 feet

Ⓒ $y - 3 = -2(x - 67)$; 121 feet

Ⓓ $y - 2 = 67(x - 3)$; 337 feet

9. A bicyclist heads east at 19 km/h. After she has traveled 24.2 kilometers, another cyclist sets out in the same direction going 30 km/h. About how long will it take the second cyclist to catch up to the first cyclist?

Ⓐ It will take the second cyclist 3.2 hours to catch up to the first cyclist.

Ⓑ It will take the second cyclist 3.7 hours to catch up to the first cyclist.

Ⓒ It will take the second cyclist 2.2 hours to catch up to the first cyclist.

Ⓓ It will take the second cyclist 1.7 hours to catch up to the first cyclist.

10. What is the equation of the graph in slope-intercept form?

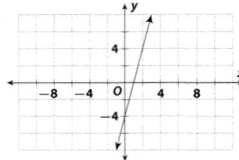

Ⓐ $y = -4x - 4$ Ⓒ $y = -5x - 4$

Ⓑ $y = 4x - 4$ Ⓓ $y = 5x - 4$

11. Solve $-2z + 3 + 7z = -12$.

Ⓐ $z = -3$ Ⓒ $z = 1$

Ⓑ $z = -15$ Ⓓ $z = -1.8$

12. Which equation has only one solution?

Ⓐ $c + 2 = c + 2$ Ⓒ $c + 2 = c - 2$

Ⓑ $c = -c + 2$ Ⓓ $c - c = 2$

13. Which ordered pair is a solution of the system of equations?
$y = 3x + 1$
$y = 5x - 1$

Ⓐ (2, 3) Ⓒ (1, 2)

Ⓑ (0, 1) Ⓓ (1, 4)

14. Which of these functions is *not* linear?

Ⓐ $y = x^2 - x$ Ⓒ $y = \frac{x}{3}$

Ⓑ $y = 1 - x$ Ⓓ $y = \frac{2}{3}x - 2x$

15. Which function has the greatest rate of change?

Ⓐ $y = -5x$

Ⓑ {(−1, −2), (1, 2), (3, 6), (5, 10), (7, 14)}

Ⓒ A fitness club charges a $200 membership fee plus monthly fees of $25.

Ⓓ $y = 3x - 16$

Mini-Tasks

16. The graph below shows an airplane's speed over a period of time. Describe the events.

The airplane accelerates quickly
on take-off, then slows down,
and then proceeds at a steady
speed.

17. Identify $\sqrt{\frac{169}{64}}$ as *rational* or *irrational*. Explain your reasoning.
rational; $\sqrt{\frac{169}{64}} = \frac{13}{8}$

Performance Task

18. Ashley reads 2 pages/minute for 10 minutes, takes a 10 minute break, and then reads at the same rate for 10 more minutes. Adam reads at the same rate the entire time. The equation for the number of pages he reads is $y = 1.2x$. How are these functions similar? How are they different?
Both have *y*-intercept 0. Adam's
graph is linear, Ashley's is not.
Ashley's has three parts: a
line with slope 2 from (0, 0) to
(10, 20), a horizontal line from
(10, 20) to (20, 20) and a line with
slope 2 from (20, 20) to (30, 40).

Grade 8

Benchmark Test

Use this test to assess students' mastery of topics in this course. The test can be used to assist with placement or as a cumulative review before high-stakes tests.

Scoring Guide for Performance Task

2 points for stating that both graphs have y-intercept 0

2 points for stating that Adam's graph is linear and Ashley's is not

2 points for correctly describing Ashley's graph

Grade 8 Student Edition

Items	Lessons	Items	Lessons
1	2.1	10	4.3
2	2.1	11	7.1
3	1.1	12	7.4
4	1.3	13	8.2
5	2.4	14	6.2
6	1.3	15	6.3
7	4.2	16	6.4
8	5.1	17	1.2
9	6.3	18	6.3

Benchmark Test

Personal Math Trainer
Online Assessment and Intervention
my.hrw.com

Selected Response

1. In the gift shop of the History of Flight museum, Elisa bought a kit to make a model of a jet airplane. The actual plane is 21 feet long with a wingspan of 17.5 feet. If the finished model will be 12 inches long, what will the wingspan be?

(A) 30.6 in.   (C) 14.4 in.
(B) 10 in.   (D) 5 in.

2. Find the angle measures in the isosceles triangle.

44°

(A) $f = 18°$ (C) $f = 68°$
(B) $f = 118°$ (D) $f = 11.7°$

3. Which ordered pair is a solution of the system of equations?
$y = 3x - 1$
$y = 5x + 1$

(A) (4, 1)   (C) (−4, −1)
(B) (1, 4)   (D) (−1, −4)

4. Melanie is making a piece of jewelry that is in the shape of a right triangle. The two shorter sides of the piece of jewelry are 9 mm and 12 mm. Find the perimeter of the piece of jewelry.

(A) 32 mm   (C) 30 mm
(B) 36 mm   (D) 34 mm

5. Find the distance, to the nearest tenth, from $T(4, -2)$ to $U(-2, 3)$.

(A) −1.0 units   (C) 0.0 units
(B) 3.4 units   (D) 7.8 units

6. Which of the following is *not* a congruence transformation?

(A) A reflection over the *x*-axis.
(B) A dilation with scale factor 0.5.
(C) A translation 1 unit left.
(D) A dilation with scale factor 1.

7. Harry and Selma start driving from the same location. Harry drives 42 miles north while Selma drives 144 miles east. How far apart are Harry and Selma when they stop?

(A) 1,764 miles   (C) 22,500 miles
(B) 150 miles   (D) 20,736 miles

8. Which triangle with side lengths given below is a right triangle?

(A) 10, 15, 20   (C) 9, 40, 41
(B) 10, 24, 25   (D) 16, 20, 25

9. Angles B and F are corresponding angles formed by a transversal intersecting two parallel lines. Angle B has a measure of 44°. What is the measure of Angle F?

(A) 44°   (C) 90°
(B) 46°   (D) 136°

10. Which transformation below preserves similarity between the preimage and image, but does not preserve congruence?

(A) reflections   (C) translations
(B) rotations   (D) dilations

© Houghton Mifflin Harcourt Publishing Company

11. An artist is creating a large conical sculpture for a park. The cone has a height of 16 m and a diameter of 25 m. Find the volume of the sculpture to the nearest hundredth.

(A) 833.33 m³   (C) 2,616.67 m³
(B) 7,850 m³   (D) 209.33 m³

12. A cylindrical barrel has a radius of 7.6 ft and a height of 10.8 ft. Tripling which dimension(s) will triple the volume of the barrel?

(A) height
(B) radius
(C) both height and radius
(D) neither height nor radius

13. Which linear equation approximates the best fit to the data?

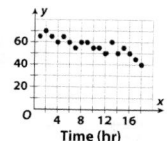

(A) $y = -2x + 65$ (C) $y = -x + 68$
(B) $y = -5x + 100$ (D) $y = -0.5x + 55$

Mini-Tasks

14. On Monday, a work group eats at Ava's café, where a lunch special is $8 and a dessert is $2. The total is $108. On Friday, the group eats at Bo's café, where a lunch special is $6 and a dessert is $3. The total is $90. Each time, the group orders the same number of lunches and the same number of desserts. How many lunches and desserts are ordered?

12 lunches, 6 desserts

15. Dilate the figure by a scale factor of 0.5 with the origin as the center of dilation.

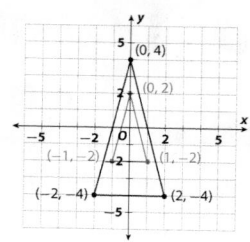

Performance Task

16. In a drought, many trees on a plot of land died. The table shows how many oak trees and pine trees survived or died.

Survived/Died	Survived	Died	Total
Oak	60	20	80
Pine	72	48	120
Total	0	68	200

a. Create a two-way relative frequency table using decimals.

Survived/Died	Survived	Died	TOTAL
Oak	0.30	0.10	0.40
Pine	0.36	0.24	0.60
TOTAL	0.66	0.34	1.00

b. As a percent, what was the joint relative frequency of pine trees that died?

_24%_

c. Compare the conditional relative frequencies, in percent form, that a tree survived given that it was an oak and that it survived given that it was a pine.

oak: 75%, pine: 60%; a greater percent of oaks survived

© Houghton Mifflin Harcourt Publishing Company

Grade 8 Student Edition

Items	Lessons
1	3.1
2	11.2
3	8.2
4	12.1
5	12.3
6	9.5
7	12.1
8	12.2

Items	Lessons
9	11.1
10	9.5, 10.3
11	13.2
12	13.1
13	14.2
14	8.4
15	10.1
16	15.2

Scoring Guide for Performance Task

a. 2 points for creating a correct two-way relative frequency table

b. 2 points for finding the correct joint relative frequency as a percent

c. 2 points for correctly comparing the conditional relative frequencies

Real Numbers, Exponents, and Scientific Notation

Contents

Teacher Notes

PLANNING AND PACING GUIDE
Instructional Path

Lesson	Lesson Objectives	Pacing*
UNIT 1 | Real Numbers, Exponents, and Scientific Notation		
Progress Tracker 1 2 3 4 5 6		
MODULE 1 | Real Numbers		1 day
1.1 Rational and Irrational Numbers	Students will rewrite rational numbers and decimals, take square roots and cube roots, and approximate irrational numbers.	2 days
1.2 Sets of Real Numbers	Students will describe relationships between sets of real numbers.	2 days
1.3 Ordering Real Numbers **Game 1.3** Root-O!	Students will order a set of real numbers. Students will evaluate square roots, including rational and irrational numbers.	3 days
Ready to Go On? **Module 1 Assessment Readiness**		1 day
MODULE 2 | Exponents and Scientific Notation		1 day
2.1 Integer Exponents **Going Further 2.1** Zero and Negative Exponents	Students will develop and use the properties of integer exponents. Students will derive the definition of a zero exponent and the definition of a negative exponent.	3 days
2.2 Scientific Notation with Positive Powers of 10 **Going Further 2.2** Comparing Very Large Numbers	Students will use scientific notation to express very large quantities. Students will compare very large numbers in scientific notation.	3 days
2.3 Scientific Notation with Negative Powers of 10 **Going Further 2.3** Comparing Very Small Numbers	Students will use scientific notation to express very small quantities. Students will compare very small numbers in scientific notation.	3 days
2.4 Operations with Scientific Notation	Students will add, subtract, multiply, and divide using scientific notation.	2 days
Ready to Go On? **Module 2 Assessment Readiness**		1 day
Study Guide Review **Unit 1 Assessment Readiness**		2 days

* Based on a 45-minute class period.

Teaching for Depth

Square Roots, Irrational Numbers, and Repeating Decimals

One or two square roots? There are two solutions of $x^2 = a$, namely $\sqrt{a}$ and $-\sqrt{a}$. For example, the two solutions of $x^2 = 121$ are 12 and −12. However, the radical symbol $\sqrt{}$ is used to indicate only the nonnegative principal square root. Therefore, $\sqrt{a^2} = |a|$.

Working with square roots gives students exposure to irrational numbers. Some key ideas are:

- A square root is irrational when the number under the square root symbol is not a perfect square.

- The decimal form of an irrational number neither terminates nor repeats.

A repeating decimal is a rational number, and students will learn to write a repeating decimal as a fraction.

Estimating Square Roots

Students estimate square roots of nonperfect squares by finding two perfect squares between which the number falls.

$$\text{For example, because } \sqrt{1} < \sqrt{2} < \sqrt{4},$$
$$\text{we know } \sqrt{2} \text{ is between 1 and 2.}$$

A more precise method involves repeated division. For example, to find $\sqrt{28}$, find a whole number whose perfect square is close to 28, such as 5. Divide 28 by that number: $28 \div 5 = 5.6$. Find the average of the quotient and divisor: $\frac{5 + 5.6}{2} = 5.3$. Continue dividing 28 by each result and averaging until you get the desired accuracy.

> **Great teaching materials do not provide great education in and of themselves. Educators who collaborate in Professional Learning Communities can have a profound impact on their students.**

TIM KANOLD on Synergy Through Collaboration

Integer Exponents

Patterns: Using patterns, you can intuitively see that any nonzero number raised to the zero power equals 1.

For example:

$$2^4 = 16$$
$$2^3 = 8 \quad \div 2$$
$$2^2 = 4 \quad \div 2$$
$$2^1 = 2 \quad \div 2$$
$$2^0 = 1 \quad \div 2$$

The exponent decreases by 1 as the value of the exponential expression is divided by the value of the base.

Properties: Using properties, we can prove that any nonzero number raised to the zero power equals 1.

(a) We know that any nonzero number divided by itself is 1.

(b) By the property of exponents, $a^x \div a^y = a^{x-y}$, for $a \neq 0$.

Using (a) and (b),

If (b) $a^x \div a^x = a^{x-x} = a^0$ and (a) $a^x \div a^x = 1$,

then $a^0 = 1$, for $a \neq 0$.

See *Going Further 2.1.*

Professional Development Videos

Module 2: Exponents and Scientific Notation

Scientific Notation

Scientific notation is used to represent very large and very small numbers in an efficient way which is easy to write and easy to read.

Error Alert: There may be confusion about the meaning of a *very large* or a *very small* number. In this context, *very large* or *very small* indicates absolute value. So a *very small* number is very close to zero. Make sure that students do not think it means a negative number with a large absolute value, such as $-999,999$.

Rules of Exponents

The rules of exponents are used when performing operations with numbers in scientific notation:

1. **Product Rule:** $a^m \cdot a^n = a^{m+n}$, for $a \neq 0$
   Example: $4^3 \cdot 4^{-1} = 4^{(3+-1)} = 4^2$

2. **Quotient Rule:** $a^m \div a^n = a^{m-n}$, for $a \neq 0$
   Example: $4^3 \div 4^{-1} = 4^{(3--1)} = 4^4$

3. **Power Rule:** $(a^m)^n = a^{m \cdot n}$, for $a \neq 0$
   Example: $(4^3)^{-1} = 4^{(3 \cdot -1)} = 4^{-3}$

UNIT 1
Real Numbers, Exponents, and Scientific Notation

CAREERS IN MATH

Astronomer

Astronomers use math to understand and predict the physical properties and motion of objects in space. They also use math as a tool to help them form and test theories about the laws that govern the universe. You will learn more about this in the Performance Tasks at the end of the unit.

For more information about careers in mathematics as well as various mathematics appreciation topics, visit the American Mathematical Society at www.ams.org.

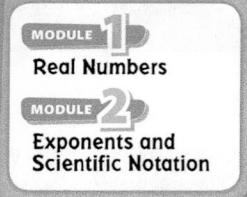

UNIT 1
Real Numbers, Exponents, and Scientific Notation

MODULE 1
Real Numbers

MODULE 2
Exponents and Scientific Notation

CAREERS IN MATH

Astronomer An astronomer is a scientist who studies and tries to interpret the universe beyond Earth. Astronomers use math to calculate distances to celestial objects and to create mathematical models to help them understand the dynamics of systems from stars and planets to black holes. If you are interested in a career as an astronomer, you should study the following mathematical subjects:
- Algebra
- Geometry
- Trigonometry
- Calculus

Research other careers that require creating mathematical models to understand physical phenomena.

Unit 1 Performance Task

At the end of the unit, check out how **astronomers** use math.

Vocabulary Preview

Use the puzzle to preview key vocabulary from this unit. Unscramble the circled letters to answer the riddle at the bottom of the page.

1. **TCREEFP SEAQUR**

P E R F E C **T**
S Q U A R E

2. **NOLRATAI RUNMEB**

R A T I **O** N A L
N U M B E R

3. **PERTIANEG MALCEDI**

R E P E A T I N G
D E C I M **A** L

4. **LAER SEBMNUR**

R E A L
N **U** M B E R **S**

5. **NIISICFTCE OITANTON**

S C I **E** N T I F I C
N O T A T I **O** N

1. Has integers as its square roots. (Lesson 1.1)
2. Any number that can be written as a ratio of two integers. (Lesson 1.1)
3. A decimal in which one or more digits repeat infinitely. (Lesson 1.1)
4. The set of rational and irrational numbers. (Lesson 1.2)
5. A method of writing very large or very small numbers by using powers of 10. (Lesson 2.2)

Q: What keeps a square from moving?

A: S Q U A R E   R O O T S !

© Houghton Mifflin Harcourt Publishing Company

Vocabulary Preview

Use the puzzle to give students a preview of important concepts in this unit. Students may work individually, in pairs, or in groups.

Digital Teacher Resources

Go online for unit-level resources.

my.hrw.com

LEARNING PROGRESSIONS AND STANDARDS ACROSS THE GRADES

Before	In this Unit	After
Students understand: • sets and subsets of rational numbers • operations with rational numbers • exponents	Students will learn about: • relationships between sets of real numbers • irrational numbers including π • ordering irrational and rational numbers • scientific notation • properties of integer exponents • scientific notation • operations with scientific notation	Students will connect: • rational and irrational numbers • irrational numbers and a number line • decimal notation and scientific notation

Module At A Glance

Module Essential Question: How can you use real numbers to solve real-world problems?

MODULE 1 | Real Numbers

Lessons at A Glance	Lesson 1.1 Rational and Irrational Numbers	Lesson 1.2 Sets of Real Numbers	Lesson 1.3 Ordering Real Numbers
	Pg. T7A	Pg. T15A	Pg. T21A
Essential Question	How do you rewrite rational numbers and decimals, take square roots and cube roots, and approximate irrational numbers?	How can you describe relationships between sets of real numbers?	How do you order a set of real numbers?
Objective	Students will rewrite rational numbers and decimals, take square roots and cube roots, and approximate irrational numbers.	Students will describe relationships between sets of real numbers.	Students will order a set of real numbers.
Vocabulary	cube root, irrational numbers, perfect cube, perfect square, principal square root, rational number, repeating decimal, square root, terminating decimal	real numbers	
Go online For all your module resources my.hrw.com	1.1 *i*Student Edition 1.1 *i*Teacher Edition 1.1 *e*Student Edition 🔧 Personal Math Trainer 📺 Math on the Spot Videos	1.2 *i*Student Edition 1.2 *i*Teacher Edition 1.2 *e*Student Edition 🔧 Personal Math Trainer 📺 Math on the Spot Videos ✖ Animated Math	1.3 *i*Student Edition 1.3 *i*Teacher Edition 1.3 *e*Student Edition 🔧 Personal Math Trainer 📺 Math on the Spot Videos

Print Resources	**1.1 Student Edition:** Lesson
	Differentiated Instruction
	  1.1 Practice and Problem Solving A/B, C, and D
	  1.1 Reteach
	  1.1 Reading Strategies
	  1.1 Success for English Learners
		1.2 Student Edition: Lesson
		Differentiated Instruction
		  1.2 Practice and Problem Solving A/B, C, and D
		  1.2 Reteach
		  1.2 Reading Strategies
		  1.2 Success for English Learners
			1.3 Student Edition: Lesson
			Differentiated Instruction
			  1.3 Practice and Problem Solving A/B, C, and D
			  1.3 Reteach
			  1.3 Reading Strategies
			  1.3 Success for English Learners

RtI

Response to Intervention

Before the Module	During the Lesson	After the Module
Are You Ready	**Guided/Independent Practice**	**Ready to Go On?**
• Prerequisite Skills Activities • Personal Math Trainer	• Reteach • Personal Math Trainer • Practice and Problem Solving D	• Reteach • Personal Math Trainer

Teacher Notes

 Check It Out!

Game	Math on the Spot Videos	Animated Math
Root-O! After Lesson 1.3	 One for every Example in every Lesson	X^2 During Lesson 1.2

Real Numbers

Real-World Video Viewing Guide

After students have watched the video, discuss the following:

- What are some different ways that biologists classify animals?
- What are some classifications of numbers mentioned in the video? natural numbers, integers, rational numbers

Professional Development Video

Author Juli Dixon models successful teaching practices as she explores the concept of real numbers in an actual eighth-grade classroom.

Real Numbers

? ESSENTIAL QUESTION

How can you use real numbers to solve real-world problems?

Since every rational and irrational number is a real number, any real-world problem that can be modeled and solved with rational or irrational numbers can be modeled and solved with real numbers.

LESSON 1.1
Rational and Irrational Numbers

LESSON 1.2
Sets of Real Numbers

LESSON 1.3
Ordering Real Numbers

© Houghton Mifflin Harcourt Publishing Company • Image Credits: ©Daniel Hershman/Getty Images

Real-World Video

Living creatures can be classified into groups. The sea otter belongs to the kingdom Animalia and class Mammalia. Numbers can also be classified into groups such as rational numbers and integers.

my.hrw.com

GO DIGITAL
my.hrw.com

my.hrw.com	Math On the Spot	Animated Math	Personal Math Trainer
Go digital with your write-in student edition, accessible on any device.	Scan with your smart phone to jump directly to the online edition, video tutor, and more.	Interactively explore key concepts to see how math works.	Get immediate feedback and help as you work through practice sets.

3

TEACHER ONLINE RESOURCES

 ONLINE TEACHER EDITION Access a full suite of teaching resources online—plan, present, and manage classes and assignments.

 MY SMART PLANNER Easily plan your classes and access all your resources online.

 INTERACTIVE WHITEBOARDS Engage students with interactive whiteboard-ready examples and a lesson quiz for each lesson.

 PERSONAL MATH TRAINER: Online Assessment and Intervention Assign automatically graded homework, quizzes, tests, and intervention activities. Prepare your students for standardized tests in short-answer and multiple-choice formats.

Reading Start-Up

Visualize Vocabulary

Use the ✔ words to complete the graphic. You can put more than one word in each section of the triangle.

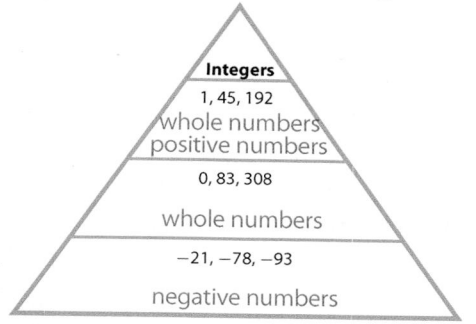

Integers
1, 45, 192
whole numbers
positive numbers

0, 83, 308

whole numbers

−21, −78, −93

negative numbers

Understand Vocabulary

Complete the sentences using the preview words.

1. One of the two equal factors of a number is a _square root_.

2. A _perfect square_ has integers as its square roots.

3. The _principal square root_ is the nonnegative square root of a number.

© Houghton Mifflin Harcourt Publishing Company

Active Reading

Layered Book Before beginning the lessons in this module, create a layered book to help you learn the concepts in this module. Label the flaps "Rational Numbers," "Irrational Numbers," "Square Roots," and "Real Numbers." As you study each lesson, write important ideas such as vocabulary, models, and sample problems under the appropriate flap.

Vocabulary

Review Words
  integers *(enteros)*
✔ negative numbers *(números negativos)*
✔ positive numbers *(números positivos)*
✔ whole number *(número entero)*

Preview Words
  cube root *(raíz cúbica)*
  irrational numbers *(número irracional)*
  perfect cube *(cubo perfecto)*
  perfect square *(cuadrado perfecto)*
  principal square root *(raíz cuadrada principal)*
  rational number *(número racional)*
  real numbers *(número real)*
  repeating decimal *(decimal periódico)*
  square root *(raíz cuadrada)*
  terminating decimal *(decimal finito)*

Reading Start-Up

Visualize Vocabulary
The summary triangle helps students review the concepts related to integers. Students should write one or more review words to match the examples in each section of the triangle.

Understand Vocabulary
Use the following explanations to help students learn the preview words.

> To terminate something means to end it. A **terminating decimal** has an ending, or a limited amount of digits. To repeat something means to do it over again. A **repeating decimal** has one or more digits that repeat and never ends.

> **Real numbers** include **rational numbers** and **irrational numbers**.

Active Reading

Integrating Language Arts
Students can use these reading and note-taking strategies to help them organize and understand new concepts and vocabulary.

Additional Resources
Differentiated Instruction
- Reading Strategies **ELL**
- Interactive multilingual glossary

LEARNING PROGRESSIONS ACROSS THE GRADES

Before	In this Module	After
Students understand:	Students will learn how to:	Students will connect that:
• write rational numbers as decimals	• express a rational number as a decimal	• the rational numbers are those with decimal expansions that terminate in 0s or eventually repeat
• describe relationships between sets and subsets of rational numbers	• approximate the value of an irrational number	• non-rational numbers are called irrational numbers
• compare rational numbers	• describe the relationship between sets of real numbers	
	• order a set of real numbers arising from mathematical and real-world contexts	

Are You Ready?

Assess Readiness

Access *Are You Ready?* assessment online, and receive instant scoring, feedback, and customized intervention or enrichment.

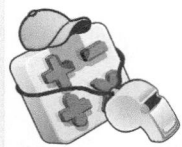

Personal Math Trainer

Online Assessment and Intervention

Additional Resources

Digital Teacher Resources

Go online for module-level resources.

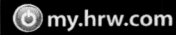
my.hrw.com

Complete these exercises to review skills you will need for this module.

Personal Math Trainer
Online Assessment and Intervention
my.hrw.com

Find the Square of a Number

EXAMPLE Find the square of $\frac{2}{3}$.

$\frac{2}{3} \times \frac{2}{3} = \frac{2 \times 2}{3 \times 3}$ Multiply the number by itself.

$= \frac{4}{9}$ Simplify.

Find the square of each number.

1. 7   <u>49</u>
2. 21   <u>441</u>
3. −3   <u>9</u>
4. $\frac{4}{5}$ <u>$\frac{16}{25}$</u>
5. 2.7   <u>7.29</u>
6. $-\frac{1}{4}$ <u>$\frac{1}{16}$</u>
7. −5.7   <u>32.49</u>
8. $1\frac{2}{5}$ <u>$1\frac{24}{25}$ or 1.96</u>

Exponents

EXAMPLE $5^3 = 5 \times 5 \times 5$ Use the base, 5, as a factor 3 times.

$= 25 \times 5$ Multiply from left to right.

$= 125$

Simplify each exponential expression.

9. 9^2 <u>81</u>
10. 2^4 <u>16</u>
11. $\left(\frac{1}{3}\right)^2$ <u>$\frac{1}{9}$</u>
12. $(-7)^2$ <u>49</u>
13. 4^3 <u>64</u>
14. $(-1)^5$ <u>−1</u>
15. 4.5^2 <u>20.25</u>
16. 10^5 <u>100,000</u>

Write a Mixed Number as an Improper Fraction

EXAMPLE $2\frac{2}{5} = 2 + \frac{2}{5}$ Write the mixed number as a sum of a whole number and a fraction.

$= \frac{10}{5} + \frac{2}{5}$ Write the whole number as an equivalent fraction with the same denominator as the fraction in the mixed number.

$= \frac{12}{5}$ Add the numerators.

Write each mixed number as an improper fraction.

17. $3\frac{1}{3}$ <u>$\frac{10}{3}$</u>
18. $1\frac{5}{8}$ <u>$\frac{13}{8}$</u>
19. $2\frac{3}{7}$ <u>$\frac{17}{7}$</u>
20. $5\frac{5}{6}$ <u>$\frac{35}{6}$</u>

© Houghton Mifflin Harcourt Publishing Company

ARE YOU READY? *Diagnostic Assessment*

RtI Response to Intervention

Use to determine if students need intervention for the module's prerequisite skills.

Skill	Missed More Than ...	Intervene With *Skills Intervention* worksheets (available online)	For Enrichment *Differentiated Instruction* (available in print and online)
Find the Square of a Number	2 questions	**Skill 11** Find the Square of a Number	**Module 1 Challenge** Extend-the-Math Lesson Activities in TE
Exponents	2 questions	**Skill 12** Exponents	**Module 1 Challenge** Extend-the-Math Lesson Activities in TE
Write a Mixed Number as an Improper Fraction	1 question	**Skill 22** Write a Mixed Number as an Improper Fraction	**Module 1 Challenge** Extend-the-Math Lesson Activities in TE

Complete these exercises to review skills you will need for this module.

Find the Square of a Number

21. Harold designed a game board that is a square grid with 18 squares on each side. How many squares are on the grid? Explain how you found your answer.

> There are 324 squares on the grid. Since the board is a square, multiply the number of squares on each side by itself: $18 \times 18 = 324$.

22. Janine estimated that the square of 4.1 is approximately 16. Justify her estimate, and then find the exact value.

> Round to the nearest whole number. 4.1 is close to 4, and $4 \times 4 = 16$, so 4.1^2 is approximately 16. The exact value is $4.1^2 = 16.81$.

Exponents

23. Wanda invested money in a savings certificate of deposit that earns 4% interest. Its value after 3 years can be found by evaluating $(1.04)^3$ and multiplying the result by the initial value.

  a. Describe how to simplify the exponential expression.

  b. The initial value of Wanda's account was $1,000. Simplify the exponential expression and interpret the result to describe how the value of Wanda's savings has changed after 3 years.

> **a.** Write the product of three factors of 1.04, or $(1.04)(1.04)(1.04)$.
>
> **b.** $1.04^3 \approx 1.125$; after 3 years, the value was about 1.125 times the initial value of $1,000, or $1,125.

Write a Mixed Number as an Improper Fraction

24. A muffin recipe calls for $2\frac{5}{8}$ cups flour, $1\frac{3}{4}$ cups yogurt, $1\frac{1}{3}$ tablespoons baking powder, and $2\frac{3}{8}$ cups blueberries. Write each of these quantities as an improper fraction.

> $\frac{21}{8}$ cups flour, $\frac{7}{4}$ cups yogurt, $\frac{4}{3}$ tablespoons baking powder, $\frac{19}{8}$ cups blueberries

25. Penny wrote the mixed number $4\frac{2}{7}$ as $\frac{8}{7}$. Describe Penny's error, and explain how she should have written the improper fraction.

> Penny multiplied 4 times 2 and used that as the numerator. She should have written 4 as the equivalent fraction $\frac{28}{7}$ and then added $\frac{28}{7}$ to $\frac{2}{7}$ to get $\frac{30}{7}$.

© Houghton Mifflin Harcourt Publishing Company

Find the Square of a Number

Exercise 21 Make sure students understand that to square a number they should multiply the number by itself.

Exercise 22 Encourage students to estimate first when finding the square of a number to check whether their answers are reasonable.

Exponents

Exercise 23a Check whether students can identify the base and the exponent. Make sure they understand when a number is in exponential form, the exponent represents how many times the base is used as a factor.

Exercise 23b Encourage students to use technology to help them find the power of a decimal.

Write a Mixed Number as an Improper Fraction

Exercise 24 Watch for students who may add the denominator, the whole number, and the numerator to get the numerator for the improper fraction.

Exercise 25 Make sure students understand that $4\frac{2}{7}$ can be written as $4 + \frac{2}{7}$, and then the whole number can be written with a denominator of 7; $\frac{28}{7} + \frac{2}{7}$.

Use to determine if students are able to apply the module's prerequisite skills.

Skill	Exercise	Depth of Knowledge (D.O.K.)	Mathematical Processes
Find the Square of a Number	21	3 Strategic Thinking	MP.2 Abstract and Quantitative Reasoning
	22	2 Skills/Concepts	MP.2 Abstract and Quantitative Reasoning
Exponents	23	2 Skills/Concepts	MP.6 Use Precise Mathematical Language
Write a Mixed Number as an Improper Fraction	24	2 Skills/Concepts	MP.1 Problem Solving
	25	2 Skills/Concepts	MP.3 Use and Evaluate Logical Reasoning

Lesson Support

Content Objective Students will learn to rewrite rational numbers and decimals, take square roots and cube roots, and approximate irrational numbers.

Professional Development

Integrate Mathematical Processes MP.6

This lesson provides an opportunity to address this Mathematical Processes standard. It calls for students to attend to precision. Students learn to express rational numbers accurately and precisely in both fractional and decimal forms, and learn to translate from one form to the other. They also learn how to precisely represent and communicate ideas about irrational numbers, square roots, and cube roots.

FOCUS

Building Background

Eliciting Prior Knowledge Have students work with a partner to review the relationship between fractions and decimals. Ask students to provide an example of writing a fraction or mixed number as a decimal and vice versa. Discuss how students chose and wrote their examples.

$$\frac{3}{4} = 0.75 \qquad 1\frac{2}{3} = 1.\overline{6}$$

$$\frac{7}{10} = 0.7 \qquad 4.5 = 4\frac{1}{2}$$

COHERENCE

Learning Progressions

In this lesson, students work with positive rational and irrational numbers. They make connections among the real numbers by converting fractions and decimals and approximating irrational numbers. Important understandings for students include the following:

- **Understand that every number has a decimal expansion.**
- **Convert a repeating decimal to a rational number.**
- **Evaluate square roots of perfect squares and cube roots of perfect cubes.**
- **Estimate an irrational number.**

Work with the real number system will continue in this unit as students extend the positive rational and irrational numbers to include negative numbers and compare and order real numbers.

RIGOR

Cluster Connections

This lesson provides an excellent opportunity to connect ideas in this cluster:

Know that there are numbers that are not rational, and approximate them by rational numbers.

Tell students, "A square garden has an area of 20 square feet."

$$\boxed{20 \text{ ft}^2}$$

Have students explain why the side length cannot be rational. Then have them approximate the length of each side of the garden to the nearest tenth and hundredth.

Sample answer: The length is the solution to $s^2 = 20$, $\sqrt{20}$, which is not a rational number. 4.5 ft; 4.47 ft; The length is between 4 and 5 feet. 20 is closer to 4.5^2 than to 4.4^2 or 4.6^2. It is also closer to 4.47^2 than to 4.46^2 or 4.48^2.

Language Support ELL

Language Objective Students will show and explain how to rewrite rational numbers and decimals, take square roots and cube roots, and approximate irrational numbers.

Leveled Strategies for English Learners ELL

Emerging
Use cards with root words *ten*, *hundred*, and *thousand* and a card with the *-th* suffix. Have students place them together to show place value. Then complete a sentence. Use the same procedure to identify decimals.

Expanding
Support students at this level of English proficiency by providing sentence frames for them to use to describe their mathematical reasoning.

  To write the fraction _____ as a decimal, I _____.

Bridging
Have students identify different meanings of the term *square* by matching examples of math problems with a written-out sentence frame that defines the usage of the term *square*: to square a number; perfect square; square root. Use this procedure also with the term *cube*.

Be sure to clarify the different uses of the term *square* when referring to square roots, perfect squares, and so on.

Linguistic Support ELL

Academic/Content Vocabulary
square In this lesson, the word *square* has multiple meanings, which can cause confusion. For example, to *square* as in "to take the square root of a number" is a verb. It is different from the nouns *square* or *square of a number*. The text also refers to *perfect square* and *principal square root* of a number, and the square root symbol is used. These different usages of *square* as a mathematical term need to be clarified. Sentence frames can be used to help define the meaning.

  To square a number means to _____. The perfect square of a number means _____.

Background Knowledge
suffixes When added to a root word, the suffix *-th* is used in math to indicate one of a specified number of parts, such as *tenth*, *hundredth*, or *thousandth*. Remind students that the suffix *-th* also indicates place value. Note that Spanish, Vietnamese, Mandarin, and other languages do not have the ending *th* sound, so teachers need to enunciate carefully.

cognates The words *terminating* and *terminal* used in this lesson have cognates in Spanish: *terminar*, meaning "to end" or "to finish." A Spanish cognate for *approximate* is *aproximar*.

Image Credits: ©Duel/Cultura/Getty Images

Rational and Irrational Numbers

① Engage

❓ ESSENTIAL QUESTION

How do you rewrite rational numbers and decimals, take square roots and cube roots, and approximate irrational numbers? **To express as a decimal, divide the numerator by the denominator. To take a square root or cube root of a number, find the number that when squared or cubed equals the original number. To approximate an irrational number, estimate a number between two consecutive perfect squares.**

Motivate the Lesson
Ask: Which type of rational number do you see more often, fractions or decimals? Which do you prefer to use? Why? Begin the lesson to find out.

② Explore

EXPLORE ACTIVITY EXAMPLE 1

ADDITIONAL EXAMPLE 1
Write each fraction as a decimal.

A $\frac{2}{5}$ 0.4

B $\frac{5}{9}$ $0.\overline{5}$

 Interactive Whiteboard
Interactive example available online

Rational and Irrational Numbers

8.1.1.1
Students will rewrite rational numbers and decimals, take square roots and cube roots, and approximate irrational numbers.

❓ ESSENTIAL QUESTION
How do you rewrite rational numbers and decimals, take square roots and cube roots, and approximate irrational numbers?

EXPLORE ACTIVITY

Expressing Rational Numbers as Decimals

Math On the Spot
ⓑ my.hrw.com

A **rational number** is any number that can be written as a ratio in the form $\frac{a}{b}$, where a and b are integers and b is not 0. Examples of rational numbers are 6 and 0.5.

6 can be written as $\frac{6}{1}$.   0.5 can be written as $\frac{1}{2}$.

Every rational number can be written as a terminating decimal or a repeating decimal. A **terminating decimal**, such as 0.5, has a finite number of digits. A **repeating decimal** has a block of one or more digits that repeats indefinitely.

EXAMPLE 1 Write each fraction as a decimal.

A $\frac{1}{4}$

The fraction bar is a division symbol.
Divide the numerator by the denominator: $1 \div 4$.

Divide until the remainder is zero, adding zeros after the decimal point in the dividend as needed.

The rational number $\frac{1}{4}$ can be written as a terminating decimal.

$$\frac{1}{4} = \boxed{0.25}$$

$$\begin{array}{r} 0.25 \\ 4\overline{)1.00} \\ -8 \\ \hline 20 \\ -20 \\ \hline 0 \end{array}$$

B $\frac{1}{3}$

Divide the numerator by the denominator: $1 \div 3$.

Divide until the remainder is zero or until the digits in the quotient begin to repeat.

Add zeros after the decimal point in the dividend as needed.

The rational number $\frac{1}{3}$ can be written as a repeating decimal, with a bar over the repeating digit(s).

$$\frac{1}{3} = \boxed{0.\overline{3}}$$

$$\begin{array}{r} 0.333 \\ 3\overline{)1.000} \\ -9 \\ \hline 10 \\ -9 \\ \hline 10 \\ -9 \\ \hline 1 \end{array}$$

© Houghton Mifflin Harcourt Publishing Company

Lesson 1.1   **7**

DIFFERENTIATE INSTRUCTION *Leveled Questions*

	EXPLORE ACTIVITY EXAMPLE 1
ⒶⓁ DOK 1 *Recall*	What operation does the fraction bar represent? division
ⓄⓁ DOK 2 *Skills/Concepts*	How can you determine the decimal equivalent of a fraction? Use long division to divide the numerator by the denominator.
ⒷⓁ DOK 3 *Strategic Thinking*	How does the denominator of a fraction in simplest form tell whether the decimal equivalent of the fraction is a terminating decimal? The decimal will terminate if the denominator has prime factors of only 2 and/or 5.

LEVELED QUESTIONS: ⒶⓁ Approaching Level | ⓄⓁ On Level | ⒷⓁ Beyond Level

YOUR TURN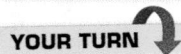

Write each fraction as a decimal.

1. $\frac{5}{11}$ ___$0.\overline{45}$___   2. $\frac{1}{8}$ ___0.125___   3. $2\frac{1}{3}$ ___$2.\overline{3}$___

Personal Math Trainer
Online Assessment and Intervention
my.hrw.com

Math On the Spot
my.hrw.com

Expressing Decimals as Rational Numbers

You can express terminating and repeating decimals as rational numbers.

EXAMPLE 2

My Notes

Write each decimal as a fraction in simplest form.

A 0.825

The decimal 0.825 means "825 thousandths." Write this as a fraction.

$\frac{825}{1000}$ *To write "825 thousandths", put 825 over 1000.*

Then simplify the fraction.

$\frac{825 \div 25}{1000 \div 25} = \frac{33}{40}$ *Divide both the numerator and the denominator by 25.*

$0.825 = \frac{33}{40}$

B $0.\overline{37}$

Let $x = 0.\overline{37}$. The number $0.\overline{37}$ has 2 repeating digits, so multiply each side of the equation $x = 0.\overline{37}$ by 10^2, or 100.

$x = 0.\overline{37}$

$(100)x = 100(0.\overline{37})$

$100x = 37.\overline{37}$ *100 times $0.\overline{37}$ is $37.\overline{37}$.*

Because $x = 0.\overline{37}$, you can subtract x from one side and $0.\overline{37}$ from the other.

$100x = 37.\overline{37}$

$\underline{-x \quad -0.\overline{37}}$

$99x = 37$ *$37.\overline{37}$ minus $0.\overline{37}$ is 37.*

Now solve the equation for x. Simplify if necessary.

$\frac{99x}{99} = \frac{37}{99}$ *Divide both sides of the equation by 99.*

$x = \frac{37}{99}$

© Houghton Mifflin Harcourt Publishing Company

YOUR TURN   MP.6

Talk About It

Check for Understanding

Ask: Can an improper fraction be written as a decimal? Give an example to support your answer. Yes; $\frac{5}{4} = 1.25$.

3 Explain

EXAMPLE 2

Focus on Technology

Point out the importance of entering a repeating decimal correctly when using a graphing calculator to convert the decimal to a fraction. The decimal $0.\overline{59}$ must be entered as 0.595959595959, not 0.59.

ADDITIONAL EXAMPLE 2
Write each decimal as a fraction in simplest form.

A 0.355 $\frac{71}{200}$

B $0.\overline{43}$ $\frac{43}{99}$

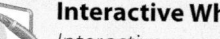
Interactive Whiteboard
Interactive example available online

	EXAMPLE 2
AL DOK 1 *Recall*	How can you tell if a decimal can be written as a rational number? If the decimal is a terminating or repeating decimal, then it can be written as a rational number.
OL DOK 2 *Skills/Concepts*	How can you use place value to write a terminating decimal as a fraction with a power of ten in the denominator? Find the place value of the decimal's last digit. Use the corresponding power of 10 as the denominator.
BL DOK 3 *Strategic Thinking*	How do you write the repeating part of a repeating decimal as a fraction? Set x equal to the repeating part of the decimal. Multiply both sides of that equation by a power of 10. Then subtract the original equation (x = repeating part) from the resulting equation. Solve for x.

TEACHER TO TEACHER

Cognitive Strategies Rational numbers terminate or repeat when written as a decimal. Irrational numbers do not terminate or repeat as decimals.

Remind students that sometimes irrational numbers have a pattern but do not repeat, such as 3.12112111211112 …

Rational and Irrational Numbers   **8**

Focus on Math Connections

Make sure students understand that the place value of the last digit in **Exercises 4** and **6** determines the denominator of the corresponding fraction or mixed number. So, for **Exercise 4**, the place value hundredths gives a denominator of 100, and for **Exercise 6**, the place value tenths gives a denominator of 10.

EXAMPLE 3

Focus on Math Connections

Make sure students understand the difference in finding $\sqrt{121}$ and solving $x^2 = 121$. The symbol $\sqrt{}$ indicates the positive or principal square root only, while the equation $x^2 = 121$ has two roots, the principal square root and its opposite.

ADDITIONAL EXAMPLE 3
Solve each equation for x.

A $x^2 = 324$ $18, -18$

B $x^2 = \frac{25}{144}$ $\frac{5}{12}, -\frac{5}{12}$

C $343 = x^3$ 7

D $x^3 = \frac{125}{512}$ $\frac{5}{8}$

 Interactive Whiteboard
Interactive example available online

Write each decimal as a fraction in simplest form.

4. 0.12 $\frac{3}{25}$

5. $0.5\overline{7}$ $\frac{19}{33}$

6. 1.4 $1\frac{2}{5}$

Personal Math Trainer
Online Assessment and Intervention
my.hrw.com

Math On the Spot
my.hrw.com

Finding Square Roots and Cube Roots

The **square root** of a positive number p is x if $x^2 = p$. There are two square roots for every positive number. For example, the square roots of 36 are 6 and −6 because $6^2 = 36$ and $(-6)^2 = 36$. The square roots of $\frac{1}{25}$ are $\frac{1}{5}$ and $-\frac{1}{5}$. You can write the square roots of $\frac{1}{25}$ as $\pm\frac{1}{5}$. The symbol $\sqrt{}$ indicates the positive, or **principal square root**.

A number that is a **perfect square** has square roots that are integers. The number 81 is a perfect square because its square roots are 9 and −9.

The **cube root** of a positive number p is x if $x^3 = p$. There is one cube root for every positive number. For example, the cube root of 8 is 2 because $2^3 = 8$. The cube root of $\frac{1}{27}$ is $\frac{1}{3}$ because $\left(\frac{1}{3}\right)^3 = \frac{1}{27}$. The symbol $\sqrt[3]{}$ indicates the cube root.

A number that is a **perfect cube** has a cube root that is an integer. The number 125 is a perfect cube because its cube root is 5.

EXAMPLE 3

Solve each equation for x.

A $x^2 = 121$

$x^2 = 121$ *Solve for x by taking the square root of both sides.*

$x = \pm\sqrt{121}$ *Apply the definition of square root.*

$x = \pm11$ *Think: What numbers squared equal 121?*

The solutions are 11 and −11.

B $x^2 = \frac{16}{169}$

$x^2 = \frac{16}{169}$ *Solve for x by taking the square root of both sides.*

$x = \pm\sqrt{\frac{16}{169}}$ *Apply the definition of square root.*

$x = \pm\frac{4}{13}$ *Think: What numbers squared equal $\frac{16}{169}$?*

The solutions are $\frac{4}{13}$ and $-\frac{4}{13}$.

Math Talk
Mathematical Processes

Can you square an integer and get a negative number? What does this indicate about whether negative numbers have square roots?

No; the square of a positive integer is positive, the square of a negative integer is positive, and the square of 0 is 0. So negative numbers do not have (real) square roots.

© Houghton Mifflin Harcourt Publishing Company

DIFFERENTIATE INSTRUCTION *Leveled Questions*

	EXAMPLE 3
AL DOK 1 *Recall*	How can a solution of an equation of the form $x^2 = p$ be negative if p is a positive number? Since the square of a negative number is positive, a negative number is also a solution of x^2 equals a positive number.
OL DOK 2 *Skills/Concepts*	In an equation of the form $x^3 = p$, can p be negative? Explain. Yes, the cube of a negative number is negative.
BL DOK 3 *Strategic Thinking*	When is the value of x in an equation of the form $x^3 = p$ greater than p? When p is a number between 0 and 1 or less than −1.

LEVELED QUESTIONS: AL Approaching Level | OL On Level | BL Beyond Level

C $729 = x^3$

$\sqrt[3]{729} = \sqrt[3]{x^3}$ Solve for x by taking the cube root of both sides.

$\sqrt[3]{729} = x$ Apply the definition of cube root.

$9 = x$ Think: What number cubed equals 729?

The solution is 9.

D $x^3 = \frac{8}{125}$

$\sqrt[3]{x^3} = \sqrt[3]{\frac{8}{125}}$ Solve for x by taking the cube root of both sides.

$x = \sqrt[3]{\frac{8}{125}}$ Apply the definition of cube root.

$x = \frac{2}{5}$ Think: What number cubed equals $\frac{8}{125}$?

The solution is $\frac{2}{5}$.

Personal Math Trainer
Online Assessment and Intervention
my.hrw.com

YOUR TURN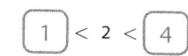

Solve each equation for x.

7. $x^2 = 196$ $\underline{x = \pm 14}$

8. $x^2 = \frac{9}{256}$ $\underline{x = \pm \frac{3}{16}}$

9. $x^3 = 512$ $\underline{x = 8}$

10. $x^3 = \frac{64}{343}$ $\underline{x = \frac{4}{7}}$

© Houghton Mifflin Harcourt Publishing Company

EXPLORE ACTIVITY 2

Estimating Irrational Numbers

Irrational numbers are numbers that are not rational. In other words, they cannot be written in the form $\frac{a}{b}$, where a and b are integers and b is not 0. Square roots of perfect squares are rational numbers. Square roots of numbers that are not perfect squares are irrational. The number $\sqrt{3}$ is irrational because 3 is not a perfect square of any rational number.

Estimate the value of $\sqrt{2}$.

A Since 2 is not a perfect square, $\sqrt{2}$ is irrational.

B To estimate $\sqrt{2}$, first find two consecutive perfect squares that 2 is between. Complete the inequality by writing these perfect squares in the boxes.

$\boxed{1} < 2 < \boxed{4}$

C Now take the square root of each number.

$\sqrt{\boxed{1}} < \sqrt{2} < \sqrt{\boxed{4}}$

D Simplify the square roots of perfect squares.

$\sqrt{2}$ is between $\underline{1}$ and $\underline{2}$.

$\boxed{1} < \sqrt{2} < \boxed{2}$

10 Unit 1

YOUR TURN MP.6

Avoid Common Errors
To avoid sign errors in **Exercise 9**, make sure that students understand that the cube of a negative number is not a positive number. Therefore, −8 is not a solution of $x^3 = 512$.

EXPLORE ACTIVITY 2

Connect Vocabulary ELL
Explain to students that the word *irrational*, when used as an ordinary word in English, means without logic or reason. In mathematics, when we say that a number is irrational it means only that the number cannot be written as the quotient of two integers.

	EXPLORE ACTIVITY 2
AL **DOK 1** *Recall*	Compare the values for 13^2 and 1.3^2. The digits are the same, but 1.3^2 has two decimal places (1.69), while 13^2 has none (169).
OL **DOK 2** *Skills/Concepts*	How do you know whether $\sqrt{2}$ is closer to 1 or closer to 2? It is closer to 1 because $\sqrt{1} < \sqrt{2} < \sqrt{4}$ and 2 is closer to 1 than to 4.
BL **DOK 3** *Strategic Thinking*	How do you know that $\sqrt{2}$ is irrational? Since 2 is not a perfect square, $\sqrt{2}$ cannot be written as a ratio of two integers, and so must be irrational.

TEACHER TO TEACHER

Number Sense Have students take turns giving irrational numbers. After the common irrational numbers of π and $\sqrt{2}$ are mentioned, remind students that the square root of any number that is not a perfect square is an irrational number. Then students can list a lot more irrational numbers, such as $\sqrt{3}$, $\sqrt{5}$, $\sqrt{6}$, $\sqrt{7}$, and so on.

Digital Teacher Resources

Go online to access all your lesson-level resources.

Differentiated Instruction
- Reteach
- Reading Strategies
- Success for English Learners
- Practice and Problem Solving A/B, C, D

Math on the Spot Videos

my.hrw.com

E Estimate that $\sqrt{2} \approx 1.5$.

$\sqrt{2} \approx 1.5$

0 1 2 3 4

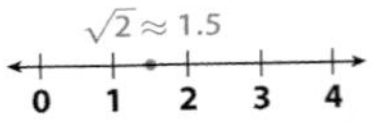

F To find a better estimate, first choose some numbers between 1 and 2 and square them. For example, choose 1.3, 1.4, and 1.5.

$1.3^2 = \underline{1.69}$ $1.4^2 = \underline{1.96}$ $1.5^2 = \underline{2.25}$

Is $\sqrt{2}$ between 1.3 and 1.4? How do you know?

No; 2 is not between 1.69 and 1.96.

Is $\sqrt{2}$ between 1.4 and 1.5? How do you know?

Yes; 2 is between 1.96 and 2.25.

$\sqrt{2}$ is between $\underline{1.4}$ and $\underline{1.5}$, so $\sqrt{2} \approx \underline{1.45}$.

G Locate and label this value on the number line.

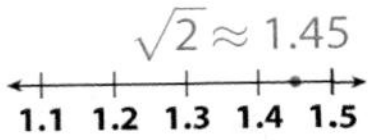

$\sqrt{2} \approx 1.45$

1.1 1.2 1.3 1.4 1.5

Reflect

11. How could you find an even better estimate of $\sqrt{2}$?

Test the squares of numbers between 1.4 and 1.5.

12. Find a better estimate of $\sqrt{2}$. Draw a number line and locate and label your estimate.

$\sqrt{2}$ is between $\underline{1.41}$ and $\underline{1.42}$, so $\sqrt{2} \approx \underline{1.415}$.

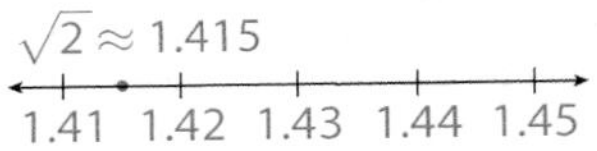

$\sqrt{2} \approx 1.415$

1.41 1.42 1.43 1.44 1.45

13. Estimate the value of $\sqrt{7}$ to two decimal places. Draw a number line and locate and label your estimate.

$\sqrt{7}$ is between $\underline{2.6}$ and $\underline{2.7}$, so $\sqrt{7} \approx \underline{2.65}$.

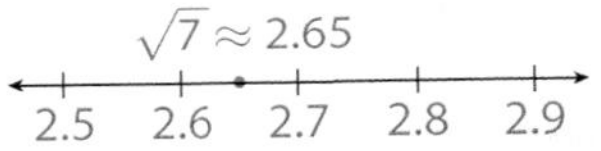

$\sqrt{7} \approx 2.65$

2.5 2.6 2.7 2.8 2.9

© Houghton Mifflin Harcourt Publishing Company

Write each fraction or mixed number as a decimal. (Explore Activity Example 1)

1. $\frac{2}{5}$ ___0.4___

2. $\frac{8}{9}$ ___$0.\overline{8}$___

3. $3\frac{3}{4}$ ___3.75___

4. $\frac{7}{10}$ ___0.7___

5. $2\frac{3}{8}$ ___2.375___

6. $\frac{5}{6}$ ___$0.8\overline{3}$___

Write each decimal as a fraction or mixed number in simplest form. (Example 2)

7. 0.675 ___$\frac{27}{40}$___

8. 5.6 ___$5\frac{3}{5}$___

9. 0.44 ___$\frac{11}{25}$___

10. $0.\overline{4}$

$10x = \boxed{4.\overline{4}}$

$-x \quad -\boxed{0.\overline{4}}$

$\boxed{9}x = \boxed{4}$

$x = \frac{4}{9}$

11. $0.\overline{26}$

$100x = \boxed{26.\overline{26}}$

$-x \quad -\boxed{0.\overline{26}}$

$\boxed{99}x = \boxed{26}$

$x = \frac{26}{99}$

12. $0.\overline{325}$

$1000x = \boxed{325.\overline{325}}$

$-x \quad -\boxed{0.\overline{325}}$

$\boxed{999}x = \boxed{325}$

$x = \frac{325}{999}$

Solve each equation for x. (Example 3)

13. $x^2 = 144$

$x = \pm\sqrt{\boxed{144}} = \pm\boxed{12}$

14. $x^2 = \frac{25}{289}$

$x = \pm\sqrt{\frac{\boxed{25}}{\boxed{289}}} = \pm\frac{\boxed{5}}{\boxed{17}}$

15. $x^3 = 216$

$x = \sqrt[3]{\boxed{216}} = \boxed{6}$

Approximate each irrational number to two decimal places without a calculator.
(Explore Activity 2)

16. $\sqrt{5} \approx \boxed{2.25}$

17. $\sqrt{3} \approx \boxed{1.75}$

18. $\sqrt{10} \approx \boxed{3.15}$

? ESSENTIAL QUESTION CHECK-IN

19. What is the difference between rational and irrational numbers?
Rational numbers can be written in the form $\frac{a}{b}$, where a and b are integers and $b \neq 0$. Irrational numbers cannot be written in this form.

© Houghton Mifflin Harcourt Publishing Company

4 Elaborate

Talk About It

Summarize the Lesson

Ask: If someone claims that a certain number is irrational but you know it is actually rational, how could you prove to that person that the number is rational? You could find a fraction equal to the number, such that the number is the ratio of two integers, with the denominator not equal to zero.

Guided Practice

Focus on Technology

Have students use a calculator to investigate the decimal equivalents of such fractions as $\frac{1}{9}$, $\frac{2}{9}$, ..., $\frac{8}{9}$ and $\frac{1}{11}$, $\frac{2}{11}$, ..., $\frac{10}{11}$. Ask them to describe the patterns they find as a result of these investigations.

Avoid Common Errors

Exercises 1–6 To avoid reversing the order of the dividend and divisor, tell students to start at the top of the fraction and read the bar as "divided by."

Engage with the Whiteboard

Have students plot each number in **Exercises 16–18** on a number line. Students should label each point with the irrational number written as a radical and as a decimal.

DIFFERENTIATE INSTRUCTION *Intervention and Additional Support*

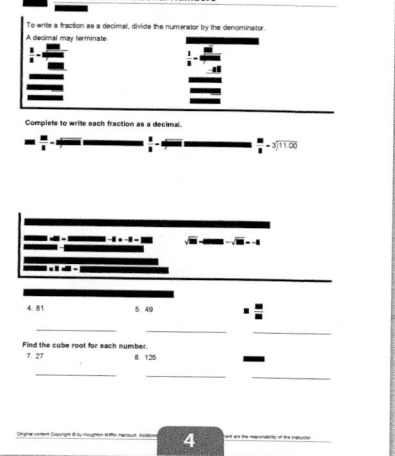

Reteach

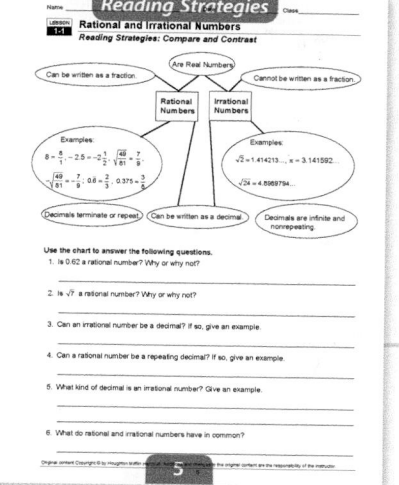

Reading Strategies

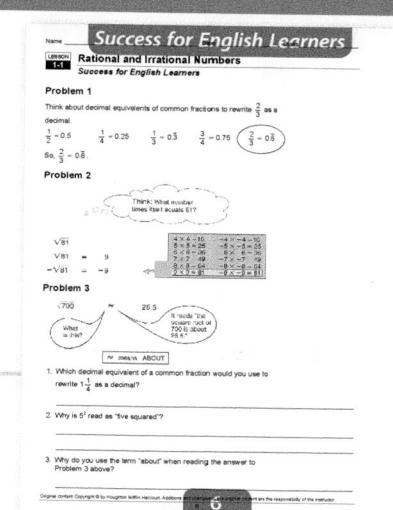

Success for English Learners

Personal Math Trainer
Daily Intervention
1.1 Homework

Pages shown are from
Differentiated Instruction.
Also available online.

5 Evaluate

 **Pressed for Time**

1.1 Differentiated Homework Assignments

(AL) **Approaching Level** 20–25, 28, 30–31

(OL) **On Level** 26–32

(BL) **Beyond Level** 28–34

*For **Below Level** students, assign Personal Math Trainer, Daily Intervention 1.1 Homework.*

Mathematical Processes	Exercises
MP.2 Reasoning	34
MP.3 Logic	30, 32
MP.4 Modeling	20–28, 31
MP.7 Using Structure	29, 33

Focus on Higher Order Thinking

Depth of Knowledge	Exercises
2 Skills/Concepts	20–27, 30–31
3 Strategic Thinking H.O.T.	28–29, 32–34

1.1 Independent Practice

Personal Math Trainer
Online Assessment and Intervention
my.hrw.com

20. A $\frac{7}{16}$-inch-long bolt is used in a machine. What is the length of the bolt written as a decimal?

0.4375 in.

21. The weight of an object on the moon is $\frac{1}{6}$ its weight on Earth. Write $\frac{1}{6}$ as a decimal.

$0.1\overline{6}$

22. The distance to the nearest gas station is $2\frac{4}{5}$ kilometers. What is this distance written as a decimal?

2.8 km

23. A baseball pitcher has pitched $98\frac{2}{3}$ innings. What is the number of innings written as a decimal?

$98.\overline{6}$ innings

24. A heartbeat takes 0.8 second. How many seconds is this written as a fraction?

$\frac{4}{5}$ second

25. There are 26.2 miles in a marathon. Write the number of miles using a fraction.

$26\frac{1}{5}$ mi

26. The average score on a biology test was $72.\overline{1}$. Write the average score using a fraction.

$72\frac{1}{9}$

27. The metal in a penny is worth about 0.505 cent. How many cents is this written as a fraction?

$\frac{101}{200}$ cent

28. **Multistep** An artist wants to frame a square painting with an area of 400 square inches. She wants to know the length of the wood trim that is needed to go around the painting.

a. If x is the length of one side of the painting, what equation can you set up to find the length of a side? _____ $x^2 = 400$

b. Solve the equation you wrote in part a. How many solutions does the equation have?

$x = \pm 20$; The equation has 2 solutions.

c. Do all of the solutions that you found in part b make sense in the context of the problem? Explain.

The solution $x = 20$ makes sense, but the solution $x = -20$ doesn't, because a painting cannot have a side length of -20 inches.

d. What is the length of the wood trim needed to go around the painting?

$4 \times 20 = 80$ inches

Lesson 1.1 **13**

© Houghton Mifflin Harcourt Publishing Company · ©Photodisc/Getty Images

---

DIFFERENTIATE INSTRUCTION *Leveled Homework/Practice*

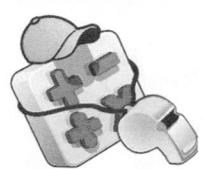

Personal Math Trainer

• 1.1 Homework

Pages shown are from *Differentiated Instruction.*
Also available online.

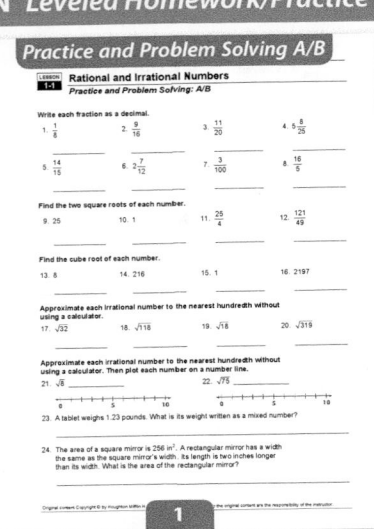

Practice and Problem Solving A/B

LESSON 1-1 Rational and Irrational Numbers
Practice and Problem Solving: A/B

Write each fraction as a decimal.

1. $\frac{1}{8}$ 2. $\frac{9}{16}$ 3. $\frac{11}{20}$ 4. $5\frac{8}{25}$

5. $\frac{14}{15}$ 6. $2\frac{7}{12}$ 7. $\frac{3}{100}$ 8. $\frac{16}{5}$

Find the two square roots of each number.

9. 25   10. 1   11. $\frac{25}{4}$ 12. $\frac{121}{49}$

Find the cube root of each number.

13. 8   14. 216   15. 1   16. 2197

Approximate each irrational number to the nearest hundredth without using a calculator.

17. $\sqrt{92}$ 18. $\sqrt{118}$ 19. $\sqrt{18}$ 20. $\sqrt{319}$

Approximate each irrational number to the nearest hundredth without using a calculator. Then plot each number on a number line.

21. $\sqrt{8}$ 22. $\sqrt{75}$

23. A tablet weighs 1.23 pounds. What is its weight written as a mixed number?

24. The area of a square mirror is 256 in². A rectangular mirror has a width the same as the square mirror's width. Its length is two inches longer than its width. What is the area of the rectangular mirror?

1

Practice and Problem Solving C

LESSON 1-1 Rational and Irrational Numbers
Practice and Problem Solving: C

Solve.

1. One nickel is $\frac{39}{500}$ inch thick. Fifteen nickels are stacked vertically. How many inches tall is the stack? Give your answer as a decimal.

2. One quarter is $\frac{191}{200}$ inch in diameter. Eight quarters are placed side-by-side along a line. How many inches long is the line of quarters? Give your answer as a decimal.

3. Is $\frac{41}{90}$ closer to $\frac{9}{11}$ or $\frac{10}{11}$? Verify your answer.

Find the two square roots of each number. (Hint: First write the decimal as a fraction.)

4. 0.25   5. 0.0625   6. $0.\overline{4}$

Approximate each irrational number to the nearest hundredth without using a calculator. Then plot each lettered point on the number line.

7. A: $\sqrt{3}$ 8. B: $\sqrt{18}$

Answer the questions below.

9. How does finding a cube root differ from finding a square root of a positive integer? How do the answers differ?

10. Each page of a photo album holds 3 rows of 4 square photos. The area of each photo is 25 cm². There is 2 cm space between photos and a 3 cm border around the group of pictures. What are the dimensions of one page of the photo album?

2

Practice and Problem Solving D

LESSON 1-1 Rational and Irrational Numbers
Practice and Problem Solving: D

Write each fraction as a decimal. The first one is done for you.

1. $\frac{1}{9}$ 2. $\frac{11}{20}$ 3. $\frac{9}{16}$

Write each decimal as a fraction in simplest form. The first one is done for you.

4. 0.268   5. 4.8   6. 0.333

$\frac{268}{1000} = \frac{129}{500}$

Find the two square roots of each number. The first one is done for you.

7. 16   8. 49   9. $\frac{25}{4}$

4, −4

Find the cube root of each number. The first one is done for you.

10. 343   11. 1   12. $\frac{8}{27}$

$7 \times 7 \times 7 = 343, 7$

Approximate each irrational number to the nearest hundredth without using a calculator. The first one is done for you.

13. $\sqrt{32}$ 14. $\sqrt{65}$ 15. $\sqrt{118}$

6.86

Solve.

16. The world's smallest country is Vatican City. It covers $\frac{17}{100}$ square mile. What is Vatican City's area written as a decimal?

17. A square sandbox has an area of 25 ft². What is the length of each of its sides? (Hint: side = $\sqrt{25}$)

3

---

29. Analyze Relationships To find $\sqrt{15}$, Beau found $3^2 = 9$ and $4^2 = 16$. He said that since 15 is between 9 and 16, $\sqrt{15}$ must be between 3 and 4. He thinks a good estimate for $\sqrt{15}$ is $\frac{3+4}{2} = 3.5$. Is Beau's estimate high, low, or correct? Explain.

His estimate is low because 15 is very close to 16,

so $\sqrt{15}$ is very close to $\sqrt{16}$, or 4. A better estimate

would be 3.8 or 3.9.

30. Justify Reasoning What is a good estimate for the solution to the equation $x^3 = 95$? How did you come up with your estimate?

Sample answer: A good estimate is $x \approx 4.5$. Because

$4^3 = 64$ and $5^3 = 125$ and 95 is about halfway between 64

and 125, $\sqrt[3]{95}$ is probably closer to 4.5 than to 4 or 5.

31. The volume of a sphere is 36π ft³. What is the radius of the sphere? Use the formula $V = \frac{4}{3}\pi r^3$ to find your answer.

3 feet

H.O.T. FOCUS ON HIGHER ORDER THINKING

32. Draw Conclusions Can you find the cube root of a negative number? If so, is it positive or negative? Explain your reasoning.

Yes; the cube root of a negative number is negative,

because a negative number cubed is always negative,

and a nonnegative number cubed is always nonnegative.

33. Make a Conjecture Evaluate and compare the following expressions.

$\sqrt{\frac{4}{25}}$ and $\frac{\sqrt{4}}{\sqrt{25}}$ $\sqrt{\frac{16}{81}}$ and $\frac{\sqrt{16}}{\sqrt{81}}$ $\sqrt{\frac{36}{49}}$ and $\frac{\sqrt{36}}{\sqrt{49}}$

Use your results to make a conjecture about a division rule for square roots. Since division is multiplication by the reciprocal, make a conjecture about a multiplication rule for square roots.

$\sqrt{\frac{4}{25}} = \frac{2}{5} = \frac{\sqrt{4}}{\sqrt{25}}$ $\sqrt{\frac{16}{81}} = \frac{4}{9} = \frac{\sqrt{16}}{\sqrt{81}}$ $\sqrt{\frac{36}{49}} = \frac{6}{7} = \frac{\sqrt{36}}{\sqrt{49}}$;

$\frac{\sqrt{a}}{\sqrt{b}} = \sqrt{\frac{a}{b}}$; $\sqrt{a} \cdot \sqrt{b} = \sqrt{a \cdot b}$

34. Persevere in Problem Solving The difference between the solutions to the equation $x^2 = a$ is 30. What is a? Show that your answer is correct.

225; the solutions to $x^2 = a$ are $x = \pm15$, and

$15 - (-15) = 30$.

© Houghton Mifflin Harcourt Publishing Company • © Ilene MacDonald/Alamy Images

Work Area

1.1 Lesson Quiz

1. Write as a decimal: $2\frac{5}{8}$, $1\frac{7}{12}$ 2.625, $1.58\overline{3}$

2. Write as a fraction: 0.34, $1.\overline{24}$ $\frac{17}{50}$, $1\frac{8}{33}$

3. Solve $x^2 = \frac{9}{49}$ for x. $x = \pm\frac{3}{7}$

4. Solve $x^3 = 216$ for x. $x = 6$

5. Estimate the value of $\sqrt{13}$ to the nearest 0.05 without using a calculator.   3.60

Differentiate Instruction

IF a student misses more than one question, THEN

Differentiate Instruction:

• 1.1 Reteach

• Personal Math Trainer

Interactive Whiteboard
Interactive Lesson quiz available online

DIFFERENTIATE INSTRUCTION *Extend-the-Math Activity* **PRE-AP**

Activity Write $\sqrt{0.9}$ on the board and invite students to conjecture what the value might be. Have them check their conjectures by squaring. Invite them to suggest ways to estimate $\sqrt{0.9}$. As a hint, point out that 0.9 is close to 1.0, and so they might use that to help guide their estimates. Lead them to see that, since 0.9^2 is 0.81 and 1.0^2 is 1, the value of $\sqrt{0.9}$ is greater than 0.9 and less than 1.0. Try squaring 0.95 to get 0.9025. A good estimate for $\sqrt{0.9}$ is 0.95.

Lesson Support

Content Objective Students will learn to describe relationships between sets of numbers.

Professional Development

Integrate Mathematical Processes MP.7

This lesson provides an opportunity to address this Mathematical Processes standard. It calls for students to discern structure to connect and communicate mathematical ideas.

Students use a Venn diagram to structure relationships between sets of numbers. They connect and communicate mathematical ideas when they make logical statements about the sets and describe which set best describes numbers applied to real-life situations.

FOCUS

Building Background

Eliciting Prior Knowledge Have students draw a number line from -5 to 5. Ask them to plot points on the number line to approximate the location of rational and irrational numbers, such as -1, $\frac{3}{4}$, 2.5, $-4\frac{2}{3}$, $\sqrt{2}$, and $-\pi$.

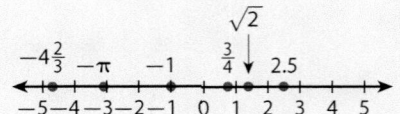

COHERENCE

Learning Progressions

In this lesson, students clarify their understanding of the real number system. They characterize sets and subsets of the real numbers. They also identify sets for real-world situations. Important understandings for students include the following:

- **Identify all of the possible subsets of the real numbers for a given number.**
- **Decide whether a statement about a subset of the real numbers is true or false.**
- **Identify the set of numbers that best describes a real-world situation.**

Understanding the relationships among the sets of numbers that make up the real numbers is essential as students are introduced to different forms of numbers throughout the school year. This lesson provides a foundation for the comparing and ordering of real numbers in the next lesson.

RIGOR

Cluster Connections

This lesson provides an excellent opportunity to connect ideas in this cluster:

Know that there are numbers that are not rational, and approximate them by rational numbers.

Have students copy this diagram, which relates the sets of real numbers.

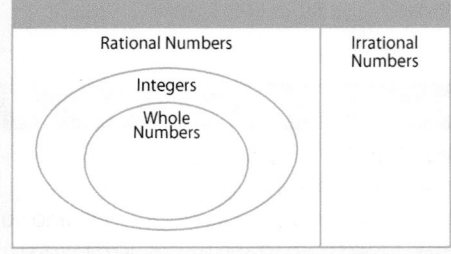

Ask students to complete the diagram by writing three examples for each set of numbers. Have students share examples and explain how they knew each number they selected belonged in the appropriate set.

Answers may vary. Check students' work.

Language Support ELL

Leveled Strategies for English Learners ELL

Emerging
Allow students to indicate *true* or *false* orally in Guided Practice Exercises 9 and 10.

Expanding
Have students use sentence frames to describe the meaning of regions and colors used in a Venn diagram. Then give them similar sentence frames orally and have them draw and shade a Venn diagram based on the oral prompts.

Bridging
Have students work in groups to draw a Venn diagram to represent sets based on real-world examples in the lesson.

To help students answer the question posed in Math Talk, provide a sentenvce frame for their answer.

The whole number _____ is a rational number because it can be written as the ratio of _____ to 1.

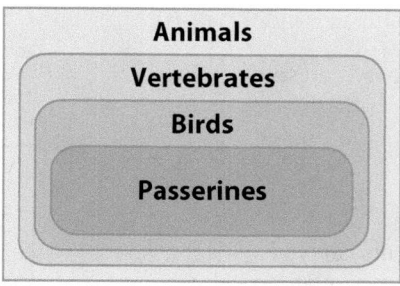
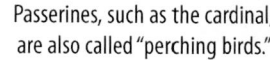

Passerines, such as the cardinal, are also called "perching birds."

Linguistic Support ELL

Academic/Content Vocabulary
Venn diagrams Students need descriptive language to describe the categories of a *Venn diagram*. Use sentence frames, such as:

The big oval represents _____.
The dark/light blue color in the middle of the big ovals represents _____.
These sets overlap because _____.

Also point out the use of the prefix *sub-*, meaning "under," in the term *subset*.

Rules and Patterns
abbreviations Be sure to point out that *mph* stands for *miles per hour* and is used to give units in a rate of speed. Students may also have seen *mpg* (miles per gallon), which gives the units in a rate of fuel efficiency.

borrowed words Terminology used in baseball, such as *inning* and *pitcher*, may require some explanation. Spanish, as well as some other languages, has borrowed these terms from English, so some students may be familiar with these words already. Despite this, whenever a word is critical to students understanding the word problem, it is best to explain the meaning.

Image Credits: ©Wikimedia

Sets of Real Numbers

1 Engage

How can you describe relationships between sets of real numbers? Sample answer: Describe them as two different sets, or one set as being a subset of another.

Motivate the Lesson

Ask: How many different types of tigers can you name? How does the set of Bengal tigers relate to the set of tigers? Begin the lesson to find out.

2 Explore

EXPLORE ACTIVITY **EXAMPLE 1**

ADDITIONAL EXAMPLE 1
Write all names that apply to each number.

A -10 integer, rational, real

B $\frac{12}{3}$ whole, integer, rational, real

 Interactive Whiteboard
Interactive example available online

 **Animated Math**

Classifying Numbers
Students build fluency in classifying numbers in this engaging, fast-paced game.

 my.hrw.com

---

8.1.1.2
Students will describe relationships between sets of real numbers.

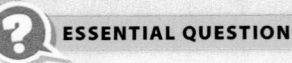 **ESSENTIAL QUESTION** How can you describe relationships between sets of real numbers?

EXPLORE ACTIVITY

Classifying Real Numbers

Biologists classify animals based on shared characteristics. A cardinal is an animal, a vertebrate, a bird, and a passerine.

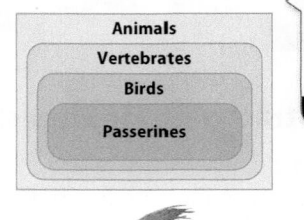
Animals / Vertebrates / Birds / Passerines

Math On the Spot
my.hrw.com

You know that the set of rational numbers consists of whole numbers, integers, decimals, and fractions. The set of **real numbers** consists of the set of rational numbers and the set of irrational numbers.

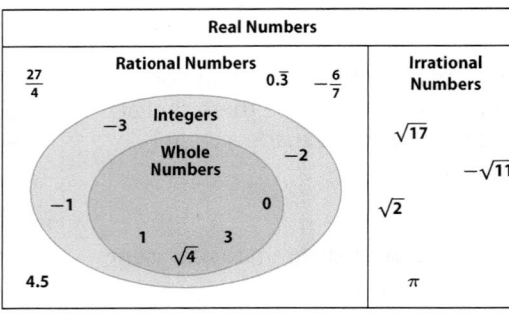

Real Numbers		
Rational Numbers		**Irrational Numbers**

$\frac{27}{4}$ $0.\overline{3}$ $-\frac{6}{7}$ $\sqrt{17}$ $-\sqrt{11}$ $\sqrt{2}$ π

Integers: -3, -2
Whole Numbers: -1, 0, 1, 3, $\sqrt{4}$
4.5

Passerines, such as the cardinal, are also called "perching birds."

EXAMPLE 1 **Write all the names that apply to each number.**

A $\sqrt{5}$
The number 5 under the square root symbol is a whole number that is not a perfect square.

irrational numbers
real numbers

B -17.84
-17.84 is a terminating decimal.

rational numbers
real numbers

C $\frac{\sqrt{81}}{9}$
$\frac{\sqrt{81}}{9} = \frac{9}{9} = 1$

whole numbers
integers
rational numbers
real numbers

Animated Math
my.hrw.com

Lesson 1.2   **15**

DIFFERENTIATE INSTRUCTION *Leveled Questions*

	EXPLORE ACTIVITY EXAMPLE 1
AL DOK 1 *Recall*	Can the number in Part B be written as a fraction? Why or why not? Yes; it is a terminating decimal, so it is a rational number.
OL DOK 2 *Skills/Concepts*	What types of numbers are between 3.1 and 3.9 on a number line? Rational, irrational, real
BL DOK 3 *Strategic Thinking*	How can a number with a radical symbol be classified as a whole number? If the radicand is a perfect square, then the square root of it is a positive integer.

LEVELED QUESTIONS: **AL** Approaching Level | **OL** On Level | **BL** Beyond Level

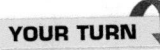

YOUR TURN

Write all names that apply to each number.

1. A baseball pitcher has pitched $12\frac{2}{3}$ innings.
   rational, real

2. The length of the side of a square that has an area of 10 square yards. irrational, real

Personal Math Trainer
Online Assessment and Intervention
my.hrw.com

Math On the Spot
my.hrw.com

Understanding Sets and Subsets of Real Numbers

By understanding which sets are subsets of types of numbers, you can verify whether statements about the relationships between sets are true or false.

EXAMPLE 2

Tell whether the given statement is true or false. Explain your choice.

A All irrational numbers are real numbers.

True. Every irrational number is included in the set of real numbers. Irrational numbers are a subset of real numbers.

B No rational numbers are whole numbers.

False. A whole number can be written as a fraction with a denominator of 1, so every whole number is included in the set of rational numbers. Whole numbers are a subset of rational numbers.

Sample answer: $8; 8 = \frac{8}{1}$

Math Talk
Mathematical Processes

Give an example of a rational number that is a whole number. Show that the number is both whole and rational.

YOUR TURN

Tell whether the given statement is true or false. Explain your choice.

3. All rational numbers are integers.

   False. Every integer is a rational number, but not every rational number is an integer. Rational numbers such as $\frac{3}{5}$ and $-\frac{5}{2}$ are not integers.

4. Some irrational numbers are integers.

   False. Real numbers are either rational or irrational numbers. Integers are rational numbers, so no integers are irrational numbers.

Personal Math Trainer
Online Assessment and Intervention
my.hrw.com

© Houghton Mifflin Harcourt Publishing Company • Image Credits: Digital Image copyright ©2004 Eyewire

	EXAMPLE 2
(AL) **DOK 1** *Recall*	What two major sets are the real numbers composed of? the rational numbers and the irrational numbers
(OL) **DOK 2** *Skills/Concepts*	How can you use the Venn diagram to answer Part B? The set of whole numbers is located inside the set of rational numbers, so all whole numbers are rational numbers. Therefore, the statement is false because SOME rational numbers are whole numbers.
(BL) **DOK 3** *Strategic Thinking*	How can you prove that the following statement is false? All integers are whole numbers. To prove a statement false, show a counterexample. Because −7 is an integer but it is not a whole number, not ALL integers are whole numbers.

Avoid Common Errors

Be sure that students read **Exercise 2** carefully before answering. The number given in the problem, 10, is the area, not the side length.

3 Explain

EXAMPLE 2

ADDITIONAL EXAMPLE 2 Tell whether the given statement is true or false. Explain your choice.

No integers are whole numbers.

False; every whole number is also an integer.

 Interactive Whiteboard
Interactive example available online

YOUR TURN MP.8

Avoid Common Errors

Students may see the word "*All*" or "*No*" in **Exercises 3–4** and immediately assume that any absolute statements like these are false. Remind them that there are true statements that begin with these words, and encourage them to provide examples.

TEACHER TO TEACHER

Home Connection Have students search with a family member or friend to find real-world situations representing rational numbers, integers, and whole numbers. Students can read through magazines, newspapers, and the Internet to find each type of number. Challenge students to find or write a real-world situation representing an irrational number. Have students share the situations they found in class the next day.

EXAMPLE 3

ADDITIONAL EXAMPLE 3
Identify the set of numbers that best describes the situation. Explain your choice.

A the amount of time that has passed since midnight The set of real numbers; time is continuous, so the amount of time can be rational or irrational.

B the number of tickets sold to a basketball game The set of whole numbers; the number of tickets sold may be 0 or a counting number.

✎ **Interactive Whiteboard**
Interactive example available online

YOUR TURN MP.2

Focus on Critical Thinking
Have students compare and contrast the classification of numbers in the answers in **Exercises 5–6**. Point out that the numbers in both exercises are real numbers, but the numbers in **Exercise 5** are nonnegative real numbers while the numbers in **Exercise 6** are negative real numbers.

Digital Teacher Resources

Go online to access all your lesson-level resources.

Differentiated Instruction
- Reteach
- Reading Strategies
- Success for English Learners
- Practice and Problem Solving A/B, C, D

Math on the Spot Videos

⬤ my.hrw.com

Math On the Spot
⬤ my.hrw.com

Identifying Sets for Real-World Situations

Real numbers can be used to represent real-world quantities. Highways have posted speed limit signs that are represented by natural numbers such as 55 mph. Integers appear on thermometers. Rational numbers are used in many daily activities, including cooking. For example, ingredients in a recipe are often given in fractional amounts such as $\frac{2}{3}$ cup flour.

EXAMPLE 3

My Notes

Identify the set of numbers that best describes each situation. Explain your choice.

A the number of people wearing glasses in a room

The set of whole numbers best describes the situation. The number of people wearing glasses may be 0 or a counting number.

B the circumference of a flying disk has a diameter of 8, 9, 10, 11, or 14 inches

The set of irrational numbers best describes the situation. Each circumference would be a product of π and the diameter, and any multiple of π is irrational.

YOUR TURN

Identify the set of numbers that best describes the situation. Explain your choice.

5. the amount of water in a glass as it evaporates
Real numbers; the amount can be any number greater than 0.

6. the number of seconds remaining when a song is playing, displayed as a negative number
Possible answer: Real numbers; the number of seconds left can be any number less than 0, depending on the display device.

Personal Math Trainer
Online Assessment and Intervention
⬤ my.hrw.com

© Houghton Mifflin Harcourt Publishing Company

DIFFERENTIATE INSTRUCTION *Leveled Questions*

	EXAMPLE 3
AL DOK 1 *Recall*	What is the relationship between the circumference of a circle and the diameter? The circumference is the diameter times π.
OL DOK 2 *Skills/Concepts*	In Part A, explain how word clues like "number of people" help you identify the appropriate number set. The phrase "number of people" suggests that you can make a count, indicating the counting numbers. But 0 must be included, so the set of whole numbers best fits the situation.
BL DOK 3 *Strategic Thinking*	In Part B, suppose the diameters, in inches, were $\frac{25}{\pi}$, $\frac{28}{\pi}$, $\frac{31}{\pi}$, and so on. What set of numbers would best describe the circumferences? Explain. Whole numbers; the circumferences, in inches, would be the whole numbers 25, 28, 31, and so on.

LEVELED QUESTIONS: **AL** Approaching Level | **OL** On Level | **BL** Beyond Level

Write all names that apply to each number. (Explore Activity Example 1)

1. $\frac{7}{8}$

rational, real

2. $\sqrt{36}$

whole, integer, rational, real

3. $\sqrt{24}$

irrational, real

4. 0.75

rational, real

5. 0

whole, integer, rational, real

6. $-\sqrt{100}$

integer, rational, real

7. $5.\overline{45}$

rational, real

8. $-\frac{18}{6}$

integer, rational, real

Tell whether the given statement is true or false. Explain your choice.
(Example 2)

9. All whole numbers are rational numbers.

True. Whole numbers are a subset of the set of rational numbers and can be written as a ratio of the whole number to 1.

10. No irrational numbers are whole numbers.

True. Whole numbers are rational numbers.

Identify the set of numbers that best describes each situation. Explain your choice. (Example 3)

11. the change in the value of an account when given to the nearest dollar

Integers; the change can be a whole dollar amount and can be positive, negative, or zero.

$\frac{1}{16}$ inch

12. the markings on a standard ruler

Rational numbers; the ruler is marked every $\frac{1}{16}$th inch.

IN.   1

? ESSENTIAL QUESTION CHECK-IN

13. What are some ways to describe the relationships between sets of numbers?

Sample answer: Describe one set as being a subset of another, or show their relationships in a Venn diagram.

© Houghton Mifflin Harcourt Publishing Company

4 Elaborate

Talk About It

Summarize the Lesson

Ask: What are some ways that number sets can be related? Sets may be subsets of other sets or they may be separate from other sets.

Guided Practice

Engage with the Whiteboard

Have students place the numbers in **Exercises 1–8** in the Venn diagram for numbers at the beginning of the lesson.

Avoid Common Errors

- **Exercise 7** Remind students that a repeating decimal is a rational number.

- **Exercises 9–10** Remind students that it only takes one counterexample to show that a statement is false.

DIFFERENTIATE INSTRUCTION *Intervention and Additional Support*

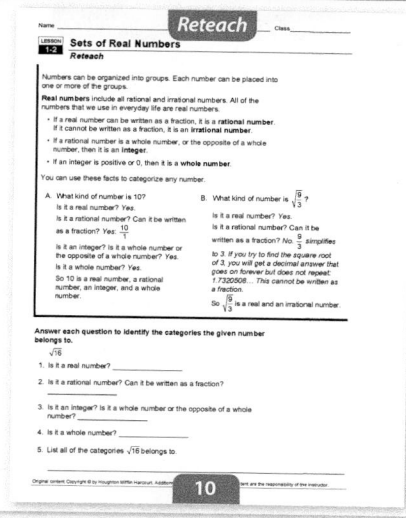

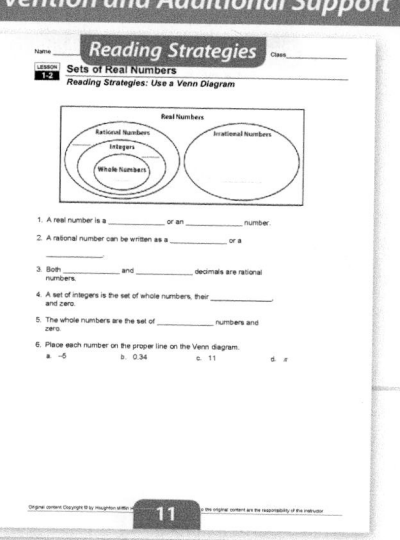

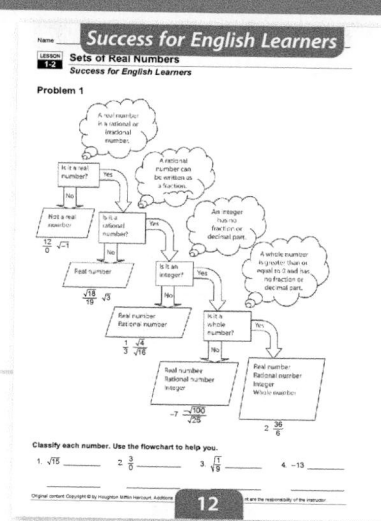

Personal Math Trainer
Daily Intervention
1.2 Homework

Pages shown are from *Differentiated Instruction*.
Also available online.

🕐 **Pressed for Time**

1.2 Differentiated Homework Assignments

(AL) Approaching Level 12–14, 16, 19, 20, 24

(OL) On Level 12, 15, 17, 18, 21, 22

(BL) Beyond Level 15, 22–24, 27, 28

*For **Below Level** students, assign Personal Math Trainer, Daily Intervention 1.2 Homework.*

Mathematical Processes	Exercises
MP.2 Reasoning	25
MP.3 Logic	22–23, 26–27, 29
MP.6 Precision	20–21
MP.7 Using Structure	14–19, 24
MP.8 Patterns	28

Focus on Higher Order Thinking

Depth of Knowledge	Exercises
1 Recall of Information	24
2 Skills/Concepts	14–23, 25
3 Strategic Thinking H.O.T.	26–29

Name_____ Class_____ Date_____

1.2 Independent Practice

Personal Math Trainer
Online Assessment and Intervention
my.hrw.com

Write all names that apply to each number. Then place the numbers in the correct location on the Venn diagram.

14. $\sqrt{9}$ whole, integer, rational, real

15. 257 whole, integer, rational, real

16. $\sqrt{50}$ irrational, real

17. $8\frac{1}{2}$ rational, real

18. 16.6 rational, real

19. $\sqrt{16}$ whole, integer, rational, real

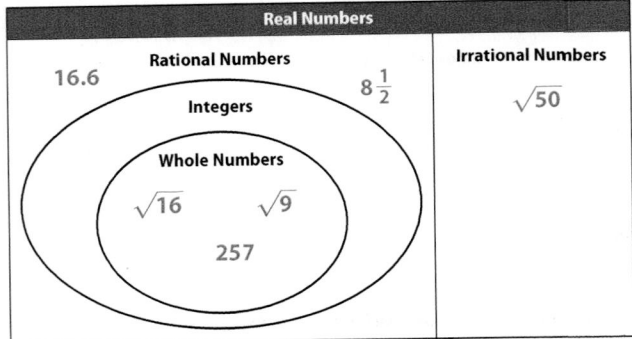

Identify the set of numbers that best describes each situation. Explain your choice.

20. the height of an airplane as it descends to an airport runway

Real numbers; the height can be any number greater than zero.

21. the score with respect to par of several golfers: 2, −3, 5, 0, −1

Integers; the scores are counting numbers, their opposites, and zero.

22. **Critique Reasoning** Ronald states that the number $\frac{1}{11}$ is not rational because, when converted into a decimal, it does not terminate. Nathaniel says it is rational because it is a fraction. Which boy is correct? Explain.

Nathaniel is correct. A rational number is a number that can be written as a fraction, and $\frac{1}{11}$ is a fraction.

© Houghton Mifflin Harcourt Publishing Company

DIFFERENTIATE INSTRUCTION *Leveled Homework/Practice*

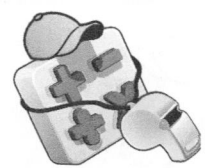

Personal Math Trainer
• 1.2 Homework

Pages shown are from *Differentiated Instruction.* **Also available online.**

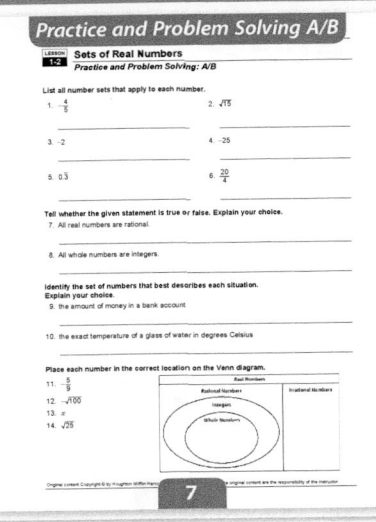

23. Critique Reasoning The circumference of a circular region is shown. What type of number best describes the diameter of the circle? Explain your answer. <u>Whole; the diameter is $\frac{\pi}{\pi} = 1$ mile.</u>

 π mi

24. Critical Thinking A number is not an integer. What type of number can it be?

It can be a rational number that is not an integer, or an irrational number.

25. A grocery store has a shelf with half-gallon containers of milk. What type of number best represents the total number of gallons?

rational number

H.O.T. FOCUS ON HIGHER ORDER THINKING

Work Area

26. Explain the Error Katie said, "Negative numbers are integers." What was her error?

The set of negative numbers also includes non-integer rational numbers and irrational numbers.

27. Justify Reasoning Can you ever use a calculator to determine if a number is rational or irrational? Explain.

Sample answer: If the calculator shows a decimal that terminates in fewer digits than what the calculator screen allows, then you can tell that the number is rational. If not, you cannot tell from the calculator display whether the number terminates because you see a limited number of digits. It may be a repeating decimal (rational), or non-terminating non-repeating decimal (irrational).

28. Draw Conclusions The decimal $0.\overline{3}$ represents $\frac{1}{3}$. What type of number best describes $0.\overline{9}$, which is $3 \cdot 0.\overline{3}$? Explain.

Whole; $3 \cdot 0.\overline{3}$ represents $3 \cdot \frac{1}{3} = 1$, so $0.\overline{9}$ is exactly 1.

29. Communicate Mathematical Ideas Irrational numbers can never be precisely represented in decimal form. Why is this?

Sample answer: In decimal form, irrational numbers never terminate and never repeat. Therefore, no matter how many decimal places you include, the number will never be precisely represented. There are always more digits.

© Houghton Mifflin Harcourt Publishing Company

✓ **Quick Check**

1.2 Lesson Quiz

1. Write all the names that apply to the number $-1.\overline{5}$. rational, real

2. Tell whether the given statement is true or false. Explain your choice.

All numbers between 1 and 2 are rational numbers.

False; $\sqrt{2}$ is an example of an irrational number between 1 and 2.

3. Identify the set of numbers that best describes the situation. Explain your choice.

The choices on a survey question change the total points for the survey by −2, −1, 0, 1, or 2 points.

Integers; each number is an integer, but only three are whole numbers.

Differentiate Instruction

IF a student misses more than one question, THEN

Differentiate Instruction:

• 1.2 Reteach

• Personal Math Trainer

Interactive Whiteboard
Interactive Lesson quiz available online

DIFFERENTIATE INSTRUCTION *Extend-the-Math Activity* **PRE-AP**

Activity Have students consider the concept of *restricted domain* for the sets of numbers that describe situations. For example, the number of sisters a person has can best be described by whole numbers, but no one has ever had 1,500 sisters. An area code is an integer or whole number between 200 and 999.

Have students use a source, such as the *Guinness Book of World Records*, and give examples of sets of numbers that describe situations where the domain is restricted. Ask whether the restriction may be changed in the future.

Lesson Support

Content Objective Students will learn to order a set of real numbers.

Professional Development

Integrate Mathematical Processes MP.4

This lesson provides an opportunity to address this Mathematical Processes standard. It calls for students to model relationships using multiple representations, including diagrams, graphs, and language as appropriate. Students use multiple representations when they use number lines to estimate the locations of and to order rational and irrational numbers given as symbols.

FOCUS

Building Background

Eliciting Prior Knowledge Have students draw a number line to compare a rational number and an irrational number, such as $-\sqrt{5}$ and $-4\frac{1}{2}$. Ask them to explain how they approximated the irrational number on the number line. Then have them identify the greater and the lesser real number. Repeat with several other pairs of real numbers in different forms.

COHERENCE

Learning Progressions

In this lesson, students order a set of real numbers. They use rational approximations to compare the sizes of irrational numbers. They also order numbers for real-world situations. Important understandings for students include the following:

- **Compare irrational numbers.**
- **Estimate the value of expressions with irrational numbers.**
- **Order a set of real numbers.**
- **Order real numbers in a real-world context.**

Work with real numbers continues throughout Grade 8 and into high school. This lesson provides students with a foundation for understanding the relative sizes of numbers in different forms in the real number system.

RIGOR

Cluster Connections

This lesson provides an excellent opportunity to connect ideas in this cluster:

Know that there are numbers that are not rational, and approximate them by rational numbers.

Tell students that there is a special number, called the golden ratio, with applications in mathematics, geometry, art, and architecture. The golden ratio is called *phi* and is represented by the Greek letter ϕ. It includes an irrational number in its definition.

$$\phi = \frac{1 + \sqrt{5}}{2}$$

Have students explain why the golden ratio is irrational. Ask them to find the two whole numbers the golden ratio lies between. Then challenge them to approximate the golden ratio to the nearest tenth.

It is irrational because it includes an irrational number in its definition. It lies between 1 and 2. To the nearest tenth, $\phi = 1.6$.

Language Support ELL

Language Objective Students will show and describe how to order a set of real numbers.

Leveled Strategies for English Learners ELL

Emerging
Label points on a number line with the terms used in ordering: *greater, greatest, less, lesser, least.* Use sentence frames to insert the correct terms.

Expanding
Have students give two or three complete sentences to compare the placement of numbers on a number line using the correct forms of the comparative and superlative adjectives.

Bridging
Have students work in pairs, with one student giving directions to the other in complete sentences to order numbers on a number line.

Math Talk To help students answer the question posed in Math Talk, make sure that students have a command of the forms for making comparisons and the superlative and the concept of opposite order so that the focus is on the math concept instead of the language skills needed to describe and explain order.

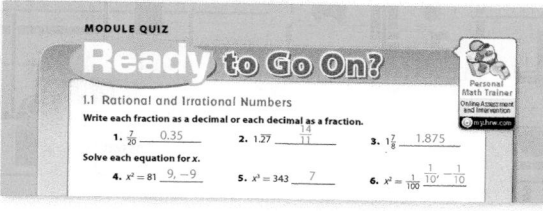

Linguistic Support ELL

Background Knowledge
The title of the module review or quiz is *Ready to Go On*. This title uses an idiomatic expression. In this context, *to go on* means "to move ahead" or "to proceed." It is different from the use of *go on* that means "having enough facts to use meaningfully," as in *having enough to go on*. Also, the intonation used in pronouncing an expression can give it different meanings. For example, when the speaker emphasizes the word *on*, he or she might be expressing disbelief, as in, "Go *ON*! You're kidding, right?" Discuss with students other ways that the phrase *go on* may be used.

Academic/Content Vocabulary
Post a chart like this to remind students of the regular comparative forms of adjectives that use the *-er* and *-est* suffixes. Add to the chart for terms that appear in examples and exercises in each lesson. Include any irregular verb forms.

Adjective	Comparative	Superlative
Far	Farther	Farthest
Large	Larger	Largest
Great	Greater	Greatest
Some	Less	Least
Some	More	Most

Ordering Real Numbers

1 Engage

❓ ESSENTIAL QUESTION

How do you order a set of real numbers? Sample answer: Find their approximate decimal values and order them.

Motivate the Lesson

Ask: What kind of numbers are you comparing when you compare the price of gasoline at two different gas stations? How do you compare two irrational numbers? Begin the lesson to find out.

2 Explore

EXPLORE ACTIVITY EXAMPLE 1

Avoid Common Errors
Caution students to read the problem carefully and think about what the radical sign means so that they do not misread the problem and answer that the two sides are equal.

ADDITIONAL EXAMPLE 1
Compare. Write $<$, $>$, or $=$.

A $\sqrt{8} - 2 \bigcirc 4 - \sqrt{8}$ $<$

B $\sqrt{20} + 1 \bigcirc 3 + \sqrt{2}$ $>$

 Interactive Whiteboard
Interactive example available online

YOUR TURN   MP.2

Focus on Technology
Calculators should not be used at this point, because developing number sense is the goal.

❓ ESSENTIAL QUESTION

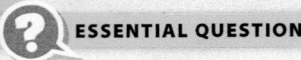 How do you order a set of real numbers?

EXPLORE ACTIVITY

Comparing Irrational Numbers

Between any two real numbers is another real number. To compare and order real numbers, you can approximate irrational numbers as decimals.

 Math On the Spot
my.hrw.com

EXAMPLE 1 Compare $\sqrt{3} + 5 \bigcirc 3 + \sqrt{5}$. Write $<$, $>$, or $=$.

STEP 1 Use perfect squares to estimate square roots.

Approximate $\sqrt{3}$. $\sqrt{3}$ is between $\sqrt{1}$ and $\sqrt{4}$, or between __1__ and __2__.

Approximate $\sqrt{5}$. $\sqrt{5}$ is between $\sqrt{4}$ and $\sqrt{9}$, or between __2__ and __3__.

STEP 2 Use your estimations to simplify the expressions.

$\sqrt{3} + 5$ is between $\boxed{1} + 5$ and $\boxed{2} + 5$, or between __6__ and __7__.

$3 + \sqrt{5}$ is between $3 + \boxed{2}$ and $3 + \boxed{3}$, or between __5__ and __6__.

So, $\sqrt{3} + 5 \enspace \boxed{>} \enspace 3 + \sqrt{5}$.

Reflect

1. If $7 + \sqrt{5}$ is equal to $\sqrt{5}$ plus a number, what do you know about the number? Why?

   The number is 7; both expressions must equal $7 + \sqrt{5}$.

2. What are the closest two integers that $\sqrt{300}$ is between?

   17 and 18

 **YOUR TURN**

 Personal Math Trainer
Online Assessment and Intervention
my.hrw.com

Compare. Write $<$, $>$, or $=$.

3. $\sqrt{2} + 4 \enspace \overset{>}{\bigcirc} \enspace 2 + \sqrt{4}$

4. $\sqrt{12} + 6 \enspace \overset{<}{\bigcirc} \enspace 12 + \sqrt{6}$

© Houghton Mifflin Harcourt Publishing Company

Lesson 1.3   **21**

DIFFERENTIATE INSTRUCTION *Leveled Questions*

	EXPLORE ACTIVITY EXAMPLE 1
AL DOK 1 *Recall*	In Step 1, how do you approximate $\sqrt{3}$? $\sqrt{1} < \sqrt{3} < \sqrt{4}$, so $1 < \sqrt{3} < 2$.
OL DOK 2 *Skills/Concepts*	Which is greater, the difference between 5 and 3, or the difference between $\sqrt{5}$ and $\sqrt{3}$? The difference between 5 and 3 is 2; the difference between $\sqrt{5}$ and $\sqrt{3}$ is approximately 1. So the difference between 5 and 3 is greater.
BL DOK 3 *Strategic Thinking*	In Step 2, how do you know what numbers each sum is between? By substituting for $\sqrt{3}$, you know the sum $\sqrt{3} + 5$ is between $1 + 5$ and $2 + 5$; by substituting for $\sqrt{5}$, you know the sum $3 + \sqrt{5}$ is between $3 + 2$ and $3 + 3$.

LEVELED QUESTIONS: **AL** Approaching Level | **OL** On Level | **BL** Beyond Level

Ordering Real Numbers

You can compare and order real numbers and list them from least to greatest.

EXAMPLE 2

Order $\sqrt{22}$, $\pi + 1$, and $4\frac{1}{2}$ from least to greatest.

STEP 1 First approximate $\sqrt{22}$.

$\sqrt{22}$ is between 4 and 5. Since you don't know where it falls between 4 and 5, you need to find a better estimate for $\sqrt{22}$ so you can compare it to $4\frac{1}{2}$.

Since 22 is closer to 25 than 16, use squares of numbers between 4.5 and 5 to find a better estimate of $\sqrt{22}$.

$4.5^2 = 20.25 \quad 4.6^2 = 21.16 \quad 4.7^2 = 22.09 \quad 4.8^2 = 23.04$

Since $4.7^2 = 22.09$, an approximate value for $\sqrt{22}$ is 4.7.

An approximate value of π is 3.14. So an approximate value of $\pi + 1$ is 4.14.

STEP 2 Plot $\sqrt{22}$, $\pi + 1$, and $4\frac{1}{2}$ on a number line.

Read the numbers from left to right to place them in order from least to greatest.

From least to greatest, the numbers are $\pi + 1$, $4\frac{1}{2}$, and $\sqrt{22}$.

YOUR TURN

Order the numbers from least to greatest. Then graph them on the number line.

5. $\sqrt{5}$, 2.5, $\sqrt{3}$ _____ $\sqrt{3}$, $\sqrt{5}$, 2.5

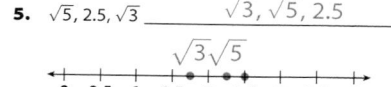

6. π^2, 10, $\sqrt{75}$ _____ $\sqrt{75}$, π^2, 10

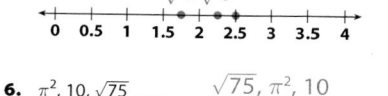

Math Talk
Mathematical Processes

If real numbers a, b, and c are in order from least to greatest, what is the order of their opposites from least to greatest? Explain.

Math Talk answer: $-c$, $-b$, $-a$; $-c$ is farthest to the left on a number line, $-b$ is in the middle, and $-a$ is farthest to the right.

22 Unit 1

Explain

EXAMPLE 2

ADDITIONAL EXAMPLE 2 Order 3π, $\sqrt{10}$, and 3.25 from greatest to least.

3π, 3.25, $\sqrt{10}$

Interactive Whiteboard
Interactive example available online

YOUR TURN MP.6

Focus on Modeling
Have students label the integers on the number line with their equivalent square root. For example, 1, 2, and 3 on the number line would be labeled $\sqrt{1}$, $\sqrt{4}$, and $\sqrt{9}$.

	EXAMPLE 2
AL) DOK 1 *Recall*	What should you do first so that you can order the three numbers? Write or approximate them all using decimal form.
OL) DOK 2 *Skills/Concepts*	How do you determine whether $\sqrt{22}$ is less than or greater than 4.5? $\sqrt{16} < \sqrt{22} < \sqrt{25}$, and $\sqrt{22}$ is closer to $\sqrt{25}$, so $\sqrt{22}$ is closer to 5 than 4. Therefore, $\sqrt{22}$ must be greater than 4.5.
BL) DOK 3 *Strategic Thinking*	Is there always a real number between any two real numbers? How can you find a real number between any given two real numbers? Sample answer: Let there be two real numbers $\frac{1}{3}$ and $\frac{1}{2}$. To find a number between them, write equivalent fractions with a much larger denominator: $\frac{1}{3} = \frac{20}{60}$ and $\frac{1}{2} = \frac{30}{60}$. Now you can see that there are many numbers between $\frac{20}{60}$ and $\frac{30}{60}$, such as $\frac{21}{60}$.

TEACHER TO TEACHER

Historical Fact The computation of pi has advanced over the years. Around AD 200, the mathematician Liu Hui of China used polygons with up to 3,072 sides to calculate pi up to 3,14159. In 1995, a group of mathematicians calculated pi to the ten billionth (10,000,000,000) digit. The current record is held by Fabrice Bellard, who calculated pi to 2.7 trillion digits. He used a desktop computer and took a total of 131 days to complete and check the result.

Ordering Real Numbers 22

EXAMPLE 3

Connect to Daily Life

Discuss how measuring across a canyon might involve different methods than measuring along a road. Explain that measurements like these are often done using calculations that approximate the distance.

ADDITIONAL EXAMPLE 3 The diameter of a meteorite in millimeters is calculated by four different methods. Order the results from least to greatest.

Joe: $\sqrt{18}$ mm, Lisa: $\frac{13}{3}$ mm,

Pablo: 4.6 mm, Julien: $\frac{4\pi}{3}$ mm

$\frac{4\pi}{3}$ mm, $\frac{13}{3}$ mm, $\sqrt{18}$ mm, 4.6 mm

 Interactive Whiteboard
Interactive example available online

YOUR TURN MP.6

Focus on Critical Thinking

Discuss with students which number is greater, $3.\overline{45}$ or 3.450? $3.\overline{45}$ or 3.455 and why. Explain that $3.\overline{45}$ can be written out as 3.4545… Make sure they understand that $3.\overline{45}$ is greater than 3.45 but less than 3.455.

Digital Teacher Resources

Go online to access all your lesson-level resources.

Differentiated Instruction
- Reteach
- Reading Strategies
- Success for English Learners
- Practice and Problem Solving A/B, C, D

Math on the Spot Videos

my.hrw.com

Ordering Real Numbers in a Real-World Context

Calculations and estimations in the real world may differ. It can be important to know not only which are the most accurate but which give the greatest or least values, depending upon the context.

Math On the Spot
my.hrw.com

EXAMPLE 3

Four people have found the distance in kilometers across a canyon using different methods. Their results are given in the table. Order the distances from greatest to least.

Distance Across Quarry Canyon (km)			
Juana	**Lee Ann**	**Ryne**	**Jackson**
$\sqrt{28}$	$\frac{23}{4}$	$5.\overline{5}$	$5\frac{1}{2}$

STEP 1 Write each value as a decimal.

$\sqrt{28}$ is between 5.2 and 5.3. Since $5.3^2 = 28.09$, an approximate value for $\sqrt{28}$ is 5.3.

$\frac{23}{4} = 5.75$

$5.\overline{5}$ is 5.555…, so $5.\overline{5}$ to the nearest hundredth is 5.56.

$5\frac{1}{2} = 5.5$

STEP 2 Plot $\sqrt{28}$, $\frac{23}{4}$, $5.\overline{5}$, and $5\frac{1}{2}$ on a number line.

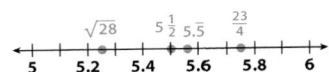

From greatest to least, the distances are:

$\frac{23}{4}$ km, $5.\overline{5}$ km, $5\frac{1}{2}$ km, $\sqrt{28}$ km.

YOUR TURN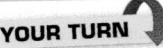

7. Four people have found the distance in miles across a crater using different methods. Their results are given below.

Jonathan: $\frac{10}{3}$, Elaine: $3.\overline{45}$, José: $3\frac{1}{2}$, Lashonda: $\sqrt{10}$

Order the distances from greatest to least.

$3\frac{1}{2}$ mi, $3.\overline{45}$ mi, $\frac{10}{3}$ mi, $\sqrt{10}$ mi

Personal Math Trainer
Online Assessment and Intervention
my.hrw.com

© Houghton Mifflin Harcourt Publishing Company

DIFFERENTIATE INSTRUCTION *Leveled Questions*

	EXAMPLE 3
(AL) DOK 1 *Recall*	How do you determine which number is greater: $5.\overline{5}$ or 5.5? When the repeating decimal is rounded to the nearest tenth or hundredth, you can see that it is greater.
(OL) DOK 2 *Skills/Concepts*	How can you determine an estimate of $\sqrt{28}$ to the nearest tenth? Because $5^2 = 25$ and $6^2 = 36$, you know that $\sqrt{28}$ is between 5 and 6, and closer to 5. Because $5.2^2 = 27.04$ and $5.3^2 = 28.09$, you know that $\sqrt{28}$ is closer to 5.3.
(BL) DOK 3 *Strategic Thinking*	How can you determine an estimate of $\sqrt{28}$ to the nearest hundredth? $5.2^2 = 27.04$ and $5.3^2 = 28.09$, so $\sqrt{28}$ is a little less than 5.3. Try finding 5.27^2, 5.28^2, and 5.29^2 to determine between which two numbers 28 falls. The value of $\sqrt{28}$ is between 5.29 and 5.30 because $5.29^2 \approx 27.98$ and $5.30^2 = 28.09$. The better estimate for $\sqrt{28}$ is 5.29 because 27.98 is closer to 28 than 28.09 is.

LEVELED QUESTIONS: (AL) Approaching Level | (OL) On Level | (BL) Beyond Level

Compare. Write <, >, or =. (Explore Activity Example 1)

1. $\sqrt{3} + 2 \;\boxed{<}\; \sqrt{3} + 3$

2. $\sqrt{11} + 15 \;\boxed{>}\; \sqrt{8} + 15$

3. $\sqrt{6} + 5 \;\boxed{<}\; 6 + \sqrt{5}$

4. $\sqrt{9} + 3 \;\boxed{<}\; 9 + \sqrt{3}$

5. $\sqrt{17} - 3 \;\boxed{>}\; -2 + \sqrt{5}$

6. $10 - \sqrt{8} \;\boxed{<}\; 12 - \sqrt{2}$

7. $\sqrt{7} + 2 \;\boxed{>}\; \sqrt{10} - 1$

8. $\sqrt{17} + 3 \;\boxed{>}\; 3 + \sqrt{11}$

9. Order $\sqrt{3}$, 2π, and 1.5 from least to greatest. Then graph them on the number line. (Example 2)

$\sqrt{3}$ is between ___1.7___ and ___1.8___, so $\sqrt{3} \approx$ ___1.75___.

$\pi \approx 3.14$, so $2\pi \approx$ ___6.28___.

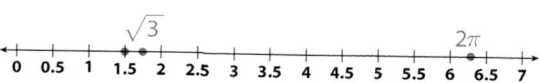

From least to greatest, the numbers are ___1.5___, ___$\sqrt{3}$___

___2π___.

10. Four people have found the perimeter of a forest using different methods. Their results are given in the table. Order their calculations from greatest to least. (Example 3)

$1 + \dfrac{\pi}{2}$ km, 2.5 km, $\dfrac{12}{5}$ km, $\sqrt{17} - 2$ km

Forest Perimeter (km)			
Leon	Mika	Jason	Ashley
$\sqrt{17} - 2$	$1 + \dfrac{\pi}{2}$	$\dfrac{12}{5}$	2.5

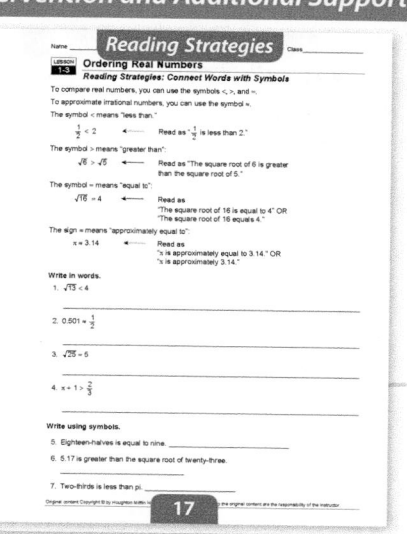

ESSENTIAL QUESTION CHECK-IN

11. Explain how to order a set of real numbers.

Sample answer: Convert each number to a decimal

equivalent, using estimation to find equivalents for

irrational numbers. Graph each number on a number line.

Read the numbers from left to right for least to greatest.

Read the numbers from right to left for greatest to least.

© Houghton Mifflin Harcourt Publishing Company • Image Credits: ©Elena Eliseeva/Alamy Images

4 Elaborate

Talk About It

Summarize the Lesson

Ask: How can you order two numbers in different forms whose decimal approximations appear to be equal? Approximate one or both numbers to an additional number of decimal places.

Guided Practice

Engage with the Whiteboard

Have students place and label additional points on the number line in **Exercise 9**. Allow the points to be in any format other than decimal.

Avoid Common Errors

- **Exercises 3–4** Caution students to read the problem carefully so that they do not misread the problem as the same numbers combined by addition on each side of the circle.

- **Exercise 10** Remind students that the calculations have units.

DIFFERENTIATE INSTRUCTION *Intervention and Additional Support*

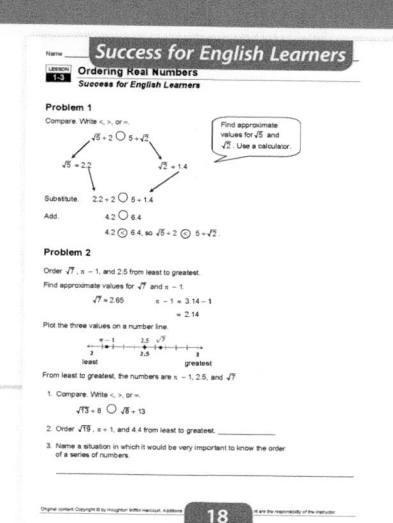

Personal Math Trainer
Daily Intervention
1.3 Homework

Pages shown are from *Differentiated Instruction.*
Also available online.

5 Evaluate

Independent Practice

1.3 Independent Practice

Personal Math Trainer

Online Assessment and Intervention

my.hrw.com

Order the numbers from least to greatest.

12. $\sqrt{7}, 2, \frac{\sqrt{8}}{2}$

$\frac{\sqrt{8}}{2}, 2, \sqrt{7}$

13. $\sqrt{10}, \pi, 3.5$

$\pi, \sqrt{10}, 3.5$

14. $\sqrt{220}, -10, \sqrt{100}, 11.5$

$-10, \sqrt{100}, 11.5, \sqrt{220}$

15. $\sqrt{8}, -3.75, 3, \frac{9}{4}$

$-3.75, \frac{9}{4}, \sqrt{8}, 3$

16. Your sister is considering two different shapes for her garden. One is a square with side lengths of 3.5 meters, and the other is a circle with a diameter of 4 meters.

  a. Find the area of the square. _____ 12.25 m²

  b. Find the area of the circle. _____ 4π m², or approximately 12.6 m²

  c. Compare your answers from parts **a** and **b**. Which garden would give your sister the most space to plant?

    The circle would give her more space to plant because it has a larger area.

17. Winnie measured the length of her father's ranch four times and got four different distances. Her measurements are shown in the table.

Distance Across Father's Ranch (km)			
1	2	3	4
$\sqrt{60}$	$\frac{58}{8}$	$7.\overline{3}$	$7\frac{3}{5}$

  a. To estimate the actual length, Winnie first approximated each distance to the nearest hundredth. Then she averaged the four numbers. Using a calculator, find Winnie's estimate.

    $\sqrt{60} \approx 7.75, \frac{58}{8} = 7.25, 7.\overline{3} \approx 7.33, 7\frac{3}{5} = 7.60$, so the average is 7.4825 km.

  b. Winnie's father estimated the distance across his ranch to be $\sqrt{56}$ km. How does this distance compare to Winnie's estimate?

    They are nearly identical. $\sqrt{56}$ is approximately 7.4833... .

Give an example of each type of number.

18. a real number between $\sqrt{13}$ and $\sqrt{14}$ _____ Sample answer: 3.7

19. an irrational number between 5 and 7 _____ Sample answer: $\sqrt{31}$

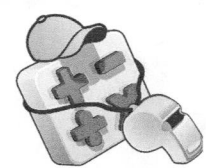

Personal Math Trainer

• 1.3 Homework

Pages shown are from *Differentiated Instruction*. **Also available online.**

© Houghton Mifflin Harcourt Publishing Company

Lesson 1.3 **25**

Pressed for Time

1.3 Differentiated Homework Assignments

AL Approaching Level	12–16, 18–20, 24
OL On Level	14–21, 24
BL Beyond Level	16–17, 20–24

*For **Below Level** students, assign Personal Math Trainer, Daily Intervention 1.3 Homework.*

Mathematical Processes	Exercises
MP.2 Reasoning	16, 18–21
MP.3 Logic	23–24
MP.4 Modeling	22
MP.5 Using Tools	12–15
MP.6 Precision	17

Focus on Higher Order Thinking

Depth of Knowledge	Exercises
1 Recall of Information	12–15
2 Skills/Concepts	16–21
3 Strategic Thinking **H.O.T.**	22–24

DIFFERENTIATE INSTRUCTION *Leveled Homework/Practice*

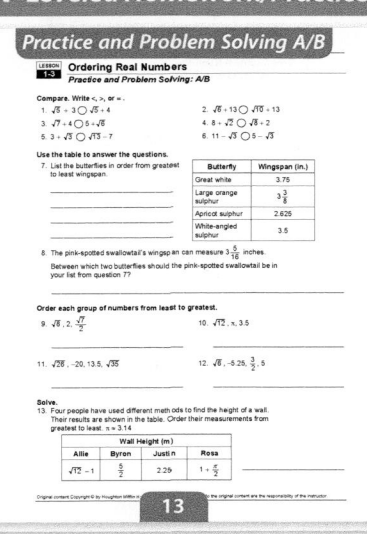

Practice and Problem Solving A/B

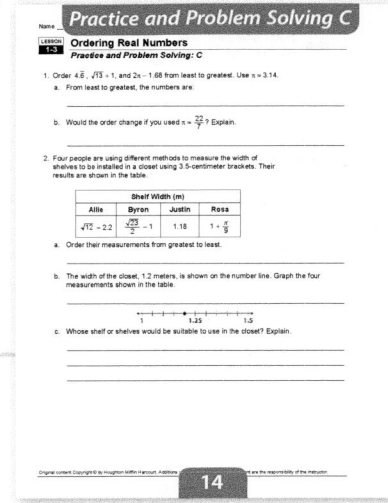

Practice and Problem Solving C

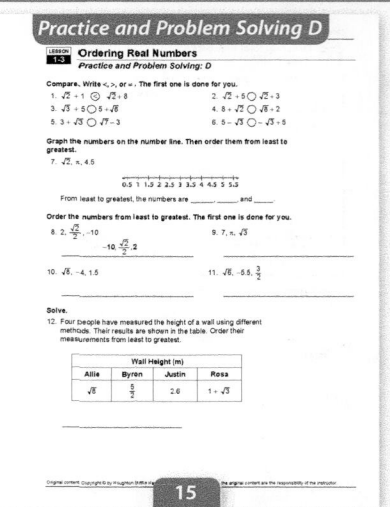

Practice and Problem Solving D

20. A teacher asks his students to write the numbers shown in order from least to greatest. Paul thinks the numbers are already in order. Sandra thinks the order should be reversed. Who is right?

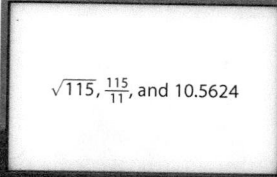

$\sqrt{115}$, $\frac{115}{11}$, and 10.5624

Neither student is correct. The answer should be $\frac{115}{11}$, 10.5624, $\sqrt{115}$.

21. **Math History** There is a famous irrational number called Euler's number, symbolized with an *e*. Like π, its decimal form never ends or repeats. The first few digits of *e* are 2.7182818284.

a. Between which two square roots of integers could you find this number?

between $\sqrt{7} \approx 2.65$ and $\sqrt{8} \approx 2.83$

b. Between which two square roots of integers can you find π?

between $\sqrt{9} \approx 3$ and $\sqrt{10} \approx 3.16$

 **FOCUS ON HIGHER ORDER THINKING**

22. **Analyze Relationships** There are several approximations used for π, including 3.14 and $\frac{22}{7}$. π is approximately 3.14159265358979…

a. Label π and the two approximations on the number line.

3.14 π $\frac{22}{7}$

3.140   3.141   3.142   3.143

b. Which of the two approximations is a better estimate for π? Explain.

$\frac{22}{7}$; it is closer to π on the number line.

c. Find a whole number *x* so that the ratio $\frac{x}{113}$ is a better estimate for π than the two given approximations. _____ 355

23. **Communicate Mathematical Ideas** What is the fewest number of distinct points that must be graphed on a number line, in order to represent natural numbers, whole numbers, integers, rational numbers, irrational numbers, and real numbers? Explain.

2 points; A rational number and an irrational number cannot be represented by the same point on the number line.

24. **Critique Reasoning** Jill says that $12.\overline{6}$ is less than 12.63. Explain her error.

She did not consider the repeating digit. 12.66…

Work Area

© Houghton Mifflin Harcourt Publishing Company Image Credits: ©3DStock/iStockPhoto.com

© Houghton Mifflin Harcourt Publishing Company Image Credits: ©3DStock/iStockPhoto.com

✔ Quick Check

1.3 Lesson Quiz

1. Compare. Write $<$, $>$, or $=$.

$\sqrt{95} - 5$ ◯ $\sqrt{62} - 2$ $\sqrt{95} - 5 < \sqrt{62} - 2$

2. Order 10.5, $\sqrt{105}$, and $3\pi + 1$ from greatest to least.   10.5, $3\pi + 1$, $\sqrt{105}$

3. A length in centimeters is calculated differently by four different people. Order their calculations from least to greatest.

K.D.: $\frac{11}{2}$ cm, Silvio: $\frac{5}{3}\pi$ cm, Paula: $5.\overline{4}$ cm, Luis: $\sqrt{33}$ cm

$\frac{5}{3}\pi$ cm, $5.\overline{4}$ cm, $\frac{11}{2}$ cm, $\sqrt{33}$ cm

Differentiate Instruction

IF a student misses more than one question, THEN

Differentiate Instruction:

• 1.3 Reteach

• Personal Math Trainer

Interactive Whiteboard

Interactive Lesson quiz available online

DIFFERENTIATE INSTRUCTION *Extend-the-Math Activity* **PRE-AP**

Activity Have students investigate whether there are infinitely many numbers between two numbers by giving examples for each of the following.

• Between any two rational numbers there is at least one other rational number.
Sample answer: 4.5 is between 4.1 and 4.8.

• Between any two irrational numbers there is at least one rational number.
Sample answer: 4.5 is between $\sqrt{11}$ and $\sqrt{29}$.

• Between any two rational numbers there is at least one irrational number.
Sample answer: $\sqrt{11}$ is between 3.1 and 3.6.

• Between any two irrational numbers there is at least one irrational number.
Sample answer: $\sqrt{17}$ is between $\sqrt{11}$ and $\sqrt{29}$.

GAME | 1.3

Root-O!

Objective
Students will evaluate square roots, including rational and irrational numbers.

Number of Players
3 or more players

Materials
- 1 *Root-O!* board per player
- 1 set of caller cards
- 25 counters (or dried beans) per player
- scratch paper

Teacher Preparation
Print and cut out materials for the players. Printing the cards on cardstock is recommended.

Game Resources

Go online to access all your game resources.
- *Root-O!* boards
- Caller cards (with answers)

my.hrw.com

Key Concepts
This game reviews square root skills. Students will:
- evaluate the square root of a perfect square
- estimate the square root of a nonperfect square number
- classify numbers as rational and irrational

Encourage students to use the square root of perfect squares to estimate the square roots of nonperfect squares.

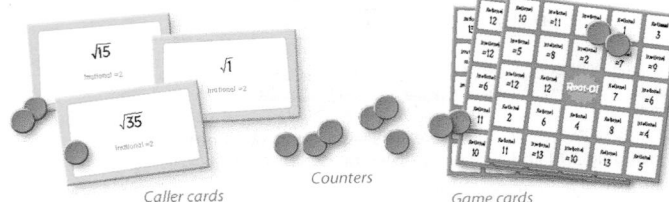

Game 1.3

INSTRUCTIONS

Playing the Game

STEP 1 Choose one person to be the caller. The caller can be a teacher, or students can take turns being caller. The caller gets a set of caller cards. All the other players get a game card and some counters. The center is a free space. Players should cover the center square before play begins.

Caller cards   Counters   Game cards

STEP 2 The caller randomly draws a caller card and reads aloud the square-root expression to the players.

STEP 3 Players write down the expression on a piece of scratch paper and determine the classification (rational or irrational) and the equivalent or approximate integer value. If the same classification and value appear on a square of his/her game card, the player covers that square with a counter.

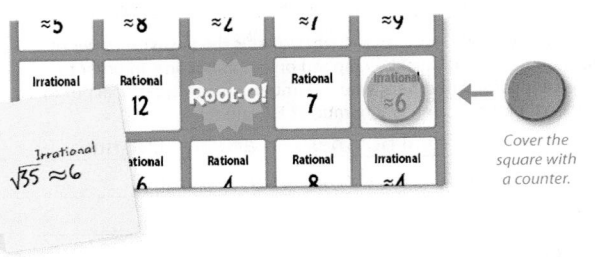

Cover the square with a counter.

© Houghton Mifflin Harcourt Publishing Company

Game 1.3 **26A**

WARM-UP EXERCISES

Classify each number as *rational* or *irrational*.

1. $\sqrt{34}$ rational
2. $\sqrt{24}$ irrational
3. $\sqrt{16}$ rational
4. $\sqrt{8}$ irrational

STEP 4 Caller will then draw another caller card to continue the game.

STEP 5 Continue the game in this way until a player covers five squares in a row horizontally, vertically, or diagonally, and calls out "Root-O!"

STEP 6 The prospective winning player will then check with the caller to verify that the squares covered on his/her game card correspond to cards that have been called. If there is a discrepancy, the player's game card is corrected and the game continues.

Winning the Game

A player who covers five squares in a horizontal, vertical, or diagonal row wins.

© Houghton Mifflin Harcourt Publishing Company

Playing the Game

STEP 1 Determine who will be the caller. The caller can be a teacher, or students can take turns being the caller. The caller gets a set of caller cards. All the other players get a game card and counters. The center is a free space. Players should cover the center square before play begins.

STEP 2 The caller randomly draws a caller card and reads aloud the square root expression to the players.

STEP 3 Players write down the expression on scratch paper and determine the classification (rational or irrational) and the equivalent or approximate integer value. If the same classification and value appears on a square of his/her game card, the player covers that square with a counter.

STEP 4 The caller will then draw another caller card to continue the game.

STEP 5 The game continues clockwise until a player covers five squares in a row horizontally, vertically, or diagonally, and calls out "Root-O!"

STEP 6 The prospective winning player should verify with the caller that the winning squares covered on his/her game card correspond to cards that have been called. If there is a discrepancy, the player's game card is corrected and the game continues.

Winning the Game

A player who covers five squares in a horizontal, vertical, or diagonal row wins.

VARIATIONS

- **Longer Variation** Instead of covering five squares in a row, have players cover squares in the patterns below to win.

Letter T

Letter I

Letter X

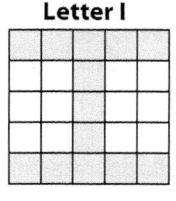

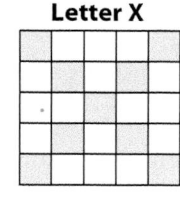

Letter N

Letter Z

Four Corners

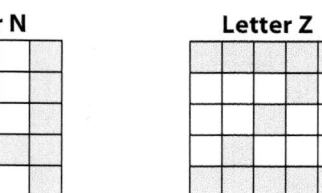

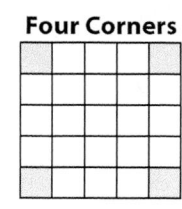

Ready to Go On?

Assess Mastery

Access *Ready to Go On?* assessment online, and receive instant scoring, feedback, and customized intervention or enrichment.

Personal Math Trainer

Online Assessment and Intervention
• Module 1 Posttest

Additional Resources

Digital Teacher Resources

Go online for module-level resources.

Assessment Resources
• Module 1 Quiz: B, p.15
• Module 1 Quiz: D, p.17

my.hrw.com

Ready to Go On?

Personal Math Trainer
Online Assessment and Intervention
my.hrw.com

1.1 Rational and Irrational Numbers

Write each fraction as a decimal or each decimal as a fraction.

1. $\frac{7}{20}$ ___0.35___   2. $1.\overline{27}$ ___$\frac{14}{11}$___   3. $1\frac{7}{8}$ ___1.875___

Solve each equation for x.

4. $x^2 = 81$ ___9, −9___   5. $x^3 = 343$ ___7___   6. $x^2 = \frac{1}{100}$ ___$\frac{1}{10}, -\frac{1}{10}$___

7. A square patio has an area of 200 square feet. How long is each side of the patio to the nearest 0.05? ___14.15 ft___

1.2 Sets of Real Numbers

Write all names that apply to each number.

8. $\frac{121}{\sqrt{121}}$ ___whole, integer, rational, real___

9. $\frac{\pi}{2}$ ___irrational, real___

10. Tell whether the statement "All integers are rational numbers" is true or false. Explain your choice.
   True; integers can be written as the quotient of two integers.

1.3 Ordering Real Numbers

Compare. Write <, >, or =.

11. $\sqrt{8} + 3$ ⊂< 8 + $\sqrt{3}$ 12. $\sqrt{5} + 11$ ⊃> $5 + \sqrt{11}$

Order the numbers from least to greatest.

13. $\sqrt{99}, \pi^2, 9.\overline{8}$ ___$\pi^2, 9.\overline{8}, \sqrt{99}$___   14. $\sqrt{\frac{1}{25}}, \frac{1}{4}, 0.\overline{2}$ ___$\sqrt{\frac{1}{25}}, 0.\overline{2}, \frac{1}{4}$___

 ESSENTIAL QUESTION

15. How are real numbers used to describe real-world situations?
   Sample answer: Real numbers, such as the rational number $\frac{1}{4}$, can describe amounts used in cooking.

© Houghton Mifflin Harcourt Publishing Company

READY TO GO ON? *Diagnostic Assessment*

RtI Response to Intervention

Use to determine if students have mastered the concepts covered in this module.

Lesson	Exercises	Content Focus	Review with *Differentiated Instruction*
1.1	1–7	Rational and Irrational Numbers	1.1 Reteach 1.1 Reading Strategies 1.1 Success for English Learners
1.2	8–10	Sets of Real Numbers	1.2 Reteach 1.2 Reading Strategies 1.2 Success for English Learners
1.3	11–14	Ordering Real Numbers	1.3 Reteach 1.3 Reading Strategies 1.3 Success for English Learners

Personal
Math Trainer
Online
Assessment and
Intervention
my.hrw.com

Selected Response

1. The square root of a number is 9. What is the other square root?

- (A) −9
- (C) 3
- (B) −3
- (D) 81

2. A square acre of land is 4,840 square yards. Between which two integers is the length of one side?

- (A) between 24 and 25 yards
- (B) between 69 and 70 yards
- (C) between 242 and 243 yards
- (D) between 695 and 696 yards

3. Which of the following is an integer but not a whole number?

- (A) −9.6
- (C) 0
- (B) −4
- (D) 3.7

4. Which statement is false?

- (A) No integers are irrational numbers.
- (B) All whole numbers are integers.
- (C) No real numbers are irrational numbers.
- (D) All integers greater than 0 are whole numbers.

5. Which set of numbers best describes the displayed weights on a digital scale that shows each weight to the nearest half pound?

- (A) whole numbers
- (B) rational numbers
- (C) real numbers
- (D) integers

6. Which of the following is not true?

- (A) $\pi^2 < 2\pi + 4$
- (C) $\sqrt{27} + 3 > \frac{17}{2}$
- (B) $3\pi > 9$
- (D) $5 - \sqrt{24} < 1$

7. Which number is between $\sqrt{21}$ and $\frac{3\pi}{2}$?

- (A) $\frac{14}{3}$
- (C) 5
- (B) $2\sqrt{6}$
- (D) $\pi + 1$

8. What number is shown on the graph?

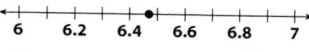

- (A) $\pi + 3$
- (C) $\sqrt{20} + 2$
- (B) $\sqrt{4} + 2.5$
- (D) $6.\overline{14}$

9. Which is in order from least to greatest?

- (A) $3.3, \frac{10}{3}, \pi, \frac{11}{4}$
- (C) $\pi, \frac{10}{3}, \frac{11}{4}, 3.3$
- (B) $\frac{10}{3}, 3.3, \frac{11}{4}, \pi$
- (D) $\frac{11}{4}, \pi, 3.3, \frac{10}{3}$

Mini-Task

10. The volume of a cube is given by $V = x^3$, where x is the length of an edge of the cube. The area of a square is given by $A = x^2$, where x is the length of a side of the square. A given cube has a volume of 1728 cubic inches.

a. Find the length of an edge.

12 in.

b. Find the area of one side of the cube.

144 in.²

c. Find the surface area of the cube.

864 in.²

d. What is the surface area in square feet?

6 ft²

© Houghton Mifflin Harcourt Publishing Company

Preparing for High Stakes Tests

Assessment Readiness Tip
Students can use estimation to eliminate some or all of the answer choices.

- **Item 2** 24 is close to 20, and 20 squared is 400. 400 is much less than 4840, so A is not likely to be correct. 242 is close to 200, and 200 squared is 40,000, which is much greater than 4840. C is not correct, and since D is greater than C, D is also incorrect.

- **Item 8** π is about 3.14, so $\pi + 3$ is about 6.14, which is much lower than the point on the graph. $6.\overline{14}$ is nearby and therefore also much too low. Answer choices A and D can be eliminated.

Avoid Common Errors

- **Item 4** Students commonly confuse real numbers and rational numbers, which may lead them to believe that C is true. Remind them that real numbers include rational and irrational numbers.

- **Item 6** If students do not read the stem carefully, they may mistakenly look for a true statement and choose any of the distractors. Remind them to always read carefully.

Items	Grade 8 Lessons	Mathematical Processes
1	1.1	MP.7
2*	9.3 (Grade 7)	MP.4
3	1.2	MP.2
4	1.2	MP.2
5	1.2	MP.4
6	1.3	MP.6
7	1.3	MP.6
8	1.3	MP.6
9	1.3	MP.6
10*	9.4, 9.5 (Grade 7)	MP.4

* Item integrates mixed review concepts from previous modules or a previous course.

DIFFERENTIATE ASSESSMENT

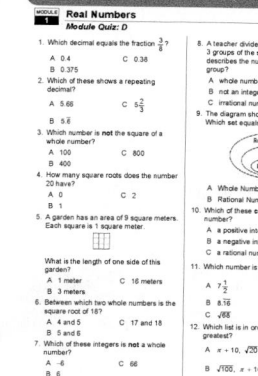

Below Level Module Quiz 1: D

17–18

On Level Module Quiz 1: B

15–16

Personal Math Trainer

Module 1
Assessment
Readiness

Pages shown are from *Assessment Resources*. **Also available online.**

Module At A Glance

Module Essential Question: How can you use scientific notation to solve real-world problems?

MODULE 2 | Exponents and Scientific Notation

Lessons at A Glance	Lesson 2.1 Integer Exponents	Lesson 2.2 Scientific Notation with Positive Powers of 10	Lesson 2.3 Scientific Notation with Negative Powers of 10
	Pg. T33A	Pg. T39A	Pg. T45A
Essential Question	How can you develop and use the properties of integer exponents?	How can you use scientific notation to express very large quantities?	How can you use scientific notation to express very small quantities?
Objective	Students will develop and use the properties of integer exponents.	Students will use scientific notation to express very large quantities.	Students will use scientific notation to express very small quantities.
Vocabulary		scientific notation	
Go online for all your module resources my.hrw.com	2.1 *i*Student Edition 2.1 *i*Teacher Edition 2.1 *e*Student Edition Personal Math Trainer Math on the Spot Videos	2.2 *i*Student Edition 2.2 *i*Teacher Edition 2.2 *e*Student Edition Personal Math Trainer Math on the Spot Videos	2.3 *i*Student Edition 2.3 *i*Teacher Edition 2.3 *e*Student Edition Personal Math Trainer Math on the Spot Videos Animated Math
Print Resources	**2.1 Student Edition:** Lesson **2.1 Student Edition:** Going Further *Differentiated Instruction* 　2.1 Practice and Problem Solving A/B, C, and D 　2.1 Reteach 　2.1 Reading Strategies 　2.1 Success for English Learners	**2.2 Student Edition:** Lesson **2.2 Student Edition:** Going Further *Differentiated Instruction* 　2.2 Practice and Problem Solving A/B, C, and D 　2.2 Reteach 　2.2 Reading Strategies 　2.2 Success for English Learners	**2.3 Student Edition:** Lesson **2.3 Student Edition:** Going Further *Differentiated Instruction* 　2.3 Practice and Problem Solving A/B, C, and D 　2.3 Reteach 　2.3 Reading Strategies 　2.3 Success for English Learners

RtI
Response to Intervention

Before the Module	During the Lesson	After the Module
Are You Ready	**Guided/Independent Practice**	**Ready to Go On?**
• Prerequisite Skills Activities • Personal Math Trainer	• Reteach • Personal Math Trainer • Practice and Problem Solving D	• Reteach • Personal Math Trainer

Module Pacing Chart			
Introduction	Instruction	Assessment	Total
1 days	11 days	1 day	13 days

Lesson 2.4
Operations with Scientific Notation

Pg. T51A

How do you add, subtract, multiply, and divide using scientific notation?

Students will add, subtract, multiply, and divide using scientific notation.

2.4 *i*Student Edition
2.4 *i*Teacher Edition
2.4 *e*Student Edition
Personal Math Trainer
Math on the Spot Videos

2.4 Student Edition: Lesson

Differentiated Instruction

- 2.4 Practice and Problem Solving A/B, C, and D
- 2.4 Reteach
- 2.4 Reading Strategies
- 2.4 Success for English Learners

Teacher Notes

Check It Out!

Math on the Spot Videos

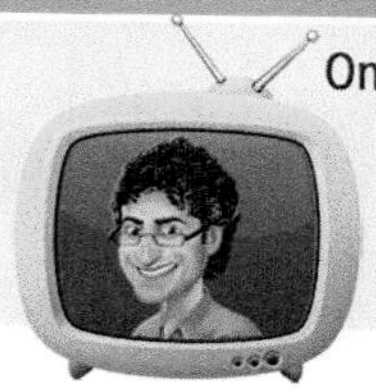

One for every Example in every Lesson

Animated Math

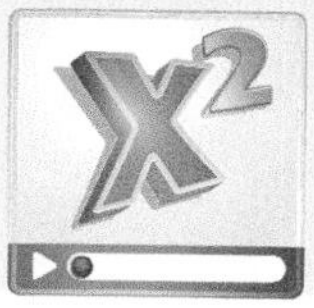

During Lesson 2.3

Exponents and Scientific Notation

Exponents and Scientific Notation

ESSENTIAL QUESTION
How can you use scientific notation to solve real-world problems?

You can simplify calculations with very large and very small numbers by first writing them in scientific notation.

● Real-World Video Viewing Guide
After students have watched the video, discuss the following:

• What are some reasons you might use scientific notation to write very large numbers?

• What symbol is used to write numbers in scientific notation? multiplication symbol

Professional Development Video
Author Juli Dixon models successful teaching practices as she explores the concept of scientific notation in an actual eighth-grade classroom.

© Houghton Mifflin Harcourt Publishing Company • Image Credits: ©Eyebyte/Alamy Images

Real-World Video
The distance from Earth to other planets, moons, and stars is a very great number of kilometers. To make it easier to write very large and very small numbers, we use scientific notation.

my.hrw.com

GO DIGITAL
my.hrw.com

my.hrw.com	Math On the Spot	Animated Math	Personal Math Trainer
Go digital with your write-in student edition, accessible on any device.	Scan with your smart phone to jump directly to the online edition, video tutor, and more.	Interactively explore key concepts to see how math works.	Get immediate feedback and help as you work through practice sets.

29

TEACHER ONLINE RESOURCES

ONLINE TEACHER EDITION Access a full suite of teaching resources online—plan, present, and manage classes and assignments.

MY SMART PLANNER Easily plan your classes and access all your resources online.

INTERACTIVE WHITEBOARDS Engage students with interactive whiteboard-ready examples and a lesson quiz for each lesson.

PERSONAL MATH TRAINER: Online Assessment and Intervention Assign automatically graded homework, quizzes, tests, and intervention activities. Prepare your students for standardized tests in short-answer and multiple-choice formats.

Reading Start-Up

Visualize Vocabulary

Use the ✔ words to complete the Venn diagram. You can put more than one word in each section of the diagram.

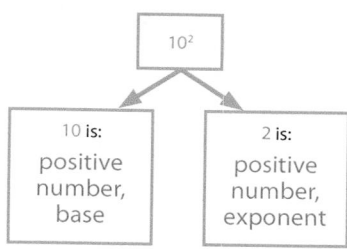

10^2

10 is: positive number, base

2 is: positive number, exponent

Understand Vocabulary

Complete the sentences using the preview words.

1. A number produced by raising a base to an exponent is a _____ power _____.

2. _____ Scientific notation _____ is a method of writing very large or very small numbers by using powers of 10.

3. A _____ rational number _____ is any number that can be expressed as a ratio of two integers.

© Houghton Mifflin Harcourt Publishing Company

Vocabulary

Review Words
✔ base (base)
✔ exponent (exponente)
integers (enteros)
✔ positive number (número positivo)
standard notation (notación estándar)

Preview Words
power (potencia)
rational number (número racional)
real numbers (número real)
scientific notation (notación científica)
whole number (número entero)

Active Reading

Two-Panel Flip Chart Create a two-panel flip chart to help you understand the concepts in this module. Label one flap "Positive Powers of 10" and the other flap "Negative Powers of 10." As you study each lesson, write important ideas under the appropriate flap. Include sample problems that will help you remember the concepts later when you look back at your notes.

Reading Start-Up

Visualize Vocabulary

The diagram helps students review the terms **base** and **exponent** and prepares them for learning about scientific notation which is the focus of this module. Students should write more than one review word in each box.

Understand Vocabulary

Use the following explanations to help students learn the preview words.

> **Scientific notation** uses the powers of 10. **Power** refers to the exponent, and 10 is the base. In scientific notation, 10 is always the base. The exponent can be any integer. Scientific notation is used for very large and very small numbers.

Active Reading

Integrating Language Arts

Students can use these reading and note-taking strategies to help them organize and understand new concepts and vocabulary.

Additional Resources

Differentiated Instruction

- Reading Strategies **ELL**
- Interactive multilingual glossary

LEARNING PROGRESSIONS ACROSS THE GRADES

Before	In this Module	After
Students understand how to: • write decimals • use exponents • add, subtract, multiply, and divide rational numbers	Students will learn how to: • apply properties of integer exponents to evaluate expressions • convert between large numbers in standard decimal notation and scientific notation • convert between small numbers in standard decimal notation and scientific notation • add, subtract, multiply, and divide numbers expressed with scientific notation	Students will connect that: • positive numbers written in scientific notation with negative exponents represent numbers between 0 and 1 • measurements written in scientific notation often use significant digits to show the precision of a measurement

Are You Ready?

Assess Readiness

Access *Are You Ready?* assessment online, and receive instant scoring, feedback, and customized intervention or enrichment.

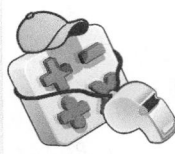

Personal Math Trainer

Online Assessment and Intervention

Additional Resources

Digital Teacher Resources

Go online for module-level resources.

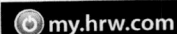

my.hrw.com

Are YOU Ready?

Complete these exercises to review skills you will need for this module.

Personal Math Trainer

Online Assessment and Intervention

my.hrw.com

Exponents

EXAMPLE $10^4 = 10 \times 10 \times 10 \times 10$

$= 10,000$

Write the exponential expression as a product.
Simplify.

Write each exponential expression as a decimal.

1. 10^2 __100__   2. 10^3 __1,000__   3. 10^5 __100,000__   4. 10^7 __10,000,000__

Multiply and Divide by Powers of 10

EXAMPLE $0.0478 \times 10^5 = 0.0478 \times 100,000$

$= 4,780$

Identify the number of zeros in the power of 10.
When multiplying, move the decimal point to the *right* the same number of places as the number of zeros.

$37.9 \div 10^4 = 37.9 \div 10,000$

$= 0.00379$

Identify the number of zeros in the power of 10.
When dividing, move the decimal point to the *left* the same number of places as the number of zeros.

Find each product or quotient.

5. 45.3×10^3 6. $7.08 \div 10^2$ 7. 0.00235×10^6 8. $3,600 \div 10^4$

__45,300__   __0.0708__   __2,350__   __0.36__

9. 0.5×10^2 10. $67.7 \div 10^5$ 11. 0.0057×10^4 12. $195 \div 10^6$

__50__   __0.000677__   __57__   __0.000195__

© Houghton Mifflin Harcourt Publishing Company

ARE YOU READY? *Diagnostic Assessment*

RtI — Response to Intervention

Use to determine if students need intervention for the module's prerequisite skills.

Skill	Missed More Than . . .	Intervene With *Skills Intervention* worksheets (available online)	For Enrichment *Differentiated Instruction* (available in print and online)
Exponents	1 question	**Skill 12** Exponents	**Module 2 Challenge** Extend-the-Math Lesson Activities in TE
Multiply and Divide by Powers of 10	2 questions	**Skill 37** Multiply and Divide by Powers of 10	**Module 2 Challenge** Extend-the-Math Lesson Activities in TE

Are YOU Ready? (cont'd)

Complete these exercises to review skills you will need for this module.

Exponents

13. Chris has an MP3 player that can store about 10^8 bytes of data. Explain how to determine the number of zeros in the product of 10^8. Then evaluate the power and state the number of bytes in words, without using exponents.

> The exponential expression can be written as the product of eight factors of 10. The number of zeros in the product is the same as the exponent, 8. The product is 1 followed by eight zeros, or 100,000,000. So the MP3 player can hold about one hundred million bytes of data.

14. To evaluate 10^4, Tyrese multiplied 10×4 to get 40. Identify Tyrese's error, and write the correct value.

> Tyrese should have multiplied $10 \times 10 \times 10 \times 10$ to get 10,000.

Multiply and Divide by Powers of 10

15. Explain how to find the product 0.8×10^3. Compare this product with 10^3.

> Identify the number of zeros in the power of 10 as three. Rewrite the product as $0.8 \times 1,000$. When multiplying, move the decimal point in 0.8 three places to the right. The product is 800. Since 10^3 is 1,000, the product is less than 10^3.

16. Jake found that the quotient $9.236 \div 10^4$ is 0.0009236. If Jake's result is correct, justify his answer. If not, give the correct decimal.

> There are four zeros in 10^4. Since the operation is division, Jake correctly moved the decimal point 4 places to the left to get 0.0009236.

17. To find the quotient $62.5 \div 10^5$, Gina first identified the number of zeros in the power of 10. When written as a decimal, 10^5 has five zeros. Describe how Gina can complete the problem.

> Move the decimal point in 62.5 five places to the left to get 0.000625.

© Houghton Mifflin Harcourt Publishing Company

Exponents

Exercise 13 Point out that the lead digit in a power of 10 is always 1, and the exponent tells how many zeros to write after the 1. Caution students that this shortcut is used only for a power of 10.

Exercise 14 Watch for students who may evaluate an exponential expression by multiplying the exponent by the base, for example: $10^4 \neq 10 \times 4$.

Multiply and Divide by Powers of 10

Exercise 15 Encourage students to look for patterns when multiplying powers of 10.

Exercise 16 Students may have difficulty adding zeros when dividing by powers of 10. Encourage students to count aloud each time they move the decimal point to the left.

Exercise 17 To check their answers, have students multiply their answers by 10^5.

Use to determine if students are able to apply the module's prerequisite skills.

Skill	Exercise	Depth of Knowledge (D.O.K.)	Mathematical Processes
Exponents	13	**2** Skills/Concepts	**MP.2** Abstract and Quantitative Reasoning
	14	**3** Strategic Thinking	**MP.3** Use and Evaluate Logical Reasoning
Multiply and Divide by Powers of 10	15	**3** Strategic Thinking	**MP.7** See Structure
	16	**3** Strategic Thinking	**MP.7** See Structure
	17	**2** Skills/Concepts	**MP.2** Abstract and Quantitative Reasoning

Lesson Support

Content Objective Students will develop and learn to use the properties of exponents.

Professional Development

Integrate Mathematical Processes MP.8

This lesson provides an opportunity to address this Mathematical Processes standard. It calls for students to notice if calculations are repeated. Students learn to recognize how repeated division defines the use of negative exponents. They then use repeated multiplication and division to discover properties of exponents and find shortcuts for simplifying expressions.

FOCUS	COHERENCE	RIGOR

Building Background

Eliciting Prior Knowledge Have students evaluate powers of 10 from 10^3 down to 10^{-3}. They are likely to write the negative powers of 10 as decimals. Ask them to write both the decimal and the fraction for the negative powers. Discuss patterns students used to evaluate the powers of 10.

$10\,3 = 1000$

$10\,2 = 100$

$10\,1 = 10$

$10\,0 = 1$

$10\,-1 = 0.1 = 1\_10$

$10\,-2 = 0.01 = 1\_100$

$10^{-3} = 0.001 = \dfrac{1}{1000}$

Learning Progressions

In this lesson, students explore and apply the properties of integer exponents. They observe patterns to write the general rules of integer exponents. Then they use these properties to generate equivalent numerical expressions. Important understandings for students include the following:

- **Recognize that there are patterns of integer exponents.**
- **Make conjectures about the properties of integer exponents.**
- **Apply the properties of integer exponents to simplify numerical expressions.**

Since Grade 5, students have used integer exponents to represent powers of 10. They have observed that $10^a \cdot 10^b = 10^{a+b}$, where a and b are whole numbers, and that $10^0 = 1$. In Grade 8, they extend to other bases the rules they have observed from studying powers of 10. They also learn and apply new properties of exponents.

Cluster Connections

This lesson provides an excellent opportunity to connect ideas in this cluster:

Work with radicals and integer exponents.

Remind students that to apply the properties of exponents, the bases must be the same. However, sometimes expressions can be manipulated to convert unequal bases to equal bases. Have students consider the following examples:

$$2\,3 \cdot 8\,4$$
$$4\,3 \cdot 16\,2$$

Ask students to demonstrate how to simplify each expression. Then challenge them to write two expressions of their own that require manipulation to convert unequal bases to equal bases.

Sample answers:

$2\,3 \cdot 8\,4 = 8\,1 \cdot 8\,4 = 8\,5$

$4\,3 \cdot 16\,2 = 4\,3 \cdot (4\,2)\,2 = 4\,3 \cdot 4\,4 = 4\,7$

Expressions may vary.

Language Support ELL

Image Credits: ©DUEL/Cultura RF/Getty Images

Language Objective Students will write an explanation of how to develop and use the properties of integer exponents.

Leveled Strategies for English Learners ELL

Emerging
Have students complete sentence frames to define mathematical terms:

In math, a product is _____.

Expanding
Have students discuss the differences between the meaning of *base* in everyday use and the mathematical definition. In mathematics, *base* does not refer to an item on a baseball field.

Bridging
Have students discuss and then write their understanding of the math terms in their own words.

Be sure that students can verbalize the difference for products involving positive exponents and those involving negative exponents, and can identify and name the mathematical symbols that signal the difference. Expanding-level and bridging-level students should be encouraged to describe and explain their thinking in problem solving.

Linguistic Support ELL

Academic/Content Vocabulary
base An understanding of the meaning of *base*, as in *base number* and *same base*, is important in this lesson. Students are asked to find patterns and describe them using terms that may be unfamiliar to them. Label examples of *base*, *exponent*, *power*, and so on. Guide the students with questions to identify the pattern and describe it in their own words before using the math terms: What number is repeated in this problem? How many times? What do we do with/to these numbers?

Background Knowledge
Clarify how the terms *base*, *product*, *expression*, *power*, and *times* are used mathematically in the lesson. Preview the lesson to anticipate potential misunderstandings and confusions between mathematical meanings and common meanings of the words. Also, be aware of phrasal terms in instruction, such as *simplify each expression* and *raising a product to a power*. Do a pre- and post- assessment to determine whether students understand the mathematical meaning of the terms.

1 Engage

? ESSENTIAL QUESTION

How can you develop and use the properties of integer exponents? Sample answer: To develop the properties of integer exponents, look for patterns in a powers table, in the multiplication and division of powers with the same base, and in powers of products. The properties can be used to simplify complicated expressions.

Motivate the Lesson

Ask: How can patterns help you simplify numbers involving negative exponents? Begin Explore Activity 1 to find out.

2 Explore

EXPLORE ACTIVITY 1

Focus on Patterns

If students have trouble seeing the patterns, point out that they should look at one row of the table at a time, and examine the two sides of the equation separately. Ask them to identify what changes on the left side and what changes on the right side.

LESSON

2.1 Integer Exponents

8.1.2.1
Students will develop and use the properties of integer exponents.

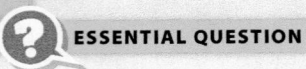

? ESSENTIAL QUESTION

How can you develop and use the properties of integer exponents?

EXPLORE ACTIVITY 1

Using Patterns of Integer Exponents

The table below shows powers of 5, 4, and 3.

$5^4 = 625$	$5^3 = 125$	$5^2 = 25$	$5^1 = 5$	$5^0 = \boxed{1}$	$5^{-1} = \boxed{\frac{1}{5}}$	$5^{-2} = \boxed{\frac{1}{25}}$
$4^4 = 256$	$4^3 = 64$	$4^2 = 16$	$4^1 = 4$	$4^0 = \boxed{1}$	$4^{-1} = \boxed{\frac{1}{4}}$	$4^{-2} = \boxed{\frac{1}{16}}$
$3^4 = 81$	$3^3 = 27$	$3^2 = 9$	$3^1 = 3$	$3^0 = \boxed{1}$	$3^{-1} = \boxed{\frac{1}{3}}$	$3^{-2} = \boxed{\frac{1}{9}}$

A What pattern do you see in the powers of 5?

As the exponent decreases by 1, the value of the power is divided by 5.

B What pattern do you see in the powers of 4?

As the exponent decreases by 1, the value of the power is divided by 4.

C What pattern do you see in the powers of 3?

As the exponent decreases by 1, the value of the power is divided by 3.

D Complete the table for the values of $5^0, 5^{-1}, 5^{-2}$.   See table above.

E Complete the table for the values of $4^0, 4^{-1}, 4^{-2}$.   See table above.

F Complete the table for the values of $3^0, 3^{-1}, 3^{-2}$.   See table above.

Reflect

1. **Make a Conjecture** Write a general rule for the value of a^0.

$$a^0 = 1$$

2. **Make a Conjecture** Write a general rule for the value of a^{-n}.

$$a^{-n} = \frac{1}{a^n}$$

© Houghton Mifflin Harcourt Publishing Company

DIFFERENTIATE INSTRUCTION *Leveled Questions*

	EXPLORE ACTIVITY 1
(AL) DOK 1 *Recall*	How do you use the pattern in the table to find the value of 5^0? You divide the power in the column before it (5) by the base (5).
(OL) DOK 2 *Skills/Concepts*	What would another row with base 2 look like? From left to right: $2^4 = 16, 2^3 = 8, 2^2 = 4, 2^1 = 2, 2^0 = 1, 2^{-1} = \frac{1}{2}, 2^{-2} = \frac{1}{4}$
(BL) DOK 3 *Strategic Thinking*	In the last two columns of the table, how is the exponent related to the denominator of the fraction? The denominator is equal to the corresponding positive power of the base. For example, for 5^{-1}, the positive power of the base is $5^1 = 5$, and that is the denominator.

LEVELED QUESTIONS: (AL) Approaching Level | (OL) On Level | (BL) Beyond Level

Exploring Properties of Integer Exponents

A Complete the following equations.

$3 \cdot 3 \cdot 3 \cdot 3 \cdot 3 = 3^{\boxed{5}}$

$(3 \cdot 3 \cdot 3 \cdot 3) \cdot 3 = 3^{\boxed{4}} \cdot 3^{\boxed{1}} = 3^{\boxed{5}}$

$(3 \cdot 3 \cdot 3) \cdot (3 \cdot 3) = 3^{\boxed{3}} \cdot 3^{\boxed{2}} = 3^{\boxed{5}}$

What pattern do you see when multiplying two powers with the same base?

The result has the same base with an exponent equal

to the sum of the exponents in the powers.

Use your pattern to complete this equation: $5^2 \cdot 5^5 = 5^{\boxed{7}}$.

B Complete the following equation:

$\frac{4^5}{4^3} = \frac{4 \cdot 4 \cdot 4 \cdot 4 \cdot 4}{4 \cdot 4 \cdot 4} = \frac{\cancel{4} \cdot \cancel{4} \cdot \cancel{4} \cdot 4 \cdot 4}{\cancel{4} \cdot \cancel{4} \cdot \cancel{4}} = 4 \cdot 4 = 4^{\boxed{2}}$

What pattern do you see when dividing two powers with the same base?

The result has the same base with an exponent equal

to the difference of the exponent in the numerator and

exponent in the denominator.

Use your pattern to complete this equation: $\frac{6^8}{6^3} = 6^{\boxed{5}}$.

C Complete the following equations:

$(5^3)^2 = (5 \cdot 5 \cdot 5)^{\boxed{2}} = (5 \cdot 5 \cdot 5) \cdot (5 \cdot 5 \cdot 5) = 5^{\boxed{6}}$

What pattern do you see when raising a power to a power?

The result has the same base with an exponent equal

to the product of the exponents.

Use your pattern to complete this equation: $(7^2)^4 = 7^{\boxed{8}}$.

Math Talk
Mathematical Processes
Do the patterns you found in parts A–C apply if the exponents are negative? If so, give an example of each.

Yes;

Part A:

$5^{-1} \cdot 5^{-2} =$
$\frac{1}{5} \cdot \frac{1}{25} = \frac{1}{125} = \frac{1}{5^3}$
$= 5^{-3} = 5^{-1 + (-2)}$

Part B:

$\frac{2^{-5}}{2^{-3}} = \frac{2^3}{2^5}$
$= \frac{2 \cdot 2 \cdot 2}{2 \cdot 2 \cdot 2 \cdot 2 \cdot 2}$
$= 2^{-2} = 2^{-5 - (-3)}$

Part C:

$(3^{-2})^{-3} = \left(\frac{1}{3^2}\right)^{-3}$
$= (3^2)^3 = 3^6$
$= 3^{-2 \cdot (-3)}$

© Houghton Mifflin Harcourt Publishing Company

		EXPLORE ACTIVITY 2
(AL)	**DOK 1** *Recall*	In Part B, why are there five factors of 4 in the numerator and only three in the denominator? 4^5 means 4 is a factor five times. 4^3 means 4 is a factor three times.
(OL)	**DOK 2** *Skills/Concepts*	In Part C, could $(5^3)^2$ be thought of as $(5^3)(5^3)$? Justify your answer. Yes, the base is (5^3), and the exponent 2 means that (5^3) is used as a factor two times, so $(5^3)^2 = (5^3) \cdot (5^3)$.
(BL)	**DOK 3** *Strategic Thinking*	Does the pattern in Part A of the Explore Activity hold for negative exponents, too? Support your answer with an example. Yes; $3^{-3} \cdot 3^2 = \frac{1}{3^3} \cdot 3^2 = \frac{3 \cdot 3}{3 \cdot 3 \cdot 3} = \frac{1}{3}$ and $3^{-3} \cdot 3^2 = 3^{-3+2} = 3^{-1} = \frac{1}{3}$

3 Explain

EXPLORE ACTIVITY 2

Engage with the Whiteboard

For each equation in Part A, have volunteers circle each factor as they count aloud. Then have students write the total number of factors in the box provided.

TEACHER TO TEACHER

Curriculum Connection After completing Explore Activity 1, challenge students to explain whether $(-a)^2$ for $a \neq 0$ will always have a positive value or a negative value. $(-a)^2$ is always positive. Then have them do the same for $-a^2$ for $a \neq 0$. $-a^2 = -(a^2)$, and its value will always be negative.

EXAMPLE 1

Focus on Critical Thinking

Make sure students understand that for expressions such as $(3 + 1)^2$ in Part B, they do not distribute the exponent to each term inside the parentheses but rather simplify inside the parentheses and then apply the exponent. That is, $(3 + 1)^2 \neq 3^2 + 1^2$ but rather $(3 + 1)^2 = 4^2$.

ADDITIONAL EXAMPLE 1
Simplify each expression.

A $5 - (6 - 4)^{-3} + (-2)^0$ $\quad 5\frac{7}{8}$

B $\dfrac{[(6 - 2)]^4}{(8 - 4)^1}$ $\quad 4^3 = 64$

Interactive Whiteboard
Interactive example available online

YOUR TURN   MP.7

Avoid Common Errors

To avoid calculation errors in expressions like those in **Exercise 6**, make sure that students understand that simplifying terms with common bases usually makes calculating easier. For example, $[(6 - 1)^2]^2 = 5^4 = 625$ and $(3 + 2)^3 = 5^3 = 125$. It is much easier to mentally simplify $\frac{5^4}{5^3} = 5$ than it is to simplify $\frac{625}{125}$.

Digital Teacher Resources

Go online to access all your lesson-level resources.

Differentiated Instruction
- Reteach
- Reading Strategies
- Success for English Learners
- Practice and Problem Solving A/B, C, D

Math on the Spot Videos

my.hrw.com

Reflect

Let *m* and *n* be integers.

3. **Make a Conjecture** Write a general rule for the value of $a^m \cdot a^n$. $\quad \dfrac{a^m \cdot a^n = a^{m+n}}{}$

4. **Make a Conjecture** Write a general rule for the value of $\frac{a^m}{a^n}$, $a \neq 0$. $\quad \dfrac{a^m}{a^n} = a^{m-n}$

5. **Make a Conjecture** Write a general rule for the value of $(a^m)^n$. $\quad (a^m)^n = a^{m \cdot n}$

Applying Properties of Integer Exponents

You can use the general rules you found in the Explore Activities to simplify more complicated expressions.

Math On the Spot
my.hrw.com

EXAMPLE 1

My Notes

Simplify each expression.

A $(5 - 2)^5 \cdot 3^{-8} + (5 + 2)^0$

$(3)^5 \cdot 3^{-8} + (7)^0$	Simplify within parentheses.
$3^{5 + (-8)} + 1$	Use properties of exponents.
$3^{-3} + 1$	Simplify.
$\frac{1}{27} + 1 = 1\frac{1}{27}$	Apply the rule for negative exponents and add.

B $\dfrac{\left[(3 + 1)^2\right]^3}{(7 - 3)^2}$

$\frac{(4^2)^3}{4^2}$	Simplify within parentheses.
$\frac{4^6}{4^2}$	Use properties of exponents.
4^{6-2}	Use properties of exponents.
$4^4 = 256$	Simplify.

© Houghton Mifflin Harcourt Publishing Company

YOUR TURN

Simplify each expression.

6. $\dfrac{[(6 - 1)^2]^2}{(3 + 2)^3}$

$\quad 5$

7. $(2^2)^3 - (10 - 6)^3 \cdot 4^{-5}$

$\quad 63\frac{15}{16}$

Personal Math Trainer
Online Assessment and Intervention
my.hrw.com

DIFFERENTIATE INSTRUCTION *Leveled Questions*

	EXAMPLE 1
AL **DOK 1** *Recall*	In the second step of Part A, how is the Multiplication Property of Exponents used? When $3^5 \cdot 3^{-8}$ is simplified to be $3^{5+(-8)}$, the property was used to add the exponents and use the common base.
OL **DOK 2** *Skills/Concepts*	How could you use order of operations and **not** the Multiplication Property of Exponents to simplify $3^5 \cdot 3^{-8}$ in the second step of Part A? Write out the factors: $3^5 \cdot 3^{-8} = \frac{3 \cdot 3 \cdot 3 \cdot 3 \cdot 3}{3 \cdot 3 \cdot 3 \cdot 3 \cdot 3 \cdot 3 \cdot 3 \cdot 3} = \frac{1}{3^3}$, or 3^{-3}.
BL **DOK 3** *Strategic Thinking*	How can you justify results in Part B without using the properties of exponents? $\frac{(4^2)^3}{4^2} = \frac{(4^2)(4^2)(4^2)}{4^2} = (4^2)(4^2)$

LEVELED QUESTIONS: **AL** Approaching Level | **OL** On Level | **BL** Beyond Level

Find the value of each power. (Explore Activity 1)

1. $8^{-1} = \dfrac{1}{8}$

2. $6^{-2} = \dfrac{1}{36}$

3. $256^0 = 1$

4. $10^2 = 100$

5. $5^4 = 625$

6. $2^{-5} = \dfrac{1}{32}$

7. $4^{-5} = \dfrac{1}{1024}$

8. $89^0 = 1$

9. $11^{-3} = \dfrac{1}{1331}$

Use properties of exponents to write an equivalent expression. (Explore Activity 2)

10. $4 \cdot 4 \cdot 4 = 4^{\boxed{3}}$

11. $(2 \cdot 2) \cdot (2 \cdot 2 \cdot 2) = 2^{\boxed{2}} \cdot 2^{\boxed{3}} = 2^{\boxed{5}}$

12. $\dfrac{6^7}{6^5} = \dfrac{6 \cdot 6 \cdot 6 \cdot 6 \cdot 6 \cdot 6 \cdot 6}{6 \cdot 6 \cdot 6 \cdot 6 \cdot 6} = 6^{\boxed{2}}$

13. $\dfrac{8^{12}}{8^9} = 8^{\boxed{12} - \boxed{9}} = 8^{\boxed{3}}$

14. $5^{10} \cdot 5 \cdot 5 = 5^{\boxed{12}}$

15. $7^8 \cdot 7^5 = 7^{\boxed{13}}$

16. $(6^2)^4 = (6 \cdot 6)^{\boxed{4}}$

$= (6 \cdot 6) \cdot (6 \cdot 6) \cdot \left(\boxed{6} \cdot \boxed{6} \right) \cdot \underline{(6 \cdot 6)}$

$= 6^{\boxed{8}}$

17. $(3^3)^3 = (3 \cdot 3 \cdot 3)^3$

$= (3 \cdot 3 \cdot 3) \cdot \left(\boxed{3} \cdot \boxed{3} \cdot \boxed{3} \right) \underline{(3 \cdot 3 \cdot 3)}$

$= 3^{\boxed{9}}$

Simplify each expression. (Example 1)

18. $(10 - 6)^3 \cdot 4^2 + (10 + 2)^2 \qquad 1168$

19. $\dfrac{(12 - 5)^7}{\left[(3 + 4)^2 \right]^2} \qquad 343$

? ESSENTIAL QUESTION CHECK-IN

20. Summarize the rules for multiplying powers with the same base, dividing powers with the same base, and raising a power to a power.

When multiplying powers with the same base, you add the exponents. When dividing powers with the same base, you subtract the exponents. When raising a power to a power, you multiply the exponents.

© Houghton Mifflin Harcourt Publishing Company

4 Elaborate

Talk About It

Summarize the Lesson

Ask: How can you simplify an expression with exponents by applying the properties of exponents? The order of operations must always be followed. Each expression within brackets or parentheses must be simplified first. Then terms with the same base that are being multiplied or divided can be simplified using the properties of exponents. Finally, any terms being added or subtracted are simplified.

Guided Practice

Avoid Common Errors

- **Exercises 1–2, 6–7, 9** Remind students that a negative exponent does not mean the answer will be a negative number.

- **Exercise 10** Remind students that when no exponent is given, it is understood that the number is raised to the power of 1.

Engage with the Whiteboard

For **Exercises 18–19**, have students underline each expression inside parentheses and then write the value of each underlined expression below it while explaining how to simplify each part of the expression.

DIFFERENTIATE INSTRUCTION *Intervention and Additional Support*

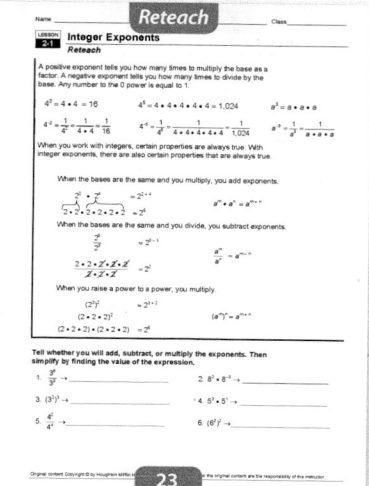

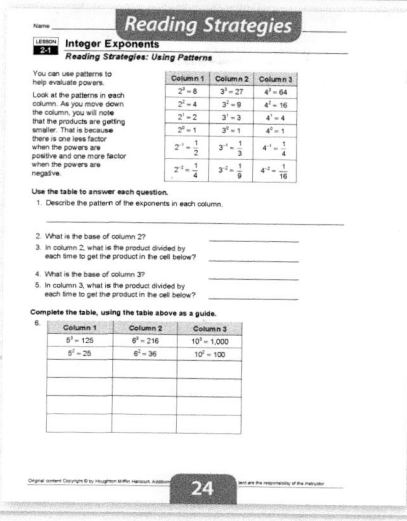

Personal Math Trainer
Daily Intervention
2.1 Homework

Pages shown are from
Differentiated Instruction.
Also available online.

⏱ Pressed for Time

2.1 Differentiated Homework Assignments

AL **Approaching Level**	21–23, 25–27, 32–33, 35	
OL **On Level**	24, 25–27, 31–35	
BL **Beyond Level**	28–31, 35–37	

*For **Below Level** students, assign Personal Math Trainer, Daily Intervention 2.1 Homework.*

Mathematical Processes	Exercises
MP.1 Problem Solving	37
MP.3 Logic	24, 28, 31, 35–36
MP.4 Modeling	23, 29–30
MP.5 Using Tools	25–27
MP.7 Using Structure	32–34

Focus on Higher Order Thinking

Depth of Knowledge	Exercises
2 Skills/Concepts	21–27, 29–30, 32–34
3 Strategic Thinking H.O.T.	28, 31, 35–37

2.1 Independent Practice

Personal Math Trainer
Online Assessment and Intervention
my.hrw.com

21. Explain why the exponents cannot be added in the product $12^3 \cdot 11^3$.

The exponents cannot be added because the bases are not the same.

22. List three ways to express 3^5 as a product of powers.

$3^5 \cdot 3^0$; $3^4 \cdot 3^1$; $3^3 \cdot 3^2$

23. **Astronomy** The distance from Earth to the moon is about 22^4 miles. The distance from Earth to Neptune is about 22^7 miles. Which distance is the greater distance and about how many times greater is it?

Earth to Neptune; 22^3, or 10,648, times greater.

24. **Critique Reasoning** A student claims that $8^3 \cdot 8^{-5}$ is greater than 1. Explain whether the student is correct or not.

The student is not correct because $8^3 \cdot 8^{-5} = 8^{3 + (-5)} = 8^{-2} = \frac{1}{8^2} = \frac{1}{64}$, which is less than 1.

Find the missing exponent.

25. $(b^2)^{\boxed{-3}} = b^{-6}$

26. $x^{\boxed{3}} \cdot x^6 = x^9$

27. $\dfrac{y^{25}}{y^{\boxed{19}}} = y^6$

28. **Communicate Mathematical Ideas** Why do you subtract exponents when dividing powers with the same base?

Dividing is the same as multiplying by the reciprocal. So when dividing powers with the same base, you add the opposite of the exponent in the denominator. This is the same as subtracting the exponents.

29. **Astronomy** The mass of the Sun is about 2×10^{27} metric tons, or 2×10^{30} kilograms. How many kilograms are in one metric ton?

10^3 kg, or 1,000 kg

30. **Represent Real-World Problems** In computer technology, a kilobyte is 2^{10} bytes in size. A gigabyte is 2^{30} bytes in size. The size of a terabyte is the product of the size of a kilobyte and the size of a gigabyte. What is the size of a terabyte?

2^{40} bytes

© Houghton Mifflin Harcourt Publishing Company • Image Credits: ©Jupiterimages/Getty Images

---

DIFFERENTIATE INSTRUCTION *Leveled Homework/Practice*

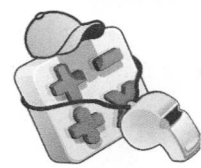

Personal Math Trainer
• 2.1 Homework

Pages shown are from *Differentiated Instruction.* **Also available online.**

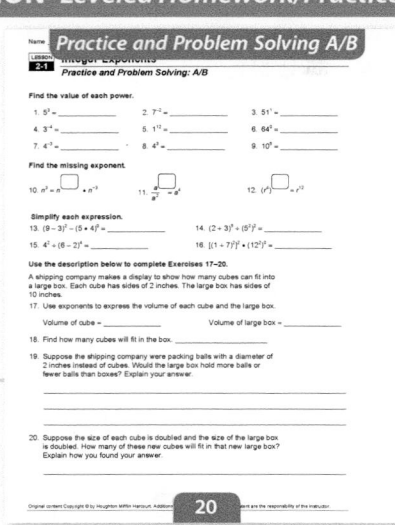

31. Write equivalent expressions for $x^7 \cdot x^{-2}$ and $\frac{x^7}{x^2}$. What do you notice? Explain how your results relate to the properties of integer exponents.

Both expressions equal x^5, so $x^7 \cdot x^{-2} = \frac{x^7}{x^2}$. When multiplying

powers with the same base, you add exponents; $7 + (-2) = 5$.

When dividing powers with the same base, you subtract

exponents; $7 - 2 = 5$. In cases like this, $x^n \cdot x^{-m} = \frac{x^n}{x^m}$.

A toy store is creating a large window display of different colored cubes stacked in a triangle shape. The table shows the number of cubes in each row of the triangle, starting with the top row.

Row	1	2	3	4
Number of cubes in each row	3	3^2	3^3	3^4

32. Look for a Pattern Describe any pattern you see in the table.

The number of cubes in each row is 3 raised to the row number.

33. Using exponents, how many cubes will be in Row 6? How many times as many cubes will be in Row 6 than in Row 3?

$\underline{\qquad 3^6; 3^3 \qquad}$

34. Justify Reasoning If there are 6 rows in the triangle, what is the total number of cubes in the triangle? Explain how you found your answer.

1,092; I evaluated $3^6, 3^5, 3^4, 3^3, 3^2$, and 3^1 and added these numbers together.

 **FOCUS ON HIGHER ORDER THINKING**

Work Area

35. Critique Reasoning A student simplified the expression $\frac{6^2}{36^2}$ as $\frac{1}{3}$. Do you agree with this student? Explain why or why not.

No; $\frac{6^2}{36^2} = \frac{6 \cdot 6}{36 \cdot 36} = \frac{6 \cdot 6}{6 \cdot 6 \cdot 6 \cdot 6} = \frac{1}{6 \cdot 6} = \frac{1}{36}$

36. Draw Conclusions Evaluate $-a^n$ when $a = 3$ and $n = 2, 3, 4$, and 5. Now evaluate $(-a)^n$ when $a = 3$ and $n = 2, 3, 4$, and 5. Based on this sample, does it appear that $-a^n = (-a)^n$? If not, state the relationships, if any, between $-a^n$ and $(-a)^n$.

For $-a^n$, you get $-9, -27, -81, -243$. For $(-a)^n$, you

get $9, -27, 81, -243$. In general, $-a^n \neq (-a)^n$. When n is

even, the two expressions are opposites; when n is odd,

the two expressions are equal.

37. Persevere in Problem Solving A number to the 12th power divided by the same number to the 9th power equals 125. What is the number?

The number is 5.

© Houghton Mifflin Harcourt Publishing Company

 Quick Check

2.1 Lesson Quiz

Find the value of each power.

1. 5^{-2} $\frac{1}{25}$

2. 3^4 81

Use properties of exponents to write an equivalent expression.

3. $(5 \cdot 5) \cdot (5 \cdot 5 \cdot 5 \cdot 5)$ 5^6

4. $\frac{(7^4)^2}{7^5}$ 7^3

Simplify each expression.

5. $(8 - 6)^5 \cdot (2)^{-4} + (2)^0$ 3

6. $\frac{[(9 - 1)]^5}{(6 + 2)^3}$ 64

Differentiate Instruction

IF a student misses more than one question, THEN

Differentiate Instruction:

- 2.1 Reteach
- Personal Math Trainer

Interactive Whiteboard
Interactive Lesson quiz available online

Activity Describe the following pattern:

$(-1)^{-1} = \boxed{}$

$(-1)^{-2} = \boxed{}$

$(-1)^{-3} = \boxed{}$

$(-1)^{-4} = \boxed{}$

Determine what $(-1)^{-100}$ would be. Justify your thinking.

$(-1)^{-1} = -1; (-1)^{-2} = 1; (-1)^{-3} = -1; (-1)^{-4} = 1;$ so the pattern is $-1, 1, -1, 1$, etc.

-1 raised to an odd number equals -1, and -1 raised to an even number equals 1. Since

-100 is an even number, then $(-1)^{-100} = 1$.

Zero and Negative Exponents

1 Engage

ESSENTIAL QUESTION

How can you derive the definition of a zero exponent and the definition of a negative exponent? Use the definition of exponents and properties of exponents to show that $x^0 = 1$ and $x^{-n} = \frac{1}{x^n}$.

Motivate the Lesson

Ask: What does it mean when an exponent is 0? What does it mean when an exponent is negative? Begin the Explore Activity to find out.

2 Explore

EXPLORE ACTIVITY 1

Focus on Reasoning

Show students that the reasoning used in Step C comes from the Transitive Property of Equality, which states:

For any real numbers a, b, and c, if $a = b$ (or $b = a$) and $b = c$, then $a = c$.

Ask students to identify what phrase is represented by a, b, and c in the *if-then* statement.

TEACHER TO TEACHER

Multiple Representations Have students work together in pairs to create various expressions that simplify to a given power. For example, given the power x^{-5}, two equivalent expressions are $\frac{x^7}{x^{12}}$ and $\frac{x^3}{x^8}$. This could be a game to see which team can create the greatest number of equivalent expressions in 10 or 15 seconds.

Zero and Negative Exponents

8.1.GF2.1
Students will derive the definition of a zero exponent and the definition of a negative exponent.

ESSENTIAL QUESTION
How can you derive the definition of a zero exponent and the definition of a negative exponent?

EXPLORE ACTIVITY 1

Definition of Zero Exponent

You can use the properties of exponents and the properties of division with x^a to show that $x^0 = 1$.

A Complete the statement: $\frac{x^a}{x^a} = x^{\boxed{a} - \boxed{a}} = x^{\boxed{0}}$

B Anything divided by itself is $\underline{\ 1\ }$, so $\frac{x^a}{x^a} = \underline{\ 1\ }$.

C If $\frac{x^a}{x^a} = x^{\boxed{0}}$ from Part A and $\frac{x^a}{x^a} = \underline{\ 1\ }$ from Part B, then $x^0 = \underline{\ 1\ }$.

Reflect

1. **Justify Reasoning** What property did you use to complete Part A?
   property of exponents for dividing powers with the same base

---

©Houghton Mifflin Harcourt Publishing Company

EXPLORE ACTIVITY 2

Definition of Negative Exponent

You can use the definition and properties of exponents with $\frac{x^3}{x^5}$ to show that $x^{-2} = \frac{1}{x^2}$.

A Complete the statement: $\frac{x^3}{x^5} = x^{\boxed{3} - \boxed{5}} = x^{\boxed{-2}}$

B Complete the statement: $\frac{x^3}{x^5} = \dfrac{x \cdot \boxed{x} \cdot \boxed{x}}{x \cdot x \cdot \boxed{x} \cdot \boxed{x} \cdot \boxed{x}} = \dfrac{1}{\boxed{x} \cdot \boxed{x}} = \dfrac{1}{x^{\boxed{2}}}$.

C If $\frac{x^3}{x^5} = x^{\boxed{-2}}$ from Part A and $\frac{x^3}{x^5} = \dfrac{1}{x^{\boxed{2}}}$ from Part B, then $x^{-2} = \dfrac{1}{x^{\boxed{2}}}$.

DIFFERENTIATE INSTRUCTION *Leveled Questions*

	EXPLORE ACTIVITY 1
(AL) DOK 1 *Recall*	What rule is being derived in this Explore Activity? $x^0 = 1$
(OL) DOK 2 *Skills/Concepts*	When you divide two powers with the same base, what do you do to the exponents? Subtract exponents of the same base.
(BL) DOK 3 *Strategic Thinking*	Explain how the Transitive Property is applied to the conclusion that $x^0 = 1$. The Transitive Property states: If $a = b$ (or $b = a$) and $b = c$, then $a = c$. Let $a = x^0$, let $b = \frac{x^a}{x^a}$, and let $c = 1$. Then the Transitive Property states: if $\frac{x^a}{x^a} = x^0$ and $\frac{x^a}{x^a} = 1$, then $x^0 = 1$.

Reflect

2. **Critique Reasoning** As you saw in Steps A–C, it can be shown that $\blacksquare^{-n} = \frac{1}{\blacksquare^n}$ for any n by using $\frac{x^a}{x^b}$, where $b > a$. Why is it necessary that $b > a$?

When you divide the powers, you subtract the exponent b from the exponent a. For the resulting exponent to be negative, it must be true that $b > a$.

Practice

1. Use x^4 to show that $x^0 = 1$.

$\frac{x^4}{x^4} = x^{4-4} = x^0$ and $\frac{x^4}{x^4} = 1$, so $x^0 = 1$

2. Use $\frac{x^4}{x^7}$ to show that $x^{-3} = \frac{1}{x^3}$.

$\frac{x^4}{x^7} = \frac{x \cdot x \cdot x \cdot x}{x \cdot x \cdot x \cdot x \cdot x \cdot x \cdot x} = \frac{1}{x^3}$, $\frac{x^4}{x^7} = x^{4-7} = x^{-3}$, so $x^{-3} = \frac{1}{x^3}$

3. Use x^6 to show that $x^0 = 1$.

$\frac{x^6}{x^6} = x^{6-6} = x^0$ and $\frac{x^6}{x^6} = 1$, so $x^0 = 1$

4. Use x^7 to show that $x^0 = 1$.

$\frac{x^7}{x^7} = 1$ and $\frac{x^7}{x^7} = x^{7-7} = x^0$, so $x^0 = 1$

5. Use $\frac{x^3}{x^9}$ to show that $x^{-6} = \frac{1}{x^6}$.

$\frac{x^3}{x^9} = \frac{x \cdot x \cdot x}{x \cdot x \cdot x \cdot x \cdot x \cdot x \cdot x \cdot x \cdot x} = \frac{1}{x^6}$ and $\frac{x^3}{x^9} = x^{-6}$, so $x^{-6} = \frac{1}{x^6}$

6. Use $\frac{x^2}{x^5}$ to show that $x^{-3} = \frac{1}{x^3}$.

$\frac{x^2}{x^5} = \frac{x \cdot x}{x \cdot x \cdot x \cdot x \cdot x} = \frac{1}{x^3}$ and $\frac{x^2}{x^5} = x^{-3}$, so $x^{-3} = \frac{1}{x^3}$

3 Explain

Connect Vocabulary

To *derive* means to obtain by reasoning. In this extension lesson, students will use reasoning to show that $x^0 = 1$ and $x^{-n} = \frac{1}{x^n}$ are true statements.

EXPLORE ACTIVITY 2

Focus on Reasoning

Point out that **Part A** uses the Division Property of Exponents to simplify, and **Part B** uses multiplicative inverses to simplify.

4 Elaborate

Summarize the Lesson

Ask: How can you derive the definitions of zero and negative exponents? Use the definition and properties of exponents to simplify an expression with a zero or negative exponent in two different ways. You then use the Transitive Property of Equality to make the conclusion that $x^0 = 1$ or $x^{-n} = \frac{1}{x^n}$.

5 Evaluate

Practice

Focus on Reasoning

Point out to students that **Exercises 1, 3, and 4** give a logically sound reason to define x^0 as equal to 1. Point out the other exercises give a logically sound reason for defining a specific negative power, but because the exact same logic can be used for any negative integer power, they can conclude the general case that $x^{-n} = \frac{1}{x^n}$.

	EXPLORE ACTIVITY 2
(AL) DOK 1 *Recall*	What rule is being derived in this Explore Activity? $x^{-n} = \frac{1}{x^n}$
(OL) DOK 2 *Skills/Concepts*	What established rules are used in each step to show that $x^{-2} = \frac{1}{x^2}$? In Step A, the Division Property of Exponents is used. In Step B, the definition of exponent is used. In Step C, the Transitive Property is used.
(BL) DOK 3 *Strategic Thinking*	The rule for negative exponents is shown using $\frac{x^3}{x^5}$. Can the rule for negative exponents also be shown using the reciprocal $\frac{x^5}{x^3}$? Explain. No; the exponent in the denominator must be greater than the exponent in the numerator in order to have a negative exponent when simplifying.

LESSON QUIZ

1. Use x^5 to show that $x^0 = 1$. $\frac{x^5}{x^5} = x^{5-5} = x^0$ and $\frac{x^5}{x^5} = 1$ so $x^0 = 1$.

2. What exponential expression can you use to show that $x^{-5} = \frac{1}{x^5}$? Sample answer: $\frac{x^3}{x^8}$ (any ratio with a common base and a difference in exponents of -5)

3. Use $\frac{x^2}{x^6}$ to show that $x^{-4} = \frac{1}{x^4}$.

$\frac{x^2}{x^6} = \frac{x \cdot x}{x \cdot x \cdot x \cdot x \cdot x \cdot x} = \frac{1}{x^4}$ and $\frac{x^2}{x^6} = x^{2-6} = x^{-4}$, so $x^{-4} = \frac{1}{x^4}$.

Lesson Support

Content Objective Students will learn to use scientific notation to express very large quantities.

Professional Development

Integrate Mathematical Processes MP.4

This lesson provides an opportunity to address this Mathematical Processes standard. It calls for students to solve problems arising in everyday life, society, and the workplace. Students use scientific notation to write very large numbers to express facts about the natural world, and they see how this notation is used by scientists in reporting scientific information.

FOCUS

Building Background

Connecting to Everyday Life Discuss examples of the uses of very large numbers with which students are familiar from a variety of subjects and areas of everyday life. From social studies, students might suggest populations; from economics, annual salaries; and from science, distances between the planets.

Sample Facts

- The average distance from the Earth to the moon is 240,000 miles.
- In 2010, the population of California was about 37,250,000.
- The annual salary of the president of the United States is $400,000.

COHERENCE

Learning Progressions

In this lesson, students use scientific notation to write very large numbers. They also interpret numbers in scientific notation and write equivalent standard notation for the numbers. Important understandings for students include the following:

- **Rewrite a number given in standard notation in scientific notation.**
- **Rewrite a number given in scientific notation in standard notation.**

Writing and interpreting numbers in scientific notation allows students to gain real-life experience working with properties of exponents. Students will extend this experience to include very small numbers in the next lesson.

RIGOR

Cluster Connections

This lesson provides an excellent opportunity to connect ideas in the cluster:

Work with radicals and integer exponents.

Tell students that very large numbers are often rounded. Discuss why this is the case by having students consider the following diameters of the outer planets.

Planet	Diameter (miles)
Jupiter	88,732
Saturn	74,975
Uranus	31,763
Neptune	30,603

Then have students choose a place to round the diameters to and write the diameters in scientific notation.

Sample answers:
8.9×10^4; 7.4×10^4; 3.2×10^4; 3.1×10^4

Language Support ELL

Leveled Strategies for English Learners ELL

Emerging
Students can respond *yes/no* or *true/false* when given a statement about the reason for using scientific notation in a given problem, such as "A scientist uses scientific notation to represent the size of large sea creatures."

Expanding
Students can classify examples of scientific notation according to what scientific discipline they are applied in. For example, scientific notations for the size of planets are posted under "Astronomy."

Bridging
Have students explain orally and then write out a description of their step-by-step process for translating numbers into scientific notation.

Math Talk

The prompt requires an explanation of why a given numerical expression is not in scientific notation. Students at all proficiency levels need explicit language for explaining the rules numbers in scientific notation.

Linguistic Support ELL

Academic/Content Vocabulary
This lesson focuses on how to translate scientific data into mathematical scientific notation. An exercise in the Independent Practice involves giving four reasons for scientific notation: shorter to write, easier to read, used by scientists everywhere, and easier to compare sizes of large numbers. English learners will benefit from making these reasons explicit. Students can find many applications of scientific notation in the exercises of the text, including several areas of science, such as entomology, zoology, and paleontology

Background Knowledge
Clarify the use of the term *translate* as it is used in mathematics "to convert a form of information from data to conclusion," or as it is used in language "to convert the form of communication from one language to another." English learners will be familiar with the meaning as it relates to translating languages, so teaching the concept of translating scientific facts and data into mathematical terms builds on their background knowledge.

Also, review with students how to read large numbers, because different countries indicate number groupings differently with commas and points.

Image Credits: ©NikoNomad/Shutterstock

Scientific Notation with Positive Powers of 10

1 Engage

? ESSENTIAL QUESTION

How can you use scientific notation to express very large quantities? Sample answer: Write the large quantity as the product of a number greater than or equal to 1 and less than 10 and a power of 10.

Motivate the Lesson

Ask: If you were given the weight of a whale in pounds as 2×10^5, how many pounds do you think that is? Begin the Explore Activity to find out.

2 Explore

EXPLORE ACTIVITY

Talk About It

Check for Understanding

Ask: In 250,000, what place is the 2 in? hundred thousands What digit is in the ten thousands place? 5

LESSON 2.2 Scientific Notation with Positive Powers of 10

8.1.2.2
Students will use scientific notation to express very large quantities.

? ESSENTIAL QUESTION

How can you use scientific notation to express very large quantities?

EXPLORE ACTIVITY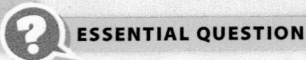

Using Scientific Notation

Scientific notation is a method of expressing very large and very small numbers as a product of a number greater than or equal to 1 and less than 10, and a power of 10.

The weights of various sea creatures are shown in the table. Write the weight of the blue whale in scientific notation.

Sea Creature	Blue whale	Gray whale	Whale shark
Weight (lb)	250,000	68,000	41,200

A Move the decimal point in 250,000 to the left as many places as necessary to find a number that is greater than or equal to 1 and less than 10.

What number did you find? _____ 2.5 _____

B Divide 250,000 by your answer to **A**. Write your answer as a power of 10.

_____ 100,000; 10^5 _____

C Combine your answers to **A** and **B** to represent 250,000.

$250,000 = \boxed{2.5} \times 10^{\boxed{5}}$

Repeat steps **A** through **C** to write the weight of the whale shark in scientific notation.

$41,200 = \boxed{4.12} \times 10^{\boxed{4}}$

Reflect

1. How many places to the left did you move the decimal point to write 41,200 in scientific notation? The decimal point moves 4 places to the left.

2. What is the exponent on 10 when you write 41,200 in scientific notation? The exponent on 10 is also 4.

© Houghton Mifflin Harcourt Publishing Company

Lesson 2.2 **39**

DIFFERENTIATE INSTRUCTION *Leveled Questions*

	EXPLORE ACTIVITY
AL DOK 1 *Recall*	When you write a very large number in scientific notation, in what direction do you move the decimal point? left
OL DOK 2 *Skills/Concepts*	Explain how many places to move the decimal point when writing a large number in scientific notation. The multiplier must be between 1 and 10. Move the decimal point so the multiplier has an appropriate value.
BL DOK 3 *Strategic Thinking*	Look at the scientific notation expressions for the blue whale and whale shark. How can you use the expressions to tell how many times more one weighs than the other? The power for the whale is 10^5 and the power for the shark is 10^4, so the whale weighs about 10 times more. Then look at the ratio of multipliers $\frac{2.5}{4.12} \approx 0.6$. So, the whale weighs about $0.6 \cdot 10 = 6$ times more than the shark.

LEVELED QUESTIONS: AL Approaching Level | OL On Level | BL Beyond Level

Math On the Spot
my.hrw.com

Writing a Number in Scientific Notation

To translate between standard notation and scientific notation, you can count the number of places the decimal point moves.

Writing Large Quantities in Scientific Notation

When the number is greater than or equal to 10, use a positive exponent.	$84,000 = 8.4 \times 10^4$	The decimal point moves 4 places to the left.

EXAMPLE 1

The distance from Earth to the Sun is about 93,000,000 miles. Write this distance in scientific notation.

STEP 1 Move the decimal point in 93,000,000 to the left until you have a number that is greater than or equal to 1 and less than 10.

9.3 0 0 0 0 0 0. *Move the decimal point 7 places to the left.*

9.3 *Remove extra zeros.*

STEP 2 Divide the original number by the result from Step 1.

10,000,000 *Divide 93,000,000 by 9.3.*

10^7 *Write your answer as a power of 10.*

STEP 3 Write the product of the results from Steps 1 and 2.

$93,000,000 = 9.3 \times 10^7$ miles *Write a product to represent 93,000,000 in scientific notation.*

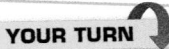

Math Talk
Mathematical Processes

Is 12×10^7 written in scientific notation? Explain.

No, because the first factor must be greater than or equal to 1 and less than 10.

YOUR TURN

Write each number in scientific notation.

3. 6,400

6.4×10^3

4. 570,000,000,000

5.7×10^{11}

5. A light-year is the distance that light travels in a year and is equivalent to 9,461,000,000,000 km. Write this distance in scientific notation.

9.461×10^{12} km

Personal Math Trainer
Online Assessment and Intervention
my.hrw.com

© Houghton Mifflin Harcourt Publishing Company

---

3 Explain

EXAMPLE 1

Avoid Common Errors

A dot used for multiplication can sometimes be confused as a decimal point when using scientific notation. Encourage students to use X instead.

ADDITIONAL EXAMPLE 1 The average distance from Earth to Mars is about 140,000,000 miles. Write this distance in scientific notation. 1.4×10^8

 Interactive Whiteboard
Interactive example available online

YOUR TURN   MP.2

Connect Multiple Representations

Single-digit estimates are often used for numbers this large rather than keep all the digits. For example, the number 9,283,000 written in scientific notation would be 9.283×10^6, but can be referred to as *about* 9×10^6. Have students estimate each number in **Exercises 3–5** as a single digit times a power of 10.

3. 6×10^3

4. 6×10^{11}

5. 9×10^{12}

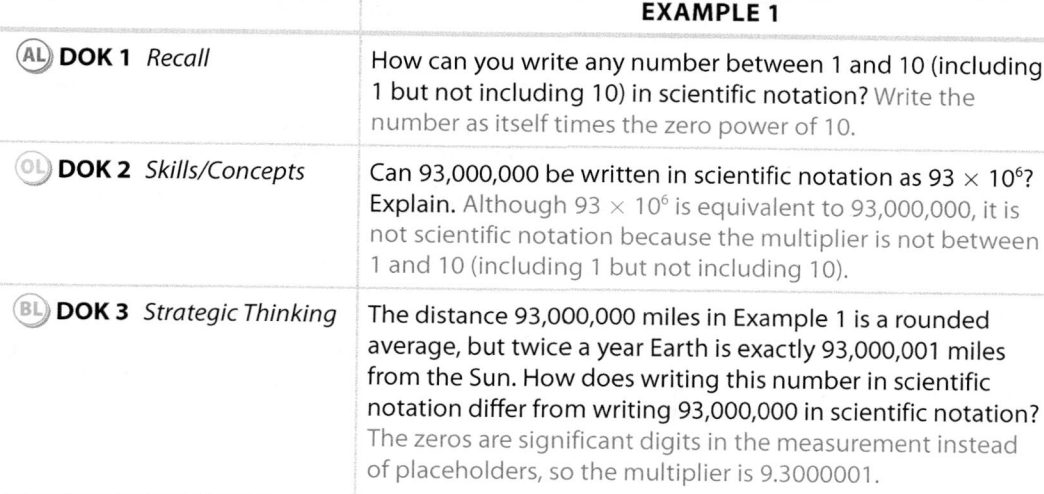

	EXAMPLE 1
AL DOK 1 *Recall*	How can you write any number between 1 and 10 (including 1 but not including 10) in scientific notation? Write the number as itself times the zero power of 10.
OL DOK 2 *Skills/Concepts*	Can 93,000,000 be written in scientific notation as 93×10^6? Explain. Although 93×10^6 is equivalent to 93,000,000, it is not scientific notation because the multiplier is not between 1 and 10 (including 1 but not including 10).
BL DOK 3 *Strategic Thinking*	The distance 93,000,000 miles in Example 1 is a rounded average, but twice a year Earth is exactly 93,000,001 miles from the Sun. How does writing this number in scientific notation differ from writing 93,000,000 in scientific notation? The zeros are significant digits in the measurement instead of placeholders, so the multiplier is 9.3000001.

TEACHER TO TEACHER

Technology Have students use the following steps to explore scientific notation on a calculator.

• Multiply 3,500,000 by 1,000,000, and interpret the result 3.5E12. 3.5×10^{12}

• Predict the display for 10 million times 3 million, then check using the calculator. 3E13

Challenge students to determine when their calculator display changes from standard notation to scientific notation. Answers may vary. Sample answer: when digits are greater than 10

EXAMPLE 2

ADDITIONAL EXAMPLE 2 Write 7.8×10^9 in standard notation. **7,800,000,000**

Interactive Whiteboard
Interactive example available online

YOUR TURN MP.7

Focus on Critical Thinking

Discuss with students how to compare the values 7.034×10^9 and 2.36×10^5 when they are expressed in scientific notation. Be sure they understand that they can compare the exponents of 10. Because 10^9 has a greater exponent than 10^5, 7.034×10^9 is greater than 2.36×10^5.

Digital Teacher Resources

Go online to access all your lesson-level resources.

Differentiated Instruction
• Reteach
• Reading Strategies
• Success for English Learners
• Practice and Problem Solving A/B, C, D

Math on the Spot Videos

Writing a Number in Standard Notation

Math On the Spot
my.hrw.com

To translate between scientific notation and standard notation, move the decimal point the number of places indicated by the exponent in the power of 10. When the exponent is positive, move the decimal point to the right and add placeholder zeros as needed.

EXAMPLE 2

My Notes

Write 3.5×10^6 in standard notation.

STEP 1 Use the exponent of the power of 10 to see how many places to move the decimal point.

6 places

STEP 2 Place the decimal point. Since you are going to write a number greater than 3.5, move the decimal point to the *right*. Add placeholder zeros if necessary.

3 5 0 0 0 0 0.

The number 3.5×10^6 written in standard notation is 3,500,000.

Reflect

6. Explain why the exponent in 3.5×10^6 is 6, while there are only 5 zeros in 3,500,000.

   The decimal point moves 6 places to the right, but one of those places is the 5 tenths in 3.5, so only 5 placeholder zeros are needed.

7. What is the exponent on 10 when you write 5.3 in scientific notation?
   The exponent on 10 is 0. $5.3 = 5.3 \times 10^0$.

YOUR TURN

Write each number in standard notation.

8. 7.034×10^9
   7,034,000,000

9. 2.36×10^5
   236,000

10. The mass of one roosting colony of Monarch butterflies in Mexico was estimated at 5×10^6 grams. Write this mass in standard notation.
    5,000,000 g

Personal Math Trainer
Online Assessment and Intervention
my.hrw.com

© Houghton Mifflin Harcourt Publishing Company • Image Credits: ©Ingram Publishing/Alamy

Lesson 2.2 **41**

DIFFERENTIATE INSTRUCTION *Leveled Questions*

	EXAMPLE 2
AL DOK 1 *Recall*	The number 3,500,000 is read "3 million, 5 hundred thousand" or "3.5 million." Explain how "3.5 million" is similar to 3,500,000 written in scientific notation. Because 10^6 is 1 million, it can be read as "3.5 million."
OL DOK 2 *Skills/Concepts*	A number in scientific notation has the power 10^0. What can you say about the value of the number? Its value is equal to the multiplier, so it must be at least 1, but less than 10.
BL DOK 3 *Strategic Thinking*	Given a number in scientific notation, explain why the exponent in the power of 10 is not always equal to the number of zeros in the corresponding number in standard notation. If the multiplier is an integer, the number of zeros equals the exponent in the power of 10, but this is not the case when the multiplier is not an integer.

LEVELED QUESTIONS: **AL** Approaching Level | **OL** On Level | **BL** Beyond Level

Write each number in scientific notation. (Explore Activity and Example 1)

1. 58,927
Hint: Move the decimal left 4 places.
5.8927×10^4

2. 1,304,000,000
Hint: Move the decimal left 9 places.
1.304×10^9

3. 6,730,000
6.73×10^6

4. 13,300
1.33×10^4

5. An ordinary quarter contains about 97,700,000,000,000,000,000,000 atoms.
9.77×10^{22}

6. The distance from Earth to the Moon is about 384,000 kilometers.
3.84×10^5

Write each number in standard notation. (Example 2)

7. 4×10^5
Hint: Move the decimal right 5 places.
400,000

8. 1.8499×10^9
Hint: Move the decimal right 9 places.
1,849,900,000

9. 6.41×10^3
6,410

10. 8.456×10^7
84,560,000

11. 8×10^5
800,000

12. 9×10^{10}
90,000,000,000

13. Diana calculated that she spent about 5.4×10^4 seconds doing her math homework during October. Write this time in standard notation. (Example 2)
54,000 s

14. The town recycled 7.6×10^6 cans this year. Write the number of cans in standard notation. (Example 2)
7,600,000 cans

? ESSENTIAL QUESTION CHECK-IN

15. Describe how to write 3,482,000,000 in scientific notation.
First move the decimal point 9 places to the left to find 3.482, a number that is greater than or equal to 1 and less than 10. Then multiply 3.482 by 10^9, using an exponent on 10 that equals the number of places you moved the decimal.

© Houghton Mifflin Harcourt Publishing Company

4 Elaborate

Talk About It

Summarize the Lesson

Ask: How can you write a very large number such as 51,200,000 in scientific notation? First, move the decimal point 7 places to the left to determine the first factor, which must be greater than or equal to 1 and less than 10. Then write the power of 10 factor with the exponent equal to 7, which is the number of places you moved the decimal to determine the first factor.

Guided Practice

Engage with the Whiteboard

For **Exercises 1–12**, have students draw and count curved arrows to show moving the decimal point the correct number of places.

Avoid Common Errors

- **Exercises 1–6** Remind students to draw arrows to avoid counting errors as they move the decimal point.

- **Exercises 7, 11–12** To avoid decimal placement errors, suggest that students place the decimal point to the right of the whole number factor before converting to standard notation.

DIFFERENTIATE INSTRUCTION *Intervention and Additional Support*

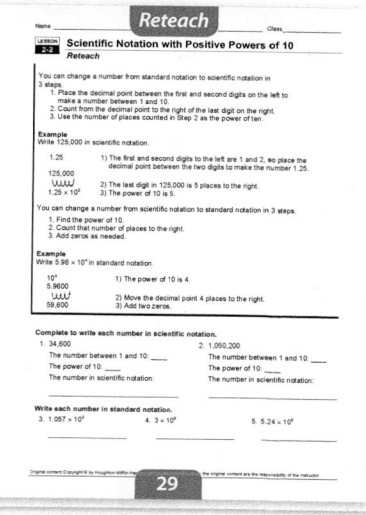

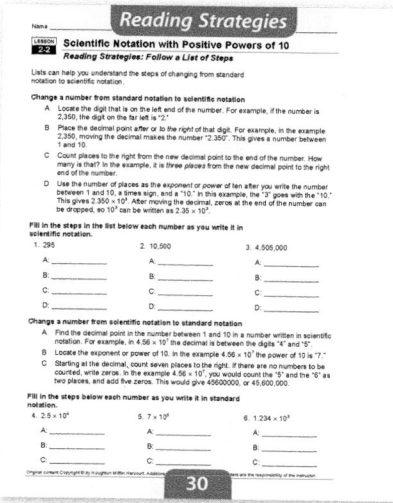

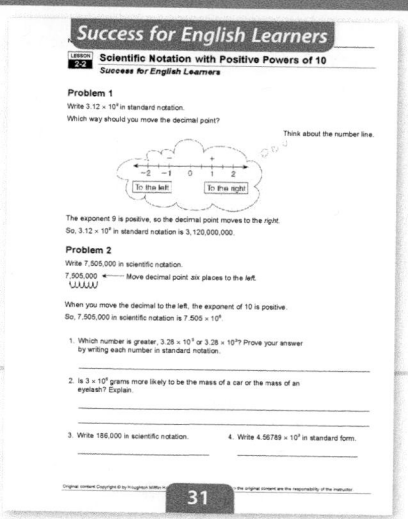

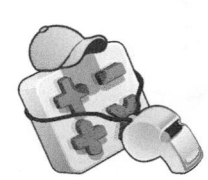

Personal Math Trainer
Daily Intervention
2.2 Homework

Pages shown are from *Differentiated Instruction*.
Also available online.

Pressed for Time

2.2 Differentiated Homework Assignments

(AL) Approaching Level 16–22, 25–27, 29

(OL) On Level 20–25, 27–30

(BL) Beyond Level 24–25, 27–31

*For **Below Level** students, assign Personal Math Trainer, Daily Intervention 2.2 Homework.*

Mathematical Processes	Exercises
MP.3 Logic	27–28
MP.4 Modeling	16–25, 29–30
MP.7 Using Structure	26, 31

Focus on Higher Order Thinking

Depth of Knowledge	Exercises
1 Recall of Information	26
2 Skills/Concepts	16–25, 27
3 Strategic Thinking H.O.T.	28–31

Name _____ Class _____ Date _____

2.2 Independent Practice

Personal Math Trainer
Online Assessment and Intervention
my.hrw.com

Paleontology Use the table for problems 16–21. Write the estimated weight of each dinosaur in scientific notation.

Estimated Weight of Dinosaurs	
Name	**Pounds**
Argentinosaurus	220,000
Brachiosaurus	100,000
Apatosaurus	66,000
Diplodocus	50,000
Camarasaurus	40,000
Cetiosauriscus	19,850

16. Apatosaurus _____ 6.6×10^4 lb

17. Argentinosaurus _____ 2.2×10^5 lb

18. Brachiosaurus _____ 1×10^5 lb

19. Camarasaurus _____ 4×10^4 lb

20. Cetiosauriscus _____ 1.985×10^4 lb

21. Diplodocus _____ 5×10^4 lb

22. A single little brown bat can eat up to 1,000 mosquitoes in a single hour. Express in scientific notation how many mosquitoes a little brown bat might eat in 10.5 hours.

   1.05×10^4 mosquitoes

23. **Multistep** Samuel can type nearly 40 words per minute. Use this information to find the number of hours it would take him to type 2.6×10^5 words.

   $108 \frac{1}{3}$ hours or 108 hours and 20 minutes

24. **Entomology** A tropical species of mite named *Archegozetes longisetosus* is the record holder for the strongest insect in the world. It can lift up to 1.182×10^3 times its own weight.

   a. If you were as strong as this insect, explain how you could find how many pounds you could lift.

   Write 1.182×10^3 in standard notation, 1,182, and then multiply by your weight.

   b. Complete the calculation to find how much you could lift, in pounds, if you were as strong as an *Archegozetes longisetosus* mite. Express your answer in both scientific notation and standard notation.

   Answers will vary. Sample answer: 94,560 lb; 9.456×10^4

25. During a discussion in science class, Sharon learns that at birth an elephant weighs around 230 pounds. In four herds of elephants tracked by conservationists, about 20 calves were born during the summer. In scientific notation, express approximately how much the calves weighed all together.

   4.6×10^3 lb

26. **Classifying Numbers** Which of the following numbers are written in scientific notation?

   0.641×10^3 9.999×10^4

   2×10^1 4.38×5^{10}

   9.999×10^4 and 2×10^1

© Houghton Mifflin Harcourt Publishing Company

DIFFERENTIATE INSTRUCTION *Leveled Homework/Practice*

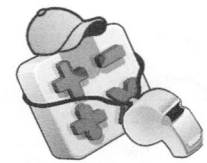

Personal Math Trainer

• 2.2 Homework

Pages shown are from *Differentiated Instruction.* **Also available online.**

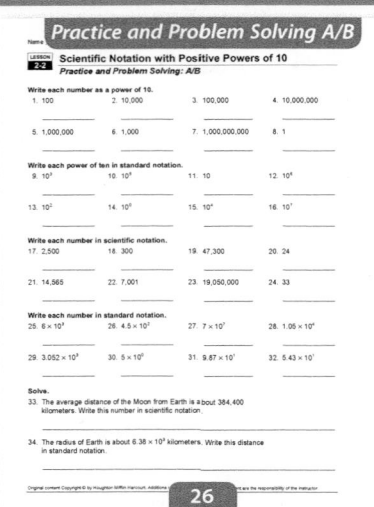

Practice and Problem Solving A/B

26

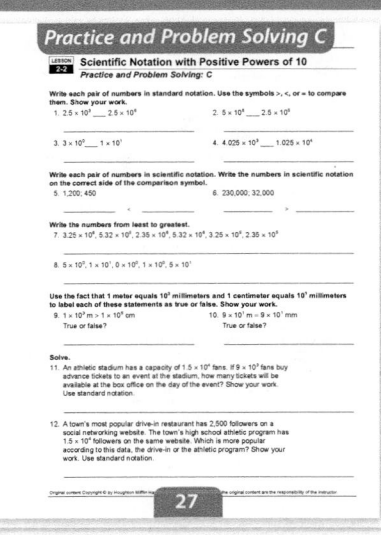

Practice and Problem Solving C

27

Practice and Problem Solving D

28

27. Explain the Error Polly's parents' car weighs about 3500 pounds. Samantha, Esther, and Polly each wrote the weight of the car in scientific notation. Polly wrote 35.0×10^2, Samantha wrote 0.35×10^4, and Esther wrote 3.5×10^4.

a. Which of these girls, if any, is correct?

None of the girls has the correct answer.

b. Explain the mistakes of those who got the question wrong.

Neither Polly nor Samantha moved the decimal point to the correct place. Esther moved the decimal point to the correct place, but wrote the wrong power of 10.

28. Justify Reasoning If you were a biologist counting very large numbers of cells as part of your research, give several reasons why you might prefer to record your cell counts in scientific notation instead of standard notation.

Sample answer: Scientific notation is shorter to write, easier to read (you see how many zeros), used by scientists everywhere, and easier to compare sizes of large numbers.

 **FOCUS ON HIGHER ORDER THINKING**

29. Draw Conclusions Which measurement would be least likely to be written in scientific notation: number of stars in a galaxy, number of grains of sand on a beach, speed of a car, or population of a country? Explain your reasoning.

The speed of a car because it is likely to be less than 100.

30. Analyze Relationships Compare the two numbers to find which is greater. Explain how you can compare them without writing them in standard notation first.

$$4.5 \times 10^6 \qquad 2.1 \times 10^8$$

2.1×10^8 is greater because the exponent 8 is greater than the exponent 6.

31. Communicate Mathematical Ideas To determine whether a number is written in scientific notation, what test can you apply to the first factor, and what test can you apply to the second factor?

Is the first factor greater than or equal to 1 and less than 10? Is the second factor a power of 10?

© Houghton Mifflin Harcourt Publishing Company

DIFFERENTIATE INSTRUCTION *Extend-the-Math Activity* **PRE-AP**

	Wattage	Hours per day	kWh per day	kWh per month	kWh per year
Pool pump	1000	6	6×10^0	2×10^2	2×10^3
Television	300	8	2×10^0	7×10^1	9×10^2
Clothes dryer	2790	4	1×10^1	3×10^2	4×10^3
Refrigerator	225	24	5×10^0	2×10^2	2×10^3

1. Use the formula Kilowatt-hour (kWh) $= \dfrac{\text{Watts} \cdot \text{hours used per day}}{1000}$ to estimate the maximum kilowatt-hour that each appliance uses per day, per month, and per year. Write your answers in scientific notation with a single-digit multiplier. Assume 30 days per month and 365 days per year.

2. Which appliance uses the least amount of energy per day? Television

3. Which appliance uses the most amount of energy per year? Clothes dryer

---

✔ **Quick Check**

2.2 Lesson Quiz

1. The approximate mass of Mars is 6.42×10^{23} kilograms. Write this mass in standard notation. 642,000,000,000,000,000,000,000 kg

2. An adult blue whale can eat about 40,000,000 krill a day. Write this number in scientific notation. 4×10^7 krill

3. Write 9 in scientific notation. 9×10^0

4. Write 1.0×10^5 in standard notation and in words. 100,000; one hundred thousand

5. Is 10.2×10^5 written in scientific notation? Explain. No; the first number is not more than 1 and less than 10.

Differentiate Instruction

IF a student misses more than one question, THEN

Differentiate Instruction:
- 2.2 Reteach
- Personal Math Trainer

 Interactive Whiteboard
Interactive Lesson quiz available online

Comparing Very Large Numbers

1 Engage

? ESSENTIAL QUESTION

How can you compare very large numbers in scientific notation? First compare the powers of 10. If the powers of 10 are the same, compare the multipliers.

Motivate the Lesson

Ask: When you are using scientific notation to represent very large quantities, how can you tell how much more one quantity is than another? Begin the Explore Activity to find out.

2 Explore

EXPLORE ACTIVITY

Avoid Common Errors

When comparing numbers in scientific notation, such as 6×10^3 and 5×10^6, students may think that the larger first number tells which is greater (6 is greater than 5). Remind students to first use the power of 10 to determine which number is greater. If the exponents are the same, you then compare the multipliers.

TEACHER TO TEACHER

Cognitive Strategies One very large named number is a *googol*—the number 1 followed by 100 zeros. An even larger named number is a *googolplex*—the number 1 followed by a googol (10^{100}) of zeros. This massive number can be represented as 10^{googol}. Have students predict what a number named as a *googolplexian* might be, and do internet research to determine if their prediction is correct. A *googolplexian* is the number 1 followed by a googolplex of zeros.

Going Further **2.2**

Comparing Very Large Numbers

8.1.GF2.2
Students will compare very large numbers in scientific notation.

? ESSENTIAL QUESTION

How can you compare very large numbers in scientific notation?

EXPLORE ACTIVITY

Comparing Very Large Numbers

A Compare 8,000 and 200 using standard notation.

$\frac{8,000}{200} = \boxed{40}$, so 8,000 is $\underline{40}$ times greater than 200.

B Compare 8,000 and 200 using scientific notation.

$8,000 = 8 \times 10^{\boxed{3}}$ and $200 = 2 \times 10^{\boxed{2}}$

First compare the powers of 10 in a ratio of greater to lesser:

$$\frac{10^3}{10^2} = 10^{\boxed{1}} = \boxed{10}$$

Then compare the corresponding multipliers: $\frac{\boxed{8}}{2} = \underline{4}$

So 8×10^3 is $10 \cdot \underline{4} = \underline{40}$ times greater than 2×10^2.

Reflect

1. When comparing two numbers in scientific notation, why would you compare the powers of 10 first to find which number is greater?

   The number with the greater exponent in the power of 10 is greater.

2. When comparing two numbers in scientific notation, if the powers of 10 are equal, how can you tell which number is greater?

   When the powers of 10 are equal, compare the multipliers to determine which is greater.

Going Further 2.2 **44A**

DIFFERENTIATE INSTRUCTION *Leveled Questions*

	EXPLORE ACTIVITY
AL DOK 1 *Recall*	How can you tell which of these two numbers is greater in scientific notation? The number with the greater exponent in the power of 10 is greater.
OL DOK 2 *Skills/Concepts*	How is a ratio used to compare numbers in both Parts A and B? A ratio of the greater number to the lesser number, when simplified, will tell you how many times greater the numerator is than the denominator.
BL DOK 3 *Strategic Thinking*	How could you show the ratio of powers of 10 and the ratio of corresponding multipliers written in standard notation? ratio of powers: $\frac{1000}{100} = 10$; ratio of corresponding multipliers: $\frac{8}{2} = 4$; so 8000 is $10 \cdot 4 = 40$ times greater than 200.

LEVELED QUESTIONS: **AL** Approaching Level | **OL** On Level | **BL** Beyond Level

Comparing Very Large Numbers in the Real World

Using scientific notation can help you compare very large numbers.

EXAMPLE

The average mass of a human is about 6×10^1 kilograms, and the average mass of an African elephant is about 6×10^3 kilograms. About how many times greater is the mass of an African elephant than the mass of a human?

$$\frac{10^3}{10^1} = 10^2 \qquad \text{Compare the powers of 10.}$$

$$\frac{6}{6} = 1 \qquad \text{Compare the multipliers.}$$

So, the mass of an African elephant is about 1×10^2, or 100 times greater than the mass of a human.

Practice

1. Complete the statements to express how many times greater 6×10^7 is than 3×10^7.

   $$\boxed{\frac{10^7}{10^7}} = 10^{\boxed{0}} = \underline{\quad 1 \quad}, \text{ and } \frac{\boxed{6}}{3} = \underline{\quad 2 \quad}$$

   So, 6×10^7 is $1 \cdot \underline{\quad 2 \quad} = \underline{\quad 2 \quad}$ times greater than 3×10^7.

2. The average mouse has a mass of about 2×10^4 milligrams, and the average housefly has a mass of about 1×10^1 milligrams. About how many times greater is the mass of a mouse than the mass of a housefly? Explain.

   $\frac{10^4}{10^1} = 10^{\blacksquare}$ ▬▬ $\frac{\blacksquare}{\blacksquare} = 2$, so a mouse weighs about $1,000 \times 2$, or about

   2,000 times greater.

Determine which quantity is greater, and determine about how many times greater.

3. Chile: about 2×10^7 people

   Argentina: about 4×10^7 people

   Argentina; $\frac{10^7}{10^7} = 1$ and $\frac{4}{2} = 2$; about 2 times greater

4. African elephant mass: 6×10^3 kg

   Asian elephant mass: 5×10^3 kg

   African elephant; $\frac{10^3}{10^3} = 1$ and $\frac{6}{5} = 1.2$; about 1.2 times greater

		EXAMPLE
(AL) **DOK 1** *Recall*		What are the numbers in standard notation? 60 and 6000
(OL) **DOK 2** *Skills/Concepts*		Which number is greater? 6×10^3
(BL) **DOK 3** *Strategic Thinking*		Use standard notation to check the answer in the example. $\frac{6000}{60} = 100$

3 Explain

EXAMPLE

ADDITIONAL EXAMPLE A locomotive engine has a mass of about 2×10^6 kg. A large SUV has a mass of about 3×10^3 kg. About how many times greater is the mass of a locomotive engine than the mass of a large SUV? $\frac{10^6}{10^3} = 10^3$ and $\frac{2}{3} \approx 0.7$, so the mass of a locomotive engine is about $10^3 \cdot 0.7 = 700$ times greater than a large SUV.

4 Elaborate

Summarize the Lesson

Ask: How can you determine the number of times greater one quantity in scientific notation is than another? Sample answer: First, determine which number is greater by comparing the powers of 10, then comparing the multipliers if needed. Then multiply the ratio of powers of 10 (greater to lesser) by the corresponding ratio of multipliers to find how many times greater the number is.

5 Evaluate

Practice

Connect to Daily Life

Point out that scientific notation is often used to give estimates. For example, in **Exercise 2**, the mass of a mouse and the mass of a housefly are given as estimates because their sizes vary so much in the real world.

LESSON QUIZ

Determine which quantity is greater, and determine about how many times greater.

1. Paraguay: about 7×10^6 people

   Brazil: about 2×10^8 people Brazil; $\frac{10^8}{10^6} = 10^2$ and $\frac{2}{7} \approx 0.29$; about 29 times greater

2. Pygmy hippopotamus mass: 2.3×10^2 kg

   Common hippopotamus mass: 1.4×10^3 kg Common hippopotamus; $\frac{10^3}{10^2} = 10$ and $\frac{1.4}{2.3} \approx 0.61$; about 6 times greater

3. An adult has about 4.94×10^{13} cells. A newborn baby has about 26,000,000,000 cells. Which has more cells, and about how many times more? Adult; $\frac{10^{13}}{10^{10}} = 10^3$ and $\frac{4.94}{2.6} = 1.9$; about 1900 times more

Comparing Very Large Numbers **44B**

Lesson Support

Content Objective Students will learn to use scientific notation to express very small quantities.

Professional Development

Integrate Mathematical Processes MP.2

This lesson provides an opportunity to address this Mathematical Processes standard. It calls for students to represent a situation symbolically. Students write very small numbers in two forms of symbolic representation: standard form and scientific notation. Students also use mathematical language to express the processes they use to convert from one representation to the other.

FOCUS

Building Background

Connecting to Everyday Life Discuss examples of the uses of very small numbers with which students are familiar from everyday life. Examples are most likely to come from science, such as measuring the size of tiny life-forms under a microscope, the weight of an atom, the size of a red or white blood cell, and so on.

Sample Facts

- An amoeba is about 0.0003 meter in length.
- The wavelength of sodium light is 0.00006 centimeter.
- The volume of a grain of sand is about 0.0000000015 cubic foot.

COHERENCE

Learning Progressions

In this lesson, students use scientific notation to write very small numbers. They also interpret numbers in scientific notation and write equivalent standard notation for the numbers. Important understandings for students include the following:

- **Rewrite a number given in standard notation in scientific notation.**
- **Rewrite a number given in scientific notation in standard notation.**

Students continue to gain experience with scientific notation and with exponents in this lesson by working with very small numbers. This lesson and the previous lessons in this cluster prepare students to express and perform calculations using scientific notation in the next and last lesson in the cluster.

RIGOR

Cluster Connections

This lesson provides an excellent opportunity to connect ideas in the cluster:

Work with radicals and integer exponents.

Students can combine scientific notation with properties of exponents to convert metric measurements. Present students with the following:

Blue light has an average wavelength of 475 nanometers. 1 nanometer is equal to 10^{-9} meter and 1 micron $= 10^{-6}$ meter.

Discuss how to write the average wavelength of blue light in scientific notation using meters and using microns.

4.75×10^{-7} m; 4.75×10^{-4} micron

Language Support ELL

Language Objective Students will explain how to use scientific notation to express very small quantities.

Leveled Strategies for English Learners ELL

Emerging
Before completing the table in Independent Practice, have students categorize the items named in the tables according to very large, large, small, and very small. Then have students compare the items. Examples: Jupiter is very large. The Moon is large. Jupiter is larger than the Moon.

Expanding
Have students create a line showing a continuum of items from very large to very small, in order. Have them orally compare two or three items using comparative suffixes *-er* and *-est*. Then label the items using scientific notation.

Bridging
Students use sentence frames and scientific notation to justify the order they chose to place items along a continuum from largest to smallest:

I know that _____ is the largest because _____.

To help students with the Guided Practice Exercises, provide sentence frames to assist with the language used to describe the value of factors and how to move the decimal point and adjust the exponent.

The decimal point should move to the right/left because _____.

The exponent should increase/decrease by _____ because _____.

Image Credits: ©lluís vinagre world photographer/Getty Images

Linguistic Support ELL

Academic/Content Vocabulary
This lesson uses the terms *negative* and *positive* for categorizing numbers. Students may also be familiar with terms *non-negative* and *non-positive*. Point out that a *non-negative* number is any number that is NOT negative. So 0 is a non-negative number. Likewise, a *non-positive* number is any number that is NOT positive. So, 0 is also a non-positive number.

Background Knowledge
For Independent Practice, in the table about the average diameter of natural fibers, explain that these fibers come from animals and most are used to make clothing. Some of the animals listed in the table (alpaca, vicuña, llama) are native to South America and may be either familiar to students from the region or unfamiliar to English learners from other countries.

Scientific Notation with Negative Powers of 10

1 Engage

? ESSENTIAL QUESTION

How can you use scientific notation to express very small quantities? Write the small quantity as the product of a number greater than or equal to 1 and less than 10 times a power of 10 with a negative exponent.

Motivate the Lesson

Ask: You have written very large numbers in scientific notation. What is a shorter way to write very small numbers, such as the weight of a butterfly egg? A single Monarch egg may weigh as little as 0.00046 grams. Begin the lesson to find out.

2 Explore

EXPLORE ACTIVITY

Focus on Patterns

Discuss with students the relationship between moving a decimal point to the left and dividing by 10. Ask them the following questions. What does moving a decimal point one place to the left do to a number? divides the number by 10 What does dividing a number by 10 do to an exponent with a base of 10? reduces the exponent by 1

Animated Math

Powers of 10
Students will explore and visualize powers of ten through virtual manipulatives.

my.hrw.com

Scientific Notation with Negative Powers of 10

8.1.2.3
Students will use scientific notation to express very small quantities.

? ESSENTIAL QUESTION

How can you use scientific notation to express very small quantities?

Animated Math
my.hrw.com

EXPLORE ACTIVITY Real World

Negative Powers of 10

You can use what you know about writing very large numbers in scientific notation to write very small numbers in scientific notation.

A typical human hair has a diameter of 0.000025 meter. Write this number in scientific notation.

A Notice how the decimal point moves in the list below. Complete the list.

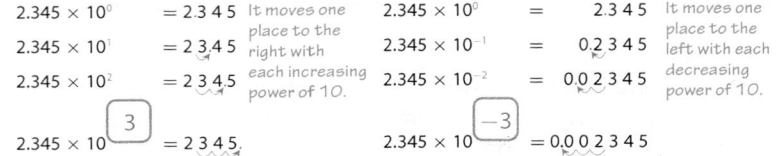

2.345×10^0	$= 2.345$	It moves one place to the right with each increasing power of 10.	2.345×10^0	$= 2.345$	It moves one place to the left with each decreasing power of 10.
2.345×10^1	$= 23.45$		2.345×10^{-1}	$= 0.2345$	
2.345×10^2	$= 234.5$		2.345×10^{-2}	$= 0.02345$	
$2.345 \times 10^{\boxed{3}}$	$= 2345$		$2.345 \times 10^{\boxed{-3}}$	$= 0.002345$	

B Move the decimal point in 0.000025 to the right as many places as necessary to find a number that is greater than or equal to 1 and less than 10. What number did you find? ___2.5___

C Divide 0.000025 by your answer to **B**. ___0.00001___

Write your answer as a power of 10. ___10^{-5}___

D Combine your answers to **B** and **C** to represent 0.000025 in scientific notation. ___$0.000025 = 2.5 \times 10^{-5}$___

Reflect

1. When you move the decimal point, how can you know whether you are increasing or decreasing the number?

    Moving left is a decrease; moving right is an increase.

2. Explain how the two steps of moving the decimal and multiplying by a power of 10 leave the value of the original number unchanged.

    One increases and the other decreases the number.

© Houghton Mifflin Harcourt Publishing Company

DIFFERENTIATE INSTRUCTION *Leveled Questions*

	EXPLORE ACTIVITY
AL DOK 1 *Recall*	When converting a number from scientific notation to standard notation, how do you know whether to move the decimal point left or right? If the exponent is positive, move it right; if the exponent is negative, move it left.
OL DOK 2 *Skills/Concepts*	What is the exponent on the power of 10 in scientific notation for a number between 0.010 and 0.099? −2
BL DOK 3 *Strategic Thinking*	In Part D, how can you use the Multiplication Property of Equality to justify that 0.000025 divided by 2.5 gives you the power of 10 to use when writing 0.000025 in scientific notation? $\frac{0.000025}{2.5} = 0.00001$, so by the Multiplication Property of Equality, $0.000025 = 2.5 \times 0.00001$, or 2.5×10^{-5}.

LEVELED QUESTIONS: **AL** Approaching Level | **OL** On Level | **BL** Beyond Level

Math On the Spot
my.hrw.com

Writing a Number in Scientific Notation

To write a number less than 1 in scientific notation, move the decimal point right and use a negative exponent.

Writing Small Quantities in Scientific Notation

When the number is between 0 and 1, use a negative exponent.	$0.0\,7\,8\,3 = 7.83 \times 10^{-2}$	*The decimal point moves 2 places to the right.*

EXAMPLE 1

The average size of an atom is about 0.00000003 centimeter across. Write the average size of an atom in scientific notation.

Move the decimal point as many places as necessary to find a number that is greater than or equal to 1 and less than 10.

STEP 1 Place the decimal point.   3.0

STEP 2 Count the number of places you moved the decimal point.   8

STEP 3 Multiply 3.0 times a power of 10. 3.0×10^{-8}

> Since 0.00000003 is less than 1, you moved the decimal point to the right and the exponent on 10 is negative.

The average size of an atom in scientific notation is 3.0×10^{-8}.

Reflect

3. **Critical Thinking** When you write a number that is less than 1 in scientific notation, how does the power of 10 differ from when you write a number greater than 1 in scientific notation?

   The exponent is negative instead of positive.

YOUR TURN

Write each number in scientific notation.

4. 0.0000829
   8.29×10^{-5}

5. 0.000000302
   3.02×10^{-7}

6. A typical red blood cell in human blood has a diameter of approximately 0.000007 meter. Write this diameter in scientific notation. 7×10^{-6} m

Personal Math Trainer
Online Assessment and Intervention
my.hrw.com

© Houghton Mifflin Harcourt Publishing Company

---

③ Explain

EXAMPLE 1

Avoid Common Errors

To prevent writing the wrong exponent, students should first predict how the answer will look. Think: 0.00000003 is a very small number. When you multiply 3.0 times a power of 10, the exponent must be negative to equal this very small value.

ADDITIONAL EXAMPLE 1 The weight of one of the smaller species of butterflies was measured at 0.0007 ounces. Write the weight of this butterfly in scientific notation. 7.0×10^{-4} ounces

 Interactive Whiteboard
Interactive example available online

YOUR TURN   MP.7

Talk About It

Check for Understanding

Ask: With 0.0000829, after you write the first part as 8.29, have you made the original number larger or smaller? larger So, if you multiply by a power of 10, what should be the sign of the exponent? negative

---

		EXAMPLE 1
(AL)	**DOK 1** *Recall*	When converting a number from standard notation to scientific notation, when do you move the decimal point left? right? Move it left if the number is greater than or equal to 10; move it right if the number is less than 1.
(OL)	**DOK 2** *Skills/Concepts*	How is the exponent in the power of 10 related to the number of places that you must move the decimal point when writing a very small number in scientific notation? The absolute value of the exponent will be equal to the number of places you moved the decimal point.
(BL)	**DOK 3** *Strategic Thinking*	Multiply two numbers in scientific notation. If the multipliers of the numbers are equal and the exponents on the powers of 10 are opposites, what is the product? Explain. It is the square of a multiplier: $(a \cdot 10^n)(a \cdot 10^{-n}) = a^2 \cdot \frac{10^n}{10^n} = a^2$.

TEACHER TO TEACHER

Activity After Example 1, have students use these steps to explore scientific notation with negative exponents on a calculator.

- Have students enter 0.000000000099 (with 10 zeros after the decimal) to a calculator and interpret the display. 9.9E–11 means 9.9×10^{-11}

- Have students compare the displays for the following numbers: 0.0000099 (with 5 zeros after the decimal) and 0.00000099 (with 6 zeros after the decimal). Ask them to discuss when their calculators display very small numbers in scientific notation. Answers may vary.

EXAMPLE 2

ADDITIONAL EXAMPLE 2 A single atom of oxygen has a mass of 2.66×10^{-23} gram. Write 2.66×10^{-23} in standard notation.
0.0000000000000000000000266

Interactive Whiteboard
Interactive example available online

YOUR TURN MP.2

Focus on Critical Thinking

Ask students to estimate the numbers in **Exercise 9** and **Exercise 10** as a single-digit times an integer power of 10, and then use scientific notation to explain which is greater. Guide them in determining about how many times as much it is.

9. 1×10^{-6}

10. $10 \times 10^{-5} = 1 \times 10^{-4}$

1×10^{-4} is 100 times greater than 1×10^{-6}.

Digital Teacher Resources

Go online to access all your lesson-level resources.

Differentiated Instruction
- Reteach
- Reading Strategies
- Success for English Learners
- Practice and Problem Solving A/B, C, D

Math on the Spot Videos

(my.hrw.com)

Math On the Spot
my.hrw.com

Writing a Number in Standard Notation

To translate between scientific notation and standard notation with very small numbers, you can move the decimal point the number of places indicated by the exponent on the power of 10. When the exponent is negative, move the decimal point to the left.

EXAMPLE 2

Platelets are one component of human blood. A typical platelet has a diameter of approximately 2.33×10^{-6} meter. Write 2.33×10^{-6} in standard notation.

STEP 1 Use the exponent of the power of 10 to see how many places to move the decimal point.   6 places

STEP 2 Place the decimal point. Since you are going to write a number less than 2.33, move the decimal point to the *left*. Add placeholder zeros if necessary.

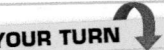
0.000000233

The number 2.33×10^{-6} in standard notation is 0.00000233.

Reflect

7. **Justify Reasoning** Explain whether 0.9×10^{-5} is written in scientific notation. If not, write the number correctly in scientific notation.

No, because the first factor is less than 1. The decimal point should move to the right and the exponent should decrease by 1: 9×10^{-6}

8. Which number is larger, 2×10^{-3} or 3×10^{-2}? Explain.

3×10^{-2} because its exponent is greater.

> **Math Talk**
> **Mathematical Processes**
>
> Describe the two factors that multiply together to form a number written in scientific notation.
>
> The first factor is a number greater than or equal to 1 and less than 10, and the second factor is a power of 10.

YOUR TURN

Write each number in standard notation.

9. 1.045×10^{-6}
0.000001045

10. 9.9×10^{-5}
0.000099

11. Jeremy measured the length of an ant as 1×10^{-2} meter. Write this length in standard notation.
0.01 m

Personal Math Trainer
Online Assessment and Intervention
my.hrw.com

© Houghton Mifflin Harcourt Publishing Company

DIFFERENTIATE INSTRUCTION *Leveled Questions*

	EXAMPLE 2
AL) DOK 1 *Recall*	Is the value of 2.33×10^{-6} greater than or less than 2.33? less
OL) DOK 2 *Skills/Concepts*	How could you check your answer in the Example? Convert 0.00000233 back to scientific notation by moving the decimal right 6 places and writing the number times 10^{-6}.
BL) DOK 3 *Strategic Thinking*	Capillaries in the human body are so small that red blood cells with a diameter of only 7×10^{-6} meter have to travel through in single file. Would platelets have to travel single file through a capillary? Explain. No; 7×10^{-6} m is 3 times the width of 2.33×10^{-6} m, so if a red blood cell can fit, 3 platelets can fit side by side.

LEVELED QUESTIONS: (AL) Approaching Level | (OL) On Level | (BL) Beyond Level

Write each number in scientific notation. (Explore Activity and Example 1)

1. 0.000487
Hint: Move the decimal right 4 places.
4.87×10^{-4}

2. 0.000028
Hint: Move the decimal right 5 places.
2.8×10^{-5}

3. 0.000059
5.9×10^{-5}

4. 0.0417
4.17×10^{-2}

5. Picoplankton can be as small as 0.00002 centimeter.
2×10^{-5}

6. The average mass of a grain of sand on a beach is about 0.000015 gram.
1.5×10^{-5}

Write each number in standard notation. (Example 2)

7. 2×10^{-5}
Hint: Move the decimal left 5 places.
0.00002

8. 3.582×10^{-6}
Hint: Move the decimal left 6 places.
0.000003582

9. 8.3×10^{-4}
0.00083

10. 2.97×10^{-2}
0.0297

11. 9.06×10^{-5}
0.0000906

12. 4×10^{-5}
0.00004

13. The average length of a dust mite is approximately 0.0001 meter. Write this number in scientific notation. (Example 1)
1×10^{-4}

14. The mass of a proton is about 1.7×10^{-24} gram. Write this number in standard notation. (Example 2)
0.0000000000000000000000017

ESSENTIAL QUESTION CHECK-IN

15. Describe how to write 0.0000672 in scientific notation.

Move the decimal point 5 places right to find 6.72, a number greater than or equal to 1 and less than 10. Then multiply 6.72 by 10^{-5}, using a negative exponent on 10 that equals the number of places you moved the decimal.

© Houghton Mifflin Harcourt Publishing Company

4 Elaborate

Talk About It

Summarize the Lesson

Ask: How can you write a number that is very close to zero, such as 0.0000078, in scientific notation? Count the number of places that the decimal point would have to move to the right to make a number greater than or equal to 1 and less than 10 for the first factor. The second factor is a power of 10 with the exponent equal to −6 to represent the number of places leftward you would need to move the decimal back to its original position.

Guided Practice

Engage with the Whiteboard

For **Exercises 1–14**, have students draw and count curved arrows to show moving the decimal point the correct number of places.

Avoid Common Errors

Exercises 1–6 Remind students to avoid counting errors as they move the decimal point by drawing arrows and counting a second time to check.

DIFFERENTIATE INSTRUCTION *Intervention and Additional Support*

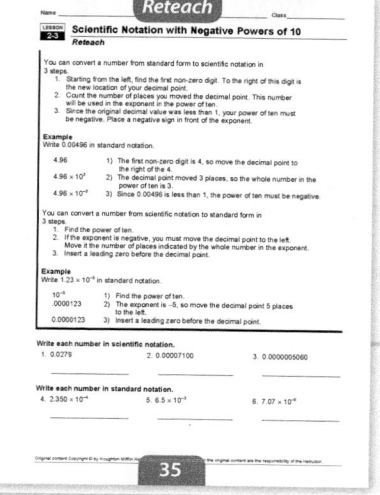

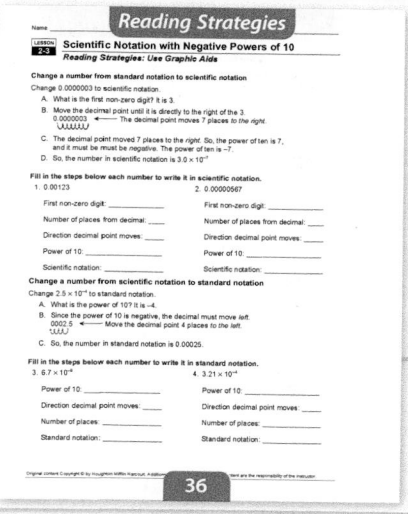

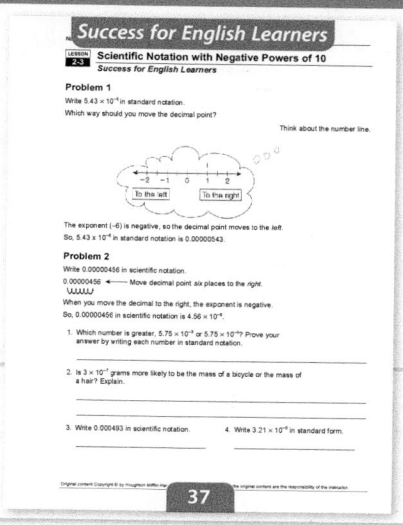

Personal Math Trainer
Daily Intervention
2.3 Homework

Pages shown are from *Differentiated Instruction.*
Also available online.

5 Evaluate

⏱ **Pressed for Time**

2.3 Differentiated Homework Assignments

Ⓐ **Approaching Level**   16–22, 25–27, 35

Ⓞ **On Level**   23–24, 28–34, 36

Ⓑ **Beyond Level**   28–37

*For **Below Level** students, assign Personal Math Trainer, Daily Intervention 2.3 Homework.*

Mathematical Processes	Exercises
MP.2 Reasoning	23
MP.3 Logic	22, 27, 36–37
MP.4 Modeling	16–21, 24–26, 28–34
MP.5 Using Tools	35

Focus on Higher Order Thinking

Depth of Knowledge	Exercises
2 Skills/Concepts	16–34
3 Strategic Thinking H.O.T.	35–37

Name_____ Class_____ Date_____

2.3 Independent Practice

Personal Math Trainer

Online Assessment and Intervention

my.hrw.com

Use the table for problems 16–21. Write the diameter of the fibers in scientific notation.

Average Diameter of Natural Fibers	
Animal	**Fiber Diameter (cm)**
Vicuña	0.0008
Angora rabbit	0.0013
Alpaca	0.00277
Angora goat	0.0045
Llama	0.0035
Orb web spider	0.015

16. Alpaca

2.77×10^{-3} cm

17. Angora rabbit

1.3×10^{-3} cm

18. Llama

3.5×10^{-3} cm

19. Angora goat

4.5×10^{-3} cm

20. Orb web spider

1.5×10^{-2} cm

21. Vicuña

8×10^{-4} cm

22. **Make a Conjecture** Which measurement would be least likely to be written in scientific notation: the thickness of a dog hair, the radius of a period on this page, the ounces in a cup of milk? Explain your reasoning.

The ounces in a cup of milk; it is more than 1 but less than 10.

23. **Multiple Representations** Convert the length 7 centimeters to meters. Compare the numerical values when both numbers are written in scientific notation.

7 cm = 0.07 m , 7 cm = 7×10^{0} cm; 0.07 m = 7×10^{-2} m. The first factors are the same; the exponents differ by 2.

24. **Draw Conclusions** A graphing calculator displays 1.89×10^{12} as 1.89E12. How do you think it would display 1.89×10^{-12}? What does the E stand for?

1.89E−12; the exponent on 10

25. **Communicate Mathematical Ideas** When a number is written in scientific notation, how can you tell right away whether or not it is greater than or equal to 1?

If the exponent on 10 is nonnegative, the number is greater than or equal to 1.

26. The volume of a drop of a certain liquid is 0.000047 liter. Write the volume of the drop of liquid in scientific notation.

4.7×10^{-5} L

27. **Justify Reasoning** If you were asked to express the weight in ounces of a ladybug in scientific notation, would the exponent of the 10 be positive or negative? Justify your response.

Negative, because a ladybug would weigh less than 1 ounce.

© Houghton Mifflin Harcourt Publishing Company

Lesson 2.3   **49**

DIFFERENTIATE INSTRUCTION *Leveled Homework/Practice*

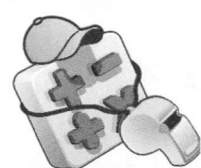

Personal Math Trainer
• 2.3 Homework

Pages shown are from *Differentiated Instruction.*
Also available online.

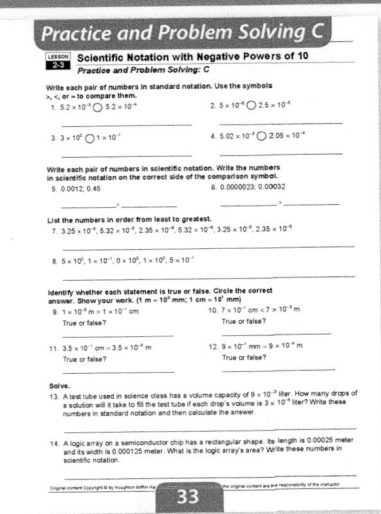

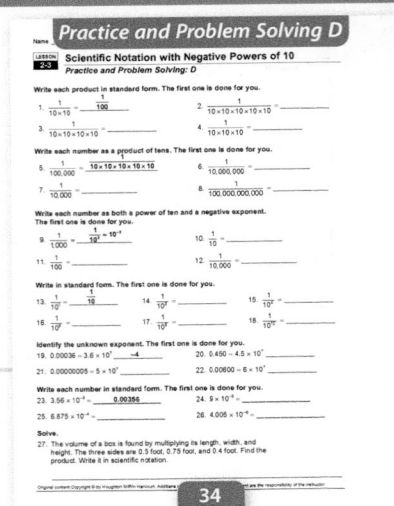

Physical Science The table shows the length of the radii of several very small or very large items. Complete the table.

	Item	Radius in Meters (Standard Notation)	Radius in Meters (Scientific Notation)
28.	The Moon	1,740,000	1.74×10^6
29.	Atom of silver	0.000000000125	1.25×10^{-10}
30.	Atlantic wolfish egg	0.0028	2.8×10^{-3}
31.	Jupiter	71,490,000	7.149×10^7
32.	Atom of aluminum	0.000000000182	1.82×10^{-10}
33.	Mars	3,397,000	3.397×10^6

34. List the items in the table in order from the smallest to the largest.

Atom of silver, atom of aluminum, Atlantic wolfish egg,

the Moon, Mars, Jupiter

 **FOCUS ON HIGHER ORDER THINKING**

35. Analyze Relationships Write the following diameters from least to greatest.
1.5×10^{-2} m 1.2×10^2 m 5.85×10^{-3} m 2.3×10^{-2} m 9.6×10^{-1} m

5.85×10^{-3} m, 1.5×10^{-2} m, 2.3×10^{-2} m,

9.6×10^{-1} m, 1.2×10^2 m

36. Critique Reasoning Jerod's friend Al had the following homework problem:

Express 5.6×10^{-7} in standard form.

Al wrote 56,000,000. How can Jerod explain Al's error and how to correct it?

Al treated the exponent as if it were positive instead

of negative and moved the decimal in the wrong

direction. The answer should be 0.00000056.

37. Make a Conjecture Two numbers are written in scientific notation. The number with a positive exponent is divided by the number with a negative exponent. Describe the result. Explain your answer.

The result will be greater than the number with the

positive exponent because the divisor is less than 1.

Work Area

© Houghton Mifflin Harcourt Publishing Company • Image Credits: ©Imagebroker/ Alamy Images

✔ Quick Check

2.3 Lesson Quiz

1. The weight of an ant is about 1.7×10^{-5} pound. Write 1.7×10^{-5} in standard notation. 0.000017

2. A bee sting delivers about 0.00005 gram of venom. Write this number in scientific notation. 5×10^{-5}

3. Write 0.77 in scientific notation. 7.7×10^{-1}

4. Write 1.0×10^{-3} in standard notation and in words. 0.001; one thousandth

5. Is 0.1×10^{-4} written in scientific notation? Explain. No; the first number is not more than 1 and less than 10.

Differentiate Instruction

IF a student misses more than one question, THEN

Differentiate Instruction:
• 2.3 Reteach
• Personal Math Trainer

Interactive Whiteboard
Interactive Lesson quiz available online

DIFFERENTIATE INSTRUCTION *Extend-the-Math Activity* **PRE-AP**

Activity Have students write 0.008 and 800 in scientific notation. Notice that both of these numbers have two zeros that are essential (since 0.008 can be written as .008). Do both exponents have the same absolute value when the numbers are written in scientific notation? Explain.

Sample answer: No; $0.008 = 8.0 \times 10^{-3}$ and $800 = 8.0 \times 10^2$. When you move the decimal to the left, the 8 counts as one place. When you move to the right, the 8 is not included in the count of the number of moves.

Comparing Very Small Numbers

1 Engage

❓ ESSENTIAL QUESTION

How can you compare very small numbers in scientific notation? First compare the powers of 10. If the powers of 10 are the same, compare the multipliers.

Motivate the Lesson

Ask: When you are using scientific notation to represent very small quantities, how can you tell how much more one quantity is than another? Begin the Explore Activity to find out.

2 Explore

EXPLORE ACTIVITY

Avoid Common Errors

When comparing numbers written in scientific notation with negative powers of 10, students may not consider the negative sign properly. For example, when comparing 4×10^{-3} and 2×10^{-6}, students may quickly decide that 2×10^{-6} is the greater number because 6 is greater than 3. Remind students to properly compare the negative exponents: 10^{-6} is less than 10^{-3} because -6 is less than -3. So, 4×10^{-3} is the greater number.

TEACHER TO TEACHER

Technology Have students use research to find something that is roughly 10 times bigger than themselves, and then something that is roughly 10 times bigger than that. Research again to find something that is roughly 10 times smaller than themselves, and then something that is roughly 10 times smaller than that. Finally, have students show that the largest thing is about 10^4 times greater than the smallest thing. Challenge students to extend the research to find something that is a million times larger than themselves and a million times smaller than themselves and then compare those two things.

Comparing Very Small Numbers

8.1.GF2.3
Students will compare very small numbers in scientific notation.

❓ ESSENTIAL QUESTION

How can you compare very small numbers in scientific notation?

EXPLORE ACTIVITY

Comparing Very Small Numbers

A Compare 0.0000003 and 0.00009 using standard notation.

Multiply the fraction by a ratio equal to 1, and simplify.

$$\frac{0.00009}{0.0000003} = \frac{0.00009}{0.0000003} \cdot \frac{10^{\boxed{7}}}{10^7} = \frac{\boxed{900}}{3} = \boxed{300}$$

So, 0.00009 is ___300___ times greater than 0.0000003.

B Compare 0.0000003 and 0.00009 using scientific notation.

$0.0000003 = 3 \times 10^{\boxed{-7}}$ and $0.00009 = 9 \times 10^{\boxed{-2}}$

First compare the powers of 10 in a ratio of greater to lesser:

$$\frac{10^{-5}}{10^{-7}} = 10^{\boxed{2}} = \boxed{100}$$

Then compare the corresponding multipliers: $\frac{\boxed{9}}{3} = \underline{\quad 3 \quad}$

So, 9×10^{-5} is $100 \cdot \underline{\quad 3 \quad} = \underline{\quad 300 \quad}$ times greater than 3×10^{-7}.

Reflect

1. Explain why 9×10^{-5} is greater than 3×10^{-7}.

   The number with the greater exponent in the power of 10 is greater. Because $-5 > -7$, 9×10^{-5} is greater than 3×10^{-7}.

2. Use both standard notation and scientific notation to explain why 1×10^{-1} is less than 1×10^0.

   Standard notation: 1×10^{-1} is equal to 0.1 and 1×10^0 is equal to 1; $0.1 < 1$.

   Scientific notation: 10^0 has a greater exponent than 10^{-1}, so 1×10^{-1} is less than 1×10^0.

© Houghton Mifflin Harcourt Publishing Company

Going Further 2.3 **50A**

DIFFERENTIATE INSTRUCTION *Leveled Questions*

	EXPLORE ACTIVITY
AL DOK 1 *Recall*	How can you tell which of these two numbers is greater in scientific notation? The number with the greater exponent in the power of 10 is greater.
OL DOK 2 *Skills/Concepts*	How is a ratio used to compare numbers in both Parts A and B? A ratio of the greater number to the lesser number, when simplified, will tell you how many times the numerator is greater than the denominator.
BL DOK 3 *Strategic Thinking*	How could you show the ratio of powers of 10 and the ratio of corresponding multipliers with these numbers written in standard notation? ratio of powers: $\frac{0.00001}{0.0000001} = 100$; ratio of corresponding multipliers: $\frac{9}{3} = 3$; so 0.00009 is $100 \cdot 3 = 300$ times greater than 0.0000003.

LEVELED QUESTIONS: **AL** Approaching Level | **OL** On Level | **BL** Beyond Level

Comparing Very Small Numbers in the Real World

Using scientific notation can help you compare very small numbers.

EXAMPLE

The thickness of a piece of paper is about 8×10^{-5} meter. The thickness of a human hair is about 2×10^{-5} meter. About how many times thicker is a piece of paper than a human hair?

$$\frac{10^{-5}}{10^{-5}} = 10^0 = 1 \qquad \text{Compare the powers of 10.}$$

$$\frac{8}{2} = 4 \qquad \text{Compare the multipliers.}$$

So, a piece of paper is about $1 \cdot 4 = 4$ times thicker than a human hair.

Practice

1. Complete the statements to express how many times greater 4×10^{-2} is than 2×10^{-4}.

$$\frac{\boxed{10^{-2}}}{10^{-4}} = 10^{\boxed{2}} = \underline{\quad 100 \quad}, \text{ and } \frac{\boxed{4}}{2} = \underline{\quad 2 \quad}$$

So, 4×10^{-2} is $100 \cdot \boxed{2} = \boxed{200}$ times greater than 2×10^{-4}.

2. The diameter of a human red blood cell is about 7×10^{-3} mm, and the diameter of a grain of salt is about 3×10^{-1} mm. Which is larger? About how many times larger? Explain.

   The grain of salt is larger because $10^{-1} > 10^{-3}$. $\frac{10^{-1}}{10^{-3}} = 10^2$ and $\frac{3}{7} \approx 0.4$,

   so the grain of salt is about 40 times larger than the red blood cell.

3. The average mass of a golden hamster is about 100 grams. The average mass of an African elephant is about 6×10^3 kilograms. About how many times greater is the mass of the elephant than the mass of the hamster? Use scientific notation to explain.

   100 grams is the same as 1×10^{-1} ▮ $\frac{▮}{▮} = 10^4$ and $\frac{6}{1} = 6$, so the

   elephant's mass is about 60,000 times greater than the hamster's mass.

4. The diameter of a cold virus cell is about 3×10^{-9} meter, and the diameter of a streptococcus bacterium cell is about 9×10^{-7} meter. Which is greater and about how many times greater?

   The streptococcus bacterium cell is larger because $10^{-7} > 10^{-9}$. $\frac{10^{-7}}{10^{-9}} = 10^2$

   and $\frac{9}{3} = 3$, so the streptococcus bacterium cell is about 300 times greater.

		EXAMPLE
(AL)	DOK 1 *Recall*	What are the numbers in standard notation? 0.00008 and 0.00002
(OL)	DOK 2 *Skills/Concepts*	Which number is greater? 8×10^{-5}
(BL)	DOK 3 *Strategic Thinking*	How can you use a ratio of these two numbers in scientific notation to check the answer in the example? $\frac{8 \times 10^{-5}}{2 \times 10^{-5}} = \frac{8}{2} = 4$

3 Explain

EXAMPLE

ADDITIONAL EXAMPLE A runner in a 1-mile race takes one stride about every 3×10^{-1} second. A beam of light travels that same mile in about 5×10^{-6} second. About how many times longer does it take the runner to take one stride in the race than for the beam of light to complete the whole mile? $\frac{10^{-1}}{10^{-6}} = 10^5$; $\frac{3}{5} = 0.6$, so it takes the runner about 60,000 times longer to take one stride than for the beam of light to go the entire mile.

4 Elaborate

Summarize the Lesson

Ask: How do you use scientific notation to determine how many times as much one quantity is than another? Sample answer: First, make sure the units are the same. Find the greater quantity by comparing the powers of 10, then comparing the multipliers if needed. Multiply the ratio of powers of 10 (greater to lesser) by the corresponding ratio of multipliers to find how many times greater the larger quantity is than the smaller quantity.

5 Evaluate

Practice

Focus on Critical Thinking
In **Exercise 3**, point out to students that the units are different in the two given measurements. After converting to the same units, one number will have a negative exponent and the other number will have a positive exponent, but the process for comparing is the same.

LESSON QUIZ

Determine which quantity is greater, and determine about how many times greater.

1. 0.0000004 and 0.0000009 9×10^{-7} is $\frac{9}{4} = 2.25$ times greater than 4×10^{-7}

2. 0.0005 and 0.0000125 5×10^{-4} is 40 times greater than 1.25×10^{-5}

3. A transistor on a computer chip in 1971 had a diameter of about 1×10^{-5} m. Forty years later, transistors have a diameter of about 2×10^{-8} m. How many times greater is the diameter of the earlier transistors than the later ones? $\frac{10^{-5}}{10^{-8}} = 10^3 = 1,000$ and $\frac{1}{2} = 0.5$; so about $1,000 \cdot 0.5 = 500$ times greater

Lesson Support

Content Objective Students will learn to add, subtract, multiply, and divide using scientific notation.

Professional Development

Integrate Mathematical Processes MP.1

This lesson provides an opportunity to address this Mathematical Process standard. It calls for students to make sense of problems and persevere in solving them. Example 2 uses a four-step problem-solving process to determine the speed of the sun as it moves in the Milky Way. Students analyze the information, formulate a plan, solve the problem, and justify and evaluate the solution.

FOCUS

Building Background

Connecting to Everyday Life In the previous two lessons, students have worked with writing numbers in scientific notation. Discuss the advantages of scientific notation and why it is used. Also review the importance of being able to interpret numbers written in scientific notation to understand the relative sizes of the numbers.

$$46,000,000,000 = 4.6 \times 10^{10}$$

$$0.000000000000592 = 5.92 \times 10^{-13}$$

COHERENCE

Learning Progressions

In this lesson, students perform calculations using scientific notation. They also interpret scientific notation generated by technology. Important understandings for students include the following:

- **Add and subtract with scientific notation.**
- **Multiply and divide with scientific notation.**
- **Use scientific notation on a calculator.**

Before students learn the properties of rational exponents, they should be adept at applying the properties of integer exponents, as demonstrated in this lesson. In this lesson students express and perform calculations with very large numbers using scientific notation. They continue to apply properties of exponents as they make computations using scientific notation.

RIGOR

Cluster Connections

This lesson provides an excellent opportunity to connect ideas in the cluster:

Work with radicals and integer exponents.

Present students with the following data:

Year	Population of California
1850	92,597
1900	1,485,053
1950	10,586,223
2000	33,871,648
2010	37,253,956

Ask students to approximate the population of California for each year shown in the table. Then ask them to use the approximations to compare differences and increases in sizes among the years.

Answers may vary. Sample answers: In 1950, the population was more than 10 times the population in 1900. In 2010, the population increased about 4×10^7 compared to the 2000 population.

Language Support ELL

Language Objective Students will demonstrate how to add, subtract, multiply, and divide using scientific notation.

Leveled Strategies for English Learners ELL

Emerging
Have students respond with "true" or "false" to statements about how scientific notation is used to describe phenomena in astronomy.

Expanding
Give students a sentence that is false about a scientific notation used in astronomy and have them change it to make the statement true.

Bridging
Have students draw and label a model of the Sun orbiting the center of the Milky Way and write a narrative description of how they calculated the rate of orbit using scientific notation.

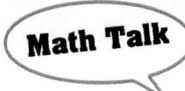
Math Talk

This prompt requires an understanding of the term *complicated*. Use familiar words such as *easy*, *hard*, or *difficult* to give students ordinary words and terms to describe and compare the challenges of the math operations.

Linguistic Support ELL

Academic/Content Vocabulary
This lesson requires background knowledge about astronomy, such as knowing that the Milky Way is the name of a galaxy and that suns orbit around its center. Students also need to know that *Sun* (with a capital *S*) refers to the planetary system's Sun, while *sun* (with a lowercase letter *s*) refers to a type of planetary body. Help students understand the mathematical formula for calculating *rate of orbiting* by giving examples from our solar system.

Background Knowledge
When teaching that E or EE represents *times a power of 10*, be aware that in the Spanish alphabet, the letter I is named "ee." Avoid confusion by writing the letter on the board while you say it.

Image Credits: ©Kevin Key/Shutterstock

Operations with Scientific Notation

LESSON 2.4 Operations with Scientific Notation

8.1.2.4
Students will add, subtract, multiply, and divide using scientific notation.

1 Engage

? ESSENTIAL QUESTION

How do you add, subtract, multiply, and divide using scientific notation? Sample answer: To add or subtract, rewrite the numbers to the same power of 10, add or subtract the multipliers, and rewrite in scientific notation. To multiply or divide, multiply or divide the multipliers, multiply or divide the powers of 10, and rewrite the answer in scientific notation.

Motivate the Lesson

Ask: How do you think you could add or subtract numbers in scientific notation without rewriting them in standard notation? What about if you wanted to multiply or divide? Begin the lesson to find out.

2 Explore

EXPLORE ACTIVITY | EXAMPLE 1

Focus on Critical Thinking

Make sure students understand why the table figure for Canada has been written with a different exponent in Method 1, Step 1.

ADDITIONAL EXAMPLE 1 Use the population table in Example 1 on the student page. How many more people live in the United States than in Canada? 2.762×10^8 people

Interactive Whiteboard
Interactive example available online

? ESSENTIAL QUESTION

How do you add, subtract, multiply, and divide using scientific notation?

EXPLORE ACTIVITY Real World

Adding and Subtracting with Scientific Notation

Numbers in scientific notation can be added and subtracted, either directly or by rewriting them in standard form.

Math On the Spot
© my.hrw.com

EXAMPLE 1 The table below shows the population of the three largest countries in North America in 2011. Find the total population of these countries.

Country	United States	Canada	Mexico
Population	3.1×10^8	3.38×10^7	1.1×10^8

Method 1:

STEP 1 Write each population with the same power of 10.

United States: $\underline{3.1} \times 10^8$

Canada: $\underline{0.338} \times 10^8$

Mexico: $\underline{1.1} \times 10^8$

STEP 2 Add the multipliers for each population.

$3.1 + \boxed{0.338} + \boxed{1.1} = \boxed{4.538}$

STEP 3 Write the final answer in scientific notation: $\underline{4.538} \times 10^8$.

Method 2:

STEP 1 Write each number in standard notation.

United States: $\underline{310,000,000}$

Canada: $\underline{33,800,000}$

Mexico: $\underline{110,000,000}$

STEP 2 Find the sum of the numbers in standard notation.

$310,000,000 + \boxed{33,800,000} + \boxed{110,000,000} = \boxed{453,800,000}$

STEP 3 Write the final answer in scientific notation: $\underline{4.538} \times 10^8$.

Lesson 2.4 **51**

© Houghton Mifflin Harcourt Publishing Company • Image Credits: ©Getty Images

DIFFERENTIATE INSTRUCTION *Leveled Questions*

	EXPLORE ACTIVITY EXAMPLE 1
AL DOK 1 *Recall*	In Step 1, why is the Canada population not written in proper scientific notation? The power of 10 has to be the same as the other two numbers in order to add the multipliers.
OL DOK 2 *Skills/Concepts*	In which method would you expect more errors to be made? Justify your answer. Method 2; it would be easy to write an incorrect number of 0s when converting between notations, and it could be hard to keep all the 0s aligned when adding.
BL DOK 3 *Strategic Thinking*	If the sum of multipliers in Step 2 were greater than 10, how would the rest of the process change? The number in Step 3 would have to be rewritten to be in scientific notation, so the exponent on the power of 10 would increase by 1.

LEVELED QUESTIONS: AL Approaching Level | OL On Level | BL Beyond Level

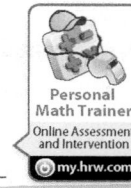

YOUR TURN

1. Using the population table above, how many more people live in Mexico than in Canada? Write your answer in scientific notation.

7.62×10^7 more people

Personal Math Trainer
Online Assessment and Intervention
my.hrw.com

Math On the Spot
my.hrw.com

Multiplying and Dividing with Scientific Notation

Numbers in scientific notation can be multiplied and divided directly by using properties of exponents.

EXAMPLE 2 *Problem Solving*

When the Sun makes an orbit around the center of the Milky Way, it travels 2.025×10^{14} kilometers. The orbit takes 225 million years. At what rate does the Sun travel? Write your answer in scientific notation.

 **Analyze Information**

The answer is the number of kilometers per year that the Sun travels around the Milky Way.

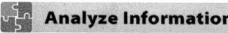 **Formulate a Plan**

Set up a division problem using $\text{Rate} = \frac{\text{Distance}}{\text{Time}}$ to represent the situation.

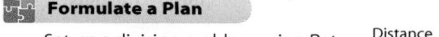 **Solve**

STEP 1 Substitute the values from the problem into the Rate formula.

$$\text{Rate} = \frac{2.025 \times 10^{14} \text{ kilometers}}{225{,}000{,}000 \text{ years}}$$

STEP 2 Write the expression for rate with years in scientific notation.

$$\text{Rate} = \frac{2.025 \times 10^{14} \text{ kilometers}}{2.25 \times 10^8 \text{ years}} \qquad 225 \text{ million} = 2.25 \times 10^8$$

STEP 3 Find the quotient by dividing the decimals and using the laws of exponents.

$2.025 \div 2.25 = 0.9$ *Divide the multipliers.*

$\dfrac{10^{14}}{10^8} = 10^{14-8} = 10^6$ *Divide the powers of 10.*

STEP 4 Combine the answers to write the rate in scientific notation.

$\text{Rate} = 0.9 \times 10^6 = 9.0 \times 10^5$ km per year

 Justify and Evaluate

Check your answer using multiplication.

$900{,}000 \times 225{,}000{,}000 = 202{,}500{,}000{,}000{,}000$, or 2.025×10^{14}. The answer is correct.

Math Talk
Mathematical Processes

Could you write 2.025×10^{14} in standard notation to do the division? Would this be a good way to solve the problem?

Yes; no; 2.025×10^{14} in standard notation is 202,500,000,000,000. Dividing this by 225,000,000 is more complicated than doing the division using scientific notation.

© Houghton Mifflin Harcourt Publishing Company • Image Credits: ©Alamy Images

---

Avoid Common Errors

Students may compare the multipliers and think Canada has a greater population than Mexico. Remind students that the power of 10 must be the same in order to compare and subtract these numbers.

3 Explain

EXAMPLE 2

Avoid Common Errors

Make sure students understand that the powers of 10 do not need to be the same when multiplying or dividing.

ADDITIONAL EXAMPLE 2 When Neptune makes an orbit around the Sun, it travels about 2.82×10^{10} km. Neptune travels at a rate of about 470,000 km/day. How many days does one orbit of Neptune take? Write your answer in scientific notation. about 6.0×10^4 days

Interactive Whiteboard
Interactive example available online

TEACHER TO TEACHER

Cooperative Learning After Example 2, have pairs of students work together to solve problems—one using standard notation and the other using scientific notation. Have students compare answers and discuss which method is faster. Have students in each pair switch roles using standard and scientific notations.

	EXAMPLE 2
AL **DOK 1** *Recall*	How is dividing two values with scientific notation like solving two division problems? The multipliers are divided and the powers of 10 are divided.
OL **DOK 2** *Skills/Concepts*	How does multiplication or division of numbers in scientific notation implement the properties of exponents? When the powers of 10 are multiplied or divided, the properties of exponents are used.
BL **DOK 3** *Strategic Thinking*	Why do powers of 10 need to be the same when adding or subtracting numbers in scientific notation, but not when multiplying or dividing numbers in scientific notation? Adding or subtracting in scientific notation is like adding or subtracting with decimals—you have to make sure the place values are lined up correctly.

YOUR TURN MP.1

Engage with the Whiteboard

For **Exercises 2–3**, have volunteers demonstrate the solution method while they explain how to multiply or divide the multipliers and the powers of 10.

EXAMPLE 3

ADDITIONAL EXAMPLE 3 Use the table in Example 3 on the student page. What is the difference between Asia's area and Europe's area? Use your calculator to find the answer. 3.36×10^{13} square meters

Interactive Whiteboard
Interactive example available online

YOUR TURN MP.5

Focus on Modeling

In **Exercises 4–6**, expressions that model scientific notation are to be rewritten in calculator notation and vice versa for **Exercises 7–9**. Ensure that students can locate the multiplier, the base, and the exponent in each.

Digital Teacher Resources

Go online to access all your lesson-level resources.

Differentiated Instruction
- Reteach
- Reading Strategies
- Success for English Learners
- Practice and Problem Solving A/B, C, D

Math on the Spot Videos

my.hrw.com

YOUR TURN

2. Light travels at a speed of 1.86×10^5 miles per second. It takes light from the Sun about 4.8×10^3 seconds to reach Saturn. Find the approximate distance from the Sun to Saturn. Write your answer in scientific notation. $\underline{8.928 \times 10^8 \text{ miles}}$

3. Light travels at the speed of 1.17×10^7 miles per minute. Pluto's average distance from the Sun is 3,670,000,000 miles. On average, how long does it take sunlight to reach Pluto? Write your answer in scientific notation. $\underline{3.14 \times 10^2 \text{ minutes}}$

Personal Math Trainer
Online Assessment and Intervention
my.hrw.com

Scientific Notation on a Calculator

On many scientific calculators, you can enter numbers in scientific notation by using a function labeled "ee" or "EE". Usually, the letter "E" takes the place of "×10". So, the number 4.1×10^9 would appear as 4.1E9 on the calculator.

Math On the Spot
my.hrw.com

EXAMPLE 3 Real World

The table shows the approximate areas for three continents given in square meters. What is the total area of these three continents? Write the answer in scientific notation using more appropriate units.

Continent	Asia	Africa	Europe
Area (m²)	4.4×10^{13}	3.02×10^{13}	1.04×10^{13}

Find $4.4 \times 10^{13} + 3.02 \times 10^{13} + 1.04 \times 10^{13}$.

Enter 4.4E13 + 3.02E13 + 1.04E13 on your calculator.

Write the results from your calculator: 8.46E13.

Write this number in scientific notation: 8.46×10^{13} m².

Square kilometers is more appropriate: 8.46×10^7 km².

> Because 1 km = 1,000 m, 1 km² = 1,000² m², or 10^6 m². Divide by 10^6.

YOUR TURN

Write each number using calculator notation.

4. 7.5×10^5 $\underline{7.5E5}$

5. 3×10^{-7} $\underline{3E-7}$

6. 2.7×10^{13} $\underline{2.7E13}$

Write each number using scientific notation.

7. 4.5E−1 $\underline{4.5 \times 10^{-1}}$

8. 5.6E12 $\underline{5.6 \times 10^{12}}$

9. 6.98E−8 $\underline{6.98 \times 10^{-8}}$

Personal Math Trainer
Online Assessment and Intervention
my.hrw.com

Lesson 2.4 **53**

© Houghton Mifflin Harcourt Publishing Company

DIFFERENTIATE INSTRUCTION *Intervention and Additional Support*

	EXAMPLE 3
AL **DOK 1** *Recall*	How do you enter the EE feature on your calculator? First enter the "2nd" or "shift" key, then the key below EE.
OL **DOK 2** *Skills/Concepts*	How do you know which operation(s) to use in this problem? The phrase "total area" indicates addition.
BL **DOK 3** *Strategic Thinking*	A kilometer is 1,000, or 10^3, meters. Explain in geometric terms why you must divide by 10^6 to convert square meters to square kilometers. Think of a square 1,000 m, or 1 km, on an edge. The large square is 1 km², and contains $1,000(1,000) = 1,000,000$ squares 1 m on an edge. Then each $1,000,000 = 10^6$ 1-m squares represents only 1 km², so you must divide the number of square meters by 10^6.

LEVELED QUESTIONS: **AL** Approaching Level | **OL** On Level | **BL** Beyond Level

Add or subtract. Write your answer in scientific notation. (Explore Activity Example 1)

1. $4.2 \times 10^6 + 2.25 \times 10^5 + 2.8 \times 10^6$

$4.2 \times 10^6 + \boxed{0.225} \times 10^{\boxed{6}} + 2.8 \times 10^6$

$4.2 + \boxed{0.225} + \boxed{2.8}$

$\boxed{7.225} \times 10^{\boxed{6}}$

2. $8.5 \times 10^3 - 5.3 \times 10^3 - 1.0 \times 10^2$

$8.5 \times 10^3 - 5.3 \times 10^3 - \boxed{0.10} \times 10^{\boxed{3}}$

$\boxed{8.5} - \boxed{5.3} - \boxed{0.10}$

$\boxed{3.1} \times 10^{\boxed{3}}$

3. $1.25 \times 10^2 + 0.50 \times 10^2 + 3.25 \times 10^2$

$\underline{\hspace{2cm} 5 \times 10^2 \hspace{2cm}}$

4. $6.2 \times 10^5 - 2.6 \times 10^4 - 1.9 \times 10^2$

$\underline{\hspace{2cm} 5.9381 \times 10^5 \hspace{2cm}}$

Multiply or divide. Write your answer in scientific notation. (Example 2)

5. $\left(1.8 \times 10^9\right)\left(6.7 \times 10^{12}\right)$ $\underline{1.206 \times 10^{22}}$

6. $\dfrac{3.46 \times 10^{17}}{2 \times 10^9}$ $\underline{1.73 \times 10^8}$

7. $\left(5 \times 10^{12}\right)\left(3.38 \times 10^6\right)$ $\underline{1.69 \times 10^{19}}$

8. $\dfrac{8.4 \times 10^{21}}{4.2 \times 10^{14}}$ $\underline{2 \times 10^7}$

Write each number using calculator notation. (Example 3)

9. 3.6×10^{11}
$\underline{\hspace{1cm} 3.6E11 \hspace{1cm}}$

10. 7.25×10^{-5}
$\underline{\hspace{1cm} 7.25E{-}5 \hspace{1cm}}$

11. 8×10^{-1}
$\underline{\hspace{1cm} 8E{-}1 \hspace{1cm}}$

Write each number using scientific notation. (Example 3)

12. 1.6E−4
$\underline{\hspace{1cm} 7.6 \times 10^{-4} \hspace{1cm}}$

13. 1.2E16
$\underline{\hspace{1cm} 1.2 \times 10^{16} \hspace{1cm}}$

14. 9E1
$\underline{\hspace{1cm} 9 \times 10^1 \hspace{1cm}}$

? **ESSENTIAL QUESTION CHECK-IN**

15. How do you add, subtract, multiply, and divide numbers written in scientific notation?

To add or subtract, rewrite the numbers to the same power of 10, add or subtract the multipliers, and rewrite the answer in scientific notation. To multiply or divide, multiply or divide the multipliers, use the rules of exponents to multiply or divide the powers of 10, and rewrite the answer in scientific notation.

© Houghton Mifflin Harcourt Publishing Company

4 Elaborate

Talk About It

Summarize the Lesson

Ask: When must the powers of 10 be the same when operating on numbers written in scientific notation? If the expressions are to be added or subtracted, the powers of 10 must be the same.

Guided Practice

Engage with the Whiteboard

For **Exercises 1–2**, have volunteers explain the process of arriving at the correct value as they complete the write-in boxes for each exercise.

Avoid Common Errors

- **Exercises 5–8** Remind students that the multipliers are operated on separately from the powers of 10.

- **Exercises 9–11** Remind students that the exponent is not written as a superscript to E but rather the same size as and to the right of E.

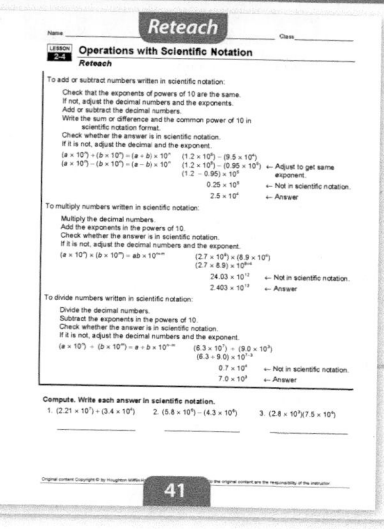

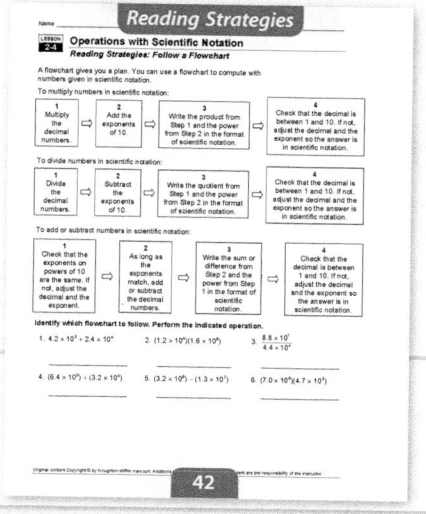

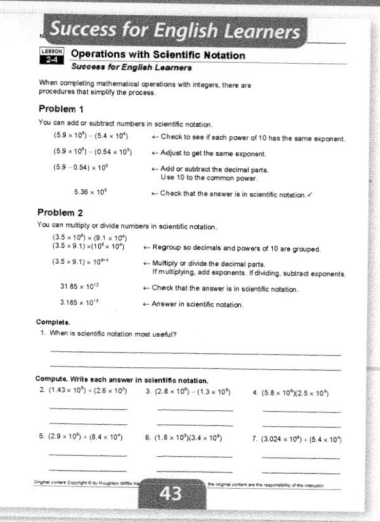

Personal Math Trainer
Daily Intervention
2.4 Homework

Pages shown are from *Differentiated Instruction.* **Also available online.**

🕐 **Pressed for Time**

2.4 Differentiated Homework Assignments

(AL) Approaching Level 16–20, 22–24, 26, 29

(OL) On Level 18–25, 27, 29

(BL) Beyond Level 16–17, 25–30

*For **Below Level** students, assign Personal Math Trainer, Daily Intervention 2.4 Homework.*

Mathematical Processes	Exercises
MP.3 Logic	29
MP.4 Modeling	16–27
MP.6 Precision	28, 30

Focus on Higher Order Thinking

Depth of Knowledge	Exercises
2 Skills/Concepts	16–27
3 Strategic Thinking H.O.T.	28–30

16. An adult blue whale can eat 4.0×10^7 krill in a day. At that rate, how many krill can an adult blue whale eat in 3.65×10^2 days?

1.46×10^{10} krill

17. A newborn baby has about 26,000,000,000 cells. An adult has about 4.94×10^{13} cells. How many times as many cells does an adult have than a newborn? Write your answer in scientific notation.

about 1.9×10^3 as many

Represent Real-World Problems The table shows the number of tons of waste generated and recovered (recycled) in 2010.

	Paper	Glass	Plastics
Tons generated	7.131×10^7	1.153×10^7	3.104×10^7
Tons recovered	4.457×10^7	0.313×10^7	0.255×10^7

18. What is the total amount of paper, glass, and plastic waste generated?

11.388×10^7, or in scientific notation 1.1388×10^8 tons

19. What is the total amount of paper, glass, and plastic waste recovered?

5.025×10^7 tons

20. What is the total amount of paper, glass, and plastic waste **not** recovered?

6.363×10^7 tons

21. Which type of waste has the lowest recovery ratio?

Plastics

Social Studies The table shows the approximate populations of three countries.

Country	China	France	Australia
Population	1.3×10^9	6.48×10^7	2.15×10^7

22. How many more people live in France than in Australia?

4.33×10^7 more people

23. The area of Australia is 2.95×10^6 square miles. What is the approximate average number of people per square mile in Australia?

about 7 people per square mile

24. How many times greater is the population of China than the population of France? Write your answer in standard notation.

about 20.1 times as great

25. Mia is 7.01568×10^6 minutes old. Convert her age to more appropriate units using years, months, and days. Assume each month to have 30.5 days.

13 years, 3 months, 22.5 days

© Houghton Mifflin Harcourt Publishing Company • Image Credits: ©Moodboard/ Alamy Images

---

DIFFERENTIATE INSTRUCTION *Leveled Homework/Practice*

Personal Math Trainer

• 2.4 Homework

Pages shown are from *Differentiated Instruction*. **Also available online.**

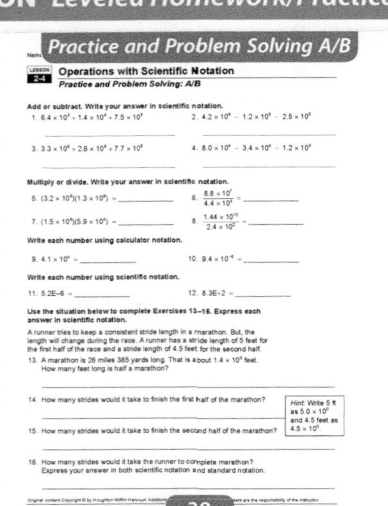

Practice and Problem Solving A/B

38

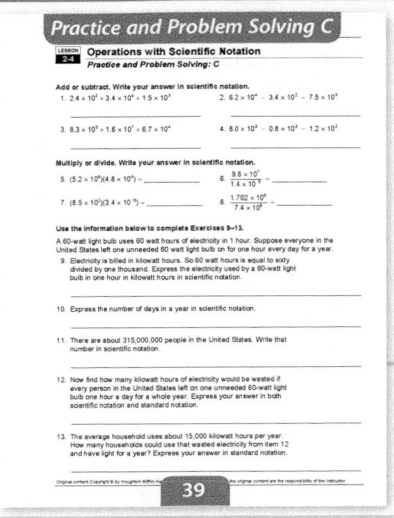

Practice and Problem Solving C

39

Practice and Problem Solving D

40

26. Courtney takes 2.4×10^4 steps during her a long-distance run. Each step covers an average of 810 mm. What total distance (in mm) did Courtney cover during her run? Write your answer in scientific notation. Then convert the distance to the more appropriate unit kilometers. Write that answer in standard form.

1.944×10^7 mm; 19.44 km

27. **Social Studies** The U.S. public debt as of October 2010 was $\$9.06 \times 10^{12}$. What was the average U.S. public debt per American if the population in 2010 was 3.08×10^8 people?

$\$2.94 \times 10^4$, or $\$29,400$ per person

 **FOCUS ON HIGHER ORDER THINKING**

28. **Communicate Mathematical Ideas** How is multiplying and dividing numbers in scientific notation different from adding and subtracting numbers in scientific notation?

You can add or subtract numbers written in scientific notation only if their powers of 10 are the same. You can multiply and divide numbers written in scientific notation that have different powers. The laws of exponents are used to combine the powers.

29. **Explain the Error** A student found the product of 8×10^6 and 5×10^9 to be 4×10^{15}. What is the error? What is the correct product?

The student is off by a power of ten. The correct product is 40×10^{15} or 4.0×10^{16}.

30. **Communicate Mathematical Ideas** Describe a procedure that can be used to simplify $\dfrac{(4.87 \times 10^{12}) - (7 \times 10^{10})}{(3 \times 10^7) + (6.1 \times 10^8)}$. Write the expression in scientific notation in simplified form.

First, simplify the numerator by rewriting both numbers to the same power of 10 (10^{10}) and subtracting to get 480×10^{10} or 4.8×10^{12}. Then, simplify the denominator by rewriting both numbers to the same power of 10 (10^7) and adding to get 64×10^7 or 6.4×10^8. Finally, divide the multipliers ($4.8 \div 6.4$) to get 0.75, use the division rule for exponents $\left(\dfrac{10^{12}}{10^8} \right)$ to get 10^4, and rewrite 0.75×10^4 in scientific notation as 7.5×10^3.

Work Area

© Houghton Mifflin Harcourt Publishing Company

2.4 Lesson Quiz

Add or subtract. Write your answer in scientific notation.

1. $3.2 \times 10^{-2} + 3.2 \times 10^{-4} + 2.8 \times 10^{-2}$
6.032×10^{-2}

2. $5.2 \times 10^4 - 1.5 \times 10^2 - 4.6 \times 10^4$ 5.85×10^3

Multiply or divide. Write your answer in scientific notation.

3. $(1.25 \times 10^4)(4 \times 10^4)$ 5×10^8

4. $\dfrac{4.5 \times 10^{28}}{3 \times 10^{15}}$ 1.5×10^{13}

5. Write 7.18×10^{-2} using calculator notation. $7.18E{-}2$

6. Write $2.898E15$ using scientific notation.
2.898×10^{15}

Differentiate Instruction

IF a student misses more than one question, THEN

Differentiate Instruction:
- 2.4 Reteach
- Personal Math Trainer

 Interactive Whiteboard
Interactive Lesson quiz available online

DIFFERENTIATE INSTRUCTION *Extend-the-Math Activity* **PRE-AP**

Activity Assume $1 \le a < 10$. When the quotient of $(6 \times 10^6) \div (a \times 10^2)$ is written in scientific notation, the power of 10 is 4. What are the possible values of a? Justify your answer.

$1 \le a \le 6$; Since $(6 \times 10^6) \div (a \times 10^2) = (6 \div a) \times 10^4$, if a is any number between 6 and 10, the value of $6 \div a$ would be less than 1. You could not write this expression in scientific notation with an exponent of 4.

Ready to Go On?

Assess Mastery

Access *Ready to Go On?* assessment online, and receive instant scoring, feedback, and customized intervention or enrichment.

Personal Math Trainer

Online Assessment and Intervention
• Module 2 Posttest

Additional Resources

Digital Teacher Resources

Go online for module-level resources.

Assessment Resources
• Module 2 Quiz: B, p.19
• Module 2 Quiz: D, p.21

my.hrw.com

Ready to Go On?

Personal Math Trainer
Online Assessment and Intervention
my.hrw.com

2.1 Integer Exponents

Find the value of each power.

1. 3^{-4} ___ $\frac{1}{81}$ ___ 2. 35^0 ___ 1 ___ 3. 4^4 ___ 256 ___

Use the properties of exponents to write an equivalent expression.

4. $8^3 \cdot 8^7$ ___ 8^{10} ___ 5. $\frac{12^6}{12^2}$ ___ 12^4 ___ 6. $(10^3)^5$ ___ 10^{15} ___

2.2 Scientific Notation with Positive Powers of 10

Convert each number to scientific notation or standard notation.

7. 2,000 ___ 2×10^3 ___ 8. 91,007,500 ___ 9.10075×10^7 ___

9. 1.0395×10^9 ___ $1,039,500,000$ ___ 10. 4×10^2 ___ 400 ___

2.3 Scientific Notation with Negative Powers of 10

Convert each number to scientific notation or standard notation.

11. 0.02 ___ 2×10^{-2} ___ 12. 0.000701 ___ 7.01×10^{-4} ___

13. 8.9×10^{-5} ___ 0.000089 ___ 14. 4.41×10^{-2} ___ 0.0441 ___

2.4 Operations with Scientific Notation

Perform the operation. Write your answer in scientific notation.

15. $7 \times 10^6 - 5.3 \times 10^6$ ___ 1.7×10^6 ___ 16. $3.4 \times 10^4 + 7.1 \times 10^5$ ___ 7.44×10^5 ___

17. $(2 \times 10^4)(5.4 \times 10^6)$ ___ 1.08×10^{11} ___ 18. $\frac{7.86 \times 10^9}{3 \times 10^4}$ ___ 2.62×10^5 ___

19. Neptune's average distance from the Sun is 4.503×10^9 km. Mercury's average distance from the Sun is 5.791×10^7 km. About how many times farther from the Sun is Neptune than Mercury? Write your answer in scientific notation.

   about 7.776×10^1 times farther

 ESSENTIAL QUESTION

20. How is scientific notation used in the real world?

   Sample answer: Very large numbers, such as distances in space, and very small numbers, such as the sizes of atomic particles, can be written in scientific notation.

© Houghton Mifflin Harcourt Publishing Company

READY TO GO ON? *Diagnostic Assessment*

RtI Response to Intervention

Use to determine if students have mastered the concepts covered in this module.

Lesson	Exercises	Content Focus	Review with *Differentiated Instruction*
2.1	1–6	Integer Exponents	**2.1** Reteach **2.1** Reading Strategies **2.1** Success for English Learners
2.2	7–10	Scientific Notation with Positive Powers of 10	**2.2** Reteach **2.2** Reading Strategies **2.2** Success for English Learners
2.3	11–14	Scientific Notation with Negative Powers of 10	**2.3** Reteach **2.3** Reading Strategies **2.3** Success for English Learners
2.4	15–19	Operations with Scientific Notation	**2.4** Reteach **2.4** Reading Strategies **2.4** Success for English Learners

Personal
Math Trainer

Online
Assessment and
Intervention

my.hrw.com

Selected Response

1. Which of the following is equivalent to 6^{-3}?

   Ⓐ 216
   Ⓒ $-\frac{1}{216}$
   Ⓑ $\frac{1}{216}$
   Ⓓ -216

2. About 786,700,000 passengers traveled by plane in the United States in 2010. What is this number written in scientific notation?

   Ⓐ $7,867 \times 10^5$ passengers
   Ⓑ 7.867×10^2 passengers
   Ⓒ 7.867×10^8 passengers
   Ⓓ 7.867×10^9 passengers

3. In 2011, the population of Mali was about 1.584×10^7 people. What is this number written in standard notation?

   Ⓐ 1.584 people
   Ⓑ 1,584 people
   Ⓒ 15,840,000 people
   Ⓓ 158,400,000 people

4. The square root of a number is between 7 and 8. Which could be the number?

   Ⓐ 72
   Ⓒ 51
   Ⓑ 83
   Ⓓ 66

5. Each entry-level account executive in a large company makes an annual salary of $\$3.48 \times 10^4$. If there are 5.2×10^2 account executives in the company, how much do they make in all?

   Ⓐ $\$6.69 \times 10^1$
   Ⓑ $\$3.428 \times 10^4$
   Ⓒ $\$3.532 \times 10^4$
   Ⓓ $\$1.8096 \times 10^7$

6. Place the numbers in order from least to greatest.
   $0.24, 4 \times 10^{-2}, 0.042, 2 \times 10^{-4}, 0.004$

   Ⓐ $2 \times 10^{-4}, 4 \times 10^{-2}, 0.004, 0.042, 0.24$
   Ⓑ $0.004, 2 \times 10^{-4}, 0.042, 4 \times 10^{-2}, 0.24$
   Ⓒ $0.004, 2 \times 10^{-4}, 4 \times 10^{-2}, 0.042, 0.24$
   Ⓓ $2 \times 10^{-4}, 0.004, 4 \times 10^{-2}, 0.042, 0.24$

7. Guillermo is $5\frac{5}{6}$ feet tall. What is this number of feet written as a decimal?

   Ⓐ 5.7 feet
   Ⓒ 5.83 feet
   Ⓑ $5.\overline{7}$ feet
   Ⓓ $5.8\overline{3}$ feet

8. A human hair has a width of about 6.5×10^{-5} meter. What is this width written in standard notation?

   Ⓐ 0.00000065 meter
   Ⓑ 0.0000065 meter
   Ⓒ 0.000065 meter
   Ⓓ 0.00065 meter

Mini-Task

9. Consider the following numbers: 7000, 700, 70, 0.7, 0.07, 0.007

   a. Write the numbers in scientific notation.
   $7 \times 10^3, 7 \times 10^2, 7 \times 10^1,$
   $7 \times 10^{-1}, 7 \times 10^{-2}, 7 \times 10^{-3}$

   b. Look for a pattern in the given list and the list in scientific notation. Which numbers are missing from the lists?
   7 and 7×10^0

   c. Make a conjecture about the missing numbers.
   7×10^0 is 7 written in
   scientific notation.

© Houghton Mifflin Harcourt Publishing Company

DIFFERENTIATE ASSESSMENT

Below Level Module Quiz 2: D

On Level Module Quiz 2: B

Personal Math Trainer

Module 2 Assessment Readiness

Pages shown are from *Assessment Resources*. **Also available online.**

Preparing for High Stakes Tests

Assessment Readiness Tip

Students can often eliminate some answer choices of multiple-choice questions using logic.

- **Item 3** 1.584 doesn't make sense as a population figure, since it's not possible to have part of a person, and 1,584 people is a very small figure for the population of a country. Therefore, answers A and B can be eliminated.

- **Item 5** The salary of several account executives must be much larger than the salary of a single executive. Answer choices A and B are smaller, while answer choice C is only slightly larger. Therefore, only answer choice D makes sense in the context.

Avoid Common Errors

- **Item 2** Caution students not to simply count the zeros in the number and select answer choice A. Remind them that they must count the number of places that the decimal point is moved to determine the correct exponent.

- **Item 8** To avoid losing their place when counting many zeros, encourage students to use the point of a pen or pencil to keep track of where they are when counting, and also to repeat counting to confirm that it is correct.

Items	Grade 8 Lessons	Mathematical Processes
1	2.1	MP.2
2	2.2	MP.4
3	2.2	MP.4
4*	1.1	MP.6
5	2.4	MP.4
6	2.3	MP.2
7*	3.1 (Grade 7)	MP.4
8	2.3	MP.4
9	2.2, 2.3	MP.7, MP.8

Item integrates mixed review concepts from previous modules or a previous course.

UNIT 1
Real Numbers, Exponents, and Scientific Notation

Study Guide Review

Vocabulary Development

Integrating Language Arts

Encourage students to practice using the unit vocabulary as they talk and write about mathematics. Understanding vocabulary will aid their understanding of the concepts.

MODULE 1

Real Numbers

Key Concepts

- An irrational number is a number that is not rational and cannot be written in the form $\frac{a}{b}$ where a and b are integers and $b \neq 0$. **(Lesson 1.1)**

- The square root of a number is the number that when multiplied by itself has the original number as the product. Every positive number has a positive and negative square root. **(Lesson 1.1)**

- The set of real numbers consists of the set of rational numbers and the set of irrational numbers. **(Lesson 1.2)**

- Between any two real numbers is another real number. **(Lesson 1.3)**

MODULE 1   Real Numbers

ESSENTIAL QUESTION

How can you use real numbers to solve real-world problems?

Key Vocabulary

cube root *(raíz cúbica)*
irrational number *(número irracional)*
perfect cube *(cubo perfecto)*
perfect square *(cuadrado perfecto)*
principal square root *(raíz cuadrada principal)*
rational number *(número racional)*
real number *(número real)*
repeating decimal *(decimal periódico)*
square root *(raíz cuadrada)*
terminating decimal *(decimal finito)*

EXAMPLE 1

Write $0.\overline{81}$ as a fraction in simplest form.

$$x = 0.\overline{81}$$
$$100x = 81.\overline{81}$$
$$\underline{-x \quad -0.\overline{81}}$$
$$99x = 81$$
$$x = \frac{81}{99}$$
$$x = \frac{9}{11}$$

EXAMPLE 2

Solve each equation for x.

A $x^2 = 289$

$x = \pm\sqrt{289}$

$x = \pm 17$

The solutions are 17 and -17.

B $x^3 = 1{,}000$

$x = \sqrt[3]{1{,}000}$

$x = 10$

The solution is 10.

EXAMPLE 3

Write all names that apply to each number.

A $5.\overline{4}$
rational, real

$5.\overline{4}$ is a repeating decimal.

B $\frac{8}{4}$
whole, integer, rational, real

$\frac{8}{4} = 2$

C $\sqrt{13}$
irrational, real

13 is a whole number that is not a perfect square.

© Houghton Mifflin Harcourt Publishing Company

EXAMPLE 4

Order 6, 2π, and $\sqrt{38}$ from least to greatest.

2π is approximately equal to 2×3.14, or 6.28.

$\sqrt{38}$ is approximately 6.15 based on the following reasoning.

$$\sqrt{36} < \sqrt{38} < \sqrt{49} \quad 6 < \sqrt{38} < 7 \quad 6.1^2 = 37.21 \quad 6.2^2 = 38.44$$

From least to greatest, the numbers are 6, $\sqrt{38}$, and 2π.

EXERCISES

Find the two square roots of each number. If the number is not a perfect square, approximate the values to the nearest 0.05.
(Lesson 1.1)

1. 16 _____ 4, −4 _____

2. $\frac{4}{25}$ _____ $\frac{2}{5}, -\frac{2}{5}$ _____

3. 225 _____ 15, −15 _____

4. $\frac{1}{49}$ _____ $\frac{1}{7}, -\frac{1}{7}$ _____

5. $\sqrt{10}$ _____ 3.15, −3.15 _____

6. $\sqrt{18}$ _____ 4.25, −4.25 _____

Write each decimal as a fraction in simplest form. (Lesson 1.1)

7. $0.\overline{5}$ _____ $\frac{5}{9}$ _____

8. $0.\overline{63}$ _____ $\frac{7}{11}$ _____

9. $0.\overline{214}$ _____ $\frac{214}{999}$ _____

Solve each equation for x. (Lesson 1.1)

10. $x^2 = 361$

_____ $x = 19$ _____

11. $x^3 = 1{,}728$

_____ $x = 12$ _____

12. $x^2 = \frac{49}{121}$

_____ $x = \frac{7}{11}$ _____

Write all names that apply to each number. (Lesson 1.2)

13. $\frac{2}{3}$

_____ rational, real _____

14. $-\sqrt{100}$

_____ integer, rational, real _____

15. $\frac{15}{5}$

_____ whole, integer, rational, real _____

16. $\sqrt{21}$

_____ irrational, real _____

Compare. Write <, >, or =. (Lesson 1.3)

17. $\sqrt{7} + 5$ $\big(<\big)$ $7 + \sqrt{5}$

18. $6 + \sqrt{8}$ $\big(<\big)$ $\sqrt{6} + 8$

19. $\sqrt{4} - 2$ $\big(<\big)$ $4 - \sqrt{2}$

Order the numbers from least to greatest. (Lesson 1.3)

20. $\sqrt{81}, \frac{72}{7}, 8.9$ _____ $8.9, \sqrt{81}, \frac{72}{7}$ _____

21. $\sqrt{7}, 2.55, \frac{7}{3}$ _____ $\frac{7}{3}, 2.55, \sqrt{7}$ _____

© Houghton Mifflin Harcourt Publishing Company

Exponents and Scientific Notation

Key Concepts

- Expressions with integer exponents can be simplified using the properties of integer exponents. **(Lesson 2.1)**

- Scientific notation is a method of expressing very large and very small numbers as a product of a number greater than or equal to 1 and less than 10, and a power of 10. **(Lesson 2.2)**

- To multiply a number by 10, move the decimal one place to the right, and to divide a number by 10, move the decimal one place to the left. **(Lessons 2.2, 2.3)**

- Numbers expressed in scientific notation can be added or subtracted by rewriting them in standard form. **(Lesson 2.4)**

- Numbers expressed in scientific notation can be multiplied or divided by applying properties of exponents. **(Lesson 2.4)**

 **MODULE 2** Exponents and Scientific Notation

Key Vocabulary
scientific notation
(notación científica)

? ESSENTIAL QUESTION

How can you use scientific notation to solve real-world problems?

EXAMPLE 1

Write each measurement in scientific notation.

A The diameter of Earth at the equator is approximately 12,700 kilometers.

Move the decimal point in 12,700 four places to the left: 1.2 7 0 0.

$12{,}700 = 1.27 \times 10^4$

B The diameter of a human hair is approximately 0.00254 centimeters.

Move the decimal point in 0.00254 three places to the right: 0.0 0 2.5 4

$0.00254 = 2.54 \times 10^{-3}$

EXAMPLE 2

Find the quotient: $\dfrac{2.4 \times 10^7}{9.6 \times 10^3}$

Divide the multipliers: $2.4 \div 9.6 = 0.25$

Divide the powers of ten: $\dfrac{10^7}{10^3} = 10^{7-3} = 10^4$

Combine the answers and write the product in scientific notation.

$0.25 \times 10^4 = 0.25 \times (10 \times 10^3) = (0.25 \times 10) \times 10^3 = 2.5 \times 10^3$

EXERCISES

Write each number in scientific notation. (Lessons 2.2, 2.3)

1. 25,500,000 2.55×10^7

2. 0.00734 7.34×10^{-3}

Write each number in standard notation. (Lessons 2.2, 2.3)

3. 5.23×10^4 52,300

4. 1.33×10^{-5} 0.0000133

Simplify each expression. (Lessons 2.1, 2.4)

5. $(9 - 7)^3 \cdot 5^0 + (8 + 3)^2$ 129

6. $\dfrac{(4+2)^2}{[(9-3)^3]^2}$ $\dfrac{1}{1{,}296}$

7. $3.2 \times 10^5 + 1.25 \times 10^4 + 2.9 \times 10^5$

   6.225×10^5

8. $(2{,}600)(3.24 \times 10^4)$

   8.424×10^7

© Houghton Mifflin Harcourt Publishing Company

1. **CAREERS IN MATH** Astronomer An astronomer is studying Proxima Centauri, which is the closest star to our Sun. Proxima Centauri is 39,900,000,000,000,000 meters away.

   a. Write this distance in scientific notation.

   3.99×10^{16} m

   b. Light travels at a speed of 3.0×10^8 m/s (meters per second). How can you use this information to calculate the time in seconds it takes for light from Proxima Centauri to reach Earth? How many seconds does it take? Write your answer in scientific notation.

   Divide the distance Proxima Centauri is from Earth by the speed of light; 1.33×10^8 s

   c. Knowing that 1 year $= 3.1536 \times 10^7$ seconds, how many years does it take for light to travel from Proxima Centauri to Earth? Write your answer in standard notation. Round your answer to two decimal places.

   4.22 years

2. Cory is making a poster of common geometric shapes. He draws a square with a side of length 4^3 cm, an equilateral triangle with a height of $\sqrt{200}$ cm, a circle with a circumference of 8π cm, a rectangle with length $\frac{122}{5}$ cm, and a parallelogram with base 3.14 cm.

   a. Which of these numbers are irrational?

   $\sqrt{200}$ and 8π

   b. Write the numbers in this problem in order from least to greatest. Approximate π as 3.14.

   $3.14, \sqrt{200}, \frac{122}{5}, 8\pi, 4^3$

   c. Explain why 3.14 is rational, but π is not.

   3.14 is a terminating decimal that can be written in the form $\frac{a}{b}$: $\frac{314}{1000}$ or $\frac{157}{500}$. π is a nonrepeating, nonterminating decimal that cannot be written in the form $\frac{a}{b}$.

© Houghton Mifflin Harcourt Publishing Company

Performance Tasks

The Performance Tasks provide students with the opportunity to apply concepts from this unit in real-world problem situations.

CAREERS IN MATH

Astronomer

In Performance Task Item 1, students can see how an astronomer uses mathematics on the job.

Scoring Guides for Performance Tasks

1. **Mathematical Processes**

   MP.1, MP.4, MP.6

Task	Possible Points (Total: 6)
a	**1 point** for writing the correct number: 3.99×10^{16} m
b	**2 points** for explanation, for example: since $d = rt$, divide the distance from Earth by the speed of light and **1 point** for the correct answer: $s = 13,300,000$ or $s = 133 \times 10^8$ s
c	**1 point** for dividing answer to **b** by 3.1536×10^7 s, **1 point** for the correct answer: 4.22 years

2. **Mathematical Processes**

   MP.3, MP.4, MP.7

Task	Possible Points (Total: 6)
a	**2 points** for choosing correct numbers: $\sqrt{200}$ and 8π
b	**2 points** for correct order: $3.14, \sqrt{200}, \frac{122}{5}, 8\pi, 4^3$
c	**2 points** for correct explanation: Because 3.14 is a terminating decimal, it can be written as a ratio of two numbers: $\frac{314}{100} = \frac{157}{50}$. On the other hand, π is irrational because it is a nonterminating, nonrepeating decimal: 3.141592654…

Assessment Readiness

Assessment Readiness Tip

Students can work backwards to find solutions for more difficult questions.

- **Item 1** Students are asked to estimate the square root of 4,220. Rather than having to go through with guessing and checking, the students can check each multiple choice solution, squaring the numbers and seeing which pair gives numbers on either side of 4,220.

Avoid Common Errors

- **Item 3** Many students automatically look for what is true, even when the question asks for what is false because that is a natural instinct when dealing with multiple choice. Suggest that students highlight the word "false," reminding them that they are looking for the statement that is *incorrect*.

- **Item 10** Students may automatically choose the positive exponent of 2 because they moved the decimal two places. Remind them that a large number will have a positive exponent once placed in scientific notation, but a small number, like 0.025, will have a negative exponent.

Items	Grade 8 Lessons	Mathematical Processes
1*	9.3 (Grade 7), 1.1	MP.4
2	1.2	MP.7
3	1.2	MP.7
4	2.2	MP.4
5	1.1, 1.3	MP.7
6	1.1, 1.3	MP.7
7	1.3	MP.2
8	2.3	MP.2
9	2.2	MP.4
10	2.3	MP.4
11*	3.1 (Grade 7), 1.1	MP.5
12	1.1	MP.5
13	2.1	MP.2
14	2.2, 2.4	MP.1
15	2.4	MP.5
16	2.4	MP.5
17	1.1	MP.2
18	2.3	MP.1

* Item integrates mixed review concepts from previous modules or a previous course.

Assessment Readiness

Personal Math Trainer
Online Assessment and Intervention
my.hrw.com

Selected Response

1. A square on a large calendar has an area of 4,220 square millimeters. Between which two integers is the length of one side of the square?

- (A) between 20 and 21 millimeters
- (B) between 64 and 65 millimeters
- (C) between 204 and 205 millimeters
- (D) between 649 and 650 millimeters

2. Which of the following numbers is rational but **not** an integer?

- (A) −9
- (C) 0
- (B) −4.3
- (D) 3

3. Which statement is false?

- (A) No integers are irrational numbers.
- (B) All whole numbers are integers.
- (C) All rational numbers are real numbers.
- (D) All integers are whole numbers.

4. In 2011, the population of Laos was about 6.586×10^6 people. What is this number written in standard notation?

- (A) 6,586 people
- (B) 658,600 people
- (C) 6,586,000 people
- (D) 65,860,000 people

5. Which of the following is **not** true?

- (A) $\sqrt{16} + 4 > \sqrt{4} + 5$
- (B) $4\pi > 12$
- (C) $\sqrt{18} + 2 < \frac{15}{2}$
- (D) $6 - \sqrt{35} < 0$

6. Which number is between $\sqrt{50}$ and $\frac{5\pi}{2}$?

- (A) $\frac{22}{3}$
- (C) 6
- (B) $2\sqrt{8}$
- (D) $\pi + 3$

7. Which number is indicated on the number line?

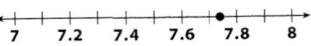

7   7.2   7.4   7.6   7.8   8

- (A) $\pi + 4$
- (B) $\frac{152}{20}$
- (C) $\sqrt{14} + 4$
- (D) $7.\overline{8}$

8. Which of the following is the number 5.03×10^{-5} written in standard form?

- (A) 503,000
- (B) 50,300,000
- (C) 0.00503
- (D) 0.0000503

9. In a recent year, about 20,700,000 passengers traveled by train in the United States. What is this number written in scientific notation?

- (A) 2.07×10^1 passengers
- (B) 2.07×10^4 passengers
- (C) 2.07×10^7 passengers
- (D) 2.07×10^8 passengers

10. A quarter weighs about 0.025 pounds. What is this weight written in scientific notation?

- (A) 2.5×10^{-2} pounds
- (B) 2.5×10^1 pounds
- (C) 2.5×10^{-1} pounds
- (D) 2.5×10^2 pounds

© Houghton Mifflin Harcourt Publishing Company

DIFFERENTIATE ASSESSMENT

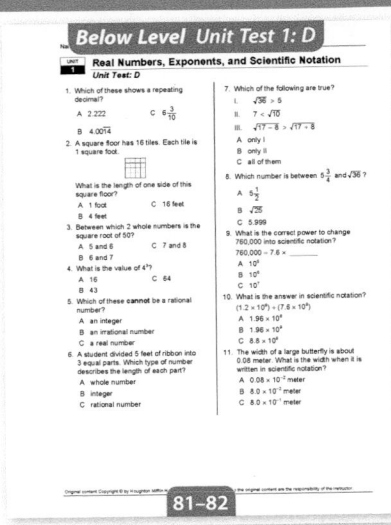

Below Level Unit Test 1: D

81–82

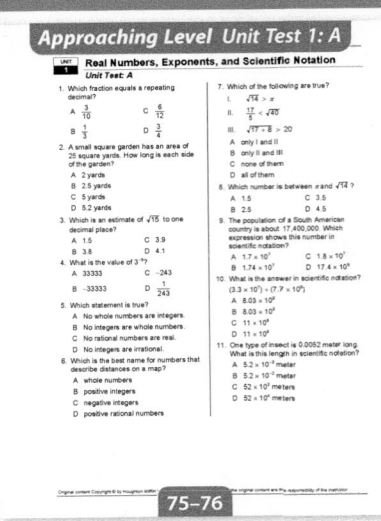

Approaching Level Unit Test 1: A

75–76

11. Which fraction is equivalent to $0.\overline{45}$?

Ⓐ $\frac{4}{9}$ Ⓒ $\frac{4}{5}$

Ⓑ $\frac{5}{9}$ Ⓓ $\frac{5}{11}$

12. What is the value of x if $x^2 = \frac{36}{81}$?

Ⓐ $\frac{2}{3}$ Ⓒ $\frac{4}{9}$

Ⓑ $\pm\frac{2}{3}$ Ⓓ $\pm\frac{4}{9}$

13. What is $\frac{[(9-2)^2]^4}{(4+3)^5}$ written in simplest form?

Ⓐ 7

Ⓑ 21

Ⓒ 49

Ⓓ 343

14. The total land area on Earth is about 6×10^7 square miles. The land area of Australia is about 3×10^6 square miles. About how many times larger is the land area on Earth than the land area of Australia?

Ⓐ 2

Ⓑ 10

Ⓒ 20

Ⓓ 60

15. What is the value of the expression $8.3 \times 10^4 - 2.5 \times 10^3 - 1.9 \times 10^4$ written in scientific notation?

Ⓐ 3.9×10^3

Ⓑ 3.9×10^4

Ⓒ 6.15×10^3

Ⓓ 6.15×10^4

16. What is the value of the expression $(2.3 \times 10^7)(1.4 \times 10^{-2})$ written in scientific notation?

Ⓐ 3.7×10^{-14}

Ⓑ 3.7×10^5

Ⓒ 0.322×10^6

Ⓓ 3.22×10^5

17. What is the value of $\sqrt[3]{64}$?

Ⓐ 2

Ⓑ 4

Ⓒ 8

Ⓓ 16

Mini-Task

18. Amanda says that a human fingernail has a thickness of about 4.2×10^{-4} meter. Justin says that a human fingernail has a thickness of about 0.42 millimeter.

a. What is the width in meters written in standard notation?

0.00042 m

b. Do Justin's and Amanda's measurements agree? Explain.

Yes; 0.00042 m × 1,000 mm/m = 0.42 mm

c. Explain why Justin's estimate of the thickness of a human fingernail is more appropriate than Amanda's estimate.

Sample answer: Since the thickness of a fingernail is a very small number, it is more appropriate to measure the thickness in millimeters than in meters.

© Houghton Mifflin Harcourt Publishing Company

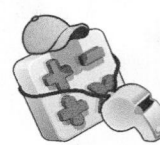

Personal Math Trainer

Online Assessment and Intervention

Additional Resources

Digital Teacher Resources

Go online for unit-level resources.

Assessment Resources

• Leveled Unit Tests: A, B, C, D
• Unit Performance Task

my.hrw.com

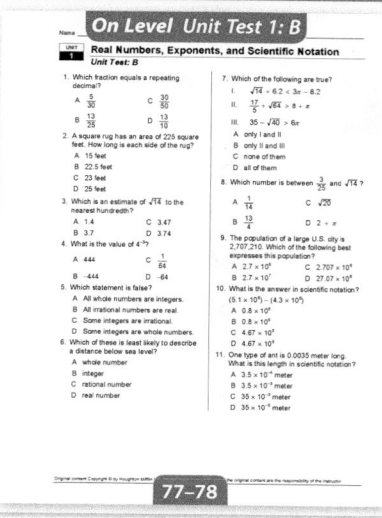

On Level *Unit Test 1: B*

Real Numbers, Exponents, and Scientific Notation
Unit Test: B

77–78

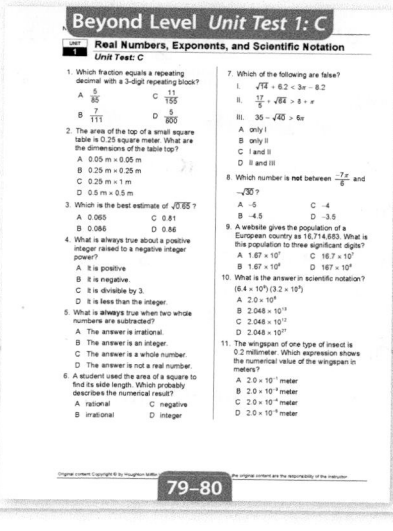

Beyond Level *Unit Test 1: C*

Real Numbers, Exponents, and Scientific Notation
Unit Test: C

79–80

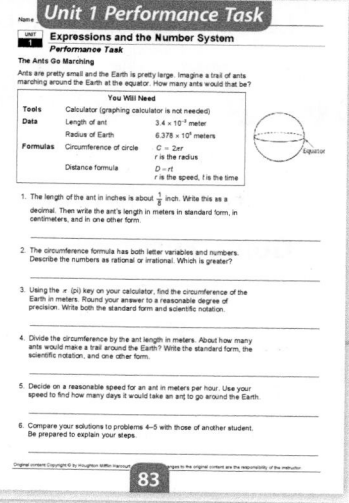

Unit 1 Performance Task

Expressions and the Number System
Performance Task

83

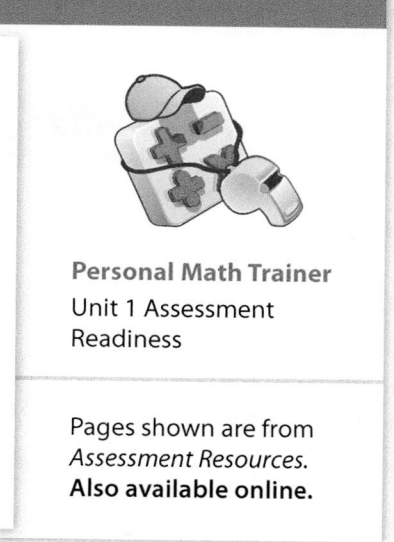

Personal Math Trainer

Unit 1 Assessment Readiness

Pages shown are from *Assessment Resources*.
Also available online.

Proportional and Nonproportional Relationships and Functions

Contents

PLANNING AND PACING GUIDE
Instructional Path

Lesson	Lesson Objectives	Pacing*
UNIT 2	**Proportional and Nonproportional Relationships and Functions**	
Progress Tracker 1 2 3 4 5 6		
MODULE 3	**Proportional Relationships**		1 day
3.1 Representing Proportional Relationships	Students will use tables, graphs, and equations to represent proportional situations.	2 days
3.2 Rate of Change and Slope **Going Further 3.2** Using Right Triangles to Explore Slope	Students will find a rate of change or a slope. Students will show that the slope of a non-vertical line is constant...	3 days
3.3 Interpreting the Unit Rate as Slope	Students will interpret the unit rate as slope.	2 days
**Ready to Go On?	Module 3 Assessment Readiness**		1 day
MODULE 4	**Nonproportional Relationships**		1 day
4.1 Representing Linear Nonproportional Relationships	Students will use tables, graphs, and equations to represent linear nonproportional situations.	2 days
4.2 Determining Slope and y-intercept	Students will determine the slope and the y-intercept of a line.	2 days
4.3 Graphing Linear Nonproportional Relationships Using Slope and y-intercept	Students will graph a line using the slope and y-intercept.	2 days
4.4 Proportional and Nonproportional Situations	Students will distinguish between proportional and nonproportional situations.	2 days
**Ready to Go On?	Module 4 Assessment Readiness**		1 day
MODULE 5	**Writing Linear Equations**		1 day
5.1 Writing Linear Equations from Situations and Graphs	Students will write an equation... given a graph or a description.	2 days
5.2 Writing Linear Equations from a Table	Students will write an equation... given a table.	2 days
5.3 Linear Relationships and Bivariate Data	Students will contrast linear and nonlinear sets of bivariate data.	3 days
**Ready to Go On?	Module 5 Assessment Readiness**		1 day
MODULE 6	**Functions**		1 day
6.1 Identifying and Representing Functions	Students will identify and represent functions.	2 days
6.2 Describing Functions **Going Further 6.2** Creating Nonlinear Functions **Activity 6.2** How Many Squares?	Students will describe functions. Students will create functions that are not linear. Students will create a function... for the number of... squares...	3 days
6.3 Comparing Functions **Going Further 6.3** Rate of Change and Initial Value	Students will use tables, graphs, and equations to compare functions. Students will interpret the rate of change and initial value... [in context].	3 days
6.4 Analyzing Graphs	Students will describe a relationship given a graph and [vice versa].	2 days
**Ready to Go On?	Module 6 Assessment Readiness**		1 day
**Study Guide Review	Unit 2 Assessment Readiness**		2 days

* Based on a 45-minute class period.

Teaching for Depth

Proportional Relationships and Slope

A proportional relationship is a special type of linear function, sometimes called a direct variation; it can be written in the form $y = kx$, where k is a nonzero constant. The constant k is called the constant of proportionality.

The graph of a proportional relationship is a straight line through the origin. The value of k is the slope of the line.

Proportional relationships can model many real-world situations, including **measurement conversions** (e.g., feet to inches) and **geometric relationships** (e.g., relationship between the circumference C and diameter d of a circle $C = \pi d$.

Nonproportional Relationships

A line that does not go through the origin represents a nonproportional linear relationship. If the x-intercept is a and the y-intercept is b, then $(a, 0)$ and $(0, b)$ are on the line, and the slope is: $m = \frac{b-0}{0-a} = -\frac{b}{a}$

Error Alert An intercept is a *value*, NOT a point.
The point $(a, 0)$ indicates that the x-intercept is the value a.
The point $(0, b)$ indicates that the y-intercept is the value b.

Slope

A slope can be positive, negative, zero, or undefined.

Positive slope

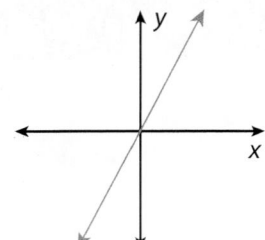

The line goes upward from left to right.

Negative slope

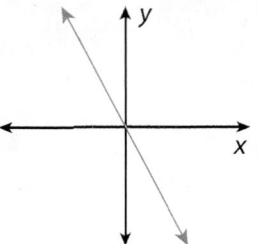

The line goes downward from left to right.

Zero slope

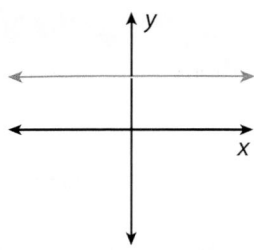

The line is horizontal.

Undefined slope

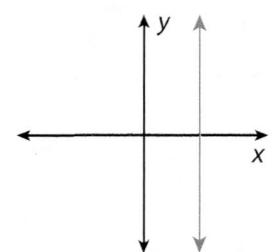

The line is vertical.

> *Mathematics involves penetrating techniques of thought that all people can use to solve problems, analyze situations, and sharpen the way they look at their world.*

EDWARD BURGER on Problem Solving Through Real-World Experiences

LESSON | 5.1

Nonproportional Relationships and Slope

The magnitude of the slope describes the steepness of the line. The line $y = x$ has a slope m of 1 and makes a 45° angle with the x-axis. A line whose slope has an absolute value between 0 and 1 is less steep than a 45° line. A line whose slope has an absolute value greater than 1 is steeper than a 45° line.

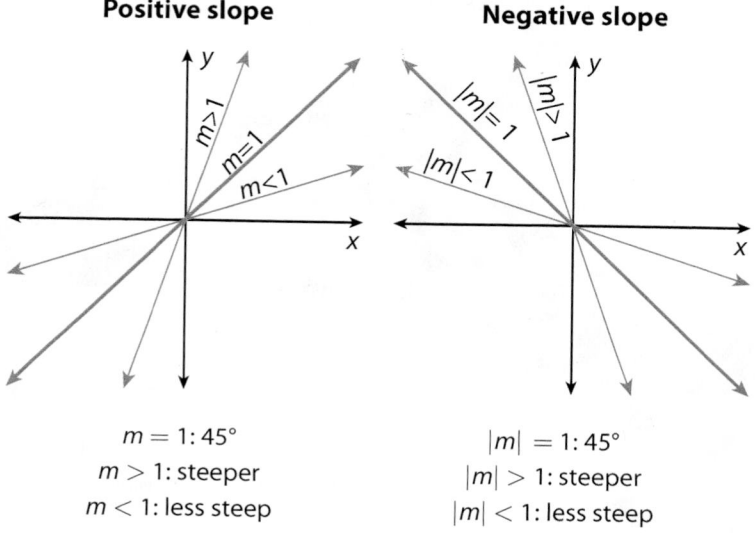

$m = 1$: 45°
$m > 1$: steeper
$m < 1$: less steep

$|m| = 1$: 45°
$|m| > 1$: steeper
$|m| < 1$: less steep

Professional Development Videos

Module 6: Functions

LESSON | 5.3

Using Bivariate Data to Approximate Values

Actual data from a relationship that tends to be somewhat linear will not be perfectly linear. A line of best fit can be used to approximate values from a real-world linear relationship. For example, a table of values generated from measurements such as temperature will not have a perfectly constant rate of change even if the relationship is generally linear in nature. Therefore, in order to approximate values in a relationship that is generally linear in nature, the ordered pairs can be plotted and a line of best fit can be drawn through them. Then the slope and y-intercept of the line of best fit can be used to write an equation that approximately describes the relationship.

LESSON | 6.1

Reasonable Domain Values

The set of all inputs for a function is called the domain. The set of all outputs of a function is called the range. For many functions the domain is the set of real numbers. However, the domain is sometimes restricted to represent real-world situations. For example, in a function that describes the costs to buy tickets, the domain may be restricted to nonnegative real numbers because negative numbers of tickets do not make sense.

LESSON | 6.2

Comparing Functions

Linear functions, such as $y = x$ and $y = 4x + 5$, are called first-degree equations because the greatest power of the variable x is 1. Quadratic functions, such as $y = x^2$ and $y = 4x^2 + 2x + 5$, are called second-degree equations because the greatest power of x is 2. Cubic functions, such as $y = x^3$ and $y = 4x^3 + x^2 + 3x + 5$, are called third-degree equations because the greatest power of x is 3.

UNIT 2
Proportional and Nonproportional Relationships and Functions

CAREERS IN MATH

Cost Estimator

Cost estimators need to accurately estimate the cost of projects such as manufacturing a product or constructing a building, taking into account prices of materials, labor costs, and all other factors that might influence the cost of a project. You will learn more about this in the Performance Tasks at the end of the unit.

For more information about careers in mathematics as well as various mathematics appreciation topics, visit the American Mathematical Society at www.ams.org.

UNIT 2
Proportional and Nonproportional Relationships and Functions

MODULE 3
Proportional Relationships

MODULE 4
Nonproportional Relationships

MODULE 5
Writing Linear Equations

MODULE 6
Functions

CAREERS IN MATH

Cost Estimator A cost estimator determines the cost of a product or project, which helps businesses decide whether or not to manufacture a product or build a structure. Cost estimators analyze the costs of labor, materials, and use of equipment, among other things. Cost estimators use math when they assemble and analyze data. If you are interested in a career as a cost estimator, you should study these mathematical subjects:
- Algebra
- Trigonometry
- Calculus

Research other careers that require analyzing costs.

Unit 2 Performance Task

At the end of the unit, check out how **cost estimators** use math.

Vocabulary Preview

Use the puzzle to preview key vocabulary from this unit. Unscramble the circled letters within the found words to answer the riddle at the bottom of the page.

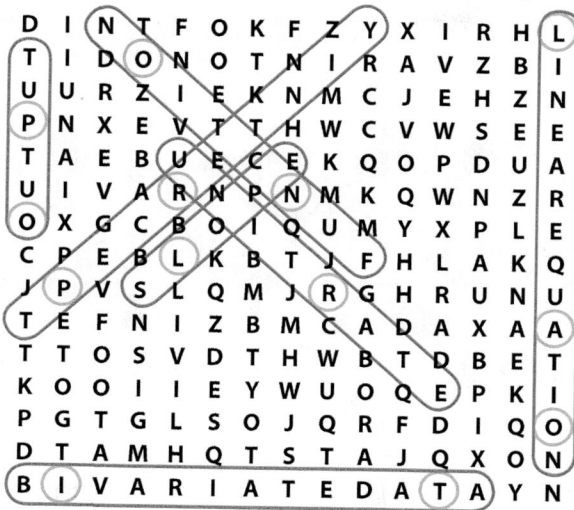

- The *y*-coordinate of the point where the graph crosses the *y*-axis. (Lesson 4.2) *y*-intercept
- A rule that assigns exactly one output to each input. (Lesson 6.1) function
- The result after applying the function machine's rule. (Lesson 6.1) output
- A rate in which the second quantity in the comparison is one unit. (Lesson 3.3) unit rate
- The ratio of change in rise to the corresponding change in run on a graph. (Lesson 3.2) slope
- A set of data that is made up of two paired variables. (Lesson 5.3) bivariate data
- An equation whose solutions form a straight line on a coordinate plane. (Lesson 4.1) linear equation

Q: How much of the money earned does a professional sports team pay its star athlete?

A: An A L L   P R O - P O R T I O N !

© Houghton Mifflin Harcourt Publishing Company

Vocabulary Preview

Use the puzzle to give students a preview of important concepts in this unit. Students may work individually, in pairs, or in groups.

Digital Teacher Resources

Go online for unit-level resources.

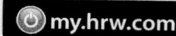

my.hrw.com

LEARNING PROGRESSIONS AND STANDARDS ACROSS THE GRADES

Before

Students understand proportional relationships:

- rates and proportionality
- linear relationships represented by tables, graphs, or equations
- constant rates of change represented by tables, descriptions, equations, or graphs

In this Unit

Students will learn about:

- linear proportional and nonproportional relationships
- unit rate and slope
- constant of proportionality
- direct variation
- equations in the form $y = mx + b$
- systems of equations
- functions

After

Students will connect:

- proportional relationships and constant rate of change
- proportionality and direct variation
- linear relationships and their graphs and equations in the form $y = mx + b$

Proportional and Nonproportional Relationships and Functions **66**

Module At A Glance

MODULE 3 | Proportional Relationships

Lessons at A Glance	Lesson 3.1 Representing Proportional Relationships	Lesson 3.2 Rate of Change and Slope	Lesson 3.3 Interpreting the Unit Rate as Slope
	Pg. T71A	Pg. T77A	Pg. T83A
Essential Question	How can you use tables, graphs, and equations to represent proportional situations?	How do you find a rate of change or a slope?	How do you interpret the unit rate as slope?
Objective	Students will use tables, graphs, and equations to represent proportional situations.	Students will find a rate of change or a slope.	Students will interpret the unit rate as slope.
Vocabulary	constant of proportionality, proportional relationship	rate of change, slope	unit rate

Go online for all your module resources my.hrw.com	3.1 *i*Student Edition 3.1 *i*Teacher Edition 3.1 *e*Student Edition 🐾 Personal Math Trainer 📺 Math on the Spot Videos	3.2 *i*Student Edition 3.2 *i*Teacher Edition 3.2 *e*Student Edition 🐾 Personal Math Trainer 📺 Math on the Spot Videos	3.3 *i*Student Edition 3.3 *i*Teacher Edition 3.3 *e*Student Edition 🐾 Personal Math Trainer 📺 Math on the Spot Videos 📊 Animated Math
Print Resources	**3.1 Student Edition**: Lesson *Differentiated Instruction* 3.1 Practice and Problem Solving A/B, C, and D 3.1 Reteach 3.1 Reading Strategies 3.1 Success for English Learners	**3.2 Student Edition**: Lesson **3.2 Student Edition**: Going Further *Differentiated Instruction* 3.2 Practice and Problem Solving A/B, C, and D 3.2 Reteach 3.2 Reading Strategies 3.2 Success for English Learners	**3.3 Student Edition**: Lesson *Differentiated Instruction* 3.3 Practice and Problem Solving A/B, C, and D 3.3 Reteach 3.3 Reading Strategies 3.3 Success for English Learners

Response to Intervention

	Before the Module	During the Lesson	After the Module
	Are You Ready	**Guided/Independent Practice**	**Ready to Go On?**
	• Prerequisite Skills Activities • Personal Math Trainer	• Reteach • Personal Math Trainer • Practice and Problem Solving D	• Reteach • Personal Math Trainer

Teacher Notes

Proportional Relationships

🔵 **Real-World Video Viewing Guide**

After students have watched the video, discuss the following:

• What two measurements are used to find the speed, or rate, of each boat? distance and time

• Which boat gives the steepest line on the graph in the video? the research boat

Professional Development Video

Author Juli Dixon models successful teaching practices as she explores the concept of proportional relationships in an actual eighth-grade classroom.

© Houghton Mifflin Harcourt Publishing Company • Image Credits: ©Angelo Giampiccolo/Shutterstock

Proportional Relationships

? ESSENTIAL QUESTION

How can you use proportional relationships to solve real-world problems?

You can solve problems about real-world proportional relationships by analyzing tables, equations, and graphs that represent them.

LESSON 3.1
Representing Proportional Relationships

LESSON 3.2
Rate of Change and Slope

LESSON 3.3
Interpreting the Unit Rate as Slope

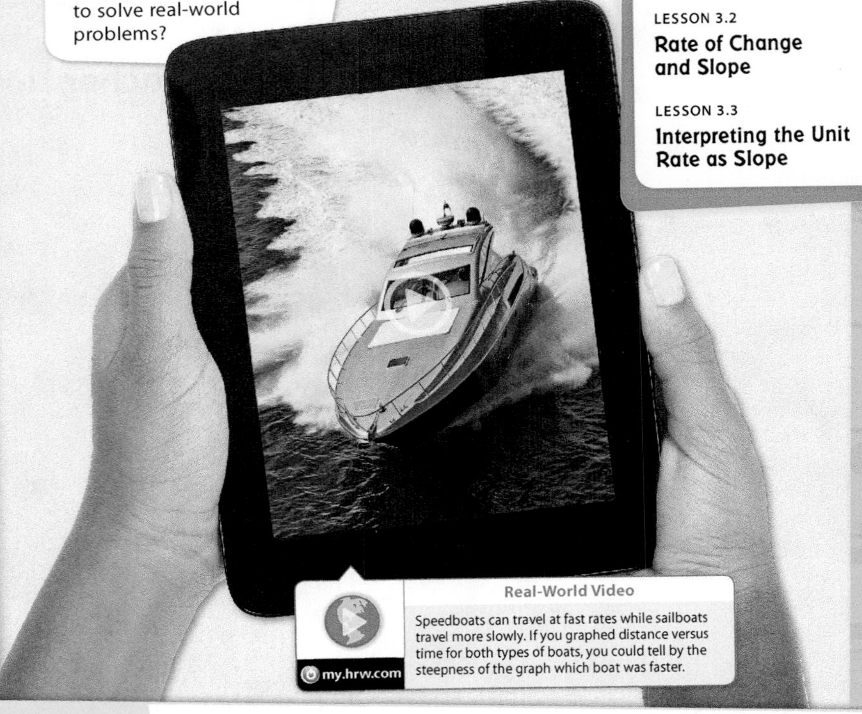

Real-World Video

Speedboats can travel at fast rates while sailboats travel more slowly. If you graphed distance versus time for both types of boats, you could tell by the steepness of the graph which boat was faster.

▶ my.hrw.com

GO DIGITAL
my.hrw.com

my.hrw.com
Go digital with your write-in student edition, accessible on any device.

Math On the Spot
Scan with your smart phone to jump directly to the online edition, video tutor, and more.

Animated Math
Interactively explore key concepts to see how math works.

Personal Math Trainer
Get immediate feedback and help as you work through practice sets.

67

TEACHER ONLINE RESOURCES

 ONLINE TEACHER EDITION Access a full suite of teaching resources online—plan, present, and manage classes and assignments.

 INTERACTIVE WHITEBOARDS Engage students with interactive whiteboard-ready examples and a lesson quiz for each lesson.

 MY SMART PLANNER Easily plan your classes and access all your resources online.

 PERSONAL MATH TRAINER: Online Assessment and Intervention Assign automatically graded homework, quizzes, tests, and intervention activities. Prepare your students for standardized tests in short-answer and multiple-choice formats.

Reading Start-Up

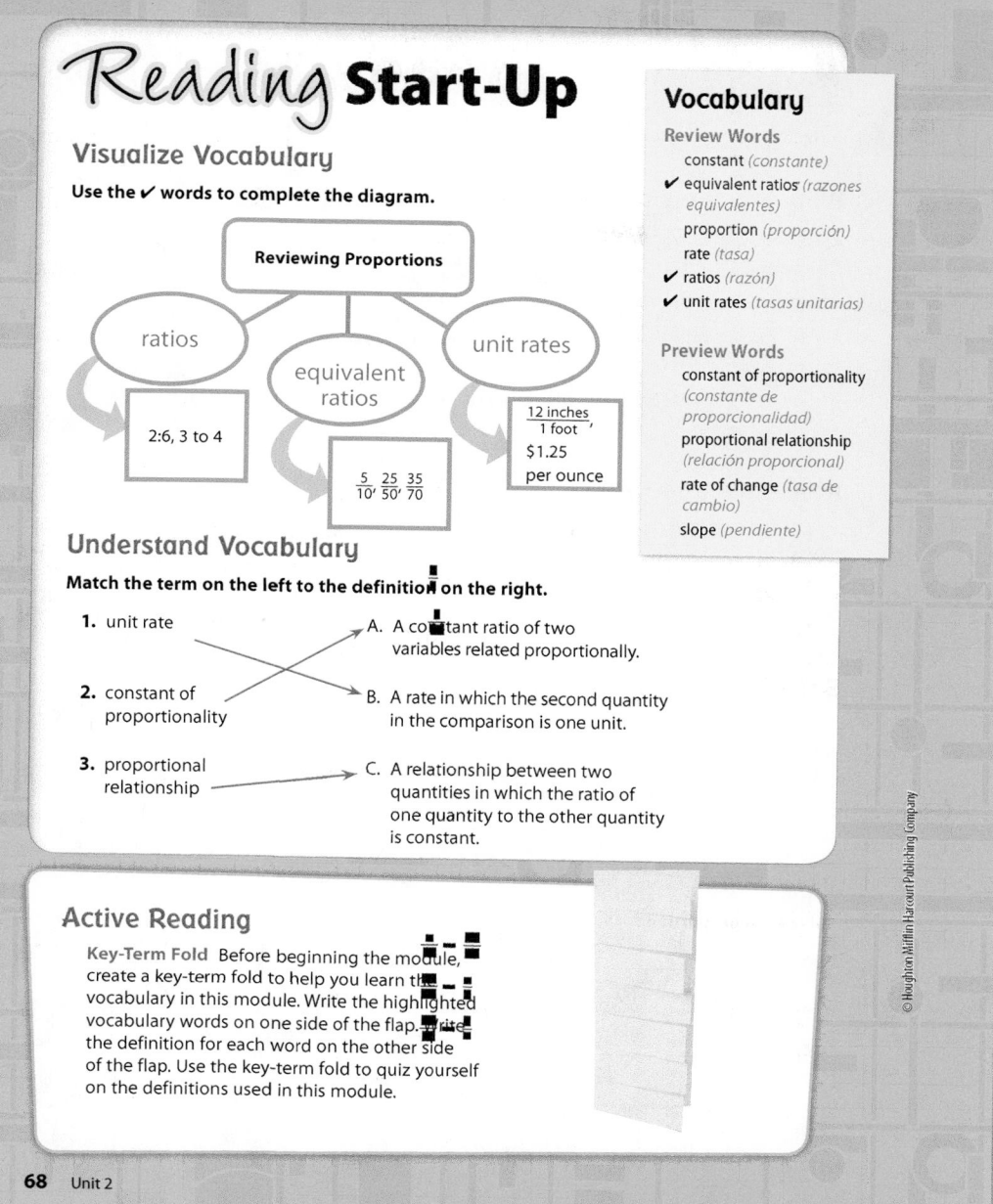

Visualize Vocabulary

Use the ✔ words to complete the diagram.

Reviewing Proportions

ratios

equivalent ratios

unit rates

2:6, 3 to 4

$\frac{5}{10}, \frac{25}{50}, \frac{35}{70}$

$\frac{12 \text{ inches}}{1 \text{ foot}}$, $1.25 per ounce

Understand Vocabulary

Match the term on the left to the definition on the right.

1. unit rate

2. constant of proportionality

3. proportional relationship

A. A constant ratio of two variables related proportionally.

B. A rate in which the second quantity in the comparison is one unit.

C. A relationship between two quantities in which the ratio of one quantity to the other quantity is constant.

© Houghton Mifflin Harcourt Publishing Company

Active Reading

Key-Term Fold Before beginning the module, create a key-term fold to help you learn the vocabulary in this module. Write the highlighted vocabulary words on one side of the flap. Write the definition for each word on the other side of the flap. Use the key-term fold to quiz yourself on the definitions used in this module.

Vocabulary

Review Words
constant (*constante*)
✔ equivalent ratios (*razones equivalentes*)
proportion (*proporción*)
rate (*tasa*)
✔ ratios (*razón*)
✔ unit rates (*tasas unitarias*)

Preview Words
constant of proportionality (*constante de proporcionalidad*)
proportional relationship (*relación proporcional*)
rate of change (*tasa de cambio*)
slope (*pendiente*)

Reading Start-Up

Visualize Vocabulary
The case diagram will help students to review concepts related to proportions. Students should write one review word in each bubble.

Understand Vocabulary
Use the following explanation to help students learn the preview words.

> ***Proportional relationships*** *can be used in many everyday situations. For example, if you need 1.5 hours to study 2 math lessons, you can figure out how much time you need to study 6 math lessons. If you know that 2 math lessons require 1.5 hours, then 4 math lessons require 3 hours, and 6 math lessons require 4.5 hours.*

> *In this lesson, you will learn how to use the* ***constant of proportionality*** *to find proportional relationships.*

Active Reading

Integrating Language Arts
Students can use these reading and note-taking strategies to help them organize and understand new concepts and vocabulary.

Additional Resources
Differentiated Instruction
- Reading Strategies **ELL**
- Interactive multilingual glossary

LEARNING PROGRESSIONS ACROSS THE GRADES

Before	In this Module	After
Students understand rates and proportional relationships: • find unit rate • use tables and verbal descriptions to represent two variable relationships • write and graph a linear relationship	Students represent and solve problems involving proportional relationships: • represent linear proportional situations with tables, graphs, and equations • use data from a table or graph to determine the rate of change or slope and *y*-intercept in mathematical and real-world problems • graph proportional relationships, interpreting the unit rate as the slope of the line that models the relationship	Students will connect: • proportional relationships with constant rate of change • proportionality and direct variation

Are You Ready?

Assess Readiness

Access *Are You Ready?* assessment online, and receive instant scoring, feedback, and customized intervention or enrichment.

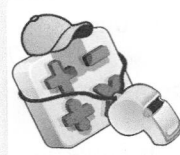

Personal Math Trainer

Online Assessment and Intervention

Additional Resources

Digital Teacher Resources

Go online for module-level resources.

my.hrw.com

Personal Math Trainer
Online Assessment and Intervention
my.hrw.com

Complete these exercises to review skills you will need for this module.

Write Fractions as Decimals

EXAMPLE $\frac{1.7}{2.5} = ?$

Multiply the numerator and the denominator by a power of 10 so that the denominator is a whole number.

$$\frac{1.7 \times 10}{2.5 \times 10} = \frac{17}{25}$$

Write the fraction as a division problem. Write a decimal point and zeros in the dividend.
Place a decimal point in the quotient. Divide as with whole numbers.

```
        0.68
   25)17.00
      −150
        200
      −200
          0
```

Write each fraction as a decimal.

1. $\frac{3}{8}$ ___0.375___
2. $\frac{0.3}{0.4}$ ___0.75___
3. $\frac{0.13}{0.2}$ ___0.65___
4. $\frac{0.39}{0.75}$ ___0.52___
5. $\frac{4}{5}$ ___0.8___
6. $\frac{0.1}{2}$ ___0.05___
7. $\frac{3.5}{14}$ ___0.25___
8. $\frac{7}{14}$ ___0.5___
9. $\frac{0.3}{10}$ ___0.03___

Solve Proportions

EXAMPLE $\frac{5}{7} = \frac{x}{14}$

$$\frac{5 \times 2}{7 \times 2} = \frac{x}{14}$$

$7 \times 2 = 14$, so multiply the numerator and denominator by 2.

$$\frac{10}{14} = \frac{x}{14}$$

$5 \times 2 = 10$

$x = 10$

Solve each proportion for x.

10. $\frac{20}{18} = \frac{10}{x}$ ___$x = 9$___
11. $\frac{x}{12} = \frac{30}{72}$ ___$x = 5$___
12. $\frac{x}{4} = \frac{4}{16}$ ___$x = 1$___
13. $\frac{11}{x} = \frac{132}{120}$ ___$x = 10$___
14. $\frac{36}{48} = \frac{x}{4}$ ___$x = 3$___
15. $\frac{x}{9} = \frac{21}{27}$ ___$x = 7$___
16. $\frac{24}{16} = \frac{x}{2}$ ___$x = 3$___
17. $\frac{30}{15} = \frac{6}{x}$ ___$x = 3$___
18. $\frac{3}{x} = \frac{18}{36}$ ___$x = 6$___

© Houghton Mifflin Harcourt Publishing Company

Module 3 **69**

ARE YOU READY? *Diagnostic Assessment*

RtI Response to Intervention

Use to determine if students need intervention for the module's prerequisite skills.

Skill	Missed More Than . . .	Intervene With *Skills Intervention* worksheets (available online)	For Enrichment *Differentiated Instruction* (available in print and online)
Write Fractions as Decimals	2 questions	**Skill 26** Write Fractions as Decimals	**Module 3 Challenge** Extend-the-Math Lesson Activities in TE
Solve Proportions	5 questions	**Skill 65** Solve Proportions	**Module 3 Challenge** Extend-the-Math Lesson Activities in TE

Complete these exercises to review skills you will need for this module.

Write Fractions as Decimals

19. Carlo invested in a mutual fund. The value of his investment increased by $\frac{1}{16}$ in one month, and then decreased by $\frac{1}{25}$ the next month. Write these fractions as decimals. Explain your method.

To find equivalent decimals, write each fraction as a division problem. Write a decimal point and zeros in the dividend. Place a decimal point in the quotient, and then divide as with whole numbers.

$$16)\overline{1.0000} = 0.0625$$
$$-96$$
$$40$$
$$-32$$
$$80$$
$$-80$$
$$0$$

$$25)\overline{1.00} = 0.04$$
$$-100$$
$$0$$

The value increased by 0.0625 and then decreased by 0.04.

20. Kay knows that the first step for writing $\frac{0.48}{6.4}$ in decimal form is to change the denominator to a whole number. Explain how she can do so without changing the value of the fraction. Then use long division to find the decimal value.

To make the denominator a whole number, multiply both the numerator and the denominator by 10:

$$\frac{0.48 \times 10}{6.4 \times 10} = \frac{4.8}{64}$$

$$64)\overline{4.800} = 0.075$$
$$-448$$
$$320$$
$$-320$$
$$0$$

The decimal value is 0.075.

Solve Proportions

21. An architect solved the proportion below in order to complete a scale drawing. Describe how to solve the proportion. Then find x.

$$\frac{12}{15} = \frac{36}{x}$$

Think of what number multiplied by 12 gives 36 in the numerator, and multiply the denominator by that number. Since $12 \times 3 = 36$, the denominator must also be multiplied by 3: $\frac{12 \times 3}{15 \times 3} = \frac{36}{45}$, so the proportion can be rewritten as $\frac{36}{45} = \frac{36}{x}$. The solution is $x = 45$.

© Houghton Mifflin Harcourt Publishing Company

Write Fractions as Decimals

Exercise 19 Make sure students do not misplace the decimal point or forget to write it in the quotient.

Exercise 20 Remind students that all decimals can be written as fractions with denominators of 10, 100, 1,000, and so on. Make sure students understand that multiplying a fraction by $\frac{10}{10}$ does not change its value because $\frac{10}{10} = 1$.

Solve Proportions

Exercise 21 Some students may first find the simplest form of $\frac{12}{15}$ and then multiply the numerator and denominator by 9. Encourage students to compare the methods they used to find the value of x.

Use to determine if students are able to apply the module's prerequisite skills.

Skill	Exercise	Depth of Knowledge (D.O.K.)	Mathematical Processes
Write Fractions as Decimals	19	**3** Strategic Thinking	**MP.1** Problem Solving
	20	**2** Skills/Concepts	**MP.2** Abstract and Quantitative Reasoning
Solve Proportions	21	**3** Strategic Thinking	**MP.7** See Structure

Lesson Support

Content Objective Students will use tables, graphs, and equations to represent proportional situations.

Professional Development

Integrate Mathematical Processes MP.4

This lesson provides an opportunity to address this Mathematical Processes standard. It calls for students to use tables and equations to model a relationship between corresponding real-world proportional values. Then students use graphs to visualize the proportional relationship and to create tables to model the relationship. In this way, students are able to use multiple representations to model real-world situations.

FOCUS

Building Background

Eliciting Prior Knowledge Have students work with a partner and review the meaning of a ratio and a proportion. If necessary, remind them that equal ratios form a proportion. Ask students to give several examples of ratios that form true proportions and ratios that do not form proportions. Have them explain their examples.

True proportion:	Not a proportion:
$\frac{2}{3} = \frac{6}{9}$	$\frac{2}{3} \neq \frac{6}{12}$

COHERENCE

Learning Progressions

In this lesson, students use tables, graphs, and equations to represent proportional situations. Important understandings for students include the following:

- **Represent proportional relationships with tables.**
- **Represent proportional relationships with equations.**
- **Identify the constant of proportionality as the multiplicative factor in a proportional relationship.**
- **Represent proportional relationships with graphs.**

Students begin to synthesize ideas about proportional relationships, which they have been developing for several years. These ideas are important in helping students develop an understanding of functions, which will be explored further throughout the year.

RIGOR

Cluster Connections

This lesson provides an excellent opportunity to connect ideas in the cluster:

Understand the connections between proportional relationships, lines, and linear equations.

Give students the following prompt: "It takes Alphonso 2 minutes to run 0.25 mile." Have students use the information to make a table and write an equation that shows the rate at which Alphonso runs. Discuss how students completed the table and identified the corresponding equation.

$y = 8x$, where y is the distance in miles and x is the time in minutes.

x	2	4	6	8
y	0.25	0.5	0.75	1

Language Support ELL

Language Objective Students will show how to use tables, graphs, and equations to represent proportional situations.

Leveled Strategies for English Learners ELL

Emerging
Have students use sentence frames to discuss ratios from a ratio table.

> *Meghan earns $12 per hour. In 1 hour, she earns _____ dollars.*
> *In 2 hours, she earns _____ dollars.*
> *In 3 hours, she earns _____ dollars.*

Expanding
Have students find examples of sentences in the text that use the term *per*. Have students state the ratio or proportional relationship in a complete sentence.

Bridging
Have students create their own word problems about real-world proportional relationships and create a chart to represent a data set to show the relationship. Then, they can write out a narrative description of the chart using complete sentences.

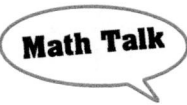

Use current exchange rates from various countries to include students' own country of origin. Other examples are conversions from the metric system to standard measurements, such as Fahrenheit to Celsius and kilos to pounds.

Number of hours	1	2	4	8
Amount earned ($)	12	24	48	96

Linguistic Support ELL

Idioms and Expressions
English uses different structures and expressions in common language to describe the concept of *per* for proportional relationships. For example, *$12 an hour* and *$12 per hour* mean the same thing. Point out these expressions that mean the same thing but are phrased differently, and have students rephrase expressions using *per*. Spanish-speakers will be familiar with the use of *por* to express these relationships.

Academic/Content Vocabulary
The term *constant* is important for describing proportional relationships. Give students several common-language words and phrases to express the notion of constancy. Examples are *does not change* and *stays the same* to define and explain the concept and math symbol for *constant of proportionality*. Using examples from the text, have students verbalize the concepts shown in a ratio chart in complete sentences. Translating the ratio chart into common language also allows for explicit teaching of terms like *hourly rate* that may be unfamiliar to some students.

1 Engage

❓ ESSENTIAL QUESTION

How can you use tables, graphs, and equations to represent proportional situations? Sample answer: If the ratio between one quantity and another is constant, you can use tables, graphs, and equations of the form $y = kx$ to represent a proportional relationship between the quantities.

Motivate the Lesson

Ask: The circumference of Earth is about 25,000 miles. How many miles did the Nautilus travel in *20,000 Leagues Under the Sea?* Begin the Explore Activity to find out.

2 Explore

EXPLORE ACTIVITY

Focus on Patterns

Point out to students that they can use a pattern to complete the table relating the distance in leagues to the distance in miles. A pattern is multiply the distance in leagues by 3 to get the number of miles (or divide miles by 3 to find leagues).

LESSON
3.1 Representing Proportional Relationships

8.2.3.1
Students will use tables, graphs, and equations to represent proportional situations.

❓ **ESSENTIAL QUESTION** How can you use tables, graphs, and equations to represent proportional situations?

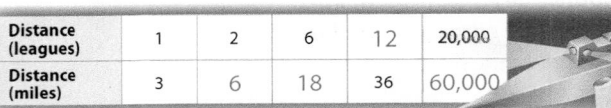

EXPLORE ACTIVITY *Real World*

Representing Proportional Relationships with Tables

In 1870, the French writer Jules Verne published *20,000 Leagues Under the Sea*, one of the most popular science fiction novels ever written. One definition of a *league* is a unit of measure equaling 3 miles.

A Complete the table.

Distance (leagues)	1	2	6	12	20,000
Distance (miles)	3	6	18	36	60,000

B What relationships do you see among the numbers in the table?

Every number in the bottom row is 3 times the number in the top row.

C For each column of the table, find the ratio of the distance in miles to the distance in leagues. Write each ratio in simplest form.

$$\frac{3}{1} = \boxed{\frac{3}{1}} \qquad \frac{6}{2} = \boxed{\frac{3}{1}} \qquad \frac{18}{6} = \boxed{\frac{3}{1}} \qquad \frac{36}{12} = \boxed{\frac{3}{1}} \qquad \frac{60,000}{20,000} = \boxed{\frac{3}{1}}$$

D What do you notice about the ratios? They are all equal to $\frac{3}{1}$.

Reflect

1. If you know the distance between two points in leagues, how can you find the distance in miles? Multiply the distance in leagues by 3.

2. If you know the distance between two points in miles, how can you find the distance in leagues? Divide the distance in miles by 3.

© Houghton Mifflin Harcourt Publishing Company

Lesson 3.1　**71**

DIFFERENTIATE INSTRUCTION *Leveled Questions*

	EXPLORE ACTIVITY
AL DOK 1 *Recall*	What is the ratio of distance in leagues to distance in miles for each column? Are they all equal? All are $\frac{1}{3}$; yes
OL DOK 2 *Skills/Concepts*	If the ratio of distance in miles to distance in leagues is always 3:1, how can you find the distance in miles that corresponds to 8 leagues? Set up and solve a proportion, such as $\frac{3}{1} = \frac{x}{8}$; $x = 24$. So, 24 miles corresponds to 8 leagues.
BL DOK 3 *Strategic Thinking*	Suppose the distances in the bottom row of the table were in feet instead of miles. Would this still be a proportional relationship? Justify your reasoning. Yes; since there are 5,280 feet in each mile, each number in the bottom row will be 3(5,280) = 15,840 times the corresponding number in the top row.

Math On the Spot
my.hrw.com

Representing Proportional Relationships with Equations

The ratio of the distance in miles to the distance in leagues is constant. This relationship is said to be *proportional*. A **proportional relationship** is a relationship between two quantities in which the ratio of one quantity to the other quantity is constant.

A proportional relationship can be described by an equation of the form $y = kx$, where k is a number called the **constant of proportionality**.

Sometimes it is useful to use another form of the equation, $k = \frac{y}{x}$.

EXAMPLE 1

Meghan earns $12 an hour at her part-time job. Show that the relationship between the amount she earned and the number of hours she worked is a proportional relationship. Then write an equation for the relationship.

Sample answer: The relationship between x, an amount of money in quarters, and y, the same amount in cents.

STEP 1 Make a table relating amount earned to number of hours.

> For every hour Meghan works, she earns $12. So, for 8 hours of work, she earns 8 × $12 = $96.

Number of hours	1	2	4	8
Amount earned ($)	12	24	48	96

STEP 2 For each number of hours, write the relationship of the amount earned and the number of hours as a ratio in simplest form.

$\frac{\text{amount earned}}{\text{number of hours}}$ $\frac{12}{1} = \frac{12}{1}$ $\frac{24}{2} = \frac{12}{1}$ $\frac{48}{4} = \frac{12}{1}$ $\frac{96}{8} = \frac{12}{1}$

Since the ratios for the two quantities are all equal to $\frac{12}{1}$, the relationship is proportional.

Math Talk
Mathematical Processes

Describe two real-world quantities with a proportional relationship that can be described by the equation $y = 25x$.

STEP 3 Write an equation.

> First tell what the variables represent.

Let x represent the number of hours.
Let y represent the amount earned.

Use the ratio as the constant of proportionality in the equation $y = kx$.

The equation is $y = \frac{12}{1}x$ or $y = 12x$.

Personal Math Trainer
Online Assessment and Intervention
my.hrw.com

YOUR TURN

3. Fifteen bicycles are produced each hour at the Speedy Bike Works. Show that the relationship between the number of bikes produced and the number of hours is a proportional relationship. Then write an equation for the relationship.

$y = 15x$

© Houghton Mifflin Harcourt Publishing Company

3 Explain

EXAMPLE 1

ADDITIONAL EXAMPLE 1 Marco earns $36.50 per hour as an accountant. Show that the relationship between the amount he earns and the number of hours he works is a proportional relationship. Then write an equation for the relationship.

$\frac{\text{amount earned}}{\text{number of hours}} = 36.5 \underline{\quad} 1 = 73 \underline{\quad} 2 = 146 \underline{\quad} 4 = 292 \underline{\quad}_8 = 36.5;$

$y = 36.5x$, where x is the number of hours, and y is the amount earned.

 Interactive Whiteboard
Interactive example available online

YOUR TURN   MP.4

Avoid Common Errors
Make sure that students divide the number of bicycles by the number of hours, not the number of hours by the number of bicycles.

	EXAMPLE 1
AL **DOK 1** *Recall*	In Step 2, which row of the table is the numerator of each ratio, and which row is the denominator? Bottom row numerator; top row denominator
OL **DOK 2** *Skills/Concepts*	At the end of 6 months, Meghan will receive a raise of $1 per hour. How will this change the equation for the relationship between number of hours worked and amount earned? It will become $y = 13x$.
BL **DOK 3** *Strategic Thinking*	In Step 3, if you had let x represent the amount earned, what would be the constant of proportionality and what would it represent? What would be the unit rate? $\frac{1}{12}$; 1 hour per 12 dollars; $\frac{1}{12}$ hour, or 5 minutes, per dollar.

TEACHER TO TEACHER

Multiple Representations Point out to students any point on the graph of a proportional relationship can be used to determine the constant of proportionality. A proportional relationship is $y = kx$, where k is the constant of proportionality. Because the coordinates of any point on the graph satisfy $y = kx$, then $k = \frac{y}{x}$ can be found using any point on the graph.

EXAMPLE 2

ADDITIONAL EXAMPLE 2 The graph shows the relationship between the number of days a car is rented and the total cost for the rental. Write an equation for this relationship. $y = 33\frac{1}{3}x$

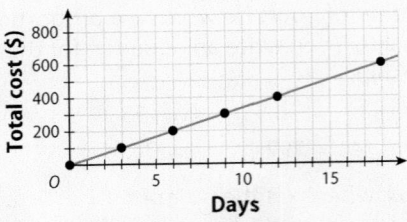

 Interactive Whiteboard
Interactive example available online

YOUR TURN MP.7

Focus on Math Connections
Make sure that students understand the connections between the rate 6 miles in 5 hours, the point (5, 6), the constant of proportionality $\frac{6}{5}$, and the equation $y = \frac{6}{5}x$.

 **Digital Teacher Resources**

Go online to access all your lesson-level resources.

Differentiated Instruction
• Reteach
• Reading Strategies
• Success for English Learners
• Practice and Problem Solving A/B, C, D

Math on the Spot Videos

my.hrw.com

Representing Proportional Relationships with Graphs

You can represent a proportional relationship with a graph. The graph will be a line that passes through the origin (0, 0). The graph shows the relationship between distance measured in miles to distance measured in leagues.

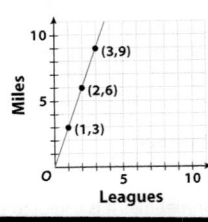

Math On the Spot
my.hrw.com

EXAMPLE 2 Real World

The graph shows the relationship between the weight of an object on the Moon and its weight on Earth. Write an equation for this relationship.

STEP 1 Use the points on the graph to make a table.

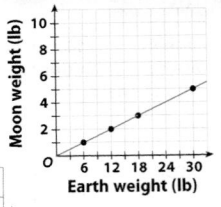

Earth weight (lb)	6	12	18	30
Moon weight (lb)	1	2	3	5

STEP 2 Find the constant of proportionality.

$\frac{\text{Moon weight}}{\text{Earth weight}}$ $\frac{1}{6} = \frac{1}{6}$ $\frac{2}{12} = \frac{1}{6}$ $\frac{3}{18} = \frac{1}{6}$ $\frac{5}{30} = \frac{1}{6}$

The constant of proportionality is $\frac{1}{6}$.

STEP 3 Write an equation.

Let x represent weight on Earth.

Let y represent weight on the Moon.

The equation is $y = \frac{1}{6}x$.   Replace k with $\frac{1}{6}$ in $y = kx$.

YOUR TURN

The graph shows the relationship between the amount of time that a backpacker hikes and the distance traveled.

4. What does the point (5, 6) represent?
   6 miles hiked in 5 hours

5. What is the equation of the relationship?
   $y = \frac{6}{5}x$

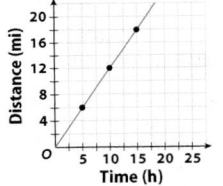

Personal Math Trainer
Online Assessment and Intervention
my.hrw.com

Lesson 3.1 **73**

© Houghton Mifflin Harcourt Publishing Company • Image Credits: ©David Epperson/PhotoDisc/Getty Images

---

DIFFERENTIATE INSTRUCTION *Leveled Questions*

	EXAMPLE 2
AL DOK 1 *Recall*	What happens to the weight of an object on the Moon as the weight of an object on Earth increases? as it decreases? Increases; decreases
OL DOK 2 *Skills/Concepts*	How do you know whether the constant of proportionality is $\frac{1}{6}$ or 6? Using the point (6, 1), the constant of proportionality is $k = \frac{y}{x} = \frac{1}{6}$.
BL DOK 3 *Strategic Thinking*	An object on Jupiter's moon Callisto weighs about $\frac{3}{4}$ as it weighs on Earth's moon. What is the constant of proportionality for the relationship comparing weights of objects on Callisto to their weights on Earth? Explain. $\frac{1}{8}$; the weight on Callisto is $\frac{3}{4}$ the weight on Earth's moon; the weight on Earth's moon is $\frac{1}{6}$ of the weight on Earth, $\frac{3}{4} \cdot \frac{1}{6} = \frac{1}{8}$.

LEVELED QUESTIONS: AL Approaching Level | OL On Level | BL Beyond Level

1. **Vocabulary** A proportional relationship is a relationship between two quantities in which the ratio of one quantity to the other quantity (**is** / **is not**) constant.

2. **Vocabulary** When writing an equation of a proportional relationship in the form $y = kx$, k represents the ___constant of proportionality___.

3. Write an equation that describes the proportional relationship between the number of days and the number of weeks in a given length of time. (Explore Activity and Example 1)

   a. Complete the table.

Time (weeks)	1	2	4	8	10
Time (days)	7	14	28	56	70

   b. Let x represent ___the time in weeks___.

   Let y represent ___the time in days___.

   The equation that describes the relationship is ___$y = 7x$___.

Each table or graph represents a proportional relationship. Write an equation that describes the relationship. (Example 1 and Example 2)

4. **Physical Science** The relationship between the numbers of oxygen atoms and hydrogen atoms in water

Oxygen atoms	2	5	17	120
Hydrogen atoms	4	10	34	240

   ___$y = 2x$___

5.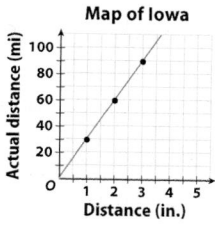
   Map of Iowa

   ___$y = 30x$___

ESSENTIAL QUESTION CHECK-IN

6. If you know the equation of a proportional relationship, how can you draw the graph of the equation?

   Sample answer: Use the equation to make a table with x-values and y-values. Then graph the points (x, y) and draw a line through the points.

© Houghton Mifflin Harcourt Publishing Company

---

4 Elaborate

Talk About It

Summarize the Lesson

Ask: When you know a relationship between variables is a proportional relationship, like the weight of an object on the Moon and on Earth from Example 2, how do you express the relationship in an equation?

Express the equation in the form $y = kx$, where k is the constant of proportionality. In Example 2, the equation relating the weight on the Moon, y, with its weight on Earth, x, is $y = \frac{1}{6}x$.

Guided Practice

Engage with the Whiteboard

Have students plot each point in the table for **Exercise 3** on the grid in **Exercise 5**, plotting weeks on the x-axis and days on the y-axis. They will have to extend the x-axis or change the scale so that each tic mark is 1 week. Then have them draw a line through the points to show that the table is a proportional relationship containing the point (0, 0).

Avoid Common Errors

- **Exercises 1–2** Remind students that the equations describing these proportional relationships have a constant of proportionality equal to the y-value divided by the x-value, not the x-value divided by the y-value.

- **Exercise 5** Remind students that the relationship shown in the graph is a proportional relationship because the line contains (0, 0).

DIFFERENTIATE INSTRUCTION *Intervention and Additional Support*

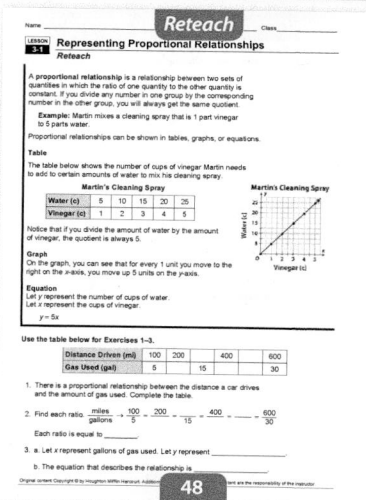

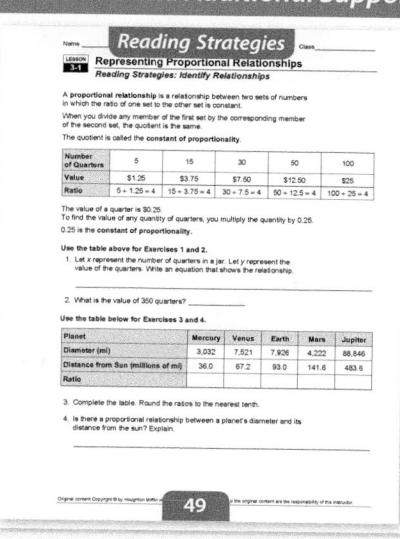

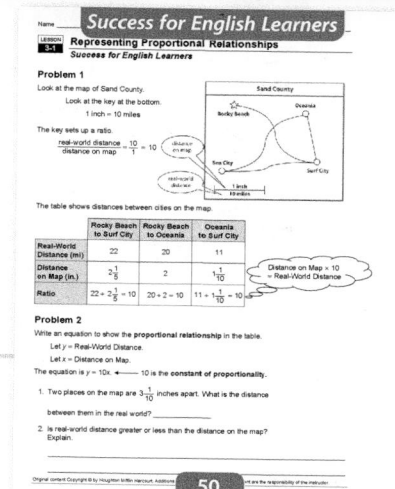

Personal Math Trainer
Daily Intervention
3.1 Homework

Pages shown are from *Differentiated Instruction*. **Also available online.**

Representing Proportional Relationships **74**

Pressed for Time

3.1 Differentiated Homework Assignments

(AL) **Approaching Level** 7–9, 11–13, 15

(OL) **On Level** 9–15

(BL) **Beyond Level** 11–16

*For **Below Level** students, assign Personal Math Trainer, Daily Intervention 3.1 Homework.*

Mathematical Processes	Exercises
MP.3 Logic	14
MP.4 Modeling	7–8, 13
MP.5 Using Tools	11–12
MP.6 Precision	9–10
MP.7 Using Structure	15–16

Focus on Higher Order Thinking

Depth of Knowledge	Exercises
2 Skills/Concepts	7–13
3 Strategic Thinking H.O.T.\	14–16

Personal Math Trainer

Online Assessment and Intervention

my.hrw.com

3.1 Independent Practice

The table shows the relationship between temperatures measured on the Celsius and Fahrenheit scales.

Celsius temperature	0	10	20	30	40	50
Fahrenheit temperature	32	50	68	86	104	122

7. Is the relationship between the temperature scales proportional? Why or why not?

No; the ratios of the numbers in each column are not equal.

8. Describe the graph of the Celsius-Fahrenheit relationship.

Sample answer: a line starting at (0, 32) and slanting upward to the right

9. **Analyze Relationships** Ralph opened a savings account with a deposit of $100. Every month after that, he deposited $20 more.

a. Why is the relationship described not proportional?

Sample answer: The account had a balance of $100 to begin with.

b. How could the situation be changed to make the situation proportional?

Sample answer: Have Ralph open the account with no money to begin with and then put $20 in every month.

10. **Represent Real-World Problems** Describe a real-world situation that can be modeled by the equation $y = \frac{1}{20}x$. Be sure to describe what each variable represents.

Sample answer: If x is the number of nickels you have, $y = \frac{1}{20}x$ is the amount of money you have in dollars.

Look for a Pattern **The variables x and y are related proportionally.**

11. When $x = 8$, $y = 20$. Find y when $x = 42$. _____ $y = 105$

12. When $x = 12$, $y = 8$. Find x when $y = 12$. _____ $x = 18$

© Houghton Mifflin Harcourt Publishing Company

DIFFERENTIATE INSTRUCTION *Leveled Homework/Practice*

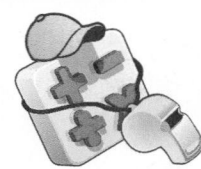

Personal Math Trainer

• 3.1 Homework

Pages shown are from *Differentiated Instruction.* **Also available online.**

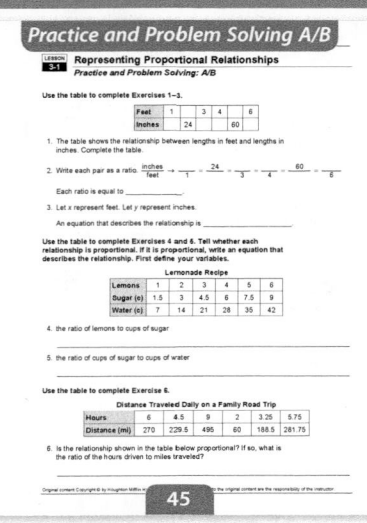

Practice and Problem Solving A/B

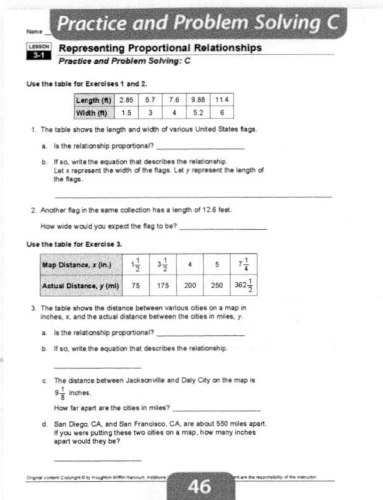

Practice and Problem Solving C

Practice and Problem Solving D

13. The graph shows the relationship between the distance that a snail crawls and the time that it crawls.

Snail Crawling

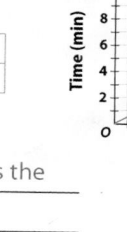

a. Use the points on the graph to make a table.

Distance (in.)	10	20	30	40	50
Time (min)	1	2	3	4	5

b. Write the equation for the relationship and tell what each variable represents.

$y = \frac{1}{10}x$, where y is the time in minutes and x is the

distance in inches

c. How long does it take the snail to crawl 85 inches? ___8.5 minutes___

H.O.T. FOCUS ON HIGHER ORDER THINKING

14. Communicate Mathematical Ideas Explain why all of the graphs in this lesson show the first quadrant but omit the other three quadrants.

Sample answer: All of the graphs represent real-world data for

which both x and y take on only nonnegative values, which

graph in the first quadrant or on the axes. If either x or y or both

could be negative, then other quadrants would be needed.

15. Analyze Relationships Complete the table.

Length of side of square	1	2	3	4	5
Perimeter of square	4	8	12	16	20
Area of square	1	4	9	16	25

a. Are the length of a side of a square and the perimeter of the square related proportionally? Why or why not?

Yes. The ratio of the perimeter of a square to its side

length is always 4.

b. Are the length of a side of a square and the area of the square related proportionally? Why or why not?

No. The ratio of the area of a square to its side length is

not constant.

16. Make a Conjecture A table shows a proportional relationship where k is the constant of proportionality. The rows are then switched. How does the new constant of proportionality relate to the original one?

It is the reciprocal of the original constant of proportionality.

76 Unit 2

© Houghton Mifflin Harcourt Publishing Company

Work Area

DIFFERENTIATE INSTRUCTION *Extend-the-Math Activity* **PRE-AP**

Activity The table and graph show values representing a proportional relationship. Use the graph labels to describe the proportional relationship. Complete the table and graph the points from the table. Then write an algebraic equation for the proportional relationship.

Hours	1	2	3	4
Calories burned	225	450	675	900

The number of calories burned by a 90-pound cyclist is proportional to the number of hours the cyclist rode. The constant of proportionality is 225, and an equation for the proportional relationship is $y = 225x$.

90-Pound Cyclist

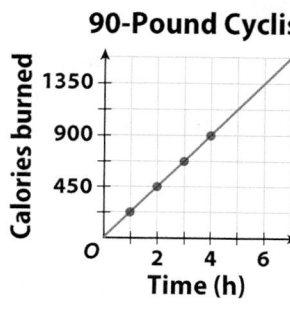

3.1 Lesson Quiz

1. Nico earns $12.50 per hour as a math tutor. Show that the relationship between the amount he earns and the number of hours he tutors is a proportional relationship. Then write the equation for the relationship.

$\frac{amount\ earned}{number\ of\ hours} = 12.5 \_\_ \frac{1}{1} = 25 \_\_ \frac{}{2} = \frac{50}{4}$
$= \frac{100}{8} = 12.5;$

$y = 12.5x$, where x is the number of hours and y is the amount earned.

2. The graph shows the relationship between the number of cups of flour and the number of cookies made. Write an equation for the proportional relationship. $y = 16x$

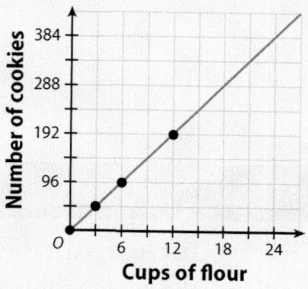

3. The table shows a proportional relationship. Write an equation that describes the relationship. $y = 28x$

Acres	5	8	15
Bushels of wheat	140	224	420

Differentiate Instruction

IF a student misses more than one question, THEN

Differentiate Instruction:

• 3.1 Reteach

• Personal Math Trainer

Interactive Whiteboard
Interactive Lesson quiz available online

Lesson Support

Content Objective Students will learn to find a rate of change and a slope.

Professional Development

Integrate Mathematical Processes MP.7

This lesson provides an opportunity to address this Mathematical Processes standard. It calls for students to discern a structure. Students find and analyze the rates of changes in input and output tables. Then students use graphs to visualize constant rates of change and to describe a constant rate of change as the slope of a line. In this way, students analyze input-output tables and graphs to make the connection between rate of change and slope.

FOCUS

Building Background

Visualizing Math Tell students that raisins cost $2 per pound. Review different ways to represent the relationship between the number of pounds bought and the total cost: use a table, write an equation, or draw a graph. Discuss the advantages of each representation. Also, discuss why the relationship is proportional.

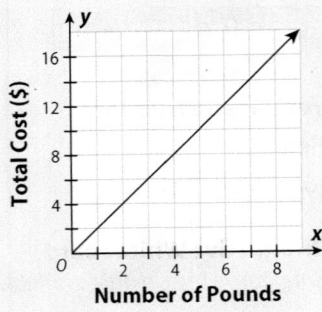

COHERENCE

Learning Progressions

In this lesson, students determine whether a rate of change is constant or variable. They find the rate of change, or the slope, from the graph of a proportional relationship. Important understandings for students include the following:

- **Use a table to determine whether the rate of change is constant or variable.**
- **Use a graph to find the rate of change.**
- **Find the slope of a line using its graph.**

Students connect the constant of proportionality to the rate of change, or slope, of a proportional relationship in equation form. They understand that the graph of a proportional relationship must be a line that passes through the origin and that the rate of change must be constant. This will facilitate the connection between the unit rate in a proportional relationship and the slope of its graph that is explored in the next lesson.

RIGOR

Cluster Connections

This lesson provides an excellent opportunity to connect ideas in the cluster:

Use functions to model relationships between quantities.

Have students refer to the following table.

x	−2	−1	0	1	2
y	−1	−0.5	0	0.5	1

Ask them to draw the line that connects the points in the coordinate plane and to find the slope of the line. Then have them graph and find the slope of the line that connects the following points.

x	2	1	0	−1	−2
y	−1	−0.5	0	0.5	1

Discuss how the graphs and their slopes are similar and how they are different.

Check students' graphs. Slopes are 0.5 and −0.5. Sample observations: The rates of change are the same but opposite in sign. The graphs slant in different directions.

Language Support ELL

Leveled Strategies for English Learners ELL

Emerging

Have students orally complete sentence frames with either "variable" or "constant" to describe a car traveling through a city and a car traveling on the freeway.

In the city, a car's speed is _____ because it stops and goes at different speeds. On the freeway, a car's speed is _____ because it goes the same speed.

Expanding

Have students work in pairs. Each partner should write a two- to three-sentence scenario, one to describe a car traveling in the city and the other to describe a car traveling on the freeway. Then students give their scenarios to other students to identify "city or freeway" and "constant or variable."

Bridging

Have students describe orally and in writing different scenarios using two to three complete sentences based on the rate-of-change problems in Guided Practice. Identify each scenario as one with a constant or variable relationship.

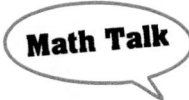

Math Talk Provide to students an example of a car traveling at a variable rate in the city with traffic and traffic lights and a car traveling at a constant rate in the country on a highway with no traffic. Have students describe and explain the difference to illustrate the contrasting meanings of *constant* and *variable*.

Image Credits: ©Gavin Hellier/Alamy

Linguistic Support ELL

Academic/Content Vocabulary

Contrast the meanings of *constant* versus *variable* relationships or ratios as used in real-world examples in this lesson. Give ordinary language equivalents. For example, *constant* means "not changing; staying the same." *Variable* means "changing; not staying the same." Spanish-speakers will recognize the terms *constant* and *variable* as cognates, but they may need to review the mathematical meanings.

Background Knowledge

In calculating and graphing slope, some ordinary words used to describe hills and mountains are used with a parallel meaning but applied differently in math. Discuss the common meanings of these terms (e.g., *slope, steep, slant, rise, run*) using illustrations of hills or mountains to support learning their mathematical usage.

Rate of Change and Slope

1 Engage

How do you find a rate of change or a slope?
Sample answer: Find the ratio of the change in output values to the change in input values in tables or graphs.

Motivate the Lesson

Ask: All cars have a speedometer and an odometer. Which one measures a rate of change? What are the two variables in this rate of change? Begin the lesson to find out.

2 Explore

EXPLORE ACTIVITY   **EXAMPLE 1**

ADDITIONAL EXAMPLE 1 Hector keeps a record of the total number of clients he has and the amount he earns as a personal trainer. Tell whether the rates of change are constant or variable. constant

	Day 1	Day 2	Day 3	Day 4
Number of clients	1	3	4	7
Amount earned ($)	45	135	180	315

 Interactive Whiteboard
Interactive example available online

YOUR TURN   MP.4

Talk About It

Check for Understanding

Ask: How are the rates of change for the table in Your Turn different from the table in Example 1? The rates of change for the table in Your Turn are variable, while the rates of change for the table in Example 1 are constant.

 ESSENTIAL QUESTION

How do you find a rate of change or a slope?

EXPLORE ACTIVITY

Investigating Rates of Change

A **rate of change** is a ratio of the amount of change in the dependent variable, or *output*, to the amount of change in the independent variable, or *input*.

EXAMPLE 1 Eve keeps a record of the number of lawns she has mowed and the money she has earned. Tell whether the rates of change are constant or variable.

	Day 1	Day 2	Day 3	Day 4
Number of lawns	1	3	6	8
Amount earned ($)	15	45	90	120

STEP 1 Identify the input and output variables.

Input: Number of lawns   **Output:** Amount earned ($)

STEP 2 Find the rates of change.

Day 1 to Day 2: $\dfrac{\text{change in \$}}{\text{change in lawns}} = \dfrac{45-15}{3-1} = \dfrac{30}{2} = 15$

Day 2 to Day 3: $\dfrac{\text{change in \$}}{\text{change in lawns}} = \dfrac{90-45}{6-3} = \dfrac{45}{3} = 15$

Day 3 to Day 4: $\dfrac{\text{change in \$}}{\text{change in lawns}} = \dfrac{120-90}{8-6} = \dfrac{30}{2} = 15$

The rates of change are constant: $ \underline{15} $ per lawn.

YOUR TURN

1. The table shows the approximate height of a football after it is kicked. Tell whether the rates of change are constant or variable.

   Find the rates of change in ft/s: ___36, 13, −10___

   The rates of change are (constant / **variable.**)

Time (s)	Height (ft)
0	0
0.5	18
1.5	31
2	26

 **Personal Math Trainer**
Online Assessment and Intervention
my.hrw.com

© Houghton Mifflin Harcourt Publishing Company

DIFFERENTIATE INSTRUCTION *Leveled Questions*

	EXPLORE ACTIVITY EXAMPLE 1
AL DOK 1 *Recall*	How can you tell which row in the table represents the input values? The number of lawns is the independent variable, so it is the input.
OL DOK 2 *Skills/Concepts*	Describe in your own words how to find the rate of change. Sample answer: Find the difference between two output values, and divide it by the corresponding difference of two input values.
BL DOK 3 *Strategic Thinking*	What might cause the rate of amount per lawn to vary in this situation? What rate could Eve use to keep it constant with different lawns? The amount per lawn could vary with the size of the lawn. Very large lawns should cost more than very small lawns to mow. She could charge a constant amount per square foot or per some area measure.

LEVELED QUESTIONS: **AL** Approaching Level | **OL** On Level | **BL** Beyond Level

Using Graphs to Find Rates of Change

You can also use a graph to find rates of change.

**The graph shows the distance Nathan bicycled over time.
What is Nathan's rate of change?**

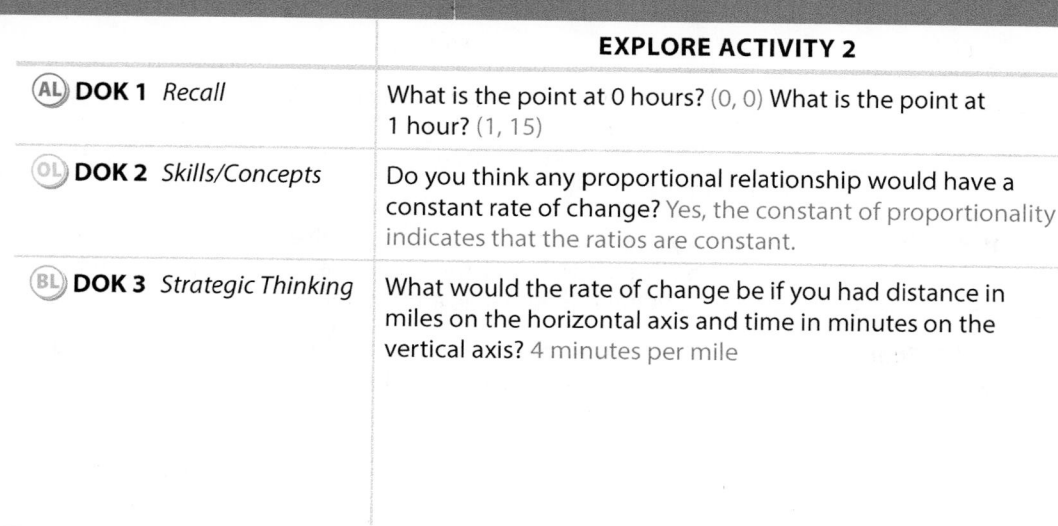

A Find the rate of change from 1 hour to 2 hours.

$$\frac{\text{change in distance}}{\text{change in time}} = \frac{30 - \boxed{15}}{2 - 1} = \frac{\boxed{15}}{1} = \boxed{15} \text{ miles per hour}$$

B Find the rate of change from 1 hour to 4 hours.

$$\frac{\text{change in distance}}{\text{change in time}} = \frac{60 - \boxed{15}}{4 - \boxed{1}} = \frac{\boxed{45}}{\boxed{3}} = \boxed{15} \text{ miles per hour}$$

C Find the rate of change from 2 hours to 4 hours.

$$\frac{\text{change in distance}}{\text{change in time}} = \frac{60 - \boxed{30}}{4 - \boxed{2}} = \frac{\boxed{30}}{\boxed{2}} = \boxed{15} \text{ miles per hour}$$

D Recall that the graph of a proportional relationship is a line through the origin. Explain whether the relationship between Nathan's time and distance is a proportional relationship.

Yes; the graph is a line through the origin.

Reflect

2. Make a Conjecture Does a proportional relationship have a constant rate of change?

Yes

3. Does it matter what interval you use when you find the rate of change of a proportional relationship? Explain.

No; in a proportional relationship, the rate of change is constant.

© Houghton Mifflin Harcourt Publishing Company

---

3 Explain

EXPLORE ACTIVITY 2

Focus on Reasoning

Discuss with students how the graph and the rate of change would be affected if Nathan rode 15 miles in the first hour, but only 12 miles in the second hour and 10 miles in the third. Students should realize that the rates of change would be variable, not constant, and they should reason that the values when graphed could not lie on a single line.

	EXPLORE ACTIVITY 2
(AL) DOK 1 *Recall*	What is the point at 0 hours? (0, 0) What is the point at 1 hour? (1, 15)
(OL) DOK 2 *Skills/Concepts*	Do you think any proportional relationship would have a constant rate of change? Yes, the constant of proportionality indicates that the ratios are constant.
(BL) DOK 3 *Strategic Thinking*	What would the rate of change be if you had distance in miles on the horizontal axis and time in minutes on the vertical axis? 4 minutes per mile

TEACHER TO TEACHER

Communicating Math Have students summarize the slopes of the lines in the graphs below in terms of rates of change. Ask them to explain how they would calculate the slopes.
positive, negative, zero, undefined

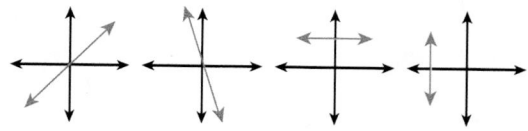

EXAMPLE 2

Engage with the Whiteboard

 Have a student draw a vertical line at $x = 4$ and place two points on it. Have another student draw a horizontal line at $y = -5$ and place two points on it. Ask students to find the slopes of the horizontal (slope is equal to 0) and vertical lines (slope is undefined).

ADDITIONAL EXAMPLE 2
Find the slope of the line.

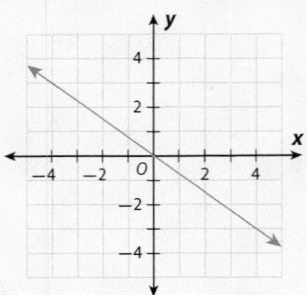

$-\dfrac{3}{4}$

Interactive Whiteboard
Interactive example available online

YOUR TURN   MP.2

Focus on Math Connections

Make sure that students understand the connections between the rate of leaking, the slope of the line, and the proportional relationship shown in the graph. Students may see that the graph is increasing and think that the amount of water is increasing. Make sure they understand that the graph shows the amount of water that has leaked out of the tank.

Digital Teacher Resources

Go online to access all your lesson-level resources.

my.hrw.com

Differentiated Instruction
• Reteach
• Reading Strategies
• Success for English Learners
• Practice and Problem Solving A/B, C, D

Math on the Spot Videos

Calculating Slope m

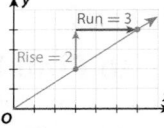 

When the rate of change of a relationship is constant, any segment of its graph has the same steepness. The constant rate of change is called the *slope* of the line.

Slope Formula

The **slope** of a line is the ratio of the change in *y*-values (rise) for a segment of the graph to the corresponding change in *x*-values (run).

$$m = \dfrac{y_2 - y_1}{x_2 - x_1}$$

EXAMPLE 2

My Notes

Find *m*, the slope of the line.

STEP 1   Choose two points on the line.
$P_1(x_1, y_1) = (-3, 2)$ $P_2(x_2, y_2) = (-6, 4)$

STEP 2   Find the change in *y*-values (rise = $y_2 - y_1$) and the change in *x*-values (run = $x_2 - x_1$) as you move from one point to the other.

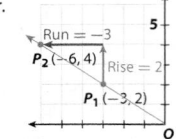

$$\text{rise} = y_2 - y_1 \qquad\qquad \text{run} = x_2 - x_1$$
$$= 4 - 2 \qquad\qquad\quad = -6 - (-3)$$
$$= 2 \qquad\qquad\qquad = -3$$

If you move up or right, the change is positive. If you move down or left, the change is negative.

STEP 3 $m = \dfrac{\text{rise}}{\text{run}} = \dfrac{y_2 - y_1}{x_2 - x_1}$
$$= \dfrac{2}{-3}$$
$$= -\dfrac{2}{3}$$

YOUR TURN

4. The graph shows the rate at which water is leaking from a tank. The slope of the line gives the leaking rate in gallons per minute. Find the slope of the line.

Rise = $\underline{\ +3\ }$ Run = $\underline{\ +4\ }$

Slope = $\underline{\dfrac{3}{4}}$

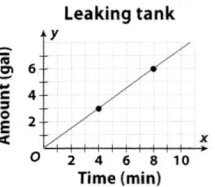

Leaking tank

Personal Math Trainer
Online Assessment and Intervention
my.hrw.com

© Houghton Mifflin Harcourt Publishing Company

Lesson 3.2   **79**

DIFFERENTIATE INSTRUCTION *Leveled Questions*

	EXAMPLE 2
AL **DOK 1** *Recall*	What do the subscripts mean in the slope formula? They indicate which point is referenced. When you choose two points, you think of one point as P_1, with subscripts of 1, and the other as P_2, with subscripts of 2.
OL **DOK 2** *Skills/ Concepts*	How do you know from the signs of the rise and run if a slope is positive or negative? If the rise is positive and the run is negative then the quotient is negative and, therefore, the slope is negative.
BL **DOK 3** *Strategic Thinking*	The operation of subtraction is not commutative, so why can you switch the order of the points used in the slope formula without changing the result? If you switch the points, the numerator's value becomes opposite and the denominator's value becomes opposite. Together, the changes cancel out any net sign change.

LEVELED QUESTIONS: **AL** Approaching Level | **OL** On Level | **BL** Beyond Level

Tell whether the rates of change are constant or variable. (Explore Activity Example 1)

1. building measurements ___constant___

Feet	3	12	27	75
Yards	1	4	9	25

2. computers sold ___variable___

Week	2	4	9	20
Number Sold	6	12	25	60

3. distance an object falls ___variable___

Distance (ft)	16	64	144	256
Time (s)	1	2	3	4

4. cost of sweaters ___constant___

Number	2	4	7	9
Cost ($)	38	76	133	171

Erica walks to her friend Philip's house. The graph shows Erica's distance from home over time. (Explore Activity 2)

5. Find the rate of change from 1 minute to 2 minutes.

$$\frac{\text{change in distance}}{\text{change in time}} = \frac{400 - \boxed{200}}{2 - \boxed{1}} = \frac{\boxed{200}}{\boxed{1}} = \boxed{200} \text{ ft per min}$$

6. Find the rate of change from 1 minute to 4 minutes. ___200 ft per min___

Find the slope of each line. (Example 2)

7.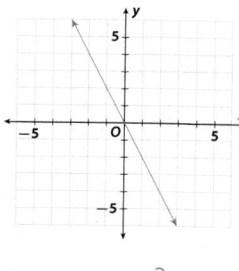

slope = ___−2___

8.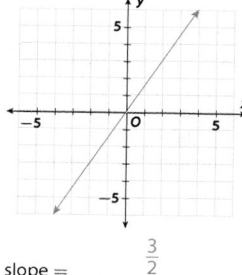

slope = ___$\frac{3}{2}$___

? ESSENTIAL QUESTION CHECK-IN

9. If you know two points on a line, how can you find the rate of change of the variables being graphed?

Sample answer: Find the coordinates of two points on the line. Then divide the change in y-values from one point to the next by the change in x-values.

④ Elaborate

Talk About It
Summarize the Lesson

Complete the graphic organizer with the students while discussing constant and variable rates of change.

Gallons	3	6	12	Items	10	20	30
Quarts	12	24	48	Cost ($)	25	50	90
Rates of change	4, 4, 4			2.5, 2.5, 3			
Constant or variable	constant			variable			

Guided Practice

Avoid Common Errors

Exercise 2 Remind students to check all pairs of values in the table before deciding if the rates of change are constant or variable.

Engage with the Whiteboard

In **Exercises 5 and 6**, have students plot the points on the graph that are indicated by the words in the exercise. For **Exercise 5**, students should plot points (1, 200) and (2, 400), which represent the distances after 1 minute and 2 mintues, respectively.

© Houghton Mifflin Harcourt Publishing Company

DIFFERENTIATE INSTRUCTION *Intervention and Additional Support*

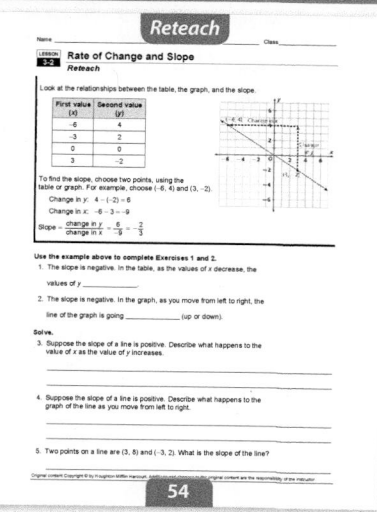

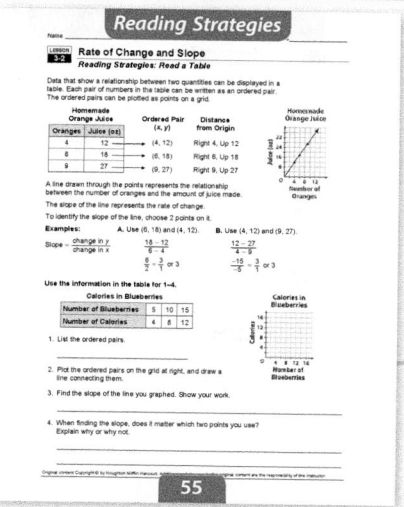

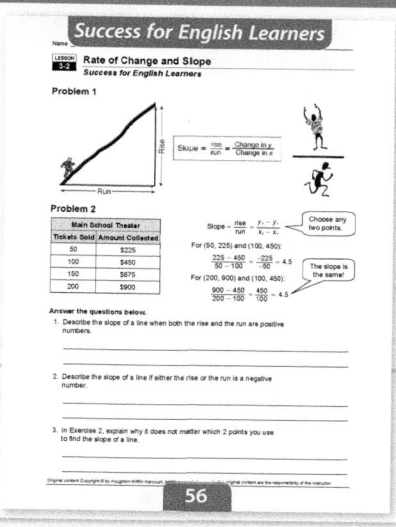

Personal Math Trainer
Daily Intervention
3.2 Homework

Pages shown are from *Differentiated Instruction.* **Also available online.**

Pressed for Time

3.2 Differentiated Homework Assignments

(AL) **Approaching Level**	10–15
(OL) **On Level**	10–12, 14–16
(BL) **Beyond Level**	12–13, 15–18

*For **Below Level** students, assign Personal Math Trainer, Daily Intervention 3.2 Homework.*

Mathematical Processes	Exercises
MP.2 Reasoning	15
MP.3 Logic	14, 18
MP.4 Modeling	11, 13
MP.5 Using Tools	12
MP.7 Using Structure	10, 16–17

Focus on Higher Order Thinking

Depth of Knowledge	Exercises
2 Skills/Concepts	11–15
3 Strategic Thinking H.O.T.	10, 16–18

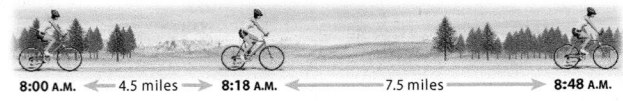
3.2 Independent Practice

Personal Math Trainer
Online Assessment and Intervention
my.hrw.com

10. Rectangle *EFGH* is graphed on a coordinate plane with vertices at *E*(−3, 5), *F*(6, 2), *G*(4, −4), and *H*(−5, −1).

   a. Find the slopes of each side.
   slope $\overline{EF} = -\frac{1}{3}$; slope $\overline{FG} = 3$; slope $\overline{GH} = -\frac{1}{3}$; slope $\overline{HE} = 3$

   b. What do you notice about the slopes of opposite sides?
   They are the same.

   c. What do you notice about the slopes of adjacent sides?
   They are negative reciprocals of one another.

11. A bicyclist started riding at 8:00 A.M. The diagram below shows the distance the bicyclist had traveled at different times. What was the bicyclist's average rate of speed in miles per hour?

8:00 A.M. ← 4.5 miles → 8:18 A.M. ← 7.5 miles → 8:48 A.M.

15 miles per hour

12. **Multistep** A line passes through (6, 3), (8, 4), and (*n*, −2). Find the value of *n*.
n = −4

13. A large container holds 5 gallons of water. It begins leaking at a constant rate. After 10 minutes, the container has 3 gallons of water left.

   a. At what rate is the water leaking?
   1 gallon every 5 minutes, or 0.2 gal/min

   b. After how many minutes will the container be empty?
   25 minutes

14. **Critique Reasoning** Billy found the slope of the line through the points (2, 5) and (−2, −5) using the equation $\frac{2-(-2)}{5-(-5)} = \frac{2}{5}$. What mistake did he make?
He used the change in *x* over the change in *y* instead of the change in *y* over the change in *x*.

© Houghton Mifflin Harcourt Publishing Company

DIFFERENTIATE INSTRUCTION *Leveled Homework/Practice*

Personal Math Trainer
• 3.2 Homework

Pages shown are from *Differentiated Instruction.*
Also available online.

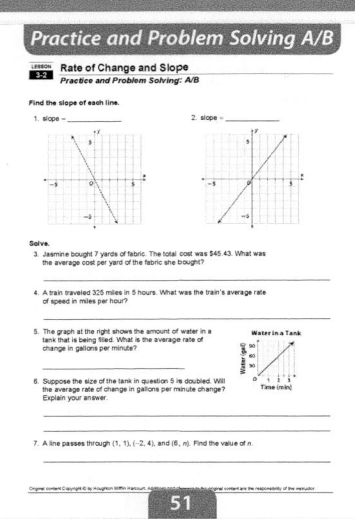

Practice and Problem Solving A/B

LESSON 3-2 Rate of Change and Slope
Practice and Problem Solving: A/B

51

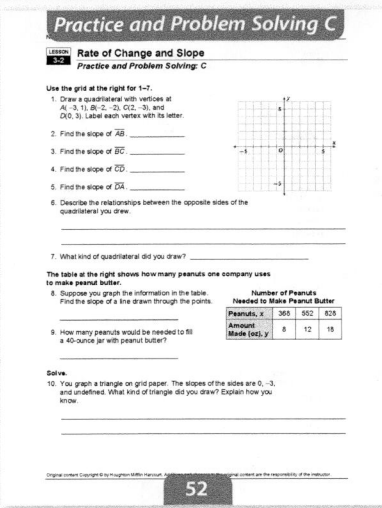

Practice and Problem Solving C

LESSON 3-2 Rate of Change and Slope
Practice and Problem Solving: C

52

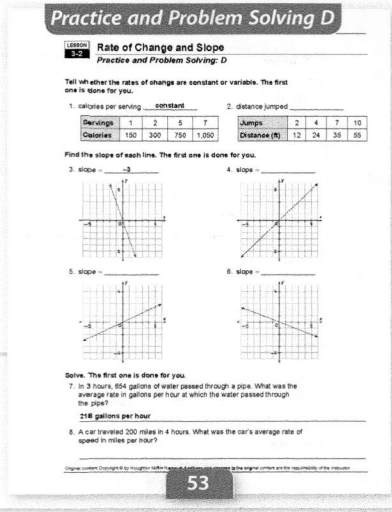

Practice and Problem Solving D

LESSON 3-2 Rate of Change and Slope
Practice and Problem Solving: D

53

15. Multiple Representations Graph parallelogram *ABCD* on a coordinate plane with vertices at *A*(3, 4), *B*(6, 1), *C*(0, −2), and *D*(−3, 1).

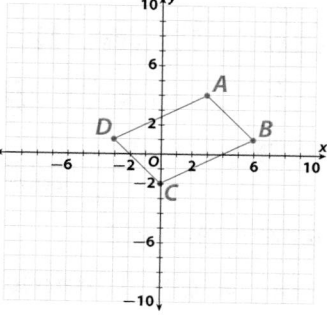

  a. Find the slope of each side.
slope $\overline{AB} = -1$; slope $\overline{BC} = \frac{1}{2}$;
slope $\overline{CD} = -1$; slope $\overline{DA} = \frac{1}{2}$

  b. What do you notice about the slopes?
The slopes of the opposite
sides are the same.

  c. Draw another parallelogram on the coordinate plane. Do the slopes have the same characteristics?
Yes; opposite sides still have the same slope.

H.O.T. FOCUS ON HIGHER ORDER THINKING

16. Communicate Mathematical Ideas Ben and Phoebe are finding the slope of a line. Ben chose two points on the line and used them to find the slope. Phoebe used two different points to find the slope. Did they get the same answer? Explain.

Yes; the slope of a line is constant. Therefore, the slope that you calculate will be the same no matter which two points you choose.

17. Analyze Relationships Two lines pass through the origin. The lines have slopes that are opposites. Compare and contrast the lines.

Sample answer: One line has a positive slope and one has a negative slope. The lines are equally steep, but one slants upward left to right while the other slants downward left to right. The lines cross at the origin.

18. Reason Abstractly What is the slope of the *x*-axis? Explain.

Zero; Sample answer: The rise along the *x*-axis is zero, while the run along the *x*-axis is not zero. The slope is $\frac{zero}{run}$ or zero.

82 Unit 2

© Houghton Mifflin Harcourt Publishing Company

Work Area

DIFFERENTIATE INSTRUCTION *Extend-the-Math Activity* **PRE-AP**

Activity The table shows the prices for various electronics during a storewide sale. Each item has the same percent discount. Complete the table and graph the points from the table. Then find the slope of the line connecting the points and give the percent discount.

Item	Tablet Computer	Disk Player	32-inch TV	Smart-phone
Original price ($)	350	375	400	200
Sale price ($)	280	300	320	160

The slope is 0.8; the percent discount is 20%.

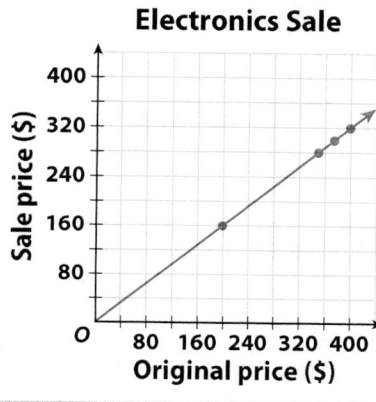

Electronics Sale

✔ **Quick Check**

3.2 Lesson Quiz

1. The table represents the number of computer tablets sold. Tell whether the rates of change are constant or variable. variable

Week	1	3	4	8
Number sold	32	96	128	224

Dev keeps a record in graph form of how far his car travels and the number of gallons of gasoline it uses.

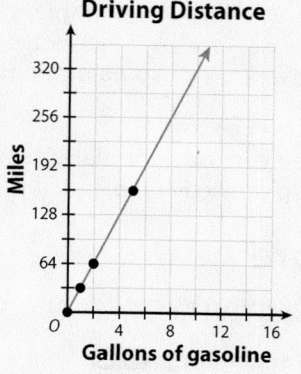

Driving Distance

2. How many miles per gallon does Dev get with his car? 32 mi/gal

3. What is the slope of the graph? 32

4. How far can Dev travel on 4 gallons of gasoline? 128 mi

5. Dev knows he only has 8 gallons of gasoline in the tank. He wants to go on a 300-mile trip. Will he have to buy more gasoline? Explain. Yes; he can only travel 256 miles on 8 gallons of gas. So he has to buy more gasoline.

Differentiate Instruction

IF a student misses more than one question, THEN

Differentiate Instruction:
• 3.2 Reteach
• Personal Math Trainer

Interactive Whiteboard
Interactive Lesson quiz available online

Using Right Triangles to Explore Slope

1 Engage

? ESSENTIAL QUESTION

How can you show that the slope of a non-vertical line is constant between any two points on a line?
Use the ratios of the vertical side lengths (rise) and the horizontal side lengths (run) of right triangles to show that the slope of a non-vertical line is constant between any two points on the line.

Motivate the Lesson

Ask: How can you use right triangles to find slope? Begin the Explore Activity to find out.

2 Explore

EXPLORE ACTIVITY

Connect Vocabulary ELL

Help students understand the meanings of *rise* and *run*. Ask them if when they are moving from side to side, whether they are going in a horizontal or a vertical direction. horizontal Ask them if when they are going up or down, whether they are going in a horizontal or a vertical direction. vertical Explain that the *rise* is the vertical change and the *run* is the horizontal change.

TEACHER TO TEACHER

Manipulatives Use geoboards to investigate the slope of a line using the triangles formed from the rise and run between any two pairs of points. Place two pegs at points on the geoboard and join the two points with a rubber band to represent a line. Then use pegs and rubber bands to create two different right triangles along the line as shown below. Find the slope of the line using each triangle and show that the slopes along the same line are always equal.

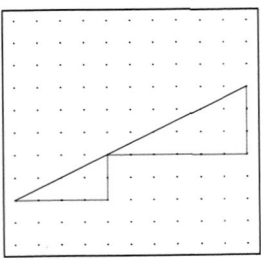

Using Right Triangles to Explore Slope

8.2.GF3.2
Students will show that the slope of a non-vertical line is constant between any two points on a line.

? ESSENTIAL QUESTION

How can you show that the slope of a non-vertical line is constant between any two points on a line?

EXPLORE ACTIVITY

Using Right Triangles to Find Slope

A Plot the points (0, 2) and (8, 6) on the grid. Draw a line through the points.

B Draw and label two different right triangles A and B with each hypotenuse on the line and a right-angle vertex at the intersection of two gridlines. Make sure that your triangles are the same shape but different sizes.

Sample answers shown.

C Use the triangles A and B that you drew to complete the table.

Triangle	Rise	Run	Rise/Run
A	1	2	$\frac{1}{2}$
B	3	6	$\frac{3}{6} = \frac{1}{2}$

D Are the ratios of *rise* to *run* of triangles A and B equivalent? Explain.
Yes, they are equivalent, because the ratios are both equal to $\frac{1}{2}$.

E Is the slope of the line constant between the points (0, 2) and (2, 3) and the points (2, 3) and (8, 6)? Explain.
Yes, because the slope between both pairs of points is $\frac{1}{2}$.

Reflect

1. How does a slope of $\frac{3}{9}$ compare with a slope of $\frac{4}{12}$?
They are equivalent; both equal $\frac{1}{3}$.

© Houghton Mifflin Harcourt Publishing Company

Going Further 3.2 **82A**

DIFFERENTIATE INSTRUCTION *Leveled Questions*

	EXPLORE ACTIVITY
AL DOK 1 *Recall*	How are right triangles used to represent slope in the coordinate plane? The rise and run of the slope are the vertical and horizontal legs of the triangle, respectively, in the coordinate plane.
OL DOK 2 *Skills/Concepts*	How are the ratios of rise to run related in the right triangles drawn from points on the line? For any pair of right triangles drawn from points on the line, the ratios of rise to run are equal.
BL DOK 3 *Strategic Thinking*	If you found the slope using two points on a graph and the slope using two different points on the same graph, and the two slopes were not equal, what does that tell you about the graph? That means the graph is not a line.

LEVELED QUESTIONS: AL Approaching Level | OL On Level | BL Beyond Level

1. Select any two pairs of points on the line graphed, draw corresponding right triangles indicating the rise and run for each pair, and show that the slope is the same between the two pairs of points.

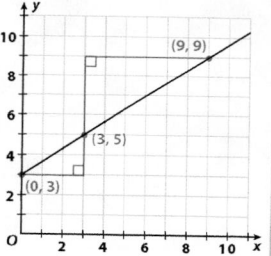

Sample answer: The ratio of the rise to run

between (0, 3) and (3, 5) and between

(3, 5) and (9, 9) is $\frac{2}{3}$, so the slope is the same

between the two pairs of points.

2. The same line is used below to generate different triangles. Verify that the slope ratios are the same for all the triangles generated by points on this line.

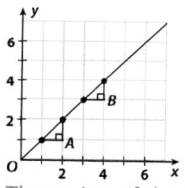 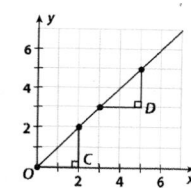 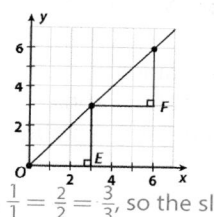

The ratios of the rise to run are equivalent, $\frac{1}{1} = \frac{2}{2} = \frac{3}{3}$, so the slope is

equal to 1.

Use slope to determine whether the given points are all on the same line.

3. (−6, −2), (0, −5), (2, −6)

$\frac{rise}{run} = \frac{-3}{6} = \frac{-1}{\blacksquare} = -\frac{1}{2}$;

yes, on same line

4. (−10, −2), (−5, 0), (10, 6)

$\frac{rise}{run} = \frac{2}{5} = \frac{6}{15} = \frac{2}{5}$;

yes, on same line

5. A line passes through the point (0, 0) and has a *rise* over *run* ratio of $\frac{4}{3}$. Give two other points that the line passes through.

Sample answer: (3, 4) and (6, 8)

6. A wheelchair ramp is allowed a maximum of one inch of rise for every foot of run. Give the dimensions of three different wheelchair ramps that would meet this requirement.

Sample answers: 36 inches long and 3 inches up; 2 feet long and

2 inches up; 66 inches long and 5.5 inches up

© Houghton Mifflin Harcourt Publishing Company

3 Explain

Talk About It

Check for Understanding

Ask: How can you use the ratios of *rise* to *run* to determine whether the points (−2, −10), (0, −4), and (2, 2) are all on one line? From one point to the next, both *rise* to *run* ratios are $\frac{6}{2}$, or 3, so they are all on one line.

4 Elaborate

Summarize the Lesson

Ask: How can you show that the slope is constant between any two pairs of points on a non-vertical line? Sample answer: Using any two points (x_1, y_1) and (x_2, y_2) on the line, form a right triangle using the rise and run between the two points as the horizontal and vertical sides of the triangle. Repeat this for any other two points (x_3, y_3) and (x_4, y_4) on the line. The ratios of rise to run will be equal for both triangles, so the slopes are equal between any two pairs of points.

5 Evaluate

Practice

Avoid Common Errors

In **Exercise 1**, make sure students select points with integer coordinates that are actually on the line. For example, students may select the point (5, 6) in error because it is close to the actual point $(5, 6\frac{1}{3})$.

LESSON QUIZ

1. Which pair of slopes could represent slopes of the same line? A

   A. $\frac{6}{3}$ and $\frac{8}{4}$ B. $\frac{3}{6}$ and $\frac{6}{3}$ C. $\frac{1}{4}$ and 4

2. Use the ratios of *rise* to *run* to determine whether the points (0, 2), (1, −1), and (3, −7) are all on one line? From one point to the next, both *rise* to *run* ratios are equal to −3, so they are all on one line.

3. Explain why it does not matter which two points on the line you choose when you find the slope of the line. The ratio of *rise* to *run* between any two points on a line is always constant.

Lesson Support

Content Objective Students will learn to interpret the unit rate as slope.

Professional Development

Integrate Mathematical Processes MP.4

This lesson provides an opportunity to address this Mathematical Processes standard. It calls for students to analyze mathematical relationships using tools such as tables and graphs. Students find and analyze the unit rate in input and output tables. Then students use graphs to find the slope of a line. In this way, students are led to make the connection between unit rate and slope.

FOCUS

Building Background

Connecting to Everyday Life Ask students to describe situations in which they use unit rates in their lives and why knowing the unit rate is useful.

Examples of Unit Rates
price per pound
price per item
miles per gallon
hourly pay
daily travel fees

COHERENCE

Learning Progressions

In this lesson, students relate the unit rate of a proportional relationship to the slope of its graph. They graph a proportional relationship and then use the graph to find the slope. Important understandings for students include the following:

- **Relate the unit rate to the slope.**
- **Use a table or a graph to find the unit rate.**
- **Use slopes to compare unit rates.**

Students recognize that in a proportional relationship, the constant of proportionality, the unit rate, and the slope of the corresponding graph are the same. As they build their understanding of proportional relationships, they will be able to compare the relationships in different ways. They will recognize that different relationships have different slopes as well as different unit rates.

RIGOR

Cluster Connections

This lesson provides an excellent opportunity to connect ideas in the cluster:

Understand the connections between proportional relationships, lines, and linear equations.

Present the following situation: Jared is on a 50-mile bike ride. He wants to finish the ride in under 4 hours. The table shows the distance, d, in miles, that Jared rides his bike in t hours.

t	0.5	0.75	1.5	2.25
d	7.5	11.25	22.5	33.75

Ask students to find the unit rate. Then ask them to explain whether Jared will meet his goal based on the data.

The unit rate is 15 mph. Sample answer: Based on the equation $d = 15t$, Jared will meet his goal.

Language Support ELL

Language Objective Students will explain how to interpret the unit rate as slope.

Leveled Strategies for English Learners ELL

Emerging

Form two groups of students. Have each group orally describe the meaning of the values in each cell of a table in terms of unit rate. Then have them use the unit rates to compare the two rates using –er words, such as *faster*.

Expanding

Form two groups of students. Have each group orally describe the meaning of the values in each cell of a table in terms of unit rate and a graph. Then have them use the unit rates to compare the two rates using –er words, such as *faster*.

Bridging

Have students compare two graphs showing different cases. Have them compare unit rates in a complete sentence and then compare the two rates using -er words, such as *faster*.

Math Talk This prompt requires students to describe how three concepts are related to each other: constant of proportionality, unit rate, and slope of a graph.

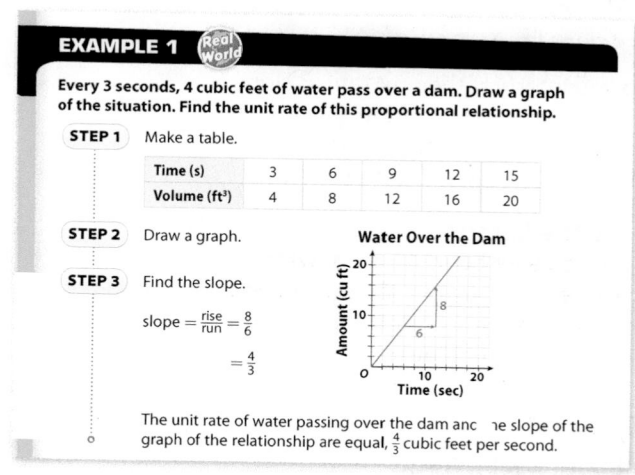

EXAMPLE 1 Real World

Every 3 seconds, 4 cubic feet of water pass over a dam. Draw a graph of the situation. Find the unit rate of this proportional relationship.

STEP 1 Make a table.

Time (s)	3	6	9	12	15
Volume (ft³)	4	8	12	16	20

STEP 2 Draw a graph.

STEP 3 Find the slope.

$$\text{slope} = \frac{\text{rise}}{\text{run}} = \frac{8}{6}$$
$$= \frac{4}{3}$$

Water Over the Dam

The unit rate of water passing over the dam and the slope of the graph of the relationship are equal, $\frac{4}{3}$ cubic feet per second.

Linguistic Support ELL

Academic/Content Vocabulary

Two aspects of the concept of *unit rate* are taught in this lesson: how a unit rate is determined and how this unit rate is represented on a graph. Note the use of the word *per* in the phrase *per hour*. Give students complete sentences to describe the change being measured. Then show how to compress the information into a phrase to define the unit rate.

Two inches of snow falls on Misty Mountain in an hour. This means that snowfall is 2 inches per hour and the unit rate is 2 inches per hour.

Background Knowledge

In the Independent Practice, several problems are based on the concept of migration of the Canadian goose. Students may be unfamiliar with the meaning of *animal migration*, but they may be aware of terms associated with *immigration*. The root word *migr-* means "to move." Various prefixes and suffixes are used to make different meanings from this root. The prefix *im-* means "into." The prefix *e-* means "to move from," as in *emigrate*.

Image Credits: ©Myotis/Shutterstock

Interpreting the Unit Rate as Slope

1 Engage

ESSENTIAL QUESTION

How do you interpret the unit rate as slope?
Sample answer: The ratio of the change in *y* to the change in *x* is the unit rate. It is also the ratio of the rise to the run, or the slope.

Motivate the Lesson

Ask: Have you ever been skiing, or watched downhill skiers on television? How can you describe the steepness of slopes numerically? Begin the lesson to find out.

2 Explore

EXPLORE ACTIVITY

Connect Multiple Representations
Ask students for the method they use to find the coordinates of points on a line. Point out that it is easiest to find the coordinates of points at the intersection of grid lines.

ESSENTIAL QUESTION

How do you interpret the unit rate as slope?

EXPLORE ACTIVITY Real World

Relating the Unit Rate to Slope

A rate is a comparison of two quantities that have different units, such as miles and hours. A **unit rate** is a rate in which the second quantity in the comparison is one unit.

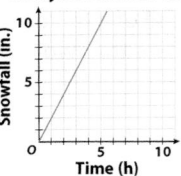

A storm is raging on Misty Mountain. The graph shows the constant rate of change of the snow level on the mountain.

A Find the slope of the graph using the points (1, 2) and (5, 10). Remember that the slope is the constant rate of change.

$$\frac{\text{change in }y\text{-value}}{\text{change in }x\text{-value}} = \frac{10 - 2}{5 - 1} = \frac{8}{4} = \frac{2}{1}$$

Misty Mountain Storm

Graph: Snowfall (in.) vs Time (h)

B Find the unit rate of snowfall in inches per hour. Explain your method.

2 inches per hour; Sample answer: The point (1, 2) is on the line, and represents 2 inches snowfall in 1 hour.

C Compare the slope of the graph and the unit rate of change in the snow level. What do you notice?

They are the same.

D Which unique point on this graph gives you the slope of the graph and the unit rate of change in the snow level? Explain how you found the point.

(1, 2); Sample answer: the unit rate is the amount of snow in 1 h. Because the line goes through the point (0, 0), the amount of snow in 1 h equals the *y*-coordinate of the point where *x* is 1. That point is (1, 2) and 2 in./h is the unit rate and the slope.

© Houghton Mifflin Harcourt Publishing Company · Image Credits: ©Cavan Images/Getty Images

Lesson 3.3 **83**

DIFFERENTIATE INSTRUCTION *Leveled Questions*

	EXPLORE ACTIVITY
AL DOK 1 *Recall*	In Part A you find slope using (1, 2) and (5, 10). What are other points you could use to find the slope? Sample answer: (0, 0), (2, 4), (3, 6), or (4, 8)
OL DOK 2 *Skills/Concepts*	Down below Misty Mountain, the same storm is bringing much lighter snow at a constant rate. The snowfall graph there contains (3, 1.5) and (5, 2.5). What is the unit rate of snowfall? 0.5 inch per hour
BL DOK 3 *Strategic Thinking*	Is it true that the point (1, *y*) with an *x*-coordinate of 1 on the graph of any proportional relationship gives the unit rate as *y*? Explain. Yes, the unit rate in a proportional relationship is the same as the slope. By definition, the unit rate is $\frac{y}{x}$, or $\frac{y}{1} = y$ in this case.

LEVELED QUESTIONS: **AL** Approaching Level | **OL** On Level | **BL** Beyond Level

Math On the Spot
my.hrw.com

Graphing Proportional Relationships

You can use a table and a graph to find the unit rate and slope that describe a real-world proportional relationship. The constant of proportionality for a proportional relationship is the same as the slope.

EXAMPLE 1

Every 3 seconds, 4 cubic feet of water pass over a dam. Draw a graph of the situation. Find the unit rate of this proportional relationship.

STEP 1 Make a table.

Time (s)	3	6	9	12	15
Volume (ft³)	4	8	12	16	20

STEP 2 Draw a graph.

STEP 3 Find the slope.

$$\text{slope} = \frac{\text{rise}}{\text{run}} = \frac{8}{6}$$

$$= \frac{4}{3}$$

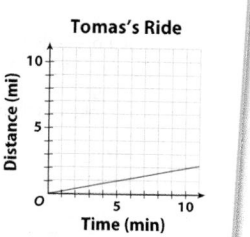

Water Over the Dam

The unit rate of water passing over the dam and the slope of the graph of the relationship are equal, $\frac{4}{3}$ cubic feet per second.

© Houghton Mifflin Harcourt Publishing Company

Math Talk
Mathematical Processes

In a proportional relationship, how are the constant of proportionality, the unit rate, and the slope of the graph of the relationship related?

They are the same.

Reflect

1. **What If?** Without referring to the graph, how do you know that the point $\left(1, \frac{4}{3}\right)$ is on the graph?

   Sample answer: The point $(1, r)$ is on any graph of a proportional relationship, where r equals the unit rate.

YOUR TURN

2. Tomas rides his bike at a steady rate of 2 miles every 10 minutes. Graph the situation. Find the unit rate of this proportional relationship.

   His unit rate and the slope of a graph of the ride both equal $\frac{1}{5}$ mi/min.

Tomas's Ride

Personal Math Trainer
Online Assessment and Intervention
my.hrw.com

---

3 Explain

EXAMPLE 1

ADDITIONAL EXAMPLE 1 Every 10 seconds an escalator step rises 6 feet. Draw a graph of the situation. Find the unit rate of this proportional relationship.

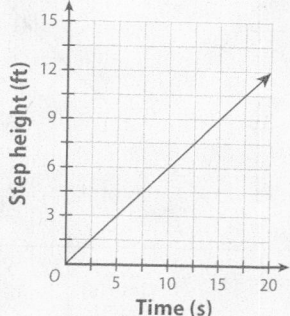

$\frac{3}{5}$ feet per second

Interactive Whiteboard
Interactive example available online

Animated Math

Proportional Relationships
Students explore how changing the parameters of a real-world proportional relationship affects tables and graphs.

my.hrw.com

YOUR TURN MP.7

Avoid Common Errors
Note that in the Example the time is given first, and then the volume. In **Exercise 2,** the distance is given first, and then the time. Caution students to read the information carefully before deciding on the independent variable.

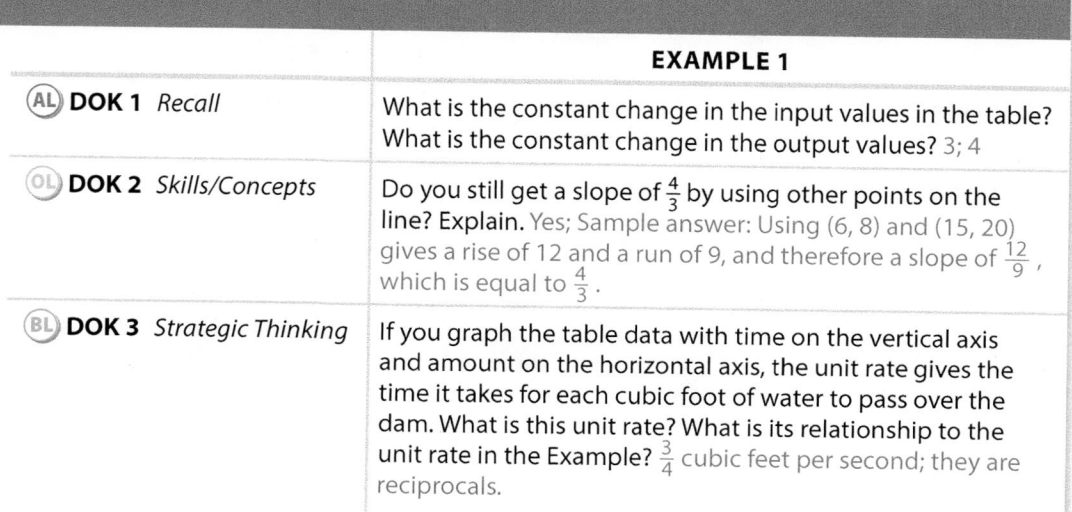

	EXAMPLE 1
AL **DOK 1** *Recall*	What is the constant change in the input values in the table? What is the constant change in the output values? 3; 4
OL **DOK 2** *Skills/Concepts*	Do you still get a slope of $\frac{4}{3}$ by using other points on the line? Explain. Yes; Sample answer: Using (6, 8) and (15, 20) gives a rise of 12 and a run of 9, and therefore a slope of $\frac{12}{9}$, which is equal to $\frac{4}{3}$.
BL **DOK 3** *Strategic Thinking*	If you graph the table data with time on the vertical axis and amount on the horizontal axis, the unit rate gives the time it takes for each cubic foot of water to pass over the dam. What is this unit rate? What is its relationship to the unit rate in the Example? $\frac{3}{4}$ cubic feet per second; they are reciprocals.

TEACHER TO TEACHER

Modeling Discuss with students a familiar unit rate such as 60 mph in terms of the slope, 60 mi/h, of an equation that represents the proportional relationship between distance d in miles and time t in hours: $d = 60t$.

EXAMPLE 2

ADDITIONAL EXAMPLE 2 The equation $y = 1.2x$ represents the rate, in beats per second, that Lee's heart beats. The graph represents the rate that Nancy's heart beats.

Determine whose heart is beating at a faster rate.

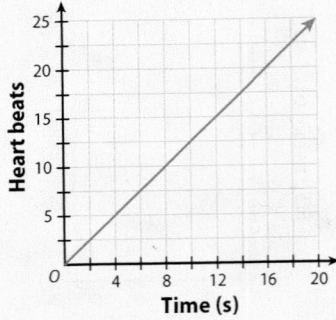

1.25 > 1.2; Nancy's heart is beating faster.

 Interactive Whiteboard
Interactive example available online

YOUR TURN MP.2

Connect Multiple Representations
Students find the greater rate from an equation and a table. In Example 2, students found the greater rate from an equation and a graph. Students should feel confident they can find the greater rate using any two representations.

 **Digital Teacher Resources**

Go online to access all your lesson-level resources.

Differentiated Instruction
• Reteach
• Reading Strategies
• Success for English Learners
• Practice and Problem Solving A/B, C, D
Math on the Spot Videos

my.hrw.com

Using Slopes to Compare Unit Rates
You can compare proportional relationships presented in different ways.

Math On the Spot  my.hrw.com

EXAMPLE 2

The equation $y = 2.75x$ represents the rate, in barrels per hour, that oil is pumped from Well A. The graph represents the rate that oil is pumped from Well B. Which well pumped oil at a faster rate?

Well B Pumping Rate

STEP 1 Use the equation $y = 2.75x$ to make a table for Well A's pumping rate, in barrels per hour.

Time (h)	1	2	3	4
Quantity (barrels)	2.75	5.5	8.25	11

STEP 2 Use the table to find the slope of the graph of Well A.

slope = unit rate = $\frac{5.5 - 2.75}{2 - 1} = \frac{2.75}{1} = 2.75$ barrels/hour

STEP 3 Use the graph to find the slope of the graph of Well B.

slope = unit rate = $\frac{\text{rise}}{\text{run}} = \frac{10}{4} = 2.5$ barrels/hour

STEP 4 Compare the unit rates.

2.75 > 2.5, so Well A's rate, 2.75 barrels/hour, is faster.

Reflect
3. Describe the relationships among the slope of the graph of Well A's rate, the equation representing Well A's rate, and the constant of proportionality.

Sample answer: The slope and the constant of proportionality equal the value 2.75 in the equation $y = 2.75x$.

YOUR TURN
4. The equation $y = 375x$ represents the relationship between x, the time that a plane flies in hours, and y, the distance the plane flies in miles for Plane A. The table represents the relationship for Plane B. Find the slope of the graph for each plane and the plane's rate of speed. Determine which plane is flying at a faster rate of speed.

Time (h)	1	2	3	4
Distance (mi)	425	850	1275	1700

A: 375, 375 mi/h; B: 425, 425 mi/h; B is flying faster.

 Personal Math Trainer
Online Assessment and Intervention
my.hrw.com

Lesson 3.3 **85**

DIFFERENTIATE INSTRUCTION *Leveled Questions*

	EXAMPLE 2
AL **DOK 1** *Recall*	The point (2, 5) is on the line in the graph. What does it represent? Well B pumps 5 barrels of oil in 2 hours.
OL **DOK 2** *Skills/Concepts*	In the equation $y = 2.75x$, what does 2.75 represent in the proportional relationship? The value 2.75 is k, the constant of proportionality, and the unit rate 2.75 barrels per hour.
BL **DOK 3** *Strategic Thinking*	Suppose the well operator sends a graph to the office of the combined output over time of Wells A and B. What is the slope of this graph? Justify your answer. 5.25; the unit rate of the wells together is 2.75 + 2.5 = 5.25 barrels per hour, so the slope would be 5.25.

LEVELED QUESTIONS: **AL** Approaching Level | **OL** On Level | **BL** Beyond Level

© Houghton Mifflin Harcourt Publishing Company • Image Credits: ©Tom McHugh/Photo Researchers, Inc.

Give the slope of the graph and the unit rate. (Explore Activity and Example 1)

1. Jorge: 5 miles every 6 hours

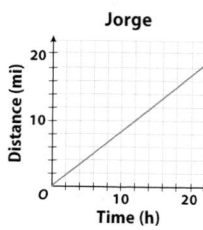

Jorge

slope = unit rate = $\frac{5}{6}$ mi/h

2. Akiko

Time (h)	4	8	12	16
Distance (mi)	5	10	15	20

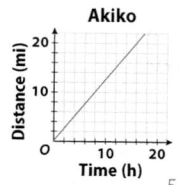

Akiko

slope = unit rate = $\frac{5}{4}$ mi/h

3. The equation $y = 0.5x$ represents the distance Henry hikes, in miles, over time, in hours. The graph represents the rate that Clark hikes. Determine which hiker is faster. Explain. (Example 2)

Clark is faster. From the equation, Henry's rate is equal to 0.5, or $\frac{1}{2}$ mile per hour. Clark's rate is the slope of the line, which is $\frac{3}{2}$, or 1.5 miles per hour.

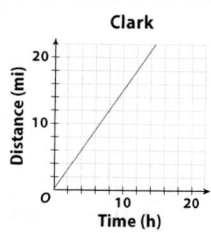

Clark

Write an equation relating the variables in each table. (Example 2)

4.

Time (x)	1	2	4	6
Distance (y)	15	30	60	90

$y = 15x$

5.

Time (x)	16	32	48	64
Distance (y)	6	12	18	24

$y = \frac{3}{8}x$

? ESSENTIAL QUESTION CHECK-IN

6. Describe methods you can use to show a proportional relationship between two variables, x and y. For each method, explain how you can find the unit rate and the slope.

Table of values: The ratio of y to x gives the unit rate and slope.

Equation: If the equation can be written as $y = mx$, then m is the unit rate and the slope. Graph: When the line passes through the origin, then the value of r at the point (1, r) is the unit rate and the slope.

© Houghton Mifflin Harcourt Publishing Company

4 Elaborate

Talk About It

Summarize the Lesson

Ask: How do you find the slope when you are only given an equation or a table?

Sample answer: For an equation such as $y = 2.6x$, the slope is the unit rate, which is the coefficient of x. For a table, the change in y divided by the change in x is the unit rate, or slope.

Guided Practice

Engage with the Whiteboard

For **Exercises 1–2**, after students complete each exercise, have them copy the graph for Akiko onto the graph for Jorge. Have them determine whether Jorge or Akiko is the faster hiker and use the graph to explain their answer. In **Exercise 3**, students should graph the equation for Henry on the graph for Clark.

Avoid Common Errors

Exercise 3 Help students understand that comparing rates, or slopes, is the same as comparing rational numbers. Students can write each unit rate as a decimal, if necessary.

DIFFERENTIATE INSTRUCTION *Intervention and Additional Support*

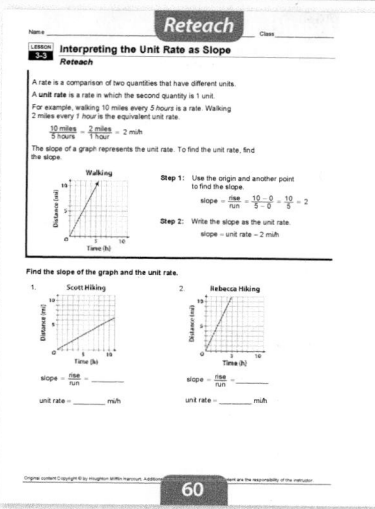

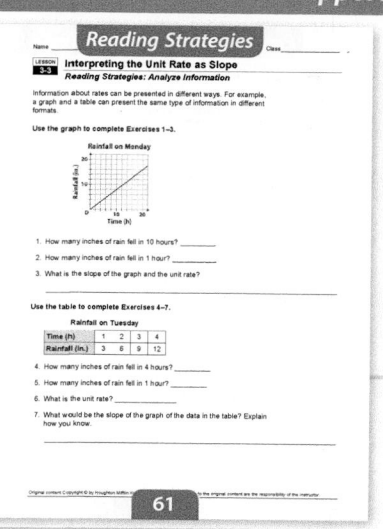

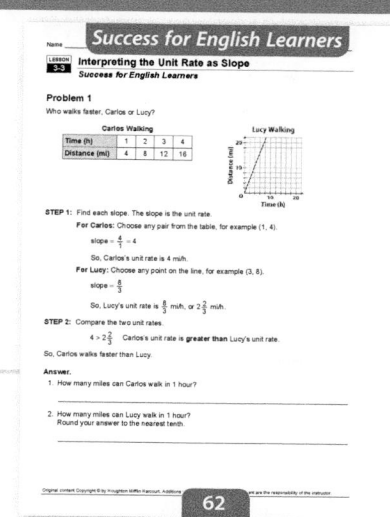

Personal Math Trainer
Daily Intervention
3.3 Homework

Pages shown are from *Differentiated Instruction.* **Also available online.**

5 Evaluate

Independent Practice

⏱ **Pressed for Time**

3.3 Differentiated Homework Assignments

AL Approaching Level	7–9, 11	
OL On Level	9–10, 12–13	
BL Beyond Level	10–11, 13	

*For **Below Level** students, assign Personal Math Trainer, Daily Intervention 3.3 Homework.*

Mathematical Processes	Exercises
MP.2 Reasoning	13
MP.3 Logic	11–12
MP.4 Modeling	7, 9–10

Focus on Higher Order Thinking

Depth of Knowledge	Exercises
1 Recall of Information	8
2 Skills/Concepts	7, 9–10
3 Strategic Thinking **H.O.T.**	11–13

Personal Math Trainer
Online Assessment and Intervention
my.hrw.com

3.3 Independent Practice

7. A Canadian goose migrated at a steady rate of 3 miles every 4 minutes.

a. Fill in the table to describe the relationship.

Time (min)	4	8	12	16	20
Distance (mi)	3	6	9	12	15

b. Graph the relationship.

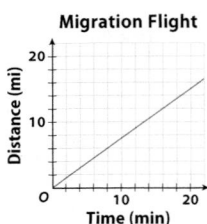

Migration Flight

c. Find the slope of the graph and describe what it means in the context of this problem.

$\frac{3}{4}$; The unit rate of migration of the goose and the slope of the graph both equal $\frac{3}{4}$ mi/min.

8. **Vocabulary** A unit rate is a rate in which the

[first quantity / **second quantity**] in the comparison is one unit.

9. The table and the graph represent the rate at which two machines are bottling milk in gallons per second.

Machine 1

Time (s)	1	2	3	4
Amount (gal)	0.6	1.2	1.8	2.4

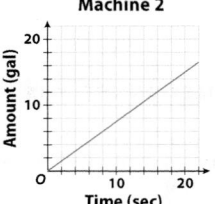

Machine 2

a. Determine the slope and unit rate of each machine.

Machine 1: slope = unit rate = $\frac{0.6}{1}$ = 0.6 gal/s;

Machine 2: slope = unit rate = $\frac{3}{4}$ = 0.75 gal/s

b. Determine which machine is working at a faster rate.

Machine 2 is working at a faster rate since 0.75 > 0.6.

© Houghton Mifflin Harcourt Publishing Company

Lesson 3.3 **87**

DIFFERENTIATE INSTRUCTION *Leveled Homework/Practice*

Personal Math Trainer
• 3.3 Homework

Pages shown are from *Differentiated Instruction*.
Also available online.

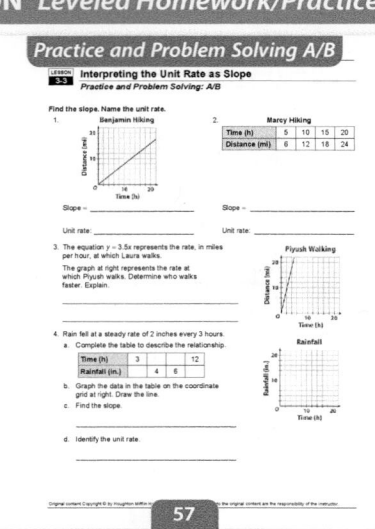

Practice and Problem Solving A/B
57

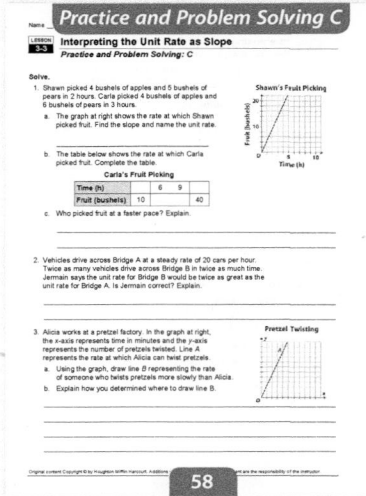

Practice and Problem Solving C
58

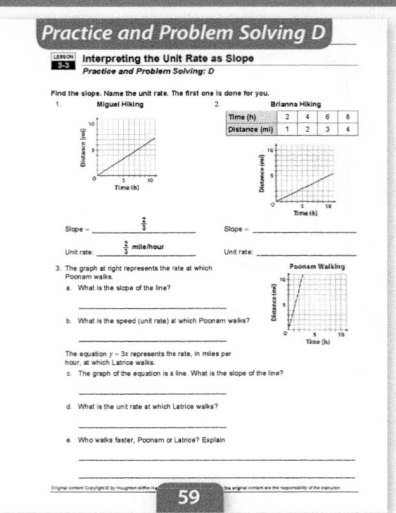

Practice and Problem Solving D
59

10. Cycling The equation $y = \frac{1}{9}x$ represents the distance y, in kilometers, that Patrick traveled in x minutes while training for the cycling portion of a triathlon. The table shows the distance y Jennifer traveled in x minutes in her training. Who has the faster training rate?

Time (min)	40	64	80	96
Distance (km)	5	8	10	12

Patrick's rate is $\frac{1}{9}$ kilometer per minute. Jennifer's rate is $\frac{1}{8}$ kilometer per minute. $\frac{1}{9} < \frac{1}{8}$, so Jennifer has the faster training rate.

 **FOCUS ON HIGHER ORDER THINKING**

11. Analyze Relationships There is a proportional relationship between minutes and dollars per minute, shown on a graph of printing expenses. The graph passes through the point (1, 4.75). What is the slope of the graph? What is the unit rate? Explain.

slope = unit rate = 4.75. If the graph of a proportional relationship passes through the point (1, r), then r equals the slope and the unit rate, which is $4.75/min.

12. Draw Conclusions Two cars start at the same time and travel at different constant rates. A graph for Car A passes through the point (0.5, 27.5), and a graph for Car B passes through (4, 240). Both graphs show distance in miles and time in hours. Which car is traveling faster? Explain.

Car B; the slope and unit rate of speed of Car A is $\frac{27.5 - 0}{0.5 - 0} = \frac{27.5}{0.5} = 55$ mi/h. The slope and unit rate of speed of Car B is $\frac{240 - 0}{4 - 0} = \frac{240}{4} = 60$ mi/h. $60 > 55$, so Car B is traveling faster.

13. Critical Thinking The table shows the rate at which water is being pumped into a swimming pool.

Time (min)	2	5	7	12
Amount (gal)	36	90	126	216

Use the unit rate and the amount of water pumped after 12 minutes to find how much water will have been pumped into the pool after $13\frac{1}{2}$ minutes. Explain your reasoning.

243 gallons; sample answer: The unit rate is $\frac{36}{2} = 18$ gal/min. So $1\frac{1}{2}$ minutes after 12 minutes, an additional $18 \times 1\frac{1}{2} = 27$ gallons will be pumped in, so the total is $216 + 27 = 243$ gal.

Work Area

© Houghton Mifflin Harcourt Publishing Company

✔ Quick Check

3.3 Lesson Quiz

1. Every 4 seconds, a ski lift chair rises 14 feet. Draw a graph of the situation. Then describe the relationship between the height of the chair and the time.

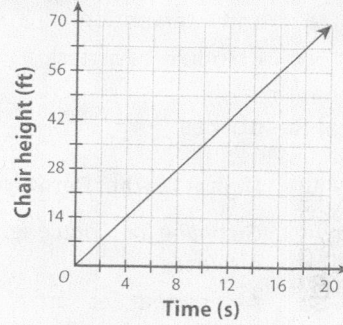

The unit rate of the height of the chair is $\frac{7}{2}$ feet per second.

2. Under Plan A, a 2-minute call costs $0.54 and a 4-minute call costs $1.08. Under Plan B, the cost for x minutes is given by $y = 0.289x$. Which plan is cheaper? Why?

Plan A; $0.27/min < $0.289/min

3. The equation $y = 13x$ represents the rate, in gallons per minute, that Tank A at an aquarium fills with water. The table represents the rate that Tank B fills with water. Determine which tank fills faster.

Time (min)	4	12	15	20
Amount (gal)	44	132	165	220

Tank A; 13 gal/min > 11 gal/min

Differentiate Instruction

IF a student misses more than one question, THEN

Differentiate Instruction:
- 3.3 Reteach
- Personal Math Trainer

 Interactive Whiteboard
Interactive Lesson quiz available online

DIFFERENTIATE INSTRUCTION *Extend-the-Math Activity* **PRE-AP**

Activity Have students select any of the proportional relationships in the lesson, given as an equation, table, or graph. Then have them consider whether there is still a proportional relationship if each of these operations is performed on the y-values.

- double the y-values yes
- divide the y-values by 10 yes
- add 5 to the y-values no
- subtract 5 from the y-values no

Then have them classify which operations kept the proportional relationship and which did not. Multiplication and division preserve the proportional relationship; addition and subtraction do not.

Ready to Go On?

Assess Mastery

Access *Ready to Go On?* assessment online, and receive instant scoring, feedback, and customized intervention or enrichment.

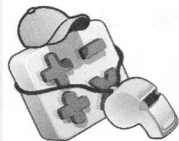

Personal Math Trainer

Online Assessment and Intervention
• Module 3 Posttest

Additional Resources

my.hrw.com

Digital Teacher Resources

Go online for module-level resources.

Assessment Resources
• Module 3 Quiz: B, p.23
• Module 3 Quiz: D, p.25

Ready to Go On?

Personal Math Trainer
Online Assessment and intervention
my.hrw.com

3.1 Representing Proportional Relationships

1. Find the constant of proportionality for the table of values.

x	2	3	4	5
y	3	4.5	6	7.5

$k = 1.5$

2. Phil is riding his bike. He rides 25 miles in 2 hours, 37.5 miles in 3 hours, and 50 miles in 4 hours. Find the constant of proportionality and write an equation to describe the situation.

$k = 12.5; y = 12.5x$

3.2 Rate of Change and Slope

Find the slope of each line.

3.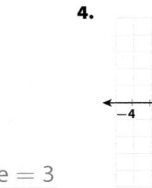

slope = 3

4.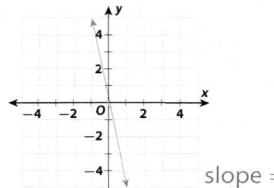

slope = −5

3.3 Interpreting the Unit Rate as Slope

5. The distance Train A travels is represented by $d = 70t$, where d is the distance in kilometers and t is the time in hours. The distance Train B travels at various times is shown in the table. What is the unit rate of each train? Which train is going faster?

Time (hours)	Distance (km)
2	150
4	300
5	375

Train A: 70 km per hour; Train B: 75 km per hour; Train B is faster.

 ESSENTIAL QUESTION

6. What is the relationship among proportional relationships, lines, rates of change, and slope?

Sample answer: The graph of a proportional relationship is a line through the origin whose slope is the unit rate of change.

© Houghton Mifflin Harcourt Publishing Company

Module 3 **89**

READY TO GO ON? *Diagnostic Assessment*

Response to Intervention

Use to determine if students have mastered the concepts covered in this module.

Lesson	Exercises	Content Focus	Review with *Differentiated Instruction*
3.1	1–2	Representing Proportional Relationships	**3.1** Reteach **3.1** Reading Strategies **3.1** Success for English Learners
3.2	3–4	Rate of Change and Slope	**3.2** Reteach **3.2** Reading Strategies **3.2** Success for English Learners
3.3	5	Interpreting the Unit Rate as Slope	**3.3** Reteach **3.3** Reading Strategies **3.3** Success for English Learners

Assessment Readiness

Personal Math Trainer

Online Assessment and Intervention

my.hrw.com

Selected Response

1. Which of the following is equivalent to 5^{-1}?

Ⓐ 4   Ⓒ $-\frac{1}{5}$

Ⓑ $\frac{1}{5}$ Ⓓ -5

2. Prasert earns $9 an hour. Which table represents this proportional relationship?

Ⓐ
Hours	4	6	8
Earnings ($)	36	54	72

Ⓑ
Hours	4	6	8
Earnings ($)	36	45	54

Ⓒ
Hours	2	3	4
Earnings ($)	9	18	27

Ⓓ
Hours	2	3	4
Earnings ($)	18	27	54

3. A factory produces widgets at a constant rate. After 4 hours, 3,120 widgets have been produced. At what rate are the widgets being produced?

Ⓐ 630 widgets per hour

Ⓑ 708 widgets per hour

Ⓒ 780 widgets per hour

Ⓓ 1,365 widgets per hour

4. A full lake begins dropping at a constant rate. After 4 weeks it has dropped 3 feet. What is the unit rate of change in the lake's level compared to its full level?

Ⓐ 0.75 feet per week

Ⓑ 1.33 feet per week

Ⓒ −0.75 feet per week

Ⓓ −1.33 feet per week

5. What is the slope of the line below?

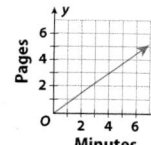

Ⓐ −2   Ⓒ $\frac{1}{2}$

Ⓑ $-\frac{1}{2}$ Ⓓ 2

6. Jim earns $41.25 in 5 hours. Susan earns $30.00 in 4 hours. Pierre's hourly rate is less than Jim's, but more than Susan's. What is his hourly rate?

Ⓐ $6.50   Ⓒ $7.35

Ⓑ $7.75   Ⓓ $8.25

Mini-Task

7. Joelle can read 3 pages in 4 minutes, 4.5 pages in 6 minutes, and 6 pages in 8 minutes.

a. Make a table of the data.

Minutes	4	6	8
Pages	3	4.5	6

b. Use the values in the table to find the unit rate.

0.75 page per minute

c. Graph the relationship between minutes and pages read.

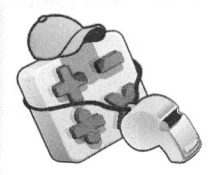

© Houghton Mifflin Harcourt Publishing Company

Preparing for High Stakes Tests

Assessment Readiness Tip

Students can use estimation to eliminate some or all of the incorrect answer choices.

- **Item 3** About 3,000 widgets are produced in 4 hours, so about 750 widgets are produced per hour. This allows students to eliminate choices A and D.

- **Item 4** If the lake has dropped 3 feet after 4 weeks, it is dropping at a rate a little slower than −1 feet per week. Only answer choice C fits the situation.

Avoid Common Errors

- **Item 2** Remind students to examine the relationship between both rows of a table before answering. The pattern 9, 18, 27 in choice C may appear correct but does not match the relationship given in the problem.

- **Item 5** Remind students how a negative sign affects the slope of a line and that slope is rise over run.

Items	Grade 8 Lessons	Mathematical Processes
1*	2.1	MP.2
2	3.1	MP.4
3	3.2	MP.4
4	3.2	MP.4
5	3.2	MP.6
6	3.3	MP.4
7	3.3	MP.4

*Item integrates mixed review concepts from previous modules or a previous course.

DIFFERENTIATE ASSESSMENT

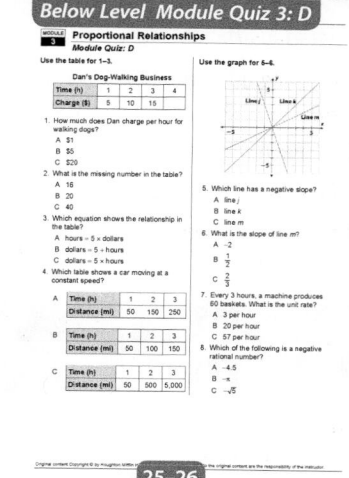

Below Level Module Quiz 3: D

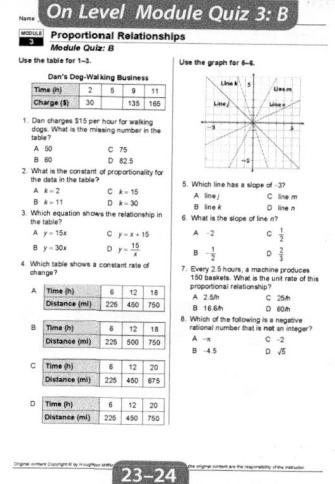

On Level Module Quiz 3: B

Personal Math Trainer Module 3 Assessment Readiness

Pages shown are from *Assessment Resources*. **Also available online.**

Module At A Glance

MODULE 4 | Nonproportional Relationships

Lessons at A Glance	Lesson 4.1 Representing Linear Nonproportional Relationships	Lesson 4.2 Determining Slope and *y*-intercept	Lesson 4.3 Graphing Linear Nonproportional Relationships using Slope and *y*-intercept
	Pg. T95A	Pg. T101A	Pg. T107A
Essential Question	How can you use tables, graphs, and equations to represent linear nonproportional situations?	How can you determine the slope and the *y*-intercept of a line?	How can you graph a line using the slope and *y*-intercept?
Objective	Students will use tables, graphs, and equations to represent linear nonproportional situations.	Students will determine the slope and the *y*-intercept of a line.	Students will graph a line using the slope and *y*-intercept.
Vocabulary	Linear equation	slope-intercept form of an equation, *y*-intercept	
Go online for all your module resources my.hrw.com	4.1 *i*Student Edition 4.1 *i*Teacher Edition 4.1 *e*Student Edition Personal Math Trainer Math on the Spot Videos Animated Math (Models?)	4.2 *i*Student Edition 4.2 *i*Teacher Edition 4.2 *e*Student Edition Personal Math Trainer Math on the Spot Videos Animated Math (Models?)	4.3 *i*Student Edition 4.3 *i*Teacher Edition 4.3 *e*Student Edition Personal Math Trainer Math on the Spot Videos Animated Math (Models?)
Print Resources	4.1 Student Edition *Differentiated Instruction* 4.1 Practice and Problem Solving A/B, C, and D 4.1 Reteach 4.1 Reading Strategies 4.1 Success for English Learners	4.2 Student Edition *Differentiated Instruction* 4.2 Practice and Problem Solving A/B, C, and D 4.2 Reteach 4.2 Reading Strategies 4.2 Success for English Learners	4.3 Student Edition *Differentiated Instruction* 4.3 Practice and Problem Solving A/B, C, and D 4.3 Reteach 4.3 Reading Strategies 4.3 Success for English Learners

RtI Response to Intervention

Before the Module	During the Lesson	After the Module
Are You Ready	Guided/Independent Practice	Ready to Go On?
• Prerequisite Skills Activities • Personal Math Trainer	• Reteach • Personal Math Trainer • Practice and Problem Solving D	• Reteach • Personal Math Trainer

Lesson 4.4
Proportional and Nonproportional Situations

Pg. 113A

How can you distinguish between proportional and nonproportional situations?

Students will distinguish between proportional and nonproportional situations.

4.4 *i*Student Edition

4.4 *i*Teacher Edition

4.4 *e*Student Edition

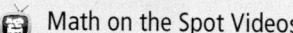 Personal Math Trainer

Math on the Spot Videos

Animated Math (Models?)

4.4 Student Edition

Differentiated Instruction

4.4 Practice and Problem Solving A/B, C, and D

4.4 Reteach

4.4 Reading Strategies

4.4 Success for English Learners

Teacher Notes

Check It Out!

Math on the Spot Videos	Animated Math
 One for every Example in every Lesson	During Lesson 4.3

Nonproportional Relationships

🔵 Real-World Video Viewing Guide

After students have watched the video, discuss the following:

- How do you find the total cost per mile for a gas-fueled vehicle? divide the total cost of one tank of gas by the distance you travel

- According to the video, why is the cost of an electric car cheaper over the lifetime of the car? The cost per mile can be quite a bit lower than the cost per mile for a gas-fueled vehicle.

Professional Development Video

Author Juli Dixon models successful teaching practices as she explores the concept of nonproportional relationships in an actual eighth-grade classroom.

MODULE 4

Nonproportional Relationships

❓ ESSENTIAL QUESTION

How can you use nonproportional relationships to solve real-world problems?

You can make tables, write equations, and draw graphs to model real-world nonproportional relationships.

LESSON 4.1
Representing Linear Nonproportional Relationships

LESSON 4.2
Determining Slope and y-intercept

LESSON 4.3
Graphing Linear Nonproportional Relationships using Slope and y-intercept

LESSON 4.4
Proportional and Nonproportional Situations

Real-World Video

The distance a car can travel on a tank of gas or a full battery charge in an electric car depends on factors such as fuel capacity and the car's efficiency. This is described by a nonproportional relationship.

🌐 my.hrw.com

© Houghton Mifflin Harcourt Publishing Company • Image Credits: ©viappy/ Shutterstock

GO DIGITAL
my.hrw.com

my.hrw.com
Go digital with your write-in student edition, accessible on any device.

Math On the Spot
Scan with your smart phone to jump directly to the online edition, video tutor, and more.

Animated Math
Interactively explore key concepts to see how math works.

Personal Math Trainer
Get immediate feedback and help as you work through practice sets.

91

TEACHER ONLINE RESOURCES

 ONLINE TEACHER EDITION Access a full suite of teaching resources online—plan, present, and manage classes and assignments.

 MY SMART PLANNER Easily plan your classes and access all your resources online.

 INTERACTIVE WHITEBOARDS Engage students with interactive whiteboard-ready examples and a lesson quiz for each lesson.

 PERSONAL MATH TRAINER: Online Assessment and Intervention Assign automatically graded homework, quizzes, tests, and intervention activities. Prepare your students for standardized tests in short-answer and multiple-choice formats.

Reading Start-Up

Visualize Vocabulary

Use the ✔ words to complete the diagram. You can put more than one word in each box.

Reviewing Slope

| Rise is the change in |
| y-coordinates |

| Run is the change in |
| x-coordinates |

$\frac{rise}{run}$ is

slope,
rate of change

© Houghton Mifflin Harcourt Publishing Company

Vocabulary

Review Words
- ordered pair (par ordenado)
- proportional relationship (relación proporcional)
- ✔ rate of change (tasa de cambio)
- ✔ slope (pendiente)
- ✔ x-coordinate (coordenada x)
- ✔ y-coordinate (coordenada y)

Preview Words
- linear equation (ecuación lineal)
- slope-intercept form of an equation (forma de pendiente-intersección)
- y-intercept (intersección con el eje y)

Understand Vocabulary

Complete the sentences using the preview words.

1. The y-coordinate of the point where a graph of a line crosses the y-axis is the _____y-intercept_____.

2. A _____linear equation_____ is an equation whose solutions form a straight line on a coordinate plane.

3. A linear equation written in the form $y = mx + b$ is the _____slope-intercept form of the equation_____.

Active Reading

Booklet Before beginning the module, create a booklet to help you learn the concepts. Write the main idea of each lesson on each page of the booklet. As you study each lesson, write important details that support the main idea, such as vocabulary and formulas. Refer to your finished booklet as you work on assignments and study for tests.

Reading Start-Up

Visualize Vocabulary
The diagram helps students review the concept of slope that is fundamental to linear relationships. Students should write one or more review words in each box to complete the definition.

Understand Vocabulary
Use the following explanation to help students learn the preview words.

> The word linear means "in the shape of a line." A **linear equation** is an equation whose solution forms a line. Linear relationships can represent either proportional or nonproportional relationships. When you graph linear equations, remember that the graph may be a line, but that does not mean the relationship is proportional.

Active Reading
Integrating Language Arts
Students can use these reading and note-taking strategies to help them organize and understand new concepts and vocabulary.

Additional Resources
Differentiated Instruction
- Reading Strategies **ELL**
- Interactive multilingual glossary

LEARNING PROGRESSIONS ACROSS THE GRADES

Before	In this Module	After
Students understand proportional and linear relationships: • use tables and verbal descriptions to describe a linear relationship • write and graph a linear relationship • represent constant rates of change given a table, verbal description, equation, or graph • determine constant of proportionality in real-world situations	Students represent and solve problems involving proportional and nonproportional relationships: • represent linear nonproportional situations with tables, graphs, and equations in the form of $y = mx + b, b \neq 0$. • use data from a table or graph to determine the rate of change or slope and y-intercept in real-world problems • distinguish between proportional and nonproportional situations using tables, graphs, and equations in the form $y = kx$ and $y = mx + b$, where $b \neq 0$	Students will connect that: • proportional relationships are in the form $y = kx$ and their graphs will pass through the origin • nonproportional relationships are in the form $y = mx + b$, where $b \neq 0$ and their graphs do not pass through the origin

Are You Ready?

Assess Readiness

Access *Are You Ready?* assessment online, and receive instant scoring, feedback, and customized intervention or enrichment.

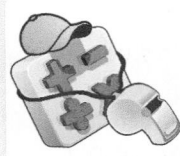

Personal Math Trainer

Online Assessment and Intervention

Additional Resources

Digital Teacher Resources

Go online for module-level resources.

© Houghton Mifflin Harcourt Publishing Company

Personal Math Trainer
Online Assessment and Intervention

my.hrw.com

Complete these exercises to review skills you will need for this module.

Integer Operations

EXAMPLE

$-7 - (-4) = -7 + 4$
$|-7| - |-4|$
$7 - 4$, or 3
$= -3$

To subtract an integer, add its opposite. The signs are different, so find the difference of the absolute values. Use the sign of the number with the greater absolute value.

Find each difference.

1. $3 - (-5)$ ___ 8
2. $-4 - 5$ ___ −9
3. $6 - 10$ ___ −4
4. $-5 - (-3)$ ___ −2
5. $8 - (-8)$ ___ 16
6. $9 - 5$ ___ 4
7. $-3 - 9$ ___ −12
8. $0 - (-6)$ ___ 6
9. $12 - (-9)$ ___ 21
10. $-6 - (-4)$ ___ −2
11. $-7 - 10$ ___ −17
12. $5 - 14$ ___ −9

Graph Ordered Pairs (First Quadrant)

EXAMPLE

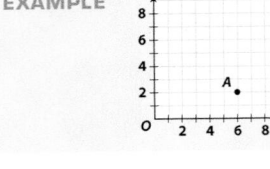

To graph a point at (6, 2), start at the origin.
Move 6 units right.
Then move 2 units up.
Graph point A(6, 2).

Graph each point on the coordinate grid.

13. B (0, 5)

14. C (8, 0)

15. D (5, 7)

16. E (2, 3)

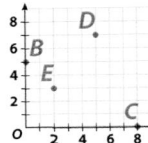

ARE YOU READY? *Diagnostic Assessment*

RtI Response to Intervention

Use to determine if students need intervention for the module's prerequisite skills.

Skill	Missed More Than . . .	Intervene With *Skills Intervention* worksheets (available online)	For Enrichment *Differentiated Instruction* (available in print and online)
Integer Operations	3 questions	**Skill 47**	**Module 4 Challenge** Extend-the-Math Lesson Activities in TE
Graph Ordered Pairs (First Quadrant)	1 question	**Skill 69**	**Module 4 Challenge** Extend-the-Math Lesson Activities in TE

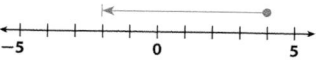

Are YOU Ready? *(cont'd)*

Complete these exercises to review skills you will need for this module.

Integer Operations

17. Describe how to find the difference: $-4 - (-12)$.

> Sample answer: To subtract an integer, add its opposite, so add $-4 + 12$. Since these numbers have different signs, add them by finding the difference of their absolute values:
> $$|12| - |-4| = 12 - 4 = 8.$$
> Use the sign of the number with the greater absolute value. The answer is 8.

18. Carla used a number line graph to analyze an integer subtraction problem. Interpret her graph to tell what the problem was, and give the solution.

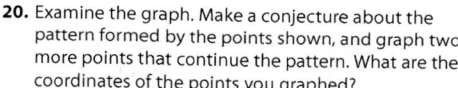

> The graph represents the difference $4 - 6$. The solution is -2.

Graph Ordered Pairs (First Quadrant)

19. A fountain is located at point A. A park bench is located at point B. Give the coordinates for the park bench and describe the location of point B relative to point A.

> The park bench (point B) is at $(7, 6)$, which is 4 units to the right and 1 unit down from point A.

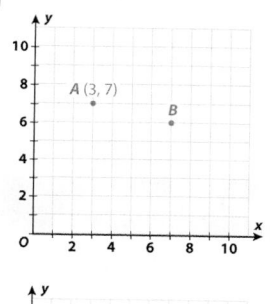

20. Examine the graph. Make a conjecture about the pattern formed by the points shown, and graph two more points that continue the pattern. What are the coordinates of the points you graphed?

> Each point is 1 unit to the right and 2 units up from the point before it. The next two points are $(4, 8)$ and $(5, 10)$.

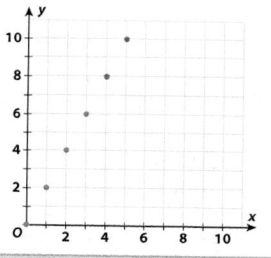

© Houghton Mifflin Harcourt Publishing Company

Integer Operations

Exercise 17 Make sure students understand that there may be more than one way to find the difference of two integers.

Exercise 18 Students may have difficulty reading a graph that represents integer subtraction. Have them identify the start of the arrow, and then have them count the number of units moving left from the start to the end of the arrow.

Graph Ordered Pairs (First Quadrant)

Exercise 19 Students may confuse the x- and y-coordinates of the new point. Point out that moving to the right or left changes the x-coordinate, and moving up or down changes the y-coordinate.

Exercise 20 Encourage students to describe their pattern verbally, and then test to see if the pattern fits all points of the graph.

Use to determine if students are able to apply the module's prerequisite skills.

Skill	Exercise	Depth of Knowledge (D.O.K.)	Mathematical Processes
Integer Operations	17	**3** Strategic Thinking	**MP.2** Abstract and Quantitative Reasoning
	18	**2** Skills/Concepts	**MP.4** Mathematical Modeling
Graph Ordered Pairs (First Quadrant)	19	**2** Skills/Concepts	**MP.2** Abstract and Quantitative Reasoning
	20	**3** Strategic Thinking	**MP.7** See Structure

Lesson Support

Content Objective Students will use tables, graphs, and equations to represent linear nonproportional situations.

Professional Development

Integrate Mathematical Processes   MP.4

This lesson provides an opportunity to address this Mathematical Processes standard. It calls for students to use equations, tables, and graphs to represent relationships. Students use equations to represent a relationship between corresponding values. Then students make tables to represent some values in the relationship. Finally, students use graphs to visualize the relationship.

FOCUS

Building Background

Eliciting Prior Knowledge Have students make tables to compare the equations $y = 2x$ and $y = 2x + 1$ for $x = 0, 1, 2, 3,$ and 4. Ask them to identify which equation represents a proportional relationship and why. Then discuss similarities and differences between the equations.

$y = 2x$					
x	0	1	2	3	4
y	0	2	4	6	8

$y = 2x + 1$					
x	0	1	2	3	4
y	1	3	5	7	9

COHERENCE

Learning Progressions

In this lesson, students use tables, graphs, and equations to represent linear nonproportional situations. They recognize that the representations look different but are equivalent. Important understandings for students include the following:

- **Represent linear relationships using tables.**
- **Recognize that linear equations can be written in the form $y = mx + b$.**
- **Represent linear relationships using equations.**

Students are introduced to the fact that while not all linear equations represent proportional situations, all have a constant rate of change. Students continue to discover and describe the characteristics of linear equations that are both proportional and nonproportional throughout this module.

RIGOR

Cluster Connections

This lesson provides an excellent opportunity to connect ideas in the cluster:

Define, evaluate, and compare functions.

Tell students that the points (2, 5) and (4, 11) lie on a line. Ask them to explain whether the equation of the line represents a proportional relationship or a nonproportional relationship.

The relationship is nonproportional. Sample explanation: If you extend the line, it does not pass through the origin.

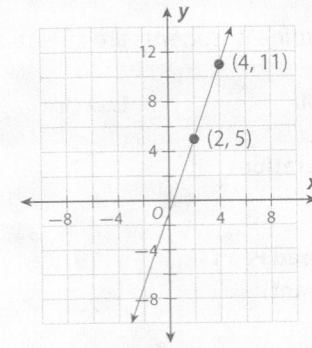

Language Support ELL

Image Credits: ©Mehmet Dilsiz/Shutterstock

Language Objective Students will show how to use tables, graphs, and equations to represent linear nonproportional situations.

Leveled Strategies for English Learners ELL

Emerging
Based on the Theme Park Costs problems in Explore Activity 2, give a group of students index cards with statements of the *x*-values (number of tickets) and *y*-values (total cost). Include costs for entrance fee, tickets for games, rides, and food. Have them read the cards aloud to each other and make a table representing the data.

Expanding
Have students create sentences orally to represent a case for each cell of a table for a fictitious student's visit to the Mountain World theme park. "Carlos paid his entrance fee and bought two tickets to ride the Go Carts. It cost him $24."

Bridging
Have students in groups of four compose a short narrative in complete sentences to tell about the costs of a fictitious student from a table and then plot points on the graph based on the data provided in their narrative.

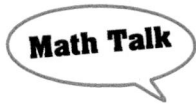

Use sentence frames based on an example from the Independent Practice to describe the process of plotting points on a graph.

Linguistic Support ELL

Academic/Content Vocabulary
This lesson makes references to points and lines in a graph representing proportional versus nonproportional relationships. Students need to review graphing terms, such as *coordinates*, *ordered pairs*, and *origin*. Display a graph with each of these features labeled. Also, display graphs of lines that represent proportional relationships and graphs of lines that represent nonproportional relationships.

Background Knowledge
To help students relate to the scenario in Explore Activity 2, have students imagine and describe what two students would do in the theme park based on rides or games available, tickets for shows or foods, and so on. Have groups of students compose a narrative of each student's visit to the park and create a table of values. Then exchange narratives and tables to have another group plot the table data onto a graph.

Representing Linear Nonproportional Relationships

1 Engage

ESSENTIAL QUESTION

How can you use tables, graphs, and equations to represent linear nonproportional situations?
Sample answer: Make a table from an equation by calculating corresponding *y*-values for different *x*-values. A table of values generates ordered pairs that you can graph.

Motivate the Lesson

Ask: The cost of cellphone service usually depends on the amount of data that is used during the month, but also has some flat monthly charges, too. How can you represent these costs with an equation? Begin the lesson to find out.

2 Explore

EXPLORE ACTIVITY   EXAMPLE 1

Focus on Patterns
Point out to students that *y*-values increase by 3 as the *x*-values increase by 1.

ADDITIONAL EXAMPLE 1 The equation $y = 2x + 5$ gives the total height, *y*, of a plant in an experiment that was 5 cm tall at the beginning of the experiment and grew 2 cm each day. Make a table of values for this situation.

x (number of days)	1	2	3	4
y (height in cm)	7	9	11	13

 Interactive Whiteboard
Interactive example available online

YOUR TURN   MP.2

Talk About It

Check for Understanding
Ask: Francisco spends $4 on transportation. Why isn't the equation $y = 12x + 4$ instead of $y = 12x - 4$? Finding earnings after transportation costs requires subtracting transportation costs from earnings.

Representing Linear Nonproportional Relationships

8.2.4.1
Students will use tables, graphs, and equations to represent linear nonproportional situations.

ESSENTIAL QUESTION

How can you use tables, graphs, and equations to represent linear nonproportional situations?

 EXPLORE ACTIVITY   Real World

Representing Linear Relationships Using Tables

You can use an equation to describe the relationship between two quantities in a real-world situation. You can use a table to show some values that make the equation true.

EXAMPLE 1 The equation $y = 3x + 2$ gives the total charge, *y*, for one person to rent a pair of shoes and bowl *x* games at Baxter Bowling Lanes based on the prices shown. Make a table of values for this situation.

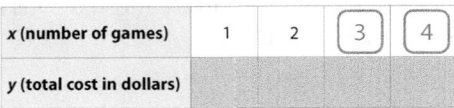
BAXTER bowling lanes
$3 per game
$2 shoe rental

STEP 1 Choose several values for *x* that make sense in context. Count by ones.

x (number of games)	1	2	3	4
y (total cost in dollars)				

STEP 2 Use the equation $y = 3x + 2$ to find *y* for each value of *x*.

x (number of games)	1	2	3	4
y (total cost in dollars)	5	8	11	14

Substitute 1 for *x*:
$y = 3(1) + 2 = 5$

YOUR TURN

1. Francisco makes $12 per hour doing part-time work on Saturdays. He spends $4 on transportation to and from work. The equation $y = 12x - 4$ gives his earnings *y*, after transportation costs, for working *x* hours. Make a table of values for this situation. Sample answer:

x (number of hours)	2	3	4	5
y (earnings in dollars)	20	32	44	56

 **Personal Math Trainer**
Online Assessment and Intervention
my.hrw.com

© Houghton Mifflin Harcourt Publishing Company

Math On the Spot
my.hrw.com

Lesson 4.1   **95**

DIFFERENTIATE INSTRUCTION *Leveled Questions*

	EXPLORE ACTIVITY EXAMPLE 1
AL DOK 1 *Recall*	Would it make sense to choose negative values for *x*? Explain. No; you cannot bowl a negative number of games.
OL DOK 2 *Skills/Concepts*	In $y = 3x + 2$, what could the 2 represent? Sample answer: the cost of renting bowling shoes
BL DOK 3 *Strategic Thinking*	If you graph this linear relationship, would a line accurately represent this situation? Explain. No; only whole number values of *x* and their corresponding *y*-values make sense in this context, so an accurate graph would be points.

EXPLORE ACTIVITY 2 (Real World)

Examining Linear Relationships

Recall that a proportional relationship is a relationship between two quantities in which the ratio of one quantity to the other quantity is constant. The graph of a proportional relationship is a line through the origin. Relationships can have a constant rate of change but not be proportional.

The entrance fee for Mountain World theme park is $20. Visitors purchase additional $2 tickets for rides, games, and food. The equation $y = 2x + 20$ gives the total cost, y, to visit the park, including purchasing x tickets.

STEP 1 Complete the table.

x (number of tickets)	0	2	4	6	8
y (total cost in dollars)	20	24	28	32	36

STEP 2 Plot the ordered pairs from the table. Describe the shape of the graph.

The points lie on a line.

STEP 3 Find the rate of change between each point and the next. Is the rate constant?

$2 per ticket; yes

Theme Park Costs

(graph: Cost ($) vs Number of tickets, points plotted rising)

STEP 4 Calculate $\frac{y}{x}$ for the values in the table. Explain why the relationship between number of tickets and total cost is not proportional.

Undefined, 12, 7, about 5.3, 4.5; the ratio of the total cost to the number of tickets sold is not constant, and the graph doesn't pass through the origin.

Reflect

2. **Analyze Relationships** Would it make sense to add more points to the graph from $x = 0$ to $x = 10$? Would it make sense to connect the points with a line? Explain.

Yes; you could add the points (1, 22), (3, 26), (5, 30), (7, 34), (9, 38), and (10, 40). No; Sample answer: The number of tickets can only be a whole number.

96 Unit 2

© Houghton Mifflin Harcourt Publishing Company

	EXPLORE ACTIVITY 2
(AL) DOK 1 *Recall*	Which ordered pair immediately indicates that the relationship is not proportional? (0, 20)
(OL) DOK 2 *Skills/Concepts*	How you can tell from examining the table that the rate of change in the relationship is constant? For each constant change of 2 in the value of *x*, the change in the value of *y* is also constant (4).
(BL) DOK 3 *Strategic Thinking*	Suppose the theme park did not charge an entrance fee, but instead charged $5 for tickets in the park. What would be the new equation for the total cost? Is there any number of tickets for which the pricing would be the same as the original pricing? Explain. $y = 5x$; There is no number of tickets that for which the two pricings would be the same because the solution of $5x = 2x + 20$ is not a whole number, and tickets can only be sold in whole-number amounts.

---

3 Explain

EXPLORE ACTIVITY 2

Avoid Common Errors
Be sure students understand the context of a problem to determine whether the graph of a linear relationship is a solid line or a set of unconnected points.

TEACHER TO TEACHER

Multiple Representations Discuss with students the strengths and weaknesses of each type of linear representation. For example, a table can only include a few ordered pairs. Likewise, a graph only displays the relationship over a limited range. Only an equation can fully represent a relationship and conclusively demonstrate that a relationship is linear.

EXAMPLE 2

ADDITIONAL EXAMPLE 2 A lake has an average depth of 4 feet. A new dam has just been completed, and the average depth of the lake will increase by $\frac{3}{4}$ foot each day for the next 8 days. The equation $y = \frac{3}{4}x + 4$ gives y, the average depth of the lake, after x days. Draw a graph of the equation. Describe the relationship. The relationship is linear but nonproportional. The graph is a line, but it does not go through the origin.

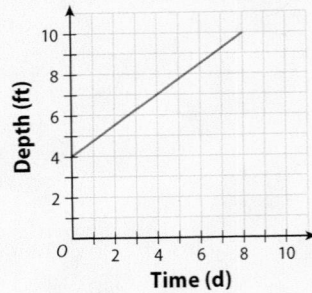

Interactive Whiteboard
Interactive example available online

YOUR TURN MP.6

Avoid Common Errors
Remind students of the rules for multiplying by a negative number. If the signs are the same, the product is positive. If the signs are different, the product is negative.

Digital Teacher Resources

Go online to access all your lesson-level resources.

Differentiated Instruction
• Reteach
• Reading Strategies
• Success for English Learners
• Practice and Problem Solving A/B, C, D

Math on the Spot Videos

Representing Linear Relationships Using Graphs

Math On the Spot
my.hrw.com

A **linear equation** is an equation whose solutions are ordered pairs that form a line when graphed on a coordinate plane. Linear equations can be written in the form $y = mx + b$. When $b \neq 0$, the relationship between x and y is *nonproportional*.

EXAMPLE 2

My Notes

The diameter of a Douglas fir tree is currently 10 inches when measured at chest height. Over the next 50 years, the diameter is expected to increase by an average growth rate of $\frac{2}{5}$ inch per year. The equation $y = \frac{2}{5}x + 10$ gives y, the diameter of the tree in inches, after x years. Draw a graph of the equation. Describe the relationship.

STEP 1 Make a table. Choose several values for x that make sense in context. To make calculations easier, choose multiples of 5.

x (years)	0	10	20	30	50
y (diameter in inches)	10	14	18	22	30

STEP 2 Plot the ordered pairs from the table. Then draw a line connecting the points to represent all the possible solutions.

STEP 3 The relationship is linear but nonproportional. The graph is a line but it does not go through the origin.

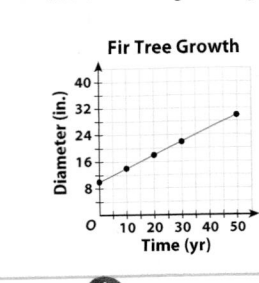

Fir Tree Growth

YOUR TURN

3. Make a table and graph the solutions of the equation $y = -2x + 1$.

x	−1	0	1	2
y	3	1	−1	−3

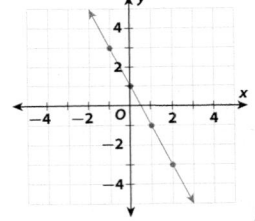

Personal Math Trainer
Online Assessment and Intervention
my.hrw.com

Lesson 4.1 **97**

DIFFERENTIATE INSTRUCTION *Leveled Questions*

		EXAMPLE 2
(AL) **DOK 1** *Recall*		How do you know from the graph that the relationship is not proportional? The graph does not go through the origin.
(OL) **DOK 2** *Skills/Concepts*		Why is there no point with an x-coordinate of 40 on the graph? The x-value of 40 is not in the table.
(BL) **DOK 3** *Strategic Thinking*		Assume that negative values of x represent years before the current time. From the graph, when would you predict that the tree began to grow? Explain. $x = -25$, or 25 years ago; Sample answer: The tree began to grow when its diameter was 0, or where the line would cross the x-axis, which is at -25.

LEVELED QUESTIONS: (AL) Approaching Level | (OL) On Level | (BL) Beyond Level

Make a table of values for each equation. (Explore Activity Example 1)

1. $y = 2x + 5$

x	−2	−1	0	1	2
y	1	3	5	7	9

2. $y = \frac{3}{8}x - 5$

x	−8	0	8	16	24
y	−8	−5	−2	1	4

Explain why each relationship is not proportional. (Explore Activity 2)

3.

x	0	2	4	6	8
y	3	7	11	15	19

First calculate $\frac{y}{x}$ for the values in the table.

Undefined, 3.5, 2.75, 2.5, 2.375;

The ratio $\frac{y}{x}$ is not constant.

4.

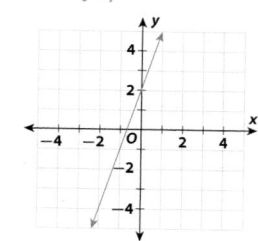

The graph is a line but it does not pass through the origin.

Complete the table for the equation. Then use the table to graph the equation. (Example 2)

5. $y = x - 1$

x	−2	−1	0	1	2
y	−3	−2	−1	0	1

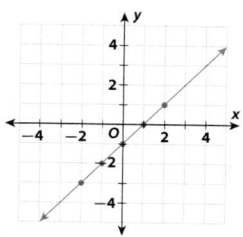

? ESSENTIAL QUESTION CHECK-IN

6. How can you choose values for x when making a table of values representing a real world situation?

Sample answer: Choose values that make sense in the context. For example, games played must be whole numbers.

© Houghton Mifflin Harcourt Publishing Company

4 Elaborate

Talk About It

Summarize the Lesson

Have students complete the graphic organizer showing at least one similarity and one difference between proportional and nonproportional linear relationships.

Similarities	Differences
Sample answer: Both graph as lines. Both have a constant rate of change.	Sample answer: Proportional linear relationship: The line passes through the origin. Nonproportional linear relationship: The line does not pass through the origin.

Guided Practice

Avoid Common Errors

- **Exercise 3** Remind students that the value of $\frac{y}{x}$ when y is 3 and x is 0 is undefined because the denominator of the fraction is 0.

- **Exercise 4** Remind students that the graph of a nonproportional linear relationship is a line that does not pass through the origin.

Engage with the Whiteboard

Have students label the coordinates of several points in **Exercise 4**. Then have them demonstrate that the x- and y-values do not form a proportion.

DIFFERENTIATE INSTRUCTION *Intervention and Additional Support*

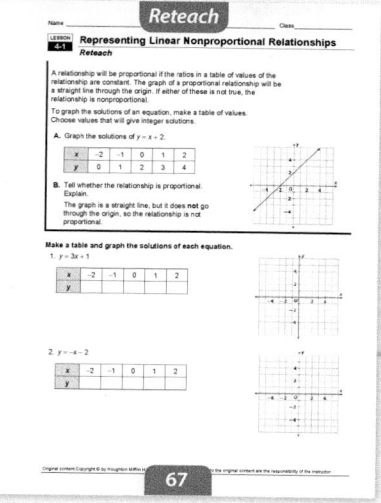

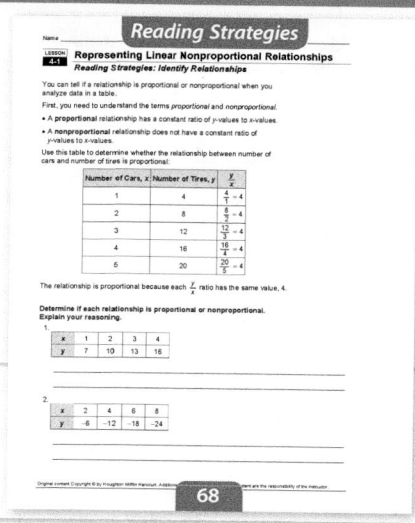

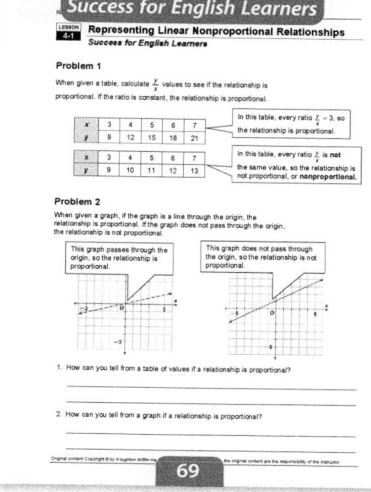

Personal Math Trainer
Daily Intervention
4.1 Homework

Pages shown are from *Differentiated Instruction*. **Also available online.**

5 Evaluate

⏱ Pressed for Time

4.1 Differentiated Homework Assignments

(AL) **Approaching Level**		7–9, 12
(OL) **On Level**		9–12
(BL) **Beyond Level**		10–13

*For **Below Level** students, assign Personal Math Trainer, Daily Intervention 4.1 Homework.*

Mathematical Processes	Exercises
MP.3 Logic	10–12
MP.4 Modeling	7–9
MP.7 Using Structure	13

Focus on Higher Order Thinking

Depth of Knowledge	Exercises
2 Skills/Concepts	7–11
3 Strategic Thinking H.O.T.	12–13

4.1 Independent Practice

Personal Math Trainer
Online Assessment and Intervention
my.hrw.com

State whether the graph of each linear relationship is a solid line or a set of unconnected points. Explain your reasoning.

7. The relationship between the number of $4 lunches you buy with a $100 school lunch card and the money remaining on the card

Set of unconnected points;

Sample answer: You cannot buy

a fractional part of a lunch.

8. The relationship between time and the distance remaining on a 3-mile walk for someone walking at a steady rate of 2 miles per hour

Solid line; Sample answer:

The distance remaining can be

measured at any moment in

time.

9. **Analyze Relationships** Simone paid $12 for an initial year's subscription to a magazine. The renewal rate is $8 per year. This situation can be represented by the equation $y = 8x + 12$, where x represents the number of years the subscription is renewed and y represents the total cost.

a. Make a table of values for this situation.   Sample answer:

x (number of years renewed)	0	1	2	3	4
y (total cost in dollars)	12	20	28	36	44

b. Draw a graph to represent the situation. Include a title and axis labels.

c. Explain why this relationship is not proportional.

Sample answer: The graph does not

include the origin. Also, the ratio of the

total cost and number of years is not

constant.

d. Does it make sense to connect the points on the graph with a solid line? Explain.

No; the number of years must be a whole

number, so total cost goes up in $8

increments.

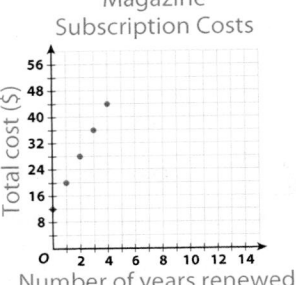

Magazine Subscription Costs

© Houghton Mifflin Harcourt Publishing Company

DIFFERENTIATE INSTRUCTION *Leveled Homework/Practice*

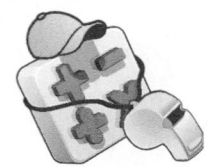

Personal Math Trainer
• 4.1 Homework

Pages shown are from *Differentiated Instruction*.
Also available online.

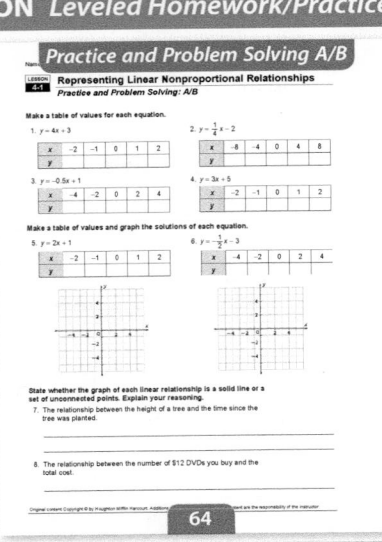

Practice and Problem Solving A/B

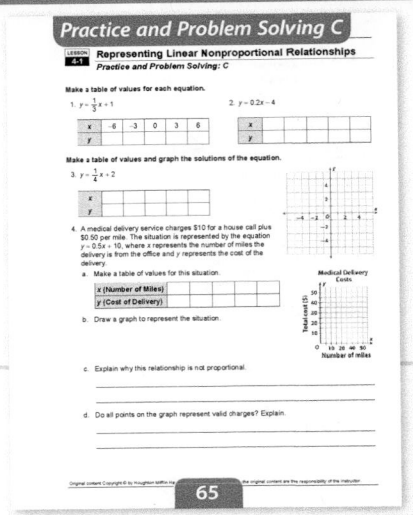

Practice and Problem Solving C

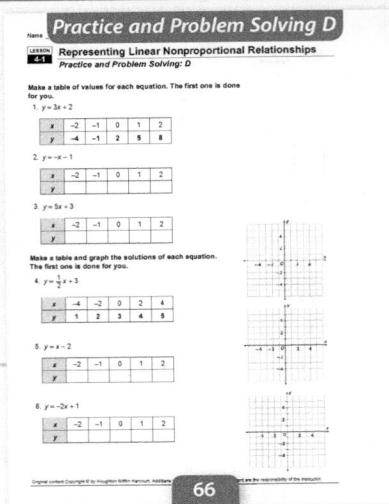

Practice and Problem Solving D

10. Analyze Relationships A proportional relationship is a linear relationship because the rate of change is constant (and equal to the constant of proportionality). What is required of a proportional relationship that is *not* required of a general linear relationship?

The graph must pass through the origin.

11. Communicate Mathematical Ideas Explain how you can identify a linear non-proportional relationship from a table, a graph, and an equation.

Sample answer: In a table, the ratios $\frac{y}{x}$ will not be equal; a graph will not pass through the origin; an equation will be in the form $y = mx + b$, where $b \neq 0$.

 **FOCUS ON HIGHER ORDER THINKING**

12. Critique Reasoning George observes that for every increase of 1 in the value of *x*, there is an increase of 60 in the corresponding value of *y*. He claims that the relationship represented by the table is proportional. Critique George's reasoning.

x	1	2	3	4	5
y	90	150	210	270	330

Sample answer: George's observation is true, but his claim is false. There is a constant rate of change. However, the relationship is not proportional because the ratio of *y* to *x* (90, 75, 70, 67.5, 66) is not constant.

13. Make a Conjecture Two parallel lines are graphed on a coordinate plane. How many of the lines could represent proportional relationships? Explain.

At most one; sample answer: A line representing a proportional relationship must pass through the origin. A line parallel to it cannot also pass through the origin, so at most one of the lines can represent a proportional relationship.

Work Area

© Houghton Mifflin Harcourt Publishing Company

100 Unit 2

DIFFERENTIATE INSTRUCTION *Extend-the-Math Activity* **PRE-AP**

Activity The equation $y = 2.5x - 1500$ represents the profit made by a manufacturer that sells a product for $2.50 each, where *y* is the profit and *x* is the number of units sold. Construct a table to find the number of units that must be sold for the manufacturer to break even. The break-even point is where profit is equal to 0. Explain the data in the table.

x	100	200	300	400	500	600
y	−1250	−1000	−750	−500	−250	0

Sample answer: When the *y*-values are negative, it means that that manufacturer has lost money. When *x* is 600, the *y*-value is 0, so the break-even point is when 600 units are sold.

✔ **Quick Check**

4.1 Lesson Quiz

A large pizza costs $10. Each topping costs an additional $2. This situation can be represented by the equation $y = 10 + 2x$, where *x* represents the number of toppings and *y* represents the total cost.

1. Make a table of values for this situation.

x	1	2	3	4
y	12	14	16	18

2. Draw a graph to represent this situation.

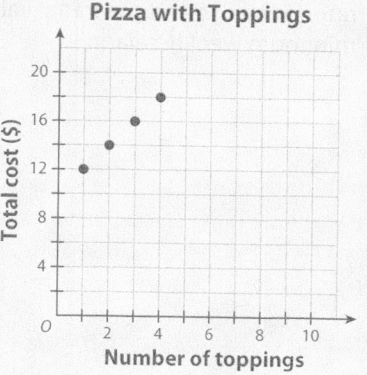

Pizza with Toppings

3. Explain why this relationship is not proportional. Sample answer: The graph does not go through the origin.

4. Does it make sense to connect the points on the graph with a solid line? Explain. No. The number of toppings must be a whole number, so the total cost goes up $2 for each additional topping.

Differentiate Instruction

IF a student misses more than one question, THEN

Differentiate Instruction:
• 4.1 Reteach
• Personal Math Trainer

Interactive Whiteboard
Interactive Lesson quiz available online

Lesson Support

Content Objective Students will learn to determine the slope and y-intercept of a line.

Professional Development

Integrate Mathematical Processes MP.7

This lesson provides an opportunity to address this Mathematical Processes standard. It calls for students to discern structure. In this lesson, students discern the relationship between slope and rate of change. In Example 1, students use a table to find the constant rate of change and the initial value and relate these to a salesperson's commission and minimum weekly salary.

FOCUS

Building Background

Eliciting Prior Knowledge Review how to find the rate of change (the slope) of a proportional relationship. Have students find the slope of a line that passes through the points $(-4, -2)$ and $(4, 2)$. Elicit that the slope is the rise over the run, or the change in x over the change in y. $m = \frac{2}{4} = \frac{1}{2}$

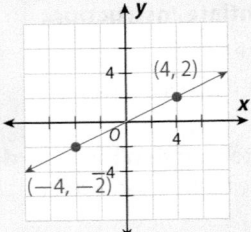

COHERENCE

Learning Progressions

In this lesson, students are introduced to the slope-intercept form of a linear equation. They determine the slope and y-intercept of linear equations from tables and from graphs. Important understandings for students include the following:

- **Determine the rate of change of a linear relationship.**
- **Determine the initial value of a linear relationship.**
- **Use the slope-intercept form of an equation of a line.**

In this lesson students derive the slope-intercept form of a linear equation. They also relate the slope to the rate of change and the y-intercept to the initial value of the linear relationship. This prepares them for graphing linear relationships using the slope and the y-intercept in the next lesson.

RIGOR

Cluster Connections

This lesson provides an excellent opportunity to connect ideas in the cluster:

Understand the connections between proportional relationships, lines, and linear equations.

Have students consider the linear equation $y = -5x + 50$. Tell them that the graph starts at the point (0, 50). Have students interpret the slope as the rate of change and the y-intercept as the initial value to write a real-world situation that could be modeled by the equation.

Sample answer: A tank filled with 50 gallons of water is being drained at a constant rate of 5 gallons per minute. After x minutes, y gallons remain in the tank.

Language Support ELL

Leveled Strategies for English Learners ELL

Emerging
In complete sentences and using common language on index cards, write out the steps for determining initial value. Have students, in groups, put the steps in chronological order to show how they used the "work backward" approach.

Expanding
Have students work in a group to create and write complete sentences describing each step in solving for initial value on index cards. Then have them put the cards with the steps in chronological order.

Bridging
Have students explain their steps in plotting points on a graph to depict a real-world problem and data table. Have them point out the *y*-intercept and what it means in relation to the table. Have students compare and contrast the rate of change (constant, not constant) and the initial value in the problem based on the *y*-intercept.

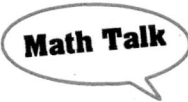

Clarify the concept of initial value as a term that refers to an unknown in a real-world math problem. To "work backward" is a strategy or approach to the data given. Draw arrows and write values on the table as students produce language to describe the "work backward" steps.

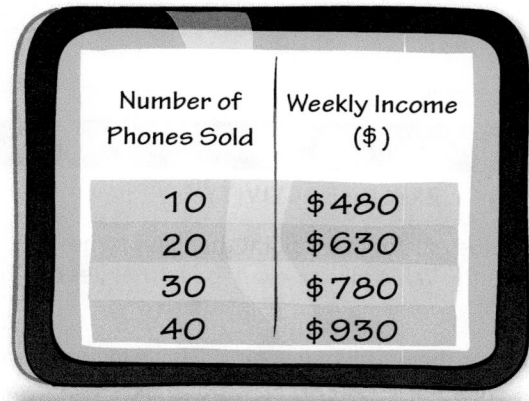

Number of Phones Sold	Weekly Income ($)
10	$480
20	$630
30	$780
40	$930

Linguistic Support ELL

Academic/Content Vocabulary
It is important to clarify some basic concepts and terms that have the same or different meanings, such as *income* and *salary*. Students may not understand what commission is and how it works. Use the table in Example 1, shown here, to point out that the weekly *salary* without any phones sold is $330, and the *commission* earned is $15 per phone.

Background Knowledge
In Independent Practice, some common expressions that may be unfamiliar to students are, *split the cost, hourly rate, group lessons,* and *private lessons*. Be sure to clarify the meaning of these expressions. Give similar examples, such as *daily rate, monthly rate,* and *yearly rate*. Elaborate by using the prefix *bi-*, meaning "every two," as in *biweekly, bimonthly,* and *biannually*.

Determining Slope and *y*-intercept

① Engage

❓ ESSENTIAL QUESTION

How can you determine the slope and the *y*-intercept of a line? Sample answer: Find the slope of the line using the coordinates of two points found on the graph. Then find the *y*-coordinate of the point where the graph crosses the *y*-axis.

Motivate the Lesson

Ask: What can the equation for a line tell you about the slope and *y*-intercept of the line? Begin the Explore Activity to find out.

② Explore

EXPLORE ACTIVITY 1

Engage with the Whiteboard

Have students draw vertical and horizontal arrows to represent the rise and the run between the points (0, 4) and (−3, 6) on the graph. Then have them do the same for two other points on the line. Next, calculate the slope using the new pair of points. Point out the slope is the same for both pairs of points.

LESSON
4.2

Determining Slope and *y*-intercept

8.2.4.2
Students will determine the slope and the y-intercept of a line.

❓ ESSENTIAL QUESTION

How can you determine the slope and the *y*-intercept of a line?

EXPLORE ACTIVITY 1

Investigating Slope and *y*-intercept

The graph of every nonvertical line crosses the *y*-axis. The **y-intercept** is the *y*-coordinate of the point where the graph intersects the *y*-axis. The *x*-coordinate of this point is always 0.

The graph represents the linear equation $y = -\frac{2}{3}x + 4$.

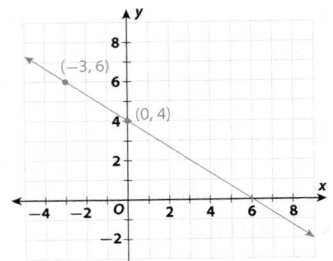

STEP 1 Find the slope of the line using the points (0, 4) and (−3, 6).

$$m = \frac{6 - \boxed{4}}{\boxed{-3} - 0} = \frac{\boxed{2}}{\boxed{-3}} = \boxed{-\frac{2}{3}}$$

STEP 2 The line also contains the point (6, 0). What is the slope using (0, 4) and (6, 0)? Using (−3, 6) and (6, 0). What do you notice?
$-\frac{2}{3}$; $-\frac{2}{3}$; it is the same as in Step 1

STEP 3 Compare your answers in Steps 1 and 2 with the equation of the graphed line.
The slope $m = -\frac{2}{3}$ is the coefficient of the variable *x* in $y = -\frac{2}{3}x + 4$.

STEP 4 Find the value of *y* when *x* = 0 using the equation $y = -\frac{2}{3}x + 4$. Describe the point on the graph that corresponds to this solution.
4; (0, 4) is where the line intersects the *y*-axis.

STEP 5 Compare your answer in Step 4 with the equation of the line.
The number 4 is the same as the number that is added to the *x*-term in the equation $y = -\frac{2}{3}x + 4$.

© Houghton Mifflin Harcourt Publishing Company

Lesson 4.2 **101**

DIFFERENTIATE INSTRUCTION *Leveled Questions*

	EXPLORE ACTIVITY 1
(AL) DOK 1 *Recall*	What is the value of *x* for every point that lies on the *y*-axis? What is the value of *y* for every point that lies on the *x*-axis? 0; 0
(OL) DOK 2 *Skills/Concepts*	What point does the graph of $y = \frac{2}{3}x + 4$ have in common with the graph of $y = -\frac{2}{3}x + 4$? How do you know? (0, 4); the constant 4 in each equation is the *y*-intercept, so both graphs contain the point (0, 4).
(BL) DOK 3 *Strategic Thinking*	Using the results from Steps 4 and 5 in the Explore Activity, what would be the equation of a line with the same slope that went through point (0, 2)? Explain. $y = -\frac{2}{3}x + 2$; the coefficient of *x* would be the same but the number added to the *x*-term would change.

LEVELED QUESTIONS: (AL) Approaching Level | (OL) On Level | (BL) Beyond Level

Math On the Spot

my.hrw.com

Determining Rate of Change and Initial Value

The linear equation shown is written in the **slope-intercept form of an equation.** Its graph is a line with **slope** m and **y-intercept** b.

$$y = mx + b$$

slope y-intercept

A linear relationship has a constant rate of change. You can find the **rate of change** m and the **initial value** b for a linear situation from a table of values.

EXAMPLE 1

A phone salesperson is paid a minimum weekly salary and a commission for each phone sold, as shown in the table. Confirm that the relationship is linear and give the constant rate of change and the initial value.

STEP 1 Confirm that the rate of change is constant.

$$\frac{\text{change in income}}{\text{change in phones sold}} = \frac{630-480}{20-10} = \frac{150}{10} = 15$$

$$\frac{\text{change in income}}{\text{change in phones sold}} = \frac{780-630}{30-20} = \frac{150}{10} = 15$$

$$\frac{\text{change in income}}{\text{change in phones sold}} = \frac{930-780}{40-30} = \frac{150}{10} = 15$$

Number of Phones Sold	Weekly Income ($)
10	$480
20	$630
30	$780
40	$930

The rate of change is a constant, **15**.

The salesperson receives a $15 commission for each phone sold.

STEP 2 Find the initial value when the number of phones sold is 0.

$-10 \quad -10$

Number of phones sold	0	10	20
Weekly income ($)	330	480	630

$-150 \quad -150$

Work backward from $x = 10$ to $x = 0$ to find the initial value.

The initial value is $330. The salesperson receives a salary of $330 each week before commissions.

YOUR TURN

Find the slope and y-intercept of the line represented by each table.

1.
x	2	4	6	8
y	22	32	42	52

$m = 5; b = 12$

2.
x	1	2	3	4
y	8	15	22	29

$m = 7; b = 1$

Personal Math Trainer

Online Assessment and Intervention

my.hrw.com

Math Talk
Mathematical Processes

How do you use the rate of change to work backward to find the initial value?

Sample answer: Work backward from the greatest number of phones to 0. Then work the weekly income back proportionally.

© Houghton Mifflin Harcourt Publishing Company

3 Explain

EXAMPLE 1

Avoid Common Errors
Focus on Patterns
Point out to students that the change in phones sold is always 10 and the change in income is always 150. In Step 2, in order to find the initial value, they need to subtract 10 from the number of phones sold and 150 from the weekly income.

ADDITIONAL EXAMPLE 1 Gregg deposits the money he makes from mowing lawns into his savings account, adding it to the money his father gave him to open the account. Confirm the relationship is linear and give the constant rate of change and the initial value.

Lawns mowed	5	10	15	20
Money saved ($)	110	170	230	290

The constant rate of change is 12. The initial value is $50.

Interactive Whiteboard
Interactive example available online

YOUR TURN   MP.7

Focus on Communication
Be sure that students can explain that in order to find the y-intercept, they need to work backward to find the y-value when x is 0.

TEACHER TO TEACHER

Cognitive Strategies When finding the slope of a line from a graph, such as in Step 1 of Explore Activity 1, have students draw in the right triangle indicating the rise and the run between two points on the line. Point out to students that it does not matter whether the right triangle is above or below the line. For a positive slope, both the rise and run will be the same sign. For a negative slope, the rise and run will have different signs.

		EXAMPLE 1
AL	**DOK 1** *Recall*	What does the rate of change for this situation describe? the constant amount the salesperson's income goes up for a constant increase in phones sold
OL	**DOK 2** *Skills/Concepts*	What is the income for a week in which the salesperson sells only 5 phones? Explain. $405; the salesperson receives a commission of $5 \times $15 = 75 on top of a weekly salary of $330.
BL	**DOK 3** *Strategic Thinking*	If you increase the initial value $60 and decrease the commission $3 for each phone sold, how many phones will the salesperson need to sell to receive the same amount of money as the salesperson in Example 1? 20 phones; the salesperson will receive $630 when the initial value is $390 and the commission is $12, or when the initial value is $330 and the commission is $15.

EXPLORE ACTIVITY 2

Focus on Math Connections

Point out that in Step 3, students are following the same steps they would use to solve a linear equation. The only difference is that there are variables instead of numbers.

Digital Teacher Resources

Go online to access all your lesson-level resources.

my.hrw.com

Differentiated Instruction
- Reteach
- Reading Strategies
- Success for English Learners
- Practice and Problem Solving A/B, C, D

Math on the Spot Videos

EXPLORE ACTIVITY 2

Deriving the Slope-intercept Form of an Equation

In the following Explore Activity, you will derive the slope-intercept form of an equation.

STEP 1 Let L be a line with slope m and y-intercept b. Circle the point that must be on the line. Justify your choice.

$(b, 0)$ $(0, b)$ $(0, m)$ $(m, 0)$

The coordinate of x is 0 in the point that includes the y-intercept.

STEP 2 Recall that slope is the ratio of change in y to change in x. Complete the equation for the slope m of the line using the y-intercept $(0, b)$ and another point (x, y) on the line.

$$m = \frac{y - \boxed{b}}{\boxed{x} - 0}$$

STEP 3 In an equation of a line, we often want y by itself on one side of the equation. Solve the equation from Step 2 for y.

$$m = \frac{y - b}{x} \qquad \text{Simplify the denominator.}$$

$$m \cdot \boxed{x} = \frac{y - b}{x} \cdot \boxed{x} \qquad \text{Multiply both sides of the equation by } \underline{\ x\ }.$$

$$m \boxed{x} = y - b$$

$$mx + \boxed{b} = y - b + \boxed{b} \qquad \text{Add } \underline{\ b\ } \text{ to both sides of the equation.}$$

$$mx + \boxed{b} = y$$

$$y = mx + \boxed{b} \qquad \text{Write the equation with } y \text{ on the left side.}$$

Reflect

3. Critical Thinking Write the equation of a line with slope m that passes through the origin. Explain your reasoning.

$y = mx$; Sample answer: Because the origin is on the y-axis, the graph crosses the y-axis at $(0, 0)$. So, the y-intercept b is 0, and $y = mx + b$ becomes $y = mx$.

© Houghton Mifflin Harcourt Publishing Company

Lesson 4.2 **103**

DIFFERENTIATE INSTRUCTION *Leveled Questions*

	EXPLORE ACTIVITY 2
(AL) DOK 1 *Recall*	How can you determine the slope and y-intercept of an equation such as $y = 3x - 2$ by just looking at the equation? The slope is the coefficient of x. For $y = 3x - 2$, the slope is 3. The y-intercept is the same as the constant, −2.
(OL) DOK 2 *Skills/Concepts*	To show that every line of the form $y = mx + b$ has a y-intercept of b, what substitution can you make for x? Substitute 0 for x.
(BL) DOK 3 *Strategic Thinking*	When you find the change in x-values and y-values in Step 2, does it make a difference in which order you subtract? Explain. Sample answer: Yes; you must subtract the x-values in the same order in which you subtract the y-values. Otherwise, you will get the wrong sign.

LEVELED QUESTIONS: (AL) Approaching Level | (OL) On Level | (BL) Beyond Level

Find the slope and *y*-intercept of the line in each graph. (Explore Activity 1)

1.

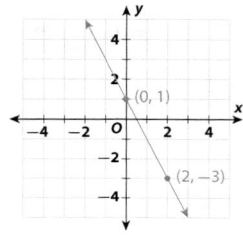

(0, 1)

(2, −3)

slope *m* = _−2_   *y*-intercept *b* = _1_

2.

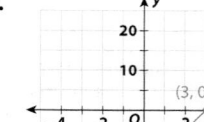

(3, 0)

(0, −15)

slope *m* = _5_   *y*-intercept *b* = _−15_

3.

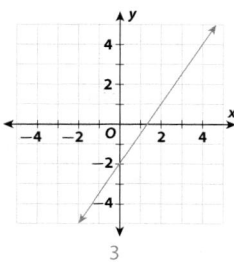

slope *m* = $\frac{3}{2}$ *y*-intercept *b* = _−2_

4.

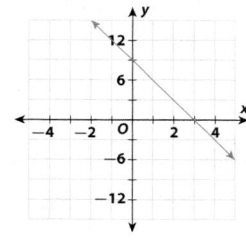

slope *m* = _−3_   *y*-intercept *b* = _9_

Find the slope and *y*-intercept of the line represented by each table. (Example 1)

5.

x	0	2	4	6	8
y	1	7	13	19	25

slope *m* = _3_   *y*-intercept *b* = _1_

6.

x	0	5	10	15	20
y	140	120	100	80	60

slope *m* = _−4_   *y*-intercept *b* = _140_

❓ ESSENTIAL QUESTION CHECK-IN

7. How can you determine the slope and the *y*-intercept of a line from a graph?

Find the slope of the line using the coordinates of two

points found on the graph. Then find the *y*-coordinate

of the point where the graph crosses the *y*-axis.

© Houghton Mifflin Harcourt Publishing Company

④ Elaborate

Talk About It

Summarize the Lesson

Ask: How can you determine the slope and *y*-intercept of a line represented by a table? Find the constant rate of change, which is the slope. Find the initial value, *y* when *x* = 0 from the table, or work backward to find it. This value will be the *y*-intercept.

Guided Practice

Engage with the Whiteboard

In **Exercises 3–4,** have students plot the two points they use to find the slope. In **Exercises 1–4,** have them draw vertical and horizontal arrows to represent the rise and run between the two plotted points.

Avoid Common Errors

Exercises 1, 4 Students must assign a negative number to the rise or the run. Remind students that since the line slants down from left to right, the slope will be negative.

DIFFERENTIATE INSTRUCTION *Intervention and Additional Support*

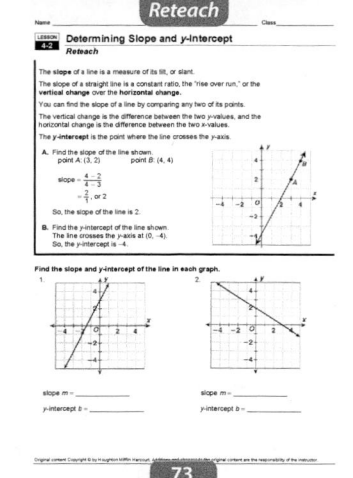

Reteach — 73

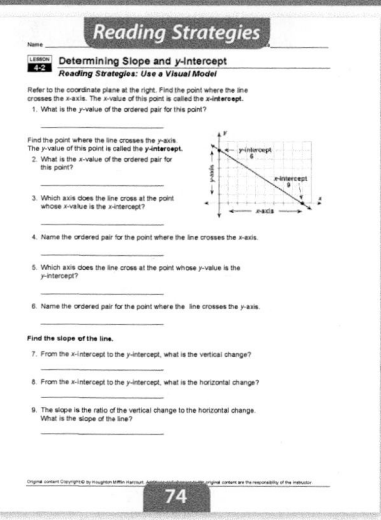

Reading Strategies — 74

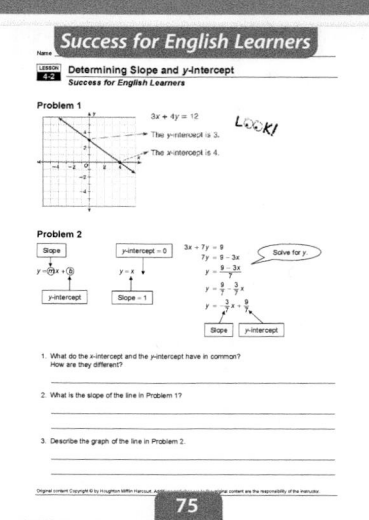

Success for English Learners — 75

Personal Math Trainer
Daily Intervention
4.2 Homework

Pages shown are from *Differentiated Instruction*. **Also available online.**

Determining Slope and *y*-intercept   **104**

⏱ Pressed for Time

4.2 Differentiated Homework Assignments

(AL) **Approaching Level**	8–9, 11–12, 14
(OL) **On Level**	10–14
(BL) **Beyond Level**	11–15

*For **Below Level** students, assign Personal Math Trainer, Daily Intervention 4.2 Homework.*

Mathematical Processes	Exercises
MP.1 Problem Solving	9–10
MP.3 Logic	13–15
MP.6 Precision	8, 11–12

Focus on Higher Order Thinking

Depth of Knowledge	Exercises
2 Skills/Concepts	8–13
3 Strategic Thinking H.O.T.	14–15

8. Some carpet cleaning costs are shown in the table. The relationship is linear. Find and interpret the rate of change and the initial value for this situation.

Rooms cleaned	1	2	3	4
Cost ($)	125	175	225	275

The rate of change is $50 per room. The initial value is $75, which is a flat fee no matter how many rooms are cleaned.

9. **Make Predictions** The total cost to pay for parking at a state park for the day and rent a paddleboat are shown.

a. Find the cost to park for a day and the hourly rate to rent a paddleboat.

$5 to park; $12 per hour

b. What will Lin pay if she rents a paddleboat for 3.5 hours and splits the total cost with a friend? Explain.

$23.50; (3.5 hours × $12 per hour + $5) ÷ 2 = $23.50

Number of Hours	Cost ($)
1	$17
2	$29
3	$41
4	$53

10. **Multi-Step** Raymond's parents will pay for him to take sailboard lessons during the summer. He can take half-hour group lessons or half-hour private lessons. The relationship between cost and number of lessons is linear.

Lessons	1	2	3	4
Group ($)	55	85	115	145
Private ($)	75	125	175	225

a. Find the rate of change and the initial value for the group lessons.

The rate of change is $30 per lesson. The initial value is $25.

b. Find the rate of change and the initial value for the private lessons.

The rate of change is $50 per lesson. The initial value is $25.

c. Compare and contrast the rates of change and the initial values.

Both rates of change are constant, but the private lessons cost more. There is a flat fee of $25 no matter which type of lessons Raymond takes.

© Houghton Mifflin Harcourt Publishing Company

DIFFERENTIATE INSTRUCTION *Leveled Homework/Practice*

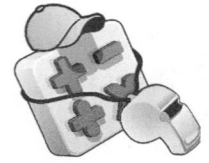

Personal Math Trainer

• 4.2 Homework

Pages shown are from *Differentiated Instruction.* **Also available online.**

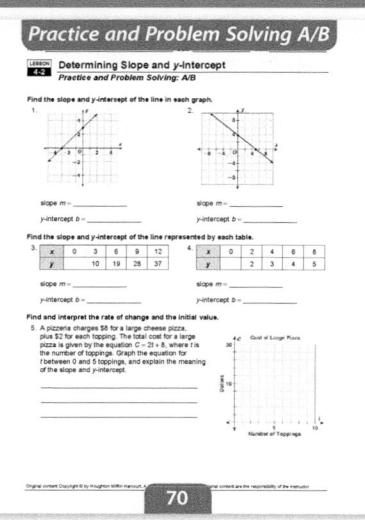

Practice and Problem Solving A/B

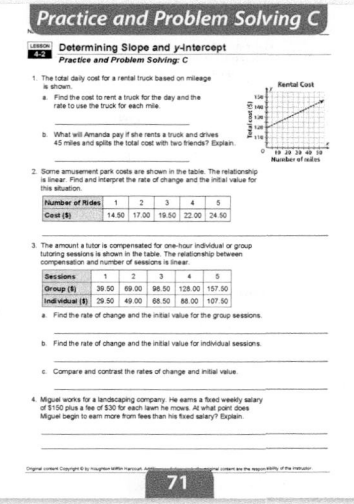

Practice and Problem Solving C

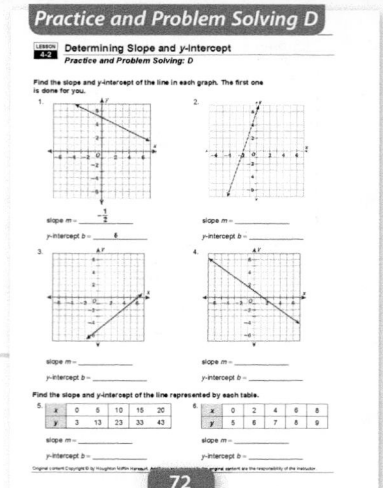

Practice and Problem Solving D

Vocabulary Explain why each relationship is not linear.

11.

x	1	2	3	4
y	4.5	6.5	8.5	11.5

Rate of change is constant from
1 to 2 to 3, but not from 3 to 4.

12.

x	3	5	7	9
y	140	126	110	92

Rate of change is not constant.
It goes from −7 to −8 to −9.

13. Communicate Mathematical Ideas Describe the procedure you performed to derive the slope-intercept form of a linear equation.

Express the slope m between a random point (x, y) on

the line and the point $(0, b)$ where the line crosses the

y-axis. Then solve the equation for y.

 **FOCUS ON HIGHER ORDER THINKING**

14. Critique Reasoning Your teacher asked your class to describe a real-world situation in which a y-intercept is 100 and the slope is 5. Your partner gave the following description: *My younger brother originally had 100 small building blocks, but he has lost 5 of them every month since.*

a. What mistake did your partner make?

The slope is positive, so the amount should be

increasing, not decreasing.

b. Describe a real-world situation that does match the situation.

Sample answer: I opened a savings account with $100 of

birthday money and I add $5 from my allowance every month.

15. Justify Reasoning John has a job parking cars. He earns a fixed weekly salary of $300 plus a fee of $5 for each car he parks. His potential earnings for a week are shown in the graph. At what point does John begin to earn more from fees than his fixed salary? Justify your answer.

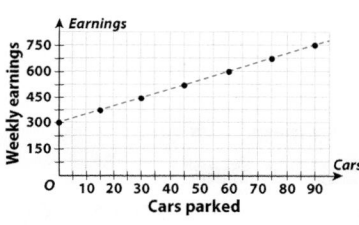

After parking 61 cars; John earns a fixed weekly salary of

$300 plus $5 for each car he parks. He earns the same in

fees as his fixed salary for parking 300 ÷ 5 = 60 cars.

Work Area

© Houghton Mifflin Harcourt Publishing Company

✔ Quick Check

4.2 Lesson Quiz

1. Find the slope and y-intercept of the line represented by the table. $m = 3, b = 1$

x	3	6	9	12
y	10	19	28	37

A large barrel that holds water is leaking. The table shows how much water is left after a specific number of minutes.

Minutes	5	10	15	20
Water (gal)	16	14	12	10

2. Find and interpret the rate of change. The rate of change is $-\frac{2}{5}$. This means that the water is leaking out at a rate of 2 gallons every 5 minutes.

3. Find and interpret the initial value. The initial value is 18 gallons. This means that the barrel originally had 18 gallons of water in it.

4. After how many minutes will the barrel be empty? Explain. The barrel will be empty after 45 minutes. Sample answer: I extended the table until the y-value was 0.

Differentiate Instruction

IF a student misses more than one question, THEN

Differentiate Instruction:
• 4.2 Reteach
• Personal Math Trainer

 Interactive Whiteboard
Interactive Lesson quiz available online

DIFFERENTIATE INSTRUCTION *Extend-the-Math Activity* **PRE-AP**

Activity Points that lie on the same line are called *collinear* points. Without graphing the ordered pairs, determine if each set of points is collinear. Explain your answer.

1. (3, 5), (5, 9), (9, 13)   No. The rate of change is not constant.

2. (−1, −4), (2, 5), (6, 17)   Yes. The rate of change is constant.

These three points are collinear. Find the missing coordinate.

3. (2, −3), (4, 3), (7, y)   12

4. (−5, 1), (−1, 9), (x, 15)   2

Lesson Support

Content Objective Students will learn to graph a line using the slope and *y*-intercept.

Professional Development

Integrate Mathematical Processes MP.6

This lesson provides an opportunity to address this Mathematical Processes standard. It calls for students to communicate precisely, including communicating through the use of symbols and graphs. In Example 2, students begin with a real-world situation represented by a linear equation, they find the *y*-intercept and slope, and then they represent the equation with a graph.

FOCUS	COHERENCE	RIGOR

FOCUS

Building Background

Eliciting Prior Knowledge Have students draw the graph of the line that passes through the points (0, 3) and (2, 0). Then have them explain how to use the graph to find the slope and the *y*-intercept of the line.

$m = -\frac{3}{2}; b = 6$

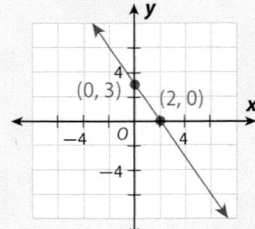

COHERENCE

Learning Progressions

In this lesson, students graph a linear relationship using the rate of change and the initial value, given the equation of the line. They use the graph of a linear function to interpret the rate of change and the initial value in terms of the real-world situation it models. Important understandings for students include the following:

- **Use slope-intercept form to graph a line.**
- **Analyze the graph of a real-world linear relationship.**
- **Use the graph of a real-world linear relationship to solve problems.**

Students demonstrate their understanding of how the rate of change and the initial value of a linear relationship relate to its graph. They also interpret the graphs to solve real-world problems.

RIGOR

Cluster Connections

This lesson provides an excellent opportunity to connect ideas in the cluster:

Use functions to model relationships between quantities.

Ask students to identify and compare the slopes and the *y*-intercepts of the equations $y = 2x + 1$ and $y = -2x + 1$. Then ask them how they think that the opposite signs in the slopes and the matching *y*-intercepts will look when the equations are graphed.

For both lines, $b = 1$ while the slopes are 2 and -2. Answers may vary.

Have students graph the lines to check their predictions.

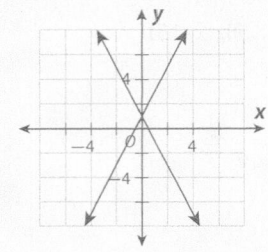

Language Support ELL

Leveled Strategies for English Learners ELL

Emerging

Using the real-world situation of Ken's exercise program in Example 2, write statements that are either true or false on index cards about Ken's weekly goals. The teacher or a more advanced student reads the statements, and students answer *true* or *false*. If the statement is false, have students change the wording to make it true.

Expanding

Have students work in small groups. Students should write a few sentences to create word problems describing different activities that a fictitious person uses in an exercise program to reach his or her goal.

Bridging

Have students write a narrative to describe how a fictitious person would use a heart meter that shows calories burned to meet his or her goals in an exercise program for a week. Have them plot a graph to show each day's calorie-burn results.

Math Talk

Concepts in this lesson require students to understand and sometimes describe steepness. Students at different levels of language proficiency need sentence frames or sentence completion activities to scaffold their descriptions. Post a chart with two labeled graphs and with sentences to describe and compare the steepness shown in each as a model.

Linguistic Support ELL

Academic/Content Vocabulary

Review expressions and phrases for comparing and contrasting the steepness of a slope: *steep, steeper than, steepest, less steep than, as steep as*, and so on. Use parallel constructions in ordinary descriptive language: *Line A shows a slope that is steeper than line B because line A is more straight up-and-down than line B*. Also use terms such as *more horizontal* and *more vertical* to give additional vocabulary for describing and comparing the slope of lines in graphs.

Background Knowledge

The term *absolute value* may be translated or interpreted literally as meaning "something emphatic, or strongly or absolutely true." This interpretation may cause confusion. Explain that *absolute value* means that the value is neither negative nor positive. Without describing direction of the line, the absolute value of the slope describes how steep the slope is.

Image Credits: ©Aleksandr Markin/Shutterstock

Graphing Linear Nonproportional Relationships Using Slope and *y*-intercept

1 Engage

? ESSENTIAL QUESTION

How can you graph a line using the slope and *y*-intercept? Sample answer: First, plot the point that contains the *y*-intercept. Then use the slope to find another point on the line and draw a line through the points.

Motivate the Lesson

Ask: Suppose you are given the slope of a line and a point on the line. How can you use that information to graph the line? Begin the lesson to find out.

2 Explore

EXPLORE ACTIVITY   EXAMPLE 1

ADDITIONAL EXAMPLE 1
Graph each equation.

A $y = 3x + 2$

B $y = -\frac{3}{4}x - 2$

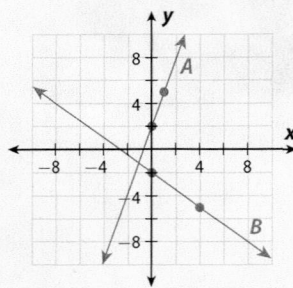

Interactive Whiteboard
Interactive example available online

Animated Math

Exploring Linear Graphs
Students explore graphs of linear relationships by changing the values of *m* and *b* using interactive sliders.

my.hrw.com

Graphing Linear Nonproportional Relationships Using Slope and *y*-intercept

8.2.4.3
Students will graph a line using the slope and *y*-intercept.

? ESSENTIAL QUESTION

How can you graph a line using the slope and *y*-intercept?

Math On the Spot
my.hrw.com

EXPLORE ACTIVITY

Using Slope-intercept Form to Graph a Line

Recall that $y = mx + b$ is the slope-intercept form of the equation of a line. In this form, it is easy to see the slope *m* and the *y*-intercept *b*. So you can use this form to quickly graph a line by plotting the point (0, *b*) and using the slope to find a second point.

Animated Math
my.hrw.com

EXAMPLE 1   Graph each equation.

A $y = \frac{2}{3}x - 1$

STEP 1 The *y*-intercept is $b = \underline{-1}$.
Plot (0, $\underline{-1}$).

STEP 2 Use the slope $m = \dfrac{2}{\underline{3}}$ to find a second point. From (0, $\underline{-1}$), count *up* $\underline{2}$ and *right* $\underline{3}$. The new point is (3, $\underline{1}$).

STEP 3 Draw a line through the points.

B $y = -\frac{5}{2}x + 3$

STEP 1 The *y*-intercept is $b = \underline{3}$. Plot (0, $\underline{3}$).

STEP 2 Use the slope $m = \dfrac{5}{\underline{2}}$ to find a second point. From ($\underline{0}$, $\underline{3}$), count *down* $\underline{5}$ and $\underline{right}$ 2 to the new point ($\underline{2}$, $\underline{-2}$), OR from ($\underline{0}$, $\underline{3}$), count *up* 5 and $\underline{left}$ 2 to the new point ($\underline{-2}$, $\underline{8}$).

STEP 3 Draw a line through the points.

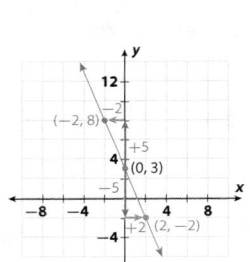

© Houghton Mifflin Harcourt Publishing Company

DIFFERENTIATE INSTRUCTION *Leveled Questions*

	EXPLORE ACTIVITY EXAMPLE 1
AL DOK 1 *Recall*	In Step 2 of part A, why do you count up 2 and right 3? The positive numerator 2 means to count up 2 units. The positive denominator 3 means to count to the right 3 units.
OL DOK 2 *Skills/Concepts*	In Step 2 of part B, does it matter whether you count down 5 and right 2 or count up 5 and left 2? Explain. No; the slope of the line is $-\frac{5}{2}$. You can write this as $\frac{-5}{2}$, for which you count down and right, or $\frac{5}{-2}$, for which you count up and left.
BL DOK 3 *Strategic Thinking*	Is a line with a positive slope always steeper than a line with a negative slope? Explain. No; the line whose slope has the larger absolute value will be steeper. The line in Part B is steeper than the line in Part A even though its slope is negative.

LEVELED QUESTIONS: **AL** Approaching Level | **OL** On Level | **BL** Beyond Level

Reflect

1. **Draw Conclusions** How can you use the slope of a line to predict the way the line will be slanted? Explain.

   A line with a positive slope will rise from left to right.

   A line with a negative slope will fall from left to right.

YOUR TURN

Graph each equation.

2. $y = \frac{1}{2}x + 1$

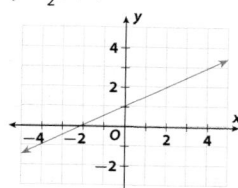

3. $y = -3x + 4$

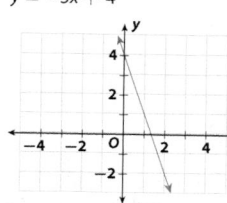

Personal Math Trainer
Online Assessment and Intervention
my.hrw.com

Analyzing a Graph

Math On the Spot
my.hrw.com

Many real-world situations can be represented by linear relationships. You can use graphs of linear relationships to visualize situations and solve problems.

EXAMPLE 2 Real World

Ken has a weekly goal of burning 2400 calories by taking brisk walks. The equation $y = -300x + 2400$ represents the number of calories y Ken has left to burn after x hours of walking which burns 300 calories per hour.

A Graph the equation $y = -300x + 2400$.

STEP 1 Write the slope as a fraction.

$m = \frac{-300}{1} = \frac{-600}{2} = \frac{-900}{3}$ Using the slope as $\frac{-900}{3}$ helps in drawing a more accurate graph.

STEP 2 Plot the point for the y-intercept: (0, 2400).

STEP 3 Use the slope to locate a second point.

From (0, 2400), count *down* 900 and *right* 3.

The new point is (3, 1500).

STEP 4 Draw a line through the two points.

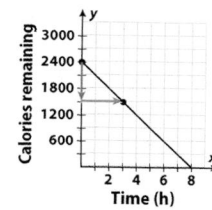

108 Unit 2

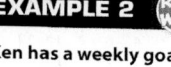

© Houghton Mifflin Harcourt Publishing Company

		EXAMPLE 2
(AL) **DOK 1**	*Recall*	How does the equation $y = -300x + 2400$ indicate that Ken is burning 300 calories each hour by walking briskly? -300 is the rate of change. Because the sign is negative, it means that Ken is using calories instead of gaining them.
(OL) **DOK 2**	*Skills/Concepts*	What does the point (3, 1500) represent? After walking 3 hours, Ken still needs to burn 1500 calories to reach his goal.
(BL) **DOK 3**	*Strategic Thinking*	Ken's friend, Tom, has a weekly goal of burning 2400 calories by jogging, and he reaches his goal after 6 hours. What equation represents the number of calories Tom has left to burn after x hours of jogging? Compare Tom's graph to the one shown in this example. $y = -400x + 2400$; The line representing Tom's graph is steeper, the x-intercept is different, and the y-intercept is the same.

YOUR TURN   MP.2

Avoid Common Errors
Make sure students correctly distinguish the slope and the y-intercept. They could write out the slope and y-intercept for each equation, or underline the slope and circle the y-intercept.

❸ Explain

EXAMPLE 2

ADDITIONAL EXAMPLE 2

A shipping company charges a fixed amount plus a certain amount per pound to ship a package. The total cost y, in dollars, to ship a package is given by the equation $y = 3x + 5$, where x is the weight of the package in pounds.

A Graph the equation.

B What is the weight of a package that can be shipped for $17? 4 lb

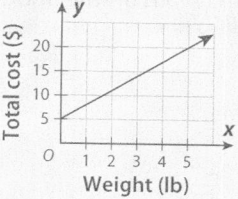

Interactive Whiteboard
Interactive example available online

TEACHER TO TEACHER

Multiple Representations Guide students in making connections between the situation, the equation, the slope, the y-intercept, and the graph. The relationship in Example 2 can be represented in words, with an equation (and statements explaining what each variable represents), and by the graph that is shown in part A. Ask students to express the relationship in their own words without an equation. For example: Ken has a goal to burn 2400 calories each week by walking fast; for each hour that he walks, he burns 300 calories.

Focus on Modeling

Have students identify the *y*-intercept of the line representing this new situation. Ask them to explain what that *y*-intercept means. Have students identify the slope of the line representing this new situation and to explain what that new slope means. Have students express the relationship in the problem in words without an equation.

Digital Teacher Resources

Go online to access all your lesson-level resources.

Differentiated Instruction
- Reteach
- Reading Strategies
- Success for English Learners
- Practice and Problem Solving A/B, C, D

Math on the Spot Videos

my.hrw.com

B After how many hours of walking will Ken have 600 calories left to burn? After how many hours will he reach his weekly goal?

STEP 1 Locate 600 calories on the *y*-axis. Read across and down to the *x*-axis.

Ken will have 600 calories left to burn after 6 hours.

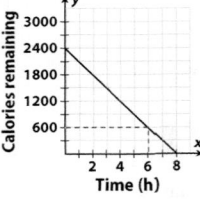

STEP 2 Ken will reach his weekly goal when the number of calories left to burn is 0. Because every point on the *x*-axis has a *y*-value of 0, find the point where the line crosses the *x*-axis.

○ Ken will reach his goal after 8 hours of brisk walking.

YOUR TURN

What If? Ken decides to modify his exercise plans from Example 2 by slowing the speed at which he walks. The equation for the modified plan is $y = -200x + 2400$.

4. Graph the equation.

5. How does the graph of the new equation compare with the graph in Example 2?

   The new graph has the same *y*-intercept but a slope of −200 instead of −300.

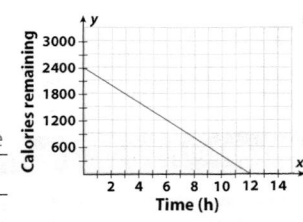

6. Will Ken have to exercise more or less to meet his goal? Explain.

   The calories left to burn will decrease more slowly with each hour of exercise, so it will take longer for Ken to meet his goal.

7. Suppose that Ken decides that instead of walking, he will jog, and that jogging burns 600 calories per hour. How do you think that this would change the graph?

   Sample answer: The *y*-intercept would not change, but the slope would become −600, which is much steeper. The line would intersect the *x*-axis when *x* = 4 hours.

Math Talk
Mathematical Processes

What do the slope and the *y*-intercept of the line represent in this situation?

The slope is −200, which means the number of calories left to burn decreases by 200 calories for every hour of walking. The *y*-intercept is 2400, which means Ken's weekly goal is to burn 2400 calories by walking.

Personal Math Trainer

Online Assessment and Intervention

my.hrw.com

© Houghton Mifflin Harcourt Publishing Company

Graph each equation using the slope and the y-intercept. (Explore Activity Example 1)

1. $y = \frac{1}{2}x - 3$

slope = $\frac{1}{2}$ y-intercept = -3

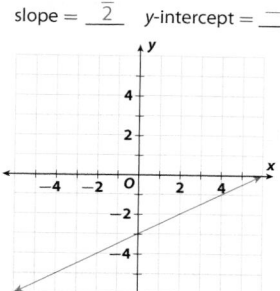

2. $y = -3x + 2$

slope = -3 y-intercept = 2

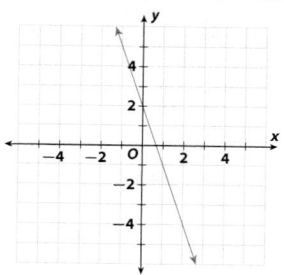

3. A friend gives you two baseball cards for your birthday. Afterward, you begin collecting them. You buy the same number of cards once each week. The equation $y = 4x + 2$ describes the number of cards, y, you have after x weeks. (Example 2)

a. Find and interpret the slope and the y-intercept of the line that represents this situation. Graph $y = 4x + 2$. Include axis labels.

Slope = 4; y-intercept = 2; you start with

2 cards and add 4 cards each week.

b. Discuss which points on the line do not make sense in this situation. Then plot three more points on the line that do make sense.

The points with coordinates that are not whole

numbers; You will not buy part of a baseball card and

you are buying only once a week.

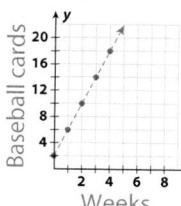

ESSENTIAL QUESTION CHECK-IN

4. Why might someone choose to use the y-intercept and the slope to graph a line?

Sample answer: You can easily identify the slope

m and y-intercept b from the slope-intercept form

$y = mx + b$ and quickly use them to locate two points

that determine the line.

© Houghton Mifflin Harcourt Publishing Company

4 Elaborate

Talk About It

Summarize the Lesson

Ask: How can you graph a line using the slope and y-intercept?

You plot the y-intercept on the y-axis. Then you use the slope to find another point and draw a line through the two points.

Guided Practice

Engage with the Whiteboard

In **Exercises 1–2,** have students change the sign of the slope and graph the new equation. Next have them change the sign of the y-intercept and graph this equation as well.

Avoid Common Errors

- **Exercises 1–2** Remind students that the y-intercept of a line is the number on the y-axis where the line intersects the y-axis.

- **Exercise 3** Students may think that any point with a whole number y-coordinate makes sense. Have students find the x-coordinate when $y = 12$. Explain that after 2 weeks you have 10 cards and after 3 weeks you have 14 cards. Since the cards are only bought once a week and you buy 4 at a time, there is no point at which you will have 12 cards.

DIFFERENTIATE INSTRUCTION *Intervention and Additional Support*

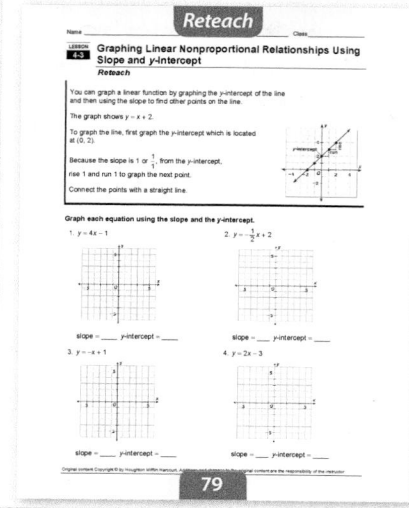

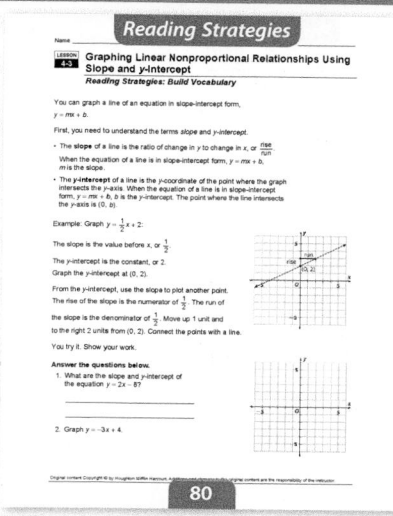

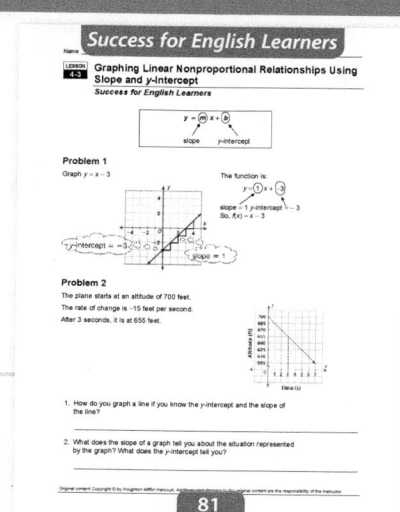

Personal Math Trainer
Daily Intervention
4.3 Homework

Pages shown are from *Differentiated Instruction*. **Also available online.**

⏱ **Pressed for Time**

4.3 Differentiated Homework Assignments

AL **Approaching Level**	6–12, 14
OL **On Level**	5, 8–14
BL **Beyond Level**	5, 12–16

*For **Below Level** students, assign Personal Math Trainer, Daily Intervention 4.3 Homework.*

Mathematical Processes	Exercises
MP.2 Reasoning	12, 15–16
MP.3 Logic	13–14
MP.4 Modeling	5
MP.5 Using Tools	6–11

Focus on Higher Order Thinking

Depth of Knowledge	Exercises
2 Skills/Concepts	6–12
3 Strategic Thinking **H.O.T.**	5, 13–16

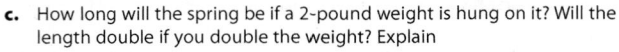
5. **Science** A spring stretches in relation to the weight hanging from it according to the equation $y = 0.75x + 0.25$ where x is the weight in pounds and y is the length of the spring in inches.

a. Graph the equation. Include axis labels.

b. Interpret the slope and the y-intercept of the line.

The slope, 0.75, means that the spring stretches by 0.75 inch with each additional pound of weight. The y-intercept, 0.25, is the unstretched length of the spring in inches.

c. How long will the spring be if a 2-pound weight is hung on it? Will the length double if you double the weight? Explain

1.75 inches; no; the length with a 4-pound weight is 3.25 in., not 3.5 in.

Look for a Pattern **Identify the coordinates of four points on the line with each given slope and y-intercept.** Sample answers are given.

6. slope = 5, y-intercept = −1
(0, −1), (1, 4), (2, 9), (3, 14)

7. slope = −1, y-intercept = 8
(0, 8), (1, 7), (2, 6), (3, 5)

8. slope = 0.2, y-intercept = 0.3
(0, 0.3), (1, 0.5), (2, 0.7), (3, 0.9)

9. slope = 1.5, y-intercept = −3
(0, −3), (1, −1.5), (2, 0), (3, 1.5)

10. slope = $-\frac{1}{2}$, y-intercept = 4
(0, 4), (2, 3), (4, 2), (6, 1)

11. slope = $\frac{2}{3}$, y-intercept = −5
(0, −5), (3, −3), (6, −1), (9, 1)

12. A music school charges a registration fee in addition to a fee per lesson. Music lessons last 0.5 hour. The equation $y = 40x + 30$ represents the total cost y of x lessons. Find and interpret the slope and y-intercept of the line that represents this situation. Then find four points on the line.

Slope = 40, so the cost per lesson is $40; y-intercept = 30, so the registration fee is $30; sample answers: (0, 30), (1, 70), (2, 110), (3, 150).

© Houghton Mifflin Harcourt Publishing Company • Image Credits: ©Steve Williams/Houghton Mifflin Harcourt

---

DIFFERENTIATE INSTRUCTION *Leveled Homework/Practice*

Personal Math Trainer

• 4.3 Homework

Pages shown are from *Differentiated Instruction*. **Also available online.**

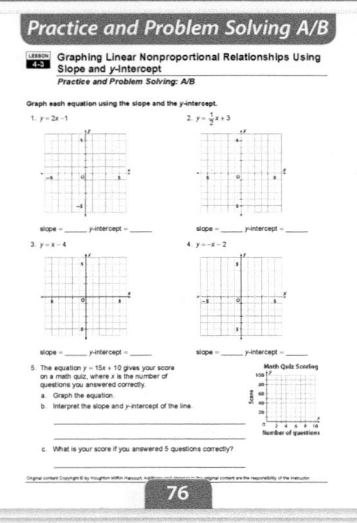

Practice and Problem Solving A/B

76

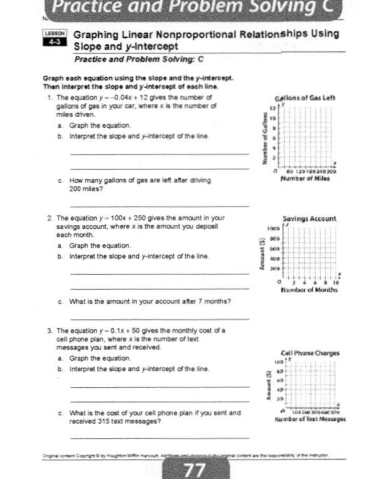

Practice and Problem Solving C

77

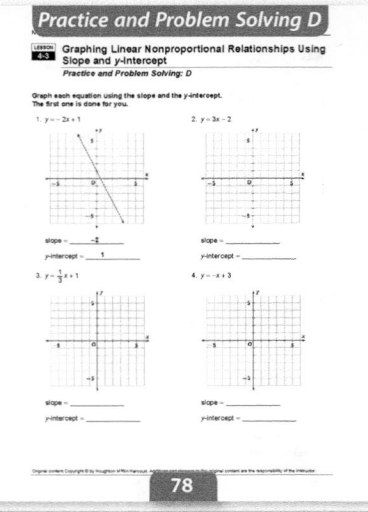

Practice and Problem Solving D

78

13. A public pool charges a membership fee and a fee for each visit. The equation $y = 3x + 50$ represents the cost y for x visits.

   a. After locating the y-intercept on the coordinate plane shown, can you move up three gridlines and right one gridline to find a second point? Explain.

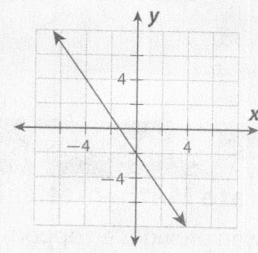

   Yes.; Since the horizontal and vertical gridlines each represent 25 units, moving up 3 gridlines and right 1 gridline represents a slope of $\frac{75}{25}$, or 3.

   b. Graph the equation $y = 3x + 50$. Include axis labels. Then interpret the slope and y-intercept.

   $m = 3$ so $3 is the charge per visit; $b = 50$ so the membership fee is $50.

   c. How many visits to the pool can a member get for $200?

   50 visits

 **FOCUS ON HIGHER ORDER THINKING**

14. Explain the Error A student says that the slope of the line for the equation $y = 20 - 15x$ is 20 and the y-intercept is 15. Find and correct the error.

The coefficient of x, -15, is the slope, not the constant term. The constant term is the y-intercept, 20.

15. Critical Thinking Suppose you know the slope of a linear relationship and a point that its graph passes through. Can you graph the line even if the point provided does *not* represent the y-intercept? Explain.

Yes; you can plot the point and use the slope to find a second point. Then draw a line through the two points.

16. Make a Conjecture Graph the lines $y = 3x$, $y = 3x - 3$, and $y = 3x + 3$. What do you notice about the lines? Make a conjecture based on your observation.

The lines appear to be parallel. Parallel lines have the same slope but different y-intercepts.

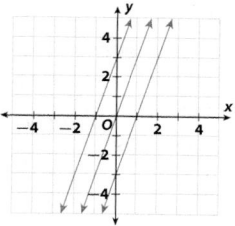

Work Area

© Houghton Mifflin Harcourt Publishing Company

DIFFERENTIATE INSTRUCTION *Extend-the-Math Activity* **PRE-AP**

Activity Have students use graphing calculators to graph on the same set of axes three linear equations whose graphs have the same slope. For example, have them graph $y = 2x$, $y = 2x + 3$, and $y = 2x - 4$. Then have them graph, on a new pair of axes, another set of linear equations whose graphs have the same slope, but different from the slope of the first set of lines. For example, have them graph $y = -3x$, $y = -3x + 2$, and $y = -3x - 1$. Ask students to make a conjecture about lines with the same slopes (they are parallel). Have them try out other sets of linear equations to test their conjectures.

✔ Quick Check

4.3 Lesson Quiz

1. Graph the equation $y = -\frac{3}{2}x - 2$.

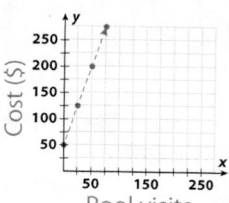

2. Maria is ordering comic books online. The equation $y = 8x + 4$ represents the total cost in dollars, y, including shipping, for ordering x number of comic books.

   a. Graph the equation.

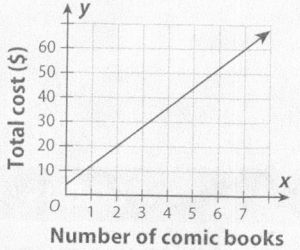

   b. If the total cost including shipping is $60, how many comic books is Maria ordering?

   7 comic books

3. Mr. Goldstein is driving to Houston. The equation $y = -45x + 270$ represents the numbers of miles that he still has to travel after driving for x hours. Find and interpret the slope and y-intercept of the line that represents this situation.

Slope $= -45$; y-intercept $= 270$; he is driving 45 miles per hour and at the beginning, had 270 miles to drive.

Differentiate Instruction

IF a student misses more than one question, THEN

Differentiate Instruction:

• 4.3 Reteach

• Personal Math Trainer

 Interactive Whiteboard

Interactive Lesson quiz available online

Lesson Support

Content Objective Students will learn to distinguish between proportional and nonproportional situations.

Professional Development

Integrate Mathematical Processes MP.6

This lesson provides an opportunity to address this Mathematical Processes standard. It calls for students to communicate mathematical ideas and arguments using precise mathematical language. Students analyze relationships represented by words, tables, equations, and graphs and must describe the relationships with terms such as *proportional, nonproportional, linear*, and *nonlinear*.

FOCUS

Building Background

Eliciting Prior Knowledge Have students work with partners to create an idea tree that relates and differentiates proportional and nonproportional linear relationships.

```
                Linear Relationships
                 /                \
          proportional        nonproportional
               |                     |
     equation of the form    equation of the form
           y = mx                y = mx + b
               |                     |
       rate of change: m      rate of change: m
        initial value: 0       initial value: b
               |                     |
       graph through the      graph through the
       origin with slope m          point
                               (0, b) with slope m
```

COHERENCE

Learning Progressions

In this lesson, students distinguish between and compare proportional and nonproportional situations represented in different ways. Important understandings for students include the following:

- **Distinguish between situations using a graph.**
- **Distinguish between situations using an equation.**
- **Distinguish between situations using a table.**
- **Compare proportional and nonproportional situations.**

Students apply and interpret the properties of proportional and nonproportional situations that they have learned about in Modules 3 and 4. The lesson provides a summary of linear functions.

RIGOR

Cluster Connections

This lesson provides an excellent opportunity to connect ideas in the cluster:

Define, evaluate, and compare functions.

Ask students to write the equation of a proportional relationship. Elicit that the rate of change of the function is the slope. Now ask them to change the equation by giving it a different initial value. Elicit that this is the *y*-intercept of a linear nonproportional relationship. Have students make tables for and then graph each equation. Discuss whether students used the proportional equation to help them make the table or to draw the graph of the nonproportional equation.

Answers may vary.

Language Support ELL

Leveled Strategies for English Learners ELL

Emerging
Have students create price tags for fictitious items in a store. Then use sentence frames to describe what a purchaser pays for the item, including sales tax.

Expanding
Using several price tags for fictitious items, have students work in pairs to create a list of items purchased and calculate the sales tax and total cost.

Bridging
Have students create a short narrative or word problem with different original shopping scenarios and exchange these with a classmate to calculate the sales tax for each purchase and total cost for the purchases.

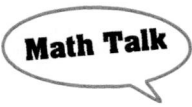

Math Talk The prompt requires the analysis of values in a table. It is preferable that the tables are related to concrete examples with real values that have been previously covered so that students can better understand the data.

Linguistic Support ELL

Academic/Content Vocabulary
An example in this lesson is based on an understanding of sales tax. Students may not be familiar with sales tax and how it is calculated on a purchase, or they may know about similar concepts, such as an *ad valorem* or *value-added* tax. Clarify the context and meaning of a sales tax to ensure that students understand that it is a percentage of a purchase price.

Multiple-Meaning Words
change This lesson uses an example of the exchange rate between Mexican pesos and dollars. Point out the multiple meanings of the word *change* in this example. The term *change* is used in describing the table of the ratio of pesos per U.S. dollar. The tourists also *change* their dollars for pesos. The word *change* also means "the amount left over after a purchase." Clarify how the word *change* is used each time.

Image Credits: ©D. Hurst/Alamy

Proportional and Nonproportional Situations

1 Engage

ESSENTIAL QUESTION

How can you distinguish between proportional and nonproportional situations? Sample answer: Determine whether the relationship is linear and the y-intercept is 0.

Motivate the Lesson

Ask: What are some things where the unit price changes as you buy more of them? Is the price proportional to the number of items you buy? Begin the lesson to find out.

2 Explore

EXPLORE ACTIVITY | EXAMPLE 1

ADDITIONAL EXAMPLE 1 The graph shows the water level as a bathtub fills. Does the graph show a linear relationship? Is the relationship proportional or nonproportional?

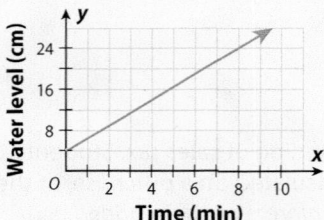

yes; nonproportional

Interactive Whiteboard
Interactive example available online

YOUR TURN | MP.2

Connect Vocabulary ELL
Saying that an equation is "nonproportional" or "nonlinear" is the same as saying that an equation is "not proportional" or "not linear". The prefix "*non-*" means not.

Proportional and Nonproportional Situations

ESSENTIAL QUESTION

How can you distinguish between proportional and nonproportional situations?

EXPLORE ACTIVITY Real World

Distinguish Between Proportional and Nonproportional Situations Using a Graph

Math On the Spot
my.hrw.com

If a relationship is nonlinear, it is nonproportional. If it is linear, it may be either proportional or nonproportional. When the graph of the linear relationship contains the origin, the relationship is proportional.

EXAMPLE 1 The graph shows the sales tax charged based on the amount spent at a video game store in a particular city. Does the graph show a linear relationship? Is the relationship proportional or nonproportional?

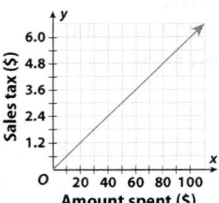

The graph shows a linear ___proportional___ relationship

because it is a ___line___ that contains the ___origin___.

YOUR TURN

Determine if each of the following graphs represents a proportional or nonproportional relationship.

1.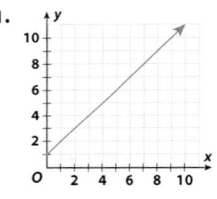

nonproportional

2.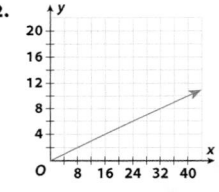

proportional

Personal Math Trainer
Online Assessment and Intervention
my.hrw.com

© Houghton Mifflin Harcourt Publishing Company

DIFFERENTIATE INSTRUCTION *Leveled Questions*

	EXPLORE ACTIVITY EXAMPLE 1
AL DOK 1 *Recall*	What characteristic of a graph indicates a constant rate of change? The graph is a straight line.
OL DOK 2 *Skills/Concepts*	What do the slope and the y-intercept of the graph represent in this situation? The slope is $0.06. It is the change in the amount of sales tax paid for each dollar spent. The y-intercept is 0, meaning you pay no sales tax if you don't buy anything.
BL DOK 3 *Strategic Thinking*	The graph of a relationship has a y-intercept of 0. Can you conclude that the relationship is proportional? Explain. No; the relationship must also be linear for it to be proportional.

LEVELED QUESTIONS: **AL** Approaching Level | **OL** On Level | **BL** Beyond Level

Math On the Spot
my.hrw.com

Distinguish Between Proportional and Nonproportional Situations Using an Equation

If an equation is not a linear equation, it represents a nonproportional relationship. A linear equation of the form $y = mx + b$ may represent either a proportional ($b = 0$) or nonproportional ($b \neq 0$) relationship.

EXAMPLE 2

The number of years since Keith graduated from middle school can be represented by the equation $y = a - 14$, where y is the number of years and a is his age. Is the relationship between the number of years since Keith graduated and his age proportional or nonproportional?

$$y = a - 14$$

The equation is in the form $y = mx + b$, with a being used as the variable instead of x. The value of m is 1, and the value of b is -14. Since b is not 0, the relationship between the number of years since Keith graduated and his age is nonproportional.

Reflect

3. Communicate Mathematical Ideas In a proportional relationship, the ratio $\frac{y}{x}$ is constant. Show that this ratio is not constant for the equation $y = a - 14$.

Sample answer: (16, 2) and (21, 7) are solutions, but $\frac{y}{x} = \frac{2}{16} = \frac{1}{8}$ and $\frac{y}{x} = \frac{7}{21} = \frac{1}{3}$

4. What If? Suppose another equation represents Keith's age in months y given his age in years a. Is this relationship proportional? Explain.

Yes; the ratio of age in months to age in years is constant.

YOUR TURN

Determine if each of the following equations represents a proportional or nonproportional relationship.

5. $d = 65t$

proportional

6. $p = 0.1s + 2000$

nonproportional

7. $n = 450 - 3p$

nonproportional

8. $36 = 12d$

nonproportional

Personal Math Trainer
Online Assessment and Intervention
my.hrw.com

© Houghton Mifflin Harcourt Publishing Company

3 Explain

EXAMPLE 2

ADDITIONAL EXAMPLE 2 The change in a test score for each incorrect answer is represented by the equation $y = -\frac{x}{2}$, where x is the number of incorrect answers. Is the relationship between the number of incorrect answers and the change in score proportional or nonproportional?
proportional

 Interactive Whiteboard
Interactive example available online

YOUR TURN   MP.2

Avoid Common Errors
Tell students that two different variables are needed for a proportional relationship. In **Exercise 8**, they may see that there is only one term on each side of the equation and assume that it is proportional.

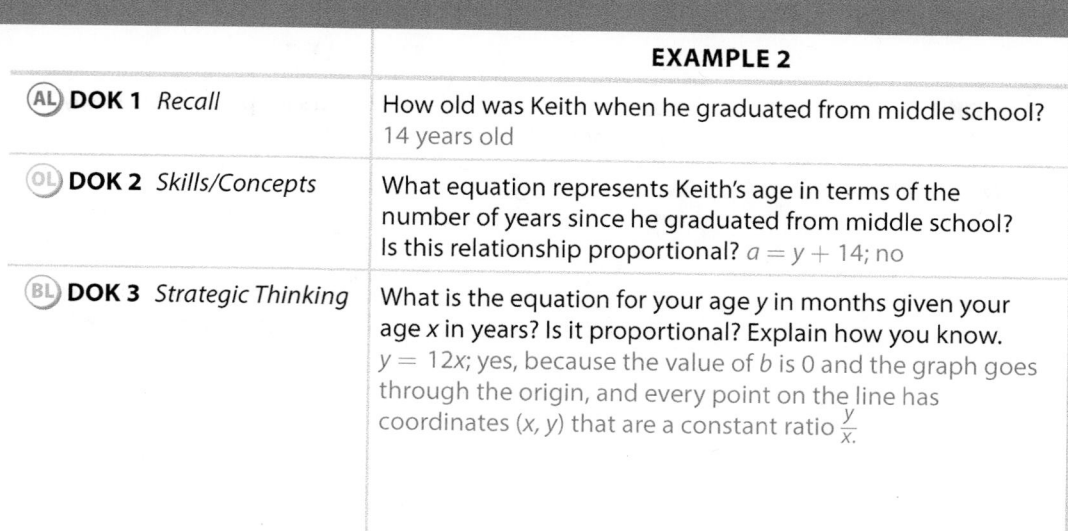

		EXAMPLE 2
AL **DOK 1** *Recall*		How old was Keith when he graduated from middle school? 14 years old
OL **DOK 2** *Skills/Concepts*		What equation represents Keith's age in terms of the number of years since he graduated from middle school? Is this relationship proportional? $a = y + 14$; no
BL **DOK 3** *Strategic Thinking*		What is the equation for your age y in months given your age x in years? Is it proportional? Explain how you know. $y = 12x$; yes, because the value of b is 0 and the graph goes through the origin, and every point on the line has coordinates (x, y) that are a constant ratio $\frac{y}{x}$.

YOUR TURN   MP.6

Focus on Critical Thinking
Suppose a fourth tourist traded 50 U.S. dollars and received 630 Mexican pesos in return, and this data were added to the table. Would this change your answer? Explain. Students should realize this would make the relationship nonlinear as the ratio is no longer 13.

EXAMPLE 3

ADDITIONAL EXAMPLE 3 The table shows the distance of a train from a station and the time it will take to arrive. The relationship is linear. Is it proportional or nonproportional?

Time (min)	25	45	65
Distance (mi)	15	30	45

nonproportional

 Interactive Whiteboard
Interactive example available online

YOUR TURN   MP.4

Focus on Math Connections
Point out to students that in Exercise 10, *y* is less than *x* so they will find ratios that are less than 1. Assure them that they can compare fractions or decimal equivalents.

Distinguish Between Proportional and Nonproportional Situations Using a Table

Math On the Spot
my.hrw.com

If there is not a constant rate of change in the data displayed in a table, then the table represents a nonlinear nonproportional relationship.

A linear relationship represented by a table is a proportional relationship when the quotient of each pair of numbers is constant. Otherwise, the linear relationship is nonproportional.

EXAMPLE 3

The values in the table represent the numbers of U.S. dollars three tourists traded for Mexican pesos. The relationship is linear. Is the relationship proportional or nonproportional?

U.S. Dollars Traded	Mexican Pesos Received
130	1,690
255	3,315
505	6,565

$\frac{1,690}{130} = \frac{169}{13} = 13$

$\frac{3,315}{255} = \frac{221}{17} = 13$

Simplify the ratios to compare the pesos received to the dollars traded.

$\frac{6,565}{505} = \frac{1313}{101} = 13$

The ratio of pesos received to dollars traded is constant at 13 Mexican pesos per U.S. dollar. This is a proportional relationship.

Math Talk
Mathematical Practices

How could you confirm that the values in the table have a linear relationship?

Compare the change in Mexican pesos to the change in U.S. dollars from each pair of numbers to the next. The results should all be the same.

YOUR TURN

Determine if the linear relationship represented by each table is a proportional or nonproportional relationship.

9.

x	y
2	30
8	90
14	150

nonproportional

10.

x	y
5	1
40	8
65	13

proportional

Personal Math Trainer
Online Assessment and Intervention
my.hrw.com

Lesson 4.4 **115**

© Houghton Mifflin Harcourt Publishing Company • Image Credits: ©Jupiter Images/ Hemera Technologies/Getty Images

---

DIFFERENTIATE INSTRUCTION *Leveled Questions*

		EXAMPLE 3
AL	**DOK 1** *Recall*	A tourist wants to trade 100 dollars for pesos. How many pesos should the tourist receive? 1300 pesos
OL	**DOK 2** *Skills/Concepts*	What would a graph of this data look like? a straight line with a slope of 13 beginning at the origin and passing through the points (130, 1690), (255, 3315), and (505, 6565)
BL	**DOK 3** *Strategic Thinking*	For this example, what equation can you use to represent the number of Mexican pesos a tourist gets for a given amount of U.S. dollars? $p = 13d$

LEVELED QUESTIONS: **AL** Approaching Level | **OL** On Level | **BL** Beyond Level

Math On the Spot
my.hrw.com

Comparing Proportional and Nonproportional Situations

You can use what you have learned about proportional and nonproportional relationships to compare similar real-world situations that are given using different representations.

EXAMPLE 4 Real World

A A laser tag league has the choice of two arenas for a tournament. In both cases, x is the number of hours and y is the total charge. Compare and contrast these two situations.

Arena A

$y = 225x$

Arena B

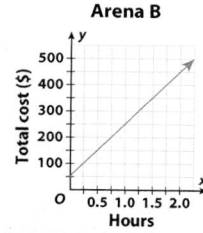

Hours

Math Talk

Mathematical Processes

How might graphing the equation for Arena A help you to compare the situations?

Sample answer: By graphing the two situations together, you can more easily see when one option is better than another.

- **Arena A's** equation has the form $y = mx + b$, where $b = 0$. So, Arena A's charges are a proportional relationship. The hourly rate, $225, is greater than Arena B's, but there is no additional fee.

- **Arena B's** graph is a line that does not include the origin. So, Arena B's charges are a nonproportional relationship. Arena B has a $50 initial fee but its hourly rate, $200, is lower.

B Jessika is remodeling and has the choice of two painters. In both cases, x is the number of hours and y is the total charge. Compare and contrast these two situations.

Painter A

$y = \$45x$

Painter B

x	0	1	2	3
y	20	55	90	125

Painter A's equation has the form $y = mx + b$, where $b = 0$. So, Painter A's charges are proportional. The hourly rate, $45, is greater than Painter B's, but there is no additional fee.

Painter B's table is a nonproportional relationship because the ratio of y to x is not constant. Because the table contains the ordered pair (0, 20), Painter B charges an initial fee of $20, but the hourly rate, $35, is less than Painter A's.

© Houghton Mifflin Harcourt Publishing Company

116 Unit 2

EXAMPLE 4

ADDITIONAL EXAMPLE 4

A John has a choice of hiring two plumbers. In both cases, x is the number of hours and y is the total charge in dollars. Compare and contrast these two situations.

Plumber A: $y = 75x$

Plumber B:

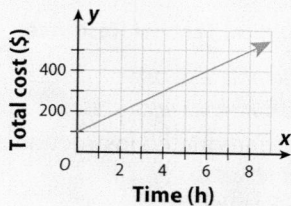

Time (h)

Plumber A's charges are a proportional relationship; Plumber B's charges are not. Plumber B charges an initial fee of $100 and a lower hourly rate.

B The bowling club has a choice between two bowling alleys. In both cases, x is the number of games and y is the total charge in dollars. Compare and contrast these two situations.

Nite Owl Lanes: $y = 3.75x + 2$

Lucky Five Lanes:

x	0	1	2	3
y	0	4.5	9	13.5

Lucky Five's charges are a proportional relationship; Nite Owl's charges are not. Nite Owl charges for shoes but its per-game rate is lower.

 Interactive Whiteboard
Interactive example available online

		EXAMPLE 4
AL	**DOK 1** *Recall*	What are the charges for 2 hours of laser tag at each arena? Arena A: $450; Arena B: $450
OL	**DOK 2** *Skills/Concepts*	What is the difference between Arena A and Arena B in the total cost for 3 hours of laser tag? Explain your reasoning. $25; Arena A charges are 3(225) = $675, and Arena B charges are 3(200) + 50 = $650.
BL	**DOK 3** *Strategic Thinking*	In Part B, how can you use the rate of change and initial value to write in the form $y = mx + b$ the total cost y of hiring Painter B? In $y = mx + b$, m represents the rate of change and b represents the initial value. Because the rate of change is $35 per hour and the initial charge is $20, $m = 35$ and $b = 20$. So, the equation is $y = 35x + 20$.

TEACHER TO TEACHER

Communicating Math Have students identify key ideas from Examples 1–3 that indicate when a linear relationship is *proportional*. A list is shown below.

- The graph contains the origin. *[Example 1]*
- The equation can be written in the form $y = mx$, because $b = 0$. *[Example 2]*
- In a table, the ratios of dependent to independent variables (y/x) is constant. *[Example 3]*

Proportional and Nonproportional Situations **116**

Connect to Daily Life

Have students consider the coupon for Test-Prep Center B and create a table or graph for this situation. Students should see that for less than 4 hours, the cost is negative. Encourage students to provide some likely restrictions on the use of the coupon.

Digital Teacher Resources

Go online to access all your lesson-level resources.

Differentiated Instruction
- Reteach
- Reading Strategies
- Success for English Learners
- Practice and Problem Solving A/B, C, D

Math on the Spot Videos

my.hrw.com

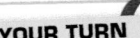

Personal Math Trainer
Online Assessment and Intervention
my.hrw.com

11. Compare and contrast the following two situations.

Test-Prep Center A	Test-Prep Center B
The cost for Test-Prep Center A is given by $c = 20h$, where c is the cost in dollars and h is the number of hours you attend.	Test-Prep Center B charges $25 per hour to attend, but you have a $100 coupon that you can use to reduce the cost.

Test-Prep Center A's charges are a proportional relationship, but B's charges are not. Center B offers a coupon that gives you an initial credit, but its hourly rate, $25, is higher than Center A's hourly rate of $20. Center B will cost more if you attend more than 20 h.

Guided Practice

Determine if each relationship is a proportional or nonproportional situation. Explain your reasoning.
(Explore Activity Example 1, Example 2, Example 4)

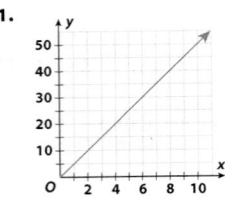

1.

Look at the origin.

Proportional; the line includes the origin.

2.

Nonproportional; the line does not include the origin.

3. $q = 2p + \frac{1}{2}$

Compare the equation with $y = mx + b$.

Nonproportional; when the equation is written in the form $y = mx + b$, the value of b is not 0.

4. $v = \frac{1}{10}u$

Proportional; when the equation is written in the form $y = mx + b$, the value of b is 0.

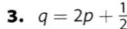

Lesson 4.4 **117**

© Houghton Mifflin Harcourt Publishing Company

The tables represent linear relationships. Determine if each relationship is a proportional or nonproportional situation. (Example 3, Example 4)

5.

x	y
3	12
9	36
21	84

Find the quotient of y and x.

Proportional; the quotient of y and x is constant, 4, for every number pair.

6.

x	y
22	4
46	8
58	10

No; the quotient of y and x is not constant for every number pair.

7. The values in the table represent the numbers of households that watched three TV shows and the ratings of the shows. The relationship is linear. Describe the relationship in other ways. (Example 4)

Number of Households that Watched TV Show	TV Show Rating
15,000,000	12
20,000,000	16
25,000,000	20

Sample answer: The TV show rating is proportional to the number of households that watched, because the quotient when you divide the rating by the number of households is always 0.0000008.

? ESSENTIAL QUESTION CHECK-IN

8. How are using graphs, equations, and tables similar when distinguishing between proportional and nonproportional linear relationships?

Sample answer: Proportional relationships exist if the y-intercepts for a graph and an equation are 0, and if the table has, or would have, a value of 0 for y when x is 0.

© Houghton Mifflin Harcourt Publishing Company

4 Elaborate

Talk About It

Summarize the Lesson

Ask: How do you know that a linear relationship given by a graph, a table, or an equation represents a nonproportional relationship? Sample answer: The y-intercept, the value of the dependent variable when $x = 0$, is not 0.

Guided Practice

Engage with the Whiteboard

Have students write the ratio of y to x for each row of the table in **Exercises 5–6**.

Avoid Common Errors

- **Exercise 4** Remind students that in $y = mx + b$ form, the value of m does not need to be an integer in order for a relationship to be proportional.

- **Exercise 7** Students should take care in dividing, due to the size of the numbers. Even using a calculator, they may find that two quotients differ by a power of ten, although they should all be the same.

DIFFERENTIATE INSTRUCTION *Intervention and Additional Support*

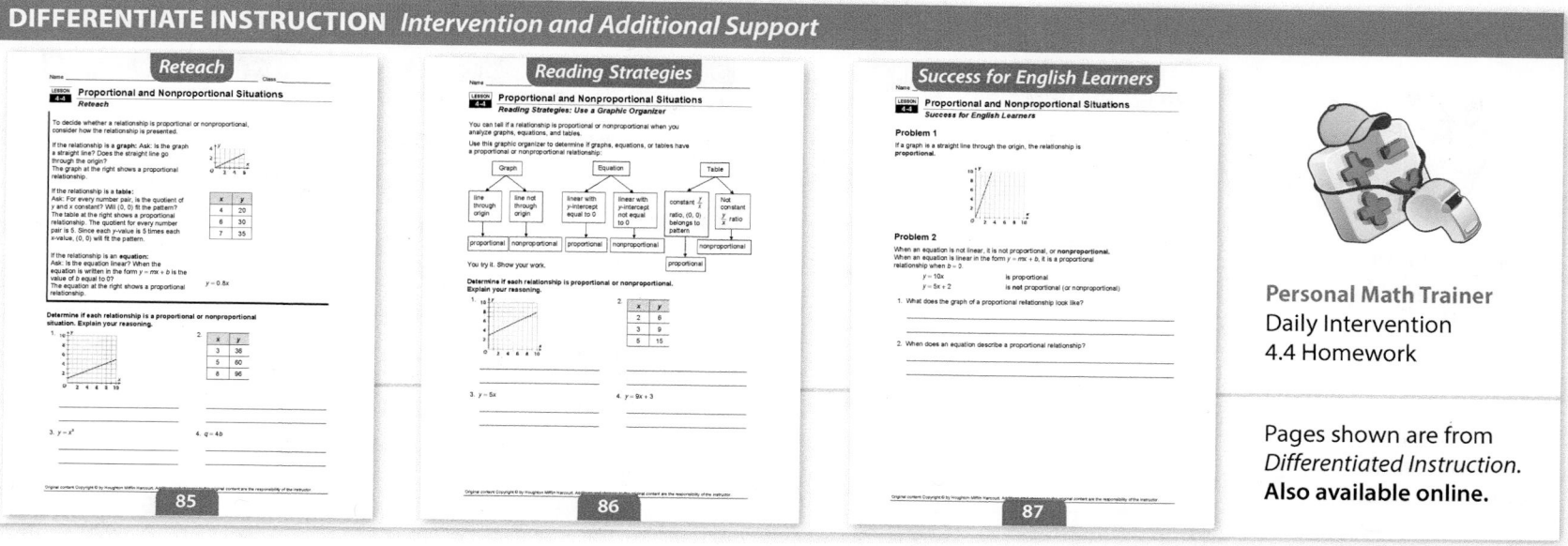

Personal Math Trainer
Daily Intervention
4.4 Homework

Pages shown are from *Differentiated Instruction.*
Also available online.

5 Evaluate

Independent Practice

⏱ **Pressed for Time**

4.4 Differentiated Homework Assignments

- (AL) **Approaching Level** 9–13
- (OL) **On Level** 10–14
- (BL) **Beyond Level** 12–15

*For **Below Level** students, assign Personal Math Trainer, Daily Intervention 4.4 Homework.*

Mathematical Processes	Exercises
MP.2 Reasoning	9, 14
MP.3 Logic	15
MP.4 Modeling	10–11
MP.6 Precision	12–13

Focus on Higher Order Thinking

Depth of Knowledge	Exercises
2 Skills/Concepts	9–13
3 Strategic Thinking H.O.T.	14–15

4.4 Independent Practice

Personal Math Trainer
Online Assessment and Intervention
my.hrw.com

9. The graph shows the weight of a cross-country team's beverage cooler based on how much sports drink it contains.

   a. Is the relationship proportional or nonproportional? Explain.

   <u>Nonproportional; the graph does not pass through the origin, so $b \neq 0$.</u>

   b. Identify and interpret the slope and the y-intercept.

   <u>$m = 0.5$, $b = 10$; each cup sports drink weighs a half pound. The empty cooler weighs 10 pounds.</u>

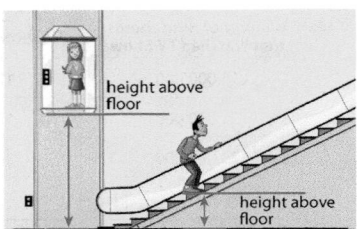

In 10–11, tell if the relationship between a rider's height above the first floor and the time since the rider stepped on the elevator or escalator is proportional or nonproportional. Explain your reasoning.

10. The elevator paused for 10 seconds after you stepped on before beginning to rise at a constant rate of 8 feet per second.

   <u>Nonproportional; sample answer: The graph of this situation will extend from (0, 0) to (10, 0) on the x-axis before rising.</u>

11. Your height, h, in feet above the first floor on the escalator is given by $h = 0.75t$, where t is the time in seconds.

   <u>Proportional; this equation has the form $y = mx + b$ where $b = 0$.</u>

12. **Analyze Relationships** Compare and contrast the two graphs.

Graph A
$y = \frac{1}{3}x$

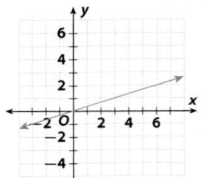

Graph B
$y = \sqrt{x}$

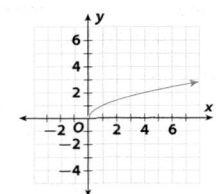

<u>Both include the origin, but only A is a line, making it linear and proportional. B is nonlinear and nonproportional.</u>

Lesson 4.4 **119**

© Houghton Mifflin Harcourt Publishing Company

DIFFERENTIATE INSTRUCTION *Leveled Homework/Practice*

Personal Math Trainer
• 4.4 Homework

Pages shown are from *Differentiated Instruction.*
Also available online.

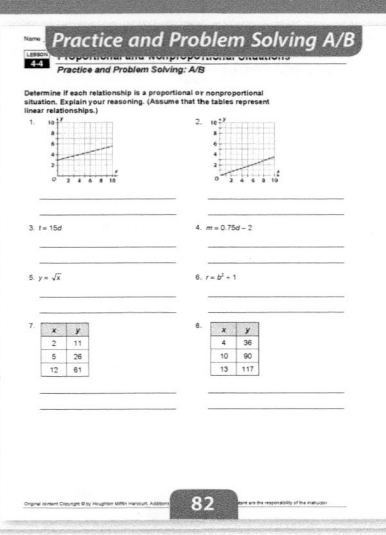

Practice and Problem Solving A/B — 82

Practice and Problem Solving C — 83

Practice and Problem Solving D — 84

13. Represent Real-World Problems Describe a real-world situation where the relationship is linear and nonproportional.

Sample answer: Amanda buys a flute for $500 and then pays $35 per week for lessons.

 **FOCUS ON HIGHER ORDER THINKING**

14. Mathematical Reasoning Suppose you know the slope of a linear relationship and one of the points that its graph passes through. How can you determine if the relationship is proportional or nonproportional?

You can plot the point, use the slope to find another point, and draw a line through the points to see if it passes through the origin.

15. Multiple Representations An entrant at a science fair has included information about temperature conversion in various forms, as shown. The variables F, C, and K represent temperatures in degrees Fahrenheit, degrees Celsius, and kelvin, respectively.

Equation A
$F = \frac{9}{5}C + 32$

Equation B
$K = C + 273.15$

Table C

Degrees Celsius	kelvin
8	281.15
15	288.15
36	309.15

a. Is the relationship between kelvins and degrees Celsius proportional? Justify your answer in two different ways.

No; using Equation B you see that the y-intercept is 273.15, not 0, so the graph does not include the origin. Using Table C you see that the quotient of K and C is not constant: about 35.1, 19.21, and 8.5875.

b. Is the relationship between degrees Celsius and degrees Fahrenheit proportional? Why or why not?

No; Equation A is in the form $y = mx + b$, with F being used instead of y and C being used instead of x. The value of b is 32. Since b is not 0, the relationship is not proportional.

Work Area

© Houghton Mifflin Harcourt Publishing Company

✔ **Quick Check**

4.4 Lesson Quiz

Explain whether each shows a proportional relationship.

1.

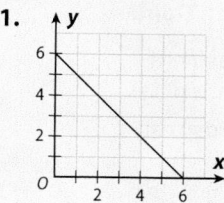

No; the graph does not go through the origin.

2.

x	9	36	63
y	7	28	49

Yes; the ratio of y to x is constant.

3. $12x = 5y$

Yes; the equation can be written in the form $y = mx + b$, and $b = 0$.

4. Compare and contrast.

Without Discount Card	With Discount Card
The cost for cat food is	The cost is given by $c = 9.5n + 5$ where n is the number of cases.

Cases	2	3
Cost ($)	21	31.50

The cost without a discount card is proportional, with a discount card it is not. The cost is more expensive with the discount card initially, but the per-case rate without it is more expensive.

Differentiate Instruction

IF a student misses more than one question, THEN

Differentiate Instruction:
• 4.4 Reteach
• Personal Math Trainer

 Interactive Whiteboard
Interactive Lesson quiz available online

DIFFERENTIATE INSTRUCTION *Extend-the-Math Activity* **PRE-AP**

Activity A *geometric progression* is a *sequence* or list of numbers with a common ratio r between the terms. One geometric progression is a sequence with a common ratio of 2:

1, 2, 4, 8, 16, 32 ...

Have students make a geometric progression using the following rule:

Choose a number between 1 and 5 for the first value of x and choose another number between 2 and 5 for r. Multiply x by r to get the first value of y. Use this value of y as the next value of x. Multiply by r again to get the next value of y.

Have them write the geometric expression and determine if it is a linear relationship.

Sample answer: 2, 6, 18, 54, 162, 486….; yes, it is linear.

Ready to Go On?

Assess Mastery

Access *Ready to Go On?* assessment online, and receive instant scoring, feedback, and customized intervention or enrichment.

Personal Math Trainer

Online Assessment and Intervention

• Module 4 Posttest

Additional Resources

Digital Teacher Resources

Go online for module-level resources.

Assessment Resources

• Module 4 Quiz: B, p.27
• Module 4 Quiz: D, p.29

my.hrw.com

Ready to Go On?

Personal Math Trainer
Online Assessment and Intervention
my.hrw.com

4.1 Representing Linear Nonproportional Relationships

1. Complete the table using the equation $y = 3x + 2$.

x	−1	0	1	2	3
y	−1	2	5	8	11

4.2 Determining Slope and y-intercept

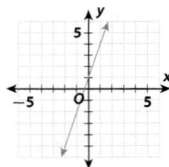

2. Find the slope and y-intercept of the line in the graph.

slope: 3; y-intercept: 1

4.3 Graphing Linear Nonproportional Relationships

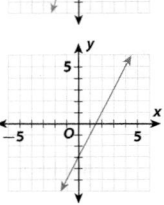

3. Graph the equation $y = 2x − 3$ using slope and y-intercept.

4.4 Proportional and Nonproportional Situations

4. Does the table represent a proportional or a nonproportional linear relationship?

x	1	2	3	4	5
y	4	8	12	16	20

proportional

5. Does the graph in Exercise 2 represent a proportional or a nonproportional linear relationship?

nonproportional

6. Does the graph in Exercise 3 represent a proportional or a nonproportional relationship?

nonproportional

 ESSENTIAL QUESTION

7. How can you identify a linear nonproportional relationship from a table, a graph, and an equation?

Table: for an ordered pair $(0, y)$, y will not be 0; graph: the y-intercept will not be 0; equation: it will have the form $y = mx + b$ where $b \neq 0$.

© Houghton Mifflin Harcourt Publishing Company

Module 4   121

READY TO GO ON? *Diagnostic Assessment*

RtI Response to Intervention

Use to determine if students have mastered the concepts covered in this module.

Lesson	Exercises	Content Focus	Review with *Differentiated Instruction*
4.1	1	Representing Linear Nonproportional Relationships	**4.1** Reteach **4.1** Reading Strategies **4.1** Success for English Learners
4.2	2	Determining Slope and y-Intercept	**4.2** Reteach **4.2** Reading Strategies **4.2** Success for English Learners
4.3	3	Graphing Linear Nonproportional Relationships Using Slope and y-Intercept	**4.3** Reteach **4.3** Reading Strategies **4.3** Success for English Learners
4.4	4–6	Proportional and Nonproportional Situations	**4.4** Reteach **4.4** Reading Strategies **4.4** Success for English Learners

Personal Math Trainer

Online Assessment and Intervention

my.hrw.com

Selected Response

1. The table below represents which equation?

x	−1	0	1	2
y	−10	−6	−2	2

Ⓐ $y = -x - 10$ Ⓒ $y = 4x - 6$
Ⓑ $y = -6x$ Ⓓ $y = -4x + 2$

2. The graph of which equation is shown below?

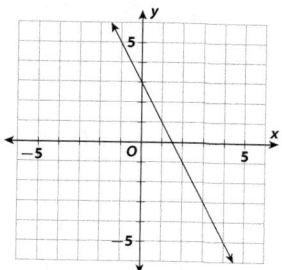

Ⓐ $y = -2x + 3$ Ⓒ $y = 2x + 3$
Ⓑ $y = -2x + 1.5$ Ⓓ $y = 2x + 1.5$

3. The table below represents a linear relationship.

x	2	3	4	5
y	4	7	10	13

What is the y-intercept?

Ⓐ −4 Ⓒ 2
Ⓑ −2 Ⓓ 3

4. Which equation represents a nonproportional relationship?

Ⓐ $y = 3x + 0$ Ⓒ $y = 3x + 5$
Ⓑ $y = -3x$ Ⓓ $y = \frac{1}{3}x$

5. The table shows a proportional relationship. What is the missing y-value?

x	4	10	12
y	6	15	?

Ⓐ 16 Ⓒ 18
Ⓑ 20 Ⓓ 24

6. What is 0.00000598 written in scientific notation?

Ⓐ 5.98×10^{-6} Ⓒ 59.8×10^{-6}
Ⓑ 5.98×10^{-5} Ⓓ 59.8×10^{-7}

Mini-Task

7. The graph shows a linear relationship.

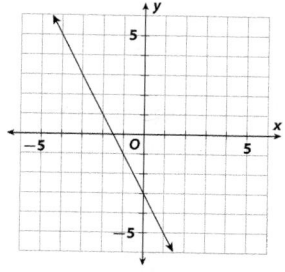

a. Is the relationship proportional or nonproportional?

nonproportional

b. What is the slope of the line?

−2

c. What is the y-intercept of the line?

−3

d. What is the equation of the line?

$y = -2x - 3$

© Houghton Mifflin Harcourt Publishing Company

Preparing for High Stakes Tests

Assessment Readiness Tip
Point out that students can create a different representation of a linear relationship if it makes them more comfortable or if it could help in solving the problem.

- **Item 1** If students plot the points given in the table and sketch the graph, it will be clear that the slope is positive. With this information, the only possible answer is C.

- **Item 2** If students are more comfortable finding an equation from a table than from a graph, encourage them to create a table using three or four points from the graph.

Avoid Common Errors

- **Item 4** Note that even though answer A is in $y = mx + b$ form, $b = 0$ and the point $(0, 0)$ satisfies the equation, so the relationship must be proportional. Point out that $y = 3x$ is an equivalent form of this equation.

- **Item 6** Remind students that the exponent reflects the number of decimal places that the decimal point must move to be to the right of the first nonzero digit. The exponent is not equal to the number of zeros to the right of the decimal point in the standard notation form.

Items	Grade 8 Lessons	Mathematical Processes
1	4.2	MP.4
2	4.2	MP.4
3	4.2	MP.2
4	4.4	MP.7
5*	3.1	MP.2
6*	2.3	MP.6
7	4.2, 4.4	MP.2, MP.4

Item integrates mixed review concepts from previous modules or a previous course.

DIFFERENTIATE ASSESSMENT

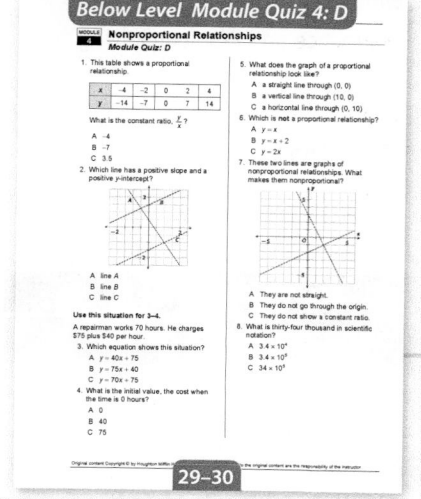

Below Level Module Quiz 4: D

29–30

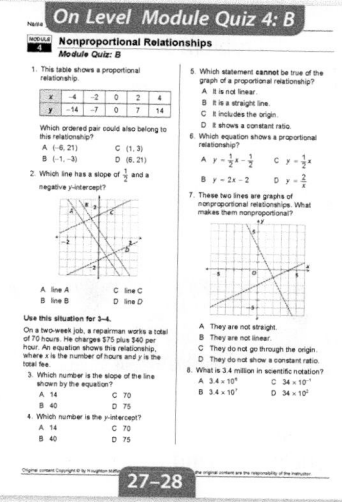

On Level Module Quiz 4: B

27–28

Personal Math Trainer

Module 4 Assessment Readiness

Pages shown are from *Assessment Resources*. **Also available online.**

Module At A Glance

MODULE 5 | Writing Linear Equations

Lessons at A Glance	Lesson 5.1 Writing Linear Equations from Situations and Graphs	Lesson 5.2 Writing Linear Equations from a Table	Lesson 5.3 Linear Relationships and Bivariate Data
	Pg. T127A	Pg. T133A	Pg. T139A
Essential Question	How do you write an equation to model a linear relationship given a graph or a description?	How do you write an equation to model a linear relationship given a table?	How can you contrast linear and nonlinear sets of bivariate data?
Objective	Students will write an equation to model a linear relationship given a graph or a description.	Students will write an equation to model a linear relationship given a table.	Students will contrast linear and nonlinear sets of bivariate data.
Vocabulary			bivariate data, nonlinear relationship
Go online for all your module resources my.hrw.com	5.1 *i*Student Edition 5.1 *i*Teacher Edition 5.1 *e*Student Edition 🐭 Personal Math Trainer 📺 Math on the Spot Videos	5.2 *i*Student Edition 5.2 *i*Teacher Edition 5.2 *e*Student Edition 🐭 Personal Math Trainer 📺 Math on the Spot Videos 𝕏 Animated Math	5.3 *i*Student Edition 5.3 *i*Teacher Edition 5.3 *e*Student Edition 🐭 Personal Math Trainer 📺 Math on the Spot Videos

Print Resources	**5.1 Student Edition:** Lesson
	Differentiated Instruction
	  5.1 Practice and Problem Solving A/B, C, and D
	  5.1 Reteach
	  5.1 Reading Strategies
	  5.1 Success for English Learners
		5.2 Student Edition: Lesson
		Differentiated Instruction
		  5.2 Practice and Problem Solving A/B, C, and D
		  5.2 Reteach
		  5.2 Reading Strategies
		  5.2 Success for English Learners
			5.3 Student Edition: Lesson
			Differentiated Instruction
			  5.3 Practice and Problem Solving A/B, C, and D
			  5.3 Reteach
			  5.3 Reading Strategies
			  5.3 Success for English Learners

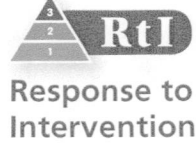

RtI

Response to Intervention

Before the Module	During the Lesson	After the Module
Are You Ready	**Guided/Independent Practice**	**Ready to Go On?**
• Prerequisite Skills Activities • Personal Math Trainer	• Reteach • Personal Math Trainer • Practice and Problem Solving D	• Reteach • Personal Math Trainer

Teacher Notes

Check It Out!

Math on the Spot Videos	Animated Math
One for every Example in every Lesson	 During Lesson 5.2

Writing Linear Equations

Real-World Video Viewing Guide

After students have watched the video, discuss the following:

- What does *x* represent in the linear equation $y = 20x + 40$? number of games that cost $20

- What does the 40 represent in the linear equation $y = 20x + 40$? cost of the $40 game

Professional Development Video

Author Juli Dixon models successful teaching practices as she explores the concept of writing linear equations in an actual eighth-grade classroom.

MODULE **5**

Writing Linear Equations

? **ESSENTIAL QUESTION**

How can you use linear equations to solve real-world problems?

You can use linear equations and their graphs to model real-world relationships involving constant rates of change.

LESSON 5.1
Writing Linear Equations from Situations and Graphs

LESSON 5.2
Writing Linear Equations from a Table

LESSON 5.3
Linear Relationships and Bivariate Data

© Houghton Mifflin Harcourt Publishing Company • Image Credits: ©Yellow Dog Productions/Getty Images

Real-World Video

Linear equations can be used to describe many situations related to shopping. If a store advertised four books for $32.00, you could write and solve a linear equation to find the price of each book.

my.hrw.com

GO DIGITAL
my.hrw.com

my.hrw.com
Go digital with your write-in student edition, accessible on any device.

Math On the Spot
Scan with your smart phone to jump directly to the online edition, video tutor, and more.

Animated Math
Interactively explore key concepts to see how math works.

Personal Math Trainer
Get immediate feedback and help as you work through practice sets.

123

TEACHER ONLINE RESOURCES

 ONLINE TEACHER EDITION Access a full suite of teaching resources online—plan, present, and manage classes and assignments.

 INTERACTIVE WHITEBOARDS Engage students with interactive whiteboard-ready examples and a lesson quiz for each lesson.

 MY SMART PLANNER Easily plan your classes and access all your resources online.

 PERSONAL MATH TRAINER: Online Assessment and Intervention Assign automatically graded homework, quizzes, tests, and intervention activities. Prepare your students for standardized tests in short-answer and multiple-choice formats.

Reading Start-Up

Visualize Vocabulary

Use the ✔ words to complete the diagram. You can put more than one word in each bubble.

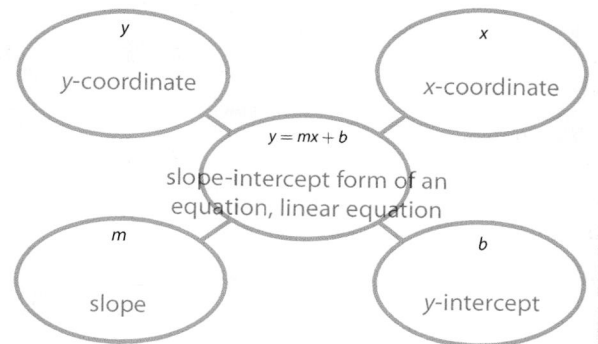

- *y* — y-coordinate
- *x* — x-coordinate
- $y = mx + b$ — slope-intercept form of an equation, linear equation
- *m* — slope
- *b* — y-intercept

© Houghton Mifflin Harcourt Publishing Company

Vocabulary

Review Words
- ✔ linear equation *(ecuación lineal)*
- ordered pair *(par ordenado)*
- proportional relationship *(relación proporcional)*
- rate of change *(tasa de cambio)*
- ✔ slope *(pendiente)*
- ✔ slope-intercept form of an equation *(forma de pendiente-intersección)*
- ✔ x-coordinate *(coordenada x)*
- ✔ y-coordinate *(coordenada y)*
- ✔ y-intercept *(intersección con el eje y)*

Preview Words
- bivariate data *(datos bivariados)*
- nonlinear relationship *(relación no lineal)*

Understand Vocabulary

Complete the sentences using the preview words.

1. A set of data that is made up of two paired variables is <u>bivariate data</u>.

2. When the rate of change varies from point to point, the relationship is a <u>nonlinear relationship</u>.

Active Reading

Tri-Fold Before beginning the module, create a tri-fold to help you learn the concepts and vocabulary in this module. Fold the paper into three sections. Label the columns "What I Know," "What I Need to Know," and "What I Learned." Complete the first two columns before you read. After studying the module, complete the third column.

Reading Start-Up

Visualize Vocabulary
The concept web helps students review vocabulary associated with linear relationships. In each bubble, students should write one or more words associated with the linear equation $y = mx + b$.

Understand Vocabulary
Use the following explanations to help students learn the preview words.

*Some relationships are **nonlinear relationships**. Nonlinear means "not in the shape of a line." In nonlinear relationships, the rate of change is not constant. Graphs that represent nonlinear relationships will not be lines.*

Many real-world situations have nonlinear relationships. For example, the growth of a plant is usually not a linear relationship because plants do not grow the same amount every day.

Active Reading

Integrating Language Arts
Students can use these reading and note-taking strategies to help them organize and understand new concepts and vocabulary.

Additional Resources
Differentiated Instruction

- Reading Strategies **ELL**
- Interactive multilingual glossary

LEARNING PROGRESSIONS ACROSS THE GRADES

Before	In this Module	After
Students understand proportional and linear relationships: • use tables and verbal descriptions to describe a linear relationship • write and graph a linear relationship	Students represent and use linear relationships: • write an equation in the form $y = mx + b$ to model a linear relationship between two quantities using verbal, numerical, tabular, and graphical representations • contrast bivariate sets of data that suggest a linear relationship with bivariate sets of data that do not suggest a linear relationship from a graphical representation	Students will connect that: • there are various forms of linear equations • in nonlinear relationships, the rate of change can vary from point to point

Assess Readiness

Access *Are You Ready?* assessment online, and receive instant scoring, feedback, and customized intervention or enrichment.

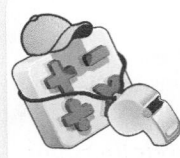

Personal Math Trainer

Online Assessment and Intervention

Additional Resources

Digital Teacher Resources

Go online for module-level resources.

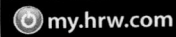

my.hrw.com

Are YOU Ready?

Complete these exercises to review skills you will need for this module.

Personal Math Trainer

Online Assessment and Intervention

my.hrw.com

Write Fractions as Decimals

EXAMPLE $\dfrac{0.5}{0.8} = ?$ Multiply the numerator and the denominator by a power of 10 so that the denominator is a whole number. $\dfrac{0.5 \times 10}{0.8 \times 10} = \dfrac{5}{8}$

$$
\begin{array}{r}
0.625 \\
8\overline{)5.000} \\
-48 \\
\overline{20} \\
-16 \\
\overline{40} \\
-40 \\
\overline{0}
\end{array}
$$

Write the fraction as a division problem.
Write a decimal point and zeros in the dividend.
Place a decimal point in the quotient.
Divide as with whole numbers.

Write each fraction as a decimal.

1. $\dfrac{3}{8}$ ___0.375___   2. $\dfrac{0.3}{0.4}$ ___0.75___   3. $\dfrac{0.13}{0.2}$ ___0.65___   4. $\dfrac{0.39}{0.75}$ ___0.52___

Inverse Operations

EXAMPLE

$5n = 20$
$\dfrac{5n}{5} = \dfrac{20}{5}$
$n = 4$

n is multiplied by 5.
To solve the equation, use the inverse operation, division.

$k + 7 = 9$
$k + 7 - 7 = 9 - 7$
$k = 2$

7 is added to *k*.
To solve the equation, use the inverse operation, subtraction.

Solve each equation using the inverse operation.

5. $7p = 28$ ___$p = 4$___   6. $h - 13 = 5$ ___$h = 18$___

7. $\dfrac{y}{3} = -6$ ___$y = -18$___   8. $b + 9 = 21$ ___$b = 12$___

9. $c - 8 = -8$ ___$c = 0$___   10. $3n = -12$ ___$n = -4$___

11. $-16 = m + 7$ ___$m = -23$___   12. $\dfrac{t}{-5} = -5$ ___$t = 25$___

© Houghton Mifflin Harcourt Publishing Company

ARE YOU READY? *Diagnostic Assessment*

Response to Intervention

Use to determine if students need intervention for the module's prerequisite skills.

Skill	Missed More Than . . .	Intervene With *Skills Intervention* worksheets (available online)	For Enrichment *Differentiated Instruction* (available in print and online)
Write Fractions as Decimals	1 question	**Skill 26** Write Fractions as Decimals	**Module 5 Challenge** Extend-the-Math Lesson Activities in TE
Inverse Operations	3 questions	**Skill 57** Inverse Operations	**Module 5 Challenge** Extend-the-Math Lesson Activities in TE

Complete these exercises to review skills you will need for this module.

Write Fractions as Decimals

13. Explain how to write $\frac{0.16}{0.5}$ as a decimal.

First, multiply the numerator and the denominator by a power of 10 so that the denominator is a whole number: $\frac{0.16 \times 10}{0.5 \times 10} = \frac{1.6}{5}$. Write the fraction as a division problem, $5\overline{)1.6}$, and add a zero to the dividend. Place a decimal point in the quotient, and then divide as with whole numbers. The decimal value is 0.32.

Inverse Operations

14. Explain why a step in solving the equation $4n = -36$ is to divide both sides by 4. Then solve the equation.

The operation involving the variable is multiplication by 4, so the inverse operation is division by 4. Dividing both sides by 4 gives $\frac{4n}{4} = -\frac{36}{4}$, which simplifies to $1n = -9$. Since $1n = n$, the solution is $n = -9$.

15. To solve the equation $\frac{d}{-8} = -8$, Lyle divided each side of the equation by -8 and concluded that $d = 1$. What was Lyle's error?

Since the variable d is divided by -8 in the equation, Lyle should have multiplied both sides by -8 to find the solution: $-8 \cdot \frac{d}{-8} = -8 \cdot (-8)$. The solution is $d = 64$.

16. The balance in Shamir's savings account at the beginning of the month was d dollars. After he deposited $175, the balance was $840.50. Write an equation to find the balance at the beginning of the month. Then show your steps as you find the beginning balance.

$$d + 175 = 840.50$$
$$d + 175 - 175 = 840.50 - 175$$
$$d = 665.50$$
The beginning balance was $665.50.

© Houghton Mifflin Harcourt Publishing Company

Write Fractions as Decimals

Exercise 13 Remind students that if they multiply the fraction by $\frac{100}{100}$, a form of 1, the fraction will have only whole numbers. Then make sure students know how to perform long division.

Inverse Operations

Exercise 14 Students may also solve this problem by multiplying both sides by $\frac{1}{4}$. Point out that multiplying by $\frac{1}{4}$ is equivalent to dividing by 4.

Exercise 15 A common error for solving one-step equations involving division is to use division to solve the problem. Point out that inverse operation of division is multiplication.

Exercise 16 A common error is to add the two numbers given in the problem. Encourage students to use a simpler problem with whole numbers to help them analyze the context of the problem.

Use to determine if students are able to apply the module's prerequisite skills.

Skill	Exercise	Depth of Knowledge (D.O.K.)	Mathematical Processes
Write Fractions as Decimals	13	**3** Strategic Thinking	**MP.2** Abstract and Quantitative Reasoning
Inverse Operations	14	**2** Skills/Concepts	**MP.2** Abstract and Quantitative Reasoning
	15	**3** Strategic Thinking	**MP.3** Use and Evaluate Logical Reasoning
	16	**3** Strategic Thinking	**MP.1** Problem Solving

Lesson Support

Content Objective Students will learn how to write an equation to model a linear relationship given a graph or a description.

Professional Development

Integrate Mathematical Processes MP.2

This lesson provides an opportunity to address this Mathematical Processes standard. It calls for students to represent a situation symbolically. Students read values from a graph and create a new representation of the linear relationship in the form of an equation.

FOCUS

Building Background

Eliciting Prior Knowledge Have students sketch the graph of $y = 3x + 2$ for $x \geq 0$. Then discuss the graph with the class. Ask students to explain how to identify the y-intercept from the graph. Then discuss how to identify the slope by applying rise-over-run to the graph. Connect the y-intercept and the slope from the graph to the equation of the line in slope-intercept form.

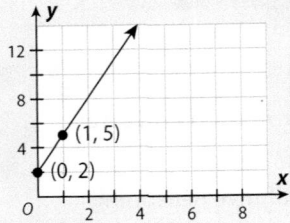

COHERENCE

Learning Progressions

In this lesson, students write equations given a graph or a real-world description of a linear relationship. Important understandings for students include the following:

- **Write an equation in slope-intercept form from a graph.**
- **Write an equation in slope-intercept form from a real-world description of a linear relationship.**

Students have graphed linear relationships using slope-intercept form and descriptions of real-life situations. In this lesson, they reverse the process and write the equation from the graph or description. They should start to understand the relationships among the equivalent forms and move easily between representations of linear relationships.

RIGOR

Cluster Connections

This lesson provides an excellent opportunity to connect ideas in the cluster:

Use functions to model relationships between quantities.

Tell students that the points $(-1, 1)$ and $(1, -7)$ lie on a line. Ask students to find the equation of the line. Discuss whether it is necessary to sketch the graph to find the equation of the line.

$y = -4x - 3$; It is not necessary to sketch the graph. You can use the points to find the slope and then substitute one of the points in $y = mx + b$ to find b.

Language Support ELL

Language Objective Students will explain how to write an equation to model a linear relationship given a graph or a description.

Leveled Strategies for English Learners ELL

Emerging
Use sentence frames to compare and contrast statements about examples of independent and dependent variables. Have students respond *yes/no* or *true/false* to correct and incorrect statements about variables.

Expanding
Have students work in groups to create, compare, and contrast sentences to identify independent and dependent variables based on real-world problems or examples.

Bridging
Have students verbalize their reasoning for identifying independent and dependent variables and for writing an equation based on a description of a real-word problem.

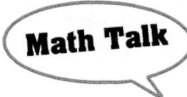

Math Talk The prompt with Example 1 focuses on the phrase through the origin in the context of a line in a graph. Remember that this is not the common use of the term origin. Post a graph that is labeled with the mathematical terms used in graphing for students to refer to visually during discussions of the process of graphing and/or the values that graphs represent.

Image Credits: ©tillsonburg/iStock/Getty Images Plus/Getty Images

Linguistic Support ELL

Academic/Content Vocabulary
This lesson uses the terms *dependent* and *independent variables*. Students will need to understand the concept of *dependence* in order to grasp the meaning of these terms. In Guided Practice, in the problem about making beaded necklaces, point out to students how the length of the necklace depends on the number of beads used. Use short, comparative sentences to describe the relationship through contrasts. "A short necklace uses fewer beads. A long necklace uses more beads. This means that the number of beads is the dependent variable."

Background Knowledge
There are several examples in this lesson that are based on an understanding of rentals, memberships, and user fees. Use some daily life experiences with rentals to frame more unfamiliar concepts and contexts involving rental situations, such as office space or memberships in craft clubs. Discuss renting an apartment or house and why those with more area (square footage) require more money. The object is to make connections between students' life experiences and new situations presented in problems and examples.

LESSON 5.1
Writing Linear Equations from Situations and Graphs

Writing Linear Equations from Situations and Graphs

8.2.5.1
Students will write an equation to model a linear relationship given a graph or a description.

1 Engage

? ESSENTIAL QUESTION

How do you write an equation to model a linear relationship given a graph or a description? Use pairs of values for input and output to determine the values for the slope m and the y-intercept b in the equation $y = mx + b$.

Motivate the Lesson

Ask: How can you compare rental costs and membership fees? Begin the Explore Activity to find out.

2 Explore

EXPLORE ACTIVITY

Connect Vocabulary ELL

Explain the terms *potter's wheel* (a rotating disk used for shaping clay) and *kiln* (an oven for baking or drying clay or pottery). Ask if any students have worked with clay. Any such students may be able to explain these terms to the class.

? ESSENTIAL QUESTION

How do you write an equation to model a linear relationship given a graph or a description?

EXPLORE ACTIVITY Real World

Writing an Equation in Slope-Intercept Form

Greta makes clay mugs and bowls as gifts at the Crafty Studio. She pays a membership fee of $15 a month and an equipment fee of $3.00 an hour to use the potter's wheel, table, and kiln. Write an equation in the form $y = mx + b$ that Greta can use to calculate her monthly costs.

A What is the input variable, x, for this situation?
the number of hours Greta uses the studio

What is the output variable, y, for this situation?
the money Greta pays the studio each month

B During April, Greta does not use the equipment at all. What will be her number of hours (x) for April? _____0_____

What will be her cost (y) for April? _____$15_____

What will be the y-intercept, b, in the equation? _____15_____

Math Talk
Mathematical Processes

What change could the studio make that would make a difference to the y-intercept of the equation?

Changing the membership fee changes the y-intercept.

C Greta spends 8 hours in May for a cost of $15 + 8($3) = _____$39_____.

In June, she spends 11 hours for a cost of _____$48_____.

From May to June, the change in x-values is _____+3_____.

From May to June, the change in y-values is _____+9_____.

What will be the slope, m, in the equation? _____3_____

D Use the values for m and b to write an equation for Greta's costs in the form $y = mx + b$: _____$y = 3x + 15$_____

© Houghton Mifflin Harcourt Publishing Company

DIFFERENTIATE INSTRUCTION *Leveled Questions*

	EXPLORE ACTIVITY
AL DOK 1 *Recall*	What information are you given about the cost Greta pays to use the pottery studio? The hourly cost is $3/h and the monthly membership is $15.
OL DOK 2 *Skills/Concepts*	How can you check that the equation $y = 3x + 15$ is correct? Substitute values of x to see if you get correct values for y: For 0 hours, $y = 3(0) + 15 = 15$, or $15; for 1 hour, $y = 3(1) + 15 = 18$, or $18. So, the equation is correct.
BL DOK 3 *Strategic Thinking*	Suppose that Clay Closet offers a membership fee of $12 per month and $3.50 per hour to use the equipment. Would Clay Closet cost less to use in May for Greta? Explain. No; Clay Closet would cost $3.5(8) + 12 = $40, which is more than Crafty Studio's cost of $39 for May.

Math On the Spot
© my.hrw.com

Writing an Equation from a Graph

You can use information presented in a graph to write an equation in slope-intercept form.

EXAMPLE 1

A video club charges a one-time membership fee plus a rental fee for each DVD borrowed. Use the graph to write an equation in slope-intercept form to represent the amount spent, y, on x DVD rentals.

STEP 1 Choose two points on the graph, (x_1, y_1) and (x_2, y_2), to find the slope.

$m = \dfrac{y_2 - y_1}{x_2 - x_1}$ — Find the change in y-values over the change in x-values.

$m = \dfrac{18 - 8}{8 - 0}$ — Substitute (0, 8) for (x_1, y_1) and (8, 18) for (x_2, y_2).

$m = \dfrac{10}{8} = 1.25$ — Simplify.

STEP 2 Read the y-intercept from the graph.

The y-intercept is 8.

STEP 3 Use your slope and y-intercept values to write an equation in slope-intercept form.

$y = mx + b$ — Slope-intercept form

$y = 1.25x + 8$ — Substitute 1.25 for m and 8 for y.

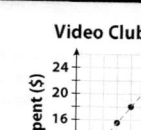

Video Club Costs
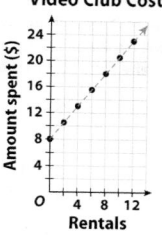

Math Talk
Mathematical Processes

If the graph of an equation is a line that goes through the origin, what is the value of the y-intercept?

The value of the y-intercept is zero.

Reflect

1. What does the value of the slope represent in this context?
   cost per DVD rental

2. Describe the meaning of the y-intercept.
   amount spent for 0 rentals, or the membership fee of $8

Personal Math Trainer
Online Assessment and Intervention
© my.hrw.com

YOUR TURN

3. The cash register subtracts $2.50 from a $25 Coffee Café gift card for every medium coffee the customer buys. Use the graph to write an equation in slope-intercept form to represent this situation.

   $y = -2.5x + 25$

Amount on Gift Card

Number of coffees

© Houghton Mifflin Harcourt Publishing Company

---

3 Explain

EXAMPLE 1

Engage with the Whiteboard

Draw arrows showing the rise and run between the two points (0, 8) and (8, 18) on the graph. Ask students what the y-intercept, rise, and run represent in terms of the membership fee and rental fee.

ADDITIONAL EXAMPLE 1 A DJ charges a setup fee plus an hourly fee to provide music for a dance party. Use the graph to write an equation in slope-intercept form to represent the amount spent, y, on x hours of music. $y = 75x + 100$

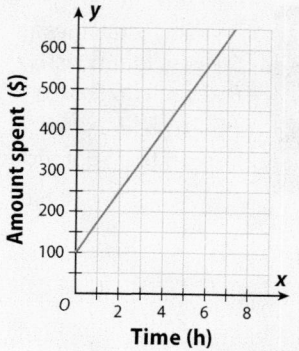

Interactive Whiteboard
Interactive example available online

YOUR TURN MP.4

Avoid Common Errors

Students may be confused about which axis is which and about the meaning of the y-intercept. Verify that they understand that the x-value is zero at the y-intercept, and that the y-intercept is the y-value of the point where the graph crosses the y-axis.

	EXAMPLE 1
AL **DOK 1** *Recall*	What points were used to find the slope? (0, 8) and (8, 18)
OL **DOK 2** *Skills/Concepts*	Describe how the graph changes if the membership fee is changed to $10. Describe how it stays the same. The y-intercept shifts up 2 units to 10; the slope, b, stays the same.
BL **DOK 3** *Strategic Thinking*	Does the average cost per video rented stay the same with each additional video rented? If not, how does it change? No; it gets cheaper because the rental fee is only charged once. For example, for 4 videos the average cost is $3.25, but for 10 videos it is $2.05.

TEACHER TO TEACHER

Communicating Math Encourage students to be precise in their use of math language.

- **y-intercept:** a numerical value not a point
- **Slope m:** ratio of rise to run or change in y over change in x, sometimes expressed as a fraction, decimal, or integer

EXAMPLE 2

ADDITIONAL EXAMPLE 2 The cost for 25 square yards of installed carpet is $650. The cost for 40 square yards of installed carpet is $950. Write an equation in slope-intercept form for the cost of the installed carpet. $y = 20x + 150$

✏️ Interactive Whiteboard
Interactive example available online

Digital Teacher Resources

Go online to access all your lesson-level resources.

Differentiated Instruction
• Reteach
• Reading Strategies
• Success for English Learners
• Practice and Problem Solving A/B, C, D

Math on the Spot Videos

Writing an Equation from a Description

You can use information from a description of a linear relationship to find the slope and y-intercept and to write an equation.

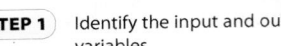

EXAMPLE 2 Real World

Math On the Spot
my.hrw.com

The rent charged for space in an office building is a linear relationship related to the size of the space rented. Write an equation in slope-intercept form for the rent at West Main Street Office Rentals.

West Main St. Office Rentals
Offices for rent at convenient locations.
Monthly Rates:
600 square feet for **$750**
900 square feet for **$1150**

STEP 1 Identify the input and output variables.

The input variable is the square footage of floor space.

The output variable is the monthly rent.

STEP 2 Write the information given in the problem as ordered pairs.

The rent for 600 square feet of floor space is $750: (600, 750)

The rent for 900 square feet of floor space is $1150: (900, 1150)

STEP 3 Find the slope.

$$m = \frac{y_2 - y_1}{x_2 - x_1} = \frac{1150 - 750}{900 - 600} = \frac{400}{300} = \frac{4}{3}$$

STEP 4 Find the y-intercept. Use the slope and one of the ordered pairs.

$y = mx + b$	Slope-intercept form
$750 = \frac{4}{3} \cdot 600 + b$	Substitute for y, m, and x.
$750 = 800 + b$	Multiply.
$-50 = b$	Subtract 800 from both sides.

STEP 5 Substitute the slope and y-intercept.

$y = mx + b$	Slope-intercept form
$y = \frac{4}{3}x - 50$	Substitute $\frac{4}{3}$ for m and -50 for b.

Reflect

4. Without graphing, tell whether the graph of this equation rises or falls from left to right. What does the sign of the slope mean in this context?

Slope is positive, so the graph rises from left to right.

This means that the rent increases as the square footage increases.

My Notes

© Houghton Mifflin Harcourt Publishing Company

Lesson 5.1 **129**

DIFFERENTIATE INSTRUCTION *Intervention and Additional Support*

	EXAMPLE 2
AL DOK 1 *Recall*	What are the independent and dependent variables? Independent is size, in square feet; dependent is monthly rent, in dollars
OL DOK 2 *Skills/Concepts*	What does the rise over the run, or the slope, represent in the problem situation? Change in rent over change in square feet, or rent per square foot
BL DOK 3 *Strategic Thinking*	If the equation for the rent were $y = \frac{4}{3}x + 25$, how would this change the rent? Explain your reasoning. It would be $75 more no matter the number of square feet because $25 - (-50) = 75$, and the variable does not have any effect on this term.

LEVELED QUESTIONS: **AL** Approaching Level | **OL** On Level | **BL** Beyond Level

Personal
Math Trainer
Online Assessment
and Intervention

my.hrw.com

YOUR TURN

5. Hari's weekly allowance varies depending on the number of chores he does. He received \$16 in allowance the week he did 12 chores, and \$14 in allowance the week he did 8 chores. Write an equation for his allowance in slope-intercept form. $y = 0.5x + 10$

Guided Practice

1. Li is making beaded necklaces. For each necklace, she uses 27 spacers, plus 5 beads per inch of necklace length. Write an equation to find how many beads Li needs for each necklace. (*Explore Activity*)

   a. input variable: ___the length of the necklace in inches___

   b. output variable: ___the total number of beads in the necklace___

   c. equation: ___$y = 5x + 27$___

2. Kate is planning a trip to the beach. She estimates her average speed to graph her expected progress on the trip. Write an equation in slope-intercept form that represents the situation. (*Example 1*)

Choose two points on the graph to find the slope.

$$m = \frac{y_2 - y_1}{x_2 - x_1} = \frac{0 - 300}{5 - 0} = \frac{-300}{5} = -60$$

Read the *y*-intercept from the graph: $b =$ ___300___

Use your slope and *y*-intercept values to write an equation in slope-intercept form. ___$y = -60x + 300$___

My Beach Trip

(graph: Distance to beach (mi) on vertical axis with 100, 200, 300; Driving time (h) 1 2 3 4 5 6 on horizontal axis; line decreasing)

3. At 59°F, crickets chirp at a rate of 76 times per minute, and at 65°F, they chirp 100 times per minute. Write an equation in slope-intercept form that represents the situation. (*Example 2*)

Input variable: ___temperature___   Output variable: ___chirps per minute___

$$m = \frac{y_2 - y_1}{x_2 - x_1} = \frac{100 - 76}{65 - 59} = \frac{24}{6} = 4$$ Use the slope and one of the ordered

pairs in $y = mx + b$ to find *b*. ___100___ = ___4___ · ___65___ + b; ___-160___ = b

Write an equation in slope-intercept form. ___$y = 4x - 160$___

? ESSENTIAL QUESTION CHECK-IN

4. Explain what *m* and *b* in the equation $y = mx + b$ tell you about the graph of the line with that equation.

___The slope of the graphed line is *m*, and the *y*-intercept is *b*.___

© Houghton Mifflin Harcourt Publishing Company

Focus on Modeling

Make sure that students understand that the number of chores Hari chooses to do is the independent, or input variable, and the allowance he receives is the dependent, or output variable.

4 Elaborate

Talk About It

Summarize the Lesson

 Ask: In a linear relationship represented by $y = mx + b$, how do you find *m*, and *b*? Use two sets of *x*- and *y*-values to find *m*, the change in *y* over the change in *x*. Then substitute *m*, *x*, and *y* in $y = mx + b$ and solve to find *b*.

Guided Practice

Engage with the Whiteboard

For **Exercise 2**, have two students label the graph with the coordinates of the two different points they choose to find the slope. Emphasize that using *any* two points on the line will result in the same slope.

Avoid Common Errors

- **Exercise 2** Ask students to predict whether the slope will be positive or negative before they do any calculations. Students may enter y_1 and y_2 in a different order than x_1 and x_2 and get the opposite slope.

- **Exercise 3** Students may use the wrong independent variable. Have them consider whether temperature is dependent upon chirps or chirps dependent upon temperature.

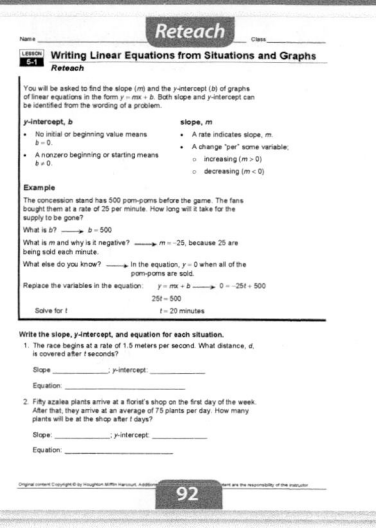

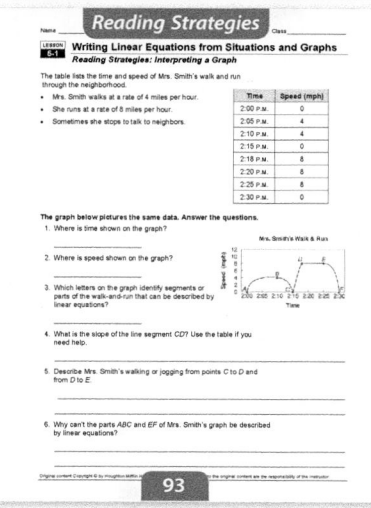

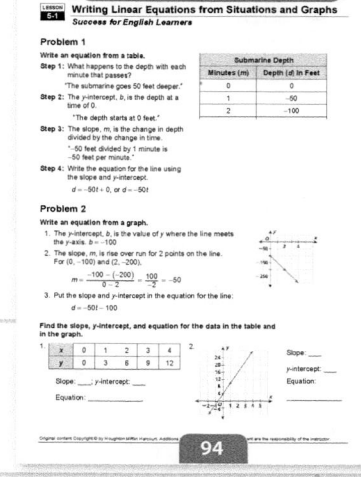

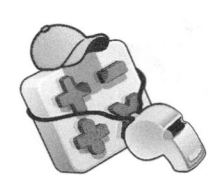

Personal Math Trainer
Daily Intervention
5.1 Homework

Pages shown are from *Differentiated Instruction.*
Also available online.

5 Evaluate

⏱ **Pressed for Time**

5.1 Differentiated Homework Assignments

AL Approaching Level	5–6, 10, 12–16	
OL On Level	6–11, 16	
BL Beyond Level	6, 10–11, 16–18	

*For **Below Level** students, assign Personal Math Trainer, Daily Intervention 5.1 Homework.*

Mathematical Processes	Exercises
MP.2 Reasoning	12–15
MP.3 Logic	16–18
MP.4 Modeling	5–6, 10–11
MP.6 Precision	7–9

Focus on Higher Order Thinking

Depth of Knowledge	Exercises
2 Skills/Concepts	5–15
3 Strategic Thinking **H.O.T.**	16–18

Name_____ Class_____ Date_____

Personal Math Trainer
Online Assessment and Intervention
my.hrw.com

5. A dragonfly can beat its wings 30 times per second. Write an equation in slope-intercept form that shows the relationship between flying time in seconds and the number of times the dragonfly beats its wings.

$$y = 30x$$

6. A balloon is released from the top of a platform that is 50 meters tall. The balloon rises at the rate of 4 meters per second. Write an equation in slope-intercept form that tells the height of the balloon above the ground after a given number of seconds.

$$y = 4x + 50$$

The graph shows a scuba diver's ascent over time.

7. Use the graph to find the slope of the line. Tell what the slope means in this context.

$m = 0.125$; the diver ascends at a rate of 0.125 m/s

8. Identify the *y*-intercept. Tell what the *y*-intercept means in this context.

-10; the diver starts 10 meters below the water's surface.

9. Write an equation in slope-intercept form that represents the diver's depth over time.

$$y = 0.125x - 10$$

Scuba Diver's Ascent

10. The formula for converting Celsius temperatures to Fahrenheit temperatures is a linear equation. Water freezes at 0 °C, or 32 °F, and it boils at 100 °C, or 212 °F. Find the slope and *y*-intercept for a graph that gives degrees Celsius on the horizontal axis and degrees Fahrenheit on the vertical axis. Then write an equation in slope-intercept form that converts degrees Celsius into degrees Fahrenheit.

$m = \frac{9}{5}$; $b = 32$; $y = \frac{9}{5}x + 32$ where $y = °F$ and $x = °C$

11. The cost of renting a sailboat at a lake is $20 per hour plus $12 for lifejackets. Write an equation in slope-intercept form that can be used to calculate the total amount you would pay for using this sailboat.

$$y = 20x + 12$$

© Houghton Mifflin Harcourt Publishing Company

Lesson 5.1 **131**

DIFFERENTIATE INSTRUCTION *Leveled Homework/Practice*

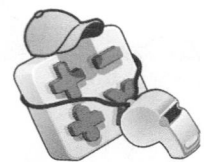

Personal Math Trainer

• 5.1 Homework

Pages shown are from *Differentiated Instruction.* **Also available online.**

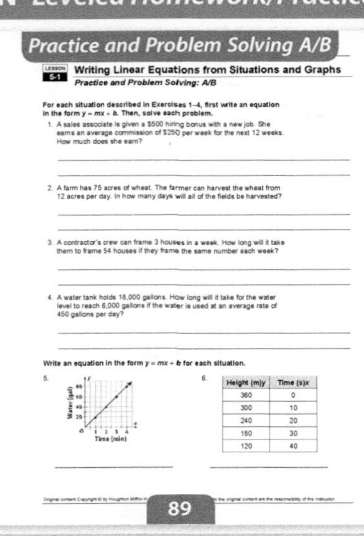

Practice and Problem Solving A/B

89

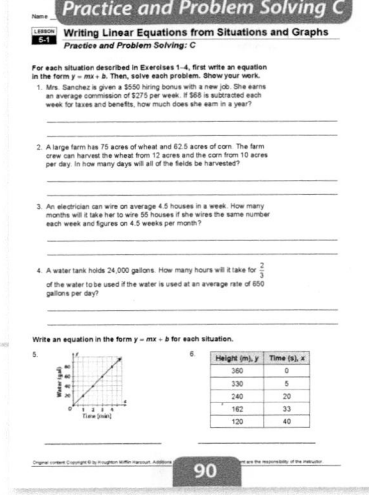

Practice and Problem Solving C

90

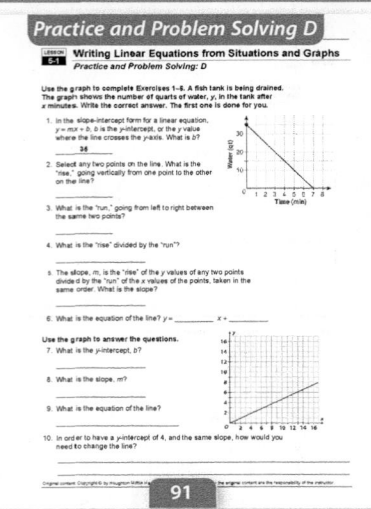

Practice and Problem Solving D

91

The graph shows the activity in a savings account.

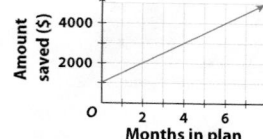

12. What was the amount of the initial deposit that started this savings account?

$1000

13. Find the slope and y-intercept of the graphed line.

$m = 500; b = 1000$

14. Write an equation in slope-intercept form for the activity in this savings account.

$y = 500x + 1000$

15. Explain the meaning of the slope in this graph.

The amount of money in the savings account increases by $500 each month.

H.O.T. FOCUS ON HIGHER ORDER THINKING

16. **Communicate Mathematical Ideas** Explain how you decide which part of a problem will be represented by the variable x, and which part will be represented by the variable y in a graph of the situation.

Examine the problem and decide what quantity you start with, or the input, and what quantity you are trying to find, or the output. Use the input quantity for x and the output quantity for y.

17. **Represent Real-World Problems** Describe what would be true about the rate of change in a situation that could *not* be represented by a graphed line and an equation in the form $y = mx + b$.

The rate of change would not be constant. Using different pairs of points in the slope formula would give you different results.

18. **Draw Conclusions** Must m, in the equation $y = mx + b$, always be a positive number? Explain.

No. A negative number for m means the dependent variable is decreasing as the independent variable increases, so the graph falls from left to right.

Work Area

© Houghton Mifflin Harcourt Publishing Company

DIFFERENTIATE INSTRUCTION *Extend-the-Math Activity* **PRE-AP**

Activity Give each pair of students a sheet of graph paper marked with the x- and y-axes, and pencils or pieces of wire or spaghetti to use for the lines to make quick graphs. One student calls out a slope (for example, $m = 0$ or 1, or 0.5, or 5, or -1) and the other places the line on the graph in the approximate position going through the origin.

Then have one student call out a slope and a y-intercept and the other place the line. If students have trouble, have them place a line with the same slope through the origin and then move it to go through the y-intercept.

 Quick Check

5.1 Lesson Quiz

1. Lee charges $3 for a basket and $2.50 for each pound of fruit picked at the orchard. Write an equation in $y = mx + b$ form for the total cost of x pounds of fruit from the orchard.
   $y = 2.50x + 3$

2. A camp charges families a fee of $625 per month for one child and a certain amount more per month for each additional child. Use the graph to write an equation in slope-intercept form to represent the amount a family with x additional children would pay.
   $y = 225x + 625$

3. Identify the y-intercept in question **2** above. Tell what the y-intercept means in this context. $b = 625$, the fixed fee for one child

4. A driving range charges $4 to rent a golf club plus $2.75 for every bucket of golf balls you hit. Write an equation that shows the total cost c of hitting b buckets of golf balls.
   $c = 2.75b + 4$

Differentiate Instruction

IF a student misses more than one question, THEN

Differentiate Instruction:

• 5.1 Reteach

• Personal Math Trainer

Interactive Whiteboard
Interactive Lesson quiz available online

Lesson Support

Content Objective Students will learn how to write an equation to model a linear relationship given a table.

Professional Development

Integrate Mathematical Processes MP.4

This lesson provides an opportunity to address this Mathematical Processes standard. It calls for students to apply mathematics to problems arising in everyday life, society, and the workplace. Students apply what they know about linear relationships to problems arising from an experiment measuring changes in temperature, measuring the flow of water, and examining the cost of a cell-phone plan. They relate details of everyday relationships to the formal summary of a linear equation in mathematical terms.

FOCUS

Building Background

Visualizing Math Ask students to consider various tables of data that model linear relationships. Then have students work with partners to create four squares that characterize such data. Students can include definitions, equations, examples, and non-examples. Discuss how their diagrams clarify the concept of linear relationships.

COHERENCE

Learning Progressions

In this lesson, students continue to write equations presented in different forms, specifically from a table. Important understandings for students include the following:

- **Draw a graph from a table and then write an equation from the graph.**
- **Write an equation from a table.**

Students continue to construct functions that model linear relationships between two quantities. They determine the rate of change, or slope, and the initial value, or y-intercept, from a description of two values presented in a table. In the last lesson of this module, students will be ready to make predictions using linear relationships and to contrast linear and nonlinear data.

RIGOR

Cluster Connections

This lesson provides an excellent opportunity to connect ideas in the cluster:

Use functions to model relationships between quantities.

Have students refer to the following table.

x	-4	-1	2	6
y	3.25	1.75	0.25	-1.75

Ask them if the data do or do not model a linear relationship and why. Then have them write the equation in slope-intercept form.

Sample answer: The data have a linear relationship since the rate of change is constant. $y = -0.5x + 1.25$

Language Support ELL

Language Objective Students will show how to write an equation to model a linear relationship given a table.

Leveled Strategies for English Learners ELL

Emerging
Post a chart with common expressions that mean the same as *increase* and *decrease*. Use sentence frames for students to complete with a common expression to review the meanings of the terms.

Expanding
Have students use sentence frames to describe the increase or decrease of quantities represented in a table.

Bridging
Have several groups of students create narratives to describe the use of a payment card from their practical real-world experiences. Have them exchange scenarios to create a table and graph to represent the decreases per usage of the payment card.

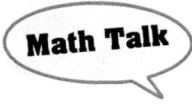

Be sure to identify the dependent variable and independent variable in the real-world problem in Explore Activity Example 1 with a word or short phrase for English learners.

Linguistic Support ELL

Background Knowledge
A Guided Practice example uses the concept of a pre-paid bus pass, in which payments are deducted per usage to produce a balance on the card. Discuss with students actual examples of this form of payment from students' real-world experiences.

Academic/Content Vocabulary
The terms *increase* and *decrease* are used frequently in this lesson. Students need other common words for these terms, such as *gets bigger* or *gets smaller*, to substitute to clarify the meaning. Also note that the terms can be used as verbs and nouns. *To increase* or *to decrease* an amount is a verb. *An increase* or *a decrease* is a noun.

Image Credits: Photodisc/ Getty Images

Writing Linear Equations from a Table

1 Engage

ESSENTIAL QUESTION

How do you write an equation to model a linear relationship given a table? Use pairs of input and output values to determine the slope m and the y-intercept b in the equation $y = mx + b$.

Motivate the Lesson

Ask: Have you ever recorded measurements in a table? Tables are often used in science labs to record temperatures, weights, and other measures. How do you use that information to write an equation? Begin the lesson to find out.

2 Explore

EXPLORE ACTIVITY   EXAMPLE 1

ADDITIONAL EXAMPLE 1 The Dailey family uses maple sap to make syrup. The table shows the temperature of the sap as it heats. Graph the data, and find the slope and y-intercept from the graph. Then write the equation for the graph in slope-intercept form.

Time (h)	0	1	2	3	4
Temp (°F)	38	83	128	173	218

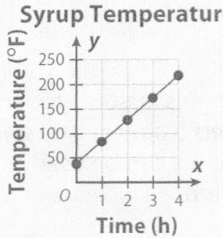

Syrup Temperature

$°F = 45h + 38$

Interactive Whiteboard
Interactive example available online

LESSON 5.2 Writing Linear Equations from a Table

8.2.5.2
Students will write an equation to model a linear relationship given a table.

ESSENTIAL QUESTION

How do you write an equation to model a linear relationship given a table?

EXPLORE ACTIVITY   Real World

Graphing from a Table to Write an Equation

You can use information from a table to draw a graph of a linear relationship and to write an equation for the graphed line.

Math On the Spot
my.hrw.com

EXAMPLE 1 The table shows the temperature of a fish tank during an experiment. Graph the data, and find the slope and y-intercept from the graph. Then write the equation for the graph in slope-intercept form.

Time (h)	0	1	2	3	4	5
Temperature (°F)	82	80	78	76	74	72

STEP 1 Graph the ordered pairs from the table (time, temperature).

STEP 2 Draw a line through the points.

STEP 3 Choose two points on the graph to find the slope: for example, choose (0, 82) and (1, 80).

Tank Temperature

(0, 82) (2, 78) (4, 74)
(1, 80) (3, 76) (5, 72)

$$m = \frac{y_2 - y_1}{x_2 - x_1} = \frac{\boxed{80} - \boxed{82}}{\boxed{1} - \boxed{0}} = \underline{-2}$$

STEP 4 Read the y-intercept from the graph.

$b = \underline{82}$

STEP 5 Use these slope and y-intercept values to write an equation in slope-intercept form.

$y = mx + b$

$y = \boxed{-2} x + \boxed{82}$

DIFFERENTIATE INSTRUCTION *Leveled Questions*

	EXPLORE ACTIVITY EXAMPLE 1
AL DOK 1 *Recall*	Describe informally what is happening in this experiment. The temperature of a fish tank is falling at a steady rate.
OL DOK 2 *Skills/Concepts*	How could you find the equation from the table without drawing a graph? Choose two points from the table to find the slope, and use (0, 82) to determine the y-intercept.
BL DOK 3 *Strategic Thinking*	How could you determine the equation from this data without the first two given data points in the table? Use any two ordered pairs to find the slope. Then find the y-intercept using the slope pattern: count backward in the first row to 0, and count backward by adding 2s in the second row to get 80 and 82. Then you know (0, 82) is on the graph, so the y-intercept is 82.

YOUR TURN

1. The table shows the volume of water released by Hoover Dam over a certain period of time. Graph the data, and find the slope and *y*-intercept from the graph. Then write the equation for the graph in slope-intercept form.

Water Released from Hoover Dam

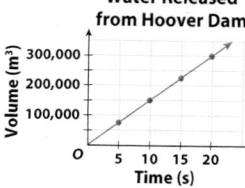

Time (s)	Volume of water (m³)
5	75,000
10	150,000
15	225,000
20	300,000

Personal Math Trainer
Online Assessment and Intervention
my.hrw.com

$m = 15,000; b = 0; y = 15,000x$

Math On the Spot
my.hrw.com

Animated Math
my.hrw.com

Writing an Equation from a Table

The information from a table can also help you to write the equation that represents a given situation without drawing the graph.

EXAMPLE 2

Elizabeth's cell phone plan lets her choose how many minutes are included each month. The table shows the plan's monthly cost *y* for a given number of included minutes *x*. Write an equation in slope-intercept form to represent the situation.

Minutes included, *x*	100	200	300	400	500
Cost of plan ($), *y*	14	20	26	32	38

STEP 1 Notice that the change in cost is the same for each increase of 100 minutes. So, the relationship is linear. Choose any two ordered pairs from the table to find the slope.

$$m = \frac{y_2 - y_1}{x_2 - x_1} = \frac{(20 - 14)}{(200 - 100)} = \frac{6}{100} = 0.06$$

STEP 2 Find the *y*-intercept. Use the slope and any point from the table.

$y = mx + b$ *Slope-intercept form*
$14 = 0.06 \cdot 100 + b$ *Substitute for y, m, and x.*
$14 = 6 + b$ *Multiply.*
$8 = b$ *Subtract 6 from both sides.*

STEP 3 Substitute the slope and *y*-intercept.

$y = mx + b$ *Slope-intercept form*
$y = 0.06x + 8$ *Substitute 0.06 for m and 8 for b.*

© Houghton Mifflin Harcourt Publishing Company

Avoid Common Errors
Remind students to refer to the slope formula on the previous page when calculating the slope. They should write out the formula and substitute the coordinates of two points.

3 Explain

EXAMPLE 2

ADDITIONAL EXAMPLE 2 Zara made an initial deposit to a bank account and then added a fixed amount every week. The table shows the money in her account. Write an equation in slope-intercept form to represent the situation.

Number of weeks, *x*	1	2	3	4	5
Balance ($), *y*	140	160	180	200	220

$y = 20x + 120$

 Interactive Whiteboard
Interactive example available online

Animated Math
Write Equations for Lines
Students explore changing the slope and *y*-intercept of a line in a dynamic graphing tool.
my.hrw.com

	EXAMPLE 2
(AL) DOK 1 *Recall*	What is the cost per minute for a 200-minute plan? $0.10
(OL) DOK 2 *Skills/Concepts*	Describe the process of using a table and the general slope-intercept form $y = mx + b$ to write the equation. Use any two ordered pairs to find the slope, *m*. Then choose any ordered pair and substitute its *x*- and *y*-values and *m* into $y = mx + b$, and solve for *b*.
(BL) DOK 3 *Strategic Thinking*	How does the average cost per minute change as the number of minutes in the plan increases? It decreases; at 100 minutes, the rate is $0.14/min, and at 400 minutes, the rate is $0.08/min.

TEACHER TO TEACHER

Cognitive Strategies Before students use data in tables to write an equation, encourage them to identify the independent and dependent variables.

• **Example 1**: Temperature depends on time.
• **Example 2**: Cost depends on minutes included.

Connect to Daily Life

For **Exercise 4**, students may not understand how sales commission works. Give one or more examples, using points from the table to make this clear, explain: The salesperson is paid $250 per week regardless of how many computers are sold. If 10 computers are sold, the total pay is $250 plus $75 for each of the 10 computers.

Digital Teacher Resources

Go online to access all your lesson-level resources.

Differentiated Instruction

- Reteach
- Reading Strategies
- Success for English Learners
- Practice and Problem Solving A/B, C, D

Math on the Spot Videos

my.hrw.com

Reflect

2. What is the base price for the cell phone plan, regardless of how many minutes are included? What is the cost per minute? Explain.

$8; $0.06; in the equation for the table, $y = 0.06x + 8$, the y-intercept, 8, is an initial amount that does not depend on the rate of change. The slope, 0.06, represents the rate of change, which is the per-minute cost.

3. **What If?** Elizabeth's cell phone company changes the cost of her plan as shown below. Write an equation in slope-intercept form to represent the situation. How did the plan change?

Minutes included, x	100	200	300	400	500
Cost of plan ($), y	30	35	40	45	50

$y = 0.05x + 25$; The fee was increased by $17, and the per-minute rate was decreased by 1 cent.

YOUR TURN

4. A salesperson receives a weekly salary plus a commission for each computer sold. The table shows the total pay, p, and the number of computers sold, n. Write an equation in slope-intercept form to represent this situation.

Number of computers sold, n	4	6	8	10	12
Total pay ($), p	550	700	850	1000	1150

$p = 75n + 250$

5. To rent a van, a moving company charges $40.00 plus $0.50 per mile. The table shows the total cost, c, and the number of miles driven, d. Write an equation in slope-intercept form to represent this situation.

Number of miles driven, d	10	20	30	40	50
Total cost ($), c	45	50	55	60	65

$c = 0.50d + 40$

The slope, or m, is the commission of $75 for each computer sold and the y-intercept, or b, is the base salary of $250.

Math Talk
Mathematical Processes
Explain the meaning of the slope and y-intercept of the equation.

Personal Math Trainer
Online Assessment and Intervention
my.hrw.com

© Houghton Mifflin Harcourt Publishing Company

1. Jaime purchased a $20 bus pass. Each time he rides the bus, a certain amount is deducted from the pass. The table shows the amount, left on his pass after x rides. Graph the data, and find the slope and y-intercept from the graph or from the table. Then write the equation for the graph in slope-intercept form. (Explore Activity Example 1)

Number of rides, x	0	4	8	12	16
Amount left on pass ($), y	20	15	10	5	0

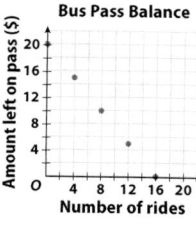

Bus Pass Balance

$m = -1.25; b = 20; y = -1.25x + 20$

The table shows the temperature (y) at different altitudes (x). This is a linear relationship. (Example 2)

Altitude (ft), x	0	2,000	4,000	6,000	8,000	10,000	12,000
Temperature (°F), y	59	51	43	35	27	19	11

2. Find the slope for this relationship.

$m = \dfrac{51 - 59}{2000 - 0} = \dfrac{-8}{2000} = -0.004$

3. Find the y-intercept for this relationship.

$b = 59$

4. Write an equation in slope-intercept form that represents this relationship.

$y = -0.004x + 59$

5. Use your equation to determine the temperature at an altitude of 5000 feet.

$y = -0.004(5000) + 59 = 39\ °F$

ESSENTIAL QUESTION CHECK-IN

6. Describe how you can use the information in a table showing a linear relationship to find the slope and y-intercept for the equation.

Use two data points from the table to find the slope, and then locate the point on the table where x is 0 to identify the y-intercept.

© Houghton Mifflin Harcourt Publishing Company • Image Credits: Photodisc/ Getty Images

4 Elaborate

Talk About It

Summarize the Lesson

Ask: How can you use values given in a table of a linear relationship to draw a graph and write an equation in $y = mx + b$ form? Use values from the table to draw a graph. Use two points to find the slope. To find the y-intercept, either read it from the graph or substitute m and any point in the table as (x, y) to solve for b in $y = mx + b$.

Engage with the Whiteboard

For **Exercise 1**, have students mark on the graph several points that are not in the table, such as the points that tell how much is left on the pass after 3 rides and after 14 rides. Label the points with their coordinates.

Focus on Communication

Have students informally describe the information that is shown in the table for **Exercises 2–5**, and what it might mean for someone who is climbing mountains. It gets colder the higher you climb.

Avoid Common Errors

Exercise 5 To avoid calculating an incorrect value, remind students that they can use the table to predict, or check, the reasonableness of the temperature. They should see that the temperature must be between 35 °F and 43 °F.

DIFFERENTIATE INSTRUCTION *Intervention and Additional Support*

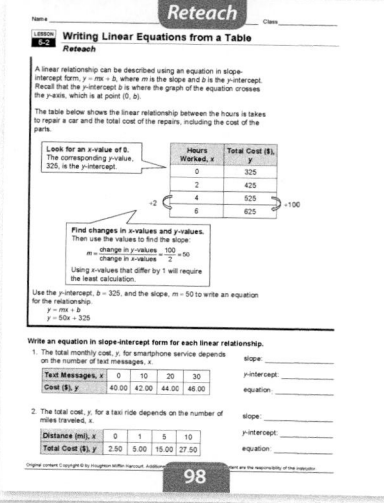

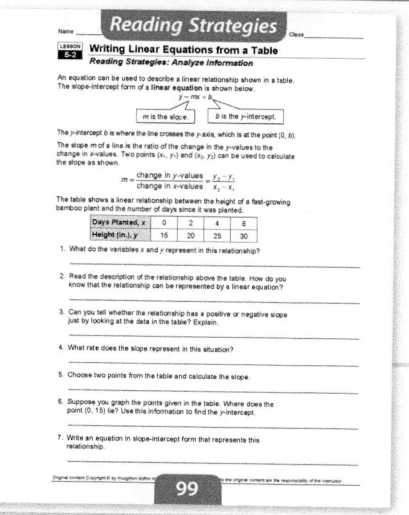

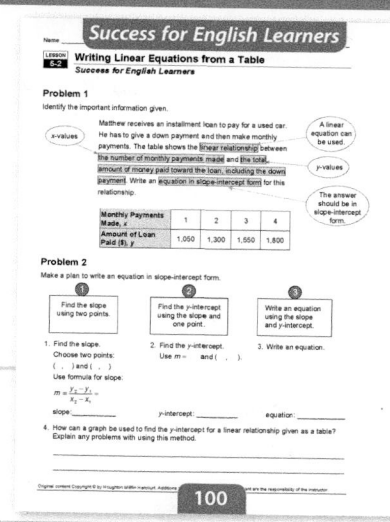

Personal Math Trainer
Daily Intervention
5.2 Homework

Pages shown are from *Differentiated Instruction*. **Also available online.**

5 Evaluate

5.2 Independent Practice

Personal Math Trainer

Online Assessment and Intervention

@my.hrw.com

7. The table shows the costs of a large cheese pizza with toppings at a local pizzeria. Graph the data, and find the slope and y-intercept from the graph. Then write the equation for the graph in slope-intercept form.

Number of toppings, t	0	1	2	3	4	5
Total cost ($), C	8	10	12	14	16	18

$m = 2; b = 8; C = 2t + 8$

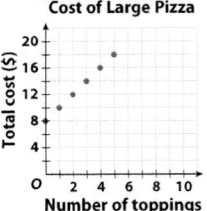

Cost of Large Pizza

8. The table shows how much an air-conditioning repair company charges for different numbers of hours of work. Graph the data, and find the slope and y-intercept from the graph. Then write the equation for the graph in slope-intercept form.

Number of hours (h), t	0	1	2	3	4	5
Amount charged ($), A	50	100	150	200	250	300

$m = 50; b = 50; A = 50t + 50$

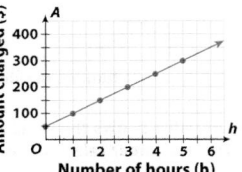

9. A friend gave Ms. Morris a gift card for a local car wash. The table shows the linear relationship of how the value left on the card relates to the number of car washes.

Number of car washes, x	0	8	12
Amount left on card ($), y	30	18	12

a. Write an equation that shows the number of dollars left on the card.

$y = -1.5x + 30$

b. Explain the meaning of the negative slope in this situation.

The amount of dollars left decreases as the number of car washes increases.

c. What is the maximum value of x that makes sense in this context? Explain.

20; after 20 washes there is no money left on the card

The tables show linear relationships between x and y. Write an equation in slope-intercept form for each relationship.

10.

x	−2	−1	0	2
y	−1	0	1	3

$y = x + 1$

11.

x	−4	1	0	6
y	14	4	6	−6

$y = -2x + 6$

Lesson 5.2 **137**

© Houghton Mifflin Harcourt Publishing Company

Pressed for Time

5.2 Differentiated Homework Assignments

AL Approaching Level	7–12, 14
OL On Level	8–14
BL Beyond Level	8–9, 12–15

*For **Below Level** students, assign Personal Math Trainer, Daily Intervention 5.2 Homework.*

Mathematical Processes	Exercises
MP.2 Reasoning	10–11
MP.3 Logic	13–15
MP.4 Modeling	7–9, 12

Focus on Higher Order Thinking

Depth of Knowledge	Exercises
2 Skills/Concepts	7–13
3 Strategic Thinking **H.O.T.**	14–15

DIFFERENTIATE INSTRUCTION *Leveled Homework/Practice*

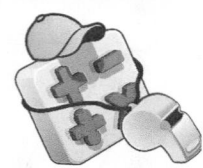

Personal Math Trainer

• 5.2 Homework

Pages shown are from *Differentiated Instruction.* **Also available online.**

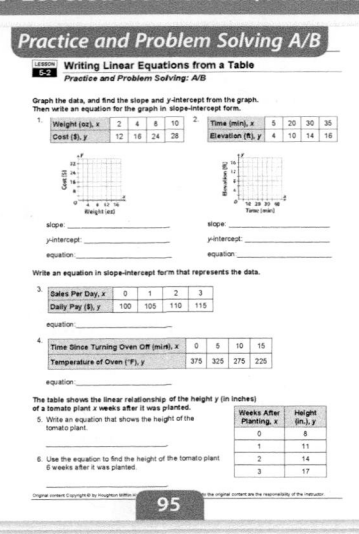

Practice and Problem Solving A/B — 95

Practice and Problem Solving C — 96

Practice and Problem Solving D — 97

12. Finance Desiree starts a savings account with $125.00. Every month, she deposits $53.50.

a. Complete the table to model the situation.

Month, x	0	1	2	3	4
Amount in Savings ($), y	125.00	178.50	232.00	285.50	339.00

b. Write an equation in slope-intercept form that shows how much money Desiree has in her savings account after x months.

$$y = 53.50x + 125.00$$

c. Use the equation to find how much money Desiree will have in savings after 11 months.

$713.50

13. Monty documented the amount of rain his farm received on a monthly basis, as shown in the table.

Month, x	1	2	3	4	5
Rainfall (in.), y	5	3	4.5	1	7

a. Is the relationship linear? Why or why not?

No, the change between weeks is constant, but the change in the amount of rain is not constant.

b. Can an equation be written to describe the amount of rain? Explain.

No; there is no apparent pattern in the table.

 **FOCUS ON HIGHER ORDER THINKING**

14. Analyze Relationships If you have a table that shows a linear relationship, when can you read the value for b, in $y = mx + b$, directly from the table without drawing a graph or doing any calculations? Explain.

If there is a point $(0, y)$ in the table, then $y = b$ because at the y-intercept the value of x is zero.

15. What If? Jaíme graphed linear data given in the form (cost, number). The y-intercept was 0. Jayla graphed the same data given in the form (number, cost). What was the y-intercept of her graph? Explain.

0; Jaíme's graph contained $(0, 0)$. Since Jayla's data were the same, but with x and y switched, her graph also contained $(0, 0)$.

Work Area

© Houghton Mifflin Harcourt Publishing Company

DIFFERENTIATE INSTRUCTION *Extend-the-Math Activity* **PRE-AP**

Activity To extend the relationships between values in a table, points on a graphed line, and ordered pairs that satisfy a linear equation, have students draw graphs that use the other three quadrants. For example, ask them to create a table of ordered pairs for the equations $y = x + 3$ and $y = -x - 2$ using both negative and positive values of x. Have them graph the points in the table and draw a line through the points. Discuss situations that might be represented by such equations, for example, charging purchases, debt, temperatures below zero, diving below sea level.

 **Quick Check**

5.2 Lesson Quiz

The table shows Eli's distance from home as he rides his bike at a steady rate after meeting a friend.

Time (h)	1	2	3	4	5
Distance (mi)	14	26	38	50	62

1. Graph the data.

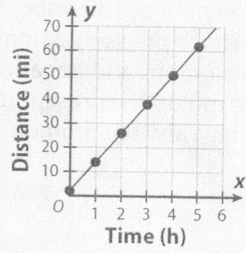

2. Find the slope and y-intercept. $m = 12; b = 2$

3. How fast does Eli ride his bike, in miles per hour? 12 mi/h

4. Write an equation in $y = mx + b$ form that represents the miles, y, that Eli goes in x hours. $y = 12x + 2$

5. If each distance were halved, what would the equation be? What would it mean in terms of the problem? Explain. $y = 6x + 1$; Eli starts 1 mile from home and goes 6 mi/h.

Differentiate Instruction

IF a student misses more than one question, THEN

Differentiate Instruction:

- 5.2 Reteach
- Personal Math Trainer

 Interactive Whiteboard
Interactive Lesson quiz available online

Lesson Support

Content Objective Students will learn how to contrast linear and nonlinear sets of bivariate data.

Professional Development

Integrate Mathematical Processes MP.6

This lesson provides an opportunity to address this Mathematical Processes standard. It calls for students to precisely communicate mathematical ideas and reasoning. Students use tables and graphs and equations to represent linear and nonlinear relationships. Students use these multiple representations to compare and contrast linear and nonlinear relationships and to communicate their understanding.

FOCUS

Building Background

Connecting to Everyday Life Ask students to write a linear equation for the canoe rental. Discuss the advantages of using an equation to describe the situation. In particular, discuss how it simplifies predictions. For example, an equation can be used to determine the cost for a given amount of time or how much time can be spent canoeing for a given cost.

> **Canoe Rental**
>
> $20 plus $5 for every hour out

COHERENCE

Learning Progressions

In this lesson, students construct scatter plots for bivariate data, identify linear and nonlinear associations, and make predictions about data with linear relationships. Important understandings for students include the following:

- **Find the equation of a linear relationship from points on a graph.**
- **Use the equation of a linear relationship to predict a value between known data.**
- **Contrast linear and nonlinear data.**

In this lesson, students identify linear associations of bivariate data and use the linear characteristics to write equations and make predictions. They also begin to investigate nonlinear data by recognizing that the rate of change of a nonlinear relationship is not constant and the graph results in a curve.

RIGOR

Cluster Connections

This lesson provides an excellent opportunity to connect ideas in the cluster:

Investigate patterns of association in bivariate data.

Have students compare the following data.

x	1	2	3	4	5
y	15	27	39	51	63

x	1	2	3	4	5
y	1	8	27	64	125

Discuss which data show a linear relationship and which do not, and challenge them to find an equation for each.

Sample answer: The first set of data has a constant rate of change, so it is linear. The equation is $y = 12x + 3$. The second set is nonlinear since the rate of change is not constant. The equation is $y = x^3$.

Language Support **ELL**

Leveled Strategies for English Learners **ELL**

Emerging
Have students measure the steps, the rise, and the handrail of a standard size stairway and then describe the measurements using sentence frames.

Expanding
Have students cut out paper strips to create a paper measuring tape of different colors to measure parts of a stairway and label horizontal distance and height of the handrail at different points. Students can then compose a sentence to describe what each paper strip measures.

Bridging
Have students work in groups to write a short narrative explaining step-by-step how to measure horizontal distance and the height of the handrail on a standard size stairway.

In Example 1, elicit from students that the slope of the equation $y = 0.8x + 3$ represents the increase in height of the handrail per foot of horizontal distance. Point out that the height and depth of most stairways are standardized and relate to concepts such as constant and rate of change.

Image Credits: ©Jack Hollingsworth/Blend Images/Alamy Images

Linguistic Support **ELL**

Academic/Content Vocabulary
An example in this lesson requires students to know the meanings of *horizontal distance* and *height* as they relate to a handrail on a staircase. Point out the relationship between *horizon* and *horizontal*. Scaffold these definitions and concepts using a tape measure or string on a stairway (also called staircase) to illustrate horizontal distance. The height of a handrail is constant for each step.

Background Knowledge
In this lesson, students discuss the cost of taxi rides for different distances. Have students use a map of their town or city or the nearest large city. Have students determine different points of origin and destinations of fictitious taxi rides and determine the cost according to the distance along a path. Students can research the taxi rates.

Linear Relationships and Bivariate Data

1 Engage

? ESSENTIAL QUESTION

How can you contrast linear and nonlinear sets of bivariate data? The graph of a linear set of data is a single line; the graph of a nonlinear set of data is not a single line.

Motivate the Lesson

Ask: Does a table of paired values always graph as a single line? Begin the lesson to find out.

2 Explore

EXPLORE ACTIVITY   EXAMPLE 1

ADDITIONAL EXAMPLE 1 The charge for a pizza changes as the number of toppings changes. Show that the relationship is linear, and then find the equation for the relationship.

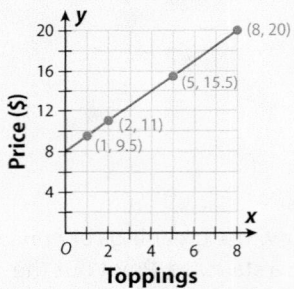

A line passes through all the graphed points so the relationship is linear. $y = 1.5x + 8$

 Interactive Whiteboard
Interactive example available online

Linear Relationships and Bivariate Data

8.2.5.3
Students will contrast linear and nonlinear sets of bivariate data.

? ESSENTIAL QUESTION

How can you contrast linear and nonlinear sets of bivariate data?

EXPLORE ACTIVITY

Finding the Equation of a Linear Relationship

You can use the points on a graph of a linear relationship to write an equation for the relationship. The equation of a linear relationship is $y = mx + b$, where m is the rate of change, or slope, and b is the value of y when x is 0.

Math On the Spot
my.hrw.com

EXAMPLE 1 A handrail runs alongside a stairway. As the horizontal distance from the bottom of the stairway changes, the height of the handrail changes. Show that the relationship is linear, and then find the equation for the relationship.

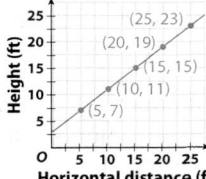

STEP 1   Show that the relationship is linear.

All of the points (5, 7), (10, 11), (15, 15), (20, 19), and (25, 23) lie on the same ___line___ , so the relationship is ___linear___ . Draw a line through the points on the graph.

STEP 2   Write the equation of the linear relationship.

Choose two points to find the slope: (5, 7) and (25, 23).

$$m = \frac{23 - \boxed{7}}{\boxed{25} - 5}$$

$$= \frac{\boxed{16}}{\boxed{20}}, \text{ or } \underline{0.8}$$

Choose a point and use the slope to substitute values for x, y, and m.

$$y = mx + b$$

$$\boxed{7} = \boxed{0.8}(5) + b$$

$$\boxed{7} = \boxed{4} + b$$

$$\boxed{3} = b$$

The equation of the linear relationship is $y = \boxed{0.8}x + \boxed{3}$.

Lesson 5.3   **139**

DIFFERENTIATE INSTRUCTION *Leveled Questions*

	EXPLORE ACTIVITY EXAMPLE 1
AL DOK 1 *Recall*	Can you draw a line through the points on the graph? Yes, the points on the graph all lie on the same line.
OL DOK 2 *Skills/Concepts*	What does the slope of the equation represent in this situation? What does the *y*-intercept represent? Slope: increase in handrail height per foot of horizontal distance; *y*-intercept: handrail height at the bottom of the stairway
BL DOK 3 *Strategic Thinking*	Do the *x*- and *y*-coordinates of the point (25, 23) represent the handrail rising 23 feet over a run of 25 feet? Justify your answer. No; the relationship is non-proportional linear. The *y*-intercept is 3, the point (25, 23) represents a rise of 20 feet over a run of 25 feet, or a slope of $\frac{4}{5} = 0.8$.

LEVELED QUESTIONS: (AL) Approaching Level | (OL) On Level | (BL) Beyond Level

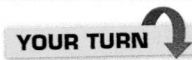

YOUR TURN

Find the equation of each linear relationship.

1.

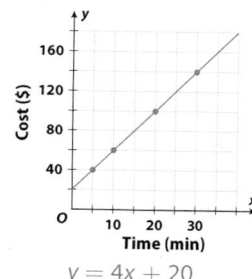

2.

Hours (x)	Number of units (y)
2	480
15	3,600
24	5,760
30	7,200
48	11,520
55	13,200

Personal Math Trainer
Online Assessment and Intervention
my.hrw.com

$y = 4x + 20$

$y = 240x$

Math On the Spot
my.hrw.com

Making Predictions

You can use an equation of a linear relationship to predict a value between data points that you already know.

EXAMPLE 2 Real World

The graph shows the cost for taxi rides of different distances. Predict the cost of a taxi ride that covers a distance of 6.5 miles.

STEP 1 Write the equation of the linear relationship.

(2, 7) and (6, 15)   Select two points.

$m = \dfrac{15 - 7}{6 - 2}$ Calculate the rate of change.

$= \dfrac{8}{4}$ Simplify.

$= 2$

$y = mx + b$

$15 = 2(6) + b$ Fill in values for x, y, and m.

$15 = 12 + b$ Simplify.

$3 = b$ Solve for b.

The equation of the linear relationship is $y = 2x + 3$.

You can check your equation using another point on the graph. Try (8, 19). Substituting gives $19 = 2(8) + 3$. The right side simplifies to 19, so $19 = 19$. ✓

© Houghton Mifflin Harcourt Publishing Company • Image Credits: © Fuse/Getty Images

140 Unit 2

YOUR TURN MP.6

Avoid Common Errors
In **Exercise 1**, students may misread the second point on the graph. Remind students to determine unlabeled values on an axis by looking at both the closest lesser axis label and the closest greater axis label.

3 Explain

EXAMPLE 2

ADDITIONAL EXAMPLE 2 The graph shows the distance of a train from a landmark as it travels at a constant speed. Use the graph to predict what the distance will be after 7.5 hours. 400 miles

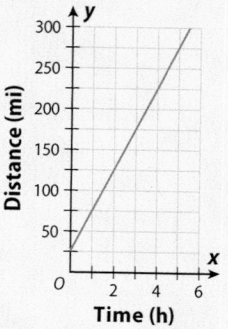

Interactive Whiteboard
Interactive example available online

		EXAMPLE 2
(AL) DOK 1 *Recall*		What other two points could be used to find the slope? (4, 11) and (8, 19)
(OL) DOK 2 *Skills/Concepts*		How can you use the graph to check your answer in Step 2? Check that the point (6.5, 16) is on the graph.
(BL) DOK 3 *Strategic Thinking*		The cost graph for a taxi ride in a second city goes through (2, 8) and (8, 17). How do the costs for a 5-mile taxi ride in the two cities compare? Explain. $0.50 less in the second city; the cost in the first city is 2(5) + 3 = $13; the cost in the second city is 1.5(5) + 5 = $12.50.

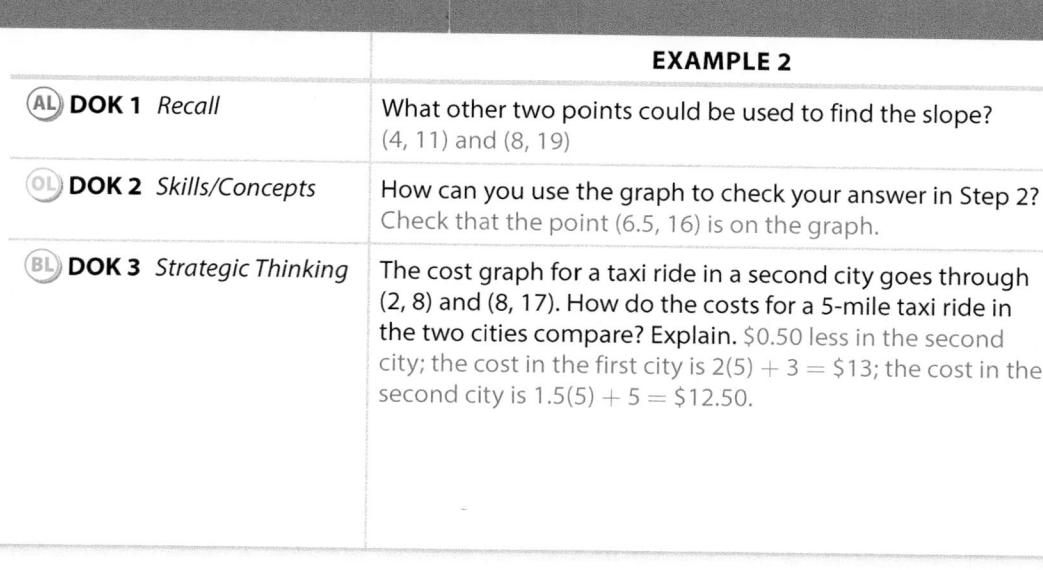

TEACHER TO TEACHER

Auditory Clues Help students understand the word *bivariate*.

• Point out the *bi-* and connect it to a familiar *bi-* word, such as *bicycle*, to help them remember that it means *two*.

• Point out the *vari-* and connect it to a familiar *vari-* word, such as *variable*, to help them remember that it means *change*.

So, *bivariate* data is data in pairs of variables.

Talk About It

Check for Understanding

Ask: What is the hourly pay graphed in this relationship? $15

STEP 2 Use your equation from Step 1 to predict the cost of a 6.5-mile taxi ride.

$y = 2x + 3$

$y = 2(6.5) + 3$ *Substitute x = 6.5.*

$y = 16$ *Solve for y.*

A taxi ride that covers a distance of 6.5 miles will cost $16.

Reflect

3. **What If?** Suppose a regulation changes the cost of the taxi ride to $1.80 per mile, plus a fee of $4.30. How does the price of the 6.5 mile ride compare to the original price?

   It is the same. The new equation is $y = 1.8x + 4.3$,

   so $y = 1.8(6.5) + 4.3 = 11.7 + 4.3 = 16$.

4. How can you use a graph of a linear relationship to predict an unknown value of y for a given value of x within the region of the graph?

   Sample answer: Use the graph to write an equation,

   and then substitute the new input into the equation

   to make the prediction.

5. How can you use a table of linear data to predict a value?

   Sample answer: Use the table of values to write

   an equation and then use the equation to make

   the prediction.

YOUR TURN

Paulina's income from a job that pays her a fixed amount per hour is shown in the graph. Use the graph to find the predicted value.

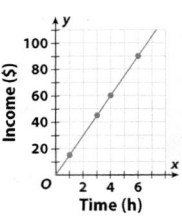

6. Income earned for working 2 hours

   $30

7. Income earned for working 3.25 hours

   $48.75

8. Total income earned for working for five 8-hour days all at the standard rate ___$600___

Personal Math Trainer

Online Assessment and Intervention

my.hrw.com

© Houghton Mifflin Harcourt Publishing Company

My Notes

Contrasting Linear and Nonlinear Data

Bivariate data is a set of data that is made up of two paired variables. If the relationship between the variables is linear, then the rate of change (slope) is constant. If the graph shows a **nonlinear relationship**, then the rate of change varies between pairs of points.

Andrew has two options in which to invest $200. Option A earns simple interest of 5%, while Option B earns interest of 5% compounded annually. The table shows the amount of the investment for both options over 20 years. Graph the data and describe the differences between the two graphs.

Year, x	Option A Total ($)	Option B Total ($)
0	200.00	200.00
5	250.00	255.26
10	300.00	325.78
15	350.00	415.79
20	400.00	530.66

STEP 1 Graph the data from the table for Options A and B on the same coordinate grid.

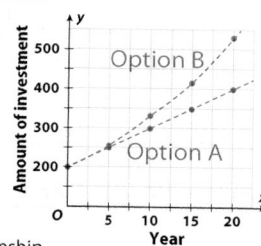

STEP 2 Find the rate of change between pairs of points for Option A and classify the relationship.

Option A	Rate of Change
(0, 200) and (5, 250)	$m = \frac{250 - 200}{5 - 0} = \underline{10}$
(5, 250) and (10, 300)	$m = \frac{300 - 250}{10 - 5} = 10$
(10, 300) and (15, 350)	$m = \frac{350 - 300}{15 - 10} = 10$

The rate of change between the data values is __constant__, so

the graph of Option A shows a __linear__ relationship.

© Houghton Mifflin Harcourt Publishing Company

Engage with the Whiteboard

Have students extend the coordinate plane and the two lines, and make conjectures about the total amounts after 25 and 30 years. Students should be able to determine that for Option A, simple interest, there will be $450 after 25 years and $500 after 30 years. Students will only be able to estimate the values for Option B; the exact values are $677.27 after 25 years and $864.39 after 30 years.

DIFFERENTIATE INSTRUCTION *Leveled Questions*

	EXPLORE ACTIVITY 2
(AL) DOK 1 *Recall*	What does bivariate mean in relation to data? the data are represented by two variables, paired with each other
(OL) DOK 2 *Skills/Concepts*	Compare values for Option A with those for Option B. How are the two options alike and how are they different? The beginning amounts are equal, but the rates at which they increase differ. Option A grows a constant rate of $50 each 5 years. Option B grows $55.26 the first 5 years, but grows by larger and larger amounts over successive 5-year intervals.
(BL) DOK 3 *Strategic Thinking*	Consider the relationship that represents the *difference* of the amounts in the accounts over 5-year intervals. Is this relationship linear? Explain. No; differences don't change by the same amount over each interval. The differences are $5.26, $25.78, $65.79, and $130.66.

LEVELED QUESTIONS: (AL) Approaching Level | (OL) On Level | (BL) Beyond Level

Digital Teacher Resources

Go online to access all your lesson-level resources.

my.hrw.com

Differentiated Instruction
- Reteach
- Reading Strategies
- Success for English Learners
- Practice and Problem Solving A/B, C, D

Math on the Spot Videos

STEP 3 Find the rate of change between pairs of points for Option B and classify the relationship.

Option B	Rate of Change
(0, 200) and (5, 255.26)	$m = \frac{252.26 - 200}{5 - 0} \approx$ <u>10.5</u>
(5, 255.26) and (10, 325.78)	$m = \frac{325.78 - 252.26}{10 - 5} \approx 14.7$
(10, 325.78) and (15, 415.79)	$m = \frac{415.79 - 325.78}{15 - 10} \approx 18.0$

The rate of change between the data values is <u>not constant</u>, so the graph of Option B shows a <u>nonlinear</u> relationship.

Reflect

9. Why are the graphs drawn as lines or curves and not discrete points?

   Sample answer: You can calculate the value of the account at any time as the money grows. All points along the line or curve are reasonable and possible.

10. Can you determine by viewing the graph if the data have a linear or nonlinear relationship? Explain.

    Sample answer: Yes. If all of the data lie on a line, then the data have a linear relationship. If the graph is a curve (or not a line), then the data have a nonlinear relationship.

11. **Draw Conclusions** Find the differences in the account balances to the nearest dollar at 5 year intervals for Option B. How does the length of time that money is in an account affect the advantage that compound interest has over simple interest?

    $55, $71, $90, $115; the longer that the money is in the account, the greater the relative advantage of it earning compound interest will be.

© Houghton Mifflin Harcourt Publishing Company

Use the following graphs to find the equation of the linear relationship. (Explore Activity Example 1)

1.

Distance (mi) vs *Amount of gas (gal)*

$y = 30x$

2.

Cost ($) vs *Time (h)*

$y = 2.5x + 2$

3. The graph shows the relationship between the number of hours a kayak is rented and the total cost of the rental. Write an equation of the relationship. Then use the equation to predict the cost of a rental that lasts 5.5 hours. (Example 2)

Cost ($) vs *Time (h)*

$y = 20x + 30; \$140$

Does each of the following graphs represent a linear relationship? Why or why not? (Explore Activity 2)

4.

Yes, because the graph has a constant rate of change.

5.

No, because the graph does not have a constant rate of change.

? ESSENTIAL QUESTION CHECK-IN

6. How can you tell if a set of bivariate data shows a linear relationship?

Sample answer: Graph the data points. If the points lie along a straight line, the data is linear.

© Houghton Mifflin Harcourt Publishing Company • Image Credits: ©Comstock/Getty Images

4 Elaborate

Talk About It

Summarize the Lesson

Ask: If you were given two graphed lines, one of a linear set of data and the other of a nonlinear set of data, how could you tell which line goes with which set of data? The graph of the linear set of data will be a single line.

Guided Practice

Engage with the Whiteboard

In **Exercises 1–2**, have students draw a line through the points and the y-axis. Have them label the y-intercept. In **Exercises 4–5**, have students attempt to draw a line through all the points.

Avoid Common Errors

• **Exercise 2** Some students may attempt to draw a line through all of the points and the origin and decide that the relationship is not linear. Remind students that the origin is not necessarily part of the graph unless it is marked as such.

• **Exercises 4–5** Remind students that the line must contain *all* of the points and that a line is always straight.

DIFFERENTIATE INSTRUCTION *Intervention and Additional Support*

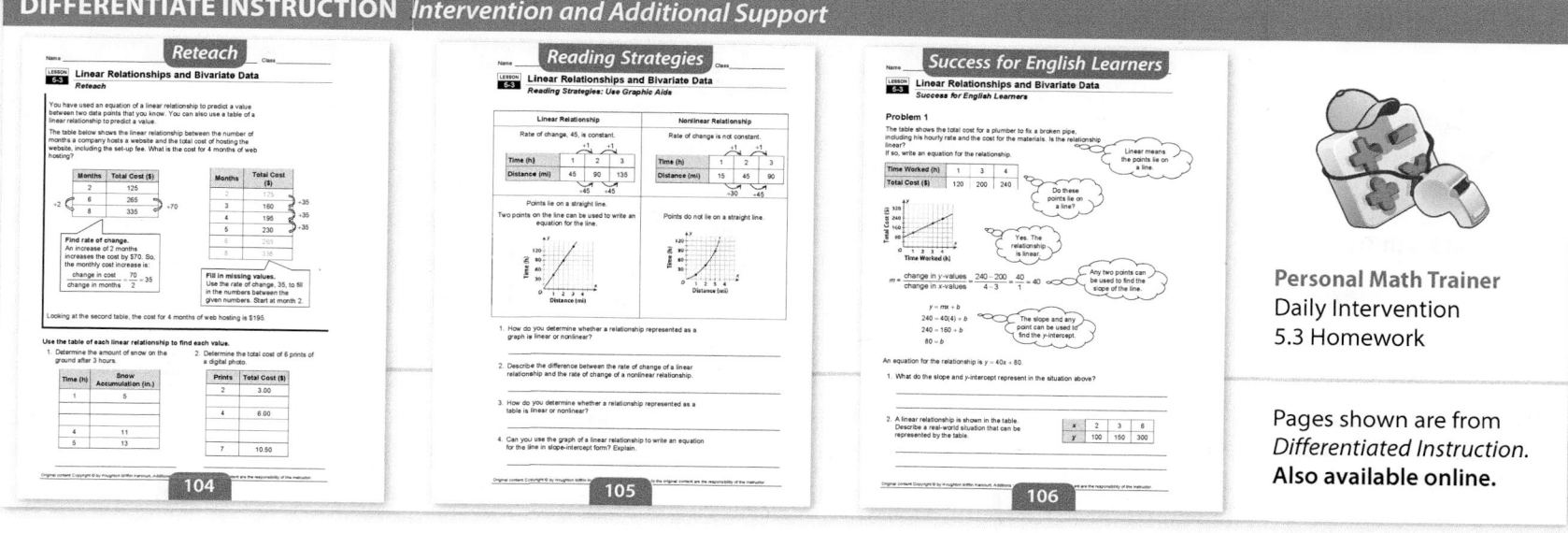

Personal Math Trainer
Daily Intervention
5.3 Homework

Pages shown are from
Differentiated Instruction.
Also available online.

Pressed for Time

5.3 Differentiated Homework Assignments

(AL) **Approaching Level**   7–13, 18

(OL) **On Level**   9–15, 18

(BL) **Beyond Level**   13–18

*For **Below Level** students, assign Personal Math Trainer, Daily Intervention 5.3 Homework.*

Mathematical Processes	Exercises
MP.2 Reasoning	9–12, 15
MP.3 Logic	7–8, 14, 16–18
MP.4 Modeling	13

Focus on Higher Order Thinking

Depth of Knowledge	Exercises
2 Skills/Concepts	7–13
3 Strategic Thinking H.O.T.	14–18

Personal Math Trainer

Online Assessment and Intervention

my.hrw.com

Does each of the following tables represent a linear relationship? Why or why not?

7.

Number of boxes	Weight (kg)
3	15
9	45
21	105

Yes, because the rate of change is constant.

8.

Day	Height (cm)
5	30
8	76.8
14	235.2

No, because the rate of change is not constant.

Explain whether or not you think each relationship is linear.

9. the cost of equal-priced DVDs and the number purchased

Linear; the rate of change is the cost of a DVD, which is constant.

10. the height of a person and the person's age

Not linear; the rate of growth is less as a person gets older.

11. the area of a square quilt and its side length

Not linear; the rate of change in the area of a square increases at a greater rate than the side length increases.

12. the number of miles to the next service station and the number of kilometers

Linear; the rate of change between units is the conversion factor, which is constant.

13. **Multistep** The Mars Rover travels 0.75 feet in 6 seconds. Add the point to the graph. Then determine whether the relationship between distance and time is linear, and if so, predict the distance that the Mars Rover would travel in 1 minute.

The relationship is linear; the equation of the linear relationship is $y = 0.125x$, so the Mars Rover would travel 7.5 feet in 60 seconds.

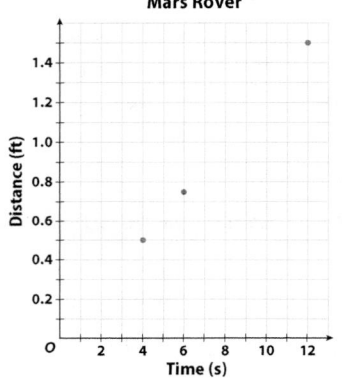

Mars Rover

© Houghton Mifflin Harcourt Publishing Company

DIFFERENTIATE INSTRUCTION *Leveled Homework/Practice*

Personal Math Trainer

• 5.3 Homework

Pages shown are from *Differentiated Instruction*. **Also available online.**

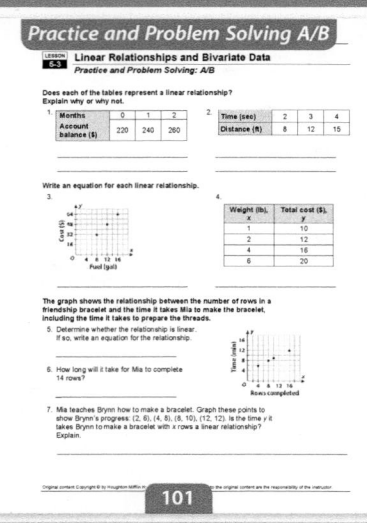

Practice and Problem Solving A/B

101

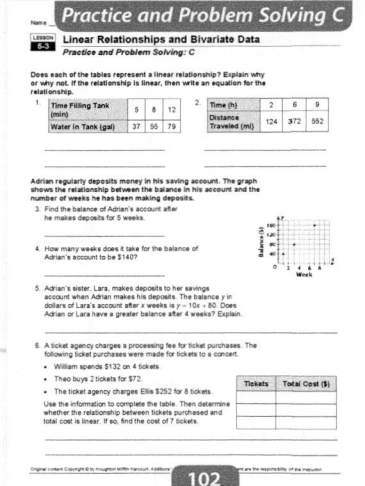

Practice and Problem Solving C

102

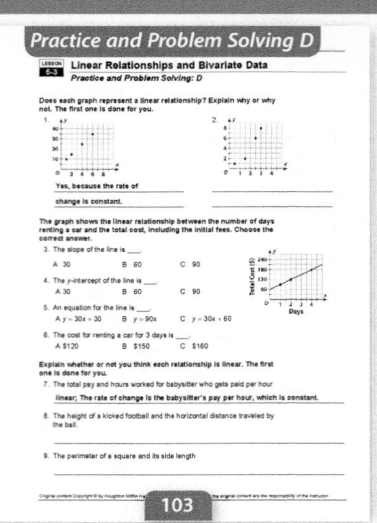

Practice and Problem Solving D

103

14. Make a Conjecture Zefram analyzed a linear relationship, found that the slope-intercept equation was $y = 3.5x + 16$, and made a prediction for the value of y for a given value of x. He realized that he made an error calculating the y-intercept and that it was actually 12. Can he just subtract 4 from his prediction if he knows that the slope is correct? Explain.

Yes; decreasing the value of b by 4 decreases the value of $mx + b$ by 4 because the value of mx stays the same.

 **FOCUS ON HIGHER ORDER THINKING**

15. Communicate Mathematical Ideas The table shows a linear relationship. How can you predict the value of y when $x = 6$ without finding the equation of the relationship?

x	y
4	38
8	76
12	114

Sample answer: Because $x = 6$ lies halfway between $x = 4$ and $x = 8$, the y-value should lie halfway between the corresponding y-values.

16. Critique Reasoning Louis says that if the differences between the values of x are constant between all the points on a graph, then the relationship is linear. Do you agree? Explain.

No; the rate of change must be constant, and the rate of change is the difference in y-values divided by the difference in x-values.

17. Make a Conjecture Suppose you know the slope of a linear relationship and one of the points that its graph passes through. How could you predict another point that falls on the graph of the line?

Find the equation of the linear relationship using the slope and given point, and then insert any x-value to find a y-value on the graph of the line.

18. Explain the Error Thomas used (7, 17.5) and (18, 45) from a graph to find the equation of a linear relationship as shown. What was his mistake?

$$m = \frac{45 - 7}{18 - 17.5} = \frac{38}{0.5} = 79$$
$$y = 79x + b$$
$$45 = 79 \cdot 18 + b$$
$$45 = 1422 + b, \text{ so } b = -1377$$

The equation is $y = 79x - 1377$.

He calculated the slope incorrectly.

Work Area

© Houghton Mifflin Harcourt Publishing Company

DIFFERENTIATE INSTRUCTION *Extend-the-Math Activity* **PRE-AP**

Activity The formula for compound interest is $A = P\left(1 + \frac{r}{n}\right)^{nt}$, where A is the total amount of money after n years, including interest, and P is the principal, or initial investment. The annual rate of interest as a decimal is r. If the interest is compounded annually, $n = 1$, since n is the number of times the interest is compounded per year. The total number of years is t. Use a calculator or an online compound interest calculator to find the amount after 4 years for Option B of the Explore Activity. $243.10

 Quick Check

5.3 Lesson Quiz

x	1	2	3	4	5
y	5	8	12	14	17

1. Does this table represent a linear relationship? Why or why not? No, the slope is not the same between 2 and 3 and between 3 and 4.

2. Change one value in this table so that this table does represent a linear relationship. Change y to 11 for $x = 3$.

Explain whether or not each relationship is linear.

3. The number of inches in a student's height and the height in feet Yes, the rate of change is a constant 12 inches per foot.

4. The radius of a circle and its area No; the rate of change is not constant.

5. An amusement park charges a price for admission and a price for each ride. Joe spent $10.50 and went on 4 rides. Janie spent $14.25 and went on 9 rides. Write a linear equation for the amount spent and predict the amount you would spend to go on 17 rides. $a = 0.75r + 7.5$; $20.25

Differentiate Instruction

IF a student misses more than one question, THEN

Differentiate Instruction:
- 5.3 Reteach
- Personal Math Trainer

Interactive Whiteboard
Interactive Lesson quiz available online

Ready to Go On?

Assess Mastery

Access *Ready to Go On?* assessment online, and receive instant scoring, feedback, and customized intervention or enrichment.

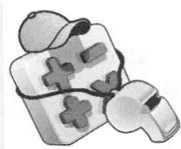

Personal Math Trainer

Online Assessment and Intervention
• Module 5 Posttest

Additional Resources

Digital Teacher Resources

Go online for module-level resources.

Assessment Resources
• Module 5 Quiz: B, p.31
• Module 5 Quiz: D, p.33

© my.hrw.com

Ready to Go On?

Personal Math Trainer
Online Assessment and Intervention
my.hrw.com

5.1 Writing Linear Equations from Situations and Graphs

Write the equation of each line in slope-intercept form.

1.

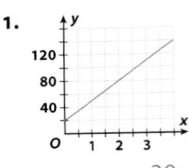

$y = 30x + 20$

2.

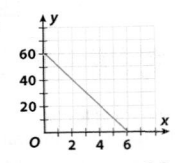

$y = -10x + 60$

5.2 Writing Linear Equations from a Table

Write the equation of each linear relationship in slope-intercept form.

3.

x	0	100	200	300
y	1.5	36.5	71.5	106.5

$y = 0.35x + 1.5$

4.

x	25	35	45	55
y	94	88	82	76

$y = -0.6x + 109$

5.3 Linear Relationships and Bivariate Data

Write the equation of the line that connects each set of data points.

5.

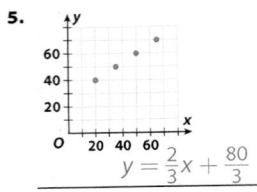

$y = \frac{2}{3}x + \frac{80}{3}$

6.

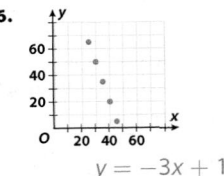

$y = -3x + 140$

 ESSENTIAL QUESTION

7. Write a real-world situation that can be represented by a linear relationship.

Sample answer: A video game rental store charges

$3 per game and a membership fee of $10.

© Houghton Mifflin Harcourt Publishing Company

READY TO GO ON? *Diagnostic Assessment*

RtI — Response to Intervention

Use to determine if students have mastered the concepts covered in this module.

Lesson	Exercises	Content Focus	Review with *Differentiated Instruction*
5.1	1–2	Writing Linear Equations from Situations and Graphs	**5.1** Reteach **5.1** Reading Strategies **5.1** Success for English Learners
5.2	3–4	Writing Linear Equations from a Table	**5.2** Reteach **5.2** Reading Strategies **5.2** Success for English Learners
5.3	5–6	Linear Relationships and Bivariate Data	**5.3** Reteach **5.3** Reading Strategies **5.3** Success for English Learners

Personal Math Trainer
Online Assessment and Intervention
my.hrw.com

Selected Response

1. An hourglass is turned over with the top part filled with sand. After 3 minutes, there are 855 mL of sand in the top half. After 10 minutes, there are 750 mL of sand in the top half. Which equation represents this situation?

(A) $y = 285x$

(B) $y = -10.5x + 900$

(C) $y = -15x + 900$

(D) $y = 75x$

2. Which graph shows a linear relationship?

(A)
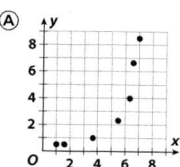

(B)
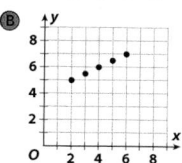

(C)
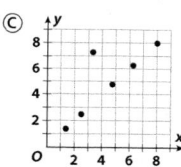

(D)
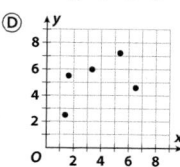

3. What are the slope and y-intercept of the relationship shown in the table?

x	10,000	20,000	30,000
y	2,500	3,000	3,500

(A) slope = 0.05, y-intercept = 1,500

(B) slope = 0.5, y-intercept = 1,500

(C) slope = 0.05, y-intercept = 2,000

(D) slope = 0.5, y-intercept = 2,000

4. Which is the sum of $3.15 \times 10^7 + 9.3 \times 10^6$? Write your answer in scientific notation.

(A) 4.08×10^7

(B) 4.08×10^6

(C) 0.408×10^8

(D) 40.8×10^6

Mini-Task

5. Franklin's faucet was leaking, so he put a bucket underneath to catch the water. After a while, Franklin started keeping track of how much water was in the bucket. His data is in the table below.

Hours	2	3	4	5
Quarts	5	6.5	8	9.5

a. Is the relationship linear or nonlinear?

linear

b. Write the equation for the relationship.

$y = 1.5x + 2$

c. Predict how much water will be in the bucket after 14 hours if Franklin doesn't stop the leak.

23 quarts

© Houghton Mifflin Harcourt Publishing Company

Preparing for High Stakes Tests

Assessment Readiness Tip
Encourage students to highlight or underline important information to help them solve problems.

- **Item 1** Students need to focus on the information they will need to find the slope and y-intercept of the equation. They should highlight "3 minutes" and "855 mL of sand" and then "10 minutes" and "750 mL of sand" to isolate what they need.

- **Item 5** Students, after reading the entire problem, should realize that they only need the information in the table. They should highlight the table and then use that information to answer the questions.

Avoid Common Errors

- **Item 2** Remind students that a linear relationship has every single point in the graph on a line. Some students may incorrectly think that a relationship that is mostly linear, as in answer choice C, is acceptable.

- **Item 3** Some students might invert the slope since the x-values are written in the top row of the table and the y-values are in the bottom row. Remind the students to write out the formula for finding the slope, and check that they are substituting from the correct cells of the table.

Items	Grade 8 Lessons	Mathematical Processes
1	5.2	MP.4
2	5.3	MP.4
3	5.2	MP.2
4*	2.4	MP.6
5	5.1, 5.2	MP.4

*Item integrates mixed review concepts from previous modules or a previous course.

DIFFERENTIATE ASSESSMENT

Below Level Module Quiz 5: D

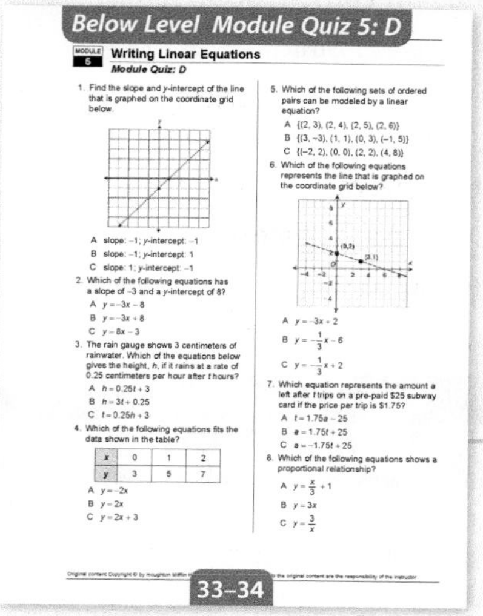

Writing Linear Equations
Module Quiz: D

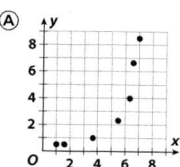

33–34

On Level Module Quiz 5: B

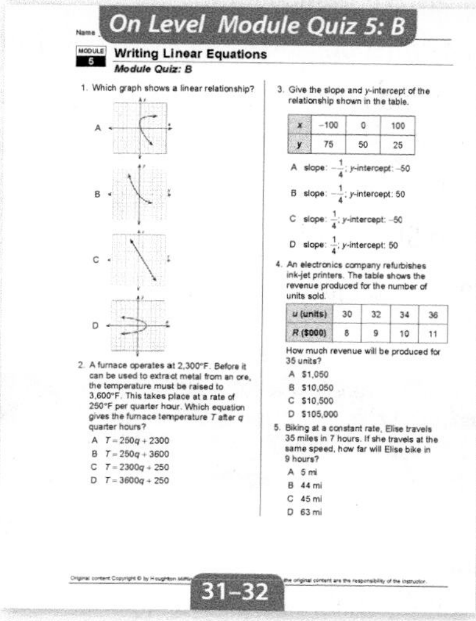

Writing Linear Equations
Module Quiz: B

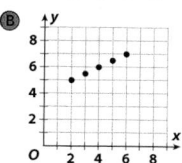

31–32

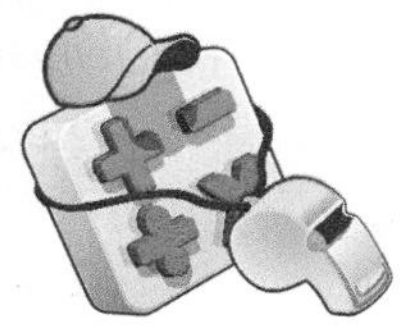

Personal Math Trainer
Module 5 Assessment Readiness

Pages shown are from *Assessment Resources*. **Also available online.**

Module At A Glance

MODULE 6 | Functions

Lessons at A Glance	Lesson 6.1 Identifying and Representing Functions	Lesson 6.2 Describing Functions	Lesson 6.3 Comparing Functions
	Pg. T153A	Pg. T161A	Pg. T167A
Essential Question	How can you identify and represent functions?	What are some characteristics that you can use to describe functions?	How can you use tables, graphs, and equations to compare functions?
Objective	Students will identify and represent functions.	Students will use characteristics to describe functions.	Students will use tables, graphs, and equations to compare functions.
Vocabulary	function, input, output	linear equation, linear function	
Go online for all your module resources my.hrw.com	6.1 *i*Student Edition 6.1 *i*Teacher Edition 6.1 *e*Student Edition Personal Math Trainer Math on the Spot Videos	6.2 *i*Student Edition 6.2 *i*Teacher Edition 6.2 *e*Student Edition Personal Math Trainer Math on the Spot Videos Animated Math	6.3 *i*Student Edition 6.3 *i*Teacher Edition 6.3 *e*Student Edition Personal Math Trainer Math on the Spot Videos
Print Resources	**6.1 Student Edition:** Lesson *Differentiated Instruction* 6.1 Practice and Problem Solving A/B, C, and D 6.1 Reteach 6.1 Reading Strategies 6.1 Success for English Learners	**6.2 Student Edition:** Lesson **6.2 Student Edition:** Going Further *Differentiated Instruction* 6.2 Practice and Problem Solving A/B, C, and D 6.2 Reteach 6.2 Reading Strategies 6.2 Success for English Learners	**6.3 Student Edition:** Lesson **6.3 Student Edition:** Going Further *Differentiated Instruction* 6.3 Practice and Problem Solving A/B, C, and D 6.3 Reteach 6.3 Reading Strategies 6.3 Success for English Learners

RtI

Response to Intervention

Before the Module	During the Lesson	After the Module
Are You Ready	**Guided/Independent Practice**	**Ready to Go On?**
• Prerequisite Skills Activities • Personal Math Trainer	• Reteach • Personal Math Trainer • Practice and Problem Solving D	• Reteach • Personal Math Trainer

Lesson 6.4
Analyzing Graphs

Pg. T173A

How can you describe a relationship given a graph and sketch a graph given a description?

Students will describe a relationship given a graph and sketch a graph given a description.

6.4 *i*Student Edition

6.4 *i*Teacher Edition

6.4 *e*Student Edition

Personal Math Trainer

Math on the Spot Videos

6.4 Student Edition: Lesson

Differentiated Instruction

    6.4 Practice and Problem Solving A/B, C, and D

    6.4 Reteach

    6.4 Reading Strategies

    6.4 Success for English Learners

Teacher Notes

Check It Out!

Game	Math on the Spot Videos	Animated Math
 How Many Squares? After Lesson 6.2	 One for every Example in every Lesson	X^2 During Lesson 6.2

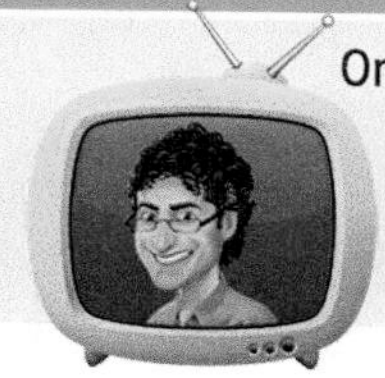

Functions

Real-World Video Viewing Guide

After students have watched the video, discuss the following:

- How many results, or outputs, does each action, or input, have when using the robot to perform surgery? one
- What types of functional relationships in the real world does the video discuss? robotic surgery, video games

Professional Development Video

Author Juli Dixon models successful teaching practices as she explores the concept of functions in an actual eighth-grade classroom.

Functions

? ESSENTIAL QUESTION

How can you use functions to solve real-world problems?

You can draw tables and graphs and evaluate functions for values of the variables that represent real-world situations.

LESSON 6.1
Identifying and Representing Functions

LESSON 6.2
Describing Functions

LESSON 6.3
Comparing Functions

LESSON 6.4
Analyzing Graphs

Real-World Video

Computerized machines can assist doctors in surgeries such as laser vision correction. Each action the surgeon takes results in one end action by the machine. In math, functions also have a one-in-one-out relationship.

my.hrw.com

© Houghton Mifflin Harcourt Publishing Company • Image Credits: ©Huntstock/Getty Images

GO DIGITAL

my.hrw.com

my.hrw.com	**Math On the Spot**	**Animated Math**	**Personal Math Trainer**
Go digital with your write-in student edition, accessible on any device.	Scan with your smart phone to jump directly to the online edition, video tutor, and more.	Interactively explore key concepts to see how math works.	Get immediate feedback and help as you work through practice sets.

149

TEACHER ONLINE RESOURCES

 ONLINE TEACHER EDITION Access a full suite of teaching resources online—plan, present, and manage classes and assignments.

 MY SMART PLANNER Easily plan your classes and access all your resources online.

INTERACTIVE WHITEBOARDS Engage students with interactive whiteboard-ready examples and a lesson quiz for each lesson.

 PERSONAL MATH TRAINER: Online Assessment and Intervention Assign automatically graded homework, quizzes, tests, and intervention activities. Prepare your students for standardized tests in short-answer and multiple-choice formats.

Reading Start-Up

Visualize Vocabulary

Use the ✔ words to complete the diagram. You can put more than one word in each section of the diagram.

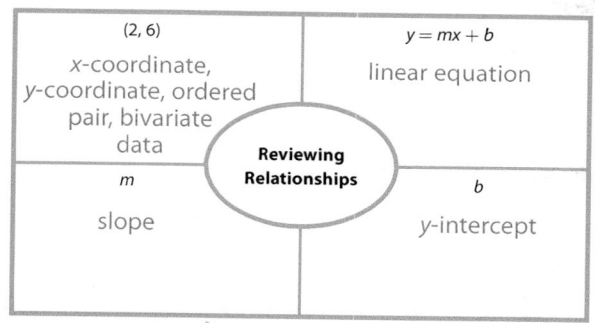

(2, 6)	$y = mx + b$
x-coordinate, y-coordinate, ordered pair, bivariate data	linear equation
m	b
slope	y-intercept

Reviewing Relationships

Understand Vocabulary

Complete the sentences using the preview words.

1. A rule that assigns exactly one output to each input is a ___function___.

2. The value that is put into a function is the ___input___.

3. The result after applying the function machine's rule is the ___output___.

© Houghton Mifflin Harcourt Publishing Company

Vocabulary

Review Words
✔ bivariate data *(datos bivariados)*
✔ linear equation *(ecuación lineal)*
  nonlinear relationship *(relación no lineal)*
✔ ordered pair *(par ordenado)*
  proportional relationship *(relación proporcional)*
✔ slope *(pendiente)*
✔ x-coordinate *(coordenada x)*
✔ y-coordinate *(coordenada y)*
✔ y-intercept *(intersección con el eje y)*

Preview Words
  function *(función)*
  input *(valor de entrada)*
  linear function *(función lineal)*
  output *(valor de salida)*

Active Reading

Double-Door Fold Create a double-door fold to help you understand the concepts in this module. Label one flap "Proportional Functions" and the other flap "Non-proportional Functions." As you study each lesson, write important ideas under the appropriate flap. Include any sample problems that will help you remember the concepts when you look back at your notes.

Reading Start-Up

Visualize Vocabulary
The four-section graphic helps students review vocabulary associated with linear relationships. Students should write one or more review words that apply to the given information in each section.

Understand Vocabulary
Use the following explanations to help students learn the preview words.

> A **function** is a special rule. You can think of a function as a machine. What you put into the machine is called the **input**. The input is altered according to the rule to produce the **output** of the machine.

Active Reading
Integrating Language Arts
Students can use these reading and note-taking strategies to help them organize and understand new concepts and vocabulary.

Additional Resources
Differentiated Instruction
- Reading Strategies **ELL**
- Interactive multilingual glossary

LEARNING PROGRESSIONS ACROSS THE GRADES

Before	In this Module	After
Students understand proportional and linear relationships: • use tables and verbal descriptions to describe a linear relationship • write and graph a linear relationship	Students represent and use functions: • identify functions using sets of ordered pairs, tables, mappings, and graphs • identify examples of proportional and nonproportional functions that arise from mathematical and real-world problems • distinguish between proportional and nonproportional situations using tables, graphs, and equations in the form $y = kx$ or $y = mx + b$, where $b \neq 0$ • analyze and interpret graphs	Students will connect relationships and functions: • linear functions • relations • quadratic functions • exponential functions

Are You Ready?

Assess Readiness

Access *Are You Ready?* assessment online, and receive instant scoring, feedback, and customized intervention or enrichment.

Personal Math Trainer

Online Assessment and Intervention

Additional Resources

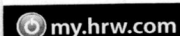

Digital Teacher Resources

Go online for module-level resources.

my.hrw.com

Complete these exercises to review skills you will need for this module.

Personal Math Trainer

Online Assessment and Intervention

my.hrw.com

Evaluate Expressions

EXAMPLE Evaluate $3x - 5$ for $x = -2$.

$3x - 5 = 3(-2) - 5$ Substitute the given value of x for x.

$\qquad = -6 - 5$ Multiply.

$\qquad = -11$ Subtract.

Evaluate each expression for the given value of x.

1. $2x + 3$ for $x = 3$ _____ 9

2. $-4x + 7$ for $x = -1$ _____ 11

3. $1.5x - 2.5$ for $x = 3$ _____ 2

4. $0.4x + 6.1$ for $x = -5$ _____ 4.1

5. $\frac{2}{3}x - 12$ for $x = 18$ _____ 0

6. $-\frac{5}{8}x + 10$ for $x = -8$ _____ 15

Connect Words and Equations

EXAMPLE Erik's earnings equal 9 dollars per hour.   Define the variables used in the situation.

e = earnings; h = hours   Identify the operation involved. "Per" indicates multiplication.
multiplication

$e = 9 \times h$ Write the equation.

Define the variables for each situation. Then write an equation.

7. Jana's age plus 5 equals her sister's age.
   j = Jana's age; s = sister's age; $j + 5 = s$

8. Andrew's class has 3 more students than Lauren's class.
   a = Andrew's class; l = Lauren's class; $a = 3 + l$

9. The bank is 50 feet shorter than the firehouse.
   b = bank's height; f = firehouse's height; $b = f - 50$

10. The pencils were divided into 6 groups of 2.
    p = pencils; $\frac{p}{6} = 2$

Module 6 **151**

© Houghton Mifflin Harcourt Publishing Company

ARE YOU READY? *Diagnostic Assessment*

▲ RtI Response to Intervention

Use to determine if students need intervention for the module's prerequisite skills.

Skill	Missed More Than . . .	Intervene With *Skills Intervention* worksheets (available online)	For Enrichment *Differentiated Instruction* (available in print and online)
Evaluate Expressions	1 question	**Skill 54** Evaluate Expressions	**Module 6 Challenge** Extend-the-Math Lesson Activities in TE
Connect Words and Equations	1 question	**Skill 56** Connect Words and Equations	**Module 6 Challenge** Extend-the-Math Lesson Activities in TE

Complete these exercises to review skills you will need for this module.

Evaluate Expressions

11. Explain how to evaluate the expression $4x - 8$ for $x = 5$.

> Substitute 5 for x in the expression $4x - 8$ to get $4(5) - 8$. Simplify to get $20 - 8$, and then subtract to get 12.

12. When you evaluate the expression $-2.5x - 6.5$ for $x = -4$, is the result positive, negative, or zero? Justify your answer.

> Positive; the expression can be evaluated as shown:
> $$-2.5x - 6.5 = -2.5(-4) - 6.5 \quad \text{Substitute} -4 \text{ for } x.$$
> $$= 10 - 6.5 \quad \text{Multiply.}$$
> $$= 3.5 \quad \text{Subtract.}$$

13. Evaluate the expression $-5x + 4$ for $x = -2, -1, 0, 1,$ and 2. Then describe a pattern in the results.

> $14, 9, 4, -1, -6$
> Each value after the first is five less than the previous value.

Connect Words and Equations

14. Monica is 3 inches taller than her sister. Define variables for Monica's height and her sister's height. Then write a plan for finding Monica's height if you know her sister's height.

> Sample answer: Let s = sister's height and m = Monica's height. Write an equation: $m = s + 3$.
> Substitute the sister's height for s in the equation and solve for m to find Monica's height.

15. The number of students in the eighth grade class is three less than twice the number of students in the sixth grade. Ariana defined variables for the situation and used them to express the number of students in the eighth grade in terms of the number of students in the sixth grade. Her work is shown. What was Ariana's error?

> e = number of eighth grade students
> s = number of sixth grade students
> $s = 2e - 3$

> The variables are reversed in the equation. The equation should be $e = 2s - 3$.

© Houghton Mifflin Harcourt Publishing Company

Evaluate Expressions

Exercise 11 Encourage students to solve the problem on their own and then compare their solutions with other student results.

Exercise 12 Make sure students use mathematical terms to describe how to evaluate an expression.

Exercise 13 Extend the exercise by asking students to make a connection between their pattern and the coefficient of the variable, -5.

Connect Words and Equations

Exercise 14 Students may write an alternate plan and solve this problem by writing the equation $s = m - 3$. Point out the similarities and differences in the plan, and make sure they know how to use their plan to find Monica's age.

Exercise 15 Students may switch the variables when connecting words to equations. Encourage them to substitute numbers for the variables and check the reasonableness of their answers in the context of the problem.

Use to determine if students are able to apply the module's prerequisite skills.

Skill	Exercise	Depth of Knowledge (D.O.K.)	Mathematical Processes
Evaluate Expressions	11	**2** Skills/Concepts	**MP.2** Abstract and Quantitative Reasoning
	12	**3** Strategic Thinking	**MP.6** Use Precise Mathematical Language
	13	**2** Skills/Concepts	**MP.6** Use Precise Mathematical Language
Connect Words and Equations	14	**3** Strategic Thinking	**MP.4** Mathematical Modeling
	15	**3** Strategic Thinking	**MP.3** Use and Evaluate Logical Reasoning

Lesson Support

Content Objective Students will learn how to identify and represent functions.

Professional Development

Integrate Mathematical Processes MP.4

This lesson provides an opportunity to address this Mathematical Processes standard. It calls for students to represent relationships using diagrams, tables, graphs, and symbols. Students learn to identify and represent a function using a set of ordered pairs, a mapping diagram, words, a table, an equation, and a graph. These multiple representations are used to communicate the idea of a function.

FOCUS

Building Background

Eliciting Prior Knowledge Have students work with partners or in small groups to draw graphs of lines with different slopes and different y-intercepts, each on its own coordinate plane. Students do not need to write the equations of the lines. Have students share their graphs. Then discuss the unique relationship between x and y that each graph shows. Elicit that a rule is applied to x to produce each y for each of the lines.

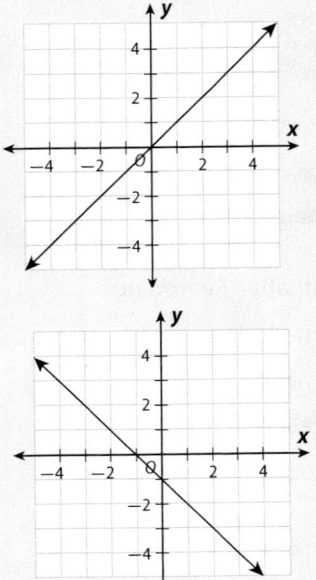

COHERENCE

Learning Progressions

In this lesson, students are introduced to functions. They recognize that a function is a rule that produces a unique output for a given input. Important understandings for students include the following:

- **Identify functions from mapping diagrams.**
- **Identify functions from tables.**
- **Identify functions from graphs.**

Students are introduced to functions represented in a variety of ways. The mapping diagrams provide a way to visualize that a function is a rule that assigns to each input exactly one output. The tables and graphs connect back to the linear relationships from the previous module. In addition, students observe that the graph of a function is the set of ordered pairs consisting of an input and the corresponding output.

RIGOR

Cluster Connections

This lesson provides an excellent opportunity to connect ideas in the cluster:

Define, evaluate, and compare functions.

Have students create mapping diagrams, tables, and graphs of the lines $y = 3$ and $x = 2$. Discuss how each representation makes it possible to identify the line that is a function and the line that is not a function.

Check students' work. $y = 3$ is a horizontal line and is a function. $x = 2$ is a vertical line and is not a function.

Language Support ELL

Language Objective Students will demonstrate how to identify and represent functions.

Leveled Strategies for English Learners ELL

Emerging

Use sentence frames to give a format or structure for identifying input and output pairs.

The input in this table is _____. The output in this table is _____.

The number of pencils the student buys is paired with _____.

Expanding

Have students describe a mapping diagram or graph and explain in a few sentences why the mapping diagram shows that the relationship is or is not a function.

Bridging

Have students draw and label a mapping diagram and write a narrative in a few sentences describing what the diagram represents and why it does or does not show a function.

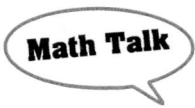

The prompt uses *mapping diagrams* to illustrate and reinforce the definition of a function. Ensure that students can verbalize what the sets and arrows in a diagram represent and can describe the steps in mapping the input and output values.

Mapping Diagram
Input   Output

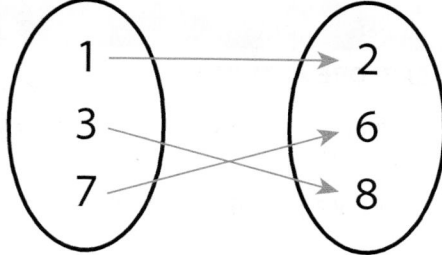

Linguistic Support ELL

Academic/Content Vocabulary

The concepts of ordered pairs and the pairing of input and output are used to distinguish functions from non-functions. The analogy of a machine that applies a rule to the input to derive the output is used to illustrate the concept. Have students use sentence frames to identify pairs in mapping diagrams, tables, and graphs.

Background Knowledge

This lesson focuses on mapping as a process to display a relationship between input and output. The terms *input* and *output* to define and describe functions are presented in this lesson. Point out that *mapping* is the word used for the process of creating a mapping diagram to show the relationship between elements in a set of inputs and elements in a set of outputs using arrows.

1 Engage

ESSENTIAL QUESTION

How can you identify and represent functions?
Sample answer: Some ways to represent a function are a mapping diagram, a table, a graph, and ordered pairs. To determine whether a relationship is a function, check that each input value is matched with only one output value.

Motivate the Lesson
Ask: Can any relationship between variables be described with a function? Begin the lesson to find out.

2 Explore

EXPLORE ACTIVITY

Focus on Patterns
After students have filled in the first three rows of the table, guide them to find more than one pattern in the table.

? ESSENTIAL QUESTION
How can you identify and represent functions?

EXPLORE ACTIVITY   *Real World*

Understanding Relationships

Carlos needs to buy some new pencils from the school supply store at his school. Carlos asks his classmates if they know how much pencils cost. Angela says she bought 2 pencils for $0.50. Paige bought 3 pencils for $0.75, and Spencer bought 4 pencils for $1.00.

Carlos thinks about the rule for the price of a pencil as a machine. When he puts the number of pencils he wants to buy into the machine, the machine applies a rule and tells him the total cost of that number of pencils.

Input  Output

	Number of Pencils	Rule	Total Cost
i.	2	?	$0.50
ii.	3	?	$0.75
iii.	4	?	$1.00
iv.	x	$0.25x$	
v.	12	0.25×12	$3.00

A Use the prices in the problem to fill in total cost in rows **i–iii** of the table.

B Describe any patterns you see. Use your pattern to determine the cost of 1 pencil.

When the number of pencils increases by 1, the
cost of the pencils increases by $0.25; 1 pencil
must cost $0.25.

© Houghton Mifflin Harcourt Publishing Company

DIFFERENTIATE INSTRUCTION *Leveled Questions*

	EXPLORE ACTIVITY
(AL) DOK 1 *Recall*	What is the input and what is the output? Input is number of pencils; output is total cost.
(OL) DOK 2 *Skills/Concepts*	How did you find the cost of 1 pencil? Because the number of pencils times the cost of 1 pencil is the total cost, I divided the total cost by the number of pencils.
(BL) DOK 3 *Strategic Thinking*	The "pencil price machine" gives a single price for each number of pencils. Do you think you could run the machine backwards to give you a single number of pencils for each price? Explain your reasoning. Yes; the machine multiplies the number of pencils by 0.25, so if you run it backwards, it will divide each price by 0.25 to give a single number of pencils.

C Use the pattern you identified to write the rule applied by the machine. Write the rule as an algebraic expression and fill in rule column row **iv** of the table.

D Carlos wants to buy 12 pencils. Use your rule to fill in row **v** of the table to show how much Carlos will pay for 12 pencils.

Reflect

1. How did you decide what operation to use in your rule?

   Since one pencil costs $0.25, the cost of any number of pencils is a

   multiple of $0.25. This means I have to use multiplication.

2. **What If?** Carlos decides to buy erasers in a package. There are 6 pencil-top erasers in 2 packages of erasers.

   a. Write a rule in words for the number of packages Carlos needs to buy to get *x* erasers. Then write the rule as an algebraic expression.

   divide the number of erasers by 3; $\frac{x}{3}$

   b. How many packages does Carlos need to buy to get 18 erasers?

   $\frac{18}{3} = 6$ packages

Math On the Spot

my.hrw.com

Identifying Functions from Mapping Diagrams

A **function** assigns exactly one output to each input. The value that is put into a function is the **input**. The result is the **output**.

A mapping diagram can be used to represent a relationship between input values and output values. A mapping diagram represents a function if each input value is paired with only one output value.

EXAMPLE 1

Determine whether each relationship is a function.

A

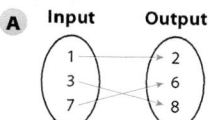

Input Output

1   2
3   6
7   8

Since each input value is paired with only one output value, the relationship is a function.

© Houghton Mifflin Harcourt Publishing Company

---

3 Explain

Connect Vocabulary **ELL**

Remind students that a function is a rule that explains what to do with the input value to get the output value. The rule may involve one or more operations but each input value results in *exactly* one output.

TEACHER TO TEACHER

Cognitive Strategies Discuss some different uses of the term *function* in our modern society.

- When used as a verb, *function* means to work properly.

- When used as a noun, *function* means an activity or intended purpose (e.g., the *function* of that bridge is to provide access across the water).

EXAMPLE 1

ADDITIONAL EXAMPLE 1
Determine whether each relationship is a function.

A

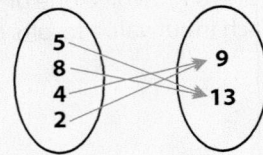

function

B

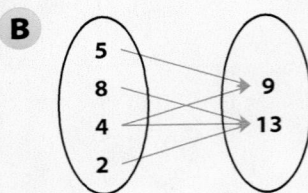

not a function

 Interactive Whiteboard
Interactive example available online

YOUR TURN   MP.3

Focus on Modeling

In **Exercise 4**, the input values 8 and 9 are both connected to the output value 1. Explain that as long as each input value is connected to only one output, the relationship is still a function.

Determine whether each relationship is a function.

B

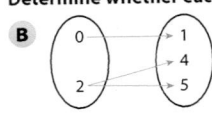 Since 2 is paired with more than one output value (both 4 and 5), the relationship is not a function.

Reflect

3. Is it possible for a function to have more than one input value but only one output value? Provide an illustration to support your answer.

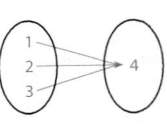

Yes

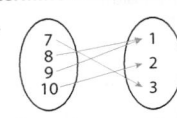 **YOUR TURN**

Determine whether each relationship is a function. Explain.

4.

function; each input value is paired with only one output value

5.

not a function; the input value is paired with more than one output value

 **Personal Math Trainer**
Online Assessment and Intervention
my.hrw.com

Math Talk
Anno: Sample answer: There is never more than one arrow coming from each input value.

Math Talk
Mathematical Processes
What is always true about a mapping diagram that represents a function?

Identifying Functions from Tables

Relationships between input values and output values can also be represented using tables. The values in the first column are the input values. The values in the second column are the output values. The relationship represents a function if each input value is paired with only one output value.

EXAMPLE 2

Determine whether each relationship is a function.

A

Input	Output
5	7
10	6
15	15
20	2
25	15

Since 15 is a repeated output value, one output value is paired with two input values. If this occurs in a relationship, the relationship can still be a function.

Since each input value is paired with only one output value, the relationship is a function.

 **Math On the Spot**
my.hrw.com

My Notes

© Houghton Mifflin Harcourt Publishing Company

DIFFERENTIATE INSTRUCTION *Intervention and Additional Support*

	EXAMPLE 1
(AL) DOK 1 *Recall*	What do you look for in a mapping diagram to indicate that the relationship is a function? Each input value is paired with only one output value, so there is only one arrow from each input to an output.
(OL) DOK 2 *Skills/Concepts*	If the input contains some integers and every input maps to the output 0, is the relationship a function? Explain. Yes; if there is no input that is mapped to more than one output, then it is a function.
(BL) DOK 3 *Strategic Thinking*	Suppose a mapping diagram has 3 different numbers in the input oval and 4 different numbers in the output oval. All the numbers have arrows coming from or pointing to them. Does the diagram represent a function? Explain. No; there are more different outputs than inputs, so an input must be paired with more than one different output.

LEVELED QUESTIONS: (AL) Approaching Level | (OL) On Level | (BL) Beyond Level

Determine whether each relationship is a function.

B

Input	Output
1	10
5	8
4	6
1	4
7	2

Since 1 is a repeated input value, one input value is paired with two output values. Look back at the rule for functions. Is this relationship a function?

Since the input value 1 is paired with more than one output value (both 10 and 4), the relationship is not a function.

Reflect

6. What is always true about the numbers in the first column of a table that represents a function? Why must this be true?

They must all be different numbers, because if a number is repeated, then that input value is paired with more than one output value and the relationship is not a function.

YOUR TURN

Determine whether each relationship is a function. Explain

7.

Input	Output
53	53
24	24
32	32
17	17
45	45

function; each input value is paired with only one output value

8.

Input	Output
14	52
8	21
27	16
36	25
8	34

not a function; the input value 8 is paired with more than one output value

Personal Math Trainer
Online Assessment and Intervention
my.hrw.com

© Houghton Mifflin Harcourt Publishing Company

156 Unit 2

EXAMPLE 2

Avoid Common Errors

Some students think that if there is an output value that corresponds to more than one input value, the relationship is not a function. Remind students that a function is a rule that assigns exactly one output to each input, but two or more input values can give the same output value.

ADDITIONAL EXAMPLE 2
Determine whether each relationship is a function.

A

Input	Output
2	10
4	12
6	24
4	8

not a function

B

Input	Output
2	10
4	10
6	6
8	8

function

 Interactive Whiteboard
Interactive example available online

YOUR TURN MP.5

Focus on Math Connections

Suggest that students draw a mapping diagram for each table to help them determine which of the relationships are functions.

	EXAMPLE 2
AL DOK 1 *Recall*	In Part A, for a relationship that is a function, does it matter how many times a number repeats in the output column? No
OL DOK 2 *Skills/Concepts*	In Part B, what is a single change you can make to the table so that it represents a function? Sample answer: Change one of the 1s in the Input column to a 2.
BL DOK 3 *Strategic Thinking*	A school uses a spreadsheet input/output table to match students to their homerooms. Can you tell whether the table represents a function? Explain. Yes; it must represent a function because it cannot match a student to more than one homeroom.

EXAMPLE 3

Focus on Critical Thinking

Introduce the vertical line test: If each vertical line passes through at most one point on a graph of a relationship; the relationship is a function. If there is at least one vertical line that passes through more than one point, the relationship is not a function. Have students explain why the vertical line test works.

ADDITIONAL EXAMPLE 3 The graph shows the relationship between the width of a sticker and the length of the sticker sold at an art store. Is the relationship represented by the graph a function? Explain why. Yes; for each *x*-value, there is only one *y*-value.

Stickers

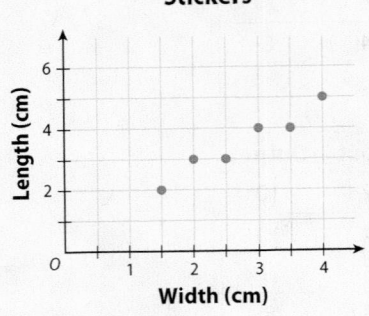

Interactive Whiteboard
Interactive example available online

YOUR TURN   MP.4

Focus on Patterns

Point out to students that the graph of a function can be isolated points rather than a line. Remind them that what matters is whether the graph passes the vertical line test.

Digital Teacher Resources

Go online to access all your lesson-level resources.

Differentiated Instruction
• Reteach
• Reading Strategies
• Success for English Learners
• Practice and Problem Solving A/B, C, D

Math on the Spot Videos

my.hrw.com

Identifying Functions from Graphs

Graphs can be used to display relationships between two sets of numbers. Each point on a graph represents an ordered pair. The first coordinate in each ordered pair is the input value. The second coordinate is the output value. The graph represents a function if each input value is paired with only one output value.

Math On the Spot
my.hrw.com

EXAMPLE 3

The graph shows the relationship between the number of hours students spent studying for an exam and the exam grades. Is the relationship represented by the graph a function?

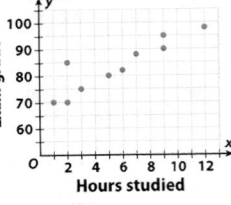

Hours Studied and Exam Grade

The input values are the number of hours spent studying by each student. The output values are the exam grades. The points represent the following ordered pairs:

(1, 70)	(2, 70)	(2, 85)	(3, 75)	(5, 80)
(6, 82)	(7, 88)	(9, 90)	(9, 95)	(12, 98)

Notice that 2 is paired with both 70 and 85, and 9 is paired with both 90 and 95. Therefore, since these input values are paired with more than one output value, the relationship is not a function.

Reflect

9. Many real-world relationships are functions. For example, the amount of money made at a car wash is a function of the number of cars washed. Give another example of a real-world function.

   Sample answer: The amount earned at an hourly-wage

   is a function of the number of hours worked.

© Houghton Mifflin Harcourt Publishing Company

YOUR TURN

10. The graph shows the relationship between the heights and weights of the members of a basketball team. Is the relationship represented by the graph a function? Explain.

    not a function; input values are

    paired with more than one output

    values; (70, 164) and (70, 174)

Heights and Weights of Team Members

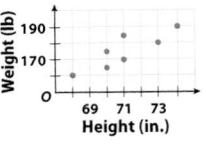

Personal Math Trainer
Online Assessment and Intervention
my.hrw.com

Lesson 6.1 **157**

DIFFERENTIATE INSTRUCTION *Leveled Questions*

	EXAMPLE 3
(AL) DOK 1 *Recall*	What is the input 2 paired with? 70 and 85
(OL) DOK 2 *Skills/Concepts*	If you know that a student scored at least a 90 on the exam, can you draw any conclusions about how long the student studied? If so, what? Yes; the student studied at least 9 hours (either 9 or 12 hours).
(BL) DOK 3 *Strategic Thinking*	How could you change two data points to make the relationship between hours studied and exam grade a function? Sample answer: Change (2, 85) to (4, 85) and change (9, 90) to (10, 90).

LEVELED QUESTIONS: (AL) Approaching Level | (OL) On Level | (BL) Beyond Level

Complete each table. In the row with *x* as the input, write a rule as an algebraic expression for the output. Then complete the last row of the table using the rule. (Explore Activity)

1.

Input	Output
Tickets	Cost ($)
2	40
5	100
7	140
x	20x
10	200

2.

Input	Output
Minutes	Pages
2	1
10	5
20	10
x	$\frac{x}{2}$
30	15

3.

Input	Output
Muffins	Cost ($)
1	2.25
3	6.75
6	13.50
x	2.25x
12	27.00

Determine whether each relationship is a function. (Examples 1 and 2)

4.

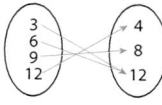

function; each input value is

paired with only one output value

5.

Input	Output
3	20
4	25
5	30
4	35
6	40

not a function; the input value 4 is

paired with more than one output

value

6. The graph shows the relationship between the weights of 5 packages and the shipping charge for each package. Is the relationship represented by the graph a function? Explain.

Yes; each input value is paired with only one

output value.

Weights and Shipping Costs

© Houghton Mifflin Harcourt Publishing Company

? ESSENTIAL QUESTION CHECK-IN

7. What are four different ways of representing functions? How can you tell if a relationship is a function?

Mapping diagrams, tables, graphs, ordered pairs; a relationship is a

function if each input value is paired with only one output value.

---

4 Elaborate

Talk About It

Summarize the Lesson

Ask: How do you know that a relationship represented by a mapping diagram, a table of values, or a graph is a function? In a mapping diagram there will be only one arrow drawn from each input value. In a table of values, each input value (*x*-value) will correspond to only one output value (*y*-value). The graph of a function will pass the vertical line test.

Guided Practice

Engage with the Whiteboard

For **Exercise 6**, invite a student to draw a mapping diagram using the ordered pairs from the graph. This should help students confirm that the relationship is a function.

Avoid Common Errors

- **Exercise 1–3** Remind students that the rule they write must work for each and every input and output pair.

- **Exercise 4** Remind students that for the relationship to be a function, each input value can only be connected with one output value.

- **Exercise 5** Remind students that the relationship is not a function if there is at least one input value that corresponds to more than one output value.

DIFFERENTIATE INSTRUCTION *Intervention and Additional Support*

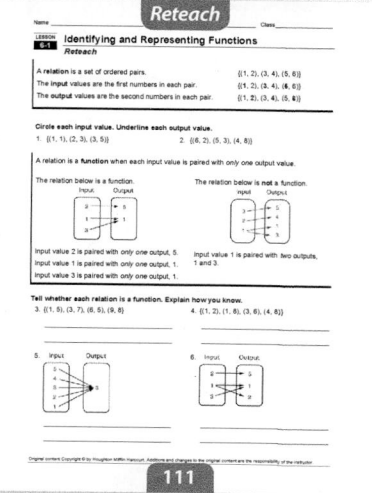

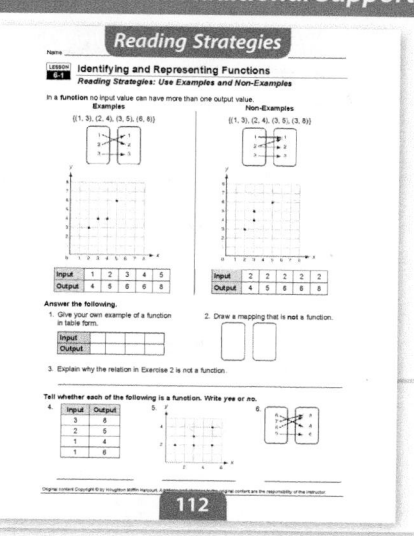

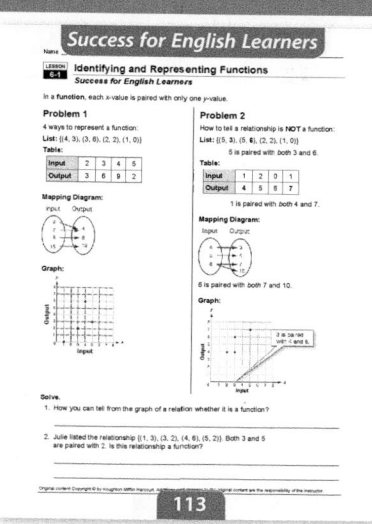

Personal Math Trainer
Daily Intervention
6.1 Homework

Pages shown are from *Differentiated Instruction.*
Also available online.

Identifying and Representing Functions **158**

Pressed for Time

6.1 Differentiated Homework Assignments

(AL) Approaching Level 8–14

(OL) On Level 10–15

(BL) Beyond Level 12–16

For **Below Level** students, assign Personal Math Trainer, Daily Intervention 6.1 Homework.

Mathematical Processes	Exercises
MP.2 Reasoning	15
MP.3 Logic	11, 14, 16
MP.4 Modeling	12
MP.6 Precision	8–10, 13

Focus on Higher Order Thinking

Depth of Knowledge	Exercises
1 Recall of Information	8–10
2 Skills/Concepts	13
3 Strategic Thinking H.O.T.	11–12, 14–16

6.1 Independent Practice

Personal Math Trainer
Online Assessment and Intervention

my.hrw.com

Determine whether each relationship represented by the ordered pairs is a function. Explain.

8. (2, 2), (3, 1), (5, 7), (8, 0), (9, 1)

function; each input value is paired with only one output value

9. (0, 4), (5, 1), (2, 8), (6, 3), (5, 9)

not a function; the input value 5 is paired with more than one output value

10. Draw Conclusions Joaquin receives $0.40 per pound for 1 to 99 pounds of aluminum cans he recycles. He receives $0.50 per pound if he recycles more than 100 pounds. Is the amount of money Joaquin receives a function of the weight of the cans he recycles? Explain your reasoning.

Yes. For each pound of aluminum he recycles (input), there can only be one dollar amount representing the amount of money he receives (outcome).

11. A biologist tracked the growth of a strain of bacteria, as shown in the graph.

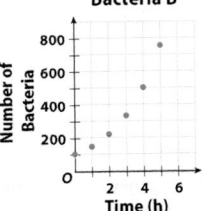

Bacteria B

a. Explain why the relationship represented by the graph is a function.

There is only one number of bacteria for each number of hours, so each input is paired with only one output.

b. What If? Suppose there was the same number of bacteria for two consecutive hours. Would the graph still represent a function? Explain.

Yes. Each input value would still be paired with only one output value.

12. Multiple Representations Give an example of a function in everyday life, and represent it as a graph, a table, and a set of ordered pairs. Describe how you know it is a function.

Check students' work

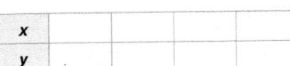

x				
y				

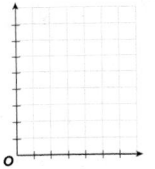

© Houghton Mifflin Harcourt Publishing Company

DIFFERENTIATE INSTRUCTION *Leveled Homework/Practice*

Personal Math Trainer

• 6.1 Homework

Pages shown are from *Differentiated Instruction.* **Also available online.**

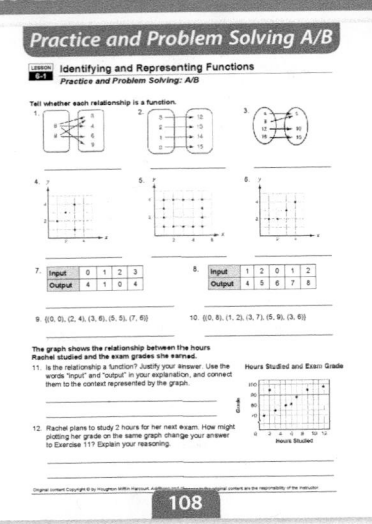

Practice and Problem Solving A/B

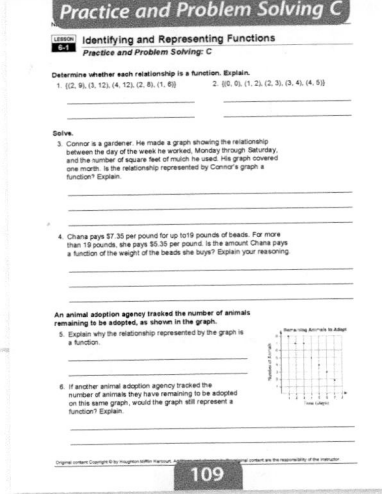

Practice and Problem Solving C

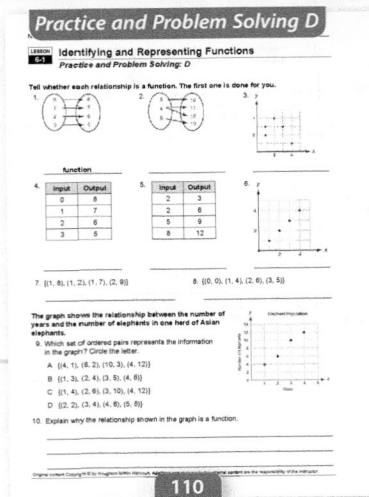

Practice and Problem Solving D

The graph shows the relationship between the weights of six wedges of cheese and the price of each wedge.

Cost of Cheese

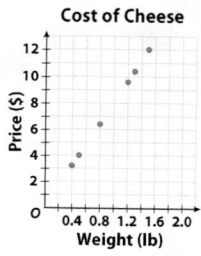

13. Is the relationship represented by the graph a function? Justify your reasoning. Use the words "input" and "output" in your explanation, and connect them to the context represented by the graph.

Yes. Each input value (the weight) is paired with only

one output value (the price).

14. Analyze Relationships Suppose the weights and prices of additional wedges of cheese were plotted on the graph. Might that change your answer to question 13? Explain your reasoning.

Sample answer: No. The points appear to lie along

a straight line. Any additional wedge of cheese

will probably also lie along this line, and the

relationship will remain a function.

 **FOCUS ON HIGHER ORDER THINKING**

15. Justify Reasoning A mapping diagram represents a relationship that contains three different input values and four different output values. Is the relationship a function? Explain your reasoning.

It does not represent a function. For the input values

to be paired with all four output values, at least one of

the input values would be paired with more than one

output value.

16. Communicate Mathematical Ideas An onion farmer is hiring workers to help harvest the onions. He knows that the number of days it will take to harvest the onions is a function of the number of workers he hires. Explain the use of the word "function" in this context.

The number of days it will take to harvest the onions

depends on the number of workers he hires. The input

values of the function are the number of workers.

The output values are the number of days. For any

particular number of workers, the job will take a certain

number of days.

© Houghton Mifflin Harcourt Publishing Company • Image Credits: ©Brand X Pictures/Getty Images

Work Area

6.1 Lesson Quiz

1. There are 12 iron-on patches in 4 packages. Each package has the same number of patches. Write a rule in words for the number of packages Leah needs to buy to get x patches. Then write the rule as an algebraic expression. Divide the number of patches by 3; $\frac{x}{3}$

Determine whether each relationship is a function.

2.

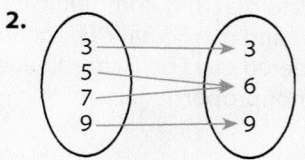

function

3.

Input	2	5	8	5
Output	7	10	13	7

not a function

4. Is the relationship represented by the graph a function? Explain. No; at least one of the input values is paired with more than one output value; in fact, many of the input values are paired with more than one output value.

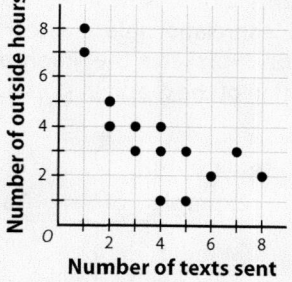

Differentiate Instruction

IF a student misses more than one question, THEN

Differentiate Instruction:

• 6.1 Reteach

• Personal Math Trainer

 Interactive Whiteboard
Interactive Lesson quiz available online

DIFFERENTIATE INSTRUCTION *Extend-the-Math Activity* **PRE-AP**

Activity The inverse of a relationship is found by switching the coordinates in each ordered pair of the relationship. So, for each ordered pair (x, y) in the relationship, the ordered pair (y, x) will appear in its inverse. Graph the function {(1, 3), (2, 4), (3, 5), (−1, 1), (−3, −1)}, find its inverse, and graph the inverse. Is the inverse of this function a function? Try to find a counterexample to determine whether the inverse of a function is always a function.

Inverse of the function: {(3, 1), (4, 2), (5, 3), (1, −1), (−1, −3)}; yes, the inverse of the function is a function. Sample answer (counterexample): function: {(5, 2), (7, 2), (−3, 1), (−5, 0)}; inverse of the function: {(2, 5), (2, 7), (1, −3), (0, −5)}; the inverse is not a function. So, the inverse of a function is not always a function.

Lesson Support

Content Objective Students will learn how to tell if a function is linear or not.

Professional Development

Integrate Mathematical Processes MP.6

This lesson provides an opportunity to address this Mathematical Processes standard. It calls for students to precisely communicate mathematical ideas and reasoning. Students model real-world and mathematical functions by creating a table of values and then graphing the ordered pairs on a coordinate grid. They determine whether the functions are proportional or nonproportional, and linear or nonlinear.

FOCUS

Building Background

Eliciting Prior Knowledge Have students work with a partner to fill in the frame with a summary of the different forms of linear relationships with which they are familiar. Students should write a real-world example of a linear relationship, create a table for the relationship, sketch the graph, and write the equation of the graph in slope-intercept form.

Real-World Example	Table
Graph	Equation

COHERENCE

Learning Progressions

In this lesson, students recognize that the equation of a line, $y = mx + b$, is a linear function whose graph is always a straight line. They also use the shape of graphs to identify functions that are not linear. Important understandings for students include the following:

- **Graph a linear function.**
- **Determine whether a function is linear.**

Students connect linear equations of the form $y = mx + b$ to linear functions and their corresponding graphs. They recall that a linear relationship may or may not be proportional and that it has a constant rate of change called the slope, m, and an initial value called the y-intercept, b. This prepares them for comparing linear functions with real-life applications in the next lesson.

RIGOR

Cluster Connections

This lesson provides an excellent opportunity to connect ideas in the cluster: **Define, evaluate, and compare functions.**

Remind students of the formulas for converting temperatures: $°F = \frac{9}{5} \cdot °C + 32$ and $°C = \frac{5}{9}(°F - 32)$. Have students decide whether or not the equations are linear functions and why.

Both formulas are linear functions. Sample explanation: The first is in the form $y = mx + b$ and the second can be put in that form by applying the distributive property to the right side of the equation.

Language Support `ELL`

Language Objective Students will explain how to tell if a function is linear or not.

Leveled Strategies for English Learners `ELL`

Emerging
Give students statements about the features of a graph and have them tell whether the statement is true or false.

Expanding
Have students compare and contrast the features of two graphs.

Graph A shows a linear relationship because _____.

Graph B shows a nonlinear relationship because _____.

Bridging
Have students identify which of three or four graphs represents a linear or nonlinear relationship and give a short explanation orally describing the features of the graph they used to select the correct graph. Then have them write out their explanation.

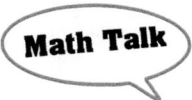 **Math Talk**

The prompt requires students to distinguish between linear and nonlinear relationships based on analysis of data represented in a table and in a graph. Keep in mind that students need to be comfortable using the terms for describing the graph itself before using the more abstract and complex language needed to describe the relationship that a graph represents.

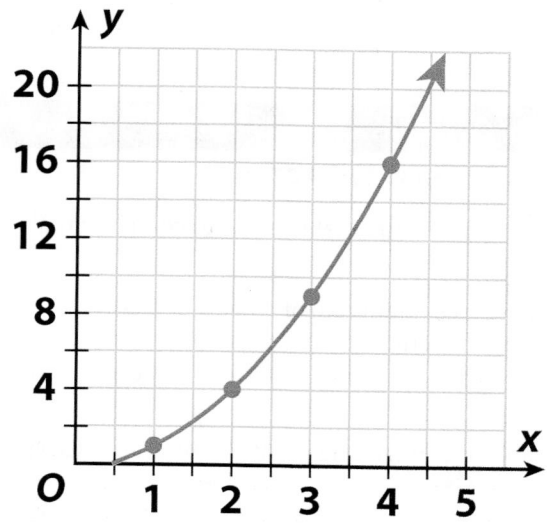

Have students use words to describe this graph in Example 2.

Linguistic Support `ELL`

Academic/Content Vocabulary
This lesson focuses on the difference between linear and nonlinear relationships, as depicted on graphs. The language students use to describe graphs is different from the language they use to describe the real-world situations that those graphs represent. Teach terms for describing graphs, such as *not straight, curved, doesn't go through the origin, vertical,* or *nonvertical.*

Background Knowledge
formula In Independent Practice, there is an exercise involving the amount of milk formula remaining after feeding a whale calf. Later in the lesson, geometry formulas are used. Keep in mind that with the non-mathematical use of the word *formula*, students may be thinking of a mathematical formula. It is important to distinguish between uses of terms in mathematics when these have a different meaning from those used in a real-world situation.

Describing Functions

1 Engage

❓ ESSENTIAL QUESTION

What are some characteristics that you can use to describe functions? Sample answer: A function can be linear or nonlinear. A linear function can be proportional or nonproportional.

Motivate the Lesson

Ask: Suppose that it started raining today at a constant rate and you make a table showing the amount of rain that has fallen after 1 hour, 2 hours, 3 hours, and so on. What kind of function would that table represent? Begin the Explore Activity to find out.

2 Explore

EXPLORE ACTIVITY

Focus on Patterns
After students complete parts A and B, have them describe the patterns that they see in the table and graph. Is the relationship linear? Is it proportional?

6.2 Describing Functions

❓ ESSENTIAL QUESTION

What are some characteristics that you can use to describe functions?

EXPLORE ACTIVITY 🌎 Real World

Investigating a Constant Rate of Change

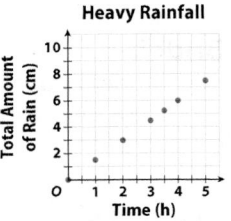

The U.S. Department of Agriculture defines heavy rain as rain that falls at a rate of 1.5 centimeters per hour.

A The table shows the total amount of rain that falls in various amounts of time during a heavy rain. Complete the table.

Time (h)	0	1	2	3	4	5
Total Amount of Rain (cm)	0	1.5	3	4.5	6	7.5

B Plot the ordered pairs from the table on the coordinate plane at the right.

C How much rain falls in 3.5 hours? <u>5.25 cm</u>

D Plot the point corresponding to 3.5 hours of heavy rain.

E What do you notice about all of the points you plotted?
All of the points lie along a line.

F Is the total amount of rain that falls a function of the number of hours that rain has been falling? Why or why not?
Yes. For any given input of time, there can be one and only one output of total amount of rain.

Heavy Rainfall

(graph: Total Amount of Rain (cm) vs Time (h))

Reflect

1. Suppose you continued to plot points for times between those in the table, such as 1.2 hours or 4.5 hours. What can you say about the locations of these points?
The points would fill in the gaps along the line determined by the existing points of the graph.

© Houghton Mifflin Harcourt Publishing Company

Lesson 6.2 **161**

DIFFERENTIATE INSTRUCTION *Leveled Questions*

	EXPLORE ACTIVITY
AL DOK 1 *Recall*	What is the rate of change that you use to complete the table in Part A? 1.5 cm/h
OL DOK 2 *Skills/Concepts*	When you have a constant rate of change, is the relationship a function? Explain. Yes; if the rate of change is constant then there will not be more than one output for any input.
BL DOK 3 *Strategic Thinking*	Is it reasonable to connect the points in the graph? Explain. Yes; the function is continuous and a line connecting the points makes sense because the domain is time in hours, and fractions of an hour make sense.

LEVELED QUESTIONS: AL Approaching Level | OL On Level | BL Beyond Level

Math On the Spot
my.hrw.com

Graphing Linear Functions

The relationship you investigated in the previous activity can be represented by the equation $y = 1.5x$, where x is the time and y is the total amount of rain. The graph of the relationship is a line, so the equation is a **linear equation**. Since there is exactly one value of y for each value of x, the relationship is a function. It is a **linear function** because its graph is a nonvertical line.

EXAMPLE 1

The temperature at dawn was 8 °F and increased steadily 2 °F every hour. The equation $y = 2x + 8$ gives the temperature y after x hours. State whether the relationship between the time and the temperature is proportional or nonproportional. Then graph the function.

STEP 1 Compare the equation with the general linear equation $y = mx + b$.
$y = 2x + 8$ is in the form $y = mx + b$, with $m = 2$ and $b = 8$.
Therefore, the equation is a linear equation. Since $b \neq 0$, the relationship is nonproportional.

STEP 2 Choose several values for the input x. Substitute these values for x in the equation to find the output y.

x	$2x + 8$	y	(x, y)
0	$2(0) + 8$	8	$(0, 8)$
2	$2(2) + 8$	12	$(2, 12)$
4	$2(4) + 8$	16	$(4, 16)$
6	$2(6) + 8$	20	$(6, 20)$

STEP 3 Graph the ordered pairs. Then draw a line through the points to represent the solutions of the function.

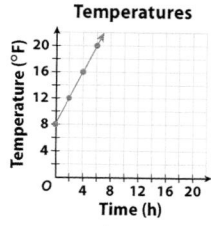

Temperatures

Math Talk
Mathematical Processes

Carrie said that for a function to be a linear function, the relationship it represents must be proportional. Do you agree or disagree? Explain.

Disagree; sample answer: the only requirement is that the graph of the function be a nonvertical line. Whether the graph passes through the origin (proportional) or not (nonproportional) does not matter.

YOUR TURN

2. State whether the relationship between x and y in $y = 0.5x$ is proportional or nonproportional. Then graph the function.

proportional

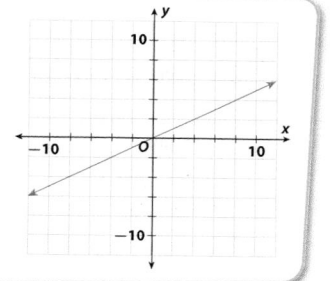

Personal Math Trainer
Online Assessment and Intervention
my.hrw.com

© Houghton Mifflin Harcourt Publishing Company

162 Unit 2

---

3 Explain

EXAMPLE 1

ADDITIONAL EXAMPLE 1 Vance charges $20 an hour to plow the snow off of driveways. The equation $y = 20x$ gives the cost y in dollars for x hours. State whether the relationship between the time and the cost is proportional or nonproportional. Then graph the function.
Since $b = 0$, the graph is proportional.

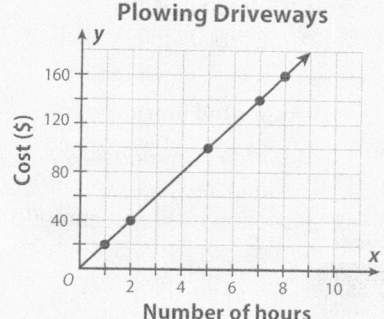

Plowing Driveways

Interactive Whiteboard
Interactive example available online

YOUR TURN   MP.8

Avoid Common Errors
Students may graph the equation incorrectly. Suggest that students determine and graph at least three ordered pairs.

	EXAMPLE 1
AL DOK 1 *Recall*	What is the input and what is the output in this relationship? Time is input; temperature is output.
OL DOK 2 *Skills/Concepts*	In Step 2, what x-values should you choose and why? Sample answer: Because x represents time in hours during a day, the x-values should be non-negative, easy to work with, and less than 12.
BL DOK 3 *Strategic Thinking*	In Step 1, the y-intercept is not equal to zero, so the relationship is not proportional. What is another way to verify that the relationship is not proportional? For a proportional relationship, $k = \frac{y}{x}$, where k is constant, is true. In this relationship, $\frac{12}{2} \neq \frac{16}{4}$, so $k = \frac{y}{x}$ is not true. So, this is not a proportional relationship.

TEACHER TO TEACHER

Curriculum Connection (Geometry) Have students complete tables of values for perimeter and area of a square, where x is the side length of the square.

Perimeter: $(0, 0), (1, 4), (2, 8), (3, 12), \ldots$

Area: $(0, 0), (1, 1), (2, 4), (3, 9), \ldots$

Point out that both relationships are functions; the perimeter function is linear and the area function is nonlinear. Challenge students to think of other nonlinear functions from the real-world. Sample answers: a volume function; distance between a soccer ball and an observer during a soccer game.

EXAMPLE 2

ADDITIONAL EXAMPLE 2 A rectangular field is x feet wide and $x + 2$ feet long. The equation $y = x^2 + 2x$ gives the area of the field in square feet. Determine whether the relationship between x and y is linear and, if so, whether it is proportional. The graph is not a line, so the relationship is not linear. Since it is not a line, it is also not proportional.

Interactive Whiteboard
Interactive example available online

Animated Math
Identify Functions
Students explore an interactive function machine, entering inputs to discover the rule.

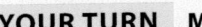
🔘 my.hrw.com

YOUR TURN   MP.1

Focus on Math Connections
Make sure that students understand the connection between the numbers in the table having a constant rate of change and the relationship being linear.

Digital Teacher Resources
Go online to access all your lesson-level resources.

Differentiated Instruction
• Reteach
• Reading Strategies
• Success for English Learners
• Practice and Problem Solving A/B, C, D

Math on the Spot Videos

🔘 my.hrw.com

Determining Whether a Function is Linear

Math On the Spot
🔘 my.hrw.com

The linear equation in Example 1 has the form $y = mx + b$, where m and b are real numbers. Every equation in the form $y = mx + b$ is a linear equation. The linear equations represent linear functions. Equations that cannot be written in this form are not linear equations, and therefore are not linear functions.

EXAMPLE 2

A square tile has a side length of x inches. The equation $y = x^2$ gives the area of the tile in square inches. Determine whether the relationship between x and y is linear and, if so, if it is proportional.

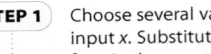
Animated Math
🔘 my.hrw.com

STEP 1 Choose several values for the input x. Substitute these values for x in the equation to find the output y.

x	x^2	y	(x, y)
1	1^2	1	(1, 1)
2	2^2	4	(2, 4)
3	3^2	9	(3, 9)
4	4^2	16	(4, 16)

STEP 2 Graph the ordered pairs.

STEP 3 Identify the shape of the graph. The points suggest a curve, not a line. Draw a curve through the points to represent the solutions of the function.

STEP 4 Describe the relationship between x and y.

The graph is not a line so the relationship is not linear.

Only a linear relationship can be proportional, so the relationship is not proportional.

Math Talk
Mathematical Processes
How can you use the numbers in the table to decide whether or not the relationship between x and y is linear?

Sample answer: I can check to see whether the rate of change is constant. Since it is not constant, the relationship is not linear.

YOUR TURN

3. A soda machine makes $\frac{2}{3}$ gallon of soda every minute. The total amount y that the machine makes in x minutes is given by the equation $y = \frac{2}{3}x$. Determine whether the relationship between x and y is linear and, if so, if it is proportional.

Time (min), x	0	3	6	9
Amount (gal), y	0	2	4	6

Making Soda
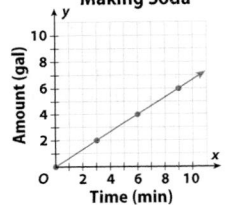

linear; proportional

Personal Math Trainer
Online Assessment and Intervention
🔘 my.hrw.com

© Houghton Mifflin Harcourt Publishing Company

Lesson 6.2 **163**

DIFFERENTIATE INSTRUCTION *Leveled Questions*

	EXAMPLE 2
(AL) **DOK 1** *Recall*	What does x represent? What does y represent? *x is side length of a square; y is area of the square.*
(OL) **DOK 2** *Skills/Concepts*	How can you use the equation to determine that this function is not linear? *The equation $y = x^2$ cannot be written in the form $y = mx + b$, so the function is not linear.*
(BL) **DOK 3** *Strategic Thinking*	Can you think of another function that is not linear? *Sample answers: $y = x^3$ or $y = \frac{1}{x}$*

LEVELED QUESTIONS: (AL) Approaching Level | (OL) On Level | (BL) Beyond Level

Plot the ordered pairs from the table. Then graph the function represented by the ordered pairs and tell whether the function is linear or nonlinear. (Examples 1 and 2)

1. $y = 5 - 2x$

Input, x	−1	1	3	5
Output, y	7	3	−1	−5

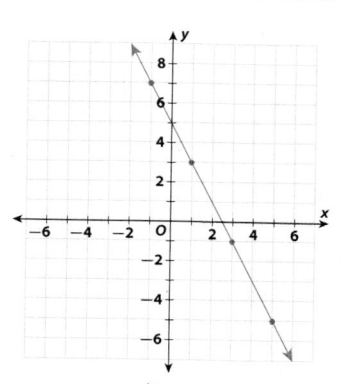

linear

2. $y = 2 - x^2$

Input, x	−2	−1	0	1	2
Output, y	−2	1	2	1	−2

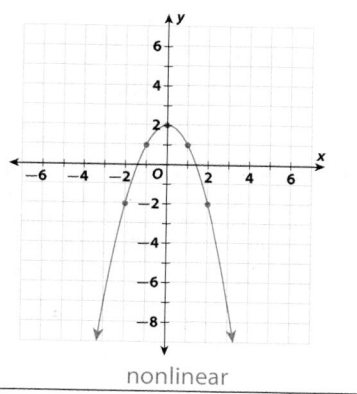

nonlinear

Explain whether each equation is a linear equation. (Example 2)

3. $y = x^2 - 1$

No; the equation cannot be written in the form $y = mx + b$, and the graph of the solutions is not a line.

4. $y = 1 - x$

Yes; the equation can be written in the form $y = mx + b$, and the graph of the solutions is a line.

 ESSENTIAL QUESTION CHECK-IN

5. Explain how you can use a table of values, an equation, and a graph to determine whether a function represents a proportional relationship.

A table of values will include (0, 0) and show a constant rate of change. An equation will be of the form $y = mx$. A graph will be a line passing through the origin.

© Houghton Mifflin Harcourt Publishing Company

4 Elaborate

Talk About It

Summarize the Lesson

Ask: How can you show that the relationship between x and y given in the form of an equation is a linear relationship and also a proportional relationship? Sample answer: First make a table of values for the equation and graph the ordered pairs; if the rate of change in the table is constant and the graph is a line through (0, 0), then the relationship is a proportional linear relationship.

Guided Practice

Engage with the Whiteboard

Have students verify their answers to **Exercises 3–4** by graphing the equations on the coordinate grids shown in **Exercises 1–2**.

Avoid Common Errors

- **Exercise 1** Remind students that $y = 5 - 2x$ is the same as $y = -2x + 5$.
- **Exercise 5** Remind students that the graph of a proportional relationship is a line that goes through the origin.

DIFFERENTIATE INSTRUCTION *Intervention and Additional Support*

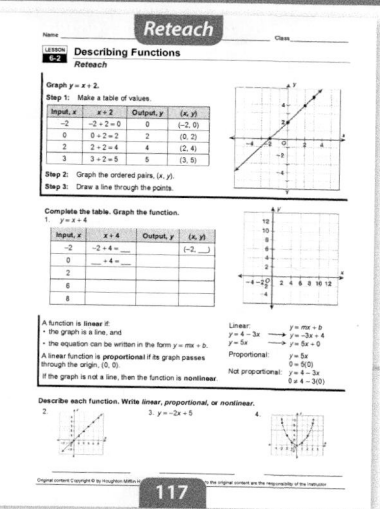

117

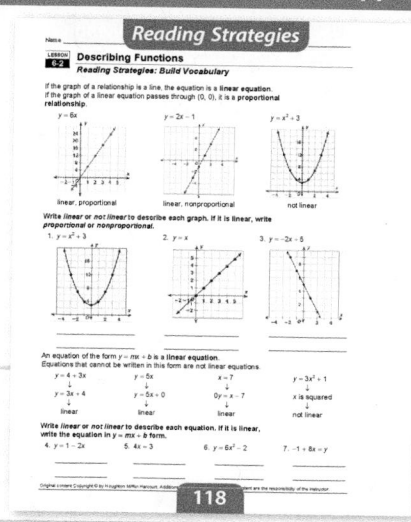

118

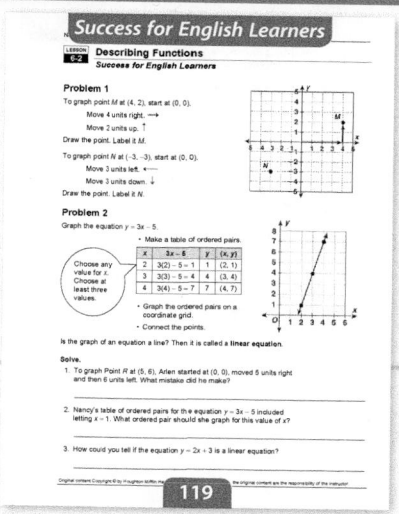

119

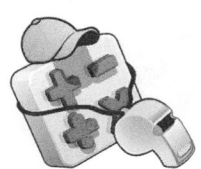

Personal Math Trainer
Daily Intervention
6.2 Homework

Pages shown are from *Differentiated Instruction*. **Also available online.**

⏱ **Pressed for Time**

6.2 Differentiated Homework Assignments

(AL) **Approaching Level**	6–10, 12	
(OL) **On Level**	8–13	
(BL) **Beyond Level**	10–15	

*For **Below Level** students, assign Personal Math Trainer, Daily Intervention 6.2 Homework.*

Mathematical Processes	Exercises
MP.2 Reasoning	6, 11–13
MP.3 Logic	7–10, 14
MP.5 Using Tools	15

Focus on Higher Order Thinking

Depth of Knowledge	Exercises
2 Skills/Concepts	6–10
3 Strategic Thinking H.O.T.	11–15

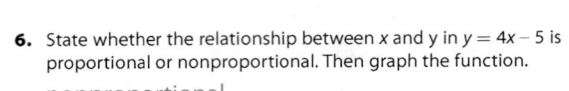
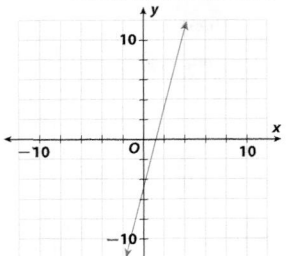

6. State whether the relationship between x and y in $y = 4x - 5$ is proportional or nonproportional. Then graph the function.

nonproportional

7. The Fortaleza telescope in Brazil is a radio telescope. Its shape can be approximated with the equation $y = 0.013x^2$. Is the relationship between x and y linear? Is it proportional? Explain.

No. The relationship is not linear because x is squared, so it will not be proportional.

8. Kiley spent $20 on rides and snacks at the state fair. If x is the amount she spent on rides, and y is the amount she spent on snacks, the total amount she spent can be represented by the equation $x + y = 20$. Is the relationship between x and y linear? Is it proportional? Explain.

If you solve for y, the relationship is $y = -x + 20$. Since the equation is in the form $y = mx + b$ with $m = -1$ and $b = 20$, the equation is linear. It is not proportional because $b \neq 0$.

9. **Represent Real-World Problems** The drill team is buying new uniforms. The table shows y, the total cost in dollars, and x, the number of uniforms purchased.

Number of uniforms, x	1	3	5	9
Total cost ($), y	60	180	300	540

a. Use the data to draw a graph. Is the relationship between x and y linear? Explain.

Yes. The graph of the solutions lie in a line.

b. Use your graph to predict the cost of purchasing 12 uniforms.

$720

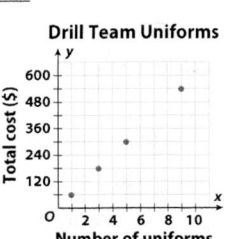
Drill Team Uniforms

10. Marta, a whale calf in an aquarium, is fed a special milk formula. Her handler uses a graph to track the number of gallons of formula y the calf drinks in x hours. Is the relationship between x and y linear? Is it proportional? Explain.

Yes, it is linear; all of the points lie along a line. Yes, it is proportional; the graph contains the point (0, 0).

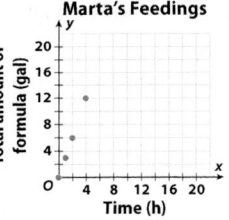
Marta's Feedings

© Houghton Mifflin Harcourt Publishing Company

DIFFERENTIATE INSTRUCTION *Leveled Homework/Practice*

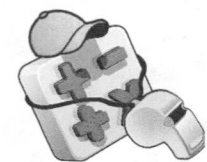

Personal Math Trainer
• 6.2 Homework

Pages shown are from *Differentiated Instruction.*
Also available online.

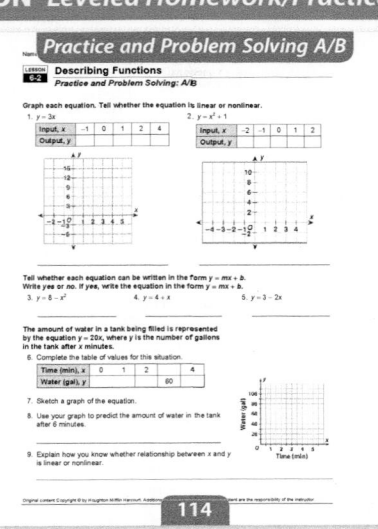
Practice and Problem Solving A/B
114

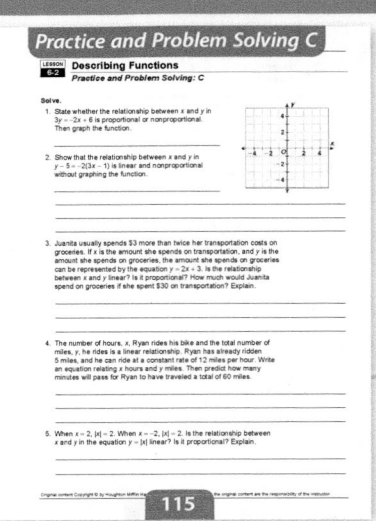
Practice and Problem Solving C
115

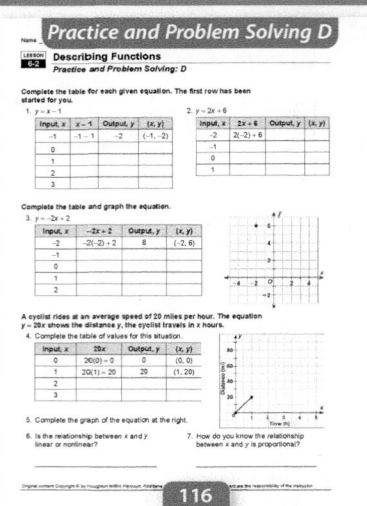
Practice and Problem Solving D
116

11. Critique Reasoning A student claims that the equation $y = 7$ is not a linear equation because it does not have the form $y = mx + b$. Do you agree or disagree? Why?

Disagree; the equation can be written in the form

$y = mx + b$ where m is 0, and the graph of the

solutions is a horizontal line.

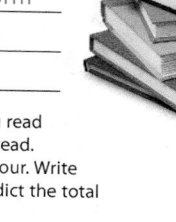

12. Make a Prediction Let x represent the number of hours you read a book and y represent the total number of pages you have read. You have already read 70 pages and can read 30 pages per hour. Write an equation relating x hours and y pages you read. Then predict the total number of pages you will have read after another 3 hours.

$y = 30x + 70$; 160 pages

 **FOCUS ON HIGHER ORDER THINKING**

13. Draw Conclusions Rebecca draws a graph of a real-world relationship that turns out to be a set of unconnected points. Can the relationship be linear? Can it be proportional? Explain your reasoning.

The relationship will be linear if the points all lie on the

same line. The relationship will be proportional if it is linear

and if a line through the points passes through the origin.

14. Communicate Mathematical Ideas Write a real-world problem involving a proportional relationship. Explain how you know the relationship is proportional.

Sample answer: Jacob charges $30 to mow a lawn.

How much does he earn mowing lawns?

The relationship is proportional because the equation of

the relationship is $y = 30x$ and is in the form $y = mx$.

15. Justify Reasoning Show that the equation $y + 3 = 3(2x + 1)$ is linear and that it represents a proportional relationship between x and y.

$y + 3 = 3(2x + 1)$	
$y + 3 = 6x + 3$	Use the Distributive Property.
$y = 6x$	Subtract 3 from both sides.

The equation is in the form $y = mx + b$, so it is linear.

Since $b = 0$, it represents a proportional relationship.

Work Area

© Houghton Mifflin Harcourt Publishing Company • Image Credits: ©Photodisc/Getty Images

---

DIFFERENTIATE INSTRUCTION *Extend-the-Math Activity* **PRE-AP**

Activity The inverse of a function is found by switching the coordinates in each ordered pair of the function. Given the nonlinear function $y = x^2 - 2$, find the equation for its inverse. Graph both relations on the same graph. Tell whether the inverse of the function is a function. Explain how you know.

The inverse of $y = x^2 - 2$ is $x = y^2 - 2$. The graph shows that the inverse is not a function because each value of x, except for $x = -2$, results in two different values of y; for example (2, 2) and (2, −2).

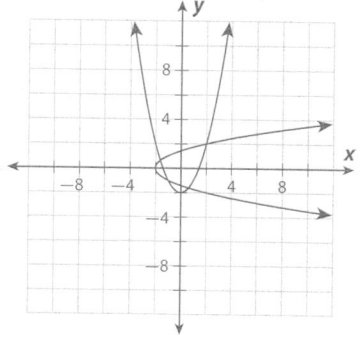

✔ **Quick Check**

6.2 Lesson Quiz

1. State whether the relationship between x and y in $y = 2x - 3$ is proportional or nonproportional. Then graph the function.
nonproportional

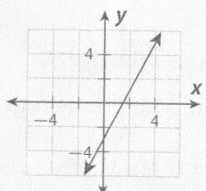

2. State whether the relationship between x and y in $y = x^2 - 1$ is linear and, if so, if it is proportional or nonproportional. Then graph the function. not linear, nonproportional

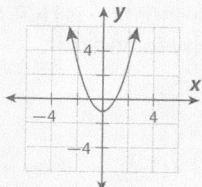

3. The table shows y, the total number of cups of water needed to make x cups of rice.

x	1	3	5	7
y	2.5	7.5	12.5	17.5

a. Use the data to draw a graph. Is the relationship between x and y linear? Explain. Yes, it is linear; the graph of the solutions lie in a straight line.

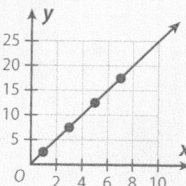

b. Use your graph to predict the number of cups of water to use when using 10 cups of rice. 25 cups of water

Differentiate Instruction

IF a student misses more than one question, THEN

Differentiate Instruction:

• 6.2 Reteach

• Personal Math Trainer

 Interactive Whiteboard
Interactive Lesson quiz available online

Creating Nonlinear Functions

1 Engage

❓ ESSENTIAL QUESTION

How can you create functions that are not linear?
Create a table of values in which there is not a common difference between x- and y-values; or draw a graph in which the points do not all fall on one line.

Motivate the Lesson

Ask: What situations can you think of that are linear? How do you know they are linear? How do you know when a situation is NOT linear? Begin the Explore Activity to find out.

2 Explore

EXPLORE ACTIVITY

Focus on Critical Thinking
In Part A, point out to students that just because an equation is not written in the form $y = mx + b$ does not mean that the equation is not linear. If the equation *can* be written in the form $y = mx + b$, then it is linear. For example, $5x = 4 - y$ is linear because it can be written as $y = -5x + 4$.

TEACHER TO TEACHER

Focus on Modeling Have students write five ordered pairs where the change between x-values is constant. Have half the class select their y-values so that the change between each is also constant. Have the other half choose their y-values so that the change is not constant. Check that students assign exactly one output to each input. Have students from each group graph their functions for the class and show that they are linear or nonlinear functions, as expected.

Going Further **6.2**

Creating Nonlinear Functions

8.2.GF6.2
Students will create functions that are not linear.

❓ ESSENTIAL QUESTION
How can you create functions that are not linear?

EXPLORE ACTIVITY

Creating Functions That Are Not Linear

A A linear function can be written in the form $y = mx + b$. If a function cannot be written in the form $y = mx + b$, it is not linear. Use this information to write a function that is *not* linear.

Sample answer: $y = 5x^2 + 4$

B A table of values for a linear function shows a constant difference in corresponding output values when there is a constant difference in the input values. Use this information to create a table of values for a function that is *not* linear. Sample answer:

x	0	2	4	6
f(x)	9	3	1	3

C A graph of a linear function consists of points that all lie along a line. Use this information to create a graph of a function that is *not* linear. Sample graph shown.

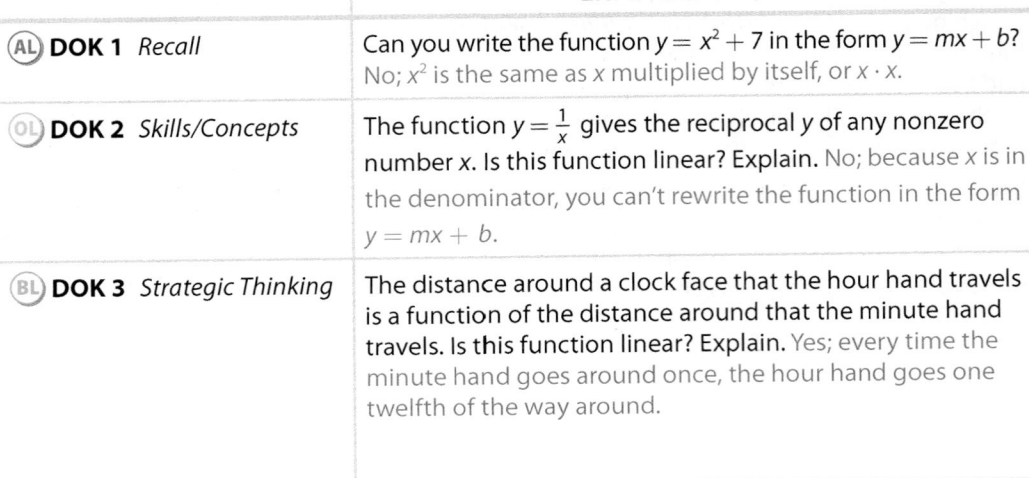

D The perimeter P of a square with side length x is given by the linear function $P = 4x$. Create a nonlinear function based on a geometry formula that you know. HINT: What do you know about the area A of a square with side length x?

Sample answers: Area of a square $A = x^2$; volume of a sphere with radius r: $V = \frac{4}{3}\pi r^3$

© Houghton Mifflin Harcourt Publishing Company

Reflect

1. Explain why the values in your table in Part B are nonlinear. Explain why the graph you created in Part C is not linear.

Sample answer: In Part B, there is a constant difference in input values but not a constant difference in output values. In Part C, the graph is not a straight line.

Going Further 6.2 **166A**

DIFFERENTIATE INSTRUCTION *Leveled Questions*

	EXPLORE ACTIVITY
AL **DOK 1** *Recall*	Can you write the function $y = x^2 + 7$ in the form $y = mx + b$? No; x^2 is the same as x multiplied by itself, or $x \cdot x$.
OL **DOK 2** *Skills/Concepts*	The function $y = \frac{1}{x}$ gives the reciprocal y of any nonzero number x. Is this function linear? Explain. No; because x is in the denominator, you can't rewrite the function in the form $y = mx + b$.
BL **DOK 3** *Strategic Thinking*	The distance around a clock face that the hour hand travels is a function of the distance around that the minute hand travels. Is this function linear? Explain. Yes; every time the minute hand goes around once, the hour hand goes one twelfth of the way around.

LEVELED QUESTIONS: **AL** Approaching Level | **OL** On Level | **BL** Beyond Level

Marco has read 7 books for a summer reading club. He plans to read 2 books each week for the rest of the summer. The table shows the total number of books he will read over time.

Week, x	0	1	2	3	4
Total books read, f(x)	7	9	11	13	15

1. Create a table to show the reading plan for another book club member whose plan is represented with a nonlinear function.

Week, x	0	1	2	3	4
Total books read, f(x)	2	5	6	7	9

2. Explain how you know the second book club member's plan is not linear.

There is a constant difference of 1 in the input values, while the difference in output values varies from 1 to 3.

For each linear situation described, give an adapted description that is not linear. Sample answers given.

3. An art museum charges $6.50 per ticket.

The same art museum charges $5 per ticket for groups of 20 or more.

4. A hat collector gets 2 new hats each month.

The same hat collector gets additional hats whenever attending a hat show.

5. A game club gives members 200 points for beginning membership and 50 points for each game purchased.

The same club gives 200 points to begin and 25, 50, or 75 points for games purchased, depending on their retail value.

Determine whether the graph is linear or nonlinear. Then write a situation for the graph. Sample answers given.

6.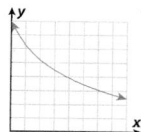

Nonlinear. The temperature of a hot beverage decreases as it cools.

7.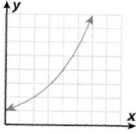

Nonlinear. The size of a bacteria colony doubles every hour.

8.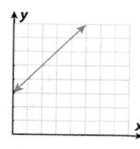

Linear. A scooter rental costs a flat fee plus an hourly cost for rental.

© Houghton Mifflin Harcourt Publishing Company

166B Unit 2

---

3 Explain

Avoid Common Errors

Caution students to make sure that the nonlinear function they create is still a function. Remind them that a function cannot have two different outputs for the same input.

4 Elaborate

Summarize the Lesson

Ask: How can you create a function that is not a linear function? You can create a table with x-values that have a constant difference but y-values that do not.

5 Evaluate

Practice

Focus on Patterns

In **Exercise 1**, ask students to compare the x-values and the y-values in the table they are to complete with the x-values and the y-values in the table they are given. The x-values are the same, with a constant difference. The y-values in the given table have a constant difference, but the y-values in the table to complete should NOT all have a constant difference.

LESSON QUIZ

1. The table shows the temperature over 4 hours. Find temperatures to replace the question marks so that the function relationship is (a) linear and (b) nonlinear. (a) 80 and 88; (b) 79 and 91 (for example)

Hours, x	0	1	2	3	4
Temperature in °F, f(x)	76	?	84	?	92

2. Consider this linear situation: "Each month, $200 is withdrawn from a savings account that initially contains $2500." Give an adapted description that is not linear. Each month, 10% of the savings account is withdrawn.

3. Is the graph shown linear or nonlinear? Write a situation for the graph.

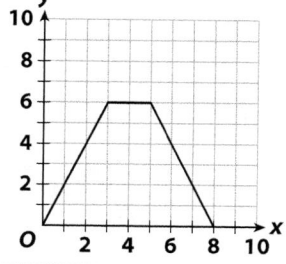

Nonlinear. Sample answer: a hiker hikes away from camp at 2 mi/h for 3 hours, has lunch and rests for 2 hours, and then hikes back at 2 mi/h.

Creating Nonlinear Functions **166B**

How Many Squares?

Objective
Students will create a function $f(n)$ for the number of different-sized squares that can be found in an $n \times n$ square grid.

Grouping
2–4 students per group (suggested)

Materials
• grid paper

Teacher Preparation
Make sure students have the required materials.

Key Concepts
This activity reviews perfect squares and functions. Students will:
• recognize geometric patterns
• recognize number patterns and perfect squares
• write a function to describe the patterns observed
• verify that a given function describes a given pattern

Encourage students to describe the geometric and number patterns observed and use inductive reasoning to extend the patterns to larger grid sizes.

How Many Squares?

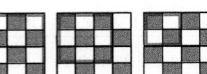

INSTRUCTIONS

STEP 1 How many squares (of all sizes) can you find in the 4×4 square grid?
There are four different sizes of squares in the grid.

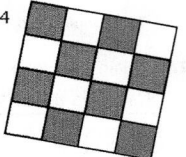

Count the number of each size square in the 4×4 square grid. The table shows you how to find them all.

Size of square	Number of squares	Identification of squares
4×4	1	
3×3	4	
2×2	9	
1×1	16	
Total	30	

The total number of squares in the 4×4 square grid is:

$f(4) = 1 $ ■■ ■■ ■ $16 = 30$

Notice the pattern. All the terms in $f(4)$ are perfect squares:

$f(4) = 1^{■} + 2^{■} + 3^{■} + 4^2$

© Houghton Mifflin Harcourt Publishing Company

WARM-UP EXERCISES

1. List the first six perfect-square integers. 1, 4, 9, 16, 25, 36

2. Write an expression for the first six perfect-square integers given $n = 1$.
   $n^2, (n + 1)^2, (n + 2)^2, (n + 3)^2, (n + 4)^2, (n + 5)^2$

3. Evaluate the function $f(n) = \dfrac{n(n + 1)(2n + 1)}{6}$ for $n = 5$. 55

STEP 2 Draw a 5 × 5 square grid. Find the total number of different-sized squares in the grid to complete the table. Look for a pattern.

Size of square	5×5	4×4	3×3	2×2	1×1
Identification of squares					
Number of squares	1	4	9	16	25

The total number of squares in the 5 × 5 square grid is:

$f(5) = 1 + 4 + \boxed{9} + \boxed{16} + \boxed{25} = \boxed{55}$

STEP 3 Repeat with a 6 × 6 grid and a 7 × 7 grid. Verify the pattern.
Check students' work.
$f(6) = \underline{1 + 4 + 9 + 16 + 25 + 36 = 91}$
$f(7) = \underline{1 + 4 + 9 + 16 + 25 + 36 + 49 = 140}$

STEP 4 Use the pattern to write a function for the total number $f(n)$ of different-sized squares in an $n \times n$ grid.

$f(n) = 1^2 + 2^2 + \boxed{3}^2 + \cdots + \boxed{n^2}$

STEP 5 The function for the total number $f(n)$ of different-sized squares in an $n \times n$ grid can also be written $\blacksquare = \frac{\blacksquare + 1)(2n + 1)}{6}$. Verify that this function works for 5 × 5, 6 × 6, and 7 ■ 7 square grids.

$f(5) = \dfrac{\boxed{5}\left(\boxed{5} + 1\right)\left(2 \times \boxed{5} + 1\right)}{6} = \boxed{55}$

$f(6) = \dfrac{\boxed{6}\left(\boxed{6} + 1\right)\left(2 \times \boxed{6} + 1\right)}{6} = \boxed{91}$

$f(7) = \dfrac{\boxed{7}\left(\boxed{7} + 1\right)\left(2 \times \boxed{7} + 1\right)}{6} = \boxed{140}$

This function gives the correct totals for 5 × 5, 6 × 6, and 7 × 7 square grids.

© Houghton Mifflin Harcourt Publishing Company

Instructions

STEP 1 Working in small groups, students read through Step 1, which shows how to count all the different squares in a 4 × 4 square grid.

STEP 2 Students draw a 5 × 5 square grid and repeat the process of counting squares in the 5 × 5 square grid.

STEP 3 Students repeat Step 2 with a 6 × 6 square grid and a 7 × 7 square grid.

STEP 4 Students write a function for the total number $f(n)$ of different-sized squares in an $n \times n$ grid.

STEP 5 Students are given an explicit formula for the number $f(n)$ of different-sized squares in an $n \times n$ grid and asked to verify that it works for the 5 × 5, 6 × 6, and 7 × 7 square grids.

TEACHER NOTES

- **Discussion** For Step 4, help students develop a function from the pattern.
- **Extension** Challenge students to develop the function $f(n) = \frac{n(n + 1)(2n + 1)}{6}$.
- **Whole-Class Variation** Work with the entire class together. Display the grids and count squares together. Work through the reasoning to create the function together.

Lesson Support

Content Objective Students will learn how to use tables, graphs, and equations to compare functions.

Professional Development

Integrate Mathematical Processes MP.3

This lesson provides an opportunity to address this Mathematical Processes standard. It calls for students to analyze mathematical relationships to connect and communicate mathematical ideas. Students compare linear relationships whether they are modeled with a verbal description, tables, equations, or graphs. By comparing linear relationships, students analyze the mathematical relationships of different real-world settings.

FOCUS

Building Background

Connecting to Everyday Life Discuss situations in which students might find it useful to compare properties of two different functions. For example, students might want to compare the costs of different telephone services or different rental costs. Have students identify the properties they would use to compare two linear functions. Students should identify the slope or unit rate of change and the y-intercept or initial value. They might also identify whether or not the relationship is proportional.

Bik's Bikes-For-Two
$8 per hour
plus $10 service charge

Tony's Tandems
$10 per hour
plus $5 service charge

COHERENCE

Learning Progressions

In this lesson, students compare properties of two linear functions represented in different ways. Important understandings for students include the following:

- **Compare a table and an equation that model a real-life situation.**
- **Compare a graph and a description that model a real-life situation.**

Students convert data in a table to a linear function to compare it with a different linear function. They also use the information in a description to write a function they can use to compare to a function shown on a graph. They use properties of the linear functions, slopes in particular, to make relevant comparisons.

RIGOR

Cluster Connections

This lesson provides an excellent opportunity to connect ideas in the cluster:

Define, evaluate, and compare functions.

Present the following situation: A 50-gallon water tank is being drained at a rate of 2.5 gallons per minute. A 75-gallon tank is being drained at a rate that is represented in the table.

Time (min)	2	4	6	8
Gallons	68.5	62	55.5	49

Which tank is being drained more quickly? Explain.

The 75-gallon tank is being drained more quickly since it is draining at a rate of 3.25 gallons per minute while the 50-gallon tank is draining at a rate of 2.5 gallons per minute.

Language Support ELL

Language Objective Students will discuss how to use tables, graphs, and equations to compare functions.

Leveled Strategies for English Learners ELL

Emerging
Create sentence frames to practice comparative terms like *greater than/less than* or *steeper/less steep* for comparing two linear graphs. Ask students to select a graph to identify the features of the lines described.

Expanding
Have students give a few sentences to compare two lines on a graph.

Bridging
Have students create detailed scenarios of different layaway plans for purchases of similar items, such as articles of clothing or laptop computers. Have them graph the two plans and then write a short rationale to describe which plan is better and why.

 **Math Talk**

Use Guided Practice to help students with different levels of proficiency by asking them for a straightforward sentence or two to define what the slopes and *y*-intercepts of two sets of data from one situation represent. Remember to clarify what is meant by terms such as *service* or *plan* based on alternatives or choices presented in the scenarios.

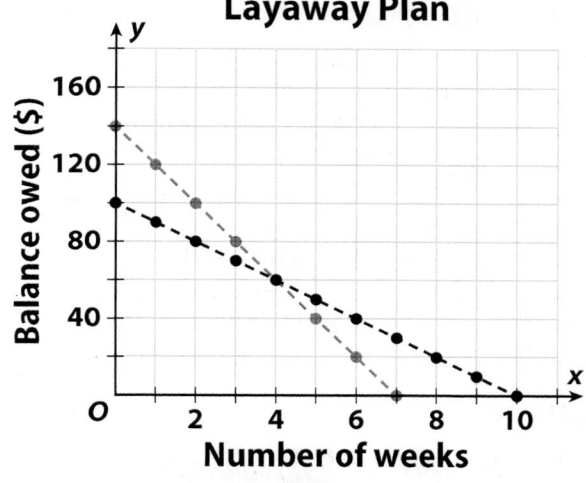

Graph of the layaway plans in Explore Activity 3

Linguistic Support ELL

Academic/Content Vocabulary
In this lesson, students need to compare two functions on one graph. Review terms for describing how the incline or steepness of the slope of the function line represents differences in the rate of change. It is also helpful to scaffold the concepts by using two separate graphs and labeling what the lines represent with words or short phrases before showing a graph with both lines to make the comparison.

Background Knowledge
A layaway plan at two stores is compared on one graph. Students may not be familiar with what a layaway plan is or these related terms: *down payment,* or *initial payment; weekly payment; balance owed.* Create two scenarios with details about two layaway purchases, including the price of the purchase and the number of weeks the purchaser has to pay down the balance owed.

Comparing Functions

1 Engage

❓ ESSENTIAL QUESTION

How can you use tables, graphs, and equations to compare functions? Sample answer: You can compare functions by graphing each function and comparing the graphs, or by writing each function as an equation and comparing the equations.

Motivate the Lesson

Ask: If you are given the graph of two linear functions, how can you compare the slopes of the lines representing the functions? Begin the lesson to find out.

2 Explore

EXPLORE ACTIVITY EXAMPLE 1

ADDITIONAL EXAMPLE 1 Melanie and Patrick have different phone services. The relationship of the monthly cost, y dollars, to send or receive x text messages, is a linear function. The cost of Patrick's texting is described by y = 0.03x + 5. The cost of Melanie's texting is shown in the table.

Melanie's Monthly Texting Cost					
x	5	10	15	20	25
y	1.25	2.50	3.75	5.00	6.25

A Write an equation to represent Melanie's monthly texting cost. y = 0.25x

B Which service is cheaper when 50 texts are sent or received in one month? Patrick's service would cost $6.50. Melanie's would cost $12.50. Patrick's is cheaper.

📝 **Interactive Whiteboard**
Interactive example available online

LESSON
6.3 Comparing Functions

8.2.6.3
Students will use tables, graphs, and equations to compare functions.

 ESSENTIAL QUESTION How can you use tables, graphs, and equations to compare functions?

EXPLORE ACTIVITY

Comparing a Table and an Equation

You can compare functions by writing them both as equations.

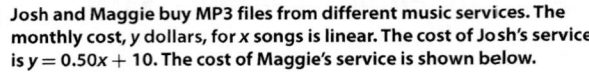

EXAMPLE 1 Josh and Maggie buy MP3 files from different music services. The monthly cost, y dollars, for x songs is linear. The cost of Josh's service is y = 0.50x + 10. The cost of Maggie's service is shown below.

Monthly Cost of MP3s at Maggie's Music Service					
Songs, x	5	10	15	20	25
Cost ($), y	4.95	9.90	14.85	19.80	24.75

A Write an equation to represent the monthly cost of Maggie's service.

STEP 1 Choose any two ordered pairs from the table to find the slope: for example, (5, 4.95) and (10, 9.90).

$$m = \frac{y_2 - y_1}{x_2 - x_1} = \frac{\boxed{9.90} - 4.95}{10 - \boxed{5}} = \frac{\boxed{4.95}}{\boxed{5}} = \frac{0.99}{}$$

STEP 2 Find the y-intercept. Use the slope and any point.

Begin with slope-intercept form. y = mx + b

Substitute for y, m, and x. 4.95 = $\boxed{0.99}$ · $\boxed{5}$ + b

$\boxed{0}$ = b

STEP 3 Write the equation in slope-intercept form.

y = $\boxed{0.99}$ x + $\boxed{0}$, or y = $\boxed{0.99}$ x

B Which service is cheaper when 30 songs are downloaded?

Josh's service:
y = 0.50x + 10
y = 0.50 · $\boxed{30}$ + 10 = $\boxed{25}$

Maggie's service:
y = 0.99x
y = 0.99 · $\boxed{30}$ = $\boxed{29.7}$

Josh's service is cheaper for 30 songs.

DIFFERENTIATE INSTRUCTION *Leveled Questions*

	EXPLORE ACTIVITY EXAMPLE 1
AL DOK 1 *Recall*	What information is given in a table and what information is given in an equation? The cost of Josh's service is given in an equation; the cost of Maggie's service is given in the table.
OL DOK 2 *Skills/Concepts*	How can you describe each service's cost in words using the meanings of the slopes and y-intercepts? Josh pays a $10/month fee but only pays $0.50 per song. Maggie has no monthly fee but pays $0.99 per song.
BL DOK 3 *Strategic Thinking*	What additional information is available to compare the functions if you compare their graphs? Sample answer: You can see from the graphs which music service has a greater rate per song by comparing the slopes, and you can see the number of songs for which the two services charge the same amount (intersection point).

LEVELED QUESTIONS: **AL** Approaching Level | **OL** On Level | **BL** Beyond Level

EXPLORE ACTIVITY (cont'd)

YOUR TURN

1. Quentin is choosing between ■■ books at the bookstore or buying online versions of the books ■■■ tablet. The cost, y dollars, of ordering books online for x books is $y = $ ■■ $+ 1.50$. The cost of buying the books at the bookstore is shown in the table. Which method of buying books is more expensive if Quentin wants to buy 6 books?

Personal Math Trainer

Online Assessment and Intervention

my.hrw.com

Cost of Books at the Bookstore					
Books, x	1	2	3	4	5
Cost (\$), y	7.50	15.00	22.50	30.00	37.50

Buying at the bookstore is more expensive.

EXPLORE ACTIVITY 2 Real World

Comparing a Table and a Graph

The table and graph show how many words Morgan and Brian typed correctly on a typing test. For both students, the relationship between words typed correctly and time is linear.

Morgan's Typing Test					
Time (min)	2	4	6	8	10
Words	30	60	90	120	150

Brian's Typing Test

(graph: Words vs Time (min), straight line through origin)

A Find Morgan's unit rate.

$m = \dfrac{60 - 30}{4 - 2} = \dfrac{30}{2} = 15$; 15 words per minute

B Find Brian's unit rate.

$m = \dfrac{80 - 40}{4 - 2} = \dfrac{40}{2} = 20$; 20 words per minute

C Which student types more correct words per minute?

Brian types 5 more correct words per minute.

Reflect

2. Katie types 17 correct words per minute. Explain how a graph of Katie's test results would compare to Morgan's and Brian's.

Katie's graph would go through the origin. Katie's graph would be less steep than Brian's but steeper than Morgan's.

168 Unit 2

	EXPLORE ACTIVITY 2
(AL) **DOK 1** *Recall*	How can you find the unit rates for the functions? Write each slope as a fraction with a denominator of 1.
(OL) **DOK 2** *Skills/Concepts*	What point on the graph gives Brian's unit rate? (1, 20)
(BL) **DOK 3** *Strategic Thinking*	You can see from the graph through (0, 0) that the relationship for Brian is proportional. How can you tell from the table that the relationship for Morgan is proportional? $\dfrac{30}{2} = \dfrac{60}{4} = 15$, and so on, so it's proportional because $\dfrac{y}{x}$ is constant for all ordered pairs (x, y).

YOUR TURN MP.1

Talk About It

Check for Understanding

Ask: How can you determine that ordering online is not always less expensive? Make a table with $x = 1, 2, 3, 4,$ and 5, and find $y = 6.95x + 1.50$ for each x-value. Comparing the values of y in the new table to the table for the bookstore will show that the bookstore's cost is sometimes less.

3 Explain

EXPLORE ACTIVITY 2

Engage with the Whiteboard

 Have a volunteer draw a graph of Morgan's test results on the same coordinate grid as Brian's test results. This will help them visualize which graph is steeper.

TEACHER TO TEACHER

Activity In small groups, with toothpicks, have students do the following activity.

1. Create a sequence using a quantity of toothpicks that *increases by a constant amount.* Sample answer:

1   2   3   4

(figures of triangles made of toothpicks)

2. Let x represent the figure number and let y represent the number of toothpicks used in the figure. Make a table of values for x and y.

x	1	2	3	4
y	3	5	7	9

3. Identify the constant rate of change. Write an equation representing y as a function of x, and graph the function. Constant rate of change of 2; $y = 2x + 1$

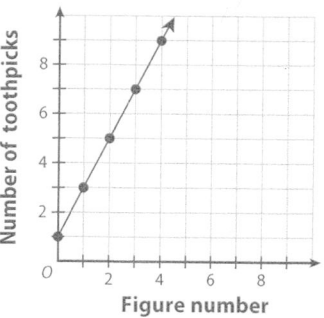

(graph: Number of toothpicks vs Figure number)

Comparing Functions **168**

EXPLORE ACTIVITY 3

Focus on Communication

Have students discuss the advantages and disadvantages of the two different plans. The discussion should include the amount of the initial payment, the amounts of the weekly payments, and how fast the balance will be paid off.

Digital Teacher Resources

Go online to access all your lesson-level resources.

my.hrw.com

Differentiated Instruction
- Reteach
- Reading Strategies
- Success for English Learners
- Practice and Problem Solving A/B, C, D

Math on the Spot Videos

EXPLORE ACTIVITY 3 Real World

Comparing a Graph and a Description

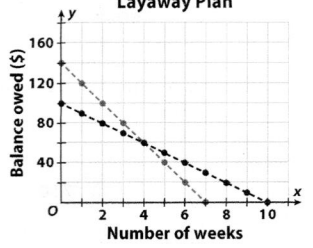

Layaway Plan

Jamal wants to buy a new game system that costs $200. He does not have enough money to buy it today, so he compares layaway plans at different stores.

The plan at Store A is shown on the graph.

Store B requires an initial payment of $60 and weekly payments of $20 until the balance is paid in full.

A Write an equation in slope-intercept form for Store A's layaway plan. Let x represent number of weeks and y represent balance owed.

$$y = -10x + 100$$

B Write an equation in slope-intercept form for Store B's layaway plan. Let x represent number of weeks and y represent balance owed.

$$y = -20x + 140$$

C Sketch a graph of the plan at Store B on the same grid as Store A.

D How can you use the graphs to tell which plan requires the greater down payment? How can you use the equations?

The y-intercept (balance owed at week 0) for Store A is less than Store B, so Store A requires a greater down payment. Compare the values of b in the equations.

E How can you use the graphs to tell which plan requires the greater weekly payment?

The slope (rate of change) for Store B is steeper, so Store B requires a greater weekly payment of $20, as opposed to $10 for Store A.

F Which plan allows Jamal to pay for the game system faster? Explain.

Store B; the balance owed at Store B is $0 after only 7 weeks.

© Houghton Mifflin Harcourt Publishing Company

DIFFERENTIATE INSTRUCTION *Leveled Questions*

	EXPLORE ACTIVITY 3
AL DOK 1 *Recall*	What does the slope represent? the y-intercept? slope: weekly payment; y-intercept: amount owed after the down payment
OL DOK 2 *Skills/Concepts*	How can you use the graph of the plan at Store A to write a description of that plan? The point (0, 100) is the amount to be paid back. The slope -10 shows weekly payments of $10. The point (10, 0) shows that it will take 10 weeks to pay back the $100.
BL DOK 3 *Strategic Thinking*	What does comparing the graphs of the layaway plans allow you to see that comparing the equations does not? Sample answer: They both allow you to compare the down payments (y-intercepts) and weekly payments (slopes), but the graphs also allow you to compare when the system is paid off (x-intercept).

LEVELED QUESTIONS: AL Approaching Level | **OL** On Level | **BL** Beyond Level

Guided Practice

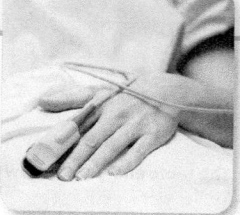

Doctors have two methods of calculating maximum heart rate. With the first method, maximum heart rate, *y*, in beats per minute is $y = 220 - x$, where *x* is the person's age. Maximum heart rate with the second method is shown in the table. (Explore Activity Example 1)

Age, *x*	20	30	40	50	60
Heart rate (bpm), *y*	194	187	180	173	166

1. Which method gives the greater maximum heart rate for a 70-year-old?

The second method (159 bpm vs. 150 bpm) gives the greater heart rate.

2. Are heart rate and age proportional or nonproportional for each method?

Heart rate and age are nonproportional for each method.

Aisha runs a tutoring business. With Plan 1, students may choose to pay $15 per hour. With Plan 2, they may follow the plan shown on the graph. (Explore Activity 2 and 3)

Tutoring Fees

Cost ($) vs. Time (h)

3. Describe the plan shown on the graph.

Students pay a $40 fee and $5 per hour.

4. Sketch a graph showing the $15 per hour option.

5. What does the intersection of the two graphs mean?

With both plans, it costs $60 for 4 hours of tutoring.

6. Which plan is cheaper for 10 hours of tutoring?

Plan 2 ($90 vs. $150) is cheaper for 10 hours of tutoring.

7. Are cost and time proportional or nonproportional for each plan?

Cost and time are proportional for Plan 1 and nonproportional for Plan 2.

? ESSENTIAL QUESTION CHECK-IN

8. When using tables, graphs, and equations to compare functions, why do you find the equations for tables and graphs?

You find the equations so that you can substitute numbers into them and compare results.

④ Elaborate

Talk About It

Summarize the Lesson

Ask: How can you use a graph of a linear function to write an equation for the function? Let the *y*-intercept be *b* in the equation $y = mx + b$. Use two points on the graph to find the slope of the graph. Substitute the value of the slope for *m*.

Guided Practice

Avoid Common Errors

- **Exercises 1–2** Remind students that the equation $y = 220 - x$ can be also be written as $y = -1x + 220$ so that it is in the familiar $y = mx + b$ form.

- **Exercise 7** Remind students that the graph of a proportional relationship is a line that goes through the origin, (0, 0). Two different lines cannot both represent proportional relationships unless they intersect at the origin.

Engage with the Whiteboard

Have students draw the graph in **Exercise 4**. Then for **Exercise 5** have a student label the coordinates of the intersection of the two graphs. Before starting **Exercise 6**, have students draw a box around the range of hours for which Plan 1 is cheaper (up to 4 hours), and in a different color draw a box around the hours that Plan 2 is cheaper.

© Houghton Mifflin Harcourt Publishing Company • Image Credits: ©PhotoAlto/Getty Images

---

DIFFERENTIATE INSTRUCTION *Intervention and Additional Support*

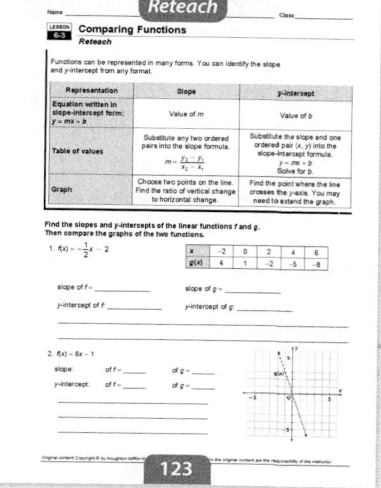

Reteach

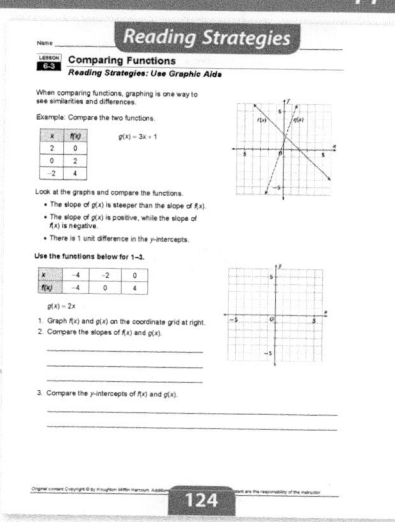

Reading Strategies

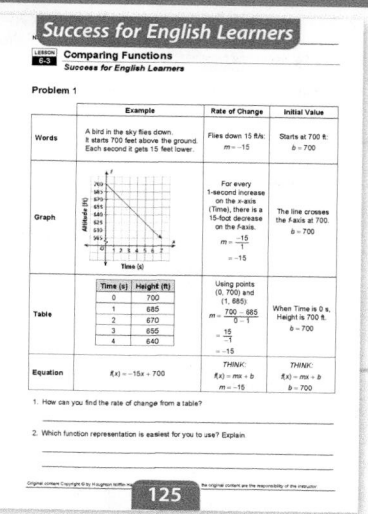

Success for English Learners

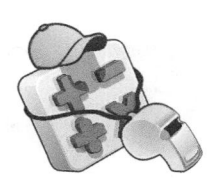

Personal Math Trainer
Daily Intervention
6.3 Homework

Pages shown are from *Differentiated Instruction*.
Also available online.

Pressed for Time

6.3 Differentiated Homework Assignments

AL **Approaching Level** 9–13, 15

OL **On Level** 11–16

BL **Beyond Level** 13–17

*For **Below Level** students, assign Personal Math Trainer, Daily Intervention 6.3 Homework.*

Mathematical Processes	Exercises
MP.2 Reasoning	16
MP.3 Logic	13, 15, 17
MP.4 Modeling	9–12, 14

Focus on Higher Order Thinking

Depth of Knowledge	Exercises
2 Skills/Concepts	9–14
3 Strategic Thinking **H.O.T.**	15–17

Name _____ Class _____ Date _____

Personal Math Trainer

Online Assessment and Intervention

my.hrw.com

The table and graph show the miles driven and gas used for two scooters.

Scooter A

Distance (mi), x	Gas used (gal), y
150	2
300	4
450	6
600	8
750	10

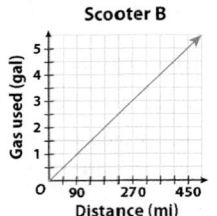

Scooter B

9. Which scooter uses fewer gallons of gas when 1350 miles are driven?

Scooter B (15 gallons vs. 18 gallons) uses fewer gallons of gas.

10. Are gas used and miles proportional or nonproportional for each scooter?

Gas used and miles are proportional for each scooter.

A cell phone company offers two texting plans to its customers. The monthly cost, y dollars, of one plan is $y = 0.10x + 5$, where x is the number of texts. The cost of the other plan is shown in the table.

Number of texts, x	100	200	300	400	500
Cost ($), y	20	25	30	35	40

■ Which plan is cheaper for under 200 texts? ___ the first plan

■ The graph of the first plan does not pass through the origin. What does this indicate?

x and y are nonproportional. There is a monthly charge of $5 even if no texting was done.

■ Brianna wants to buy a digital camera for a photography class. One store offers the camera for $50 down and a payment plan of $20 per month. The payment plan for a second store is described by $y = 15x + 80$, where y is the total cost in dollars and x is the number of months. Which camera is cheaper when the camera is paid off in 12 months? Explain.

The camera at the second store; the cost at the first store is $290 and the cost at the second store is $260.

DIFFERENTIATE INSTRUCTION *Leveled Homework/Practice*

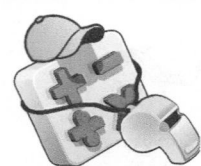

Personal Math Trainer

• 6.3 Homework

Pages shown are from *Differentiated Instruction.* **Also available online.**

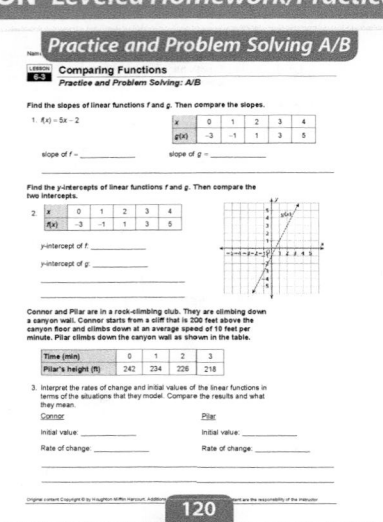

Practice and Problem Solving A/B

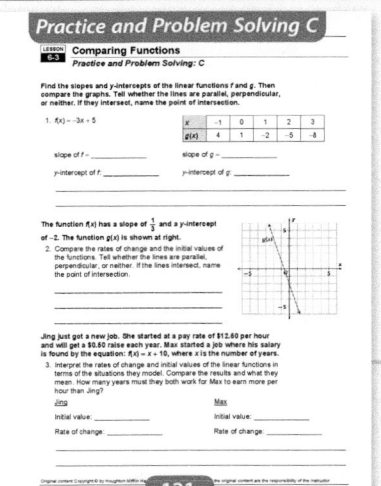

Practice and Problem Solving C

Practice and Problem Solving D

14. The French club and soccer team are washing cars to earn money. The amount earned, y dollars, for washing x cars is a linear function. Which group makes the most money per car? Explain.

French Club	
Number of cars, x	Amount earned ($), y
2	10
4	20
6	30
8	40
10	50

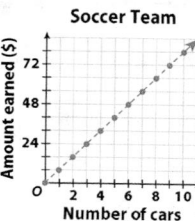
Soccer Team

The soccer team; the unit rate, or cost per car, for the French club is $5 per car. The unit rate for the soccer team is $8 per car.

 **FOCUS ON HIGHER ORDER THINKING**

15. Draw Conclusions Gym A charges $60 a month plus $5 per visit. The monthly cost at Gym B is represented by $y = 5x + 40$, where x is the number of visits per month. What conclusion can you draw about the monthly costs of the gyms?

Since the rate per visit is the same, the monthly cost of Gym A is always more than Gym B.

16. Justify Reasoning Why will the value of y for the function ▪–▪▪ + 1 always be greater than that for the function $y = 4x + 2$ when ▪▪ 1?

Since $y = 5x + 1$ has a steeper slope, once its y-value becomes greater, it will remain greater.

17. Analyze Relationships The equations of two functions are $y = -21x + 9$ and $y = -24x + 8$. Which function is changing more quickly? Explain.

$y = -24x + 8$ is changing more quickly because even though -24 is less than -21, the absolute value of -24 is greater than the absolute value of -21. So, a slope of -24 is steeper.

Work Area

DIFFERENTIATE INSTRUCTION *Extend-the-Math Activity* **PRE-AP**

Activity Introduce function notation. If x represents the input value (domain) of a function and y represents the output value (range), then the function notation for y is $f(x)$, read "f of x", where f names the function. So, for the function represented by the equation $y = 3x + 2$, the function notation is $f(x) = 3x + 2$. $f(x)$ represents the value in the range that corresponds to the value of x in the domain. For example, $f(0)$ is the value in the range that corresponds to the value 0 in the domain, so $f(0) = 3(0) + 2 = 2$. Letters other than f are also used to name functions. For example, if $h(x) = x + 1$, then $h(3) = 3 + 1 = 4$. Have students use these two functions to find $f(3)$, $f(-3)$, $h(3)$, $h(-3)$, and $f(h(2))$.

$f(3) = 11$, $f(-3) = -7$, $h(3) = 4$, $h(-3) = -2$,

$f(h(2)) = f(2 + 1) = f(3) = 11$

 **Quick Check**

6.3 Lesson Quiz

The table and graph show the relationships between the number of miles driven and amount of gas used for two different cars.

Car A				
Miles, x	25	50	75	100
Gas (gal), y	1	2	3	4

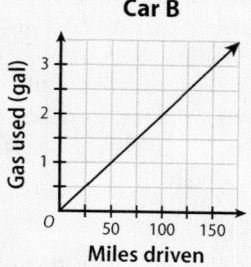
Car B

1. Which car uses fewer gallons of gas when 200 miles are driven? Car B

2. Are the relationships proportional or nonproportional? proportional for both cars

3. Write equations in slope-intercept form for Car A and Car B. Let x represent miles driven and y represent gallons of gas used. Car A: $y = 0.04x$; Car B: $y = 0.02x$

The monthly cost, in y dollars, to download x movies is a linear function. The cost of Nate's service is described by $y = 4x + 6$. The table shows the cost of Beth's service.

Movies, x	2	4	6	8
Cost ($), y	10	20	30	40

4. Write an equation to represent the monthly cost of Beth's service. $y = 5x$

5. Which service is cheaper for 8 movies in one month? Nate's service ($38 vs. $40) is cheaper.

Differentiate Instruction

IF a student misses more than one question, THEN

Differentiate Instruction:
- 6.3 Reteach
- Personal Math Trainer

 Interactive Whiteboard
Interactive Lesson quiz available online

Rate of Change and Initial Value

1 Engage

? ESSENTIAL QUESTION

How can you interpret the rate of change and initial value of a linear function in terms of the situation it models? The rate of change is indicated by the slope; the units are those of the rise over the run. The initial value is the value of the function when the independent variable is 0. The units of the initial value are the same as those of the dependent variable.

Motivate the Lesson

Ask: When modeling a situation with the graph of a linear function, how do you know what the slope and y-intercept mean and what units to use? Begin the Explore Activity to find out.

2 Explore

EXPLORE ACTIVITY

Focus on Communication
Emphasize to students that the y-intercept is a value, not an ordered pair or a point. The y-intercept is the corresponding dependent value when the independent value is 0. When modeling, the y-intercept does not *represent* the initial value, it *is* the initial value.

TEACHER TO TEACHER

Cooperative Learning Have students work in small groups to solve the following problem:

At a neighborhood pizza restaurant, a medium, traditional-crust, 3-topping pizza costs $8.60, and a medium, traditional-crust, 4-topping pizza costs $9.80. Find the rate of change and tell what it means. the cost per topping: $1.20 Find the initial value and tell what it means. the cost of the medium traditional-crust pizza before adding ingredients: $5.00 Write a linear equation for the cost of a medium traditional-crust pizza at this restaurant. $y = 1.2x + 5$ If students need a hint to get started, tell them to try and find the cost per ingredient first.

Rate of Change and Initial Value

8.2.GF6.3
Students will interpret the rate of change and initial value of a linear function in terms of the situation it models.

? ESSENTIAL QUESTION

How can you interpret the rate of change and initial value of a linear function in terms of the situation it models?

EXPLORE ACTIVITY

Determining Rate of Change and Initial Value

A pitcher with a maximum capacity of 4 cups contains 1 cup of apple juice concentrate. A faucet is turned on, filling the pitcher at a rate of $\frac{1}{4}$ cup per second. The amount A of liquid in the pitcher (in cups) is a function $A(t)$ of the time t (in seconds) that the water is running.

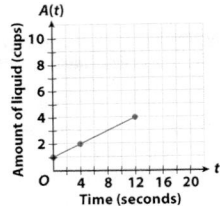

A The y-intercept, ____1____ , is the initial amount in cups in the pitcher at time 0. Plot the point that corresponds to the y-intercept.

B The slope is the rate of change: ___$\frac{1}{4}$___ cup per second, or 1 cup every ___4___ seconds. So, the rise is ___1___ and the run is ___4___.

C Use the rise and run to move from the first point to a second point on the line, and plot a second point.
Check students' graphs.

D Connect the points and extend the line to the maximum value of the function, where $A(t) = $ ___4___ cups.

Reflect

1. How do you know what the maximum value of the function is in Part D?
The problem states that the pitcher has a maximum capacity of 4 cups.

Going Further 6.3 **172A**

© Houghton Mifflin Harcourt Publishing Company

DIFFERENTIATE INSTRUCTION *Leveled Questions*

	EXPLORE ACTIVITY
(AL) **DOK 1** *Recall*	What is the rate of change with units for this situation? $\frac{1}{4}$ cup per second
(OL) **DOK 2** *Skills/Concepts*	What does the function $A(t)$ represent in this situation? the amount of liquid in the pitcher at time t
(BL) **DOK 3** *Strategic Thinking*	How do you know that the rate of change of $\frac{1}{4}$ cup per second is the same as 1 cup every 4 seconds? Multiply the numerator and denominator of the ratio by 4: $\frac{4 \cdot \frac{1}{4} \text{ cup}}{4 \cdot 1 \text{ sec}} = \frac{1 \text{ cup}}{4 \text{ sec}}$

LEVELED QUESTIONS: (AL) Approaching Level | (OL) On Level | (BL) Beyond Level

The increase in pressure ■ (in pounds per square inch, or psi) is a linear function of the depth ■ (in feet) to which a scuba diver descends. This function, ■■ = 0.445d + 14.7, is graphed.

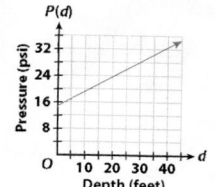

1. What is the initial value, and what does it represent?

   The initial value is 14.7 psi, the pressure at

   $d = 0$, or at the surface of the water.

2. What is the rate of change, and what does it represent?

   The rate of change is 0.445 psi per foot. It represents how quickly the

   pressure increases as the depth increases.

The cost of catering for a scholarship presentation dinner is $300 plus $10 per student. The cost C is a function of the number n of students.

3. Write the linear function C(n).

   $C(n) = 10n + 300$

4. What are the initial value and rate of change, and what do they represent?

   The initial value is $300, the cost of having a meal catered before

   per-person charges are added. The rate of change is $10 per student.

   It represents how quickly the cost increases as the number of students

   increases.

The cost for a plumber to make a repair is $50 for the service call plus $75 per hour.

5. Write the linear function C(t).

   $C(t) = 75t + 50$

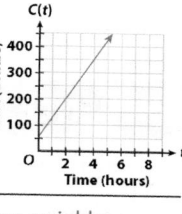

6. Identify the initial value, the rate of change, and their meanings.

   The initial value is $50, the charge for the service

   call. The rate of change is $75 per hour. It represents how quickly

   the charge in dollars increases as the time in hours increases.

© Houghton Mifflin Harcourt Publishing Company

---

3 Explain

Focus on Modeling

Discuss with students that the units of the *rise* are cups and the units of the *run* are seconds, so the units for the rate of change are cups per second. Be sure to use units to show students how the function $A(t) = \frac{1}{4}t + 1$ models the situation:

A cups $= \dfrac{\text{cups}}{\text{seconds}} \cdot t \ \text{seconds} + \text{cups}.$

4 Elaborate

Summarize the Lesson

Ask: How are the units of the rate of change and initial value determined in a linear function model? See answer below.

5 Evaluate

Practice

Focus on Modeling

Discuss with students whether each situation in the exercises is discrete or continuous.

- For **Exercises 1–2**, the pressure function is continuous because the domain values are measures of depth in feet, which are continuous (e.g., 1.5 ft is possible).

- For **Exercises 3–4**, the cost function is discrete because the domain values are numbers of students

- For **Exercises 5–6**, the cost function is continuous because the domain values are measures of time

---

Answer to Elaborate

The units for the rate of change are rate units obtained by dividing the units of the dependent variable by the units of the independent variable. The units for the initial value are always those of the dependent variable.

Answers to Lesson Quiz

1. Rate of change = 60 mi/h; initial value is 300 mi, her beginning distance from the beach

2. $H(t) = 2.5t + 10$

3. The initial value is 10 cm, the height at $t = 0$, or noon. The rate of change is 5 cm per 2 hours, which is 2.5 cm per hour. The rate of change indicates how quickly the height increases with time.

LESSON QUIZ

1. Tamika is planning a trip to the beach at an average constant speed. The function for the distance in miles she is from the beach as she travels is $d(t) = -60t + 300$, where t is time in hours. Identify and interpret the rate of change and initial value of the function.

A bamboo plant is 10 centimeters tall at noon and grows at a rate of 5 centimeters every 2 hours.

2. Write the linear function for height H in centimeters as a function of time t in hours, $H(t)$.

3. Identify the initial value, the rate of change, and their meanings.

Lesson Support

Content Objective Students will learn how to describe a relationship given a graph and sketch a graph given a description.

Professional Development

Integrate Mathematical Processes MP.4

This lesson provides an opportunity to address this Mathematical Process standard. It calls for students to model with mathematics. Students apply mathematics to describe a relationship arising in everyday life. They use a given graph or sketch a graph to model a complicated real-world situation, draw conclusions, and reflect on whether the results make sense. The graph helps them to interpret the situation in ways that the information written in the problem does not permit.

FOCUS

Building Background

Connecting to Everyday Life Describe the following situation. Paul went on a 4-hour bike ride. The first hour he rode at an average rate of 8 mph, the second hour at 12 mph, the third hour at 6 mph, and the last hour at 9.5 mph. Discuss why each hour can be represented as a linear function but the entire ride cannot.

Paul's Bike Ride	
Time (hr)	Rate (mph)
0–1	8
1–2	12
2–3	6
3–4	9.5

COHERENCE

Learning Progressions

In this lesson, students describe the functional relationship between two quantities by analyzing graphs. Important understandings for students include the following:

- **Interpret piecewise graphs.**
- **Match graphs to situations.**
- **Sketch a graph for a situation.**

Students explore segmented or piecewise graphs that show changing slopes over time. They also select a graph that corresponds to a given verbal description. Finally, students sketch a generalized graph based on a verbal situation. In this final lesson of the module, students apply their understanding of linear and nonlinear functions to real-life situations that may have changing or non-constant rates of change.

RIGOR

Cluster Connections

This lesson provides an excellent opportunity to connect ideas in the cluster:

Use functions to model relationships between quantities.

Show students the following graph.

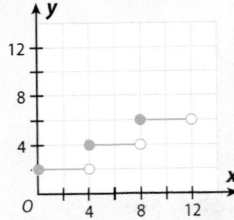

Ask students to describe a situation that could be represented by the steps in the graph. Have them explain their thinking to support their answer.

Sample answer: The graph could represent fixed costs for a given amount of time—for example, a cost of $2 for renting a bike for up to 4 hours, with a jump in price to $4 from 4 hours up to 8 hours, with another jump to $6 from 8 hours up to 10 hours.

Language Support ELL

Language Objective Students will explain how to describe a relationship given a graph and sketch a graph given a description.

Leveled Strategies for English Learners ELL

Emerging
Give students descriptions of a graph to identify if the statement is true or false—for example, "The curve here on this graph is shallow/deep." True/False

Expanding
Have students complete sentences using prompts to indicate possible meanings of a graph when they are familiar with the real-world situation it represents—for example:

This curve slopes downward here and then is flat. This may mean that _____.

Bridging
Have students give a rationale orally to explain why they matched a particular graph with the description of its corresponding situation—for example:

I chose Graph 1 because _____.

 Review the language needed to describe lines that are straight and continuous versus lines that are curved before asking students to identify the type of relationship represented. Use sentence frames and more structured sentence prompts versus narrative descriptions according to students' language proficiency levels.

Park Visitors

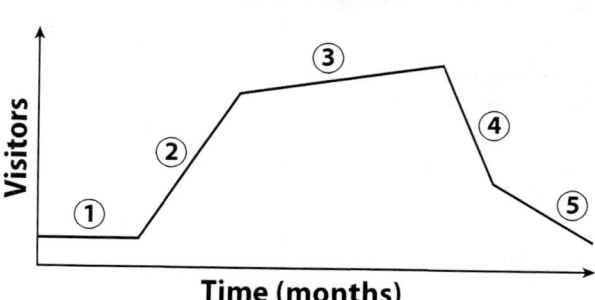

Graph of roller coaster park visitors from Explore Activity 1

Linguistic Support ELL

Academic/Content Vocabulary
This lesson employs language for describing the patterns of lines and curves that represent data in graphs: *decline/rise, shift, upward/downward, increase/decrease, steep/shallow curve*, etc. There are also other terms to indicate what the shape of the line/curve may mean in relationship to the situation described, such as *slant, coincide, trend, constant,* and *progress.* Teach the descriptive language for lines and curves of graphs, emphasizing words for opposites and changes in the line.

Rules and Patterns
When interpreting graphs, keep in mind that the grammatical structures of *may/might, can/could,* and *will/would* are challenging for English learners. For example, the question "How might this affect the number of students?" can be very challenging to answer. Instead, first describe the graph and then use "This means that.." to connect the description of the graph to the real world. This allows the students to focus on the more concrete and visual representation before engaging in the more challenging task of inferring the possible meaning of the graph and describing it with a new language.

Analyzing Graphs

1 Engage

? ESSENTIAL QUESTION

How can you describe a relationship given a graph and sketch a graph given a description? Sample answer: Determine where the function is increasing, decreasing, or constant. Analyze the rate of change to determine if the function is changing quickly or slowly. Describe what these features mean in the context of the problem. Use the same features to sketch a graph.

Motivate the Lesson

Ask: What can the features of a graph tell you about the attendance at a roller coaster park? Begin the Explore Activity to find out.

2 Explore

EXPLORE ACTIVITY 1

Focus on Patterns
Point out to students that the graph shows when park attendance stayed constant, increased, and decreased over time. An analysis of the graph would include possible explanations as to why the attendance was constant, increased, or decreased during each particular time segment.

LESSON
6.4 Analyzing Graphs

8.2.6.4
Students will describe a relationship given a graph and sketch a graph given a description.

? ESSENTIAL QUESTION

How can you describe a relationship given a graph and sketch a graph given a description?

EXPLORE ACTIVITY 1

Interpreting Graphs

A roller coaster park is open from May to October each year. The graph shows the number of park visitors over its season.

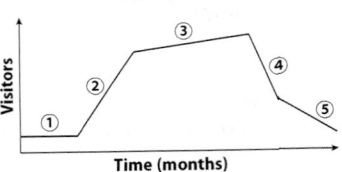

Park Visitors

(graph: y-axis labeled "Visitors", x-axis labeled "Time (months)"; segments labeled ① ② ③ ④ ⑤)

A Segment 1 shows that attendance during the opening weeks of the park's season stayed constant. Describe what Segment 2 shows.

A steep upward slope shows that attendance rises quickly.

B Based on the time frame, give a possible explanation for the change in attendance represented by Segment 2.

The increase might coincide with summer break from school.

C Which segments of the graph show decreasing attendance? Give a possible explanation.

Segments 4 and 5; the decrease might coincide with the end of summer break when school starts again.

Reflect

1. Explain how the slope of each segment of the graph is related to whether attendance increases or decreases.

A positive slope shows that attendance increases.

A negative slope shows that attendance decreases.

DIFFERENTIATE INSTRUCTION *Leveled Questions*

	EXPLORE ACTIVITY 1
(AL) DOK 1 *Recall*	Which segments are constant? Which are increasing? Which are decreasing? Segment 1 is constant; segments 2 and 3 are increasing; segments 4 and 5 are decreasing.
(OL) DOK 2 *Skills/Concepts*	What does it mean when a segment of the graph is horizontal? It means that the number of visitors is not changing with time; neither increasing nor decreasing.
(BL) DOK 3 *Strategic Thinking*	Which segment do you think would most likely have a slope greater than 1? Between 0 and 1? Segment 2; segment 3

LEVELED QUESTIONS: (AL) Approaching Level | (OL) On Level | (BL) Beyond Level

© Houghton Mifflin Harcourt Publishing Company · Image Credits: ©Purestock/Getty Images

EXPLORE ACTIVITY 2

Matching Graphs to Situations

Grace, Jet, and Mike are studying 100 words for a spelling bee.

- Grace started by learning how to spell many words each day, but then learned fewer and fewer words each day.
- Jet learned how to spell the same number of words each day.
- Mike started by learning how to spell only a few words each day, but then learned a greater number of words each day.

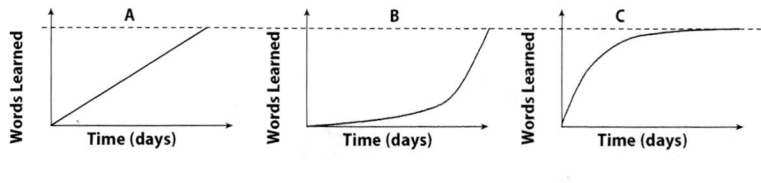

Jet   Mike   Grace

A Describe the progress represented by Graph A.

Graph A shows a constant rate. This means the student learned how to spell the same number of words each day.

B Describe the progress represented by Graph B.

Graph B begins with a shallow curve and gets steeper. This means the student learned a few words at first, and then learned more at the end.

C Describe the progress represented by Graph C.

Graph C begins with a steep curve that gets more shallow. This student learned many words at first, and then learned fewer words at the end.

D Determine which graph represents each student's study progress and write the students' names under the appropriate graphs.

Math Talk
Mathematical Processes

Tell whether each graph is linear or nonlinear and proportional or nonproportional.

(A) linear; proportional
(B) nonlinear; nonproportional
(C) nonlinear; nonproportional

Reflect

2. What would it mean if one of the graphs slanted downward?

A student forgot how to spell words that he or she had already learned.

© Houghton Mifflin Harcourt Publishing Company

EXPLORE ACTIVITY 2

Focus on Modeling

Make sure students understand that a nearly horizontal line on the graph means that few new words are learned each day, while a nearly vertical line means that the number of words learned is increasing rapidly.

EXPLORE ACTIVITY 2

(AL) **DOK 1** *Recall*	Which graph shows a constant rate? Graph A
(OL) **DOK 2** *Skills/Concepts*	What is the difference between a graph that is constant and a graph that shows a constant rate? A graph that is constant is horizontal; a graph that shows a constant rate is linear.
(BL) **DOK 3** *Strategic Thinking*	How are Graphs B and C alike and how are they different? Graphs B and C are both increasing over time. Graph B begins increasing slowly and then finishes by increasing more quickly. Graph C begins increasing quickly and then finishes by increasing more slowly.

TEACHER TO TEACHER

Curriculum Connection (Literature) Have students work in small groups.

1. Choose a familiar fable or folk tale that involves time and at least one other quantity such as distance. Sample answer: Tortoise and the Hare

2. Write the relevant information from the story in a short paragraph.

3. Draw a graph that represents the relationship between the variables in the tale. Check students' graphs.

EXPLORE ACTIVITY 3

Engage with the Whiteboard

 For Parts A and C, have several volunteers sketch graphs that describe the situation. Point out the ways in which the graphs can vary but still be correct.

Digital Teacher Resources

Go online to access all your lesson-level resources.

Differentiated Instruction
- Reteach
- Reading Strategies
- Success for English Learners
- Practice and Problem Solving A/B, C, D

Math on the Spot Videos

⏻ my.hrw.com

EXPLORE ACTIVITY 3

Sketching a Graph for a Situation

Mrs. Sutton provides free math tutoring to her students every day after school. No one comes to tutoring sessions during the first week of school. Over the next two weeks, use of the tutoring service gradually increases.

A Sketch a graph showing the number of students who use the tutoring service over the first three weeks of school.

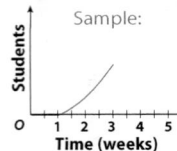

Sample:

B Mrs. Sutton's students are told that they will have a math test at the end of the fifth week of school. How do you think this will affect the number of students who come to tutoring?

Sample answer: More students might come to tutoring before the test. After the test, the number might decrease.

C Considering your answer to **B**, sketch a graph showing the number of students who might use the tutoring service over the first six weeks of school.

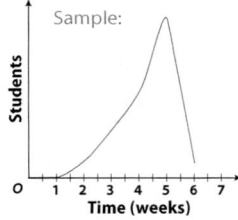

Sample:

Reflect

3. If Mrs. Sutton offers bonus credit to students who come to tutoring, how might this affect the number of students?

Sample answer: More students might come to tutoring.

4. How would your answer to Question 3 affect the graph?

Sample answer: The graph would shift upward because more students would participate. Overall, trends would stay the same.

© Houghton Mifflin Harcourt Publishing Company

Lesson 6.4 **175**

DIFFERENTIATE INSTRUCTION *Leveled Questions*

	EXPLORE ACTIVITY 3
(AL) DOK 1 *Recall*	What should the graph in Part A show for the number of students during the first week? The graph should show that no students attend during the first week.
(OL) DOK 2 *Skills/Concepts*	How might the graph change if the teacher gives a test every week? Sample answer: During the first week it would climb to its highest point immediately before the test, followed by a steep drop after the test. This pattern would repeat for each week around the test time.
(BL) DOK 3 *Strategic Thinking*	Describe what tutoring situation might cause the graph to start high, and then decrease? Sample answer: If Mrs. Sutton offered bonus points during the first week of school for those who come to tutoring sessions.

LEVELED QUESTIONS: (AL) Approaching Level | (OL) On Level | (BL) Beyond Level

In a lab environment, colonies of bacteria follow a predictable pattern of growth. The graph shows this growth over time. (Explore Activity 1)

Bacterial Growth Curve

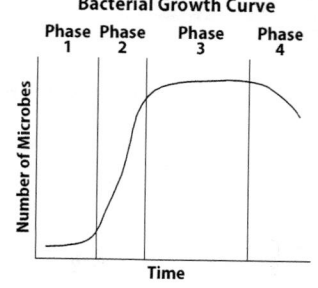

1. What is happening to the population during Phase 2?

   The graph is increasing quickly. This shows a period of rapid growth.

2. What is happening to the population during Phase 4?

   The number of bacteria is decreasing.

The graphs give the speeds of three people who are riding snowmobiles. Tell which graph corresponds to each situation. (Explore Activity 2)

Graph 1	Graph 2	Graph 3
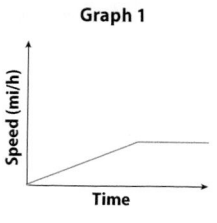	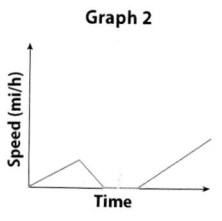	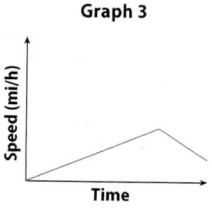

3. Chip begins his ride slowly but then stops to talk with some friends. After a few minutes, he continues his ride, gradually increasing his speed.

   Graph 2

4. Linda steadily increases her speed through most of her ride. Then she slows down as she nears some trees.

   Graph 3

5. Paulo stood at the top of a diving board. He walked to the end of the board, and then dove forward into the water. He plunged down below the surface, then swam straight forward while underwater. Finally, he swam forward and upward to the surface of the water. Draw a graph to represent Paulo's elevation at different distances from the edge of the pool. (Explore Activity 3)

Paulo's elevation

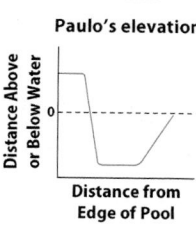

© Houghton Mifflin Harcourt Publishing Company

④ Elaborate

Talk About It

Summarize the Lesson

 Ask: How do the features of a graph help you interpret a real-world situation? The axis labels and units tell you what quantities are being compared. The slope, height, and length of different sections of the graph describe how the quantities are related.

Guided Practice

Avoid Common Errors

- **Exercises 1–2** Suggest that students analyze the graph before answering these exercises. They should note that the phases have different widths, meaning the time involved for each phase is different.

- **Exercises 3–4** There may be confusion interpreting these graphs, as all three graphs begin with a steady increase in speed. Suggest that students examine all three graphs to see what happens after the steady increase before answering these exercises.

Engage with the Whiteboard

For **Exercise 5**, have a volunteer sketch a graph that represents the situation. Have another volunteer sketch a graph that is different but still correct.

DIFFERENTIATE INSTRUCTION *Intervention and Additional Support*

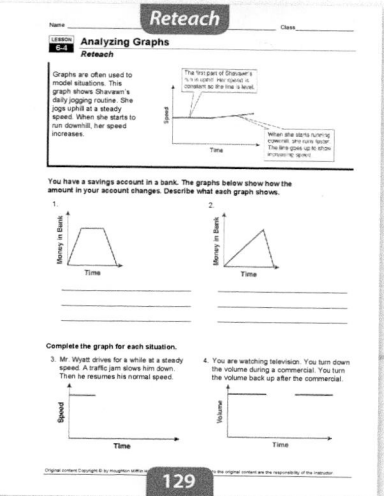

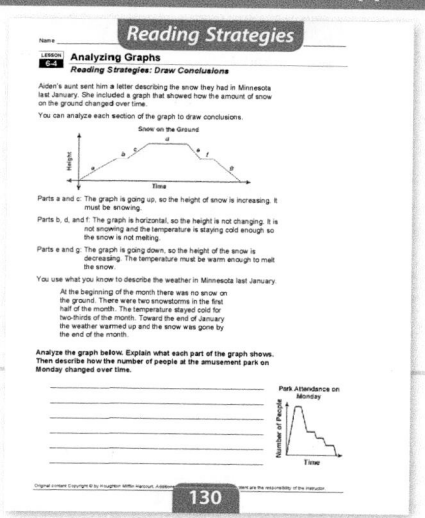

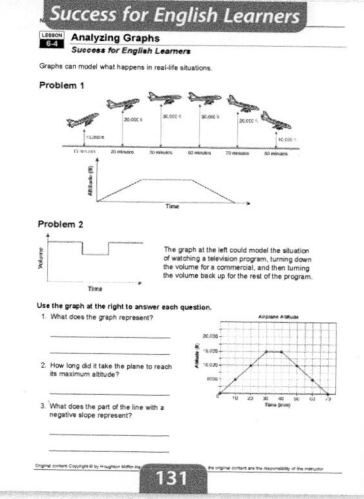

Personal Math Trainer
Daily Intervention
6.4 Homework

Pages shown are from *Differentiated Instruction.*
Also available online.

Analyzing Graphs **176**

Pressed for Time

6.4 Differentiated Homework Assignments

AL **Approaching Level**	6–13	
OL **On Level**	9–15	
BL **Beyond Level**	11–16	

*For **Below Level** students, assign Personal Math Trainer, Daily Intervention 6.4 Homework.*

Mathematical Processes	Exercises
MP.2 Reasoning	10, 12–13
MP.3 Logic	14
MP.4 Modeling	6–8, 11, 15–16
MP.6 Precision	9

Focus on Higher Order Thinking

Depth of Knowledge	Exercises
2 Skills/Concepts	6–13
3 Strategic Thinking **H.O.T.**	14–16

Name_____ Class_____ Date_____

6.4 Independent Practice

Personal Math Trainer
Online Assessment and Intervention
my.hrw.com

Tell which graph corresponds to each situation below.

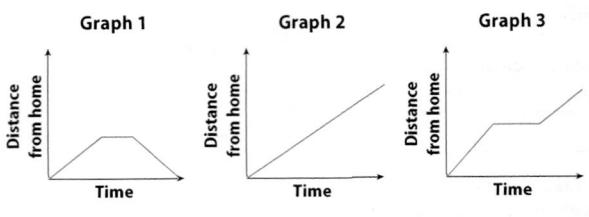

Graph 1   Graph 2   Graph 3

(y-axis: Distance from home; x-axis: Time)

6. Arnold started from home and walked to a friend's house. He stayed with his friend for a while and then walked to another friend's house farther from home.

Graph 3

7. Francisco started from home and walked to the store. After shopping, he walked back home.

Graph 1

8. Celia walks to the library at a steady pace without stopping.

Graph 2

Regina rented a motor scooter. The graph shows how far away she is from the rental site after each half hour of riding.

9. **Represent Real-World Problems** Use the graph to describe Regina's trip. You can start the description like this: "Regina left the rental shop and rode for an hour…"

Regina left the rental shop and rode for an hour. She took a half-hour rest and then started back. She changed her mind and continued for another half hour. She took a half-hour break and then returned to the rental shop.

Distance from Rental Site

(y-axis: Distance (mi), values 4, 8, 12, 16, 20, 24, 28; x-axis: Time (h), values 1–6)

10. **Analyze Relationships** Determine during which half hour Regina covered the greatest distance.

From 0.5 to 1.0 hour.

© Houghton Mifflin Harcourt Publishing Company • Image Credits: ©Adobe Image Library/Getty Images

---

DIFFERENTIATE INSTRUCTION *Leveled Homework/Practice*

Personal Math Trainer
• 6.4 Homework

Pages shown are from *Differentiated Instruction*. **Also available online.**

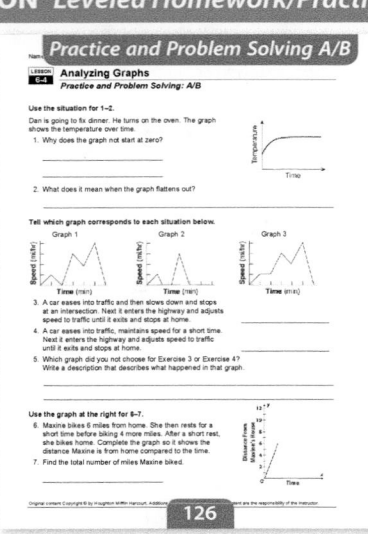

Practice and Problem Solving A/B

126

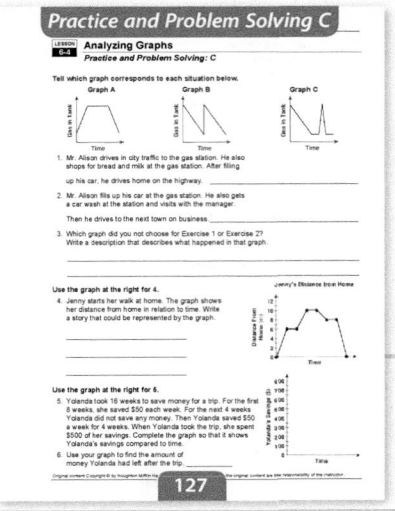

Practice and Problem Solving C

127

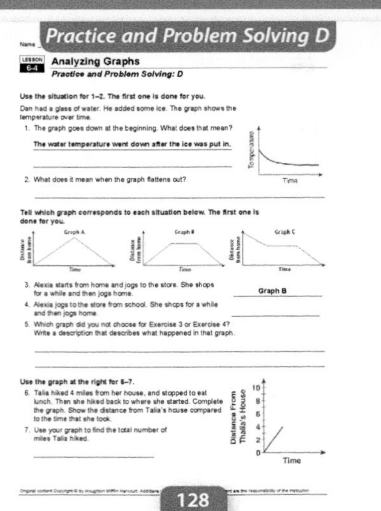

Practice and Problem Solving D

128

The data in the table shows the speed of a ride at an amusement park at different times one afternoon.

Time	3:20	3:21	3:22	3:23	3:24	3:25
Speed (mi/h)	0	14	41	62	8	0

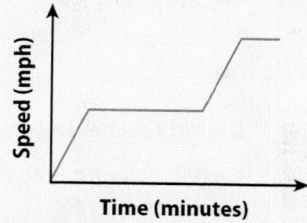

11. Sketch a graph that shows the speed of the ride over time.

12. Between which times is the ride's speed increasing the fastest?
3:21 to 3:22

13. Between which times is the ride's speed decreasing the fastest?
3:23 to 3:24

 H.O.T. FOCUS ON HIGHER ORDER THINKING

A woodland area on an island contains a population of foxes. The graph describes the changes in the population over time.

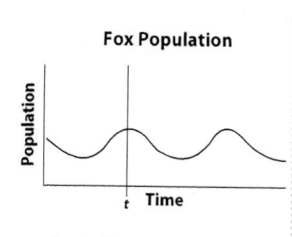
Fox Population

14. **Justify Reasoning** What is happening to the fox population before time *t*? Explain your reasoning.
The population is decreasing at first, but begins to increase again. The graph declines and then begins to rise midway through the time period.

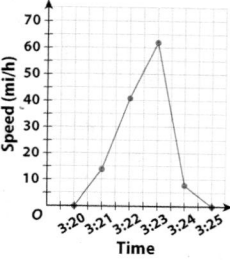

15. **What If?** Suppose at time *t*, a conservation organization moves a large group of foxes to the island. Sketch a graph to show how this action might affect the population on the island after time *t*.

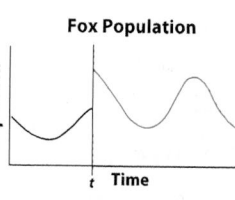
Fox Population

16. **Make a Prediction** At some point after time *t*, a forest fire destroys part of the woodland area on the island. Describe how your graph from problem 15 might change.
The graph would show a steep decline at the point that represents the fire. Then as the forest regrows, the gradual increasing and decreasing pattern would resume.

178 Unit 2

Work Area

© Houghton Mifflin Harcourt Publishing Company · Image Credits: ©Eric Isselée/Shutterstock

---

DIFFERENTIATE INSTRUCTION *Extend-the-Math Activity* **PRE-AP**

Analyze Relationships Gabe and Mike are in a 3-mile race. The graph shows the distance of each runner (in miles) as a function of time (in minutes). Describe the progress of the race. Sample answer: Gabe has the early lead in the race, but he stops for about 10 minutes. After 14 minutes, Mike passes Gabe, then wins the race 6 minutes before Gabe finishes.

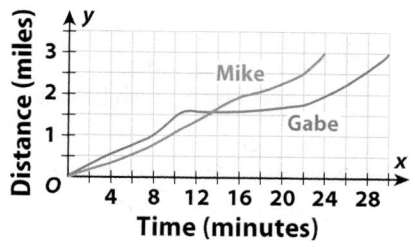

✔ Quick Check

6.4 Lesson Quiz

1. The graph shows the speed of Denise's car during a trip. Describe what the graph shows. Sample answer: The graph shows Denise accelerating to a moderate speed, driving at that speed for a while, then accelerating again to a higher speed and maintaining the higher speed for a while.

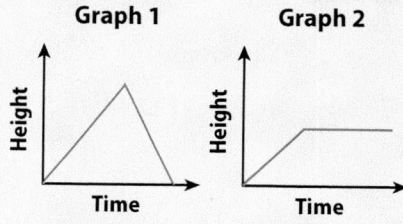

Tell which graph corresponds to each situation below.

Graph 1   Graph 2

2. A woman climbs up a hill and then runs down the hill. Graph 1

3. A child climbs the porch steps and sits on a chair on the porch. Graph 2

4. Sketch a graph that shows the height over time of a man who climbs up a ladder, fixes a roof gutter, and then climbs back down the ladder. Sample answer:

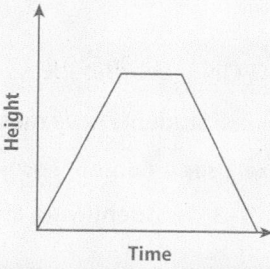

Differentiate Instruction
IF a student misses more than one question, THEN

Differentiate Instruction:
• 6.4 Reteach
• Personal Math Trainer

 Interactive Whiteboard
Interactive Lesson quiz available online

Ready to Go On?

Assess Mastery

Access *Ready to Go On?* assessment online, and receive instant scoring, feedback, and customized intervention or enrichment.

Personal Math Trainer

Online Assessment and Intervention
• Module 6 Posttest

Additional Resources

Digital Teacher Resources

Go online for module-level resources.

Assessment Resources
• Module 6 Quiz: B, p.35
• Module 6 Quiz: D, p.37

🔵 my.hrw.com

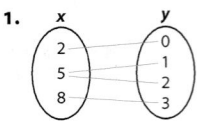

Ready to Go On?

Personal Math Trainer
Online Assessment and Intervention
🔵 my.hrw.com

6.1 Identifying and Representing Functions

Determine whether each relationship is a function.

1.

x	y
2	0
5	1
8	2
	3

_____no_____

2.

Input, x	Output, y
−1	6
3	5
6	5

_____yes_____

3. (2, 5), (7, 2), (−3, 4), (2, 9), (1, 1)

_____no_____

6.2 Describing Functions

Determine whether each situation is linear or nonlinear, and proportional or nonproportional.

4. Joanna is paid $14 per hour.

_____linear; proportional_____

5. Alberto started out bench pressing 50 pounds. He then added 5 pounds every week.

_____linear; nonproportional_____

6.3 Comparing Functions

6. Which function is changing more quickly? Explain.

Function 2; absolute value of Function 2 slope is greater

Function 1

(graph with y-axis marked 4, 8, 12, 16, 20 and x-axis marked 2, 4, 6, 8, 10, showing a line decreasing from (0, 20) to about (6, 0))

Function 2

Input, x	Output, y
2	11
3	6.5
4	2

6.4 Analyzing Graphs

7. Describe a graph that shows Sam running at a constant rate.

a line that starts at (0, 0) with a constant positive slope

? ESSENTIAL QUESTION

8. How can you use functions to solve real-world problems?

You can use a function to find an unknown value, or to predict a value.

© Houghton Mifflin Harcourt Publishing Company

READY TO GO ON? *Diagnostic Assessment*

🔺 **RtI** Response to Intervention

Use to determine if students have mastered the concepts covered in this module.

Lesson	Exercises	Content Focus	Review with *Differentiated Instruction*
6.1	1–3	Identifying and Representing Functions	**6.1** Reteach **6.1** Reading Strategies **6.1** Success for English Learners
6.2	4–5	Describing Functions	**6.2** Reteach **6.2** Reading Strategies **6.2** Success for English Learners
6.3	6	Comparing Functions	**6.3** Reteach **6.3** Reading Strategies **6.3** Success for English Learners
6.4	7	Analyzing Graphs	**6.4** Reteach **6.4** Reading Strategies **6.4** Success for English Learners

Personal Math Trainer
Online Assessment and Intervention
my.hrw.com

Selected Response

1. Which table shows a proportional function?

Ⓐ
x	0	5	10
y	3	15	30

Ⓑ
x	0	5	10
y	10	20	30

Ⓒ
x	0	5	10
y	0	50	100

Ⓓ
x	0	5	10
y	10	5	0

2. What is the slope and y-intercept of the function shown in the table?

x	1	4	7
y	6	12	18

Ⓐ $m = -2; b = -4$

Ⓑ $m = -2; b = 4$

Ⓒ $m = 2; b = 4$

Ⓓ $m = 4; b = 2$

3. The table below shows some input and output values of a function.

Input	4	5	6	7
Output	14	17.5		24.5

What is the missing output value?

Ⓐ 20

Ⓑ 21

Ⓒ 22

Ⓓ 23

4. Tom walked to school at a steady pace, met his sister, and they walked home at a steady pace. Describe this graph.

Ⓐ V-shaped

Ⓑ upside down V-shaped

Ⓒ Straight line sloping up

Ⓓ Straight line sloping down

Mini-Task

5. Linear functions can be used to find the price of a building based on its floor area. Below are two of these functions.

$y = 40x + 15,000$

Floor Area (ft²)	400	700	1,000
Price ($1,000s)	32	56	80

a. Find and compare the slopes.

slope of 1st function is 40;

slope of 2nd function is 80;

slope of 2nd function is greater.

b. Find and compare the y-intercepts.

y-inter of 1st function is 15,000;

y-inter of 2nd function is 0;

y-inter of 1st function is greater.

c. Describe each function as proportional or nonproportional.

1st function is nonproportional;

2nd function is proportional

© Houghton Mifflin Harcourt Publishing Company

Preparing for High Stakes Tests

Assessment Readiness Tip

Students can often eliminate some answer choices of multiple-choice questions using logic.

- **Item 1** Students should realize that in a proportional relationship, when $x = 0$, $y = 0$. Since all four tables show the value of y when $x = 0$, students can quickly eliminate choices A, B, and D. They should then confirm that the correct choice, C, has a constant rate of change.

- **Item 2** Students should recognize that y increases as x increases. Therefore, the slope is positive and they can eliminate choices A and B.

Avoid Common Errors

- **Item 2** Students may have difficulty finding the y-intercept of the function, since the table does not provide the value of y when $x = 0$. Students should find the slope first, and deduce that when x decreases by 1, y decreases by 2.

- **Item 5** Students should recognize that x in the first function represents the floor area. They should write an equation for the table to compare the two functions, making sure that they use x to represent the floor area, not the price.

Items	Grade 8 Lessons	Mathematical Processes
1	6.2	MP.6
2*	5.2	MP.6
3	6.1	MP.2
4	6.4	MP.4
5	6.3	MP.4

* Item integrates mixed review concepts from previous modules or a previous course.

DIFFERENTIATE ASSESSMENT

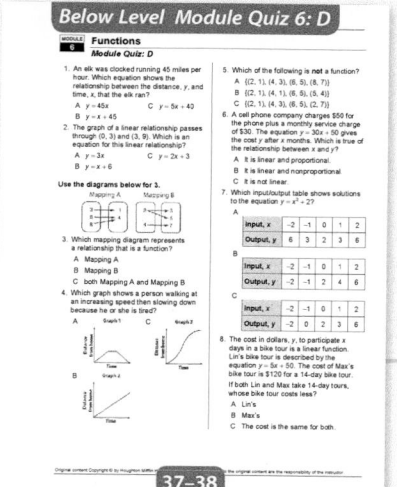

Below Level Module Quiz 6: D
37–38

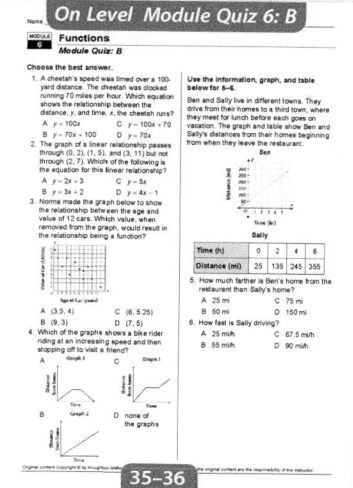

On Level Module Quiz 6: B
35–36

Personal Math Trainer
Module 6 Assessment Readiness

Pages shown are from *Assessment Resources*. **Also available online.**

Proportional and Nonproportional Relationships and Functions

Study Guide Review

Vocabulary Development

Integrating Language Arts

Encourage students to practice using the unit vocabulary as they talk and write about mathematics. Understanding vocabulary will aid their understanding of the concepts.

Proportional Relationships

Key Concepts

- Proportional relationships can be described by an equation of the form $y = kx$, where k is the constant of proportionality. **(Lesson 3.1)**

- A rate of change is the ratio of the amount of change in the output to the amount of change in the input. **(Lesson 3.2)**

- A relationship with a constant rate of change forms a line, and the rate of change is the slope of the line. **(Lesson 3.2)**

- The unit rate and the constant of proportionality are the same as the slope of a linear relationship. **(Lesson 3.3)**

MODULE 3 Proportional Relationships

Key Vocabulary

constant of proportionality *(constante de proporcionalidad)*

proportional relationship *(relación proporcional)*

slope *(pendiente)*

? ESSENTIAL QUESTION

How can you use proportional relationships to solve real-world problems?

EXAMPLE 1

Write an equation that represents the proportional relationship shown in the graph.

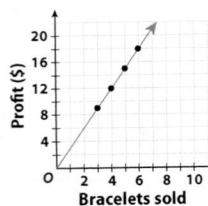

Use the points on the graph to make a table.

Bracelets sold	3	4	5	6
Profit ($)	9	12	15	18

Let x represent the number of bracelets sold.

Let y represent the profit.

The equation is $y = 3x$.

EXAMPLE 2

Find the slope of the line.

$$\text{slope} = \frac{\text{rise}}{\text{run}}$$

$$= \frac{3}{-4}$$

$$= -\frac{3}{4}$$

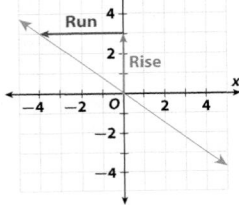

© Houghton Mifflin Harcourt Publishing Company

EXERCISES

1. The table represents a proportional relationship. Write an equation that describes the relationship. Then graph the relationship represented by the data. (Lessons 3.1, 3.3, 3.4)

Time (x)	6	8	10	12
Distance (y)	3	4	5	6

$y = \frac{1}{2}x$

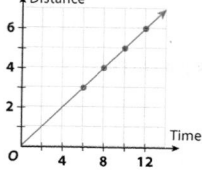

Find the slope and the unit rate represented on each graph. (Lesson 3.2)

2.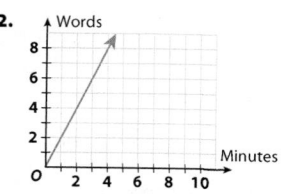

slope = unit rate = 2 words/min

3.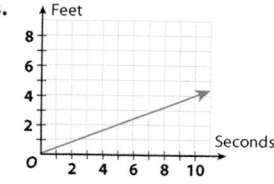

slope = unit rate = 0.4 ft/s

 **Nonproportional Relationships**

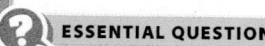

? ESSENTIAL QUESTION

How can you use nonproportional relationships to solve real-world problems?

EXAMPLE 1

Jai is saving to buy his mother a birthday gift. Each week, he saves $5. He started with $25. The equation $y = 5x + 25$ gives the total Jai has saved, y, after x weeks. Draw a graph of the equation. Then describe the relationship.

Use the equation to make a table. Then, graph the ordered pairs from the table, and draw a line through the points.

x (weeks)	0	1	2	3	4
y (savings in dollars)	25	30	35	40	45

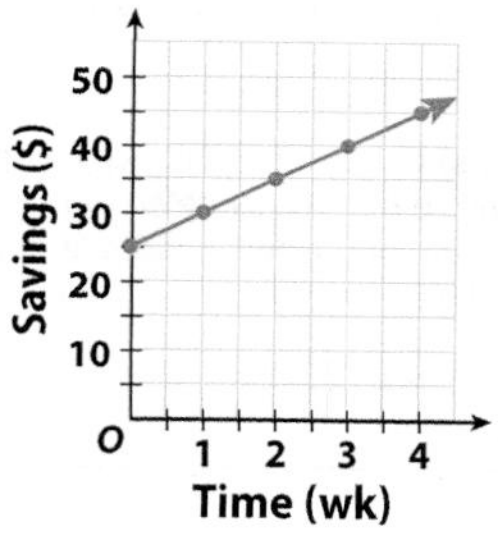

The relationship is linear but nonproportional.

182 Unit 2

© Houghton Mifflin Harcourt Publishing Company

Nonproportional Relationships

Key Concepts

- Linear relationships can be written in the slope-intercept form, $y = mx + b$, where m is the slope and b is the y-intercept. When $b \neq 0$, the relationship between the variables is nonproportional. **(Lessons 4.1, 4.2, 4.3)**

- The y-intercept is the y-coordinate of the point where the graph intersects the y-axis. **(Lesson 4.2)**

- In a linear relationship $y = mx + b$, when $b \neq 0$, the relationship between the variables is nonproportional. **(Lessons 4.1, 4.4)**

Key Vocabulary

linear equation
  (ecuación lineal)
slope-intercept form of an
  equation *(forma de
  pendiente-intersección)*
y-intercept
  (intersección con el eje y)

EXAMPLE 2

Graph $y = -\frac{1}{2}x - 2$.

The slope is $\frac{-1}{2}$, or $-\frac{1}{2}$.

The y-intercept is -2.

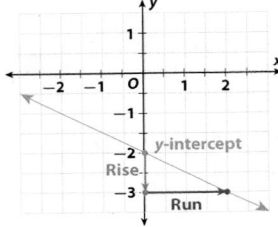

EXERCISES

Complete each table. Explain whether the relationship between x and y is proportional or nonproportional and whether it is linear. (Lesson 4.1)

1. $y = 10x - 4$

x	0	2	4	6
y	−4	16	36	56

nonproportional, linear

2. $y = -\frac{3}{2}x$

x	0	1	2	3
y	0	−1.5	−3	−4.5

proportional, linear

3. Find the slope and y-intercept for the linear relationship shown in the table. Graph the line. Is the relationship proportional or nonproportional? (Lessons 4.2, 4.4)

x	−4	−1	0	1
y	−4	2	4	6

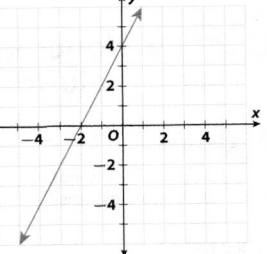

slope ___2___

y-intercept ___4___

The relationship is ___nonproportional___.

4. Tom's Taxis charges a fixed rate of $4 per ride plus $0.50 per mile. Carla's Cabs does not charge a fixed rate but charges $1.00 per mile. (Lesson 4.3)

a. Write an equation that represents the cost of Tom's Taxis. ___$y = 0.5x + 4$___

b. Write an equation that represents the cost of Carla's cabs. ___$y = x$___

c. Steve calculated that for the distance he needs to travel, Tom's Taxis will charge the same amount as Carla's Cabs. Graph both equations. How far is Steve going to travel and how much will he pay?

Steve is going to travel 8 miles and will pay $8.00.

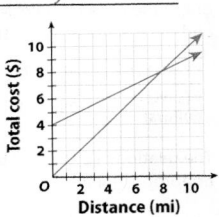

© Houghton Mifflin Harcourt Publishing Company

? ESSENTIAL QUESTION

How can you use linear equations to solve real-world problems?

Key Vocabulary
bivariate data *(datos bivariados)*
nonlinear relationship *(relación no lineal)*

EXAMPLE 1

Jose is renting a backhoe for a construction job. The rental charge for a month is based on the number of days in the month and a set charge per month. In September, which has 30 days, Jose paid $700. In August, which has 31 days, he paid $715. Write an equation in slope-intercept form that represents this situation.

$(x_1, y_1), (x_2, y_2) \rightarrow (30, 700), (31, 715)$	Write the information given as ordered pairs.
$m = \dfrac{y_2 - y_1}{x_2 - x_1} = \dfrac{715 - 700}{31 - 30} = 15$	Find the slope.
$y = mx + b$	Slope-intercept form
$715 = 15(31) + b$	Substitute for y, m, and x to find b.
$250 = b$	Solve for b.
$y = 15x + 250$	Write the equation.

EXAMPLE 2

Determine if the graph shown represents a linear or nonlinear relationship.

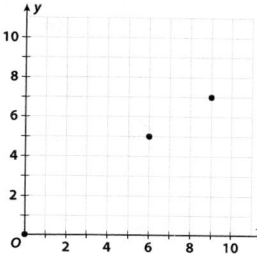

Points	Rate of Change
(0, 0) and (6, 5)	$m = \dfrac{5 - 0}{6 - 0} = \dfrac{5}{6}$
(6, 5) and (9, 7)	$m = \dfrac{7 - 5}{9 - 6} = \dfrac{2}{3}$
(0, 0) and (9, 7)	$m = \dfrac{7 - 0}{9 - 0} = \dfrac{7}{9}$

The rates of change are not constant. The graph represents a nonlinear relationship.

Key Concepts

- The equation of a linear relationship can be written in slope-intercept form if you know the slope and the *y*-intercept. **(Lessons 5.1, 5.2, 5.3)**

- A set of data made up of two paired variables is bivariate data and can have a linear or a nonlinear relationship. **(Lesson 5.3)**

- Bivariate data has a linear relationship if the rate of change is constant. Bivariate data with a nonlinear relationship will not have a constant rate of change. **(Lesson 5.3)**

© Houghton Mifflin Harcourt Publishing Company

EXERCISES

1. Ms. Thompson is grading math tests. She is giving everyone that took the test a 10-point bonus. Each correct answer is worth 5 points. Write an equation in slope-intercept form that represents the scores on the tests. (Lesson 5.1)

   $y = 5x + 10$

The table shows a pay scale based on years of experience. (Lessons 5.1, 5.2)

Experience (years), x	0	2	4	6	8
Hourly pay ($), y	9	14	19	24	29

2. Find the slope for this relationship. $\dfrac{5}{2}$

3. Find the y-intercept. 9

4. Write an equation in slope-intercept form that represents this relationship. $y = \dfrac{5}{2}x + 9$

5. Graph the equation, and use it to predict the hourly pay of someone with 10 years of experience.

   Someone with 10 years of experience will be paid $34 an hour.

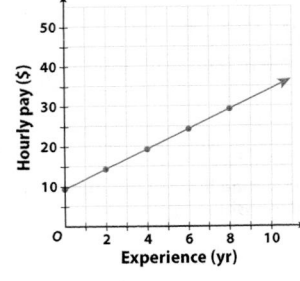

Does each of the following graphs represent a linear relationship? Why or why not? (Lesson 5.3)

6.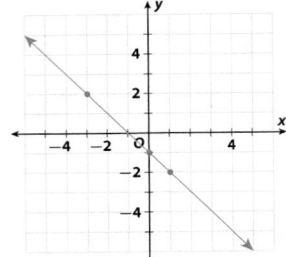

   Yes; the rate of change is -1 between every pair of points.

7.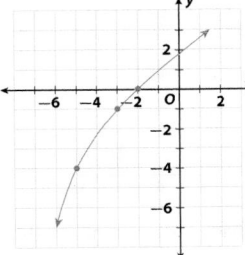

   No; the rates of change are different between different pairs of points.

© Houghton Mifflin Harcourt Publishing Company

Key Vocabulary
function *(función)*
input *(valor de entrada)*
linear function *(función lineal)*
output *(valor de salida)*

ESSENTIAL QUESTION

How can you use functions to solve real-world problems?

EXAMPLE 1

Determine whether each relationship is a function.

A

Input	Output
3	10
4	4
5	2
4	0
6	5

The relationship is not a function, because an input, 4, is paired with 2 different outputs, 4 and 0.

B

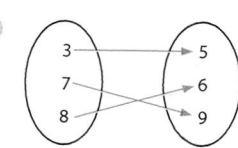

Since each input value is paired with only one output value, the relationship is a function.

EXAMPLE 2

Sally and Louis are on a long-distance bike ride. Sally bikes at a steady rate of 18 miles per hour. The distance y that Sally covers in x hours is given by the equation $y = 18x$. Louis's speed can be found by using the numbers in the table. Who will travel farther in 4 hours and by how much?

Louis's Biking Speed			
Time (h), x	3	5	7
Distance (mi), y	60	100	140

Each distance in the table is 20 times each number of hours. Louis's speed is 20 miles per hour, and his distance covered is represented by $y = 20x$.

Sally's ride:

$y = 18x$

$y = 18(4)$

$y = 72$

Louis's ride:

$y = 20x$

$y = 20(4)$

$y = 80$

Sally will ride 72 miles in 4 hours. Louis will ride 80 miles in 4 hours. Louis will go 8 miles farther.

Key Concepts

- A function is a rule that assigns exactly one output to each input. *(Lesson 6.1)*
- Nonvertical lines are linear functions. All linear equations in the form $y = mx + b$ are linear functions. *(Lesson 6.2)*
- Two functions can be compared by comparing the slopes and *y*-intercepts. *(Lesson 6.3)*
- Understanding the shape of a graph and its slope are important to interpreting the meaning of a graph. *(Lesson 6.4)*

© Houghton Mifflin Harcourt Publishing Company

EXERCISES

Determine whether each relationship is a function. (Lesson 6.1)

1.

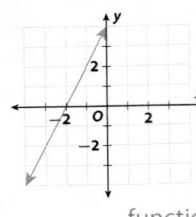

_____function_____

2.

Input	Output
−1	8
0	4
1	8
2	16

_____function_____

Tell whether the function is linear or nonlinear. (Lesson 6.2)

3. $y = 5x + \frac{1}{2}$ _____linear_____

4. $y = x^2 + 3$ _____nonlinear_____

5. Elaine has a choice of two health club memberships. The first membership option is to pay $500 now and then pay $150 per month. The second option is shown in the table. Elaine plans to go to the club for 12 months. Which option is cheaper? Explain. (Lesson 6.3)

Months, x	1	2	3
Total paid ($), y	215	430	645

The first option is cheaper. $500 + 12($150) = $2300, which is less than 12($215) = $2580.

_____

6. Jenny rode her bike around her neighborhood. Use the graph to describe Jenny's bike ride. (Lesson 6.4)

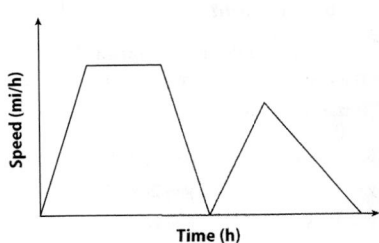

Sample answer: Jenny starts by riding her bike at an increasing speed. Then she rides at a steady rate. She then slows down to a full stop. She starts again riding at an increasing speed until she reaches a maximum speed that was lower than her previous steady rate, then starts slowing down again to a full stop.

© Houghton Mifflin Harcourt Publishing Company

1. **CAREERS IN MATH** | Cost Estimator To make MP3 players, a cost estimator determined it costs a company $1500 per week for overhead and $45 for each MP3 player made.

   a. Define a variable to represent the number of players made. Then write an equation to represent the company's total cost c.

   let p = number of players; $c = 1500 + 45p$

   b. One week, the company spends $5460 making MP3 players. How many players were made that week? Show your work.

   $5460 = 1500 + 45p$, $3960 = 45p$, $p = 88$; the company made 88 players.

   c. If the company sells MP3 players for $120, how much profit would it make if it sold 80 players in one week? Explain how you found your answer.

   $4500; I subtracted the cost of making 80 players from the total revenue.

2. A train from Portland, Oregon, to Los Angeles, California, travels at an average speed of 60 miles per hour and covers a distance of 963 miles. Susanna is taking the train from Portland to Los Angeles to see her aunt. She needs to arrive at her aunt's house by 8 p.m. It takes 30 minutes to get from the train station to her aunt's house.

   a. By what time does the train need to leave Portland for Susanna to arrive by 8 p.m.? Explain how you got your answer. As part of your explanation, write a function that you used in your work.

   3:27 a.m.; Use $d = rt$ with $d = 963$ mi and $r = 60$ mi/h to solve for t, the travel time from Portland to Los Angeles. $t = 963 \div 60 = 16.05$ h, or 16 h, 3 min. Add 30 min to get to her aunt's house: 16 h 33 min. Counting back from 8 p.m. gives a time of 3:27 a.m.

   b. Susanna does not want to leave Portland later than 10 p.m. or earlier than 6 a.m. Does the train in part **a** meet her requirements? If not, give a new departure time that would allow her to still get to her aunt's house on time, and find the arrival time of that train.

   No, the train leaves too early. Susanna needs to take a train that leaves by 10 p.m. A 10 p.m. train would arrive in Los Angeles at 2:03 p.m. the next day, and Susanna would be at her aunt's house at 2:33 p.m.

© Houghton Mifflin Harcourt Publishing Company

Performance Tasks

The Performance Tasks provide students with the opportunity to apply concepts from this unit in real-world problem situations.

CAREERS IN MATH

Cost Estimator

In Performance Task Item 1, students can see how a cost estimator uses mathematics on the job.

Scoring Guides for Performance Tasks

1. **Mathematical Processes**

   MP.3, MP.4

Task	Possible Points (Total: 6)
a	**1 point** for defining a variable, for example, p. **1 point** for writing equation: $c = 1500 + 45p$
b	**1 point** for correct answer and work: $5460 = 1500 + 45p \rightarrow 3960 = 45p \rightarrow p = 88$
c	**2 points** for explanation and **1 point** for correct answer: The cost to make 80 MP3 players in one week is $5100. If they sell the players for $120 each, they will make $9600 that week. Subtracting costs, this gives a profit of $4500.

2. **Mathematical Processes**

   MP.2, MP.3, MP.4, MP.6

Task	Possible Points (Total: 6)

a **1 point** for correctly writing the function $d = 60t$, with t as the time in hours and d as the distance in miles (OR equivalent function).
1 point for correctly calculating the departure time from Portland: 3:27 a.m.
1 point for the explanation, for example: I used the distance function $d = rt$ with $d = 963$ miles and $r = 60$ mi/h to solve for t, the time it takes the train to go from Portland to Los Angeles. $t = 963 \div 60 = 16.05$ hours, or 16 hours, 3 minutes. I added 30 minutes to this time for Susanna to get to her aunt's house, giving a total time of 16 hours 33 minutes. Counting back from 8 p.m. gives a time of 3:27 a.m.

b **1 point** for noting that the departure time in part **a** is not acceptable.
2 points for choosing a departure time that is acceptable and calculating the arrival time, for example: A train leaving at 10 p.m. would get Susanna to Los Angeles at 2:03 p.m. and to her aunt's house by 2:33 p.m.

Assessment Readiness

Avoid Common Errors

- **Item 2** Students may see the repeated *y*-coordinate of 3 in answer choice C, and eliminate it as a possible correct answer. Remind them that functions written as a set of ordered pairs may have repeated *y*-coordinates but not repeated *x*-coordinates.

Items	Grade 8 Lessons	Mathematical Processes
1	3.1	MP.4
2	6.1	MP.2
3*	1.2	MP.7
4	3.2	MP.2
5	4.2	MP.6
6	4.1	MP.2
7*	2.3	MP.2
8	4.1	MP.6
9	4.4	MP.7
10	4.4	MP.7
11	4.2, 5.2	MP.1
12	6.3	MP.4

* Item integrates mixed review concepts from previous modules or a previous course.

Assessment Readiness

Personal Math Trainer
Online Assessment and Intervention
my.hrw.com

Selected Response

1. Rickie earns $7 an hour babysitting. Which table represents this proportional relationship?

   Ⓐ
Hours	4	6	8
Earnings ($)	28	42	56

   Ⓑ
Hours	4	6	8
Earnings ($)	28	35	42

   Ⓒ
Hours	2	3	4
Earnings ($)	7	14	21

   Ⓓ
Hours	2	3	4
Earnings ($)	14	21	42

2. Which of the relationships below is a function?

   Ⓐ (6, 3), (5, 2), (6, 8), (0, 7)
   Ⓑ (8, 2), (1, 7), (−1, 2), (1, 9)
   Ⓒ (4, 3), (3, 0), (−1, 3), (2, 7)
   Ⓓ (7, 1), (0, 0), (6, 2), (0, 4)

3. Which set best describes the numbers used on the scale for a standard thermometer?

   Ⓐ whole numbers
   Ⓑ rational numbers
   Ⓒ real numbers
   Ⓓ integers

4. Which term refers to slope?

   Ⓐ rate of change Ⓒ *y*-intercept
   Ⓑ equation   Ⓓ coordinate

5. The graph of which equation is shown below?

   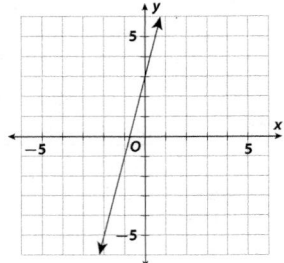

   Ⓐ $y = 4x + 3$
   Ⓑ $y = -4x - 0.75$
   Ⓒ $y = -4x + 3$
   Ⓓ $y = 4x - 0.75$

6. Which equation represents a nonproportional relationship?

   Ⓐ $y = 5x$
   Ⓑ $y = -5x$
   Ⓒ $y = 5x + 3$
   Ⓓ $y = -\frac{1}{5}x$

7. Which number is 7.0362×10^{-4} written in standard notation?

   Ⓐ 0.000070362
   Ⓑ 0.00070362
   Ⓒ 7.0362
   Ⓓ 7036.2

© Houghton Mifflin Harcourt Publishing Company

DIFFERENTIATE ASSESSMENT

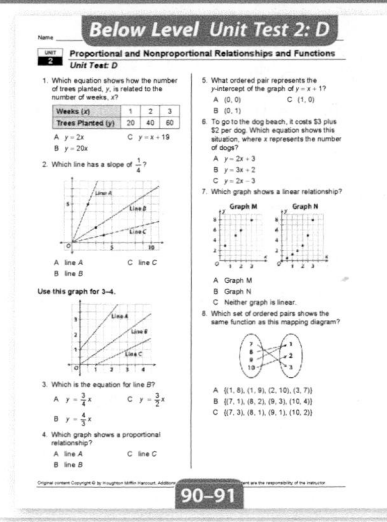
Below Level Unit Test 2: D
90–91

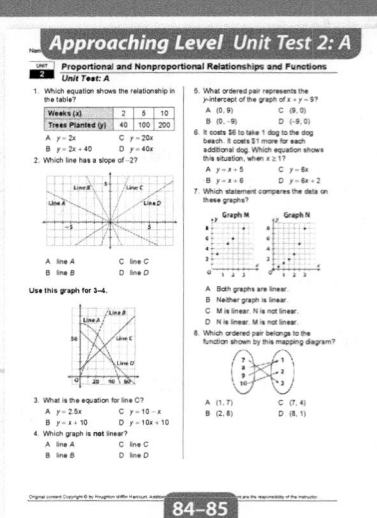
Approaching Level Unit Test 2: A
84–85

8. Which term does not correctly describe the relationship shown in the table?

x	0	2	4
y	0	70	140

Ⓐ function

Ⓑ linear

Ⓒ proportional

Ⓓ nonproportional

9. As part of a science experiment, Greta measured the amount of water flowing from Container A to Container B. Container B had half a gallon of water in it to start the experiment. Greta found that the water was flowing at a rate of two gallons per hour. Which equation represents the amount of water in Container B?

Ⓐ $y = 2x$

Ⓑ $y = 0.5x$

Ⓒ $y = 2x + 0.5$

Ⓓ $y = 0.5x + 2$

10. Carl and Jeannine both work at appliance stores. Carl earns a weekly salary of $600 plus $40 for each appliance he sells. The equation $p = 50n + 550$ represents the amount of money Jeannine earns in a week, p ($), as a function of the number of appliances she sells, n. Which of the following statements is true?

Ⓐ Carl has a greater salary and a greater rate per appliance sold.

Ⓑ Jeannine has a greater salary and a greater rate per appliance sold.

Ⓒ Carl will earn more than Jeannine if they each sell 10 appliances in a given week.

Ⓓ Both Carl and Jeannine earn the same amount if they each sell 5 appliances in a given week.

190 Unit 2

Mini-Task

11. The table below represents a linear relationship.

x	2	3	4	5
y	14	17	20	23

a. Find the slope for this relationship.

$$\frac{3}{1}$$

b. Find the y-intercept. Explain how you found it.

8; possible answer: I graphed the relationship and found the point where the graph crossed the y-axis.

c. Write an equation in slope-intercept form that represents this relationship.

$$y = 3x + 8$$

 Estimate your answer before solving the problem. Use your estimate to check the reasonableness of your answer.

12. Jacy has a choice of cell phone plans. Plan A is to pay $260 for the phone and then pay $70 per month for service. Plan B is to get the phone for free and pay $82 per month for service.

a. Write an equation to represent the total cost, c, of Plan A for m months.

$$c = 260 + 70m$$

b. Write an equation to represent the total cost, c, of Plan B for m months.

$$c = 82m$$

c. If Jacy plans to keep the phone for 24 months, which plan is cheaper? Explain.

Plan A is cheaper. Plan A will cost $1,940 for 24 months and Plan B will cost $1,968 for 24 months.

© Houghton Mifflin Harcourt Publishing Company

Avoid Common Errors

- **Item 9** Some students will realize that 2 and 0.5 must appear in the correct equation but may have a hard time deciding which value should be the coefficient of x. Remind them that the coefficient of x is the slope, which is the rate of change.

Assessment Readiness Tip

Students can highlight or underline key terms, important information, or equations in a word problem.

- **Item 10** With longer word problems, sometimes students can lose track of the information they really need. By highlighting or underlining that information, they can keep better track. If the students highlight Carl's sentence and Jeannine's equation, they can better compare the situations by isolating what they need.

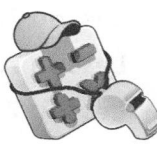

Personal Math Trainer

Online Assessment and Intervention

Additional Resources

Digital Teacher Resources

Go online for unit-level resources.

Assessment Resources

- Leveled Unit Tests: A, B, C, D
- Unit Performance Task

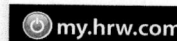 my.hrw.com

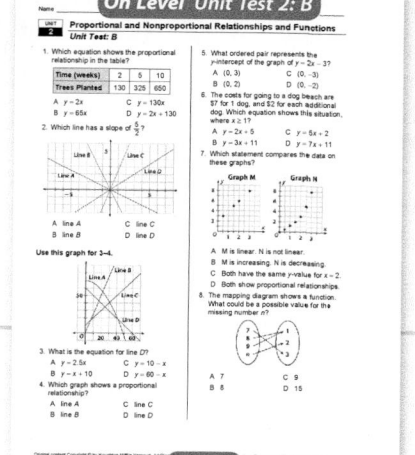

On Level Unit Test 2: B

86–87

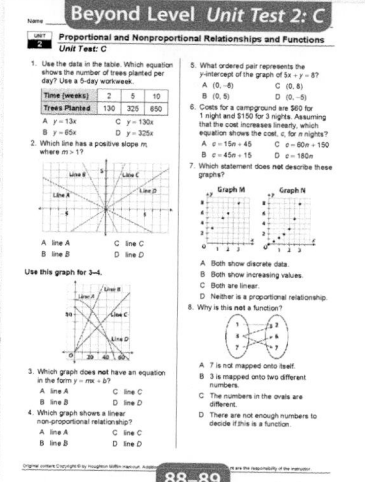

Beyond Level Unit Test 2: C

88–89

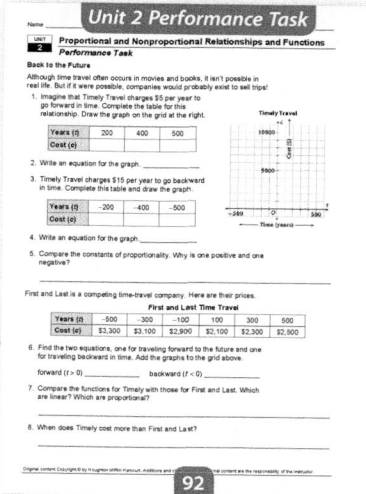

Unit 2 Performance Task

92

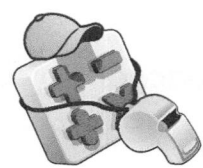

Personal Math Trainer

Unit 2 Assessment Readiness

Pages shown are from *Assessment Resources*. **Also available online.**

Solving Equations and Systems of Equations

Contents

Teacher Notes

PLANNING AND PACING GUIDE
Instructional Path

Lesson	Lesson Objectives	Pacing*
UNIT 3 Solving Equations and Systems of Equations		
Progress Tracker 1 2 **3** 4 5 6		
MODULE 7 Solving Linear Equations		1 day
7.1 Equations with the Variable on Both Sides	Students will represent and solve equations with the variable on both sides.	2 days
7.2 Equations with Rational Numbers	Students will solve equations with rational number coefficients and constants.	2 days
7.3 Equations with the Distributive Property	Students will use the Distributive Property to solve equations.	1 days
7.4 Equations with Many Solutions or No Solution	Students will give examples of equations with a given number of solutions.	2 days
Activity 7.4 Mathy Plants	Students will solve multistep equations and use the value of the variables to decode the answer to a riddle.	
Ready to Go On? **Module 7 Assessment Readiness**		1 day
MODULE 8 Solving Systems of Linear Equations		1 day
8.1 Solving Systems of Linear Equations by Graphing	Students will solve a system of equations by graphing.	1 day
8.2 Solving Systems by Substitution	Students will use substitution to solve a system of linear equations.	2 days
8.3 Solving Systems by Elimination	Students will solve a system of linear equations by adding or subtracting.	3 days
8.4 Solving Systems by Elimination with Multiplication	Students will solve a system of linear equations by multiplying.	3 days
8.5 Solving Special Systems	Students will solve systems with no solution or infinitely many solutions.	2 days
Ready to Go On? **Module 8 Assessment Readiness**		1 day
Study Guide Review **Unit 3 Assessment Readiness**		2 days

* Based on a 45-minute class period.

Teaching for Depth

Writing and Solving Equations with the Variable on Both Sides

When solving equations with the variable on both sides, students should remember that the goal is to isolate the terms containing variables on one side of the equation and the constants on the other side. Variable terms may be grouped on either side of the equation. Consider the two methods shown below for solving $2x + 8 = 3x - 1$.

Method 1

$$
\begin{array}{rcl}
2x + 8 &=& 3x - 7 \\
-3x && -3x \\
\hline
-x + 8 &=& -7 \\
-8 && -8 \\
\hline
-x &=& -15 \\
\dfrac{-x}{-1} &=& \dfrac{-15}{-1} \\
x &=& 15
\end{array}
$$

Method 2

$$
\begin{array}{rcl}
2x + 8 &=& 3x - 7 \\
-2x && -2x \\
\hline
8 &=& x - 7 \\
+7 && +7 \\
\hline
15 &=& x
\end{array}
$$

Both methods are equally valid, but in this case, one requires fewer steps and simpler calculations than the other.

Error Alert Encourage students to check their solutions in the *original* equation. This is important because a mistake might have been made in the solution process, and one of the "transformed" equations may no longer be equivalent to the original equation.

The Distributive Property

The Distributive Property only holds true for multiplication over addition or subtraction:

1. **Multiplication over addition:** $a(b + c) = ab + bc$
   Example: $3(b + 5) = 3b + 15$

2. **Multiplication over subtraction:** $a(b - c) = ab - bc$
   Example: $3(b - 5) = 3b - 15$

3. **Division over addition:** $\dfrac{b + c}{a} = \dfrac{b}{a} + \dfrac{c}{a}$
   Example: $\dfrac{b + 6}{2} = \dfrac{b}{2} + 3$

4. **Division over subtraction:** $\dfrac{b - c}{a} = \dfrac{b}{a} - \dfrac{c}{a}$
   Example: $\dfrac{b - 6}{2} = \dfrac{b}{2} - 3$

Equations with Many Solutions or No Solution

A one-variable linear equation may have **no solution**, **one solution**, or **infinitely many solutions**.

The equation $x + 4 = x + 2$ has no solution because it is false for every real number. The equation $x + 3 = 3 + x$ has infinitely many solutions because it is true for every real number.

Using set notation, no solution is called the *empty set* and written as $\{\}$ or $\varnothing$.

> *The careful development of algebraic reasoning creates a deep and solid foundation of algebra readiness skills that prepares students for success in higher mathematics courses.*

MARTHA SANDOVAL-MARTINEZ
on Promoting Algebra Readiness

Solving Systems by Graphing

Solving a system of equations by graphing has a limitation that algebraic methods do not. These solutions can only be an approximation. You must verify by substitution that it is a solution in order to be sure.

Only an algebraic method of solving systems, such as substitution or elimination (which students will learn later), can determine the exact solution.

Solving Systems by Algebraic Methods

A system of two linear equations can have 0, 1, or infinitely many solutions.

Consistent independent system: Most of the systems that students solve in this course have one unique solution because the lines intersect at one point.

Inconsistent system: Sometimes the two lines in a system are **parallel**, so they never intersect. In this case, the system has **0 solutions**. Algebraically, the result will be a **false statement**, such as $3 = -2$.

Consistent dependent system: Sometimes the two lines in a system are the **same line** represented with two different equations. In this case, the system has **infinitely many solutions**. Algebraically, the result will be a **true statement**, such as $4 = 4$.

Professional Development Videos

Module 7: Solving Linear Equations

Matrices and Row Operations

A system of equations can be solved using matrices and row operations. Possible row operations are:

> 1. Any two rows can be interchanged.
>
> 2. Multiply a row by a nonzero constant.
>
> 3. Any row can be replaced with the sum of that row and another.

Solve $\begin{cases} 2x + y = 1 \\ 3x - 5y = 8 \end{cases}$.

Represent the system with an augmented matrix.

$$\begin{cases} 2x + y = 1 \\ 3x - 5y = 8 \end{cases} \rightarrow \left[\begin{array}{cc:c} 2 & 1 & 1 \\ 3 & -5 & 8 \end{array}\right]$$

Multiply row 1 by 5.

$$5 \times \left[\begin{array}{cc:c} 2 & 1 & 1 \\ 3 & -5 & 8 \end{array}\right] \rightarrow \left[\begin{array}{cc:c} 10 & 5 & 5 \\ 3 & -5 & 8 \end{array}\right]$$

Add rows 1 and 2, and replace row 1.

$$\left[\begin{array}{cc:c} 10 & 5 & 5 \\ 3 & -5 & 8 \end{array}\right] \rightarrow \left[\begin{array}{cc:c} 13 & 0 & 13 \\ 3 & -5 & 8 \end{array}\right]$$

Use row 1 to solve for x.

$$13x = 13$$

$$x = 1$$

Substitute 1 for x in an original equation to solve for y.

$$2x + y = 1$$

$$2(1) + y = 1$$

$$y = -1$$

UNIT 3

Solving Equations and Systems of Equations

UNIT 3

Solving Equations and Systems of Equations

MODULE 7
Solving Linear Equations

MODULE 8
Solving Systems of Linear Equations

CAREERS IN MATH

Hydraulic Engineer

Hydraulic engineering is based on the mathematical understanding of how fluids behave, including pressure at different depths and the nature of fluid flow. You will learn more about how hydraulic engineers calculate the pressure of fluids in the Performance Tasks at the end of the unit.

For more information about careers in mathematics as well as various mathematics appreciation topics, visit the American Mathematical Society at www.ams.org.

© Houghton Mifflin Harcourt Publishing Company · Image Credits: © David R. Frazier Photolibrary, Inc./Alamy Images

CAREERS IN MATH

Hydraulic Engineer A hydraulic engineer specializes in the behavior of fluids, mainly water. A hydraulic engineer applies the mathematics of fluid dynamics to the collection, transport, measurement, and regulation of water and other fluids.

If you are interested in a career in hydraulic engineering, you should study the following mathematical subjects:
- Algebra
- Geometry
- Trigonometry
- Probability and Statistics
- Calculus

Research other careers that require the understanding of the mathematics of fluid dynamics.

Unit 3 Performance Task

At the end of the unit, check out how **hydraulic engineers** use math.

Unit 3 **191**

Vocabulary Preview

Use the puzzle to preview key vocabulary from this unit. Unscramble the circled letters to answer the riddle at the bottom of the page.

1. **FIACALRONT INFEOCIECTF**

   F R A C T I O N A L
   C O E F F I C I E N T

2. **LCMADEI CINETFOEFIC**

   D E C I M A L
   C O E F F I C I E N T

3. **UQAOTENI**

   E Q U A T I O N

4. **ROPWE**

   P O W E R

5. **TNUSITBUOSIT DOHMTE**

   S U B S T I T U T I O N
   M E T H O D

1. A number that is multiplied by the variable in an algebraic expression, where the number is a fraction. (Lesson 7.2) *fractional coefficient*

2. A number that is multiplied by the variable in an algebraic expression, where the number is a decimal. (Lesson 7.2) *decimal coefficient*

3. A mathematical statement that two expressions are equal. (Lesson 7.1) *equation*

4. A number that is formed by repeated multiplication of the same factor. Multiply by this to remove decimals from an unsolved equation. (Lesson 7.2) *power*

5. A process used to solve systems of linear equations by solving an equation for one variable and then substituting the resulting expression for that variable into the other equation. (Lesson 8.2) *substitution method*

Q: What is the best time to divide a half dollar between two people?

A: at a Q U A R T E R   T O   T W O !

© Houghton Mifflin Harcourt Publishing Company

Use the puzzle to give students a preview of important concepts in this unit. Students may work individually, in pairs, or in groups.

Digital Teacher Resources

Go online for unit-level resources.

my.hrw.com

LEARNING PROGRESSIONS AND STANDARDS ACROSS THE GRADES

Before	In this Unit	After
Students understand equations: • write and solve two-step equations	Students will learn about: • solving equations with the variable on both sides and with rational number coefficients and constants • solving systems of equations by graphing, substitution, or elimination	Students will connect: • solving multistep equations with the variable on both sides • solving multistep equations with rational number coefficients and constants • real-world situations and systems of equations.

Module At A Glance

MODULE 7 | Solving Linear Equations

Lessons at A Glance	Lesson 7.1 Equations with the Variable on Both Sides	Lesson 7.2 Equations with Rational Numbers	Lesson 7.3 Equations with the Distributive Property
	Pg. T197A	Pg. T203A	Pg. T209A
Essential Question	How can you represent and solve equations with the variable on both sides?	How can you solve equations with rational number coefficients and constants?	How do you use the Distributive Property to solve equations?
Objective	Students will represent and solve equations with the variable on both sides.	Students will solve equations with rational number coefficients and constants.	Students will use the Distributive Property to solve equations.
Vocabulary			

Go online for all your module resources my.hrw.com 	7.1 *i*Student Edition 7.1 *i*Teacher Edition 7.1 *e*Student Edition 🐭 Personal Math Trainer 📺 Math on the Spot Videos ✗ Animated Math	7.2 *i*Student Edition 7.2 *i*Teacher Edition 7.2 *e*Student Edition 🐭 Personal Math Trainer 📺 Math on the Spot Videos	7.3 *i*Student Edition 7.3 *i*Teacher Edition 7.3 *e*Student Edition 🐭 Personal Math Trainer 📺 Math on the Spot Videos

Print Resources	**7.1 Student Edition:** Lesson
	Differentiated Instruction
	  7.1 Practice and Problem Solving A/B, C, and D
	  7.1 Reteach
	  7.1 Reading Strategies
	  7.1 Success for English Learners
		7.2 Student Edition: Lesson
		Differentiated Instruction
		  7.2 Practice and Problem Solving A/B, C, and D
		  7.2 Reteach
		  7.2 Reading Strategies
		  7.2 Success for English Learners
			7.3 Student Edition: Lesson
			Differentiated Instruction
			  7.3 Practice and Problem Solving A/B, C, and D
			  7.3 Reteach
			  7.3 Reading Strategies
			  7.3 Success for English Learners

RtI Response to Intervention

Before the Module	During the Lesson	After the Module
Are You Ready	**Guided/Independent Practice**	**Ready to Go On?**
• Prerequisite Skills Activities • Personal Math Trainer	• Reteach • Personal Math Trainer • Practice and Problem Solving D	• Reteach • Personal Math Trainer

Lesson 7.4
Equations with Many Solutions or No Solution

Pg. T215A

How can you give examples of equations with a given number of solutions?

Students will give examples of equations with a given number of solutions.

7.4 *i*Student Edition

7.4 *i*Teacher Edition

7.4 *e*Student Edition

Personal Math Trainer

Math on the Spot Videos

7.4 Student Edition: Lesson

Differentiated Instruction

7.4 Practice and Problem Solving
A/B, C, and D

7.4 Reteach

7.4 Reading Strategies

7.4 Success for English Learners

Teacher Notes

Activity	Math on the Spot Videos	Animated Math
Mathy Plants After Lesson 7.4	One for every Example in every Lesson	During Lesson 7.1

Check It Out!

Solving Linear Equations

Real-World Video Viewing Guide

After students have watched the video, discuss the following:

- How can you use equations to determine which dealership to work for?

- What is commission? a percentage based on the final sales price

Professional Development Video

Author Juli Dixon models successful teaching practices as she explores the concept of equations and inequalities with the variable on both sides in an actual eighth-grade classroom.

Solving Linear Equations

MODULE **7**

? ESSENTIAL QUESTION

How can you use equations with the variable on both sides to solve real-world problems?

You can model real-world problems with equations and use algebraic methods to solve the equations.

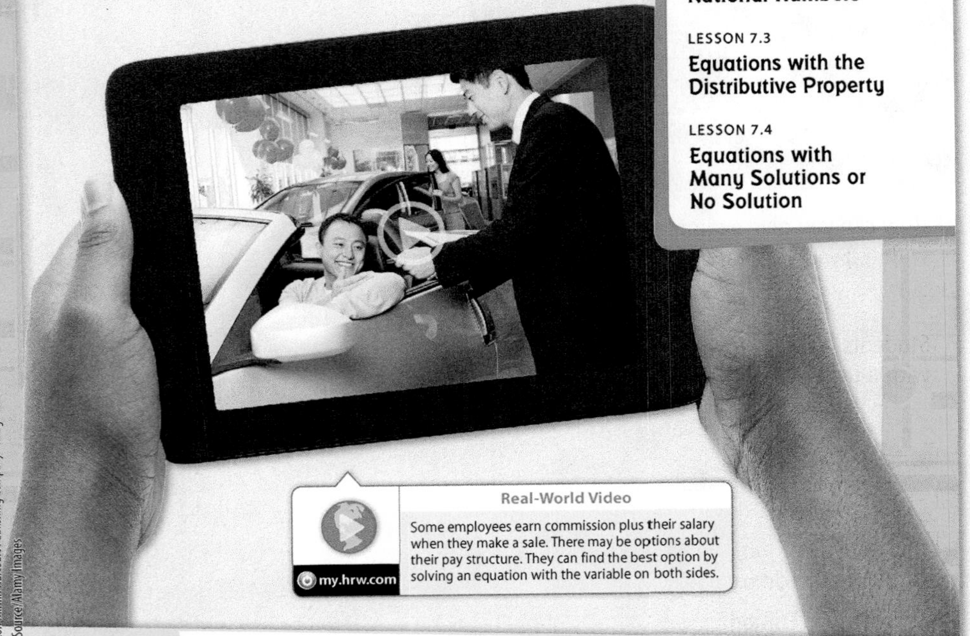

Real-World Video

Some employees earn commission plus their salary when they make a sale. There may be options about their pay structure. They can find the best option by solving an equation with the variable on both sides.

my.hrw.com

GO DIGITAL
my.hrw.com

my.hrw.com
Go digital with your write-in student edition, accessible on any device.

Math On the Spot
Scan with your smart phone to jump directly to the online edition, video tutor, and more.

Animated Math
Interactively explore key concepts to see how math works.

Personal Math Trainer
Get immediate feedback and help as you work through practice sets.

193

TEACHER ONLINE RESOURCES

ONLINE TEACHER EDITION Access a full suite of teaching resources online—plan, present, and manage classes and assignments.

MY SMART PLANNER Easily plan your classes and access all your resources online.

INTERACTIVE WHITEBOARDS Engage students with interactive whiteboard-ready examples and a lesson quiz for each lesson.

PERSONAL MATH TRAINER: Online Assessment and Intervention Assign automatically graded homework, quizzes, tests, and intervention activities. Prepare your students for standardized tests in short-answer and multiple-choice formats.

© Houghton Mifflin Harcourt Publishing Company • Image Credits: © Image Source/Alamy Images

Reading Start-Up

Visualize Vocabulary

Use the ✔ words to complete the bubble map. You may put more than one word in each oval.

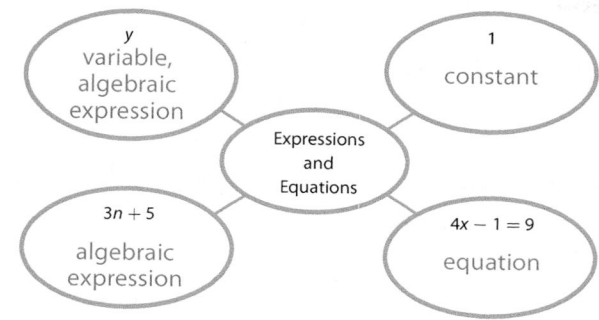

- y — variable, algebraic expression
- 1 — constant
- Expressions and Equations
- $3n + 5$ — algebraic expression
- $4x - 1 = 9$ — equation

© Houghton Mifflin Harcourt Publishing Company

Vocabulary

Review Words
- ✔ algebraic expression *(expresión algebraica)*
- coefficient *(coeficiente)*
- common denominator *(denominador común)*
- ✔ constant *(constante)*
- ✔ equation *(ecuación)*
- integers *(entero)*
- least common multiple *(mínimo común múltiplo)*
- operations *(operaciones)*
- solution *(solución)*
- ✔ variable *(variable)*

Understand Vocabulary

Complete the sentences using the review words.

1. A value of the variable that makes an equation true is a ___solution___.

2. The set of all whole numbers and their opposites are ___integers___.

3. An ___algebraic expression___ is an expression that contains at least one variable.

Active Reading

Layered Book Before beginning the module, create a layered book to help you learn the concepts in this module. At the top of the first flap, write the title of the book, "Solving Linear Equations." Then label each flap with one of the lesson titles in this module. As you study each lesson, write important ideas, such as vocabulary and formulas, under the appropriate flap.

Reading Start-Up

Visualize Vocabulary
The concept web helps students review vocabulary associated with equations and inequalities. Students should write one or more review words in each oval. As a class, add additional ovals to the graphic and brainstorm additional terms and definitions related to the content in this module.

Understand Vocabulary
Use the following explanation to help students review the vocabulary words.

> An expression includes numbers and operations. An **algebraic expression** includes at least one variable. A **variable** represents an unknown number. The word variable means "able to change." A term in an expression that never changes is called a **constant**.

Active Reading

Integrating Language Arts
Students can use these reading and note-taking strategies to help them organize and understand new concepts and vocabulary.

Additional Resources
Differentiated Instruction
- Reading Strategies **ELL**
- Interactive multilingual glossary

LEARNING PROGRESSIONS ACROSS THE GRADES

Before	In this Module	After
Students understand equations: • write and solve two-step equations	Students will learn about: • solving equations with the variable on both sides and with rational number coefficients and constants	Students will solve: • multistep equations with the variable on one or both sides • equations with rational number coefficients and constants

Are You Ready?

Assess Readiness

Access *Are You Ready?* assessment online, and receive instant scoring, feedback, and customized intervention or enrichment.

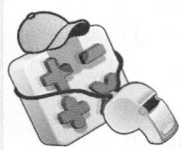

Personal Math Trainer

Online Assessment and Intervention

Additional Resources

Digital Teacher Resources

Go online for module-level resources.

Complete these exercises to review skills you will need for this module.

Personal Math Trainer
Online Assessment and Intervention
my.hrw.com

Find Common Denominators

EXAMPLE Find the LCD of 3, 5, and 10.

3: 3, 6, 9, 12, 15, 18, 21, 24, 27, 30,...   List the multiples of each number.
5: 5, 10, 15, 20, 25, 30, 35,...   Choose the least multiple the lists have in common.
10: 10, 20, 30, 40, 50,...   LCD(3, 5, 10) = 30

Find the LCD.

1. 8, 12 ___24___   2. 9, 12 ___36___   3. 15, 20 ___60___   4. 8, 10 ___40___

Multiply Decimals by Powers of 10

EXAMPLE 3.719×100 Count the zeros in 100: 2 zeros
$3.719 \times 100 = 371.9$ Move the decimal point 2 places to the right.

Find the product.

5. 0.683×100 6. $9.15 \times 1,000$ 7. 0.005×100 8. $1,000 \times 1,000$
___68.3___   ___9,150___   ___0.5___   ___1,000,000___

Connect Words and Equations

EXAMPLE Two times a number decreased by 5 is −6.
Two times x decreased by 5 is −6.   Represent the unknown with a variable.
$2x - 5$ is -6 *Times* means multiplication.
$2x - 5 = -6$ *Decreased by* means subtraction.
   Place the equal sign.

Write an algebraic equation for the sentence.

9. The difference between three times a number and 7 is 14. ___$3x - 7 = 14$___

10. The quotient of five times a number and 7 is no more than 10. ___$\frac{5x}{7} \leq 10$___

11. 14 less than 3 times a number is 5 more than half of the number. ___$3x - 14 = \frac{1}{2}x + 5$___

© Houghton Mifflin Harcourt Publishing Company

ARE YOU READY? *Diagnostic Assessment*

RtI Response to Intervention

Use to determine if students need intervention for the module's prerequisite skills.

Skill	Missed More Than...	Intervene With *Skills Intervention* worksheets (available online)	For Enrichment *Differentiated Instruction* (available in print and online)
Find Common Denominators	1 question	**Skill 23** Find Common Denominators	**Module 7 Challenge** Extend-the-Math Lesson Activities in TE
Multiply Decimals by Powers of 10	1 question	**Skill 41** Multiply Decimals by Powers of 10	**Module 7 Challenge** Extend-the-Math Lesson Activities in TE
Connect Words and Equations	1 question	**Skill 56** Connect Words and Equations	**Module 7 Challenge** Extend-the-Math Lesson Activities in TE

Complete these exercises to review skills you will need for this module.

Find Common Denominators

12. Explain how to find the least common denominator (LCD) of 12 and 18. Find the LCD.

List the multiples of 12: 12, 24, 36, 48, 60, 72, . . .
List the multiples of 18: 18, 36, 54, 72, 90, 108, . . .
Choose the least multiple the lists have in common: the LCD is 36.

Multiply Decimals by Powers of 10

13. How can you find the product $8.14 \times 1,000$ without multiplying? Explain.

1,000 is a power of 10. Count the number of zeros in 1,000. There are three zeros, so move the decimal point in 8.14 three places to the right.
$8.140 \times 1,000 = 8,140$

Connect Words and Equations

14. Write an algebraic equation for the following sentence, explaining each step of your reasoning:
Twelve less than twice a number is nine more than the number.

Use a variable expression to represent each word phrase.
Let n = the number. Then:
  the phrase "twice the number" is represented by $2n$,
  the phrase "twelve less than twice the number" is represented by $2n - 12$,
  and the phrase "nine more than the number" is represented by $n + 9$.
Write an equation representing the situation: $2n - 12 = n + 9$

15. Sarah's age is four more than twice her brother's age. Write two equivalent algebraic equations that can be used to find their ages.

Let b = the brother's age and s = Sarah's age.
Equation 1: $s = 2b + 4$
Equation 2: $b = \frac{s - 4}{2}$

© Houghton Mifflin Harcourt Publishing Company

Find Common Denominators

Exercise 12 Make sure students understand that there is only one least common denominator. Once they find a common multiple, they can stop writing multiples in their lists.

Multiply Decimals by Powers of 10

Exercise 13 Encourage students to solve these types of problems using mental math. They can check their work with technology.

Connect Words and Equations

Exercise 14 Encourage students to analyze the phrases in the sentence separately as they connect the words to algebraic expressions. For example, in the sentence, "is" translates to "=" and the word phrases on either side of "is" translate directly into the two sides of an equation. Have students compare how they translated the sentence.

Exercise 15 Discuss how different algebraic equations can produce equivalent results in the context of a real-world situation. Have students verify that both equations give the same solution.

Use to determine if students are able to apply the module's prerequisite skills.

Skill	Exercise	Depth of Knowledge (D.O.K.)	Mathematical Processes
Find Common Denominators	12	**2** Skills/Concepts	**MP.2** Abstract and Quantitative Reasoning
Multiply Decimals by Powers of 10	13	**2** Skills/Concepts	**MP.2** Abstract and Quantitative Reasoning
Connect Words and Equations	14	**3** Strategic Thinking	**MP.6** Use Precise Mathematical Language
	15	**3** Strategic Thinking	**MP.7** See Structure

Lesson Support

Content Objective Students will learn how to represent and solve equations with the variable on both sides.

Professional Development

Integrate Mathematical Processes MP.4

This lesson provides an opportunity to address this Mathematical Processes standard. It calls for students to apply mathematics to problems arising in everyday life, society, and the workplace. Students use information about two related real-world situations to write and solve an equation with the same variable on both sides of the equation. Students must also describe a real-world situation that could be modeled by a given equation.

FOCUS

Building Background

Eliciting Prior Knowledge Have students create a sequence diagram to organize and identify the steps they would follow to solve a two-step equation, such as $4x - 9 = -33$. Then have them follow the steps in their diagrams to solve the equation. $4x = -24; x = -6; -24 = -24$

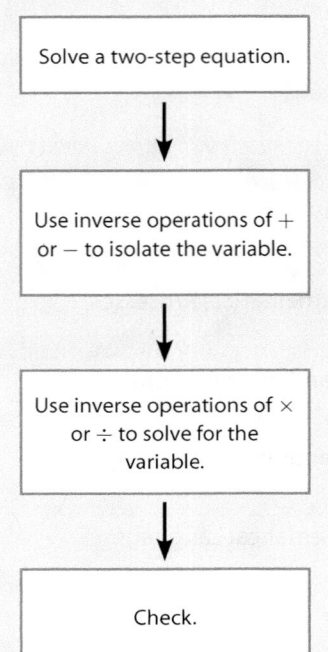

COHERENCE

Learning Progressions

In this lesson, students solve equations with the variable on both sides. The equations have integer coefficients and constants. Important understandings for students include the following:

- **Model and solve an equation with the variable on both sides using algebra tiles.**
- **Solve an equation with the variable on both sides.**
- **Write a real-world situation that could be modeled by a given equation.**

By Grade 8, students have the necessary experience to solve an equation that has a linear expression on each side of the equal sign. In this lesson they solve equations with the variable on both sides that arise from real-life situations. They also write a situation that could correspond to an equation with the variable on both sides.

RIGOR

Cluster Connections

This lesson provides an excellent opportunity to connect ideas in the cluster:

Analyze and solve linear equations and pairs of simultaneous linear equations.

Tell students that a square and an equilateral triangle have the same perimeter. The length of each side of the square, in feet, is $x + 8$. The length of each side of the equilateral triangle, in feet, is $4x$. Ask them to find the length of each side of the square and the triangle and the perimeter of each figure.

square: 12 ft; equilateral triangle: 16 ft; perimeter: 48 ft

Language Support ELL

Language Objective Students will demonstrate how to represent and solve equations with the variable on both sides.

Leveled Strategies for English Learners ELL

Emerging

Give students statements identifying parts of an equation and what they represent and have them state whether the statement is true or false. After they have identified the elements and symbols, make statements based on a familiar real-life example. "The constant plus the variable on the left side of the equation represents the total cost of dog-sitting for a day." True/False

Expanding

Give students sentence frames to help them explain the elements of an equation based on a familiar real-world situation.

The constant plus the variable on the left side of the equation gives you _____.

Bridging

Have students working in small groups match a few equations with their corresponding real-world situations. Then have them use prompts to give a rationale for selecting that situation.

Math Talk The prompt in Example 1's Math Talk refers to tiles and to "both sides." Students need to be aware that "both sides" refers to both sides of the equal sign. Students need to have words to label or name each tile and sentences to describe the step-by-step movement of tiles to find the solution for the variable.

Derrick's Dog Sitting

$12 plus $5 per hour

Darlene's Dog Sitting

$18 plus $3 per hour

Linguistic Support ELL

Academic/Content Vocabulary

This lesson teaches operations with equations in which students need to understand various terms: *variable, constant, left side/right side of the equation, equal sign.* Have a visual representation of an equation with the components labeled. Refer to this labeled equation as a model when naming variables and constants based on real-life situations.

Background Knowledge

In the Independent Practice, an exercise compares two dog-sitting businesses. Students may be unfamiliar with the expression *dog-sitting*. The word *sitting* in the expression means "taking care of" and is used in other expressions, such as *house-sitting* or *plant-sitting*.

Equations with the Variable on Both Sides

1 Engage

ESSENTIAL QUESTION

How can you represent and solve equations with the variable on both sides? Sample answer: You can use algebra tiles to model and solve equations with the variable on both sides. You can also use inverse operations to get the variable terms on one side of the equal sign and the constant terms on the other side, and then divide both sides by the coefficient of the resulting variable term.

Motivate the Lesson

Ask: How can you use zero pairs to help you solve an equation? Begin the Explore Activity to find out.

2 Explore

EXPLORE ACTIVITY

Focus on Reasoning

Have students model subtracting x from both sides of the equation and then adding 1 to both sides of the equation. Then have students start with the original equation again and model adding 1 to both sides of the equation and then subtracting x from both sides of the equation. Have students compare the solutions that are obtained in both ways.

Equations with the Variable on Both Sides

ESSENTIAL QUESTION

How can you represent and solve equations with the variable on both sides?

EXPLORE ACTIVITY

Modeling an Equation with a Variable on Both Sides

Algebra tiles can model equations with a variable on both sides.

KEY
$\boxed{+} = 1$
$\boxed{-} = -1$
$\boxed{+} \; \boxed{-} = 0$
$\boxed{} = x$

Use algebra tiles to model and solve $x + 5 = 3x - 1$.

Model $x + 5$ on the left side of the mat and $3x - 1$ on the right side.
Remember that $3x - 1$ is the same as $3x + \underline{(-1)}$.

Remove one x-tile from both sides. This represents subtracting $\underline{x}$ from both sides of the equation.

Place one +1-tile on both sides. This represents adding $\underline{1}$ to both sides of the equation. Remove zero pairs.

Separate each side into 2 equal groups.
One x-tile is equivalent to $\underline{3}$ +1-tiles.
The solution is $\underline{x} = \underline{3}$.

> **Math Talk**
> Mathematical Processes
> Why is a positive unit tile added to both sides in the third step?
>
> To get the variable tiles alone on one side you need to create a 0 pair by adding a positive unit tile.

Reflect

1. How can you check the solution to $x + 5 = 3x - 1$ using algebra tiles?
   In the original model, replace each x-tile with three +1-tiles. Remove any zero pairs and see if the equation balances.

Lesson 7.1 **197**

DIFFERENTIATE INSTRUCTION *Leveled Questions*

	EXPLORE ACTIVITY
(AL) **DOK 1** *Recall*	After removing zero pairs, what equation does the mat represent? $6 = 2x$
(OL) **DOK 2** *Skills/Concepts*	What property does separating each side into equal groups represent? Division Property of Equality
(BL) **DOK 3** *Strategic Thinking*	Does it matter the order in which you perform your operations? Explain. Yes; you can add 1 to both sides and remove zero pairs before subtracting x from both sides. Dividing both sides into 2 equal groups must be done after all addition and subtraction. Because it is reversing the order of operations, addition/subtraction is done before multiplication/division.

LEVELED QUESTIONS: (AL) Approaching Level | (OL) On Level | (BL) Beyond Level

© Houghton Mifflin Harcourt Publishing Company

Math On the Spot
my.hrw.com

Animated Math
my.hrw.com

Solving an Equation with the Variable on Both Sides

Equations with the variable on both sides can be used to compare costs of real-world situations. To solve these equations, use inverse operations to get the variable terms on one side of the equation.

EXAMPLE 1

Andy's Rental Car charges an initial fee of $20 plus an additional $30 per day to rent a car. Buddy's Rental Car charges an initial fee of $36 plus an additional $28 per day. For what number of days is the total cost charged by the companies the same?

STEP 1 Write an expression representing the total cost of renting a car from Andy's Rental Car.

$$\text{Initial fee} + \text{Cost for } x \text{ days}$$
$$20 + 30x$$

STEP 2 Write an expression representing the total cost of renting a car from Buddy's Rental Car.

$$\text{Initial fee} + \text{Cost for } x \text{ days}$$
$$36 + 28x$$

STEP 3 Write an equation that can be solved to find the number of days for which the total cost charged by the companies would be the same.

$$\text{Total cost at Andy's} = \text{Total cost at Buddy's}$$
$$20 + 30x = 36 + 28x$$

STEP 4 Solve the equation for x.

$$
\begin{array}{rcll}
20 + 30x &=& 36 + 28x & \text{Write the equation.} \\
\underline{-28x} & & \underline{-28x} & \text{Subtract } 28x \text{ from both sides.} \\
20 + 2x &=& 36 & \\
\underline{-20} & & \underline{-20} & \text{Subtract 20 from both sides.} \\
2x &=& 16 & \\
\dfrac{2x}{2} &=& \dfrac{16}{2} & \text{Divide both sides by 2.} \\
x &=& 8 &
\end{array}
$$

The total cost is the same if the rental is for 8 days.

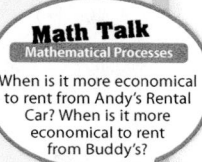

Math Talk
Mathematical Processes

When is it more economical to rent from Andy's Rental Car? When is it more economical to rent from Buddy's?

Math Talk: It's more economical to rent from Andy's if you're renting for less than 8 days. It's more economical to rent from Buddy's if you're renting for more than 8 days.

© Houghton Mifflin Harcourt Publishing Company • Image Credits: ©Roderick Chen/Getty Images

198   Unit 3

---

3 Explain

EXAMPLE 1

ADDITIONAL EXAMPLE 1 Peppy Pets charges a flat fee of $15 plus $3 per hour to keep a dog during the day. Happy Hounds charges a flat fee of $21 plus $1 per hour. For how many hours is the total fee charged by the companies the same?
3 hours

 Interactive Whiteboard
Interactive example available online

Animated Math

Solving Equations with Variables on Both Sides
Students build fluency in solving equations using an interactive game.

my.hrw.com

	EXAMPLE 1
(AL) DOK 1 *Recall*	What does each side of the equation in Step 3 represent? The left side represents the total cost of rental from Andy's; the right side represents the total cost of rental from Buddy's.
(OL) DOK 2 *Skills/Concepts*	How can you determine what the total cost is when it is the same? Because $x = 8$, it is the same rental cost for 8 days, so substitute 8 for x in either side of the equation.
(BL) DOK 3 *Strategic Thinking*	If you graphed Andy's Rental Car costs and Buddy's Rental Car costs as two different linear equations, what information could you get from observing the graph? You could view the initial fees as the y-intercepts, the daily rates as the slopes, and the point of intersection as the number of days for which the costs are the same.

TEACHER TO TEACHER

Technology Using the expressions in Example 1, demonstrate for students how the situation can be represented on a graphing calculator. Have students enter the expression $20 + 30x$ in Y1 and $36 + 28x$ in Y2, and graph the lines on the same screen. The x-value for the point of intersection $(8, 260)$ is the number of days (8) for which the cost of either rental agency is the same. The y-value is the total cost ($260).

Equations with the Variable on Both Sides   **198**

Avoid Common Errors

Students may represent each expression using addition instead of subtraction. Remind them that "leaking" implies decreasing, so subtraction should be used.

EXAMPLE 2

ADDITIONAL EXAMPLE 2 Write a real-world situation that could be modeled by the equation $40x = 100 + 15x$. Sample answer: One house sitter charges $40 a day. Another house sitter charges an initial fee of $100 plus $15 per day. After how many days is the fee charged by the two sitters the same?

 Interactive Whiteboard
Interactive example available online

YOUR TURN   MP.2

Connect to Daily Life

Have students state a real-world situation for this equation that they themselves might encounter, such as the variety of deals for purchasing yearly passes to an amusement park or for cell phone services.

Digital Teacher Resources

Go online to access all your lesson-level resources.

Differentiated Instruction
• Reteach
• Reading Strategies
• Success for English Learners
• Practice and Problem Solving A/B, C, D

Math on the Spot Videos

my.hrw.com

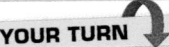 **YOUR TURN**

2. A water tank holds 256 gallons but is leaking at a rate of 3 gallons per week. A second water tank holds 384 gallons but is leaking at a rate of 5 gallons per week. After how many weeks will the amount of water in the two tanks be the same?

64 weeks

 **Personal Math Trainer**
Online Assessment and Intervention
my.hrw.com

Writing a Real-World Situation from an Equation

As shown in Example 1, an equation with the variable on both sides can be used to represent a real-world situation. You can reverse this process by writing a real-world situation for a given equation.

 **Math On the Spot**
my.hrw.com

EXAMPLE 2

Write a real-world situation that could be modeled by the equation $150 + 25x = 55x$.

STEP 1   The left side of the equation consists of a constant plus a variable term. It could represent the total cost for doing a job where there is an initial fee plus an hourly charge.

STEP 2   The right side of the equation consists of a variable term. It could represent the cost for doing the same job based on an hourly charge only.

STEP 3   The equation $150 + 25x = 55x$ could be represented by this situation: A handyman charges $150 plus $25 per hour for house painting. A painter charges $55 per hour. How many hours would a job have to take for the handyman's fee and the painter's fee to be the same?

YOUR TURN

3. Write a real-world situation that could be modeled by the equation $30x = 48 + 22x$.

Sample answer: One tennis club charges $30 per session to play tennis. Another tennis club charges an annual fee of $48 plus $22 per session. After how many sessions is the cost at the two clubs the same?

 **Personal Math Trainer**
Online Assessment and Intervention
my.hrw.com

© Houghton Mifflin Harcourt Publishing Company

Lesson 7.1   **199**

DIFFERENTIATE INSTRUCTION *Leveled Questions*

	EXAMPLE 2
AL DOK 1 *Recall*	What does the variable *x* represent in the real-world situation in Step 3? the number of hours that it takes to paint the house
OL DOK 2 *Skills/Concepts*	Why do you think the situation for the right side of the equation was given as an hourly charge without an initial fee? There is no constant to represent an initial fee added to the variable term.
BL DOK 3 *Strategic Thinking*	What is another situation that could be modeled by the equation? Sample answer: A bicyclist riding a constant 25 mi/hour has traveled 150 miles along a highway when a car traveling a constant 55 mi/hour leaves from the same place that the bicyclist started. How long (in hours) will it take the car to catch up to the bicyclist?

LEVELED QUESTIONS: **AL** Approaching Level | **OL** On Level | **BL** Beyond Level

Use algebra tiles to model and solve each equation. (Explore Activity)

1. $x + 4 = -x - 4$ _____ $x = -4$

2. $2 - 3x = -x - 8$ _____ $x = 5$

3. At Silver Gym, membership is $25 per month, and personal training sessions are $30 each. At Fit Factor, membership is $65 per month, and personal training sessions are $20 each. In one month, how many personal training sessions would Sarah have to buy to make the total cost at the two gyms equal? (Example 1)

   4 personal training sessions

4. Write a real-world situation that could be modeled by the equation $120 + 25x = 45x$. (Example 2)

   Sample answer: A DJ charges a flat fee of $120 plus $25 an hour. A second DJ charges $45 an hour. After how many hours is the charge for the two DJs the same?

5. Write a real-world situation that could be modeled by the equation $100 - 6x = 160 - 10x$. (Example 2)

   Sample answer: Xavier has $100 in his lunch account. He spends $6 for lunch each day. Zack has $160 in his lunch account. He spends $10 each day. After how many days will the boys have the same amount of money in their accounts?

 ESSENTIAL QUESTION CHECK-IN

6. How can you solve an equation with the variable on both sides?

   You can solve the equation by using inverse operations to get the variable terms on one side of the equal sign and the constant terms on the other side, and then dividing both sides by the coefficient of the resulting variable term.

© Houghton Mifflin Harcourt Publishing Company

4 Elaborate

Talk About It

Summarize the Lesson

Ask: What is the method for solving an equation with the same variable on both sides of the equation? Add or subtract the same terms, for example $3x$ or 7, on both sides of the equation to get the variable term on one side of the equation and the constant term on the other side of the equation. Then solve the resulting equation by dividing both sides by the coefficient of the variable.

Engage with the Whiteboard

For **Exercise 3**, write an "x" next to the coefficients of the variable. Circle the constants. Explain that x represents the number of personal training sessions that a person buys in one month. Have a student write an expression for the cost of a gym membership at Silver Gym for one month and x personal training sessions. Then have another student write an expression for the cost of a gym membership at Fit Factor for one month and x personal training sessions.

Avoid Common Errors

- **Exercise 1** Remind students that their model should involve making 0 pairs. An x on one side and a $-x$ on the other is not an example of a 0 pair.

- **Exercise 5** Remind students that the equation shows expressions that involve subtraction, so their situation should involve some decrease from a total amount.

DIFFERENTIATE INSTRUCTION *Intervention and Additional Support*

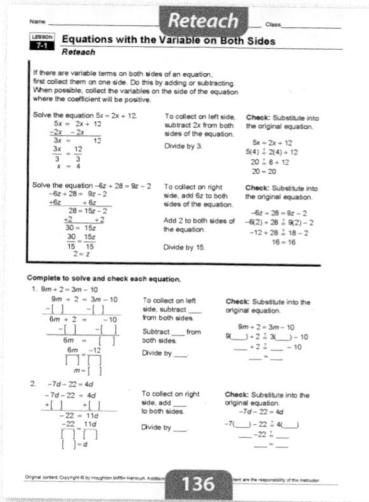

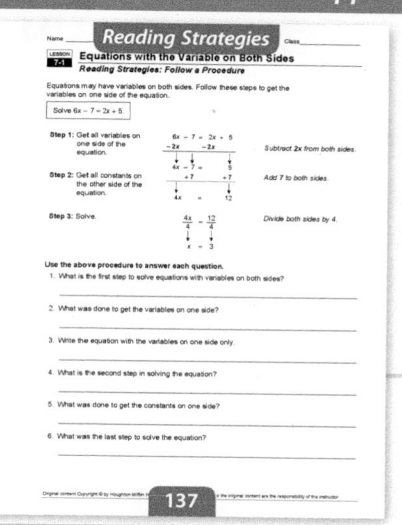

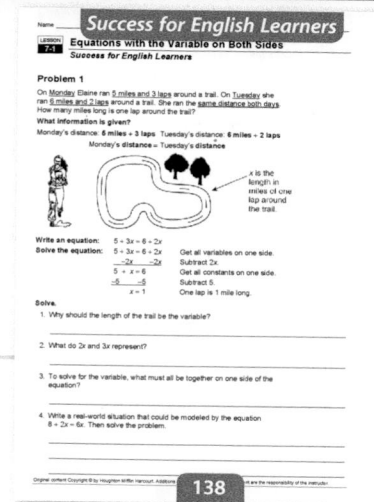

Personal Math Trainer
Daily Intervention
7.1 Homework

Pages shown are from *Differentiated Instruction*. **Also available online.**

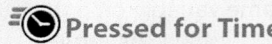

Pressed for Time

7.1 Differentiated Homework Assignments

AL Approaching Level 7–12, 14

OL On Level 8–14

BL Beyond Level 8, 12–15

*For **Below Level** students, assign Personal Math Trainer, Daily Intervention 7.1 Homework.*

Mathematical Processes	Exercises
MP.2 Reasoning	8, 13, 15
MP.3 Logic	14
MP.4 Modeling	7
MP.5 Using Tools	12
MP.6 Precision	9–11

Focus on Higher Order Thinking

Depth of Knowledge	Exercises
2 Skills/Concepts	7–12
3 Strategic Thinking H.O.T.	13–15

Name _____ Class _____ Date _____

7.1 Independent Practice

Personal Math Trainer

Online Assessment and Intervention

my.hrw.com

7. Derrick's Dog Sitting and Darlene's Dog Sitting are competing for new business. The companies ran the ads shown.

> Derrick's Dog Sitting
> $12 plus $5 per hour

> Darlene's Dog Sitting
> $18 plus $3 per hour

a. Write and solve an equation to find the number of hours for which the total cost will be the same for the two services.

$12 + 5x = 18 + 3x$; $x = 3$; 3 hours

b. **Analyze Relationships** Which dog sitting service is more economical to use if you need 5 hours of service? Explain.

Darlene's Dog Sitting; the cost would be $33, as opposed to $37 at Derrick's Dog Sitting.

8. Country Carpets charges $22 per square yard for carpeting, and an additional installation fee of $100. City Carpets charges $25 per square yard for the same carpeting, and an additional installation fee of $70.

a. Write and solve an equation to find the number of square yards of carpeting for which the total cost charged by the two companies will be the same.

$22x + 100 = 25x + 70$; $x = 10$; 10 square yards

b. **Justify Reasoning** Mr. Shu wants to hire one of the two carpet companies to install carpeting in his basement. Is he more likely to hire Country Carpets or City Carpets? Explain your reasoning.

Country Carpets; Mr. Shu's basement is probably larger than 10 square yards, and Country Carpets is cheaper than City Carpets for amounts greater than 10 square yards.

Write an equation to represent each relationship. Then solve the equation.

9. Two less than 3 times a number is the same as the number plus 10.

$3x - 2 = x + 10$; $x = 6$

10. A number increased by 4 is the same as 19 minus 2 times the number.

$x + 4 = 19 - 2x$; $x = 5$

11. Twenty less than 8 times a number is the same as 15 more than the number.

$8x - 20 = x + 15$; $x = 5$

© Houghton Mifflin Harcourt Publishing Company

DIFFERENTIATE INSTRUCTION *Leveled Homework/Practice*

Personal Math Trainer
• 7.1 Homework

Pages shown are from *Differentiated Instruction.*
Also available online.

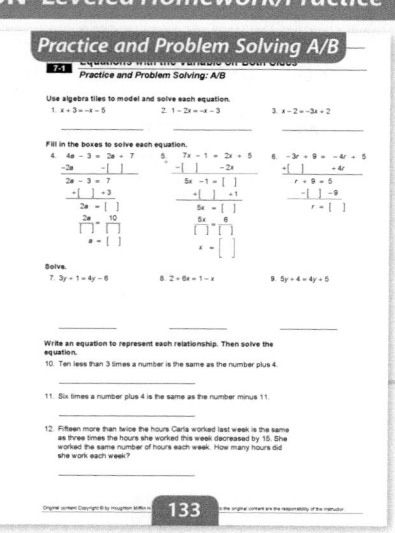

12. The charges for an international call made using the calling card for two phone companies are shown in the table.

Phone Company	Charges
Company A	35¢ plus 3¢ per minute
Company B	45¢ plus 2¢ per minute

a. What is the length of a phone call that would cost the same no matter which company is used?

10 minutes

b. **Analyze Relationships** When is it better to use the card from Company B?

Company B is a better choice whenever you expect

a phone call will take more than 10 minutes.

 **FOCUS ON HIGHER ORDER THINKING**

13. **Draw Conclusions** Liam is setting up folding chairs for a meeting. If he arranges the chairs in 9 rows of the same length, he has 3 chairs left over. If he arranges the chairs in 7 rows of that same length, he has 19 left over. How many chairs does Liam have?

$9x + 3 = 7x + 19$; $x = 8$; 75 chairs

14. **Explain the Error** Rent-A-Tent rents party tents for a flat fee of $365 plus $125 a day. Capital Rentals rents party tents for a flat fee of $250 plus $175 a day. Delia wrote the following equation to find the number of days for which the total cost charged by the two companies would be the same:

$$365x + 125 = 250x + 175$$

Find and explain the error in Delia's work. Then write the correct equation.

Delia multiplied the flat fee, instead of the daily rate, by

the number of days x. The total cost for each company

is the flat fee plus the product of the daily rate and the

number of days; $365 + 125x = 250 + 175x$.

15. **Persevere in Problem Solving** Lilliana is training for a marathon. She runs the same distance every day for a week. On Monday, Wednesday, and Friday, she runs 3 laps on a running trail and then runs 6 more miles. On Tuesday and Sunday, she runs 5 laps on the trail and then runs 2 more miles. On Saturday, she just runs laps. How many laps does Lilliana run on Saturday?

$3x + 6 = 5x + 2$; $x = 2$; 6 laps

Work Area

© Houghton Mifflin Harcourt Publishing Company

 **Quick Check**

7.1 Lesson Quiz

Solve each equation.

1. $3x + 5 = -x - 7$ $x = -3$

2. $3 - 5x = -9 + x$ $x = 2$

3. Joe's Canoes charges an initial fee of $20 plus $4 an hour. Callie's Canoes charges a flat rate of $14 an hour. Find the number of hours for which the total amount that both places charge would be the same. 2 hours

4. Write a real-world situation that could be modeled by the equation $500 + 250x = 300x$. Sample answer: One car dealer sells a car with a $500 down payment and payments of $250 per month. Another car dealer sells the same type of car with no down payment and monthly payments of $300 per month. After how many months will the buyers have paid the same amount?

Differentiate Instruction

IF a student misses more than one question, THEN

Differentiate Instruction:

• 7.1 Reteach

• Personal Math Trainer

 Interactive Whiteboard
Interactive Lesson quiz available online

DIFFERENTIATE INSTRUCTION *Extend-the-Math Activity* **PRE-AP**

Activity The numbers 5, 7, and 9 are an example of three consecutive odd integers. Write and solve an equation for the problem below.

Find three consecutive odd integers whose sum is 121 minus twice the first integer.

Let $x =$ the first number, $x + 2 =$ the second number, and $x + 4 =$ the third number. Then $x + (x + 2) + (x + 4) = 121 - 2x$, or $5x = 115$. Therefore, $x = 23$. The consecutive odd integers are 23, 25, and 27.

Lesson Support

Content Objective Students will learn how to solve equations with rational number coefficients and constants.

Professional Development

Integrate Mathematical Processes MP.6

This lesson provides an opportunity to address this Mathematical Processes standard. It calls for students to communicate precisely. Students write equations involving fractions or decimals to represent real-world situations and solve real-world problems. They also create real-world situations that can be modeled by equations involving fractions or decimals.

FOCUS

Building Background

Eliciting Prior Knowledge Have students explain how they would modify the sequence diagram to explain how to solve an equation with the variable on both sides. They should recognize that they must now include an additional step: collect like terms.

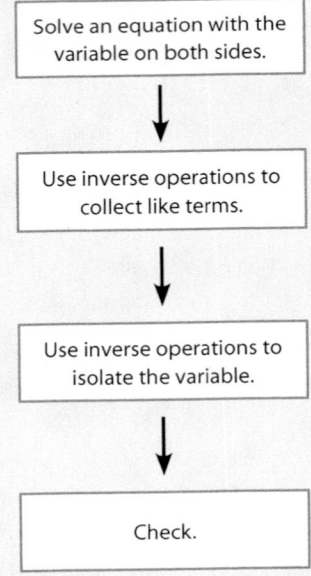

Solve an equation with the variable on both sides.

↓

Use inverse operations to collect like terms.

↓

Use inverse operations to isolate the variable.

↓

Check.

COHERENCE

Cluster Connections

In this lesson, students solve equations with the variable on both sides that have rational coefficients and constants. Important understandings for students include the following:

- **Solve an equation that involves fractions.**
- **Solve an equation that involves decimals.**
- **Write a real-world situation that could be modeled by a given equation with rational numbers.**

Students write equivalent forms to simplify expressions with fraction and decimal coefficients and constants to collect like terms and solve multi-step equations. They continue to relate the equations to real-life situations to reinforce the importance of fluency in solving equations in a variety of forms.

RIGOR

Cluster Connections

This lesson provides an excellent opportunity to connect ideas in the cluster:

Analyze and solve linear equations and pairs of simultaneous linear equations.

Ask students to explain how they would solve the following equation:

$$\frac{6 + 8x}{2} = 5x$$

Discuss solution methods and the reasons for the selected method.

$x = 3$

Language Support ELL

Language Objective Students will explain how to solve equations with rational number coefficients and constants.

Leveled Strategies for English Learners ELL

Emerging
Have students work in mixed language proficiency level groups to brainstorm some real-world applications that they can write about in this lesson.

Expanding
Have students make a list of settings for word problems for this lesson. Encourage them to think of the various activities they participate in during the day, including school, meals, sports, and homework.

Bridging
Have students read over some real-world problems and make a list of characteristics that make a good real-world problem.

Point out that the constant on the right side of the equation in Example 1 is not a fraction. Ask whether they must multiply the constant by the LCM, and provide a sentence frame to complete.

You need to multiply each term by the LCM, 10, because _____.

Linguistic Support ELL

Academic/Content Vocabulary
In this lesson, students are challenged to write real-world problems for a given equation. This is a very challenging task for English learners because it requires linguistic skill and cultural familiarity. Students may be familiar with day-to-day experiences that would fit the equation but may not know the words in English to describe them. Allow students to work together to create these real-world applications.

Background Knowledge
Your Turn problems allow students to try out their understanding after examining a worked-out example. Have students work with a partner on Your Turn exercises, asking them to write out a justification for why they believe their answer is correct. This will let students know that it is not just getting the right answer that matters. It is important that they understand the process.

Image Credits: ©Monkey Business Images/Shutterstock

1 Engage

❓ ESSENTIAL QUESTION

How can you solve equations with rational number coefficients and constants? Sample answer: Start by eliminating the fractions or decimals from the equation by multiplying both sides of the equation by the same factor. Continue by isolating the variable using the same steps that were used for solving equations with integer coefficients and constants.

Motivate the Lesson

Ask: Fractions can appear in the equations that you will be solving. What are some ways to create a new equation with no fractions and the same solution as the original equation? Begin the lesson to find out.

2 Explore

EXPLORE ACTIVITY   EXAMPLE 1

ADDITIONAL EXAMPLE 1 Solve
$\frac{3}{5}x + \frac{1}{4} = \frac{7}{20}x - 4$. $x = -17$

 Interactive Whiteboard
Interactive example available online

LESSON
7.2
Equations with
Rational Numbers

8.3.7.2
Students will solve equations
with rational number
coefficients and constants.

❓ **ESSENTIAL QUESTION**   How can you solve equations with rational number coefficients and constants?

EXPLORE ACTIVITY

Solving an Equation That Involves Fractions

To solve an equation with the variable on both sides that involves fractions, start by eliminating the fractions from the equation.

EXAMPLE 1 Solve $\frac{7}{10}n + \frac{3}{2} = \frac{3}{5}n + 2$.

STEP 1 Determine the least common multiple of the denominators: ____10____

STEP 2 Multiply both sides of the equation by the LCM.

$$10\left(\frac{7}{10}n + \frac{3}{2}\right) = 10\left(\frac{3}{5}n + 2\right)$$

$$\boxed{1}\,10\left(\frac{7}{10_1}n\right) + \boxed{5}\,10\left(\frac{3}{2_1}\right) = \boxed{2}\,10\left(\frac{3}{5_1}n\right) + 10(2)$$

$$\boxed{7}\,n + \boxed{15} = \boxed{6}\,n + \boxed{20}$$

STEP 3 Use inverse operations to solve the equation.

$$7n + 15 = 6n + 20$$

Subtract 15 from both sides.

$$\frac{-\boxed{15} \qquad -\boxed{15}}{\boxed{7n} = 6n + \boxed{5}}$$

Subtract 6n from both sides.

$$\frac{-\boxed{6n} \qquad -\boxed{6n}}{n = \boxed{5}}$$

Reflect

1. What is the advantage of multiplying both sides of the equation by the least common multiple of the denominators in the first step?

   It simplifies the calculations by eliminating all the fractions.

2. **What If?** What happens in the first step if you multiply both sides by a common multiple of the denominators that is not the LCM?

   You would eliminate the fractions, but the result would

   be an equation with greater integer coefficients.

© Houghton Mifflin Harcourt Publishing Company

DIFFERENTIATE INSTRUCTION *Leveled Questions*

	EXPLORE ACTIVITY EXAMPLE 1
(AL) DOK 1 *Recall*	What happens to the fractions in the equation when both sides are multiplied by the LCM in Step 2? An equivalent equation without fractions is produced.
(OL) DOK 2 *Skills/Concepts*	Can you eliminate fractions by multiplying both sides of the equation by a common denominator that is not the LCM? Explain. Yes; for instance, multiplying both sides by 20 results in $14n + 30 = 12n + 40$, which is equivalent.
(BL) DOK 3 *Strategic Thinking*	Write an equivalent equation that has all fraction coefficients with common denominators of 10. How is this like the equivalent equation produced in Step 2 by multiplying both sides by 10? $\frac{7}{10}n + \frac{15}{10} = \frac{6}{10}n + \frac{20}{10}$. The numerators match the whole numbers in Step 2.

LEVELED QUESTIONS: (AL) Approaching Level | (OL) On Level | (BL) Beyond Level

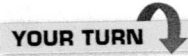

YOUR TURN

Solve.

3. $\frac{1}{7}k - 6 = \frac{3}{7}k + 4$ $\quad k = -35$

4. $\frac{5}{6}y + 1 = -\frac{1}{2}y + \frac{1}{4}$ $\quad y = -\frac{9}{16}$

Personal Math Trainer
Online Assessment and Intervention
my.hrw.com

Math On the Spot
my.hrw.com

Solving an Equation that Involves Decimals

Solving an equation with the variable on both sides that involves decimals is similar to solving an equation with fractions. But instead of first multiplying both sides by the LCM, multiply by a power of 10 to eliminate the decimals.

EXAMPLE 2 (Real World)

Javier walks from his house to the zoo at a constant rate. After walking 0.75 mile, he meets his brother, Raul, and they continue walking at the same constant rate. When they arrive at the zoo, Javier has walked for 0.5 hour and Raul has walked for 0.2 hour. What is the rate in miles per hour at which the brothers walked to the zoo?

STEP 1 Write an equation for the distance from the brothers' house to the zoo, using the fact that distance equals rate times time. Let r = the brothers' walking rate.

$$\underbrace{0.2r + 0.75}_{\text{distance to zoo}} = \underbrace{0.5r}_{\text{distance to zoo}}$$

STEP 2 Multiply both sides of the equation by $10^2 = 100$.

> Multiplying by 100 clears the equation of decimals. Multiplying by 10 does not: $10 \times 0.75 = 7.5$.

$$100(0.2r) + 100(0.75) = 100(0.5r)$$
$$20r + 75 = 50r$$

STEP 3 Use inverse operations to solve the equation.

$$\begin{array}{rl} 20r + 75 = & 50r \qquad \text{Write the equation.} \\ \underline{-20r \qquad -20r} & \qquad \text{Subtract } 20r \text{ from both sides.} \\ 75 = & 30r \\ \dfrac{75}{30} = & \dfrac{30r}{30} \qquad \text{Divide both sides by 30.} \\ 2.5 = & r \end{array}$$

So, the brothers' constant rate of speed was 2.5 miles per hour.

© Houghton Mifflin Harcourt Publishing Company

Avoid Common Errors

Make sure that students understand that when multiplying by the LCM all terms on the left and on the right of the equal sign get multiplied by the LCM, not just the fractions.

3 Explain

EXAMPLE 2

ADDITIONAL EXAMPLE 2 Sasha walks to school at a constant rate. She meets her friend Hannah 0.6 kilometer along the way, and they continue walking at the same constant rate. When they get to school, Sasha has walked for 0.6 hour and Hannah has walked for 0.45 hour. What is the rate in kilometers per hour at which they walked to school? 4 km/h

 Interactive Whiteboard
Interactive example available online

	EXAMPLE 2
(AL) DOK 1 *Recall*	In Step 2, why are both sides of the equation multiplied by 100? to get an equivalent equation without decimal coefficients
(OL) DOK 2 *Skills/Concepts*	Can you eliminate decimals by multiplying both sides of the equation by a power of 10 greater than 100? Explain. Yes; for instance, multiplying both sides by 1000 results in $200r + 750 = 500r$, which is equivalent because the solution is $r = 2.5$.
(BL) DOK 3 *Strategic Thinking*	Explain how you know what power of 10 to use to clear an equation of decimals. The coefficient with the greatest number of decimal places determines the power of 10 that will clear decimals. If the greatest number of decimal places is 2, then multiplying by 10 to a power of 2, or 10^2, will clear decimals.

TEACHER TO TEACHER

Game To practice solving equations with rational numbers, write expressions on cards. Separate the cards into two sets. For example, Set A: $6 - \frac{1}{2}x$ and Set B: -20. Place all the cards face down. The teacher draws a card from each set to form an equation. Have teams race to solve the equations. The team with the most points wins.

Avoid Common Errors

Make sure that students understand that the variable represents the weight of a cubic foot of water. Students may be tempted to add 37.44 to 1.9x. Explain that for the two sides of the equation to be equal, they must subtract 37.44 from 1.9x or add 37.44 to 1.3x.

EXAMPLE 3

ADDITIONAL EXAMPLE 3 Write a real-world situation that can be modeled by the equation $5.25x + 3.25 = 1.75x + 10.25$. Sample answer: One sandbox has 3.25 pounds of sand. You are filling the sandbox with a bucket that holds 5.25 pounds of sand. Another sandbox has 10.25 pounds of sand. Your brother is filling it with a bucket that holds 1.75 pounds of sand. How many buckets of sand will it take to have the same weight of sand in each sandbox?

 Interactive Whiteboard
Interactive example available online

YOUR TURN   MP.3

Talk About It

Check for Understanding

Ask: Given the sample answer for **Exercise 6**, what does x represent in the equation?
x represents the weight of rice in the bin when it is full.

Digital Teacher Resources

Go online to access all your lesson-level resources.

Differentiated Instruction
• Reteach
• Reading Strategies
• Success for English Learners
• Practice and Problem Solving A/B, C, D

Math on the Spot Videos

my.hrw.com

5. Logan has two aquariums. One aquarium contains 1.3 cubic feet of water and the other contains 1.9 cubic feet of water. The water in the larger aquarium weighs 37.44 pounds more than the water in the smaller aquarium. Write an equation with a variable on both sides to represent the situation. Then find the weight of 1 cubic foot of water.

$1.9x = 1.3x + 37.44$; 62.4 lb

 **Personal Math Trainer** Online Assessment and Intervention **my.hrw.com**

Writing a Real-World Situation from an Equation

Real-world situations can often be represented by equations involving fractions and decimals. Fractions and decimals can represent quantities such as weight, volume, capacity, time, and temperature. Decimals can also be used to represent dollars and cents.

 Math On the Spot **my.hrw.com**

EXAMPLE 3

Write a real-world situation that can be modeled by the equation $0.95x = 0.55x + 60$.

The left side of the equation consists of a variable term. It could represent the total cost for x items.

The right side of the equation consists of a variable term plus a constant. It could represent the total cost for x items plus a flat fee.

The equation $0.95x = 0.55x + 60$ could be represented by this situation: Toony Tunes charges $0.95 for each song you download. Up With Downloads charges $0.55 for each song but also charges an annual membership fee of $60. How many songs must a customer download in a year so that the cost will be the same at both websites?

My Notes

YOUR TURN

6. Write a real-world problem that can be modeled by the equation $\frac{1}{3}x + 10 = \frac{3}{5}x$.

Sample answer: A bin of rice at a store is one third full. After 10 additional pounds of rice is added to the bin, the bin is three fifths full. How much rice does the bin hold when it is full?

 **Personal Math Trainer** Online Assessment and Intervention **my.hrw.com**

© Houghton Mifflin Harcourt Publishing Company

DIFFERENTIATE INSTRUCTION *Leveled Questions*

	EXAMPLE 3
(AL) DOK 1 *Recall*	What does the variable x represent in the real-world situation? the number of songs downloaded
(OL) DOK 2 *Skills/Concepts*	What is the difference between what a variable term represents and what a constant term represents? A variable term describes a quantity that changes, such as a rate (distance changes per time); a constant term describes a quantity that is not changing.
(BL) DOK 3 *Strategic Thinking*	Can you think of an equation and corresponding situation that has no solution? Sample answer: $2x + 1 = 2x$ has no solution. One person starts 1 mile away from the park and walks due east at 2 miles per hour. Another person starts at the park and walks due east at 2 miles per hour. After how much time will they meet? (They will never meet.)

LEVELED QUESTIONS: **(AL)** Approaching Level | **(OL)** On Level | **(BL)** Beyond Level

1. Sandy is upgrading her Internet service. Fast Internet charges $60 for installation and $50.45 per month. Quick Internet has free installation but charges $57.95 per month. (Example 2)

   a. Write an equation that can be used to find the number of months at which the Internet service would cost the same.

$$60 + 50.45x = 57.95x$$

   b. Solve the equation.

$$x = 8; \text{ 8 months}$$

Solve. (Explore Activity Example 1 and Example 2)

2. $\frac{3}{4}n - 18 = \frac{1}{4}n - 4$

$$n = 28$$

3. $6 + \frac{4}{5}b = \frac{9}{10}b$

$$b = 60$$

4. $\frac{2}{11}m + 16 = 4 + \frac{6}{11}m$

$$m = 33$$

5. $2.25t + 5 = 13.5t + 14$

$$t = -0.8$$

6. $3.6w = 1.6w + 24$

$$w = 12$$

7. $-0.75p - 2 = 0.25p$

$$p = -2$$

8. Write a real-world problem that can be modeled by the equation $1.25x = 0.75x + 50$. (Example 3)

Sample answer: A store charges $1.25 per bathroom tile and lets you use their installation tools for free. Another store charges $0.75 per tile but charges you $50 to use their tools. How many tiles would you need to buy for the total cost to be the same?

 ESSENTIAL QUESTION CHECK-IN

9. How does the method for solving equations with fractional or decimal coefficients and constants compare with the method for solving equations with integer coefficients and constants?

The methods are essentially the same. The only extra step is that you begin solving by eliminating the fractions or the decimals from the equation.

© Houghton Mifflin Harcourt Publishing Company

4 Elaborate

Talk About It

Summarize the Lesson

Ask: How do you determine what to multiply an equation by so that you eliminate fractions or decimals from the equation? If the equation has fractions in it, multiply both sides of the equation by the LCM (or any common multiple) of the denominators. If the equation has decimals in it, multiply both sides of the equation by the appropriate power of 10 to eliminate the decimals.

Guided Practice

Engage with the Whiteboard

For **Exercise 1**, have a student write an expression for how much Fast Internet charges. Have another student write an expression for Quick Internet. In **Exercises 2–4**, have students write the LCM for the fractions in each equation.

Avoid Common Errors

Exercises 2–7 Remind students that the solution of an equation can be a decimal or a fraction, even though they eliminated fractions or decimals from the original equation.

DIFFERENTIATE INSTRUCTION *Intervention and Additional Support*

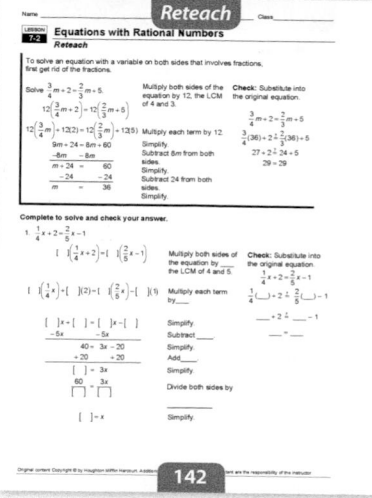

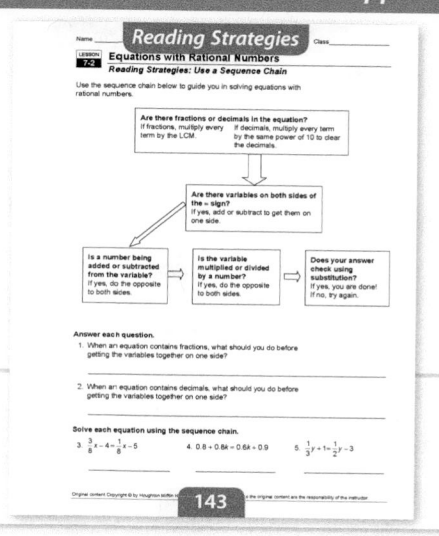

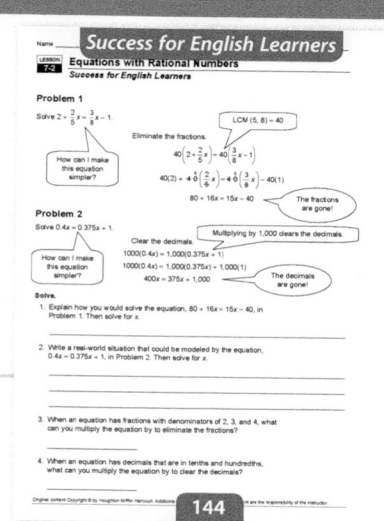

Personal Math Trainer
Daily Intervention
7.2 Homework

Pages shown are from *Differentiated Instruction*. **Also available online.**

5 Evaluate

Independent Practice

⏱ Pressed for Time

7.2 Differentiated Homework Assignments

(AL) Approaching Level 10–13, 16, 18

(OL) On Level 12–14, 17–19

(BL) Beyond Level 15, 17, 19–21

*For **Below Level** students, assign Personal Math Trainer, Daily Intervention 7.2 Homework.*

Mathematical Processes	Exercises
MP.2 Reasoning	21
MP.3 Logic	18
MP.4 Modeling	14–17
MP.5 Using Tools	10–13, 19
MP.8 Patterns	20

Focus on Higher Order Thinking

Depth of Knowledge	Exercises
2 Skills/Concepts	10–18
3 Strategic Thinking **H.O.T.**	19–21

7.2 Independent Practice

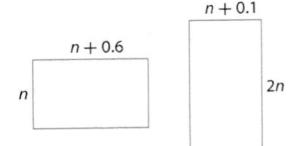
Personal Math Trainer
@my.hrw.com
Online Assessment and Intervention

10. Members of the Wide Waters Club pay $105 per summer season, plus $9.50 each time they rent a boat. Nonmembers must pay $14.75 each time they rent a boat. How many times would a member and a non-member have to rent a boat in order to pay the same amount?

20 times

11. Margo can purchase tile at a store for $0.79 per tile and rent a tile saw for $24. At another store she can borrow the tile saw for free if she buys tiles there for $1.19 per tile. How many tiles must she buy for the cost to be the same at both stores?

60 tiles

12. The charges for two shuttle services are shown in the table. Find the number of miles for which the cost of both shuttles is the same.

	Pickup Charge ($)	Charge per Mile ($)
Easy Ride	10	0.10
Best	0	0.35

40 miles

13. **Multistep** Rapid Rental Car charges a $40 rental fee, $15 for gas, and $0.25 per mile driven. For the same car, Capital Cars charges $45 for rental and gas and $0.35 per mile.

a. For how many miles is the rental cost at both companies the same?

_100 mi_

b. What is that cost?

_$80_

14. Write an equation with the solution $x = 20$. The equation should have the variable on both sides, a fractional coefficient on the left side, and a fraction anywhere on the right side.

Sample answer: $\frac{4}{5}x - 3 = \frac{3}{10}x + 7$

15. Write an equation with the solution $x = 25$. The equation should have the variable on both sides, a decimal coefficient on the left side, and a decimal anywhere on the right side. One of the decimals should be written in tenths, the other in hundredths.

Sample answer: $0.4x - 5 = 0.08x + 3$

16. **Geometry** The perimeters of the rectangles shown are equal. What is the perimeter of each rectangle?

$n + 0.1$

$n + 0.6$

n $2n$

3.2 units

17. **Analyze Relationships** The formula $F = 1.8C + 32$ gives the temperature in degrees Fahrenheit (F) for a given temperature in degrees Celsius (C). There is one temperature for which the number of degrees Fahrenheit is equal to the number of degrees Celsius. Write an equation you can solve to find that temperature and then use it to find the temperature.

$C = 1.8C + 32; -40°F = -40°C$

© Houghton Mifflin Harcourt Publishing Company

DIFFERENTIATE INSTRUCTION *Leveled Homework/Practice*

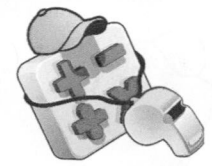

Personal Math Trainer

• 7.2 Homework

Pages shown are from *Differentiated Instruction.*
Also available online.

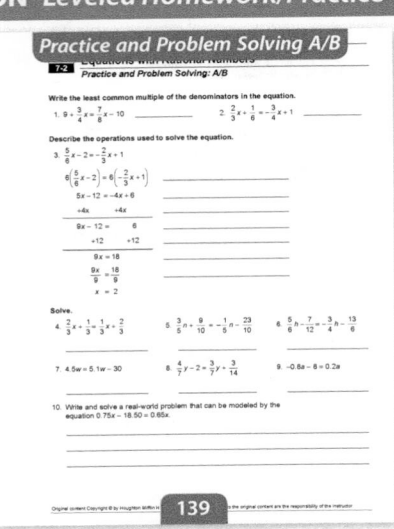
Practice and Problem Solving A/B
139

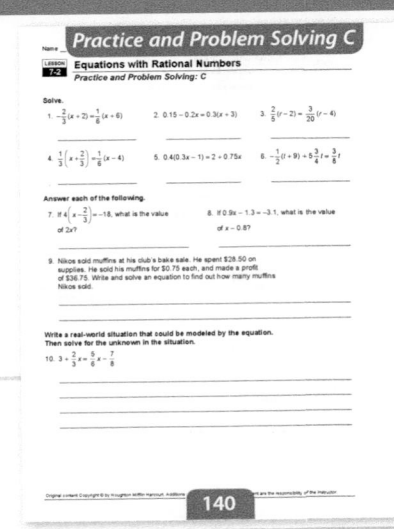
Practice and Problem Solving C
140

Practice and Problem Solving D
141

18. Explain the Error Agustin solved an equation as shown. What error did Agustin make? What is the correct answer?

Agustin multiplied only the terms with fractional coefficients by the LCD. He should have multiplied all the terms. The correct answer is $x = -12$.

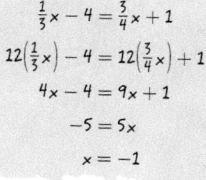

$$\tfrac{1}{3}x - 4 = \tfrac{3}{4}x + 1$$
$$12\left(\tfrac{1}{3}x\right) - 4 = 12\left(\tfrac{3}{4}x\right) + 1$$
$$4x - 4 = 9x + 1$$
$$-5 = 5x$$
$$x = -1$$

H.O.T. FOCUS ON HIGHER ORDER THINKING

19. Draw Conclusions Solve the equation $\tfrac{1}{2}x - 5 + \tfrac{2}{3}x = \tfrac{7}{6}x + 4$. Explain your results.

When you attempt to solve the equation, you eliminate the variable from both sides of the equation, leaving a false statement such as $-30 = 24$. Since the statement is false, the equation must not have a solution.

20. Look for a Pattern Describe the pattern in the equation. Then solve the equation.

$$0.3x + 0.03x + 0.003x + 0.0003x + \ldots = 3$$

Each term on the left side of the equation is one tenth of the previous term. Since the pattern continues without end, the sum of the terms is $0.3333 \ldots x$, which equals $\tfrac{1}{3}x$. Since $\tfrac{1}{3}x = 3$, $x = 9$.

21. Critique Reasoning Jared wanted to find three consecutive even integers whose sum was 4 times the first of those integers. He let k represent the first integer, then wrote and solved this equation: $k + (k + 1) + (k + 2) = 4k$. Did he get the correct answer? Explain.

No; the solution to his equation is $k = 3$, giving 3, 4, and 5 as the three integers. However, 3 and 5 are not even integers. He should have used the equation $k + (k + 2) + (k + 4) = 4k$, which gives $k = 6$ and the correct answer 6, 8, 10.

Work Area

© Houghton Mifflin Harcourt Publishing Company

7.2 Lesson Quiz

Solve each equation.

1. Solve $\tfrac{7}{8}x - \tfrac{1}{2} = \tfrac{3}{16}x + 5$. $x = 8$

2. Marsha is changing her phone service. One data package charges an initial fee of $50 and $13.25 per month. The other has no initial fee but charges $25.75 per month for the same data package. After how many months would Marsha have paid the same amount for either data package? 4 months

3. Write a real-world situation that can be modeled by the equation $8.35x = 4.25x + 36.90$. Sample answer: Mark paid $8.35 per pound for fish at one market. Then he found another market that charges a member's fee of $36.90 a year plus $4.25 per pound for fish. How many pounds of fish would Mark need to buy for the total cost to be the same?

4. The perimeter of one square is given as $4x$. Its perimeter is equal to the perimeter of a rectangle given as $2.5x + 3.75$. What is the perimeter of each figure? 10 units

Differentiate Instruction

IF a student misses more than one question, THEN

Differentiate Instruction:

• 7.2 Reteach

• Personal Math Trainer

Interactive Whiteboard
Interactive Lesson quiz available online

DIFFERENTIATE INSTRUCTION *Extend-the-Math Activity* **PRE-AP**

Activity The following equation is nonlinear but becomes linear when the fractions are eliminated from the equation. Solve the equation.

$$\frac{x}{x-2} = 2 + \frac{3}{x-2}$$

$$\frac{x}{x-2} = 2 + \frac{3}{x-2}$$
$$(x-2)\left(\frac{x}{x-2}\right) = \left(2 + \frac{3}{x-2}\right)(x-2)$$
$$x = 2x - 4 + 3$$
$$x = 2x - 1$$
$$x = 1$$

Lesson Support

Content Objective Students will learn how to use the Distributive Property to solve equations.

Professional Development

Integrate Mathematical Processes MP.1

This lesson provides an opportunity to address this Mathematical Process standard. It calls for students to make sense of problems and persevere in solving them.

Example 3 uses a four-step problem-solving process to determine the amount of a restaurant bill before a discount was applied. Students analyze the information, formulate a plan, solve the problem, and justify and evaluate the solution.

FOCUS

Building Background

Eliciting Prior Knowledge Have students complete a definition and example chart for the Distributive Property. Ask them to provide an algebraic definition and to include examples with positive and negative signs.

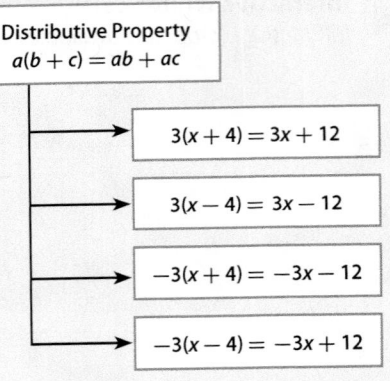

Distributive Property
$a(b + c) = ab + ac$

$3(x + 4) = 3x + 12$

$3(x - 4) = 3x - 12$

$-3(x + 4) = -3x - 12$

$-3(x - 4) = -3x + 12$

COHERENCE

Learning Progressions

In this lesson, students use the Distributive Property to solve equations with the variable on both sides. Important understandings for students include the following:

- **Solve an equation using the Distributive Property on one side.**
- **Solve an equation using the Distributive Property on both sides.**
- **Solve a real-world problem using the Distributive Property.**

Students focus on using the Distributive Property to solve equations in a separate lesson to help them become confident in accurately applying the property to solve multi-step equations. Students are solving increasingly difficult equations and must identify the order and necessity of the steps that can be used to solve the equations.

RIGOR

Cluster Connections

This lesson provides an excellent opportunity to connect ideas in the cluster:

Analyze and solve linear equations and pairs of simultaneous linear equations.

Provide students with the following variation of an equation that requires the Distributive Property to solve:

$$-3(2x - 4 + 6x + 7) = \frac{1}{2}(-36x + 18)$$

Discuss the steps students used to solve the equation and why.

Sample answer: Use the Distributive Property on both sides
$(-6x + 12 - 18x - 21 = -18x + 9)$; simplify
$(-24x - 9 = -18x + 9)$; add 9 to both sides
$(-24x = -18x + 18)$; add 18x to both sides
$(-6x = 18)$; divide both sides by -6 ($x = -3$).

Language Support ELL

Language Objective Students will demonstrate how to use the Distributive Property to solve equations.

Leveled Strategies for English Learners ELL

Emerging
Write out the steps of solving an equation using the Distributive Property on sentence strips of paper. Read the statements aloud with the students as they work through solving the equation. Then scramble the steps and have students determine when they are back in the correct order.

Expanding
Work an example of solving an equation using the Distributive Property, describing each step aloud as students write out the steps on sentence strips. Then scramble the steps and have students work in groups to place them in the correct order.

Bridging
Have students write out a description of how to solve an equation using the Distributive Property. Then have students solve an equation and read each step as it is performed.

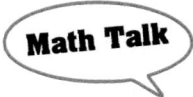

Math Talk The prompt uses the term eliminate as in eliminate a fraction. Make sure that students understand that eliminate means "to do away with" or "to make something disappear." Explain that nothing actually disappears but that the values are just expressed in a different way.

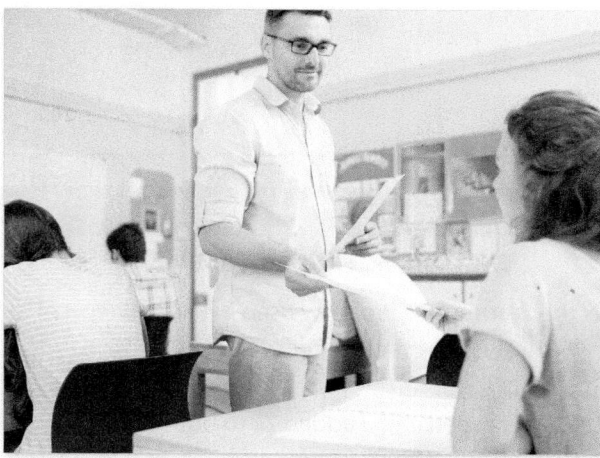

Image Credits: ©Wavebreak/iStock/Getty Images Plus/Getty Images

Linguistic Support ELL

Academic/Content Vocabulary
Teaching the meaning of the term *Distributive Property* and application of the property requires an understanding of the verb *to distribute*. Use other expressions, such as *to give shares of* or *to give out*, to facilitate discussion of the meaning and application of the term in math. Think of real-world examples such as dealing (giving out) cards to players in a card game. The cards are "distributed" equally. Review the operations of addition, multiplication, and division involved in "distributing" a set of concrete objects. Show how parentheses are used to signal groupings of the numbers that represent different sets of the concrete objects.

Background Knowledge
The Independent Practice has problems involving deriving equations to calculate differences in students' ages. Encourage students to research the ages of family members and apply this process to real-world cases of age differences. Have students work in groups to create age-difference problems, working to solve from two people's current ages or from information about the multiples of their age difference to derive an equation. This application provides an opportunity for cultural connections.

Equations with the Distributive Property

1 Engage

How do you use the Distributive Property to solve equations? Sample answer: Distribute a factor to all terms within parentheses, then solve for the variable.

Motivate the Lesson

Ask: How can the Distributive Property and inverse operations help you simplify equations? Begin the lesson to find out.

2 Explore

EXPLORE ACTIVITY **EXAMPLE 1**

ADDITIONAL EXAMPLE 1

Solve each equation.

A $2(x - 6) + 3 = 4 + x$ $x = 13$

B $3x - 8 = 10 - 3(x - 4)$ $x = 5$

 Interactive Whiteboard
Interactive example available online

LESSON
7.3 **Equations with the Distributive Property**

8.3.7.3
Students will use the Distributive Property to solve equations.

? **ESSENTIAL QUESTION**

How do you use the Distributive Property to solve equations?

EXPLORE ACTIVITY

Using the Distributive Property

The Distributive Property can be useful in solving equations.

EXAMPLE 1 Solve each equation.

A $3(x - 5) + 1 = 2 + x$

STEP 1 Use the Distributive Property.

Distribute 3 to the terms inside the parentheses. $3x - \boxed{15} + 1 = 2 + x$

Simplify. $\boxed{3x - 14} = 2 + x$

STEP 2 Use inverse operations to solve the equation.

Subtract ___x___ from both sides.

$$3x - 14 = 2 + x$$
$$-\boxed{x} \qquad -\boxed{x}$$
$$\overline{2x - 14 = 2}$$

Add ___14___ to both sides.

$$+\boxed{14} = +\boxed{14}$$
$$\overline{2x \qquad = \quad 16}$$

Divide both sides by 2.

$$x = \boxed{8}$$

B $5 - 7k = -4(k + 1) - 3$

STEP 1 Use the Distributive Property.

Distribute ___-4___ to the terms inside the parentheses. $5 - 7k = \boxed{-4k} - 4 - 3$

Simplify. $5 - 7k = \boxed{-4k - 7}$

STEP 2 Use inverse operations to solve the equation.

Add ___$4k$___ to both sides.

$$5 - 7k = -4k - 7$$
$$+4k \qquad +\boxed{4k}$$
$$\overline{5 - 3k = \qquad -7}$$

Subtract ___5___ from both sides.

$$-\boxed{5} \qquad -\boxed{5}$$
$$\overline{-3k = \quad -12}$$

Divide both sides by ___-3___.

$$k = \boxed{4}$$

© Houghton Mifflin Harcourt Publishing Company

DIFFERENTIATE INSTRUCTION *Leveled Questions*

	EXPLORE ACTIVITY EXAMPLE 1
AL DOK 1 *Recall*	How is the Distributive Property used in Part A, Step 1? The 3 is distributed to the terms in the expression in parentheses, $x - 5$.
OL DOK 2 *Skills/Concepts*	What would happen if you added $7k$ to both sides of the equation in Part B, Step 2? You would get $5 = 3k - 7$, which is equivalent, with the variable on the right side.
BL DOK 3 *Strategic Thinking*	Is the Distributive Property used to rewrite an equation where an expression is being subtracted, such as $7 - (2a + 3) = 12$? Explain. Yes; it is the same as multiplying the expression in parentheses by -1, so $7 - (2a + 3) = 12$ can be rewritten as $7 - 1(2a + 3) = 12$, and then as $7 - 2a - 3 = 12$.

LEVELED QUESTIONS: **AL** Approaching Level | **OL** On Level | **BL** Beyond Level

YOUR TURN

Solve each equation.

1. $y - 5 = 3 - 9(y + 2)$ $y = -1$ 2. $2(x - 7) - 10 = 12 - 4x$ $x = 6$

Personal
Math Trainer

Online Assessment
and Intervention

my.hrw.com

Math On the Spot

my.hrw.com

Using the Distributive Property on Both Sides

Some equations require the use of the Distributive Property on both sides.

EXAMPLE 2

Solve: $\frac{3}{4}(x - 13) = -2(9 + x)$

STEP 1 Eliminate the fraction.

$\frac{3}{4}(x - 13) = -2(9 + x)$

$4 \times \frac{3}{4}(x - 13) = 4 \times [-2(9 + x)]$ Multiply both sides by 4.

$3(x - 13) = -8(9 + x)$

Math Talk
Mathematical Processes

How can you eliminate fractions if there is a fraction being distributed on both sides of an equation?

Multiply both sides of the equation by the LCD of the fractions before applying the Distributive Property.

STEP 2 Use the Distributive Property.

$3x - 39 = -72 - 8x$ Distribute 3 and −8 to the terms within the parentheses.

STEP 3 Use inverse operations to solve the equation.

$3x - 39 = -72 - 8x$

$\underline{+ 8x \qquad\qquad + 8x}$ Add 8x to both sides.

$11x - 39 = -72$

$\underline{\quad + 39 \quad + 39}$ Add 39 to both sides.

$11x = -33$

$\frac{11x}{11} = \frac{-33}{11}$ Divide both sides by 11.

$x = -3$

© Houghton Mifflin Harcourt Publishing Company

Personal
Math Trainer

Online Assessment
and Intervention

my.hrw.com

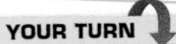

YOUR TURN

Solve each equation.

3. $-4(-5 - b) = \frac{1}{3}(b + 16)$ $b = -4$ 4. $\frac{3}{5}(t + 18) = -3(2 - t)$ $t = 7$

	EXAMPLE 2
AL DOK 1 *Recall*	What is the result of multiplying both sides of the equation by 4 in Step 1? The fraction is eliminated.
OL DOK 2 *Skills/Concepts*	Why is the leading fraction eliminated before using the Distributive Property? Using the Distributive Property before eliminating fractions would cause there to be more fractions.
BL DOK 3 *Strategic Thinking*	How do you know what number to choose when multiplying both sides of the equation in order to eliminate fractions? You can use any common multiple of the denominators in the fractions in the equation. When you use the least common multiple, the numbers will be as simplified as possible. If you use a greater common multiple, you may have to simplify again later in the solution process.

Avoid Common Errors

For **Exercise 1**, to prevent errors with signs encourage students to distribute −9 instead of 9.

3 Explain

EXAMPLE 2

ADDITIONAL EXAMPLE 2 Solve
$-\frac{3}{5}(5 - 2y) = -3(y - 5) - 18.$ $y = 0$

 Interactive Whiteboard
Interactive example available online

YOUR TURN MP.8

Engage with the Whiteboard

For **Exercises 3–4**, have volunteers demonstrate while they explain how to find the LCD and use the Distributive Property to solve each equation.

TEACHER TO TEACHER

Curriculum Connection (Geometry) After completing Example 2, draw the two rectangles shown below on the board.

A	3
$x + 1$	

B	2
$3 + x$	

Tell students that the areas of these two rectangles are equal. Have them write and solve an equation for x. Then have them state the dimensions of each rectangle. Rectangle A: 3 × 4; Rectangle B: 2 × 6

EXAMPLE 3

ADDITIONAL EXAMPLE 3 Every year Chana uses her income from her job to pay for 80% of her college tuition. Next year Chana will need to contribute $2,000 toward her tuition. Next year the tuition will be $600 more than this year's tuition. How much is this year's tuition? $1,900

Interactive Whiteboard
Interactive example available online

YOUR TURN   MP.1

Engage with the Whiteboard

For **Exercise 5**, have volunteers underline the information needed to write an equation describing the situation. Have other volunteers write and solve the equation.

Digital Teacher Resources

Go online to access all your lesson-level resources.

my.hrw.com

Differentiated Instruction
• Reteach
• Reading Strategies
• Success for English Learners
• Practice and Problem Solving A/B, C, D

Math on the Spot Videos

Math On the Spot
my.hrw.com

Solving a Real-World Problem Using the Distributive Property

Solving a real-world problem may involve using the Distributive Property.

EXAMPLE 3 Problem Solving

The Coleman family had their bill at a restaurant reduced by $7.50 because of a special discount. They left a tip of $8.90, which was 20% of the reduced amount. How much was their bill before the discount?

 Analyze Information

The answer is the amount before the discount.

 Formulate a Plan

Use an equation to find the amount before the discount.

Solve

STEP 1 Write the equation $0.2(x - 7.5) = 8.9$, where x is the amount of the Coleman family's bill before the discount.

STEP 2 Use the Distributive Property: $0.2x - 1.5 = 8.9$

STEP 3 Use inverse operations to solve the equation.

$$0.2x - 1.5 = 8.9$$
$$\underline{+1.5 \quad +1.5} \qquad \text{Add 1.5 to both sides.}$$
$$0.2x = 10.4$$
$$\frac{0.2x}{0.2} = \frac{10.4}{0.2} \qquad \text{Divide both sides by 0.2.}$$
$$x = 52$$

The Coleman family's bill before the discount was $52.00.

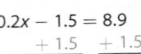 **Justify and Evaluate**

$52.00 - $7.50 = $44.50 and $0.2($44.50) = $8.90. This is the amount of the tip the Colemans left. The answer is reasonable.

Math Talk
Mathematical Processes

Why do you use 0.2 in Step 1?

0.2 is 20% written as a decimal.

 YOUR TURN

5. The Smiths spend 8% of their budget on entertainment. Their total budget this year is $2,000 more than last year, and this year they plan to spend $3,840 on entertainment. What was their total budget last year? _$46,000_

Personal Math Trainer
Online Assessment and Intervention
my.hrw.com

Lesson 7.3 **211**

© Houghton Mifflin Harcourt Publishing Company • Image Credits: ©Monkey Business Images/Shutterstock

---

DIFFERENTIATE INSTRUCTION *Leveled Questions*

	EXAMPLE 3
AL DOK 1 *Recall*	How does the equation $0.2(x - 7.5) = 8.9$ represent this situation? The original amount of the bill was reduced by $7.50, so that is $x - 7.5$, where x is the original amount; 20% of the reduced amount is represented by $0.2(x - 7.5)$, and that equals $8.90, the amount tipped.
OL DOK 2 *Skills/Concepts*	How can you mentally determine that $52 is a reasonable answer? You can round $8.90 to $9 and then work backward: $52 - $9 = $43; 20% of $43 is double 10% of $43, so it's $8.60; since $8.60 is close to $8.90, $52 is a reasonable answer.
BL DOK 3 *Strategic Thinking*	Why wouldn't you want to multiply both sides of the equation by 10 before using the Distributive Property? The decimals 0.2 and 8.9 would be eliminated, but 7.5 would not be eliminated because it is within the parentheses.

LEVELED QUESTIONS: **AL** Approaching Level | **OL** On Level | **BL** Beyond Level

Solve each equation.

1. $4(x + 8) - 4 = 34 - 2x$
(Explore Activity Ex. 1)

$\boxed{4} \ x + \boxed{32} - 4 = 34 - 2x$

$\boxed{4} \ x + \boxed{28} = 34 - 2x$

$\boxed{6} \ x + \boxed{28} = 34$

$\boxed{6} \ x = \boxed{6}$

$\dfrac{\boxed{6} \ x}{\boxed{6}} = \dfrac{\boxed{6}}{\boxed{6}}$

$x = \boxed{1}$

2. $\frac{2}{3}(9 + x) = -5(4 - x)$ (Ex. 2)

$\boxed{3} \times \frac{2}{3}(9 + x) = \boxed{3} \times [-5(4 - x)]$

$\boxed{2} \ (9 + x) = \boxed{-15} \ (4 - x)$

$\boxed{18} + \boxed{2} \ x = \boxed{-60} \ \boxed{+} \ \boxed{15} \ x$

$\boxed{-13} \ x = \boxed{-78}$

$\dfrac{\boxed{-13} \ x}{\boxed{-13}} = \dfrac{\boxed{-78}}{\boxed{-13}}$

$x = \boxed{6}$

3. $-3(x + 4) + 15 = 6 - 4x$
(Explore Activity Ex. 1)
$x = 3$

4. $10 + 4x = 5(x - 6) + 33$
(Explore Activity Ex. 1)
$x = 7$

5. $x - 9 = 8(2x + 3) - 18$
(Explore Activity Ex. 1)
$x = -1$

6. $-6(x - 1) - 7 = -7x + 2$
(Explore Activity Ex. 1)
$x = 3$

7. $\frac{1}{10}(x + 11) = -2(8 - x)$ (Ex. 2)
$x = 9$

8. $-(4 - x) = \frac{3}{4}(x - 6)$ (Ex. 2)
$x = -2$

9. $-8(8 - x) = \frac{4}{5}(x + 10)$ (Ex. 2)
$x = 10$

10. $\frac{1}{2}(16 - x) = -12(x + 7)$ (Ex. 2)
$x = -8$

11. Sandra saves 12% of her salary for retirement. This year her salary was $3,000 more than in the previous year, and she saved $4,200. What was her salary in the previous year? (Example 3)

Write an equation. $\qquad 0.12(x + 3,000) = 4,200$

Sandra's salary in the previous year was $\qquad \$32,000$.

? ESSENTIAL QUESTION CHECK-IN

12. When solving an equation using the Distributive Property, if the numbers being distributed are fractions, what is your first step? Why?

You eliminate the fractions by using their LCD. The resulting computations will be less complicated without fractions.

© Houghton Mifflin Harcourt Publishing Company

4 Elaborate

Talk About It

Summarize the Lesson

Ask: How can the Distributive Property help you solve equations? When an equation contains an expression in parentheses multiplied by a factor, the Distributive Property allows you to distribute the factor and get rid of the parentheses. This allows the equation to be solved.

Guided Practice

Engage with the Whiteboard

For **Exercises 1–2**, have volunteers explain the process of arriving at the correct value as they complete the write-in boxes for each exercise. Have other volunteers show how to check the answers using substitution.

Avoid Common Errors

• **Exercises 3, 6–10** Students may apply the negative sign to only the first term when distributing. Remind students that negative factors must be distributed to both terms within the parentheses.

• **Exercises 7–10** Remind students to eliminate the fractions before using inverse operations.

DIFFERENTIATE INSTRUCTION *Intervention and Additional Support*

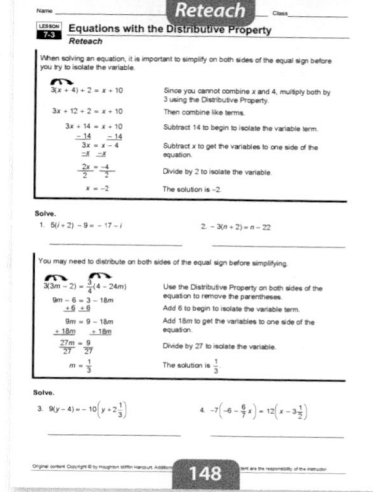

Reteach
148

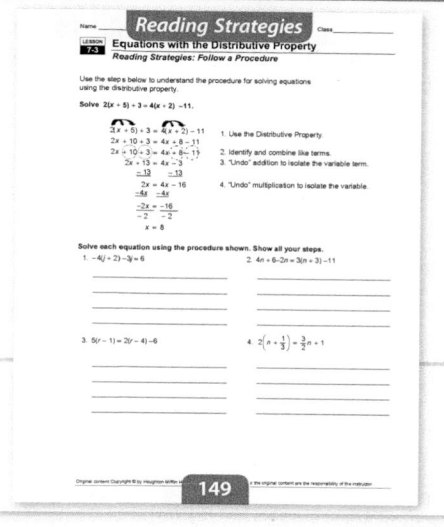

Reading Strategies
149

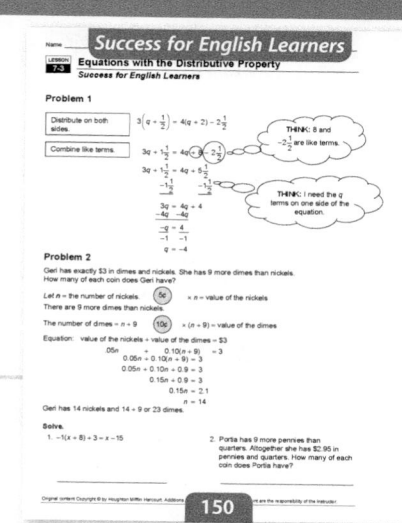

Success for English Learners
150

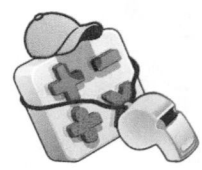

Personal Math Trainer
Daily Intervention
7.3 Homework

Pages shown are from *Differentiated Instruction.*
Also available online.

⏱ **Pressed for Time**

7.3 Differentiated Homework Assignments

AL Approaching Level 13–16, 18

OL On Level 14–18

BL Beyond Level 14, 17–19

*For **Below Level** students, assign Personal Math Trainer, Daily Intervention 7.3 Homework.*

Mathematical Processes	Exercises
MP.2 Reasoning	16
MP.3 Logic	15, 18
MP.4 Modeling	13–14, 17
MP.8 Patterns	19

Focus on Higher Order Thinking

Depth of Knowledge	Exercises
2 Skills/Concepts	13–14, 16–17
3 Strategic Thinking H.O.T.	15, 18–19

7.3 Independent Practice

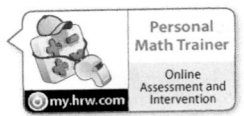

Personal Math Trainer
Online Assessment and Intervention
my.hrw.com

13. Multistep Martina is currently 14 years older than her cousin Joey. In 5 years she will be 3 times as old as Joey. Use this information to answer the following questions.

a. If you let x represent Joey's current age, what expression can you use to represent Martina's current age?

$x + 14$

b. Based on your answer to part a, what expression represents Joey's age in 5 years? What expression represents Martina's age in 5 years?

Joey's age in 5 years: $x + 5$; Martina's age in 5 years: $x + 19$

c. What equation can you write based on the information given?

$3(x + 5) = x + 19$

d. What is Joey's current age? What is Martina's current age?

Joey: 2 years old; Martina: 16 years old

14. As part of a school contest, Sarah and Luis are playing a math game. Sarah must pick a number between 1 and 50 and give Luis clues so he can write an equation to find her number. Sarah says, "If I subtract 5 from my number, multiply that quantity by 4, and then add 7 to the result, I get 35." What equation can Luis write based on Sarah's clues and what is Sarah's number?

$4(x - 5) + 7 = 35$; 12

15. Critical Thinking When solving an equation using the Distributive Property that involves distributing fractions, usually the first step is to multiply by the LCD to eliminate the fractions in order to simplify computation. Is it necessary to do this to solve $\frac{1}{2}(4x + 6) = \frac{1}{3}(9x - 24)$? Why or why not?

It is not necessary. In this case, distributing the fractions directly results in whole number coefficients and constants.

16. Solve the equation given in Exercise 15 with and without using the LCD of the fractions. Are your answers the same?

Yes; using either method gives $x = 11$.

© Houghton Mifflin Harcourt Publishing Company

DIFFERENTIATE INSTRUCTION *Leveled Homework/Practice*

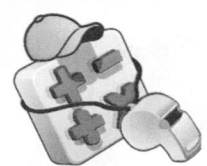

Personal Math Trainer

• 7.3 Homework

Pages shown are from *Differentiated Instruction*. **Also available online.**

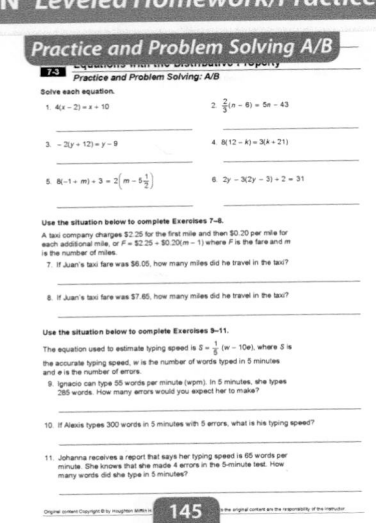

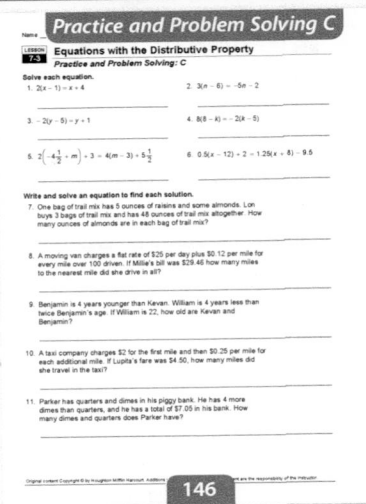

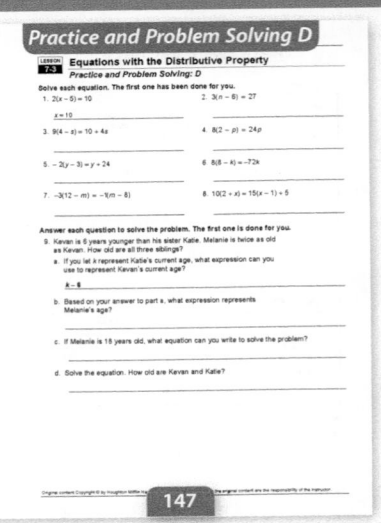

17. Represent Real-World Problems A chemist mixed x milliliters of 25% acid solution with some 15% acid solution to produce 100 milliliters of a 19% acid solution. Use this information to fill in the missing information in the table and answer the questions that follow.

	ml of Solution	Percent Acid as a Decimal	ml of Acid
25% Solution	x	0.25	$0.25x$
15% Solution	$100 - x$	0.15	$0.15(100 - x)$
Mixture (19% Solution)	100	0.19	19

a. What is the relationship between the milliliters of acid in the 25% solution, the milliliters of acid in the 15% solution, and the milliliters of acid in the mixture? The milliliters of acid in the 25% solution plus the milliliters of acid in the 15% solution equals the milliliters of acid in the mixture.

b. What equation can you use to solve for x based on your answer to part a? $0.25x + 0.15(100 - x) = 19$

c. How many milliliters of the 25% solution and the 15% solution did the chemist use in the mixture? The chemist used 40 ml of the 25% solution and 60 ml of the 15% solution.

 **FOCUS ON HIGHER ORDER THINKING**

Work Area

18. Explain the Error Anne solved $5(2x) - 3 = 20x + 15$ for x by first distributing 5 on the left side of the equation. She got the answer $x = -3$. However, when she substituted -3 into the original equation for x, she saw that her answer was wrong. What did Anne do wrong, and what is the correct answer? Anne did not need to use the Distributive Property. The parentheses are only around $2x$ and are used to represent $5 \cdot 2x$, not $5(2x - 3)$. The correct answer is $x = -1.8$.

19. Communicate Mathematical Ideas Explain a procedure that can be used to solve $5[3(x + 4) - 2(1 - x)] - x - 15 = 14x + 45$. Then solve the equation. Use the Distributive Property to distribute both 3 and 2 inside the square parentheses on the left side. Combine like terms inside the square parentheses. Then use the Distributive Property again to distribute 5. Combine like terms on the left side and use inverse operations to solve the equation. $x = 1$

DIFFERENTIATE INSTRUCTION *Extend-the-Math Activity* **PRE-AP**

Activity When solving an equation with one variable, it is possible to have one solution, no solutions, or infinitely many solutions. Determine how many solutions each of the following equations has. Justify your answers.

- $-x + 3(x - 2) = 2(x - 2) - 3$ no solution; the equation simplifies to $-6 \neq -7$, so no value for x will make the equation true.
- $3x - 4 = 2(x - 1)$ one solution; the equation simplifies to $x = 2$.
- $3x + 2(4x - 6) = 7x + 4(x - 3)$ infinitely many solutions; the equation simplifies to $-12 = -12$, so any value for x will make the equation true.

© Houghton Mifflin Harcourt Publishing Company • Image Credits: ©O. Hurst/Alamy Images

✔ **Quick Check**

7.3 Lesson Quiz

Solve each equation.

1. $5(x + 6) + 11 = 25 - 3x$ $x = -2$

2. $-\frac{3}{8}(-6 - 2y) = \frac{1}{2}(2y - 3) - 1$ $y = 19$

Solve.

3. Kyle saves 8% of his income for a new car. This year his salary was $2,000 less than in the previous year, and he saved $3,000. What was his salary in the previous year? $39,500

4. Leslie is currently 8 years older than her neighbor Bill. In 4 years she will be 2 times as old as Bill. Let x equal Bill's current age.

a. What expression represents Leslie's current age? $x + 8$

b. What expression represents Bill's age in 4 years? What expression represents Leslie's age in 4 years? $x + 4$; $x + 12$ or $2(x + 4)$

c. What equation can you write based on the given information? $x + 12 = 2(x + 4)$

d. What is Bill's current age? What is Leslie's current age? Bill: 4 years old; Leslie: 12 years old

Differentiate Instruction

IF a student misses more than one question, THEN

Differentiate Instruction:

- 7.3 Reteach
- Personal Math Trainer

 Interactive Whiteboard
Interactive Lesson quiz available online

Lesson Support

Content Objective Students will learn how to give examples of equations with a given number of solutions.

Professional Development

Integrate Mathematical Processes MP.8

This lesson provides an opportunity to address this Mathematical Process standard. It calls for students to look for and express regularity in repeated reasoning. Students should see patterns in the processes of simplifying and building equations. They should notice that linear equations in one variable that have no solutions always result in a false statement after the x term has been eliminated. Using this pattern, students use the work-backward strategy to reinstate an x value on both sides of a false statement involving two numbers. The result is a linear equation that has no solutions.

FOCUS

Building Background

Eliciting Prior Knowledge Ask students to try to solve the equation $x + 5 = x + 6$, to describe what happens, and to explain why it happens. Students will find that when they subtract x from both sides, the variable vanishes and they are left with a nonsensical equation, $5 = 6$. Show that it was the original equation that was nonsensical: no number x has a property that results in the same number whether 5 or 6 is added to it. Conclusion: some equations have no solution.

$$
\begin{array}{rcl}
x + 5 &=& x + 6 \\
-x & & -x \\
\hline
5 &=& 6
\end{array}
$$

COHERENCE

Learning Progressions

In this lesson, students decide whether a linear equation has one, zero, or infinitely many solutions. Important understandings for students include the following:

- **Determine whether an equation has one, zero, or infinitely many solutions.**
- **Write equations with a given number of solutions.**

Students transform a given linear equation into simpler forms until they arrive at an equivalent form in which the equation has one, zero, or infinitely many solutions. They also work backward to construct examples of linear equations with a given number of solutions. This lesson prepares students for each of the possible solutions they will encounter when they solve simultaneous equations, both algebraically and graphically, in the next module.

RIGOR

Cluster Connections

This lesson provides an excellent opportunity to connect ideas in the cluster:

Analyze and solve linear equations and pairs of simultaneous linear equations.

Have students examine the following equation:

$$-\frac{2}{3}\left(6x + 9\right) = -7x + 3x$$

Ask them whether the equation has one, zero, or infinitely many solutions. Ask them to explain their conclusion. No solution, since $-6 \neq 0$. Then have them transform the equation into (a) an equation with infinitely many solutions, and (b) an equation with one solution, including its solution.

Answers may vary. Sample answers: infinitely many: $-\frac{2}{3}\left(6x + 9\right) = -7x + 3x - 6$; one: $-\frac{2}{3}\left(6x + 9\right) = -7x + 4x$ with solution $x = -6$

Language Support `ELL`

Language Objective Students will explain how to write equations that have a given number of solutions.

Leveled Strategies for English Learners `ELL`

Emerging
Group the students into pairs. Have each student create three equations—one with no solution, one with one solution, and one with many solutions. Have the pairs trade equations, simplify, and identify which equation is which.

Expanding
Have students make a three-column chart to compare the meanings of *none*, *many*, and *infinitely many* by listing some things that fit each category.

None	Many	Infinitely Many
unicorns	students	stars
flying pigs	pets	sand grains

Bridging
Have students write in their own words an explanation of the phrase *infinitely many*.

 **Math Talk**

To help students answer the question posed in Math Talk, provide them with a sentence frame.

You substitute values for x into the original equation because _____ .

Linguistic Support `ELL`

Academic/Content Vocabulary
In this lesson, students encounter the quantity *infinitely many* in terms of the number of solutions. Make sure they understand these words and encourage them to think of other uses of the word *infinite* to be sure they understand its meaning.

Background Knowledge
Example 2 suggests to students that they use the strategy of "working backward." Explain the word *backward* by physically walking backward and telling students that the word *backward* describes a direction. The opposite of *backward* is *forward*.

Image Credits: ©Design Pics Inc/Alamy Stock Photo

Equations with Many Solutions or No Solution

1 Engage

ESSENTIAL QUESTION

How can you give examples of equations with a given number of solutions? Sample answer: Equations that simplify to the form $x = a$ have one solution, equations that simplify to $a = a$ have many solutions, and equations that simplify to the form $a = b$, where $a \neq b$, have no solution.

Motivate the Lesson

Ask: What is the greatest number of solutions an equation can have? Begin the lesson to find out.

2 Explore

EXPLORE ACTIVITY   EXAMPLE 1

ADDITIONAL EXAMPLE 1

Use the properties of equality to simplify each equation. Tell whether the equation has one, zero, or infinitely many solutions.

A $3x - 6 = 4 + 2x$ $x = 10$; one

B $3x - 8 = 3(x - 4) + 1$ $-8 = -11$; zero

C $3x - 7 = 3(x - 3) + 2$ $-7 = -7$; infinitely many

 Interactive Whiteboard
Interactive example available online

LESSON 7.4

8.3.7.4
Students will give examples of equations with a given number of solutions.

Equations with Many Solutions or No Solution

ESSENTIAL QUESTION

How can you give examples of equations with a given number of solutions?

Math On the Spot
my.hrw.com

EXPLORE ACTIVITY

Determining the Number of Solutions

So far, when you solved a linear equation in one variable, you found one value of x that makes the equation a true statement. When you simplify some equations, you may find that they do not have one solution.

EXAMPLE 1 Use the properties of equality to simplify each equation. Tell whether the final equation is a true statement.

A $4x - 3 = 2x + 13$

Add __3__ to both sides.

Subtract __2x__ from both sides.

Divide both sides by __2__.

$$4x - 3 = 2x + 13$$
$$+3 \quad = \quad +3$$
$$4x = 2x + 16$$
$$-2x \quad -2x$$
$$2x = 16$$
$$\frac{2x}{2} = \frac{16}{2}$$
$$x = 8$$

The statement is true. There is one solution.

B $4x - 5 = 2(2x - 1) - 3$

Apply the Distributive Property.

Simplify.

Subtract __4x__ from both sides.

$$4x - 5 = 2(2x - 1) - 3$$
$$4x - 5 = 4x - 2 - 3$$
$$4x - 5 = 4x - 5$$
$$-4x \quad -4x$$
$$-5 = -5$$

The statement is true. There are many solutions.

© Houghton Mifflin Harcourt Publishing Company

Lesson 7.4 **215**

DIFFERENTIATE INSTRUCTION *Leveled Questions*

	EXPLORE ACTIVITY EXAMPLE 1
(AL) DOK 1 *Recall*	In Part C, what does a false statement indicate about the solution? It means that there is no solution because any value substituted for x will result in a false statement.
(OL) DOK 2 *Skills/Concepts*	In Parts A and B both results are true. How do you know which result indicates one solution and which result indicates infinitely many solutions? In Part A, the result is only true when you substitute 8 for x. In Part B, the result is true no matter what values are substituted for x.
(BL) DOK 3 *Strategic Thinking*	How could you write your own equation that has infinitely many solutions? Sample answer: You could begin with $x = x$ and use properties of equality to generate equivalent equations that also have infinitely many solutions.

LEVELED QUESTIONS: **(AL)** Approaching Level | **(OL)** On Level | **(BL)** Beyond Level

C $4x + 2 = 4x - 5$

Subtract __2__ from both sides.

Subtract __4x__ from both sides.

$$4x + 2 = 4x - 5$$
$$-\boxed{2} \quad -\boxed{2}$$
$$4x = 4x - 7$$
$$-\boxed{4x} \quad -\boxed{4x}$$
$$0 = -7$$

The statement is false. There is no solution.

Reflect

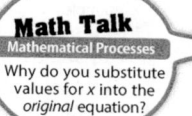

Math Talk
Mathematical Processes

Why do you substitute values for *x* into the *original* equation?

1. What happens when you substitute any value for *x* in the original equation in part B? in the original equation in part C?

In part B, any value of *x* will result in a true statement.

In part C, any value of *x* will result in a false statement.

YOUR TURN

Use the properties of equality to simplify each equation. Tell whether the final equation is a true statement.

2. $2x + 1 = 5x - 8$ 3. $3(4x + 3) - 2 = 12x + 7$ 4. $3x - 9 = 5 + 3x$

    True   True   False

Personal
Math Trainer
Online Assessment
and Intervention
my.hrw.com

Math On the Spot
my.hrw.com

Writing Equations with a Given Number of Solutions

When you simplify an equation using the properties of equality, you will find one of three results.

Result	What does this mean?	How many solutions?
$x = a$	When the value of *x* is *a*, the equation is a true statement.	1
$a = a$	Any value of *x* makes the equation a true statement.	Infinitely many
$a = b$, where $a \neq b$	There is no value of *x* that makes the equation a true statement.	0

You can use these results to write a linear equation that has a given number of solutions.

© Houghton Mifflin Harcourt Publishing Company

216 Unit 3

YOUR TURN   MP.3

Focus on Critical Thinking
Point out to students that they can sometimes see that an equation is false without finding the final equation. An example of this could be **Exercise 4**. But for now, suggest that they still complete the steps for simplifying each equation.

TEACHER TO TEACHER

Cooperative Learning Group students into pairs. Have each student create three equations— one with one solution, one with many solutions, and one with no solution. Have the pairs trade equations, simplify, and identify which equation is which.

3 Explain

EXAMPLE 2

ADDITIONAL EXAMPLE 2 Write a linear equation in one variable that has many solutions.

Sample answer: $4x + 17 = 4(x + 3) + 5$

 Interactive Whiteboard
Interactive example available online

YOUR TURN   MP.3

Engage with the Whiteboard

 For **Exercise 8**, have three or more volunteers complete the equation with a different value and show why the value they chose creates an equation with no solution.

Digital Teacher Resources

Go online to access all your lesson-level resources.

Differentiated Instruction
• Reteach
• Reading Strategies
• Success for English Learners
• Practice and Problem Solving A/B, C, D

Math on the Spot Videos

my.hrw.com

EXAMPLE 2

Write a linear equation in one variable that has no solution.

You can use the strategy of working backward:

STEP 1 Start with a false statement such as $3 = 5$. Add the same variable term to both sides.

$3 + x = 5 + x$ *Add x to both sides.*

STEP 2 Next, add the same constant to both sides and combine like terms on each side of the equation.

$10 + x = 12 + x$ *Add 7 to both sides.*

STEP 3 Verify that your equation has no solutions by using properties of equality to simplify your equation.

$$10 + x = 12 + x$$
$$\underline{ - x = - x}$$
$$10 = 12$$

Reflect

5. Explain why the result of the process above is an equation with no solution.

You started with a false statement and performed balanced operations on both sides of the equation. This does not change the true or false nature of the original statement.

> **Math Talk**
> Mathematical Processes
>
> What type of statement do you start with to write an equation with infinitely many solutions? Give an example.

You start with a true statement because when you solve an equation that has infinitely many solutions, you arrive at a true statement; $8 = 8$

YOUR TURN   For Ex. 8, any number except 1

Tell whether each equation has one, zero, or infinitely many solutions.

6. $6 + 3x = x - 8$ _____ One solution

7. $8x + 4 = 4(2x + 1)$ _____ Infinitely many solutions

Complete each equation so that it has the indicated number of solutions.

8. No solution: $3x + 1 = 3x +$ _____ Sample answer: 6

9. Infinitely many: $2x - 4 = 2x -$ _____ 4

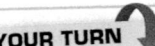 Personal Math Trainer
Online Assessment and Intervention
my.hrw.com

© Houghton Mifflin Harcourt Publishing Company

DIFFERENTIATE INSTRUCTION *Leveled Questions*

	EXAMPLE 2
AL DOK 1 *Recall*	Does adding the same number to both sides of a false statement change the fact that the statement is false? **Explain.** No, it produces an equivalent statement, which will also be false.
OL DOK 2 *Skills/Concepts*	What is another operation that you could perform on both sides of the equation in Step 2 to produce an equivalent equation that also has no solution? Sample answer: You could subtract 7 (or any number) from both sides.
BL DOK 3 *Strategic Thinking*	Is it true that applying properties of equality to a false statement always produces a false statement? If not, what is a counterexample? True except for using zero with the Multiplication Property of Equality. Multiplying both sides of the false statement $3 = 2$ by 0 results in the true statement $0 = 0$.

LEVELED QUESTIONS: AL Approaching Level | OL On Level | BL Beyond Level

Use the properties of equality to simplify each equation. Tell whether the final equation is a true statement. (Explore Activity Example 1)

1.

$$3x - 2 = 25 - 6x$$

$$\underline{+6x} \qquad \underline{+6x}$$

$$\boxed{9x} - 2 = \boxed{25}$$

$$\boxed{+2} = \boxed{+2}$$

$$\boxed{9}x = \boxed{27}$$

$$\frac{\boxed{9}x}{\boxed{9}} = \frac{\boxed{27}}{\boxed{9}}$$

$$x = \boxed{3}$$

The statement is $\boxed{\text{true}}$.

2.

$$2x - 4 = 2(x - 1) + 3$$

$$2x - 4 = \boxed{2x - 2} + 3$$

$$2x - 4 = 2x + \boxed{1}$$

$$\underline{-\boxed{2x}} \qquad \underline{-\boxed{2x}}$$

$$\boxed{-4} = \boxed{1}$$

The statement is $\boxed{\text{false}}$.

3. How many solutions are there to the equation in Exercise 2? _____ none _____
(Explore Activity Example 1)

4. After simplifying an equation, Juana gets 6 = 6. Explain what this means.
(Explore Activity Example 1)

Any value of x will result in a true statement; infinitely many solutions.

Write a linear equation in one variable that has infinitely many solutions. (Example 2)

5. Start with a _____ true _____ statement. $\qquad 10 = \boxed{10}$

Add the _____ same variable _____ to both sides. $\qquad 10 + x = \boxed{10 + x}$

Add the _____ same constant _____ to both sides. $\qquad 10 + x + 5 = \boxed{10 + x + 5}$

Combine _____ like _____ terms. $\qquad \boxed{15 + x} = \boxed{15 + x}$

 ESSENTIAL QUESTION CHECK-IN

6. Give an example of an equation with an infinite number of solutions. Then make one change to the equation so that it has no solution.

Sample answer: infinitely many solutions: $2x + 1 = 2x + 1$; no

solution: $2x + 1 = 2x$

© Houghton Mifflin Harcourt Publishing Company

4 Elaborate

Talk About It

Summarize the Lesson

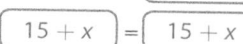 **Ask:** James wrote the equation $3x + 1 = 3x + 8$. He wants to change only one term so that the equation has exactly one solution. What are some ways he could change the equation? What are some ways he could not change the equation? He could change the x terms so that their coefficients are different, for example $2x + 1 = 3x + 8$ or $3x + 1 = 2x + 8$. A change to one of the constant terms would not work.

Guided Practice

Engage with the Whiteboard

For **Exercises 1, 2, and 5,** have volunteers explain the process of arriving at the correct values or words as they complete each of the write-in boxes.

Avoid Common Errors

- **Exercise 2** In the fourth line, students could subtract 1 from each side, resulting in $2x - 5 = 2x$. In this case, an extra line would be needed to arrive at the correct solution. Point out that although this solution method is correct, subtracting $2x$ allows you to arrive at the correct solution more quickly.

- **Exercise 5** Students may attempt to fill in the blanks on the left side, then proceed to the right side. Point out that they will need to refer to both sides to be able to fill in the blanks correctly.

DIFFERENTIATE INSTRUCTION *Intervention and Additional Support*

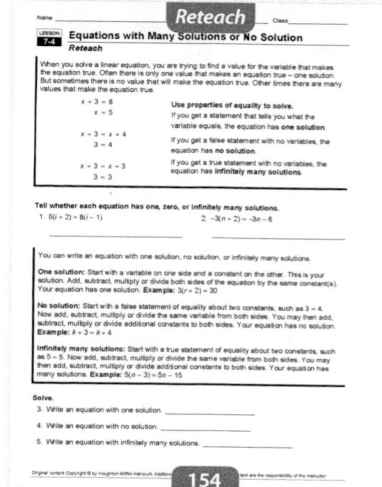

154

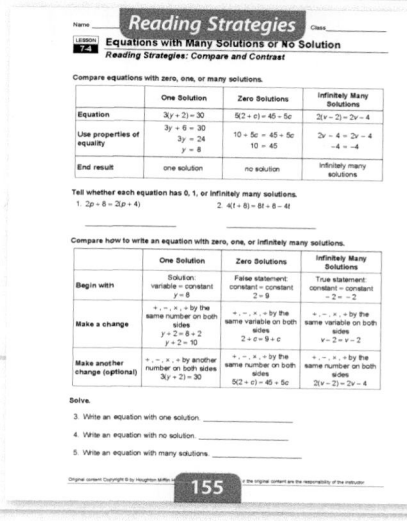

155

156

Personal Math Trainer
Daily Intervention
7.4 Homework

Pages shown are from *Differentiated Instruction.*
Also available online.

5 Evaluate

Independent Practice

7.4 Independent Practice

my.hrw.com Personal Math Trainer — Online Assessment and Intervention

Tell whether each equation has one, zero, or infinitely many solutions.

7. $-(2x + 2) - 1 = -x - (x + 3)$

$0 = 0$; infinitely many solutions

8. $-2(z + 3) - z = -z - 4(z + 2)$

$z = -1$; one solution

Create an equation with the indicated number of solutions.

9. No solution:

$3\left(x - \dfrac{4}{3}\right) = 3x + \boxed{5}$

Any number except -4. A sample is given.

10. Infinitely many solutions:

$2(x - 1) + 6x = 4\left(\boxed{2x} - 1\right) + 2$

11. One solution of $x = -1$:

$5x - (x - 2) = 2x - \left(\boxed{x + 1}\right)$

12. Infinitely many solutions:

$-(x - 8) + 4x = 2\left(\boxed{x + 4}\right) + x$

13. Persevere in Problem Solving The Dig It Project is designing two gardens that have the same perimeter. One garden is a trapezoid whose nonparallel sides are equal. The other is a quadrilateral. Two possible designs are shown at the right.

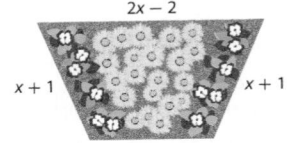

a. Based on these designs, is there more than one value for x? Explain how you know this.

Yes; because the perimeters are equal you get the equation $(2x - 2) + (x + 1) + x + (x + 1)$ $= (2x - 9) + (x + 1) + (x + 8) + x$, or $5x = 5x$. Since $5x = 5x$ is a true statement there are an infinite number of values for x.

b. Why does your answer to part a make sense in this context?

The condition was that the two perimeters are to be equal. However, a specific number was not given, so there are an infinite number of possible perimeters.

c. Suppose the Dig It Project wants the perimeter of each garden to be 60 meters. What is the value of x in this case? How did you find this?

12; Sample answer: I used the trapezoid and wrote the equation $(2x - 2) + (x + 1) + x + (x + 1) = 60$. Solving this gives $x = 12$.

© Houghton Mifflin Harcourt Publishing Company

Lesson 7.4 **219**

Pressed for Time

7.4 Differentiated Homework Assignments

AL **Approaching Level** 7–12, 15

OL **On Level** 9–15, 17

BL **Beyond Level** 11–14, 16–17

For **Below Level** students, assign Personal Math Trainer, Daily Intervention 7.4 Homework.

Mathematical Processes	Exercises
MP.2 Reasoning	7–12
MP.3 Logic	14, 16–17
MP.4 Modeling	13, 15

Focus on Higher Order Thinking

Depth of Knowledge	Exercises
2 Skills/Concepts	7–12
3 Strategic Thinking H.O.T.	13–17

DIFFERENTIATE INSTRUCTION *Leveled Homework/Practice*

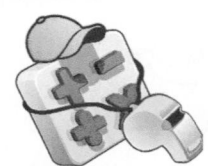

Personal Math Trainer
• 7.4 Homework

Pages shown are from *Differentiated Instruction.* Also available online.

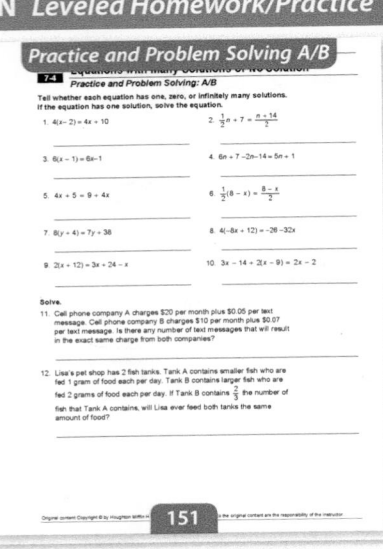

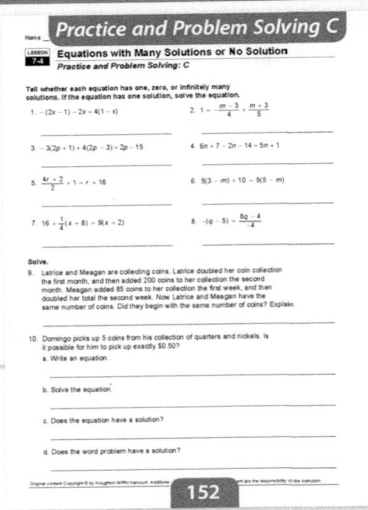

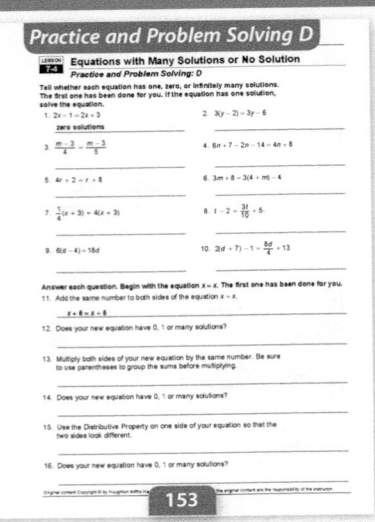

14. Critique Reasoning Lisa says that the indicated angles cannot have the same measure. Marita disagrees and says she can prove that they can have the same measure. Who do you agree with? Justify your answer.

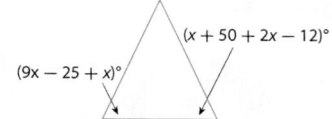

$(9x - 25 + x)°$ $(x + 50 + 2x - 12)°$

Marita; If the angles have the same measure, $9x - 25 + x = x + 50 + 2x - 12$. Solving this equation gives a single solution, $x = 9$. Since $9(9) - 25 + 9 = 81 - 25 + 9 = 65$ and $9 + 50 + 2(9) - 12 = 59 + 18 - 12 = 65$, each angle measures $65°$.

15. Represent Real-World Problems Adele opens an account with $100 and deposits $35 a month. Kent opens an account with $50 and also deposits $35 a month. Will they have the same amount in their accounts at any point? If so, in how many months and how much will be in each account? Explain.

No; setting the expressions equal to each other and solving gives $100 + 35x = 50 + 35x$, or $100 = 50$, which is false.

 **FOCUS ON HIGHER ORDER THINKING**

16. Communicate Mathematical Ideas Frank solved an equation and got the result $x = x$. Sarah solved the same equation and got $12 = 12$. Frank says that one of them is incorrect because you cannot get different results for the same equation. What would you say to Frank? If both results are indeed correct, explain how this happened.

The results may appear different, but their meaning is the same. Both are true statements, so the equation has infinitely many solutions. Frank solved the equation by eliminating 12, while Sarah eliminated x.

17. Critique Reasoning Matt said $2x - 7 = 2(x - 7)$ has infinitely many solutions. Is he correct? Justify Matt's answer or show how he is incorrect.

Matt is incorrect. He applied the Distributive Property to the right side incorrectly. Correctly simplified, the equation is $0 = -7$, which is false, meaning no solution.

© Houghton Mifflin Harcourt Publishing Company

Work Area

✔ **Quick Check**

7.4 Lesson Quiz
Use the properties of equality to simplify each equation. Tell whether the equation has one, zero, or infinitely many solutions.

1. $5x + 6 = 2 + 3x$ $x = -2$; one solution
2. $2(6 - 2y) = -1(4y - 9)$ $12 = 9$; no solution
3. $2z - 6 = 2(z + 2) - 10$ $-6 = -6$; infinitely many solutions

Complete each equation so that it has the indicated number of solutions.

4. no solution: $5x + 1 = 5x +$ ____ Sample answer: 8
5. one solution: $3x - 3 =$ __$x + 11$ Sample answer: 2
6. infinitely many: $8x - 7 = 8x -$ ____ 7

Differentiate Instruction
IF a student misses more than one question, THEN

Differentiate Instruction:
• 7.4 Reteach
• Personal Math Trainer

 Interactive Whiteboard
Interactive Lesson quiz available online

DIFFERENTIATE INSTRUCTION *Extend-the-Math Activity* **PRE-AP**

Activity The larger of two numbers is twice the smaller. Their sum is three times their difference. Find the numbers.

Let $y =$ the smaller number. Let $2y =$ the larger number.
$y + 2y = 3(2y - y)$
   $3y = 6y - 3y$
   $3y = 3y$
    $y = y$
There are infinitely many solutions.

ACTIVITY 7.4

Mathy Plants

Objective
Students will solve multistep equations and use the values of the variables to decode the answer to a riddle.

Grouping
2 students per group (optional)

Materials
- student textbook

Teacher Preparation
Make sure students have the required materials.

Key Concepts
This activity provides students with practice solving multistep equations. Students will:
- solve multistep linear equations
- solve linear equations with rational number coefficients
- solve linear equations whose solutions require expanding expressions using the Distributive Property
- solve linear equations whose solutions require collecting like terms

Encourage students to discuss different methods for solving an equation and decide which method is most efficient.

Mathy Plants

INSTRUCTIONS

STEP 1   Solve each equation for the variable.

A	-14	$3a + 17 = -25$
B	0	$2b - 25 + 5b = 7 - 32$
C	5	$2.7c - 4.5 = 3.6c - 9$
D	6	$\frac{5}{\blacksquare}\blacksquare + \frac{1}{\blacksquare}\blacksquare + \frac{1}{\blacksquare}\blacksquare + \frac{1}{\blacksquare}\blacksquare = 6$
E	-10	$4\blacksquare - \blacksquare\blacksquare - \blacksquare - \blacksquare$
F	17	$420 - \blacksquare\blacksquare\blacksquare - 73$
G	-16	$2(\blacksquare\ \blacksquare\blacksquare - \blacksquare = -20$
H	9	$2h + 7 = -3h + 52$
I	-2	$96i + 245 = 53$
J	13	$3j + 7 = 46$
K	2	$\frac{\blacksquare}{\blacksquare} - \frac{3}{\blacksquare}\blacksquare - \frac{1}{2}$
L	20	$30\blacksquare\ \blacksquare\blacksquare\blacksquare = 50l - 160$
M	2	$4\blacksquare - \blacksquare\frac{\blacksquare}{\blacksquare} - \frac{67}{8}$
N	-5	$24 - \blacksquare\blacksquare - 54$
O	10	$8.4o - 6.8 = 14.2 + 6.3o$
P	-3	$4p - p + 8 = 2p + 5$

© Houghton Mifflin Harcourt Publishing Company   Photo credit: ©gmutlu/E+/Getty Images

---

WARM-UP EXERCISES

Solve each equation.

1. $7a + 16 - 3a = -4$ -5
2. $\frac{7k}{8} - \frac{3}{4} - \frac{5k}{16} = \frac{3}{8}$ 2
3. $\frac{1}{2}(6x - 4) = 4x - 9$ 7
4. $\frac{y}{3} + 11 = \frac{y}{2} - 3$ 84

STEP 1 Students solve the equations.

STEP 2 Students use the solutions to decode the answer to the riddle.

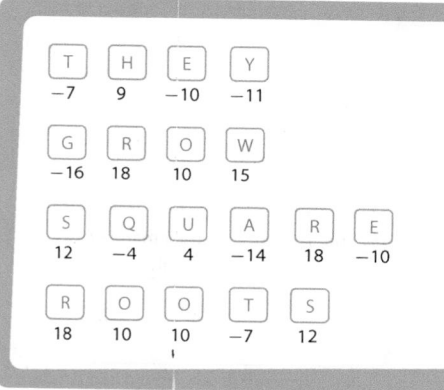

Q	-4	▪ —▪▪ — $3q + 40$
R	18	▪ ▪▪ $\frac{!}{!}$ — ▪ — 8
S	12	$\frac{!}{!}$ — $\frac{!}{!}$ ▪ $\frac{!}{!}$ — $\frac{!}{!}$
T	-7	▪ —▪▪ — $4t + 17$
U	4	▪▪ ▪▪▪ $= 66 + 23u + 31$
V	-1	▪▪▪ ▪▪ ▪▪▪ —▪▪
W	15	▪▪ ▪▪▪ —▪▪ — ▪ ▪ $15 + 2w - 3w$
X	7	▪ ▪▪ ▪▪ ▪▪ ▪▪ $= 75$
Y	-11	$\frac{!—▪}{5}$ — $\frac{!—▪}{8}$
Z	8	— $11 = 25 - 4.5z$

STEP 2 Use the value of each variable to decode the answer to the riddle.

What happens to plants that live in a math classroom?

T	H	E	Y
-7	9	-10	-11

G	R	O	W
-16	18	10	15

S	Q	U	A	R	E
12	-4	4	-14	18	-10

R	O	O	T	S
18	10	10	-7	12

© Houghton Mifflin Harcourt Publishing Company

TEACHER NOTES

- **Discussion** Discuss the methods students used to solve each equation. Find out if there are different methods that students used to solve the same equation, and discuss why students chose their method. Lead students to see that there are many methods that are valid.

- **Extension** Have students work together in groups of four to write new equations for the letters of the alphabet. Have each group write a message in code and trade equations and messages with another group to solve.

- **Variations** Students can work independently or in groups.

Ready to Go On?

Assess Mastery

Access *Ready to Go On?* assessment online, and receive instant scoring, feedback, and customized intervention or enrichment.

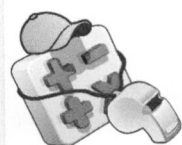

Personal Math Trainer

Online Assessment and Intervention
• Module 7 Posttest

Additional Resources

Digital Teacher Resources

Go online for module-level resources.

Assessment Resources
• Module 7 Quiz: B, p.39
• Module 7 Quiz: D, p.41

Ready to Go On?

Personal Math Trainer
Online Assessment and Intervention
my.hrw.com

7.1 Equations with the Variable on Both Sides

Solve.

1. $4a - 4 = 8 + a$ ___ $a = 4$

2. $4x + 5 = x + 8$ ___ $x = 1$

3. Hue is arranging chairs. She can form 6 rows of a given length with 3 chairs left over, or 8 rows of that same length if she gets 11 more chairs. Write and solve an equation to find how many chairs are in that row length.

$$6c + 3 = 8c - 11; c = 7; 7 \text{ chairs}$$

7.2 Equations with Rational Numbers

Solve.

4. $\frac{2}{3}n - \frac{2}{3} = \frac{n}{6} + \frac{4}{3}$ ___ $n = 4$

5. $1.5d + 3.25 = 1 + 2.25d$ ___ $d = 3$

6. Happy Paws charges $19.00 plus $1.50 per hour to keep a dog during the day. Woof Watchers charges $14.00 plus $2.75 per hour. Write and solve an equation to find for how many hours the total cost of the services is equal.

$$19 + 1.5h = 14 + 2.75h; h = 4; 4 \text{ hours}$$

7.3 Equations with the Distributive Property

Solve.

7. $14 + 5x = 3(-x + 3) - 11$ ___ $x = -2$

8. $\frac{1}{4}(x - 7) = 1 + 3x$ ___ $x = -1$

9. $-5(2x - 9) = 2(x - 8) - 11$ ___ $x = 6$

10. $3(x + 5) = 2(3x + 12)$ ___ $x = -3$

7.4 Equations with Many Solutions or No Solution

Tell whether each equation has one, zero, or infinitely many solutions.

11. $5(x - 3) + 6 = 5x - 9$ ___ infinitely many solutions

12. $5(x - 3) + 6 = 5x - 10$ ___ zero solutions

13. $5(x - 3) + 6 = 4x + 3$ ___ one solution

READY TO GO ON? *Diagnostic Assessment*

RtI Response to Intervention

Use to determine if students have mastered the concepts covered in this module.

Lesson	Exercises	Content Focus	Review with *Differentiated Instruction*
7.1	1–3	Equations with the Variable on Both Sides	**7.1** Reteach **7.1** Reading Strategies **7.1** Success for English Learners
7.2	4–6	Equations with Rational Numbers	**7.2** Reteach **7.2** Reading Strategies **7.2** Success for English Learners
7.3	7–10	Equations with the Distributive Property	**7.3** Reteach **7.3** Reading Strategies **7.3** Success for English Learners
7.4	11–13	Equations with Many Solutions or No Solution	**7.4** Reteach **7.4** Reading Strategies **7.4** Success for English Learners

© Houghton Mifflin Harcourt Publishing Company

Personal Math Trainer

Online Assessment and Intervention

my.hrw.com

Selected Response

1. Two cars are traveling in the same direction. The first car is going 40 mi/h, and the second car is going 55 mi/h. The first car left 3 hours before the second car. Which equation could you solve to find how many hours it will take for the second car to catch up to the first car?

Ⓐ $55t + 3 = 40t$

Ⓑ $55t + 165 = 40t$

Ⓒ $40t + 3 = 55t$

Ⓓ $40t + 120 = 55t$

2. Which linear equation is represented by the table?

x	-2	1	3	6
y	7	4	2	-1

Ⓐ $y = -x + 5$ Ⓒ $y = x + 3$

Ⓑ $y = 2x - 1$ Ⓓ $y = -3x + 11$

3. Shawn's Rentals charges $27.50 per hour to rent a surfboard and a wetsuit. Darla's Surf Shop charges $23.25 per hour to rent a surfboard plus $17 extra for a wetsuit. For what total number of hours are the charges for Shawn's Rentals the same as the charges for Darla's Surf Shop?

Ⓐ 3   Ⓒ 5

Ⓑ 4   Ⓓ 6

4. Which of the following is irrational?

Ⓐ -8 Ⓒ $\sqrt{11}$

Ⓑ 4.63 Ⓓ $\frac{1}{3}$

5. Greg and Jane left a 15% tip after dinner. The amount of the tip was $9. Greg's dinner cost $24. Which equation can you use to find x, the cost of Jane's dinner?

Ⓐ $0.15x + 24 = 9$

Ⓑ $0.15(x + 24) = 9$

Ⓒ $15(x + 24) = 9$

Ⓓ $0.15x = 24 + 9$

6. For the equation $3(2x - 5) = 6x + k$, which value of k will create an equation with infinitely many solutions?

Ⓐ 15   Ⓒ 5

Ⓑ -5 Ⓓ -15

7. Which of the following is equivalent to 2^{-4}?

Ⓐ $\frac{1}{16}$ Ⓒ -2

Ⓑ $\frac{1}{8}$ Ⓓ -16

Mini-Task

8. Use the figures below for parts a and b.

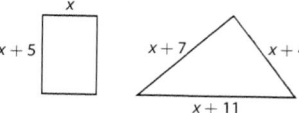

a. Both figures have the same perimeter. Solve for x.

$x = 12$

b. What is the perimeter of each figure?

58 units

© Houghton Mifflin Harcourt Publishing Company

Preparing for High Stakes Tests

Assessment Readiness Tip

Students can choose between testing the answer choices or writing and solving an equation or inequality.

- **Item 3** Students can find the two expressions to represent this problem, $27.5x$ and $17 + 23.25x$, set them equal to each other, and then solve. However, they may find it easier and quicker to test the answer choices.

- **Item 6** Students may initially assume that testing individual answer choices is the only way to find the solution because the given equation has two unknowns. However, if they simplify the equation, they will find that the x terms cancel out, leaving the correct value of k as the answer.

Avoid Common Errors

- **Item 5** Remind students that since the tip was applied to the cost of both meals, parentheses must be used to ensure the addition is performed before the multiplication.

- **Item 8** Students may only sum x and $x + 5$ when finding the perimeter of the rectangle. Remind them that they must sum the lengths of all four sides, so x and $x + 5$ must both be used twice.

Items	Grade 8 Lessons	Mathematical Processes
1	7.1	MP.4
2*	5.2	MP.4
3	7.2	MP.4
4*	1.1	MP.6
5	7.2	MP.4
6	7.4	MP.2
7*	2.1	MP.6
8	7.1	MP.4

Item integrates mixed review concepts from previous modules or a previous course.

DIFFERENTIATE ASSESSMENT

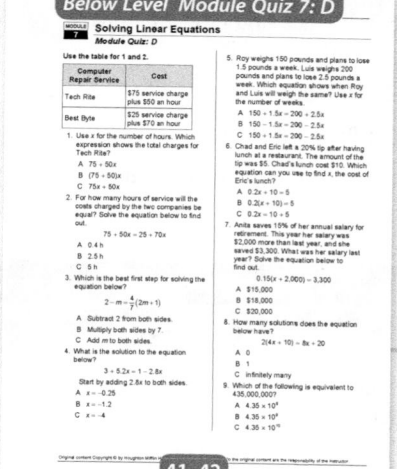

Below Level Module Quiz 7: D

41–42

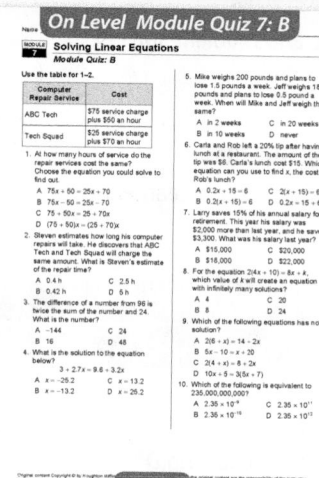

On Level Module Quiz 7: B

39–40

Personal Math Trainer

Module 7 Assessment Readiness

Pages shown are from *Assessment Resources*. **Also available online.**

Module At A Glance

MODULE 8 | Solving Systems of Linear Equations

Lessons at A Glance	Lesson 8.1 Solving Systems of Linear Equations by Graphing	Lesson 8.2 Solving Systems by Substitution	Lesson 8.3 Solving Systems by Elimination
	Pg. T227A	Pg. T235A	Pg. T243A
Essential Question	How can you solve a system of equations by graphing?	How do you use substitution to solve a system of linear equations?	How do you solve a system of linear equations by adding or subtracting?
Objective	Students will solve a system of equations by graphing.	Students will use substitution to solve a system of linear equations.	Students will solve a system of linear equations by adding or subtracting.
Vocabulary	solution of a system of equations, system of equations	substitution method	elimination method
Go online for all your module resources my.hrw.com	8.1 iStudent Edition 8.1 iTeacher Edition 8.1 eStudent Edition Personal Math Trainer Math on the Spot Videos Animated Math	8.2 iStudent Edition 8.2 iTeacher Edition 8.2 eStudent Edition Personal Math Trainer Math on the Spot Videos	8.3 iStudent Edition 8.3 iTeacher Edition 8.3 eStudent Edition Personal Math Trainer Math on the Spot Videos
Print Resources	**8.1 Student Edition:** Lesson *Differentiated Instruction* 8.1 Practice and Problem Solving A/B, C, and D 8.1 Reteach 8.1 Reading Strategies 8.1 Success for English Learners	**8.2 Student Edition:** Lesson *Differentiated Instruction* 8.2 Practice and Problem Solving A/B, C, and D 8.2 Reteach 8.2 Reading Strategies 8.2 Success for English Learners	**8.3 Student Edition:** Lesson *Differentiated Instruction* 8.3 Practice and Problem Solving A/B, C, and D 8.3 Reteach 8.3 Reading Strategies 8.3 Success for English Learners

RtI — Response to Intervention

Before the Module	During the Lesson	After the Module
Are You Ready	**Guided/Independent Practice**	**Ready to Go On?**
• Prerequisite Skills Activities • Personal Math Trainer	• Reteach • Personal Math Trainer • Practice and Problem Solving D	• Reteach • Personal Math Trainer

Teacher Notes

Lesson 8.4
Solving Systems by Elimination with Multiplication

Pg. T251A

How do you solve a system of linear equations by multiplying?

Students will solve a system of linear equations by adding or subtracting.

8.4 *i*Student Edition
8.4 *i*Teacher Edition
8.4 *e*Student Edition
Personal Math Trainer
Math on the Spot Videos

8.4 Student Edition: Lesson
Differentiated Instruction
8.4 Practice and Problem Solving A/B, C, and D
8.4 Reteach
8.4 Reading Strategies
8.4 Success for English Learners

Lesson 8.5
Solving Special Systems

Pg. T259A

How do you solve a system with no solutions or infinitely many solutions?

Students will solve a system with no solutions or infinitely many solutions.

8.5 *i*Student Edition
8.5 *i*Teacher Edition
8.5 *e*Student Edition
Personal Math Trainer
Math on the Spot Videos

8.5 Student Edition: Lesson
Differentiated Instruction
8.5 Practice and Problem Solving A/B, C, and D
8.5 Reteach
8.5 Reading Strategies
8.5 Success for English Learners

Check It Out!

Math on the Spot Videos	Animated Math
One for every Example in every Lesson	During Lesson 8.1

Solving Systems of Linear Equations

Real-World Video Viewing Guide

After students have watched the video, discuss the following:

- How can a system of equations be used to determine how long it will take two people to travel the same distance if they leave at different times?

- What does the intersection of the two graphs represent in the video? the time of arrival

Professional Development Video

Author Juli Dixon models successful teaching practices as she explores the concept of systems of equations in an actual eighth-grade classroom.

Solving Systems of Linear Equations

MODULE 8

You can use systems of linear equations to find ordered pairs where two quantities are the same, such as costs for services from two different businesses.

? ESSENTIAL QUESTION

How can you use systems of equations to solve real-world problems?

LESSON 8.1
Solving Systems of Linear Equations by Graphing

LESSON 8.2
Solving Systems by Substitution

LESSON 8.3
Solving Systems by Elimination

LESSON 8.4
Solving Systems by Elimination with Multiplication

LESSON 8.5
Solving Special Systems

© Houghton Mifflin Harcourt Publishing Company • Image Credits: ©Kenny Ferguson/Alamy Images

Real-World Video

The distance contestants in a race travel over time can be modeled by a system of equations. Solving such a system can tell you when one contestant will overtake another who has a head start, as in a boating race or marathon.

my.hrw.com

GO DIGITAL
my.hrw.com

my.hrw.com
Go digital with your write-in student edition, accessible on any device.

Math On the Spot
Scan with your smart phone to jump directly to the online edition, video tutor, and more.

Animated Math
Interactively explore key concepts to see how math works.

Personal Math Trainer
Get immediate feedback and help as you work through practice sets.

223

TEACHER ONLINE RESOURCES

ONLINE TEACHER EDITION Access a full suite of teaching resources online—plan, present, and manage classes and assignments.

INTERACTIVE WHITEBOARDS Engage students with interactive whiteboard-ready examples and a lesson quiz for each lesson.

MY SMART PLANNER Easily plan your classes and access all your resources online.

PERSONAL MATH TRAINER: Online Assessment and Intervention Assign automatically graded homework, quizzes, tests, and intervention activities. Prepare your students for standardized tests in short-answer and multiple-choice formats.

Reading Start-Up

Visualize Vocabulary

Use the ✔ words to complete the graphic.

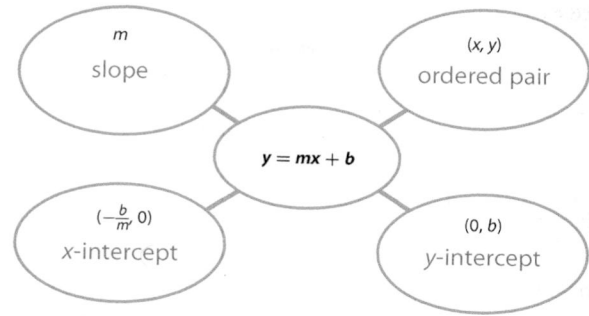

- m — slope
- (x, y) — ordered pair
- $y = mx + b$
- $\left(-\frac{b}{m}, 0\right)$ — x-intercept
- $(0, b)$ — y-intercept

Understand Vocabulary

Complete the sentences using the preview words.

1. A __solution of a system of equations__ is any ordered pair
   that satisfies all the equations in a system.

2. A set of two or more equations that contain two or more variables is
   called a __system of equations__.

Active Reading

Four-Corner Fold Before beginning the module, create a four-corner fold to help you organize what you learn about solving systems of equations. Use the categories "Solving by Graphing," "Solving by Substitution," "Solving by Elimination," and "Solving by Multiplication." As you study this module, note similarities and differences among the four methods. You can use your four-corner fold later to study for tests and complete assignments.

© Houghton Mifflin Harcourt Publishing Company

Vocabulary

Review Words

- linear equation *(ecuación lineal)*
- ✔ ordered pair *(par ordenado)*
- ✔ slope *(pendiente)*
- slope-intercept form *(forma pendiente intersección)*
- x-axis *(eje x)*
- ✔ x-intercept *(intersección con el eje x)*
- y-axis *(eje y)*
- ✔ y-intercept *(intersección con el eje y)*

Preview Words

- solution of a system of equations *(solución de un sistema de ecuaciones)*
- system of equations *(sistema de ecuaciones)*

Reading Start-Up

Visualize Vocabulary

The concept web helps students review vocabulary associated with the slope-intercept form of a linear equation. Students should write one review word in each oval.

Understand Vocabulary

Use the following explanations to help students learn the preview words.

A **system of equations** is a set of two or more equations that have the same variables. A **solution of a system of equations** is an ordered pair that satisfies all equations in the system simultaneously.

Active Reading

Integrating Language Arts

Students can use these reading and note-taking strategies to help them organize and understand new concepts and vocabulary.

Additional Resources

Differentiated Instruction

- Reading Strategies **ELL**
- Interactive multilingual glossary

LEARNING PROGRESSIONS ACROSS THE GRADES

Before	In this Module	After
Students understand: • how to solve linear equations • how to graph linear equations	Students will learn how to: • solve systems of two linear equations in two variables using graphing, elimination, and substitution • analyze special systems that have no solution or an infinite number of solutions • represent real-world situations using systems of equations	Students will connect: • graphical and algebraic representations of systems of equations and their solutions

Are You Ready?

Assess Readiness

Access *Are You Ready?* assessment online, and receive instant scoring, feedback, and customized intervention or enrichment.

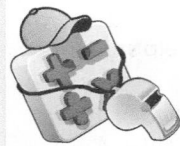

Personal Math Trainer

Online Assessment and Intervention

Additional Resources

Digital Teacher Resources

Go online for module-level resources.

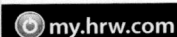

my.hrw.com

Personal Math Trainer
Online Assessment and Intervention

Complete these exercises to review skills you will need for this module.

Simplify Algebraic Expressions

EXAMPLE   Simplify $5 - 4y + 2x - 6 + y$.
$-4y + y + 2x - 6 + 5$ Group like terms.
$-3y + 2x - 1$ Combine like terms.

Simplify.

1. $14x - 4x + 21$

$10x + 21$

2. $-y - 4x + 4y$

$3y - 4x$

3. $5.5a - 1 + 21b + 3a$

$8.5a + 21b - 1$

4. $2y - 3x + 6x - y$

$y + 3x$

Graph Linear Equations

EXAMPLE   Graph $y = -\frac{1}{3}x + 2$.
Step 1: Make a table of values.

x	$y = -\frac{1}{3}x + 2$	(x, y)
0	$y = -\frac{1}{3}(0) + 2 = 2$	$(0, 2)$
3	$y = -\frac{1}{3}(3) + 2 = 1$	$(3, 1)$

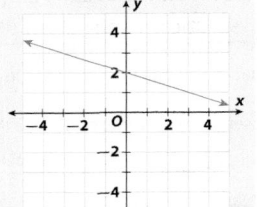

Step 2: Plot the points.
Step 3: Connect the points with a line.

Graph each equation.

5. $y = 4x - 1$

6. $y = \frac{1}{2}x + 1$

7. $y = -x$

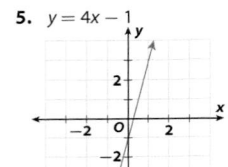
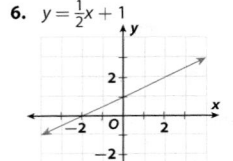
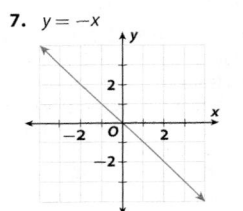

© Houghton Mifflin Harcourt Publishing Company

ARE YOU READY? *Diagnostic Assessment*

RtI Response to Intervention

Use to determine if students need intervention for the module's prerequisite skills.

Skill	Missed More Than . . .	Intervene With *Skills Intervention* worksheets (available online)	For Enrichment *Differentiated Instruction* (available in print and online)
Simplify Algebraic Expressions	1 question	**Skill 55** Simplify Algebraic Expressions	**Module 8 Challenge** Extend-the-Math Lesson Activities in TE
Graph Linear Equations	1 question	**Skill 64** Graph Linear Equations	**Module 8 Challenge** Extend-the-Math Lesson Activities in TE

Complete these exercises to review skills you will need for this module.

Simplify Algebraic Expressions

8. Simplify $18x - 5 - 5x + 9$. Show your work, and explain each step.

$18x - 5x - 5 + 9$	Group like terms.
$(18 - 5)x + (-5 + 9)$	Combine like terms.
$13x + 4$	Simplify.

9. Marina said that $-x - 8 + 5y + 9x$ can be simplified to $13y - 8$. What was her error?

Marina added all the coefficients of the variables instead of grouping the x terms separately from the y term. The correct simplified expression is $8x + 5y - 8$.

Graph Linear Equations

10. Complete the table of values to determine four points that can be used to graph $y = 3x + 2$.

x	y = 3x + 2	(x, y)
−1	$y = 3(-1) + 2$	(−1, −1)
0	$y = 3(0) + 2$	(0, 2)
1	$y = 3(1) + 2$	(1, 5)
2	$y = 3(2) + 2$	(2, 8)

11. Graph the equation $y = -3x + 1$. Is the point $(-1, 4)$ on the graph? Why or why not?

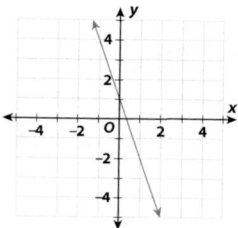

Yes; because $4 = -3(-1) + 1$.

© Houghton Mifflin Harcourt Publishing Company

Simplify Algebraic Expressions

Exercise 8 Students often make errors rearranging like terms when subtraction is involved in simplifying an algebraic expression. Suggest that they rewrite all subtraction as addition of the opposite to avoid these errors.

Exercise 9 Make sure students understand that like terms must have the same variable (and exponent if there is one) when they simplify algebraic expressions.

Graph Linear Equations

Exercise 10 Help students make the connection between using the equation of a graph in the second column and the coordinates of points on the graph in the third column.

Exercise 11 Students can check if a point is on the graph of an equation by substituting the x- and y-coordinates of the point into the equation.

Use to determine if students are able to apply the module's prerequisite skills.

Skill	Exercise	Depth of Knowledge (D.O.K.)	Mathematical Processes
Simplify Algebraic Expressions	8	**2** Skills/Concepts	**MP.7** See Structure
	9	**3** Strategic Thinking	**MP.3** Use and Evaluate Logical Reasoning
Graph Linear Equations	10	**2** Skills/Concepts	**MP.7** See Structure
	11	**3** Strategic Thinking	**MP.7** See Structure

Lesson Support

Content Objective Students will learn how to solve a system of equations by graphing.

Professional Development

Integrate Mathematical Processes MP.3

This lesson provides an opportunity to address this Mathematical Processes standard. It calls for students to reason logically about what it means for a system of two linear equations in two variables to have a unique solution or infinitely many solutions, both graphically and algebraically. Students also have the opportunity to make conjectures about the conditions under which a system of three linear equations in two variables will have a unique solution.

FOCUS

Building Background

Eliciting Prior Knowledge Have students create an information wheel to write the tools they can use to graph a linear equation. They should include as graphing tools the slope and *y*-intercept of a linear equation in slope-intercept form, making a table with at least two ordered pairs, and plotting the ordered pairs in the coordinate plane.

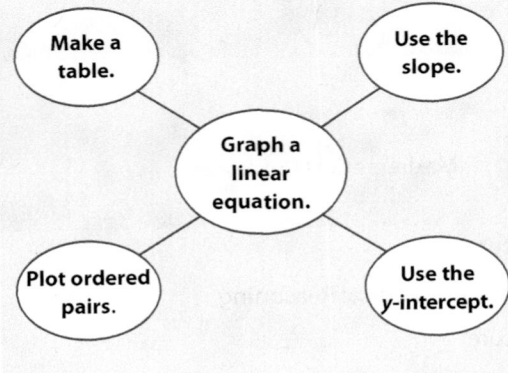

COHERENCE

Learning Progressions

In this lesson, students solve a system of two linear equations by graphing the equations and identifying the point of intersection of the lines. Important understandings for students include the following:

- **Solve a system of linear equations by graphing.**
- **Rewrite a linear equation written in standard form in slope-intercept form.**
- **Solve problems using systems of linear equations graphically.**

In Grade 8, students start to solve problems that lead to simultaneous equations. This lesson introduces students to the graphical method that can be used to solve a system. It introduces students to real-world problem situations that are solved by formulating and then solving a linear system. The emphasis on context helps students recognize the usefulness of setting up and solving these systems.

RIGOR

Cluster Connections

This lesson provides an excellent opportunity to connect ideas in the cluster:

Analyze and solve linear equations and pairs of simultaneous linear equations.

Ask students whether the ordered pair (2, 1) is a solution of the following system:

$$\begin{cases} x - y = 3 \\ 2x + y = 3 \end{cases}$$

After they test the point in the equations, ask them to solve the system by graphing.

no; (2, −1)

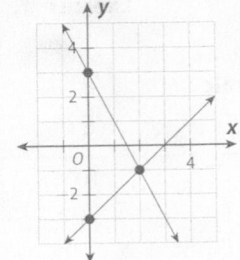

Language Support **ELL**

Language Objective Students will demonstrate how to solve a system of equations by graphing.

Leveled Strategies for English Learners **ELL**

Emerging
In order to make the concept easier to grasp, have students work in small teams to select a problem from this lesson, role play, and show the solution.

Expanding
Have students plan a party that must stay within a budget. Pairs of students will create a system of linear equations that represents how a certain amount of money will be spent on two items. For example, one pair works with pizza and drinks and another with plates and cups.

Bridging
Have students observe as another group plans a party that must stay within a budget. Students prepare to report on the steps that were taken to plan the party so that it would stay on budget.

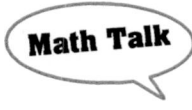

To help students answer Reflect questions in this lesson, provide sentence frames for them to use.

Linguistic Support **ELL**

Academic/Content Vocabulary
Demonstrate for English learners to help them better understand systems of equations.

Have students model a problem that involves two objects moving at different speeds. Beginning with two students at the same location, have one walk forward at a slow, steady pace. A few seconds later, have the other student walk along the same path at a faster speed until the second student catches up with the first student. Ask whether the second person could catch up if he or she walked the same speed or a slower speed. The point at which the second person catches up models the point at which the two lines intersect.

Cognates and Borrowed Words
Students will be using the word *equation* frequently in algebra. *Equation* is a cognate with Spanish. English and Spanish share many words from Latin, including many roots, prefixes, and suffixes. Many words in English that end with *-tion* are shared with Spanish words ending in *-ción*. These shared words are known as cognates. Some are shown below.

English *-tion*	Spanish *-ción*
multiplication	multiplicación
equation	ecuación
solution	solución
elimination	eliminación

Image Credits: ©Monkey Business Images/Shutterstock

1 Engage

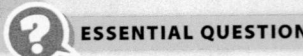

ESSENTIAL QUESTION

How can you solve a system of equations by graphing? Sample answer: Find the ordered pair at the point where the graphs of the equations intersect.

Motivate the Lesson

Ask: Do you think you could catch up with your friend before he gets home if you leave school 10 minutes later but travel twice as fast? Begin the Explore Activity to find out.

2 Explore

EXPLORE ACTIVITY

Focus on Reasoning

Elicit from students that the solution is the ordered pair represented by the point where the two lines intersect.

LESSON 8.1 Solving Systems of Linear Equations by Graphing

8.3.8.1
Students will solve a system of equations by graphing.

? ESSENTIAL QUESTION

How can you solve a system of equations by graphing?

EXPLORE ACTIVITY

Investigating Systems of Equations

You have learned several ways to graph a linear equation in slope-intercept form. For example, you can use the slope and y-intercept or you can find two points that satisfy the equation and connect them with a line.

> Slope-intercept form is $y = mx + b$, where m is the slope and b is the y-intercept.

A Graph the pair of equations together: $\begin{cases} y = 3x - 2 \\ y = -2x + 3 \end{cases}$.

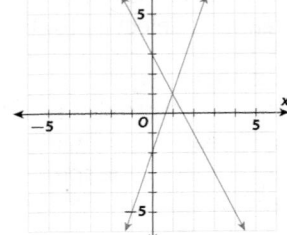

B Explain how to tell whether $(2, -1)$ is a solution of the equation $y = 3x - 2$ without using the graph.

Substituting $(2, -1)$ into the equation results in a false statement, so it is not a solution.

C Explain how to tell whether $(2, -1)$ is a solution of the equation $y = -2x + 3$ without using the graph.

Substituting $(2, -1)$ into the equation results in a true statement, so it is a solution.

D Use the graph to explain whether $(2, -1)$ is a solution of each equation.

If $(2, -1)$ is on the line, it is a solution. So, $(2, -1)$ is not a solution of $y = 3x - 2$ but it is a solution of $y = -2x + 3$.

E Determine if the point of intersection is a solution of both equations.

Point of intersection: $\left(\boxed{1}, \boxed{1} \right)$

$y = 3x - 2$

$\boxed{1} = 3\boxed{1} - 2$

$1 = \boxed{1}$

$y = -2x + 3$

$\boxed{1} = -2\boxed{1} + 3$

$1 = \boxed{1}$

The point of intersection **is** / **is not** the solution of both equations.

© Houghton Mifflin Harcourt Publishing Company

DIFFERENTIATE INSTRUCTION *Leveled Questions*

	EXPLORE ACTIVITY
AL DOK 1 *Recall*	What is the point of intersection for the two lines graphed? (1, 1)
OL DOK 2 *Skills/Concepts*	Given the coordinates of a point and an equation of a line, how do you know if the point is on the line? All points that satisfy the equation are points that are on the graph of the equation.
BL DOK 3 *Strategic Thinking*	Why do you think that a solution of a system of equations is given by the coordinates of the point of intersection of the graphs of the equations? A solution of both equations will be a point on both graphs, so it must be an intersection.

Math On the Spot
my.hrw.com

Solving Systems Graphically

An ordered pair (x, y) is a solution of an equation in two variables if substituting the x- and y-values into the equation results in a true statement. A **system of equations** is a set of equations that have the same variables. An ordered pair is a **solution of a system of equations** if it is a solution of every equation in the set.

Since the graph of an equation represents all ordered pairs that are solutions of the equation, if a point lies on the graphs of two equations, the point is a solution of both equations and is, therefore, a solution of the system.

EXAMPLE 1

My Notes

Solve each system by graphing.

A $\begin{cases} y = -x + 4 \\ y = 3x \end{cases}$

> **STEP 1** Start by graphing each equation.
>
> **STEP 2** Find the point of intersection of the two lines. It appears to be (1, 3). Check by substitution to determine if it is a solution to both equations.

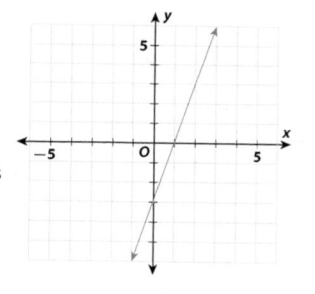

$$y = -x + 4 \qquad y = 3x$$
$$3 \overset{?}{=} -(1) + 4 \qquad 3 \overset{?}{=} 3(1)$$
$$3 = 3 \checkmark \qquad 3 = 3 \checkmark$$

> ○ The solution of the system is (1, 3).

B $\begin{cases} y = 3x - 3 \\ y = 3(x - 1) \end{cases}$

> **STEP 1** Start by graphing each equation.
>
> **STEP 2** Identify any ordered pairs that are solutions of both equations.
>
> The graphs of the equations are the same line. So, every ordered pair that is a solution of one equation is also a solution of the other equation. The system has
> ○ infinitely many solutions.

© Houghton Mifflin Harcourt Publishing Company

228 Unit 3

Connect Vocabulary **ELL**

A *system* is a set of things working together. If any one of the things is not working, then the system does not work. Similarly, an ordered pair is the solution of a system of equations only if it is the solution for each equation.

EXAMPLE 1

ADDITIONAL EXAMPLE 1
Solve each system by graphing.

A $\begin{cases} y = -2x - 4 \\ y = 3x + 1 \end{cases}$ $(-1, -2)$

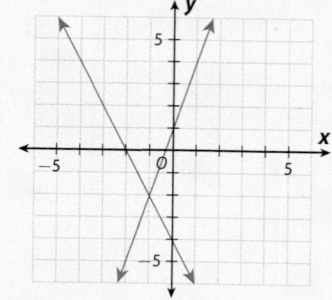

B $\begin{cases} y = -2x - 4 \\ y = -2(x + 2) \end{cases}$ infinitely many solutions

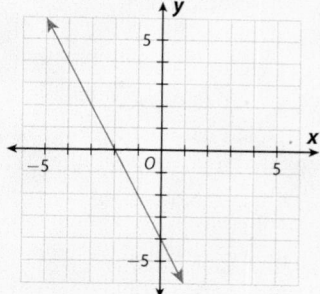

 Interactive Whiteboard
Interactive example available online

	EXAMPLE 1
AL **DOK 1** *Recall*	What is the process for solving a linear system by graphing? Graph the lines; find the point of intersection; verify that it is a solution of both equations.
OL **DOK 2** *Skills/Concepts*	How do you verify that the apparent point of intersection is a solution of the equation? Use substitution to check that the coordinates of the point satisfy both equations.
BL **DOK 3** *Strategic Thinking*	Why is it necessary to check the point of intersection that you read from the graph? Justify your reasoning. Reading the point of intersection from the graph is an approximation based on the appearance of the graph, so it must be verified mathematically.

TEACHER TO TEACHER

Kinesthetic Experience Model a problem with two objects moving at different speeds. Have two students stand at the same location. Then have one student walk slowly forward. A few seconds later, have another student walk quickly along the same path until the students catch up. The point at which they catch up is the point at which they intersect (the elapsed time and distance traveled is the same for both). Ask whether the second student will catch up if they walked the same speed.

Focus on Modeling

Review methods of graphing lines. Students can either use a table of values or plot the *y*-intercept and use the slope to plot additional points on the line. Explain that if either line is not drawn accurately, the solution point will not be correct.

Reflect

1. A system of linear equations has infinitely many solutions. Does that mean any ordered pair in the coordinate plane is a solution?

   No, only ordered pairs that lie on the graph are solutions.

2. Can you show algebraically that both equations in part B represent the same line? If so, explain how.

   Yes; by simplifying the second equation, $y = 3(x - 1) = 3x - 3$, you can see that both equations are identical.

YOUR TURN

Solve each system by graphing. Check by substitution.

3. $\begin{cases} y = -x + 2 \\ y = -4x - 1 \end{cases}$ $(-1, 3)$

   Check:

$y = -x + 2$	$y = -4x - 1$
$3 = -(-1) + 2$	$3 = -4(-1) - 1$
$3 = 3 \checkmark$	$3 = 3 \checkmark$

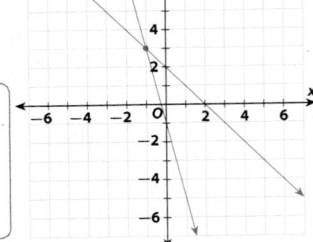

4. $\begin{cases} y = -2x + 5 \\ y = 3x \end{cases}$ $(1, 3)$

   Check:

$y = -2x + 5$	$y = 3x$
$3 = -2(1) + 5$	$3 = 3(1)$
$3 = 3 \checkmark$	$3 = 3 \checkmark$

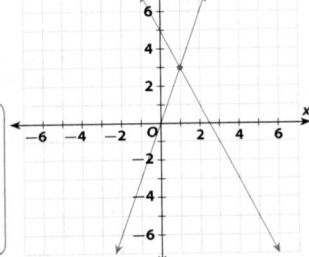

Personal
Math Trainer
Online Assessment
and Intervention
my.hrw.com

© Houghton Mifflin Harcourt Publishing Company

Math On the Spot
my.hrw.com

Solving Problems Using Systems of Equations

When using graphs to solve a system of equations, it is best to rewrite both equations in slope-intercept form for ease of graphing.

To write an equation in slope-intercept form starting from $ax + by = c$:

$$ax + by = c$$

$$by = c - ax \qquad \text{Subtract } ax \text{ from both sides.}$$

$$y = \frac{c}{b} - \frac{ax}{b} \qquad \text{Divide both sides by } b.$$

$$y = -\frac{a}{b}x + \frac{c}{b} \qquad \text{Rearrange the equation.}$$

EXAMPLE 2

Keisha and her friends visit the concession stand at a football game. The stand charges $2 for a hot dog and $1 for a drink. The friends buy a total of 8 items for $11. Tell how many hot dogs and how many drinks they bought.

STEP 1   Let x represent the number of hot dogs they bought and let y represent the number of drinks they bought.

Write an equation representing the **number of items they purchased.**

Number of hot dogs	+	Number of drinks	=	Total items
x	+	y	=	8

Write an equation representing the **money spent on the items.**

Cost of 1 hot dog times number of hot dogs	+	Cost of 1 drink times number of drinks	=	Total cost
$2x$	+	$1y$	=	11

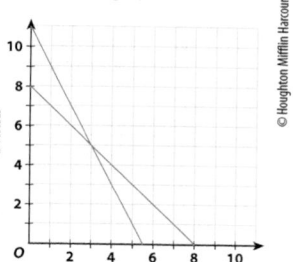

STEP 2   Write the equations in slope-intercept form. Then graph.

$$x + y = 8$$
$$y = 8 - x$$
$$y = -x + 8$$

$$2x + 1y = 11$$
$$1y = 11 - 2x$$
$$y = -2x + 11$$

Graph the equations $y = -x + 8$ and $y = -2x + 11$.

[Graph with axes labeled "Drinks" (vertical) and "Hot dogs" (horizontal), both ranging 0 to 10.]

© Houghton Mifflin Harcourt Publishing Company • Image Credits:
©Veronica Ankorhom/Houghton Mifflin Harcourt

EXAMPLE 2

ADDITIONAL EXAMPLE 2

Zander uses an online store that sells songs for $1 each and movies for $6. He used all of his $20 allowance to buy 10 items. How many songs and how many movies did he buy? 8 songs and 2 movies

Interactive Whiteboard
Interactive example available online

DIFFERENTIATE INSTRUCTION *Leveled Questions*

	EXAMPLE 2
(AL) **DOK 1** *Recall*	What do the two equations represent in this situation? One equation is the total number of items; the other equation is the total cost of the items.
(OL) **DOK 2** *Skills/Concepts*	Why can the solution only have non-negative integer values in this situation? You cannot buy part of a soda or part of a hot dog.
(BL) **DOK 3** *Strategic Thinking*	What other information can you determine from the graph of this linear system model? Sample answer: From one line, you can determine the possible combinations of items totaling 8 that were purchased at the concession stand. From the other line, you can determine the possible numbers of each item that would total $11 at the concession stand. The intercepts of each line give the minimum and maximum values.

TEACHER TO TEACHER

Home Connection Have students bring from home pizza menus and grocery store advertisements. Have students work in groups to plan a party that must stay within a budget. Each group will write a system of linear equations to represent how a given amount of money can be spent on two things. For example, show how $100 can be spent on pizza and wings; how $25 can be spent on water bottles and juice boxes; and how $10 can be spent on plates and cups.

Animated Math

Explore a System of Equations
Using a model of two runners, students discover how a graph can show where the runners' paths will intersect.

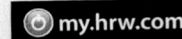
my.hrw.com

YOUR TURN   MP.4

Engage with the Whiteboard

 After graphing both lines, discuss what each line means. Point out that the graph of $2x + 4y = 20$ shows how many of each game can be played for $20 with no restriction on the number of games. Draw graphs of $x + y = 5$ and $x + y = 7$ to see how the solution of the system changes with a different total number of games played.

Digital Teacher Resources

Go online to access all your lesson-level resources.

Differentiated Instruction
• Reteach
• Reading Strategies
• Success for English Learners
• Practice and Problem Solving A/B, C, D

Math on the Spot Videos

my.hrw.com

Animated Math
my.hrw.com

STEP 3   Use the graph to identify the solution of the system of equations. Check your answer by substituting the ordered pair into both equations.

Apparent solution: (3, 5)
Check:

$x + y = 8$	$2x + y = 11$
$3 + 5 \overset{?}{=} 8$	$2(3) + 5 \overset{?}{=} 11$
$8 = 8 ✓$	$11 = 11 ✓$

The point (3, 5) is a solution of both equations.

STEP 4   Interpret the solution in the original context.

Keisha and her friends bought 3 hot dogs and 5 drinks.

Reflect

5.   **Conjecture** Why do you think the graph is limited to the first quadrant?

<u>It would not make sense to buy a negative number of</u>

<u>items or to spend a negative amount of money.</u>

YOUR TURN

6.   During school vacation, Marquis wants to go bowling and to play laser tag. He wants to play 6 total games but needs to figure out how many of each he can play if he spends exactly $20. Each game of bowling is $2 and each game of laser tag is $4.

a.   Let x represent the number of games Marquis bowls and let y represent the number of games of laser tag Marquis plays. Write a system of equations that describes the situation. Then write the equations in slope-intercept form.

<u>$x + y = 6$ and $2x + 4y = 20$; $y = -x + 6$ and</u>

<u>$y = -0.5x + 5$</u>

b.   Graph the solutions of both equations.

c.   How many games of bowling and how many games of laser tag will Marquis play?

<u>Marquis will bowl 2 games</u>

<u>and play 4 games of laser</u>

<u>tag.</u>

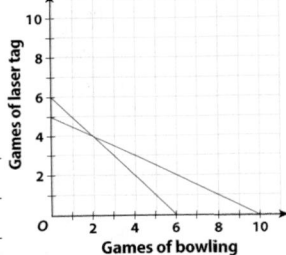

Personal Math Trainer

Online Assessment and Intervention

my.hrw.com

© Houghton Mifflin Harcourt Publishing Company

Solve each system by graphing. (Example 1)

1. $\begin{cases} y = 3x - 4 \\ y = x + 2 \end{cases}$ _____ (3, 5)

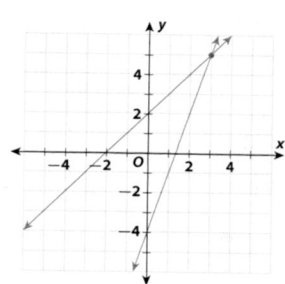

2. $\begin{cases} x - 3y = 2 \\ -3x + 9y = -6 \end{cases}$ _____ infinitely many solutions

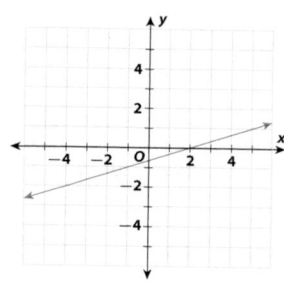

3. Mrs. Morales wrote a test with 15 questions covering spelling and vocabulary. Spelling questions (*x*) are worth 5 points and vocabulary questions (*y*) are worth 10 points. The maximum number of points possible on the test is 100. (Example 2)

   a. Write an equation in slope-intercept form to represent the number of questions on the test.

   _____ $y = -x + 15$ _____

   b. Write an equation in slope-intercept form to represent the total number of points on the test.

   _____ $y = -0.5x + 10$ _____

   c. Graph the solutions of both equations.

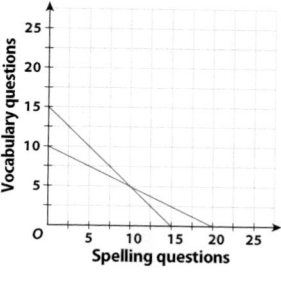

   d. Use your graph to tell how many of each question type are on the test.

   _____ 10 spelling questions and 5 vocabulary questions _____

? ESSENTIAL QUESTION CHECK-IN

4. When you graph a system of linear equations, why does the intersection of the two lines represent the solution of the system?

   Every point on a line makes a linear equation true. A point

   that is on both lines (the intersection point) makes both

   equations true.

© Houghton Mifflin Harcourt Publishing Company

4 Elaborate

Talk About It

Summarize the Lesson

Ask: Given a coordinate plane that contains the graph of two linear equations, how can you identify the solution to the system of equations? The solution is the ordered pair at the point of intersection. There are infinitely many solutions if the lines are the same line.

Guided Practice

Avoid Common Errors

- **Exercises 1–3** Remind students to check their answers algebraically after finding the solution on the graph.

- **Exercise 2** Remind students that if the graphs of both lines are the same, the entire line is the intersection and any point that solves one equation also solves the other.

Engage with the Whiteboard

For **Exercise 2**, replace the second equation with $x = 3y + 2$ and have a student graph this equation. Have students describe the solution to the new system.

DIFFERENTIATE INSTRUCTION *Intervention and Additional Support*

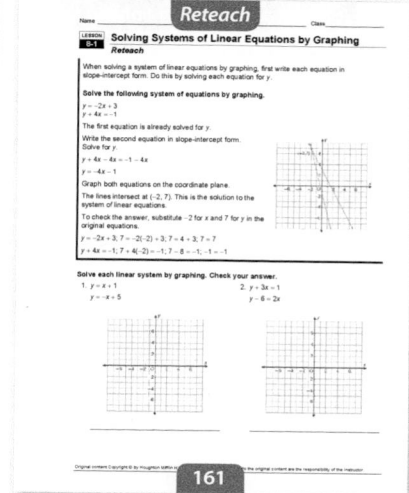

161

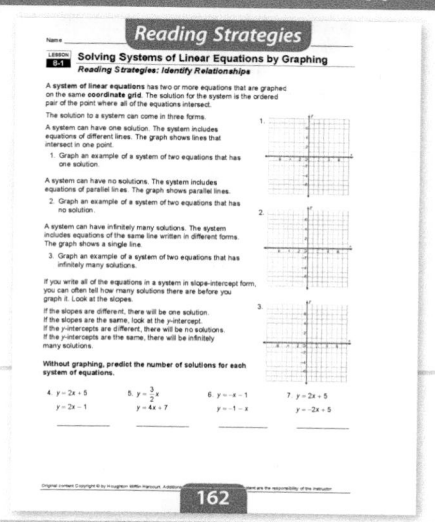

162

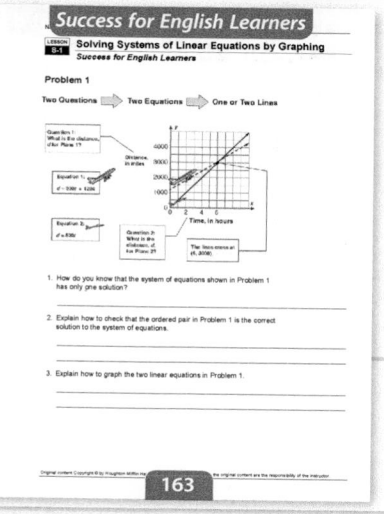

163

Personal Math Trainer
Daily Intervention
8.1 Homework

Pages shown are from *Differentiated Instruction*.
Also available online.

5 Evaluate

🕐 **Pressed for Time**

8.1 Differentiated Homework Assignments

AL **Approaching Level** 5–10

OL **On Level** 6–10

BL **Beyond Level** 8–11

*For **Below Level** students, assign Personal Math Trainer, Daily Intervention 8.1 Homework.*

Mathematical Processes	Exercises
MP.2 Reasoning	6–7
MP.3 Logic	11
MP.4 Modeling	8–10
MP.6 Precision	5

Focus on Higher Order Thinking

Depth of Knowledge	Exercises
1 Recall of Information	5
2 Skills/Concepts	6–9
3 Strategic Thinking H.O.T.	10–11

8.1 Independent Practice

Personal Math Trainer
Online Assessment and Intervention
my.hrw.com

5. **Vocabulary** A _system of equations_ is a set of equations that have the same variables.

6. Eight friends started a business. They will wear either a baseball cap or a shirt imprinted with their logo while working. They want to spend exactly $36 on the shirts and caps. Shirts cost $6 each and caps cost $3 each.

a. Write a system of equations to describe the situation. Let x represent the number of shirts and let y represent the number of caps.

$x + y = 8$

$6x + 3y = 36$

b. Graph the system. What is the solution and what does it represent?

Business Logo Wear

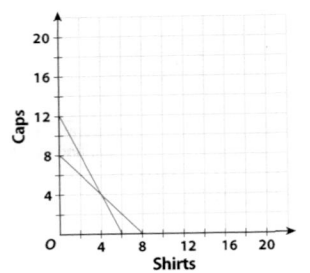

The solution is (4, 4). It represents that 4 people will get shirts and 4 people will get caps.

7. **Multistep** The table shows the cost for bowling at two bowling alleys.

	Shoe Rental Fee	Cost per Game
Bowl-o-Rama	$2.00	$2.50
Bowling Pinz	$4.00	$2.00

a. Write a system of equations, with one equation describing the cost to bowl at Bowl-o-Rama and the other describing the cost to bowl at Bowling Pinz. For each equation, let x represent the number of games played and let y represent the total cost.

$y = 2.50x + 2$

$y = 2x + 4$

b. Graph the system. What is the solution and what does it represent?

Cost of Bowling

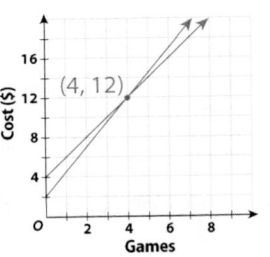

The solution is (4, 12). The cost at both alleys will be the same for 4 games bowled; that cost will be $12.

© Houghton Mifflin Harcourt Publishing Company

DIFFERENTIATE INSTRUCTION *Leveled Homework/Practice*

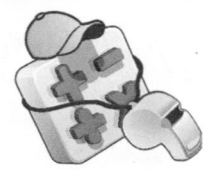

Personal Math Trainer
• 8.1 Homework

Pages shown are from *Differentiated Instruction.* **Also available online.**

Practice and Problem Solving A/B

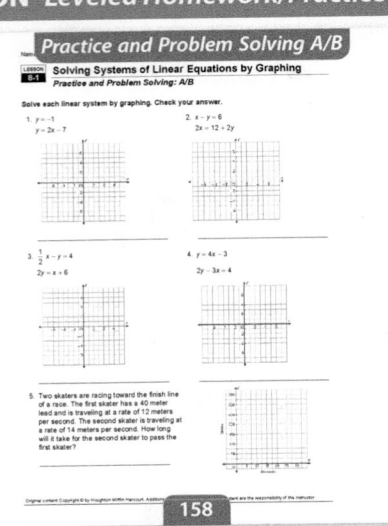

158

Practice and Problem Solving C

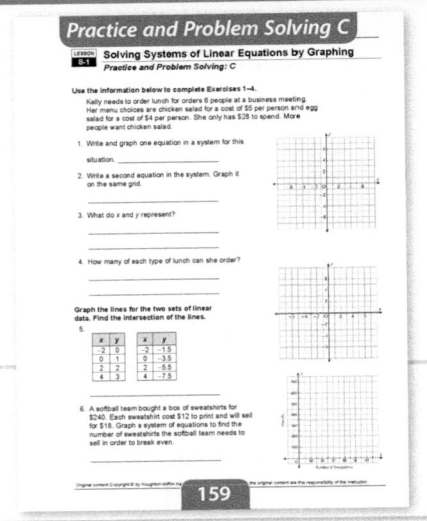

159

Practice and Problem Solving D

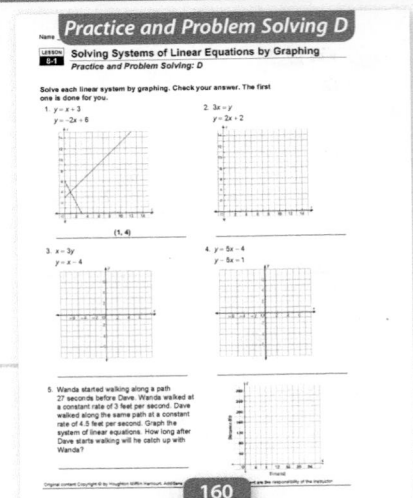

160

8. Multi-Step Jeremy runs 7 miles per week and increases his distance by 1 mile each week. Tony runs 3 miles per week and increases his distance by 2 miles each week. In how many weeks will Jeremy and Tony be running the same distance? What will that distance be?

4 weeks; 11 miles

9. Critical Thinking Write a real-world situation that could be represented by the system of equations shown below.

$$\begin{cases} y = 4x + 10 \\ y = 3x + 15 \end{cases}$$

Sample answer: Store A rents carpet cleaners for a fee of $10, plus $4 per day. Store B rents carpet cleaners for a fee of $15, plus $3 per day.

 **FOCUS ON HIGHER ORDER THINKING**

10. Multistep The table shows two options provided by a high-speed Internet provider.

	Setup Fee ($)	Cost per Month ($)
Option 1	50	30
Option 2	No setup fee	$40

a. In how many months will the total cost of both options be the same? What will that cost be?

5 months; $200

b. If you plan to cancel your Internet service after 9 months, which is the cheaper option? Explain.

Option 1 is cheaper

Option 1: cost = 30(9) + 50 = $320

Option 2: cost = 40(9) = $360

11. Draw Conclusions How many solutions does the system formed by $x - y = 3$ and $ay - ax + 3a = 0$ have for a nonzero number a? Explain.

Infinitely many; sample answer: Rearranging the left side of the 2nd equation and subtracting 3a from both sides gives $-ax + ay = -3a$. Dividing both sides by $-a$ gives $x - y = 3$. So, the equations describe the same line.

Work Area

© Houghton Mifflin Harcourt Publishing Company

DIFFERENTIATE INSTRUCTION *Extend-the-Math Activity* **PRE-AP**

Have students imagine including a third equation with the same variables to a system of two linear equations in two variables.

• What is the solution to a system of three equations in two variables? the ordered pair that solves all three equations

• How can you write a third equation to be included in a system of two linear equations in two variables and be sure you won't change the solution of the system? Use the technique for writing an equation of a line through two known points and use the point that is the solution of the original system as one of the points.

✔ **Quick Check**

8.1 Lesson Quiz

1. What is the solution to the system of equations shown? $(-5, 3)$

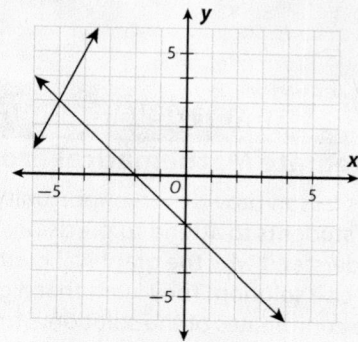

Diego works at a warehouse that ships two types of packages, a red package weighing 4 pounds and a blue package weighing 6 pounds. Diego shipped a total of 40 packages weighing 180 pounds.

2. Graph the system of linear equations.

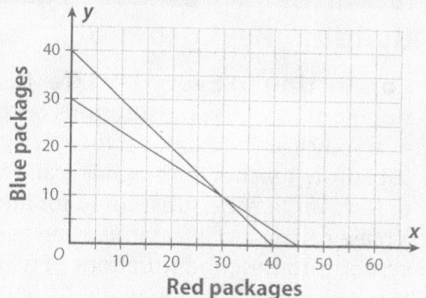

3. How many red and blue packages were in the shipment? 30 red packages and 10 blue packages

Differentiate Instruction

IF a student misses more than one question, THEN

Differentiate Instruction:

• 8.1 Reteach

• Personal Math Trainer

 Interactive Whiteboard
Interactive example available online

Lesson Support

Content Objective Students will learn how to solve a system of linear equations by substitution.

Professional Development

Integrate Mathematical Processes MP.6

This lesson provides an opportunity to address this Mathematical Process standard. It calls for students to attend to precision. Students examine graphs of systems of equations to understand why the graphical method of solving a system is not always able to provide a precise solution. They learn that a graph of a system of equations can provide an estimate of the coordinates of the solution. Students also learn to use the algebraic method of substitution to find the precise solution to a system of equations.

FOCUS

Building Background

Connecting to Everyday Life Discuss situations in which substitutions occur in everyday life. For example, there may be a substitute teacher if a teacher is absent, or one player may be substituted for another if a player is injured in a game. Then ask students to describe situations in which they use substitution in math. For example, a solution may be substituted into an original equation to check an answer, or a value may be substituted into an expression to evaluate the expression.

$$3x + 5 = -1$$
$$x \overset{?}{=} -2$$
$$3(-2) + 5 \overset{?}{=} -1$$
$$-6 + 5 \overset{?}{=} -1$$
$$-1 = -1$$

COHERENCE

Learning Progressions

In this lesson, students solve a system of two linear equations by the substitution method. Important understandings for students include the following:

- **Solve a system of linear equations algebraically using substitution.**
- **Use a graph to estimate the solution of a system before solving algebraically.**
- **Solve problems with systems of linear equations algebraically.**

In this lesson students build on the graphical foundation they set in the last lesson for solving a system. They now begin to solve a system algebraically by solving one equation for a variable and substituting it into the other equation. They refer back to the graphs of systems to both check and estimate solutions. They continue to solve problems by applying the new methodology to create and solve a system based on real-life situations.

RIGOR

Cluster Connections

This lesson provides an excellent opportunity to connect ideas in the cluster:

Analyze and solve linear equations and pairs of simultaneous linear equations.

Have students consider the following system:

$$\begin{cases} \frac{y}{2} - x = 1 \\ x + y + 7 = 0 \end{cases}$$

Explain the following method for solving the system, which is similar to the substitution method: (1) Solve both equations for the same variable. (2) Set the two expressions for that same variable equal to each other, and solve for the variable. (3) Solve for the remaining variable. Ask students to use the method to solve the system.

Sample answer: Solve each equation for x: $x = \frac{y}{2} - 1$ and $x = -y - 7$. Then $\frac{y}{2} - 1 = -y - 7$ and $y = -4$. Substituting, $x = -3$. The solution is $(-4, -3)$.

Language Support ELL

Language Objective Students will describe the steps for how to solve a system of linear equations by substitution.

Leveled Strategies for English Learners ELL

Emerging
Have students work in mixed proficiency level teams to solve the hidden-treasure problem in Example 3. Have students predict by writing out a solution they think will find the treasure.

Expanding
As students work together through the hidden-treasure problem in Example 3, have students tell how they are solving each step. Have a partner write down the steps to share with the class when finished.

Bridging
Using Example 3, have students work with a small team to predict the solution, solve the problem, and explain each step of the solution. Have students name the island if they solve the problem correctly.

To help students answer the question posed in Math Talk, provide a sentence frame for students to use to respond.

I know that (−5, −2) is not the solution because _____.

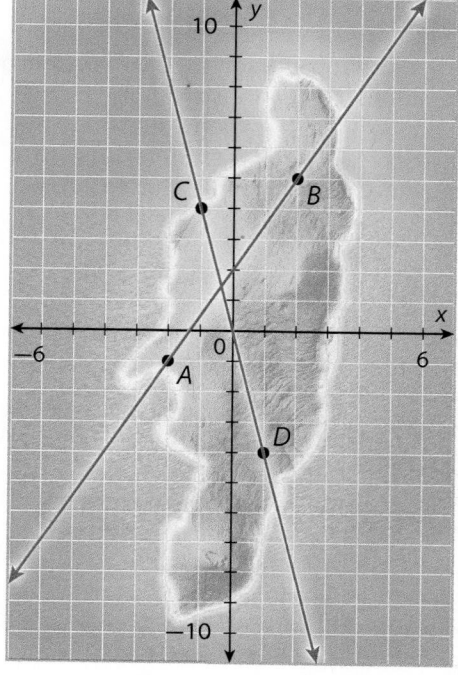

Hidden-Treasure Map from Example 3

Linguistic Support ELL

Academic/Content Vocabulary
Provide scaffolding for English learners by walking them step-by-step through Example 1 as they rephrase each step in their own words.

Background Knowledge
Students have likely had a class with a substitute teacher who takes the place of the regular classroom teacher. The idea of a substitution is also familiar in sports like soccer or basketball or in cooking, where you can substitute one ingredient for another. Help students understand the concept of the substitution method by making a connection to these situations.

Solving Systems by Substitution

1 Engage

ESSENTIAL QUESTION

How do you use substitution to solve a system of linear equations? Sample answer: Solve for one variable in one of the equations. Substitute the resulting expression for the same variable in the other equation. Substitute the solution into either original equation to find the value of the other variable.

Motivate the Lesson

Ask: How can you turn two equations with two variables into one equation with one variable? Begin the lesson to find out.

2 Explore

EXPLORE ACTIVITY   EXAMPLE 1

Focus on Critical Thinking
Make sure students understand that in Step 1 either equation could be used and either variable could be solved for. However, it is usually easier to solve for a variable that has a coefficient of 1.

ADDITIONAL EXAMPLE 1 Solve the system of linear equations by substitution. Check your answer.

$$\begin{cases} 2x + y = 5 \\ -3x + 2y = 17 \end{cases}$$

$(-1, 7)$

 Interactive Whiteboard
Interactive example available online

Solving Systems by Substitution

8.3.8.2
Students will use substitution to solve a system of linear equations.

? ESSENTIAL QUESTION

How do you use substitution to solve a system of linear equations?

EXPLORE ACTIVITY

Solving a Linear System by Substitution

The **substitution method** is used to solve systems of linear equations by solving an equation for one variable and then substituting the resulting expression for that variable into the other equation. The steps for this method are as follows:

1. Solve one of the equations for one of its variables.
2. Substitute the expression from Step 1 into the other equation and solve for the other variable.
3. Substitute the value from Step 2 into either original equation and solve to find the value of the variable in Step 1.

EXAMPLE 1 Solve the system of linear equations by substitution. Check your answer.

$$\begin{cases} -3x + y = 1 \\ 4x + y = 8 \end{cases}$$

STEP 1 Solve an equation for one variable.

Select one of the equations. $-3x + y = 1$

Solve for the variable y. $y = \boxed{3x + 1}$

STEP 2 Substitute the expression for y in the other equation, and solve for x.

Substitute $\underline{3x + 1}$ for y. $4x + \left(\boxed{3x + 1}\right) = 8$

Combine like terms. $\boxed{7x} + 1 = 8$

Subtract $\underline{1}$ from each side. $7x = \boxed{7}$

Solve for x. $x = \boxed{1}$

STEP 3 Substitute the value of x you found into one of the equations, and solve for the other variable, y.

$-3x + y = 1$

Substitute $\underline{1}$ for x. $-3\left(\boxed{1}\right) + y = 1$

Simplify. $\boxed{-3} + y = 1$

Solve for y. $y = \boxed{4}$

So $(\underline{1}, \underline{4})$ is the solution of the system.

© Houghton Mifflin Harcourt Publishing Company

Lesson 8.2   **235**

DIFFERENTIATE INSTRUCTION *Leveled Questions*

	EXPLORE ACTIVITY EXAMPLE 1
AL) DOK 1 *Recall*	What is the first step when solving a system by substitution? Solve one of the equations for one of the variables.
OL) DOK 2 *Skills/Concepts*	How do you know there is only one solution of this system? In Step 4 you can see that the graphs of the equations intersect at only one point.
BL) DOK 3 *Strategic Thinking*	Why not solve for x in Step 1? You could solve for x in Step 1, but then you would have fractions in your expression that you substitute for x in Step 2.

LEVELED QUESTIONS: **AL)** Approaching Level | **OL)** On Level | **BL)** Beyond Level

STEP 4 Check the solution by graphing.

$$-3x + y = 1$$

x-intercept: $-3x + 0 = 1 \rightarrow x = \boxed{-\dfrac{1}{3}}$

y-intercept: $3(0) + y = 1 \rightarrow y = \boxed{1}$

$$4x + y = 8$$

x-intercept: $4x + 0 = 8 \rightarrow x = \boxed{2}$

y-intercept: $4(0) + y = 8 \rightarrow y = \boxed{8}$

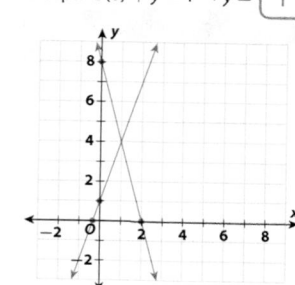

The graph confirms that the solution is (_1_ , _4_).

Reflect

1. Is it more efficient to solve $-3x + y = 1$ for x? Why or why not?

No; more steps are needed, and $x = \dfrac{1}{3}y - \dfrac{1}{3}$ is more difficult to substitute.

2. Is there another way to solve the system?

Yes; solve $4x + y = 8$ for y and substitute that expression into $-3x + y = 1$.

3. What is another way to check your solution?

Substitute (1, 4) into each equation and see if both equations are true.

 **YOUR TURN**

Solve each system of linear equations by substitution.

4. $\begin{cases} 3x + y = 11 \\ -2x + y = 1 \end{cases}$
___(2, 5)___

5. $\begin{cases} 2x - 3y = -24 \\ x + 6y = 18 \end{cases}$
___(−6, 4)___

6. $\begin{cases} x - 2y = 5 \\ 3x - 5y = 8 \end{cases}$
___(−9, −7)___

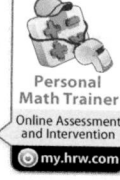

Personal Math Trainer

Online Assessment and Intervention

my.hrw.com

© Houghton Mifflin Harcourt Publishing Company

YOUR TURN MP.8

Avoid Common Errors

Some students may have difficulty deciding which equation to use in Step 1 of the solution process. Discuss what should be considered when choosing an equation to solve for a variable. For example, in **Exercise 4**, the most straightforward method would be to solve either equation for y, thereby avoiding fractions in the solution process.

TEACHER TO TEACHER

Critical Thinking Give students two or more systems of equations such as those below. Have them complete tables that show ordered pairs for each of the equations, for all integers from $x = -5$ to $x = 5$. Ask them to find the solution to each system by identifying the ordered pair that appears in both tables for that system.

$\begin{cases} 2x + y = 7 \\ x - 3y = 0 \end{cases}$

(3, 1)

$\begin{cases} 2x - 5y = 1 \\ -3x + 4y = 2 \end{cases}$

(−2, −1)

③ Explain

EXAMPLE 2

ADDITIONAL EXAMPLE 2 Solve the system.

$$\begin{cases} 2x + 6y = -1 \\ 6x - 21y = 10 \end{cases}$$

$$\left(\tfrac{1}{2}, -\tfrac{1}{3}\right)$$

 Interactive Whiteboard
Interactive example available online

Using a Graph to Estimate the Solution of a System

You can use a graph to estimate the solution of a system of equations before solving the system algebraically.

Math On the Spot
my.hrw.com

EXAMPLE 2

Solve the system $\begin{cases} x - 4y = 4 \\ 2x - 3y = -3 \end{cases}$.

STEP 1 Sketch a graph of each equation by substituting values for x and generating values of y.

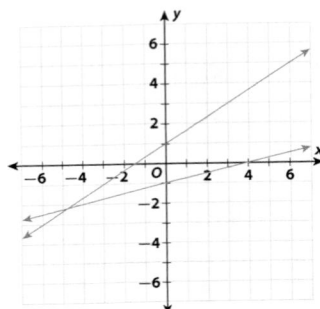

STEP 2 Find the intersection of the lines. The lines appear to intersect near $(-5, -2)$.

> **Math Talk**
> Mathematical Processes
> In Step 2, how can you tell that $(-5, -2)$ is not the solution?

The lines intersect near, but not at, $(-5, -2)$. Also, if you substitute $x = -5$ and $y = -2$ into each equation, you get false statements.

STEP 3 Solve the system algebraically.

Solve $x - 4y = 4$ for x.
$$x - 4y = 4$$
$$x = 4 + 4y$$

Substitute to find y.
$$2(4 + 4y) - 3y = -3$$
$$8 + 8y - 3y = -3$$
$$8 + 5y = -3$$
$$5y = -11$$
$$y = -\tfrac{11}{5}$$

Substitute to find x.
$$x = 4 + 4y$$
$$= 4 + 4\left(-\tfrac{11}{5}\right)$$
$$= \tfrac{20 - 44}{5}$$
$$= -\tfrac{24}{5}$$

The solution is $\left(-\tfrac{24}{5}, -\tfrac{11}{5}\right)$.

STEP 4 Use the estimate you made using the graph to judge the reasonableness of your solution.

$-\tfrac{24}{5}$ is close to the estimate of -5, and $-\tfrac{11}{5}$ is close to the estimate of -2, so the solution seems reasonable.

© Houghton Mifflin Harcourt Publishing Company

Lesson 8.2 **237**

DIFFERENTIATE INSTRUCTION *Leveled Questions*

	EXAMPLE 2
AL) DOK 1 *Recall*	How do you know that the solution $\left(-\tfrac{24}{5}, -\tfrac{11}{5}\right)$ is reasonable? The graphs appear to intersect at a point near $(-5, -2)$, which is near the solution.
OL) DOK 2 *Skills/Concepts*	How do you decide which equation and which variable to solve for in Step 3? Solve for the variable that has a coefficient of 1.
BL) DOK 3 *Strategic Thinking*	Why is the solution found by graphing always considered to be an estimate until verified? Even when the lines appear to intersect at a point with integer coordinates, the actual coordinates of the point may be other rational numbers very near to the apparent integer coordinates.

LEVELED QUESTIONS: AL) Approaching Level | OL) On Level | BL) Beyond Level

Personal
Math Trainer
Online Assessment
and Intervention
my.hrw.com

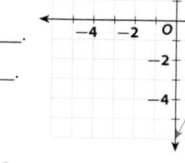

7. Estimate the solution of the system $\begin{cases} x + y = 4 \\ 2x - y = 6 \end{cases}$ by sketching a graph of each linear function. Then solve the system algebraically. Use your estimate to judge the reasonableness of your solution.

The estimated solution is ___(3, 1)___.

The algebraic solution is ___$\left(\frac{10}{3}, \frac{2}{3}\right)$___.

The solution (is/is not) reasonable because

$\frac{10}{3}$ is close to the estimate of 3,

and $\frac{2}{3}$ is close to the estimate of 1.

Math On the Spot
my.hrw.com

Solving Problems with Systems of Equations

EXAMPLE 3

As part of Class Day, the eighth grade is doing a treasure hunt. Each team is given the following riddle and map. At what point is the treasure located?

There's pirate treasure to be found. So search on the island, all around. Draw a line through A and B. Then another through C and D. Dance a jig, "X" marks the spot. Where the lines intersect, that's the treasure's plot!

$\left(-\frac{1}{3}, \frac{3}{2}\right)$; This ordered pair can be used as an estimate for the solution.

Math Talk
Mathematical Processes

Where do the lines appear to intersect? How is this related to the solution?

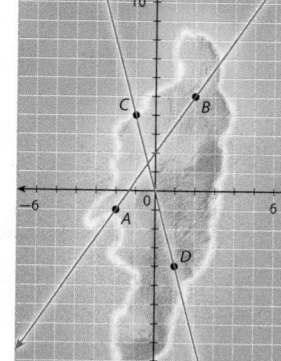

© Houghton Mifflin Harcourt Publishing Company

STEP 1 Give the coordinates of each point and find the slope of the line through each pair of points.

| A: (−2, −1) | C: (−1, 4) |
| B: (2, 5) | D: (1, −4) |

Slope:

$\frac{5 - (-1)}{2 - (-2)} = \frac{6}{4}$

$= \frac{3}{2}$

Slope:

$\frac{-4 - 4}{1 - (-1)} = \frac{-8}{2}$

$= -4$

Engage with the Whiteboard

Have a volunteer graph each of the lines and estimate the intersection. Then have another student find the algebraic solution and compare it to the estimate.

EXAMPLE 3

ADDITIONAL EXAMPLE 3 A line passes through the points (5, 3) and (−5, −2). Another line passes through the points (−6, 4) and (2, −4). Find the coordinates of the intersection of the two lines. $\left(-\frac{5}{3}, -\frac{1}{3}\right)$

Interactive Whiteboard
Interactive example available online

	EXAMPLE 3
AL DOK 1 *Recall*	What are the steps to solve this problem? Use points on each line to write the equations; then solve the system.
OL DOK 2 *Skills/Concepts*	What can you determine about the values of the solution of the system from the location of the point of intersection? The location is the second quadrant, so the x-coordinate will be negative and the y-coordinate positive.
BL DOK 3 *Strategic Thinking*	Explain why the final solution in this situation must be considered to be an estimate even though it was obtained algebraically. The coordinates of the points on the map were not given. Because the equations in the system are based on coordinates that are determined from observation, everything that follows must be considered approximate.

© Houghton Mifflin Harcourt Publishing Company

YOUR TURN MP.1

Engage with the Whiteboard

 Have volunteers write the two equations that represent the car rentals. Ask another volunteer to demonstrate how to solve the system.

Digital Teacher Resources

Go online to access all your lesson-level resources.

Differentiated Instruction
- Reteach
- Reading Strategies
- Success for English Learners
- Practice and Problem Solving A/B, C, D

Math on the Spot Videos

my.hrw.com

STEP 2 Write equations in slope-intercept form describing the line through points A and B and the line through points C and D.

Line through A and B:

Use the slope and a point to find b.

$5 = \left(\frac{3}{2}\right)2 + b$

$b = 2$

The equation is $y = \frac{3}{2}x + 2$.

Line through C and D:

Use the slope and a point to find b.

$4 = -4(-1) + b$

$b = 0$

The equation is $y = -4x$.

STEP 3 Solve the system algebraically.

Substitute $\frac{3}{2}x + 2$ for y in $y = -4x$ to find x.

$\frac{3}{2}x + 2 = -4x$

$\frac{11}{2}x = -2$

$x = -\frac{4}{11}$

Substitute to find x.

$y = -4\left(-\frac{4}{11}\right) = \frac{16}{11}$

The solution is $\left(-\frac{4}{11}, \frac{16}{11}\right)$.

YOUR TURN

8. Ace Car Rental rents cars for x dollars per day plus y dollars for each mile driven. Carlos rented a car for 4 days, drove it 160 miles, and spent $120. Vanessa rented a car for 1 day, drove it 240 miles, and spent $80. Write equations to represent Carlos's expenses and Vanessa's expenses. Then solve the system and tell what each number represents.

Carlos: $4x + 160y = 120$

Vanessa: $x + 240y = 80$

$(20, 0.25)$;

20 represents the cost per day: $20;

0.25 represents the cost per mile: $0.25

Personal Math Trainer

Online Assessment and Intervention

my.hrw.com

Lesson 8.2 **239**

TEACHER TO TEACHER

Teaching Tip Another way to use substitution to solve a system of equations is to rewrite both equations so that the same variable is isolated as shown below.

$\begin{cases} y = 3x + 1 \\ y = -4x + 8 \end{cases}$

Use the Transitive Property: $3x + 1 = -4x + 8$. Solve the equation to find $x = 1$, and then substitute 1 for x in one of the equations to find the value of y, 4.

Solve each system of linear equations by substitution. (Explore Activity Example 1)

1. $\begin{cases} 3x - 2y = 9 \\ y = 2x - 7 \end{cases}$ _____ $(5, 3)$

2. $\begin{cases} y = x - 4 \\ 2x + y = 5 \end{cases}$ _____ $(3, -1)$

3. $\begin{cases} x + 4y = 6 \\ y = -x + 3 \end{cases}$ _____ $(2, 1)$

4. $\begin{cases} x + 2y = 6 \\ x - y = 3 \end{cases}$ _____ $(4, 1)$

Solve each system. Estimate the solution first. (Example 2)

5. $\begin{cases} 6x + y = 4 \\ x - 4y = 19 \end{cases}$

Estimate _____ $(1, -4)$

Solution _____ $\left(\dfrac{7}{5}, -\dfrac{22}{5} \right)$

6. $\begin{cases} x + 2y = 8 \\ 3x + 2y = 6 \end{cases}$

Estimate _____ $(-1, 5)$

Solution _____ $\left(-1, \dfrac{9}{2} \right)$

7. $\begin{cases} 3x + y = 4 \\ 5x - y = 22 \end{cases}$

Estimate _____ $(3, -6)$

Solution _____ $\left(\dfrac{13}{4}, -\dfrac{23}{4} \right)$

8. $\begin{cases} 2x + 7y = 2 \\ x + y = -1 \end{cases}$

Estimate _____ $(-2, 1)$

Solution _____ $\left(-\dfrac{9}{5}, \dfrac{4}{5} \right)$

9. Adult tickets to Space City amusement park cost x dollars. Children's tickets cost y dollars. The Henson family bought 3 adult and 1 child tickets for $163. The Garcia family bought 2 adult and 3 child tickets for $174. (Example 3)

a. Write equations to represent the Hensons' cost and the Garcias' cost.

Hensons' cost: $3x + y = 163$

Garcias' cost: $2x + 3y = 174$

b. Solve the system.

adult ticket price: _____ $45

child ticket price: _____ $28

ESSENTIAL QUESTION CHECK-IN

10. How can you decide which variable to solve for first when you are solving a linear system by substitution?

Choose the variable whose coefficient is 1. If no coefficient is 1, choose the variable with the least positive integer coefficient.

© Houghton Mifflin Harcourt Publishing Company

4 Elaborate

Talk About It

Summarize the Lesson

Ask: How can a graph of a system of two equations help you determine if your algebraic solution is reasonable? You can see which quadrant the intersection is in and the approximate value of the intersection by looking at the graph. You can compare the algebraic solution to these two pieces of information and confirm that it is reasonable.

Guided Practice

Engage with the Whiteboard

For **Exercises 5–8**, have volunteers graph the equations on the whiteboard and estimate the solution.

Avoid Common Errors

- **Exercises 5–8** Remind students that to estimate the solution of each system they will first need to graph each system.

- **Exercise 9** Remind students to first analyze their two equations to determine which has a variable with a coefficient of 1. Then caution students to use the Distributive Property when substituting. So when $y = -3x + 163$ and $2x + 3(-3x + 163) = 174$, the 3 must be distributed to both $-3x$ and 163.

DIFFERENTIATE INSTRUCTION Intervention and Additional Support

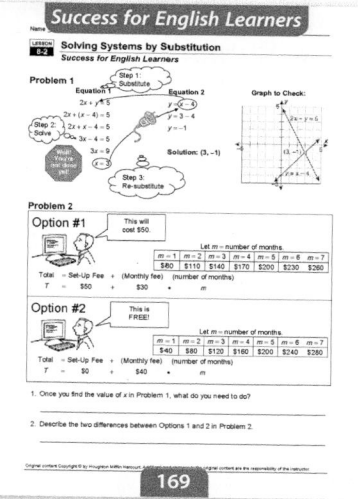

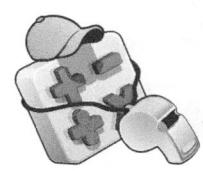

Personal Math Trainer
Daily Intervention
8.2 Homework

Pages shown are from *Differentiated Instruction*. **Also available online.**

8.2 Independent Practice

my.hrw.com — Personal Math Trainer — Online Assessment and Intervention

⏱ Pressed for Time

8.2 Differentiated Homework Assignments

(AL) Approaching Level 11–15

(OL) On Level 11, 13–16

(BL) Beyond Level 11, 14, 16–18

For Below Level students, assign Personal Math Trainer, Daily Intervention 8.2 Homework.

Mathematical Processes	Exercises
MP.1 Problem Solving	14
MP.3 Logic	11
MP.4 Modeling	12–13, 15
MP.6 Precision	17
MP.7 Using Structure	16, 18

Focus on Higher Order Thinking

Depth of Knowledge	Exercises
2 Skills/Concepts	12–15
3 Strategic Thinking H.O.T.	11, 16–18

---

11. **Check for Reasonableness** Zach solves the system $\begin{cases} x + y = -3 \\ x - y = 1 \end{cases}$ and finds the solution $(1, -2)$. Use a graph to explain whether Zach's solution is reasonable.

The graph shows that the x-coordinate of the solution is negative, so Zach's solution is not reasonable.

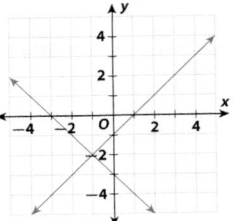

12. **Represent Real-World Problems** Angelo bought apples and bananas at the fruit stand. He bought 20 pieces of fruit and spent $11.50. Apples cost $0.50 and bananas cost $0.75 each.

a. Write a system of equations to model the problem. (Hint: One equation will represent the number of pieces of fruit. A second equation will represent the money spent on the fruit.)

$$\begin{cases} x + y = 20 \\ 0.50x + 0.75y = 11.50 \end{cases}$$

Apples $0.50
Bananas $0.75

b. Solve the system algebraically. Tell how many apples and bananas Angelo bought.

14 apples and 6 bananas

13. **Represent Real-World Problems** A jar contains n nickels and d dimes. There is a total of 200 coins in the jar. The value of the coins is $14.00. How many nickels and how many dimes are in the jar?

120 nickels and 80 dimes

14. **Multistep** The graph shows a triangle formed by the x-axis, the line $3x - 2y = 0$, and the line $x + 2y = 10$. Follow these steps to find the area of the triangle.

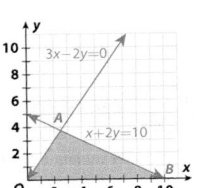

a. Find the coordinates of point A by solving the system $\begin{cases} 3x - 2y = 0 \\ x + 2y = 10 \end{cases}$.

Point A: $\left(\dfrac{5}{2}, \dfrac{15}{4}\right)$

b. Use the coordinates of point A to find the height of the triangle.

height: $\dfrac{15}{4}$ units

c. What is the length of the base of the triangle?

base: 10 units

d. What is the area of the triangle? $18\dfrac{3}{4}$ square units

© Houghton Mifflin Harcourt Publishing Company

DIFFERENTIATE INSTRUCTION *Leveled Homework/Practice*

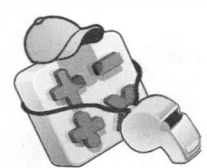

Personal Math Trainer
• 8.2 Homework

Pages shown are from *Differentiated Instruction*.
Also available online.

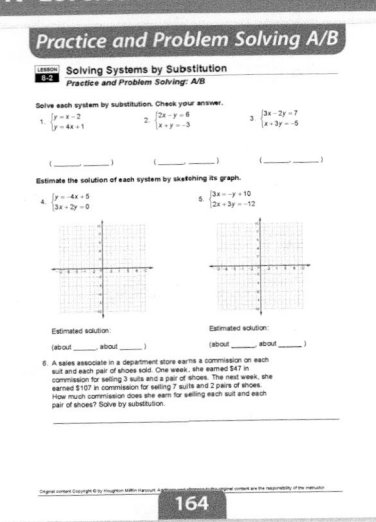

Practice and Problem Solving A/B

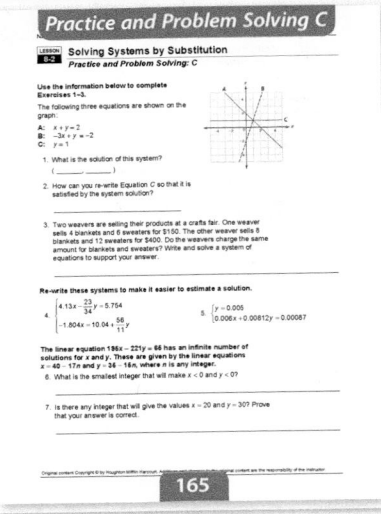

Practice and Problem Solving C

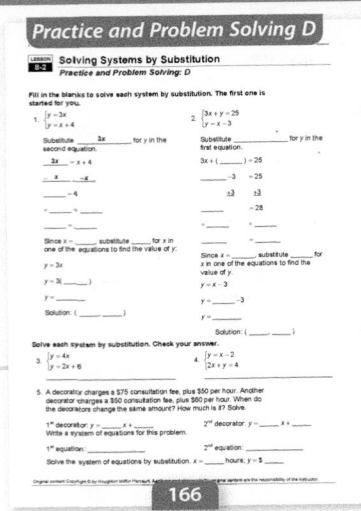

Practice and Problem Solving D

15. Jed is graphing the design for a kite on a coordinate grid. The four vertices of the kite are at $A\left(-\frac{4}{3}, \frac{2}{3}\right)$, $B\left(\frac{14}{3}, -\frac{4}{3}\right)$, $C\left(\frac{14}{3}, -\frac{16}{3}\right)$, and $D\left(\frac{2}{3}, -\frac{16}{3}\right)$. One kite strut will connect points A and C. The other will connect points B and D. Find the point where the struts cross.

$\left(\frac{8}{3}, -\frac{10}{3}\right)$

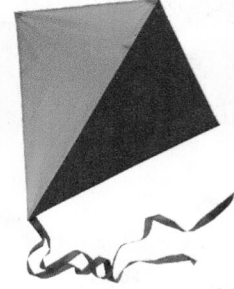

 H.O.T. FOCUS ON HIGHER ORDER THINKING

16. **Analyze Relationships** Consider the system $\begin{cases} 6x - 3y = 15 \\ x + 3y = -8 \end{cases}$. Describe three different substitution methods that can be used to solve this system. Then solve the system.

Solve the second equation for x ($x = -8 - 3y$) and then substitute that value into the first equation. Solve the first equation for y ($y = 2x - 5$) and then substitute that value into the second equation. Solve either equation for $3y$ ($3y = -8 - x$ or $3y = 6x - 15$) and then substitute that value into the other equation. Solution: $(1, -3)$

17. **Communicate Mathematical Ideas** Explain the advantages, if any, that solving a system of linear equations by substitution has over solving the same system by graphing.

The substitution method has the advantage of always giving an exact answer. Graphing produces an exact answer only if the solution is an ordered pair whose coordinates are integers.

18. **Persevere in Problem Solving** Create a system of equations of the form $\begin{cases} Ax + By = C \\ Dx + Ey = F \end{cases}$ that has $(7, -2)$ as its solution. Explain how you found the system.

Sample answer: $\begin{cases} x + 3y = 1 \\ -2x - 4y = -6 \end{cases}$; I chose random values of A, B, D, and E, substituted them into the equations, and calculated the values of C and F using $x = 7$ and $y = -2$.

Work Area

© Houghton Mifflin Harcourt Publishing Company

DIFFERENTIATE INSTRUCTION *Extend-the-Math Activity* PRE-AP

Activity Let m represent a real number. Solve the following system of equations. The solution should be in the form (x, y), and x and y will be expressed in terms of m.

$\begin{cases} 8x + y = m \\ 4x + 3y = m \end{cases}$

$\left(\frac{1}{10}m, \frac{2}{10}m\right)$

✓ Quick Check

8.2 Lesson Quiz

Solve the system of linear equations by substitution. Check your answer.

1. $\begin{cases} x + y = 5 \\ 2x - y = 7 \end{cases}$ $(4, 1)$

2. $\begin{cases} y = -2x + 6 \\ -4x - 6y = 4 \end{cases}$ $(5, -4)$

Solve each system. Estimate the solution first.

3. $\begin{cases} 3x + y = 7 \\ -7x - 5y = 25 \end{cases}$ $\left(\frac{15}{2}, -\frac{31}{2}\right)$

4. $\begin{cases} x + 3y = 9 \\ 2x + 4y = 7 \end{cases}$ $\left(-\frac{15}{2}, \frac{11}{2}\right)$

5. Jill bought oranges and bananas. She bought 12 pieces of fruit and spent $5. Oranges cost $0.50 each and bananas cost $0.25 each. Write a system of equations to model the problem. Then solve the system algebraically. How many oranges and how many bananas did Jill buy?

$x + y = 12$
$0.50x + 0.25y = 5.00$
$(8, 4)$; 8 oranges and 4 bananas

Differentiate Instruction

IF a student misses more than one question, THEN

Differentiate Instruction:

• 8.2 Reteach

• Personal Math Trainer

 Interactive Whiteboard
Interactive Lesson quiz available online

Lesson Support

Content Objective Students will learn how to solve a system of linear equations by adding or subtracting.

Professional Development

Integrate Mathematical Processes MP.1

This lesson provides an opportunity to address this Mathematical Process standard. It calls for students to make sense of problems and persevere in solving them. Students solve systems of equations using either addition or subtraction to eliminate one of the variables. Then students ask themselves if the solution they found makes sense. They use what they learned about graphing systems of equations to check the accuracy or reasonableness of the solution they found. They also learn to translate real-world problems into systems of equations and solve them.

FOCUS

Building Background

Eliciting Prior Knowledge Have students create a main idea web to summarize what they have learned about solving systems of linear equations. They should include and describe the graphical method and the algebraic method of substitution.

Sample completed web is shown.

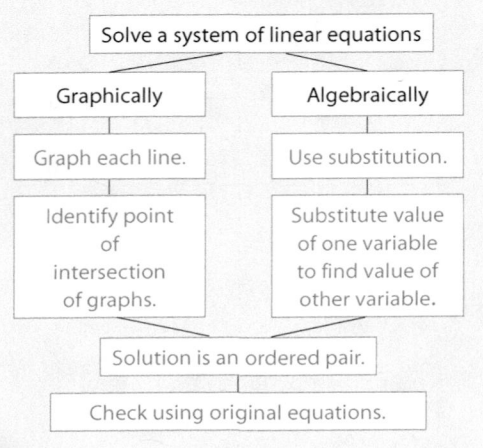

COHERENCE

Learning Progressions

In this lesson, students solve a system of two linear equations using the elimination method. Important understandings for students include the following:

- **Solve a linear system by adding.**
- **Solve a linear system by subtracting.**
- **Solve problems with systems of linear equations by elimination.**

Students continue to solve systems of equations algebraically. They learn the forms to look for to decide when the elimination method is appropriate. They recognize that there are a variety of approaches to solving a system and that with experience they will be increasingly able to select the easiest method. They continue to solve real-life problems that illustrate the importance of being able to formulate and solve a system of linear equations.

RIGOR

Cluster Connections

This lesson provides an excellent opportunity to connect ideas in the cluster:

Analyze and solve linear equations and pairs of simultaneous linear equations.

Remind students that they know how to solve equations with rational coefficients and constants. Ask them to apply what they have learned about elimination to solve the following system:

$$\begin{cases} \frac{3}{2}x - \frac{1}{3}y = 14 \\ \frac{5}{4}x + \frac{1}{3}y = 12 \end{cases}$$

$(8, -6)$

Language Support **ELL**

Language Objective Students will explain how to solve a system of linear equations by adding or subtracting.

Leveled Strategies for English Learners **ELL**

Emerging
Have students work together to solve Exercise 7. Have them show each step to demonstrate how to decide whether to add or subtract to eliminate the variable.

Expanding
Have students think of when the method of elimination is the preferred method for solving a system of linear equations.

Bridging
Have students work with a partner to select a problem from this lesson, solve it using the elimination method, and tell step-by-step how to solve it.

Explain to English learners that the question in Independent Practice Exercise 19 is not simply providing two possible methods for them to choose from, but asking them to tell why they choose the method that they do. Provide a sentence frame.

It is better to check a solution by _____ because _____.

Image Credits: ©DYashkin/iStock/Getty Images Plus/Getty Images

Linguistic Support **ELL**

Academic/Content Vocabulary
Provide scaffolding for English learners by walking them step-by-step through Example 1 as they rephrase each step in their own words.

The word *elimination* is a cognate in Spanish.

Background Knowledge
Students may hear or read the expression *process of elimination*. A process of elimination involves testing and ruling out choices one-at-a-time until only one possibility remains. In some sports tournaments, the winner is determined using a process of elimination. In this lesson, students learn the elimination method to solve a system of linear equations. Much like with the process of elimination, solving a system by elimination involves eliminating, or getting rid of, one of the variables so that only one remains.

Solving Systems by Elimination

1 Engage

❓ ESSENTIAL QUESTION

How do you solve a system of linear equations by adding or subtracting? Sample answer: Write the equations so that like terms are aligned vertically. Add or subtract the equations to eliminate either the x or y variable. Simplify to solve for the variable that was not eliminated. Then substitute that value into one of the original equations to solve for the other variable.

Motivate the Lesson

Ask: How can you turn two equations with two variables into one equation with one variable without substituting? Begin the lesson to find out.

2 Explore

EXPLORE ACTIVITY   EXAMPLE 1

ADDITIONAL EXAMPLE 1 Solve the system of equations by adding. Check your answer.

$$\begin{cases} 2x + y = 8 \\ -2x + 3y = 8 \end{cases}$$

$(2, 4)$

 Interactive Whiteboard
Interactive example available online

 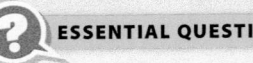 **Solving Systems by Elimination**

8.3.8.3
Students will solve a system of linear equations by adding or subtracting.

❓ ESSENTIAL QUESTION
How do you solve a system of linear equations by adding or subtracting?

EXPLORE ACTIVITY

Solving a Linear System by Adding

 Math On the Spot
ⓖ my.hrw.com

The **elimination method** is another method used to solve a system of linear equations. In this method, one variable is *eliminated* by adding or subtracting the two equations of the system to obtain a single equation in one variable. The steps for this method are as follows:

1. Add or subtract the equations to eliminate one variable.
2. Solve the resulting equation for the other variable.
3. Substitute the value into either original equation to find the value of the eliminated variable.

EXAMPLE 1 Solve the system of equations by adding. Check your answer.

$$\begin{cases} 2x - 3y = 12 \\ x + 3y = 6 \end{cases}$$

STEP 1 Add the equations.

Write the equations so that like terms are aligned.

$2x - 3y = 12$

Notice that the terms $-3y$ and ___$3y$___ are opposites.

$+ x + \boxed{3y} = 6$

Add to eliminate the variable ___y___.

$3x + \boxed{0} = 18$

Simplify.

$3x = 18$

Divide each side by ___3___.

$\dfrac{3x}{\boxed{3}} = \dfrac{18}{\boxed{3}}$

Simplify.

$x = \boxed{6}$

STEP 2 Substitute the solution into one of the original equations, and solve for y.

Use the second equation.

$x + 3y = 6$

Substitute ___6___ for the variable x.

$\boxed{6} + 3y = 6$

Subtract ___6___ from each side.

$3y = \boxed{0}$

Divide each side by ___3___ and simplify.

$y = \boxed{0}$

Lesson 8.3 **243**

© Houghton Mifflin Harcourt Publishing Company

DIFFERENTIATE INSTRUCTION *Leveled Questions*

	EXPLORE ACTIVITY EXAMPLE 1
Ⓐ **DOK 1** *Recall*	What variable is eliminated in Step 1 when the equations are added? Why? The variable y is eliminated because the y-terms, $3y$ and $-3y$, are opposites.
Ⓞ **DOK 2** *Skills/Concepts*	In Step 2, can you substitute 6 for x in the other equation, $2x - 3y = 12$? Explain. Yes, you would still get $y = 0$ because the solution of the system is a solution of both equations.
Ⓑ **DOK 3** *Strategic Thinking*	Is it better to check a solution by graphing or by substitution? Explain. Substituting into the original equations is more accurate because if the x- and y-values are not integers, graphing may not produce an accurate check. But graphing may be easier for checking to see that your solution is reasonable.

STEP 3 Write the solution as an ordered pair: (6 , 0)

STEP 4 Check the solution by graphing.

$$2x - 3y = 12$$

x-intercept: $2x - 3(0) = 12 \rightarrow x = \boxed{6}$

y-intercept: $2(0) - 3y = 12 \rightarrow y = \boxed{-4}$

$$x + 3y = 6$$

x-intercept: $x + 3(0) = 6 \rightarrow x = \boxed{6}$

y-intercept: $0 + 3y = 6 \rightarrow y = \boxed{2}$

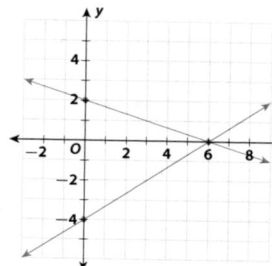

The graph confirms that the solution is (6 , 0).

Reflect

1. Can this linear system be solved by subtracting one of the original equations from the other? Why or why not?

No; if either of the original equations is subtracted from the other, neither variable will be eliminated.

2. What is another way to check your solution?

Substitute (6, 0) into each equation and see if both equations are true.

YOUR TURN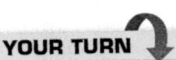

Solve each system of equations by adding. Check your answers.

3. $\begin{cases} x + y = -1 \\ x - y = 7 \end{cases}$

(3, −4)

4. $\begin{cases} 2x + 2y = -2 \\ 3x - 2y = 12 \end{cases}$

(2, −3)

5. $\begin{cases} 6x + 5y = 4 \\ -6x + 7y = 20 \end{cases}$

(−1, 2)

Personal Math Trainer

Online Assessment and Intervention

my.hrw.com

© Houghton Mifflin Harcourt Publishing Company

YOUR TURN MP.7

Avoid Common Errors

In **Exercise 5**, be sure students correctly align the terms in the equations. The constant terms should be aligned by place value, so that $4 + 20$ is correctly found to be 24, not 60.

TEACHER TO TEACHER

Number Sense Have students switch the order of the equations in Examples 1 and 2. Ask students if switching their order will affect the solution. Then have students solve the systems. Help students understand that switching the order does not affect the solution. Graphing the lines is a good way to establish this fact. The graphs (and the solution) remain the same regardless of the order in which the equations are graphed.

EXAMPLE 2

ADDITIONAL EXAMPLE 2 Solve the system of equations by adding. Check your answer.

$$\begin{cases} 2x + y = 8 \\ 2x + 3y = 4 \end{cases}$$

$(5, -2)$

Interactive Whiteboard
Interactive example available online

Solving a Linear System by Subtracting

If both equations contain the same x- or y-term, you can solve by subtracting.

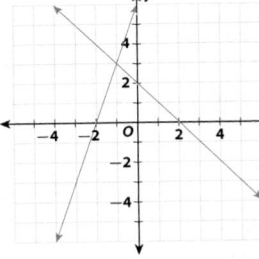
Math On the Spot
my.hrw.com

EXAMPLE 2

Solve the system of equations by subtracting. Check your answer.

$$\begin{cases} 3x + 3y = 6 \\ 3x - y = -6 \end{cases}$$

STEP 1   Subtract the equations.

$$3x + 3y = 6$$ Write the equations so that like terms are aligned.
$$-(3x - y = -6)$$ Notice that both equations contain the term 3x.

$$0 + 4y = 12$$ Subtract to eliminate the variable x.

$$4y = 12$$ Simplify and solve for y.

$$y = 3$$ Divide each side by 4 and simplify.

STEP 2   Substitute the solution into one of the original equations and solve for x.

$$3x - y = -6$$ Use the second equation.

$$3x - 3 = -6$$ Substitute 3 for the variable y.

$$3x = -3$$ Add 3 to each side.

$$x = -1$$ Divide each side by 3 and simplify.

STEP 3   Write the solution as an ordered pair: $(-1, 3)$

STEP 4   Check the solution by graphing.

$3x + 3y = 6$	$3x - y = -6$
x-intercept: 2	x-intercept: −2
y-intercept: 2	y-intercept: 6

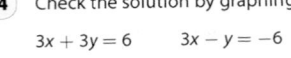

The point of intersection is $(-1, 3)$.

Reflect

6. What would happen if you added the original equations?

You would get $6x + 2y = 0$. This does not help to solve the system. Neither variable would be eliminated.

© Houghton Mifflin Harcourt Publishing Company

My Notes

DIFFERENTIATE INSTRUCTION *Leveled Questions*

	EXAMPLE 2
AL **DOK 1** *Recall*	What variable are you left to solve for in Step 1 after the equations are subtracted? After x is eliminated, solve for y.
OL **DOK 2** *Skills/Concepts*	How do you use the value of one variable found in Step 1 to find the value of the other variable in Step 2? Substitute the value of one variable into one of the original equations, and solve for the other variable.
BL **DOK 3** *Strategic Thinking*	How can you decide whether to add or subtract equations to eliminate a variable? If coefficients of like terms are equal, then subtract. If coefficients of like terms are opposites, then add.

LEVELED QUESTIONS: **AL** Approaching Level | **OL** On Level | **BL** Beyond Level

7. How can you decide whether to add or subtract to eliminate a variable in a linear system? Explain your reasoning.

If the equations have two terms that are opposites, then you can add to eliminate a variable; if the equations have two terms that are the same, then you can subtract to eliminate a variable.

Personal Math Trainer
Online Assessment and Intervention
my.hrw.com

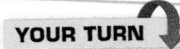

YOUR TURN

Solve each system of equations by subtracting. Check your answers.

8. $\begin{cases} 6x - 3y = 6 \\ 6x + 8y = -16 \end{cases}$

$(0, -2)$

9. $\begin{cases} 4x + 3y = 19 \\ 6x + 3y = 33 \end{cases}$

$(7, -3)$

10. $\begin{cases} 2x + 6y = 17 \\ 2x - 10y = 9 \end{cases}$

$\left(7, \dfrac{1}{2}\right)$

Math On the Spot
my.hrw.com

Solving Problems with Systems of Equations

Many real-world situations can be modeled and solved with a system of equations.

EXAMPLE 3

The Polar Bear Club wants to buy snowshoes and camp stoves. The club will spend $554.50 to buy them at Top Sports and $602.00 to buy them at Outdoor Explorer, before taxes, but Top Sports is farther away. How many of each item does the club intend to buy?

© Houghton Mifflin Harcourt Publishing Company • Image Credits: ©Jovan Nikolic/Shutterstock

	Snowshoes	Camp Stoves
Top Sports	$79.50 per pair	$39.25
Outdoor Explorer	$89.00 per pair	$39.25

Engage with the Whiteboard

For **Exercises 8–10**, have volunteers write the subtraction sign in front of the second equation in each and then demonstrate how to subtract each term from the equation on top. Close attention should be paid to subtracting negative terms. Have other volunteers demonstrate subtracting the top equation from the bottom equation.

EXAMPLE 3

ADDITIONAL EXAMPLE 3 Jeb and Lori went to a florist to buy flowers. Jeb bought 6 roses and 3 carnations for $20.25. Lori bought 8 roses and 3 carnations for $25.75. Find the price of one rose and the price of one carnation.

rose: $2.75; carnation: $1.25

Interactive Whiteboard
Interactive example available online

YOUR TURN   MP.1

Engage with the Whiteboard

Have a volunteer make a table to organize the information in the problem. Have another volunteer write the two equations for the system of equations. Ask another volunteer to demonstrate how to solve the system.

Digital Teacher Resources

Go online to access all your lesson-level resources.

Differentiated Instruction
- Reteach
- Reading Strategies
- Success for English Learners
- Practice and Problem Solving A/B, C, D

Math on the Spot Videos

my.hrw.com

TEACHER TO TEACHER

Multiple Representations Discuss with students that it is helpful to use a table to organize information given in a real-world problem. Have students complete a table for Example 3 that includes the total amount spent at each store. Point out how the table organizes the information like the system of equations is written.

	Shoes	Stoves	Total
Store A	$79.50	$39.25	$554.50
Store B	$89.00	$39.25	$602.00

STEP 1 Choose variables and write a system of equations.
Let x represent the number of pairs of snowshoes.
Let y represent the number of camp stoves.

Top Sports cost: $79.50x + 39.25y = 554.50$
Outdoor Explorer cost: $89.00x + 39.25y = 602.00$

STEP 2 Subtract the equations.

$$79.50x + 39.25y = 554.50$$
$$-(89.00x + 39.25y = 602.00)$$

Both equations contain the term 39.25y.

$$-9.50x + 0 = -47.50$$ *Subtract to eliminate the variable y.*

$$-9.50x = -47.50$$ *Simplify and solve for x.*

$$\frac{-9.50x}{-9.50} = \frac{-47.50}{-9.50}$$ *Divide each side by −9.50.*

$$x = 5$$ *Simplify.*

STEP 3 Substitute the solution into one of the original equations and solve for y.

$$79.50x + 39.25y = 554.50$$ *Use the first equation.*

$$79.50(5) + 39.25y = 554.50$$ *Substitute 5 for the variable x.*

$$397.50 + 39.25y = 554.50$$ *Multiply.*

$$39.25y = 157.00$$ *Subtract 397.50 from each side.*

$$\frac{39.25y}{39.25} = \frac{157.00}{39.25}$$ *Divide each side by 39.25.*

$$y = 4$$ *Simplify.*

STEP 4 Write the solution as an ordered pair: (5, 4)

The club intends to buy 5 pairs of snowshoes and 4 camp stoves.

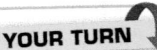
YOUR TURN

11. At the county fair, the Baxter family bought 6 hot dogs and 4 juice drinks for $16.70. The Farley family bought 3 hot dogs and 4 juice drinks for $10.85. Find the price of a hot dog and the price of a juice drink.

   hot dog: $1.95; juice drink: $1.25

Personal Math Trainer
Online Assessment and Intervention
my.hrw.com

© Houghton Mifflin Harcourt Publishing Company

DIFFERENTIATE INSTRUCTION *Leveled Questions*

	EXAMPLE 3
(AL) DOK 1 *Recall*	What information does the table give you? the price per item at each store
(OL) DOK 2 *Skills/Concepts*	How do you decide whether to add or subtract the two equations? The goal is to eliminate one of the variable terms. Since the coefficients of the variable y are the same in both equations, you subtract.
(BL) DOK 3 *Strategic Thinking*	How would the equations and solution change if you let x represent the number of camp stoves and y represent the number of pairs of snowshoes? The equations would be $39.25x + 79.50y = 554.50$ and $39.25x + 89.00y = 602.00$. The solution would be (4, 5) instead of (5, 4).

LEVELED QUESTIONS: **(AL)** Approaching Level | **(OL)** On Level | **(BL)** Beyond Level

1. Solve the system $\begin{cases} 4x + 3y = 1 \\ x - 3y = -11 \end{cases}$ by adding. (Explore Activity Example 1)

   STEP 1 Add the equations.

   $$4x + 3y = 1$$
   $$+\quad x - 3y = -11$$

   Write the equations so that like terms are aligned.

   $$5x + \boxed{0} = \boxed{-10}$$

   Add to eliminate the variable $\boxed{y}$.

   $$5x = \boxed{-10}$$

   Simplify and solve for x.

   $$x = \boxed{-2}$$

   Divide both sides by $\boxed{5}$ and simplify.

   STEP 2 Substitute into one of the original equations and solve for y.

   $$y = \boxed{3}$$ So, $\boxed{(-2, 3)}$ is the solution of the system.

   Solve each system of equations by adding or subtracting.
   (Explore Activity Example 1, Example 2)

2. $\begin{cases} x + 2y = -2 \\ -3x - 2y = -10 \end{cases}$

   $(2, -2)$

3. $\begin{cases} 3x + y = 23 \\ 3x - 2y = 8 \end{cases}$

   $(6, 5)$

4. $\begin{cases} -4x - 5y = 7 \\ 3x + 5y = -14 \end{cases}$

   $(7, -7)$

5. $\begin{cases} x - 2y = -19 \\ 5x + 2y = 1 \end{cases}$

   $(-3, 8)$

6. $\begin{cases} 3x + 4y = 18 \\ -2x + 4y = 8 \end{cases}$

   $(2, 3)$

7. $\begin{cases} -5x + 7y = 11 \\ -5x + 3y = 19 \end{cases}$

   $(-5, -2)$

8. The Green River Freeway has a minimum and a maximum speed limit. Tony drove for 2 hours at the minimum speed limit and 3.5 hours at the maximum limit, a distance of 355 miles. Rae drove 2 hours at the minimum speed limit and 3 hours at the maximum limit, a distance of 320 miles. What are the two speed limits? (Example 3)

   a. Write equations to represent Tony's distance and Rae's distance.

   Tony: $2x + 3.5y = 355$ Rae: $2x + 3y = 320$

   b. Solve the system.

   minimum speed limit: 55 mi/h   maximum speed limit: 70 mi/h

   ❓ ESSENTIAL QUESTION CHECK-IN

9. Can you use addition or subtraction to solve any system? Explain.

   no; Addition or subtraction can be used only when the coefficients of the x-terms or the y-terms are the same or opposites.

© Houghton Mifflin Harcourt Publishing Company

4 Elaborate

Talk About It

Summarize the Lesson

Ask: How do you know when to add or subtract when solving a system of equations by elimination? The goal is to eliminate one of the variable terms. If the coefficients of one variable term are the same in both equations, then you subtract. If they are opposites, you add.

Guided Practice

Engage with the Whiteboard

For **Exercise 1**, have volunteers explain the process of arriving at the correct value as they complete the write-in boxes for each step.

Avoid Common Errors

- **Exercise 3** Remind students to be cautious with the signs of the terms. Subtracting $-2y$ from y is the same as adding $2y$ to y. Suggest that if they have trouble correctly subtracting each term, they might choose to rewrite the second equation with the opposite of each term and then add the equations.

- **Exercise 8** Suggest that students organize the information in this situation in a table and identify what their variables represent.

DIFFERENTIATE INSTRUCTION *Intervention and Additional Support*

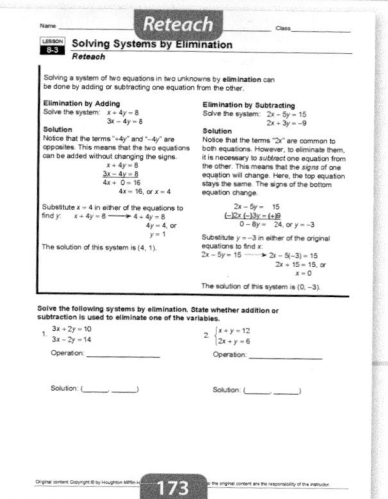

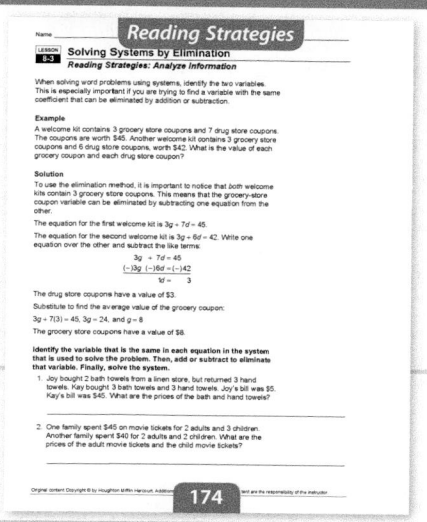

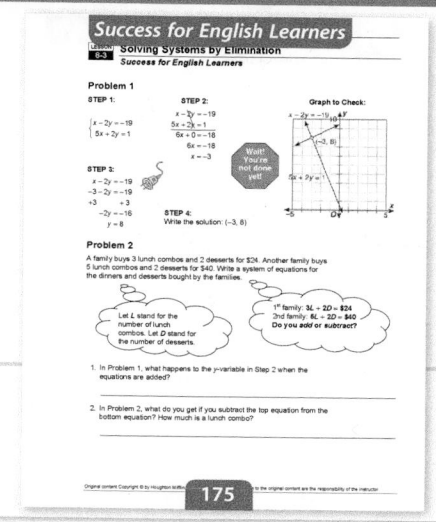

Personal Math Trainer
Daily Intervention
8.3 Homework

Pages shown are from *Differentiated Instruction*.
Also available online.

Solving Systems by Elimination **248**

⏱ Pressed for Time

8.3 Differentiated Homework Assignments

AL **Approaching Level**	10–13, 15, 17
OL **On Level**	12–15, 17
BL **Beyond Level**	14, 16–17

*For **Below Level** students, assign Personal Math Trainer, Daily Intervention 8.3 Homework.*

Mathematical Processes	Exercises
MP.2 Reasoning	12, 16
MP.3 Logic	17
MP.4 Modeling	10–11, 13–15

Focus on Higher Order Thinking

Depth of Knowledge	Exercises
1 Recall of Information	12, 16
2 Skills/Concepts	17
3 Strategic Thinking H.O.T.	10–11, 13–15

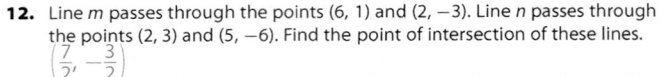

Personal Math Trainer
Online Assessment and Intervention
my.hrw.com

10. **Represent Real-World Problems** Marta bought new fish for her home aquarium. She bought 3 guppies and 2 platies for a total of $13.95. Hank also bought guppies and platies for his aquarium. He bought 3 guppies and 4 platies for a total of $18.33. Find the price of a guppy and the price of a platy.

Guppy: $3.19; platy: $2.19

11. **Represent Real-World Problems** The rule for the number of fish in a home aquarium is 1 gallon of water for each inch of fish length. Marta's aquarium holds 13 gallons and Hank's aquarium holds 17 gallons. Based on the number of fish they bought in Exercise 10, how long is a guppy and how long is a platy?

Guppy: 3 in.; platy: 2 in.

12. Line *m* passes through the points (6, 1) and (2, −3). Line *n* passes through the points (2, 3) and (5, −6). Find the point of intersection of these lines.

$\left(\frac{7}{2}, -\frac{3}{2}\right)$

13. **Represent Real-World Problems** Two cars got an oil change at the same auto shop. The shop charges customers for each quart of oil plus a flat fee for labor. The oil change for one car required 5 quarts of oil and cost $22.45. The oil change for the other car required 7 quarts of oil and cost $25.45. How much is the labor fee and how much is each quart of oil?

Labor fee: $14.95; quart of oil: $1.50

14. **Represent Real-World Problems** A sales manager noticed that the number of units sold for two T-shirt styles, style A and style B, was the same during June and July. In June, total sales were $2779 for the two styles, with A selling for $15.95 per shirt and B selling for $22.95 per shirt. In July, total sales for the two styles were $2385.10, with A selling at the same price and B selling at a discount of 22% off the June price. How many T-shirts of each style were sold in June and July combined?

280 T-shirts of style A and style B were sold in

June and July.

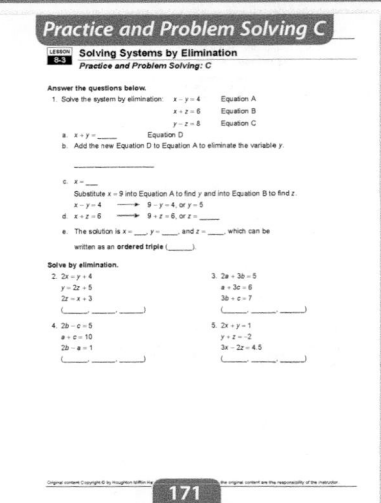

15. **Represent Real-World Problems** Adult tickets to a basketball game cost $5. Student tickets cost $1. A total of $2,874 was collected on the sale of 1,246 tickets. How many of each type of ticket were sold?

407 adult tickets and 839 student tickets

© Houghton Mifflin Harcourt Publishing Company • Image Credits: (tr) ©Johannes Kornelius/Shutterstock, (br) ©Corbis Flirt/Alamy Images

---

DIFFERENTIATE INSTRUCTION *Leveled Homework/Practice*

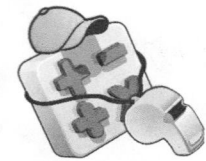

Personal Math Trainer
• 8.3 Homework

Pages shown are from *Differentiated Instruction*. **Also available online.**

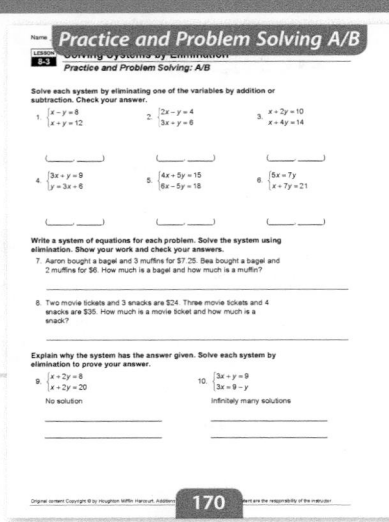

Practice and Problem Solving A/B

170

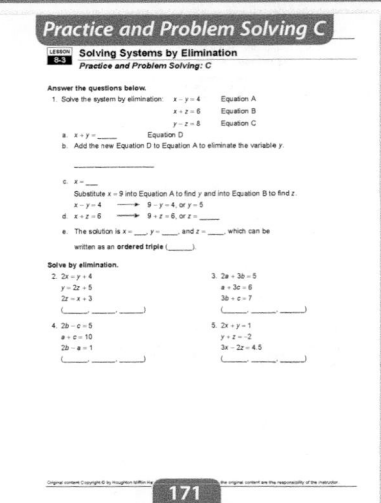

Practice and Problem Solving C

171

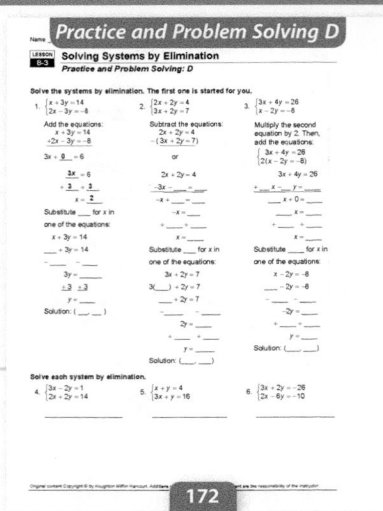

Practice and Problem Solving D

172

16. Communicate Mathematical Ideas Is it possible to solve the system $\begin{cases} 3x - 2y = 10 \\ x + 2y = 6 \end{cases}$ by using substitution? If so, explain how. Which method, substitution or elimination, is more efficient? Why?

Yes; solve the second equation for x to get $x = -2y + 6$.

Substitute $-2y + 6$ for x in the first equation to get

$3(-2y + 6) - 2y = 10$. Solve this for y to get $y = 1$. Then

substitute 1 for y in either original equation to get $x = 4$,

for a solution of (4, 1). The elimination method is more

efficient because there are fewer calculations and they

are simpler to do.

17. Jenny used substitution to solve the system $\begin{cases} 2x + y = 8 \\ x - y = 1 \end{cases}$. Her solution is shown below.

Step 1 $y = -2x + 8$ Solve the first equation for y.

Step 2 $2x + (-2x + 8) = 8$ Substitute the value of y in an original equation.

Step 3 $2x - 2x + 8 = 8$ Use the Distributive Property.

Step 4 $8 = 8$ Simplify.

a. Explain the Error Explain the error Jenny made. Describe how to correct it.

She substituted her expression for y in the same

equation she used to find y. She should substitute

her expression into the other equation.

b. Communicate Mathematical Ideas Would adding the equations have been a better method for solving the system? If so, explain why.

Yes; adding the equations would have resulted in

$3x = 9$, easily giving $x = 3$ after dividing each side

by 3. Substitution requires many more steps.

© Houghton Mifflin Harcourt Publishing Company

Work Area

 Quick Check

8.3 Lesson Quiz

Solve each system of equations by adding or subtracting.

1. $\begin{cases} x + 5y = 8 \\ 2x - 5y = 1 \end{cases}$ (3, 1)

2. $\begin{cases} 2x + y = 7 \\ -2x - 4y = -16 \end{cases}$ (2, 3)

3. $\begin{cases} 3x + 7y = 47 \\ -4x + 7y = 19 \end{cases}$ (4, 5)

4. $\begin{cases} x + 3y = -23 \\ -x + 4y = -26 \end{cases}$ (-2, -7)

5. The perimeter of a rectangle is 24 inches. Twice the length decreased by three times the width is 4 inches. What are the dimensions of the rectangle? length = 8 inches; width = 4 inches

Differentiate Instruction

IF a student misses more than one question, THEN

Differentiate Instruction:

• 8.3 Reteach

• Personal Math Trainer

Interactive Whiteboard
Interactive Lesson quiz available online

DIFFERENTIATE INSTRUCTION *Extend-the-Math Activity* **PRE-AP**

Activity The solution to a system of three equations in three variables is an ordered triple (x, y, z). You can solve the following system of equations using elimination. Add the first two equations to eliminate z. Add the resulting equation to the third equation to eliminate y. This will give you the value of x, which you can substitute into the third equation to find the value of y. Finally, substitute y in the second equation to find the value of z.

$$\begin{cases} 2x + y + z = 12 \\ 3y - z = -10 \\ x - 4y = 7 \end{cases}$$

$(3, -1, 7)$

Lesson Support

Content Objective Students will learn how to solve a system of linear equations by elimination with multiplying.

Professional Development

Integrate Mathematical Processes MP.1

This lesson provides an opportunity to address this Mathematical Process standard. It calls for students to make sense of problems and persevere in solving them. Example 3 uses a four-step problem-solving process. Students analyze the information, formulate a plan, solve the problem, and justify and evaluate the solution.

FOCUS

Building Background

Eliciting Prior Knowledge Show students two systems of equations. Discuss the method students would choose to use to solve each system. Students do not have to solve the systems. Instead ask them to focus on how they would select the method they would use and why they would use the method.

$$\begin{cases} 5x + y = 7 \\ -5x - 4y = -13 \end{cases}$$

$$\begin{cases} 3x - 4y = 13 \\ x - 4y = 7 \end{cases}$$

Solutions are (1, 2) and (3, −1). Elimination by adding would be a good method for the first system; elimination by subtracting would be a good method for the second system. Students might also choose substitution.

COHERENCE

Learning Progressions

In this lesson, students solve a system of two linear equations using the elimination method. Important understandings for students include the following:

- **Solve a linear system by multiplying and adding.**
- **Solve a linear system by multiplying and subtracting.**
- **Solve problems with systems of linear equations by elimination.**

This lesson is a culmination of the methods students have learned to solve a system. They algebraically solve linear systems in which substitution or elimination alone are increasingly difficult to use. They look for appropriate multiples to help them use the elimination method they learned in the last lesson. As with the other lessons in this module, students continue to apply the new method to solving real-life problems arising from a system of linear equations.

RIGOR

Cluster Connections

This lesson provides an excellent opportunity to connect ideas in the cluster:

Analyze and solve linear equations and pairs of simultaneous linear equations.

Remind students that they solved equations with rational number coefficients and constants by multiplying by the LCD. Point out that this same method can be used to rewrite the fractions in a system of equations. Ask them to use multiplication and elimination to solve the following system:

$$\begin{cases} \dfrac{x}{4} + \dfrac{y}{3} = -6 \\ 2x - 4y = 12 \end{cases}$$

(−12, −9)

Language Support ELL

Language Objective Students will give the steps for solving a system of linear equations by elimination with multiplying.

Leveled Strategies for English Learners ELL

Type of apple	Granny Smith	Red Delicious
Needed for a pie	5	3
Needed for a jar of applesauce	4	2

Emerging
Have students copy the table in Exercise 13 and draw a symbol to represent the different possibilities (pies and applesauce). Have students work in small groups of mixed English proficiency levels to help formulate an explanation and justification for how to solve the problem.

Expanding
Have students form teams to solve Exercise 13. As students solve the problem, have them prepare a statement that tells how they know their answer is correct.

Bridging
When students solve Exercise 13, provide them with a sentence frame to write in their math journal how they solved the problem and how they know their answer is correct.

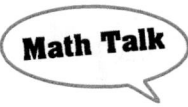 **Math Talk** To help students answer the question posed in Reflect questions, provide sentence frames for them to use.

Linguistic Support ELL

Academic/Content Vocabulary
Help students get into the routine of explaining their answer and their process when solving systems. Work collaboratively with English learners to solve Your Turn Exercise 10. As students work through the problem, have another student write down the step-by-step solution so that they can all explain how to solve the problem when it is complete.

Background Knowledge
Encourage students to discuss their answers and their solutions. Structure group work so that each student has a meaningful contribution to make to the whole group task.

Image Credits: ©Photodisc/Getty Images

Solving Systems by Elimination with Multiplication

1 Engage

 ESSENTIAL QUESTION

How do you solve a system of linear equations by multiplying? Sample answer: First, decide which variable to eliminate. Then, multiply one equation by a constant so that adding or subtracting will eliminate that variable. Finally, solve the system using the elimination method.

Motivate the Lesson

Ask: Can you solve a system of equations if adding or subtracting does not eliminate one of the variables? Begin the lesson to find out.

2 Explore

EXPLORE ACTIVITY **EXAMPLE 1**

ADDITIONAL EXAMPLE 1 Solve the system of equations by multiplying and adding.

$$\begin{cases} 2x + 5y = 8 \\ -x + 3y = 7 \end{cases}$$

$(-1, 2)$

Interactive Whiteboard
Interactive example available online

Solving Systems by Elimination with Multiplication

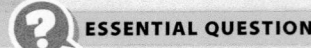 **ESSENTIAL QUESTION**

How do you solve a system of linear equations by multiplying?

Math On the Spot
my.hrw.com

EXPLORE ACTIVITY

Solving a System by Multiplying and Adding

In some linear systems, neither variable can be eliminated by adding or subtracting the equations directly. In systems like these, you need to multiply one of the equations by a constant so that adding or subtracting the equations will eliminate one variable. The steps for this method are as follows:

1. Decide which variable to eliminate.
2. Multiply one equation by a constant so that adding or subtracting will eliminate that variable.
3. Solve the system using the elimination method.

EXAMPLE 1 Solve the system of equations by multiplying and adding.

$$\begin{cases} 2x + 10y = 2 \\ 3x - 5y = -17 \end{cases}$$

STEP 1 The coefficient of y in the first equation, 10, is 2 times the coefficient of y, 5, in the second equation. Also, the y-term in the first equation is being added, while the y-term in the second equation is being subtracted. To eliminate the _y-terms_, multiply the second equation by 2 and add this new equation to the first equation.

Multiply each term in the second equation by __2__ to get opposite coefficients for the _y-terms_, and simplify.

Add the first equation to the new equation.

Add to eliminate the variable __y__.

Simplify.

Divide each side by __8__.

Simplify.

$$\boxed{2}(3x - \boxed{5}y = -17)$$
$$\boxed{6}x - \boxed{10}y = -34$$
$$\begin{array}{r} 6x - 10y = -34 \\ + \ 2x + \boxed{10y} = \ 2 \\ \hline 8x + \boxed{0}y = -32 \\ 8x = -32 \end{array}$$
$$\frac{8x}{\boxed{8}} = \frac{-32}{\boxed{8}}$$
$$x = \boxed{-4}$$

Lesson 8.4 **251**

DIFFERENTIATE INSTRUCTION *Leveled Questions*

	EXPOLRE ACTIVITY EXAMPLE 1
AL DOK 1 *Recall*	What is the first step in solving a system by multiplying and adding? Decide which variable to eliminate.
OL DOK 2 *Skills/Concepts*	How can you decide which variable to eliminate? Sample answer: Look for like terms with coefficients that are multiples of each other. Then multiply one equation by a number to make those like terms equals or opposites.
BL DOK 3 *Strategic Thinking*	How can you solve the system of equations using another method? Sample answer: Rewrite the first equation as $x + 5y = 1$, then either add the new equation to $3x - 5y = -17$, or write x as $-5y + 1$ and use substitution to solve the system.

STEP 2 Substitute the solution into one of the original equations, and solve for y.

Use the first equation. $2x + 10y = 2$

Substitute __−4__ for the variable x. $2\left(\boxed{-4}\right) + 10y = 2$

Simplify. $\boxed{-8} + 10y = 2$

Add __8__ to each side. $10y = \boxed{10}$

Divide each side by __10__, and simplify. $y = \boxed{1}$

STEP 3 Write the solution as an ordered pair: (__−4__ , __1__).

STEP 4 Check your answer algebraically.

Substitute __−4__ for x and __1__ for y in the original system.

$$\begin{cases} 2x + 10y = 2 \rightarrow 2\left(\boxed{-4}\right) + 10\left(\boxed{1}\right) = \boxed{2}\ \checkmark \\ 3x - 5y = -17 \rightarrow 3\left(\boxed{-4}\right) - 5\left(\boxed{1}\right) = \boxed{-17}\ \checkmark \end{cases}$$

The solution is correct.

Reflect

1. How can you solve this linear system by subtracting? Which is more efficient, adding or subtracting? Explain your reasoning.

Multiply the second equation by −2 and then subtract. Adding is

more efficient because the y-terms already have opposite signs.

2. Can this linear system be solved by adding or subtracting without multiplying? Why or why not?

No; without multiplying, neither variable will be eliminated.

3. What would you need to multiply the second equation by to eliminate x by adding? Why might you choose to eliminate y instead of x?

You would need to multiply the second equation by $-\frac{2}{3}$; it is simpler

to multiply by the whole number 2.

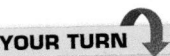

YOUR TURN

Solve each system of equations by multiplying and adding.

4. $\begin{cases} 5x + 2y = -10 \\ 3x + 6y = 66 \end{cases}$ **5.** $\begin{cases} 4x + 2y = 6 \\ 3x - y = -8 \end{cases}$ **6.** $\begin{cases} -6x + 9y = -12 \\ 2x + y = 0 \end{cases}$

    __(−8, 15)__   __(−1, 5)__ $\left(\frac{1}{2}, -1\right)$

Personal Math Trainer

Online Assessment and Intervention

my.hrw.com

© Houghton Mifflin Harcourt Publishing Company

YOUR TURN MP.7

Avoid Common Errors
Students might not be able to decide which variable to eliminate. Suggest they first check the equations for coefficients that are multiples of each other. If they exist, only one equation need be multiplied before adding or subtracting to eliminate that variable.

TEACHER TO TEACHER

Visual Clues Some students are not orderly when using elimination to solve a system. Suggest they write out the steps they are using. For example:

$$\begin{cases} 3x - 7y = 2 \\ 6x - 9y = 9 \end{cases}$$

Multiply by 2.	$\begin{cases} 6x - 14y = 4 \\ 6x - 9y = 9 \end{cases}$
Subtract.	$\begin{cases} 6x - 14y = 4 \\ -(6x - 9y = 9) \end{cases}$
Add.	$\begin{cases} 6x - 14y = 4 \\ -6x + 9y = -9 \end{cases}$

EXAMPLE 2

ADDITIONAL EXAMPLE 2 Solve the system of linear equations by multiplying and subtracting.

$$\begin{cases} 4x + y = -8 \\ 2x + 3y = 6 \end{cases}$$

$(-3, 4)$

Interactive Whiteboard
Interactive example available online

Solving a System by Multiplying and Subtracting

You can solve some systems of equations by multiplying one equation by a constant and then subtracting.

Math On the Spot
my.hrw.com

EXAMPLE 2

Solve the system of equations by multiplying and subtracting.

$$\begin{cases} 6x + 5y = 7 \\ 2x - 4y = -26 \end{cases}$$

My Notes

STEP 1 Multiply the second equation by 3 and subtract this new equation from the first equation.

$3(2x - 4y) = -26$ Multiply each term in the second equation by 3 to get the same coefficients for the x-terms.

$6x - 12y = -78$ Simplify.

$\begin{array}{r} 6x + 5y = 7 \\ -(6x - 12y = -78) \end{array}$ Subtract the new equation from the first equation.

$0x + 17y = 85$ Subtract to eliminate the variable x.

$17y = 85$ Simplify and solve for y.

$\dfrac{17y}{17} = \dfrac{85}{17}$ Divide each side by 17.

$y = 5$ Simplify.

STEP 2 Substitute the solution into one of the original equations and solve for *x*.

$6x + 5y = 7$ Use the first equation.

$6x + 5(5) = 7$ Substitute 5 for the variable y.

$6x + 25 = 7$ Simplify.

$6x = -18$ Subtract 25 from each side.

$x = -3$ Divide each side by 6 and simplify.

STEP 3 Write the solution as an ordered pair: $(-3, 5)$

STEP 4 Check your answer algebraically.
Substitute -3 for *x* and 5 for *y* in the original system.

$$\begin{cases} 6x + 5y = 7 \rightarrow 6(-3) + 5(5) = -18 + 25 = 7 \checkmark \\ 2x - 4y = -26 \rightarrow 2(-3) - 4(5) = -6 - 20 = -26 \checkmark \end{cases}$$

The solution is correct.

© Houghton Mifflin Harcourt Publishing Company

DIFFERENTIATE INSTRUCTION *Leveled Questions*

	EXAMPLE 2
(AL) DOK 1 *Recall*	What variable is eliminated first? *x*
(OL) DOK 2 *Skills/Concepts*	How would the solution process change if you multiplied the second equation by -3 instead of 3? The *x*-terms would be eliminated by adding instead of by subtracting.
(BL) DOK 3 *Strategic Thinking*	If you got $0 = 0$ at the end of Step 1, what would that tell you about the system? That would mean there are infinitely many solutions to the system and both equations represent the same line.

LEVELED QUESTIONS: (AL) Approaching Level | (OL) On Level | (BL) Beyond Level

Personal
Math Trainer
Online Assessment
and Intervention
my.hrw.com

Math On the Spot
my.hrw.com

Solve each system of equations by multiplying and subtracting.

7. $\begin{cases} 3x - 7y = 2 \\ 6x - 9y = 9 \end{cases}$

   $(3, 1)$

8. $\begin{cases} -3x + y = 11 \\ 2x + 3y = -11 \end{cases}$

   $(-4, -1)$

9. $\begin{cases} 9x + y = 9 \\ 3x - 2y = -11 \end{cases}$

   $\left(\dfrac{1}{3}, 6\right)$

Solving Problems with Systems of Equations

Many real-world situations can be modeled with a system of equations.

EXAMPLE 3 — Problem Solving

The Simon family attended a concert and visited an art museum. Concert tickets were $24.75 for adults and $16.00 for children, for a total cost of $138.25. Museum tickets were $8.25 for adults and $4.50 for children, for a total cost of $42.75. How many adults and how many children are in the Simon family?

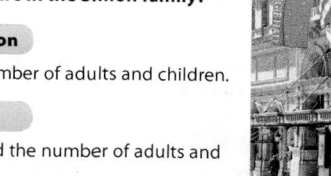

Analyze Information

The answer is the number of adults and children.

Formulate a Plan

Solve a system to find the number of adults and children.

Solve

STEP 1 Choose variables and write a system of equations. Let x represent the number of adults. Let y represent the number of children.

Concert cost: $24.75x + 16.00y = 138.25$
Museum cost: $8.25x + 4.50y = 42.75$

STEP 2 Multiply both equations by 100 to eliminate the decimals.

$100(24.75x + 16.00y = 138.25) \rightarrow 2{,}475x + 1{,}600y = 13{,}825$

$100(8.25x + 4.50y = 42.75) \rightarrow 825x + 450y = 4{,}275$

My Notes

© Houghton Mifflin Harcourt Publishing Company • Image Credits: ©Education Images/UIG/Getty Images

Engage with the Whiteboard

In **Exercise 9**, have a student volunteer show how to multiply one equation to eliminate x. Have another show how to multiply one equation to eliminate y. Point out that both methods result in the same answer.

EXAMPLE 3

ADDITIONAL EXAMPLE 3 Meghan needs to board her cats and dogs at a kennel while she is on vacation. Pet Hotel charges $42.50 for a cat and $64.00 for a dog for a total cost of $277.00. Animal Spa charges $35.50 for a cat and $50.50 for a dog, for a total cost of $222.50. How many cats and how many dogs does Meghan have?
2 cats, 3 dogs

Interactive Whiteboard
Interactive example available online

	EXAMPLE 3
AL DOK 1 *Recall*	What will the solution represent in this system of equations? the number of adults, x, and children, y, in the Simon family
OL DOK 2 *Skills/Concepts*	How do you decide which power of 10 to use to multiply the equations in Step 2? The greatest number of decimal places in any of the coefficients or constant terms is hundredths, so multiplying by 100 replaces all of the decimals with whole numbers.
BL DOK 3 *Strategic Thinking*	How would eliminating Step 2 from the solution process change the solution and the solution process? It would not change the solution. The solution process would involve working with decimals; or you could multiply the second equation by 300 instead of 3 in Step 3 to eliminate the decimals.

YOUR TURN MP.1

Talk About It
Check for Understanding

 **Ask:** If nothing else changed, would it have been possible for Seth's average biking speed to be 29.8 mi/h? Justify your answer. It would not be possible. The solution would have been approximately $(-1.23, 1)$, but it is not possible to run for a negative number of hours.

Digital Teacher Resources

Go online to access all your lesson-level resources.

Differentiated Instruction
- Reteach
- Reading Strategies
- Success for English Learners
- Practice and Problem Solving A/B, C, D

Math on the Spot Videos

my.hrw.com

STEP 3 Multiply the second equation by 3 and subtract this new equation from the first equation.

$3(825x + 450y = 4,275)$ Multiply each term in the second equation by 3 to get the same coefficients for the x-terms.

$2,475x + 1,350y = 12,825$ Simplify.

$2,475x + 1,600y = 13,825$ Subtract the new equation from the first equation.
$-(2,475x + 1,350y = 12,825)$

$0x + 250y = 1,000$ Subtract to eliminate the variable x.

$250y = 1,000$ Simplify and solve for y.

$\dfrac{250y}{250} = \dfrac{1,000}{250}$ Divide each side by 250.

$y = 4$ Simplify.

STEP 4 Substitute the solution into one of the original equations and solve for x.

$8.25x + 4.50y = 42.75$ Use the second equation.

$8.25x + 4.50(4) = 42.75$ Substitute 4 for the variable y.

$8.25x + 18 = 42.75$ Simplify.

$8.25x = 24.75$ Subtract 18 from each side.

$x = 3$ Divide each side by 8.25 and simplify.

STEP 5 Write the solution as an ordered pair: (3, 4).
There are 3 adults and 4 children in the family.

Justify and Evaluate

Substituting $x = 3$ and $y = 4$ into the original equations results in true statements. The answer is correct.

YOUR TURN

10. Contestants in the Run-and-Bike-a-thon run for a specified length of time, then bike for a specified length of time. Jason ran at an average speed of 5.2 mi/h and biked at an average speed of 20.6 mi/h, going a total of 14.2 miles. Seth ran at an average speed of 10.4 mi/h and biked at an average speed of 18.4 mi/h, going a total of 17 miles. For how long do contestants run and for how long do they bike?

Contestants run 0.75 hour and bike 0.5 hour.

Personal Math Trainer

Online Assessment and Intervention

my.hrw.com

© Houghton Mifflin Harcourt Publishing Company

TEACHER TO TEACHER

Multiple Representations Students can make a table to organize the information before writing the system of equations for Your Turn Exercise 10.

	Run	**Bike**	**Total**
Jason	5.2 mi/h	20.6 mi/h	14.2 mi
Seth	10.4 mi/h	18.4 mi/h	17 mi

Have students give the corresponding system of equations, and discuss how the table organizes the information like the system of equations is written.

$$\begin{cases} 5.2r + 20.6b = 14.2 \\ 10.4r + 18.4b = 17 \end{cases}$$

1. Solve the system $\begin{cases} 3x - y = 8 \\ -2x + 4y = -12 \end{cases}$ by multiplying and adding. (Explore Activity Example 1)

STEP 1 Multiply the first equation by 4. Add to the second equation.

$4(3x - y = 8)$ Multiply each term in the first equation by 4 to get opposite coefficients for the y-terms.

$\boxed{12}x - \boxed{4}y = \boxed{32}$ Simplify.

$+ \ (-2x) \ + \ 4y = -12$ Add the second equation to the new equation.

$10x = \boxed{20}$ Add to eliminate the variable $\boxed{y}$.

$x = \boxed{2}$ Divide both sides by $\boxed{10}$ and simplify.

STEP 2 Substitute into one of the original equations and solve for y.

$y = \boxed{-2}$ So, $\boxed{(2, -2)}$ is the solution of the system.

Solve each system of equations by multiplying first. (Explore Activity Example 1, Example 2)

2. $\begin{cases} x + 4y = 2 \\ 2x + 5y = 7 \end{cases}$ $\underline{(6, -1)}$ **3.** $\begin{cases} 3x + y = -1 \\ 2x + 3y = 18 \end{cases}$ $\underline{(-3, 8)}$ **4.** $\begin{cases} 2x + 8y = 21 \\ 6x - 4y = 14 \end{cases}$ $\underline{\left(\frac{7}{2}, \frac{7}{4}\right)}$

5. $\begin{cases} 2x + y = 3 \\ -x + 3y = -12 \end{cases}$ $\underline{(3, -3)}$ **6.** $\begin{cases} 6x + 5y = 19 \\ 2x + 3y = 5 \end{cases}$ $\underline{(4, -1)}$ **7.** $\begin{cases} 2x + 5y = 16 \\ -4x + 3y = 20 \end{cases}$ $\underline{(-2, 4)}$

8. Bryce spent $5.26 on some apples priced at $0.64 each and some pears priced at $0.45 each. At another store he could have bought the same number of apples at $0.32 each and the same number of pears at $0.39 each, for a total cost of $3.62. How many apples and how many pears did Bryce buy? (Example 3)

   a. Write equations to represent Bryce's expenditures at each store.

     First store: $\underline{0.64x + 0.45y = 5.26}$ Second store: $\underline{0.32x + 0.39y = 3.62}$

   b. Solve the system.   Number of pears: $\underline{\quad 6 \quad}$

     Number of apples: $\underline{\quad 4 \quad}$

 ESSENTIAL QUESTION CHECK-IN

9. When solving a system by multiplying and then adding or subtracting, how do you decide whether to add or subtract?

<u>If the coefficients of one variable are the same, you subtract. If the</u>

<u>coefficients of one variable are opposites, you add.</u>

© Houghton Mifflin Harcourt Publishing Company

4 Elaborate

Talk About It

Summarize the Lesson

Ask: How do you know when solving a system of equations that you must multiply before you can add or subtract? If the coefficients of one variable are not the same or are not opposites in the two equations, then you must multiply one or both of the equations until the coefficients of one variable are the same or opposites. Then, you can add or subtract to eliminate one variable.

Guided Practice

Engage with the Whiteboard

For **Exercise 1**, have volunteers explain the process of arriving at the correct values as they complete the write-in boxes for each step.

Avoid Common Errors

- **Exercise 4** Remind students that either equation can be selected and then multiplied by a number, and either variable can be eliminated. In this exercise the top equation could be multiplied by 3 so x can be eliminated, or the bottom equation could be multiplied by 2 so y can be eliminated.

- **Exercise 8** Suggest that students organize the information in this situation in a table and identify what the variables represent. Remind them that eliminating the decimals will make the solution process easier.

DIFFERENTIATE INSTRUCTION *Intervention and Additional Support*

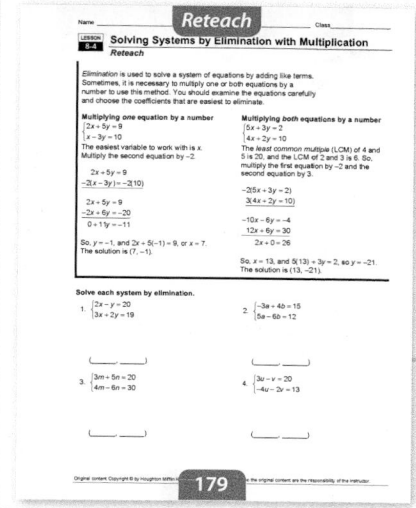

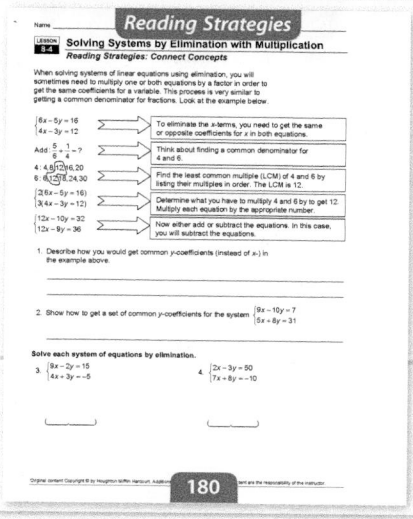

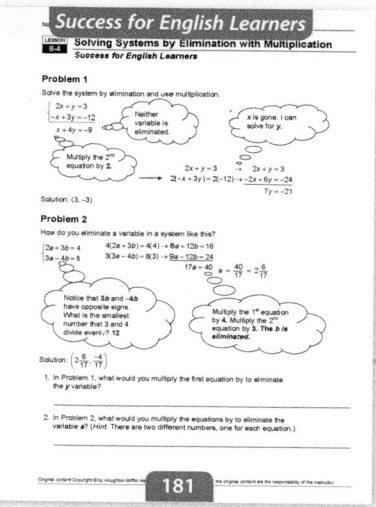

Personal Math Trainer
Daily Intervention
8.4 Homework

Pages shown are from *Differentiated Instruction*. **Also available online.**

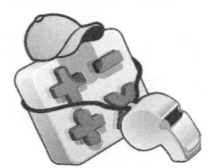

Pressed for Time

8.4 Differentiated Homework Assignments

AL Approaching Level	10–13	
OL On Level	11–13, 15	
BL Beyond Level	13–15	

For **Below Level** students, assign Personal Math Trainer, Daily Intervention 8.4 Homework.

Mathematical Processes	Exercises
MP.2 Reasoning	12
MP.3 Logic	10, 14
MP.4 Modeling	11, 13
MP.7 Using Structure	15

Focus on Higher Order Thinking

Depth of Knowledge	Exercises
2 Skills/Concepts	12–13
3 Strategic Thinking **H.O.T.**	10–11, 14–15

Name _____ Class _____ Date _____

8.4 Independent Practice

Personal Math Trainer

Online Assessment and Intervention

my.hrw.com

10. **Explain the Error** Gwen used elimination with multiplication to solve the system $\begin{cases} 2x + 6y = 3 \\ x - 3y = -1 \end{cases}$. Her work to find x is shown. Explain her error. Then solve the system.

$$2(x - 3y) = -1$$
$$2x - 6y = -1$$
$$+2x + 6y = 3$$
$$4x + 0y = 2$$

Gwen forgot to multiply the right side by 2; $\left(\frac{1}{4}, \frac{5}{12}\right)$ $x = \frac{1}{2}$

11. **Represent Real-World Problems** At Raging River Sports, polyester-fill sleeping bags sell for $79. Down-fill sleeping bags sell for $149. In one week the store sold 14 sleeping bags for $1,456.

Sleeping Bags

Nylon Down-filled, 35° $149

Flannel-lined Polyester-filled, 40° $79

a. Let x represent the number of polyester-fill bags sold and let y represent the number of down-fill bags sold. Write a system of equations you can solve to find the number of each type sold.

$$\begin{cases} 79x + 149y = 1,456 \\ x + y = 14 \end{cases}$$

b. Explain how you can solve the system for y by multiplying and subtracting.

Multiply the second equation by 79. Subtract the new equation from the first one and solve the resulting equation for y.

c. Explain how you can solve the system for y using substitution.

Solve the second equation for x. Substitute the expression for x in the first equation and solve the resulting equation for y.

d. How many of each type of bag were sold?

9 polyester-fill, 5 down-fill

12. Twice a number plus twice a second number is 310. The difference between the numbers is 55. Find the numbers by writing and solving a system of equations. Explain how you solved the system.

105 and 50; Sample answer: I multiplied the second equation in the system $\begin{cases} 2x + 2y = 310 \\ x - y = 55 \end{cases}$ by 2 and then added to eliminate the y-terms.

© Houghton Mifflin Harcourt Publishing Company

Lesson 8.4 **257**

DIFFERENTIATE INSTRUCTION *Leveled Homework/Practice*

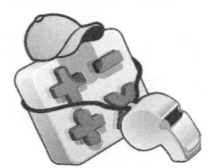

Personal Math Trainer
• 8.4 Homework

Pages shown are from *Differentiated Instruction*. **Also available online.**

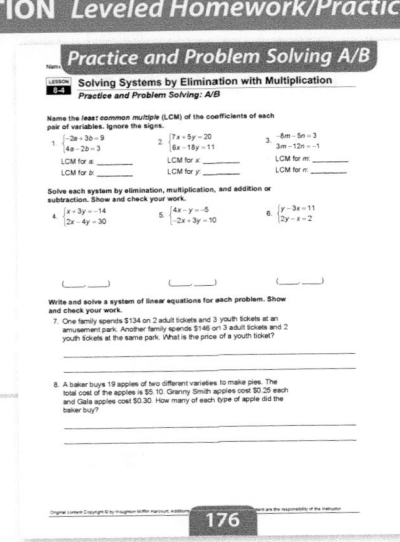

Practice and Problem Solving A/B

LESSON 8-4 Solving Systems by Elimination with Multiplication
Practice and Problem Solving: A/B

176

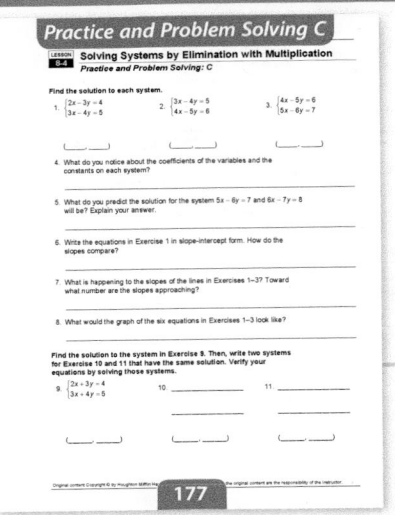

Practice and Problem Solving C

LESSON 8-4 Solving Systems by Elimination with Multiplication
Practice and Problem Solving: C

177

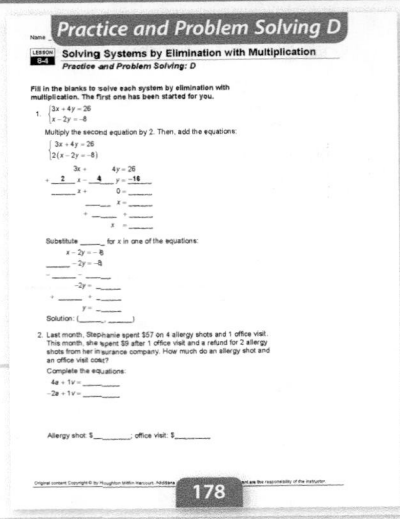

Practice and Problem Solving D

LESSON 8-4 Solving Systems by Elimination with Multiplication
Practice and Problem Solving: D

178

13. Represent Real-World Problems A farm stand sells apple pies and jars of applesauce. The table shows the number of apples needed to make a pie and a jar of applesauce. Yesterday, the farm picked 169 Granny Smith apples and 95 Red Delicious apples. How many pies and jars of applesauce can the farm make if every apple is used?

Type of apple	Granny Smith	Red Delicious
Needed for a pie	5	3
Needed for a jar of applesauce	4	2

21 pies, 16 jars of applesauce

 **FOCUS ON HIGHER ORDER THINKING**

14. Make a Conjecture Lena tried to solve a system of linear equations algebraically and in the process found the equation $5 = 9$. Lena thought something was wrong, so she graphed the equations and found that they were parallel lines. Explain what Lena's graph and equation could mean.

Lena's graph shows that the two lines do not intersect. This would seem to mean that the system has no solution. It would seem that solving an equation algebraically and getting a false statement means that the system has no solution.

15. Consider the system $\begin{cases} 2x + 3y = 6 \\ 3x + 7y = -1 \end{cases}$.

a. Communicate Mathematical Ideas Describe how to solve the system by multiplying the first equation by a constant and subtracting. Why would this method be less than ideal?

Multiply the first equation by 1.5 and subtract. This would be less than ideal because you would introduce decimals into the solution process.

b. Draw Conclusions Is it possible to solve the system by multiplying both equations by integer constants? If so, explain how.

Yes; multiply the first equation by 3 and the second equation by 2. Both x-term coefficients would be 6. Solve by eliminating the x-terms using subtraction.

c. Use your answer from part b to solve the system.

$(9, -4)$

Work Area

© Houghton Mifflin Harcourt Publishing Company Image credits: ©Photodisc/Getty Images

---

✔ Quick Check

8.4 Lesson Quiz

Solve the system of linear equations by multiplying first.

1. $\begin{cases} x + 3y = 8 \\ 2x - 5y = -6 \end{cases}$ $(2, 2)$

2. $\begin{cases} 3x + 2y = 2 \\ -2x - 4y = -12 \end{cases}$ $(-2, 4)$

3. $\begin{cases} 2x + 15y = 1 \\ -3x + 5y = 8 \end{cases}$ $(-1, 1)$

4. $\begin{cases} x + 2y = -8 \\ -8x + 5y = 1 \end{cases}$ $(-2, -3)$

5. The perimeter of a rectangle is 42 feet. The length decreased by three times the width is 1 foot. What are the dimensions of the rectangle? length = 16 ft; width = 5 ft

Differentiate Instruction

IF a student misses more than one question, THEN

Differentiate Instruction:
- 8.4 Reteach
- Personal Math Trainer

 Interactive Whiteboard
Interactive Lesson quiz available online

DIFFERENTIATE INSTRUCTION *Extend-the-Math Activity* PRE-AP

Activity The solution to a system of three equations in three variables is (x, y, z). Solve the following system of equations using elimination by multiplication and addition or subtraction. Multiply the first equation by 2. Add the first two equations to eliminate z. Add the resulting equation to the third equation, after multiplying the third equation by 4, to eliminate x. This will give you the value of y, which you can substitute into the third equation to find the value of x. Finally, substitute y in the second equation to find the value of z.

$$\begin{cases} 2x + y + 2z = 6 \\ 3y - 4z = -10 \\ x - 4y = 11 \end{cases}$$

$(3, -2, 1)$

Lesson Support

Content Objective Students will learn how to solve systems that have no solution or infinitely many solutions.

Professional Development

Integrate Mathematical Processes MP.2

This lesson provides an opportunity to address this Mathematical Process standard. It calls for students to reason abstractly and quantitatively. Upon reaching a final algebraic solution of a system of equations, students must reason abstractly to determine whether there is only one solution, no solution, or infinitely many solutions to the system. They must also reason abstractly to analyze the graphs of a system of equations and draw conclusions about the solution(s) of the system.

FOCUS	COHERENCE	RIGOR

FOCUS

Building Background

Eliciting Prior Knowledge Have students work with a partner or in small groups to create a case diagram that shows the possible solutions of a linear equation. Encourage students to construct examples for each of the three possible cases in the diagram.

Sample completed diagram is shown.

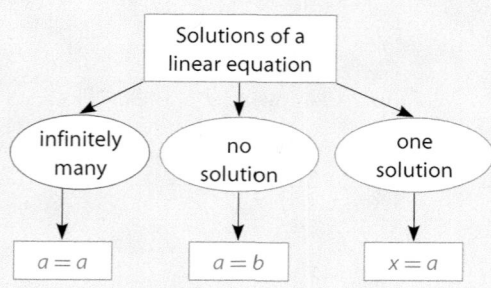

COHERENCE

Learning Progressions

In this lesson, students learn that not all systems of linear equations have a unique solution. Students also solve simple cases by inspection. Important understandings for students include the following:

- **Solve special systems by graphing.**
- **Solve special systems algebraically.**

In this unit, students have focused on linear equations and, in this module, on systems of linear equations. They have built upon their knowledge of equations from earlier grades and laid the foundation for more extensive study in algebra. This lesson provides a logical conclusion to their persistent work in finding solutions algebraically and by graphing.

RIGOR

Cluster Connections

This lesson provides an excellent opportunity to connect ideas in the cluster:

Analyze and solve linear equations and pairs of simultaneous linear equations.

Ask students to create three systems of equations, one with infinitely many solutions, one with no solutions, and one with one solution. In each case they should pair the equation $x + y = 5$ with one of the following equations: $x - y = 5$; $2x + 2y = 10$; $x + y = 10$. Discuss with students how they created each system.

infinitely many: $2x + 2y = 10$; one: $x - y = 5$; none: $x + y = 10$

Language Support ELL

Leveled Strategies for English Learners ELL

Emerging
Using visual representations, such as graphic organizers, is an excellent way to provide comprehension support for students at this English proficiency level. Using visual representations can help them demonstrate their understanding while also developing higher-level thinking. Use the graphic organizer given in *Teacher to Teacher* on p. 260.

Expanding
Use the graphic organizer given in *Teacher to Teacher* on p. 260, and have the students at this English proficiency level explain why they placed each element where they did on the graphic organizer.

Bridging
Have these students explain to other students why each step in the graphic organizer is placed where it is.

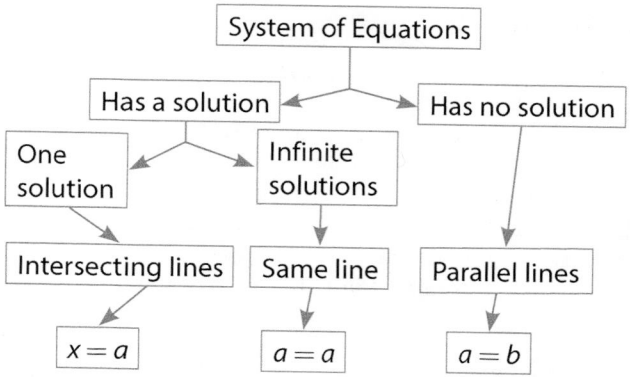

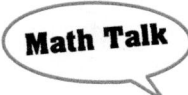

To help students answer the question posed in Math Talk, provide students with a sentence frame to respond.

When I solve the system by substitution, I get _____.

The result _____ (does / does not) change the number of solutions because _____.

Linguistic Support ELL

Academic/Content Vocabulary
In this lesson, students learn that some systems may have no solution or they may have infinitely many solutions. Explain that *infinitely many* means that the number of solutions is unlimited. Explain that the word *infinite* means "without end." Students who speak Spanish may know that the word *fin* means "end" and the word *infinito* is a cognate that means the same as *infinite*.

Background Knowledge
Form small groups of mixed English proficiency levels to work through Your Turn Exercises 6–8. Provide a sentence frame so that students can develop an explanation for their conclusions.

This system has _____ solution(s) because _____.

Solving Special Systems

1 Engage

ESSENTIAL QUESTION

How do you solve a system with no solutions or infinitely many solutions? Sample answer: The same methods of graphing, substitution, or elimination are used. If the graph shows parallel lines or if the solution gives a false statement, there is no solution. If the graph shows the lines coincide or if the solution gives a true statement for all ordered pairs, there are infinitely many solutions.

Motivate the Lesson

Ask: Equations whose graphs are intersecting lines have one solution. How many solutions do equations whose graphs are parallel lines have? Begin the Explore Activity to find out.

2 Explore

EXPLORE ACTIVITY

Engage with the Whiteboard

When discussing Step A, have a student highlight each of the equations in different colors and then highlight the corresponding lines in the same colors. When discussing Step B, have a different student highlight the two equations and the corresponding line in the same color.

Solving Special Systems

8.3.8.5
Students will solve systems with no solution or infinitely many solutions.

ESSENTIAL QUESTION   How do you solve systems with no solution or infinitely many solutions?

EXPLORE ACTIVITY

Solving Special Systems by Graphing

As with equations, some systems may have no solution or infinitely many solutions. One way to tell how many solutions a system has is by inspecting its graph.

Use the graph to solve each system of linear equations.

A $\begin{cases} x + y = 7 \\ 2x + 2y = 6 \end{cases}$

Is there a point of intersection? Explain.

No, the lines appear to be parallel; they have no points in common.

Does this linear system have a solution? Use the graph to explain.

This system has no solution; the lines have no points in common, which means there is no ordered pair that will make both equations true.

B $\begin{cases} 2x + 2y = 6 \\ x + y = 3 \end{cases}$

Is there a point of intersection? Explain.

Yes, the graphs are the same line; all points are points of intersection.

Does this linear system have a solution? Use the graph to explain.

This system has infinitely many solutions; all ordered pairs on the line will make both equations true.

Reflect

1. Use the graph to identify two lines that represent a linear system with exactly one solution. What are the equations of the lines? Explain your reasoning.

Sample answer : $x + y = 7$ and $3x - y = 1$; the lines intersect at one point.

Lesson 8.5 **259**

Graph labels: $3x - y = 1$, $x + y = 3$, $x + y = 7$, $2x + 2y = 6$

© Houghton Mifflin Harcourt Publishing Company

DIFFERENTIATE INSTRUCTION *Leveled Questions*

	EXPLORE ACTIVITY
(AL) DOK 1 *Recall*	How many solutions does the system in Part A have? the system in Part B? no solution; infinitely many solutions
(OL) DOK 2 *Skills/Concepts*	How can you tell without the graph when two lines are parallel? Identify the slopes and the y-intercepts. If the slopes are the same and the y-intercepts are different, the graphs are parallel.
(BL) DOK 3 *Strategic Thinking*	Can you describe the graph of a system of linear equations with no solution? Parallel lines; they do not intersect. with infinitely many solutions? Same line; all points are in common.

2. If each equation in a system of two linear equations is represented by a different line when graphed, what is the greatest number of solutions the system can have? Explain your reasoning.

One; because the two lines are different, they are either parallel and there is no solution, or they intersect at only one point.

3. Identify the three possible numbers of solutions for a system of linear equations. Explain when each type of solution occurs.

one solution when the lines intersect at a single point; no solution when the lines are parallel; infinitely many solutions when the lines are the same line

Math On the Spot
my.hrw.com

My Notes

Solving Special Systems Algebraically

As with equations, if you solve a system of equations with no solution, you get a false statement, and if you solve a system with infinitely many solutions, you get a true statement.

EXAMPLE 1

A Solve the system of linear equations by substitution.

$$\begin{cases} x - y = -2 \\ -x + y = 4 \end{cases}$$

STEP 1 Solve $x - y = -2$ for x:
$$x = y - 2$$

STEP 2 Substitute the resulting expression into the other equation and solve.

$$-(y - 2) + y = 4 \qquad \text{Substitute the expression for the variable } x.$$

$$2 = 4 \qquad \text{Simplify.}$$

STEP 3 Interpret the solution. The result is the false statement $2 = 4$, which means there is no solution.

STEP 4 Graph the equations to check your answer. The graphs do not intersect, so there is no solution.

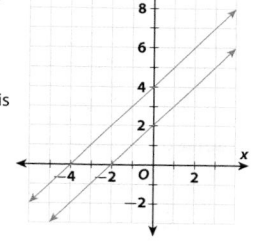

© Houghton Mifflin Harcourt Publishing Company

EXAMPLE 1

ADDITIONAL EXAMPLE 1

A Solve the system of linear equations by substitution.
$$\begin{cases} x - y = 8 \\ -x + y = 4 \end{cases} \text{ no solution}$$

B Solve the system of linear equations by elimination.
$$\begin{cases} 3x + 4y = -7 \\ -9x - 12y = 21 \end{cases} \text{ infinitely many solutions}$$

 Interactive Whiteboard
Interactive example available online

	EXAMPLE 1
(AL) DOK 1 *Recall*	When you solve a system of equations algebraically, what result indicates there is no solution? What result indicates there are infinitely many solutions? a false statement; a true statement
(OL) DOK 2 *Skills/Concepts*	In a system of equations with no solution, what happens if you substitute the coordinates of any ordered pair (x, y) in the two equations? The equations would not be satisfied no matter what values are substituted for x and y.
(BL) DOK 3 *Strategic Thinking*	In Part B, the system has infinitely many solutions. Does that mean any values for x and y are solutions? Explain. No; any values for x and y that are coordinates of points on the line are solutions of the system.

TEACHER TO TEACHER

Graphic Organizer

Have students create a concept map to show the connections between different types of systems of two equations. For example:

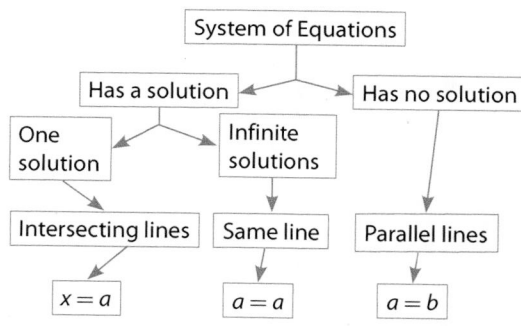

Talk About It

Check for Understanding

 **Ask:** If you were to graph the systems in **Exercises 6–8**, what would you expect each of the graphs to look like? The graph for the system in Exercise 6 would be parallel lines. The graph for the system in Exercise 7 would be lines intersecting at (10, −2). The graph for the system in Exercise 8 would be one line.

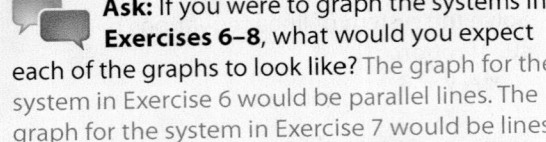

Digital Teacher Resources

Go online to access all your lesson-level resources.

Differentiated Instruction
- Reteach
- Reading Strategies
- Success for English Learners
- Practice and Problem Solving A/B, C, D

Math on the Spot Videos

my.hrw.com

B Solve the system of linear equations by elimination.

$$\begin{cases} 2x + y = -2 \\ 4x + 2y = -4 \end{cases}$$

STEP 1 Multiply the first equation by −2.

$$-2(2x + y = -2) \rightarrow -4x + (-2y) = 4$$

STEP 2 Add the new equation from Step 1 to the original second equation.

$$\begin{array}{r} -4x + (-2y) = 4 \\ + 4x + 2y = -4 \\ \hline 0x + 0y = 0 \\ 0 = 0 \end{array}$$

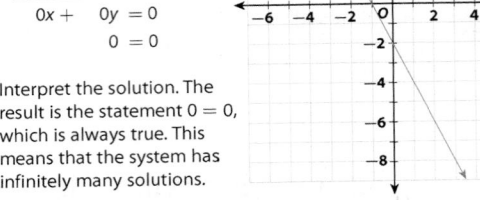

STEP 3 Interpret the solution. The result is the statement 0 = 0, which is always true. This means that the system has infinitely many solutions.

STEP 4 Graph the equations to check your answer. The graphs are the same line, so there are infinitely many solutions.

Math Talk
Mathematical Processes

What solution do you get when you solve the system in part B by substitution? Does this result change the number of solutions? Explain.

−4 = −4; no, this is still a true statement, so the system still has infinitely many solutions.

Reflect

4. If x represents a variable and a and b represent constants so that $a \neq b$, interpret what each result means when solving a system of equations.

$x = a$ The system has one solution.

$a = b$ The system has no solution.

$a = a$ The system has infinitely many solutions.

5. In part B, can you tell without solving that the system has infinitely many solutions? If so, how?

Yes; the corresponding constants and coefficients of the second equation are twice those of the first equation. Both equations represent the same line, so there are infinitely many solutions.

 **YOUR TURN**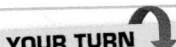

Solve each system. Tell how many solutions each system has.

6. $\begin{cases} 4x - 6y = 9 \\ -2x + 3y = 4 \end{cases}$

no solution

7. $\begin{cases} x + 2y = 6 \\ 2x - 3y = 26 \end{cases}$

(10, −2); one solution

8. $\begin{cases} 12x - 8y = -4 \\ -3x + 2y = 1 \end{cases}$

infinitely many solutions

Personal Math Trainer

Online Assessment and Intervention

my.hrw.com

© Houghton Mifflin Harcourt Publishing Company

1. Use the graph to solve each system of linear equations. (Explore Activity)

A. $\begin{cases} 4x - 2y = -6 \\ 2x - y = 4 \end{cases}$ B. $\begin{cases} 4x - 2y = -6 \\ x + y = 6 \end{cases}$ C. $\begin{cases} 2x - y = 4 \\ 6x - 3y = 12 \end{cases}$

STEP 1 Decide if the graphs of the equations in each system intersect, are parallel, or are the same line.

System A: The graphs ___are parallel___ .

System B: The graphs ___intersect___ .

System C: The graphs ___are the same line___ .

STEP 2 Decide how many points the graphs have in common.

Intersecting lines have ___one___ point(s) in common.

Parallel lines have ___no___ point(s) in common.

The same lines have ___an infinite number of___ point(s) in common.

STEP 3 Solve each system.

System A has ___no___ points in common, so it has ___no___ solution.

System B has ___1___ point in common. That point is the solution, ___(1, 5)___ .

System C has ___an infinite number of___ points in common. ___All___ ordered pairs on the line will make both equations true.

Solve each system. Tell how many solutions each system has. (Example 1)

2. $\begin{cases} x - 3y = 4 \\ -5x + 15y = -20 \end{cases}$ ___infinitely many solutions___

3. $\begin{cases} 6x + 2y = -4 \\ 3x + y = 4 \end{cases}$ ___no solution___

4. $\begin{cases} 6x - 2y = -10 \\ 3x + 4y = -25 \end{cases}$ ___$(-3, -4)$; one solution___

? ESSENTIAL QUESTION CHECK-IN

5. When you solve a system of equations algebraically, how can you tell whether the system has zero, one, or an infinite number of solutions?

If your solution gives specific values for x and y, the system has one solution, (x, y). If it gives a false statement, there is no solution. If it gives a true statement, there are infinitely many solutions.

© Houghton Mifflin Harcourt Publishing Company

4 Elaborate

Talk About It

Summarize the Lesson

Ask: How can you tell that a system has one, none, or infinitely many solutions? The graph of a system with one solution is a pair of intersecting lines. The algebraic solution will provide a value for x and a value for y. The graph of a system with no solutions is a pair of parallel lines. The algebraic solution will provide a false statement. The graph of a system with infinitely many solutions is one line. The algebraic solution will provide a true statement.

Guided Practice

Engage with the Whiteboard

For **Exercise 1,** have volunteers explain their thinking as they fill in the blanks for each step. Ask volunteers to point out or highlight the equations involved as they are referred to in the steps.

Avoid Common Errors

· **Exercise 3** If students attempt to solve this exercise by elimination, they may incorrectly identify it as having infinitely many solutions, because they will reach a point where they see that the left sides of both equations are identical. Explain that for there to be infinitely many solutions, the right sides of the equations must also be identical.

· **Exercises 2–4** Suggest that students graph each system on its own coordinate grid and then use the graph to verify their answers.

DIFFERENTIATE INSTRUCTION *Intervention and Additional Support*

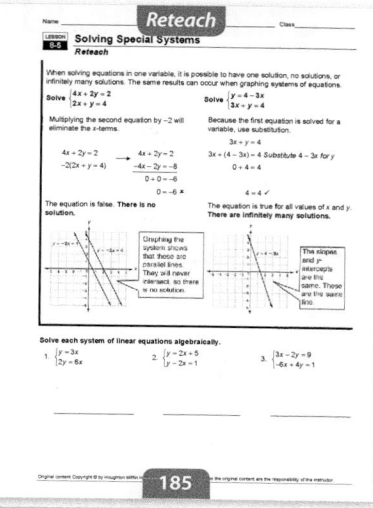

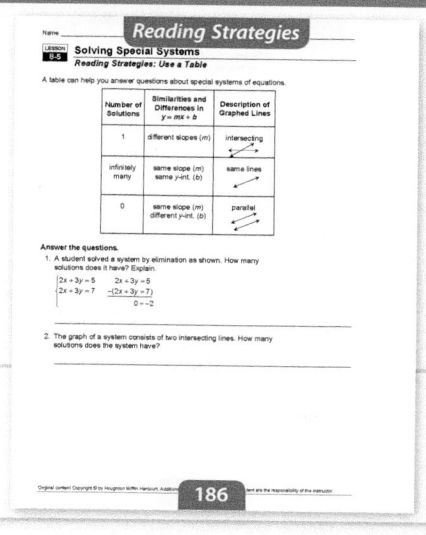

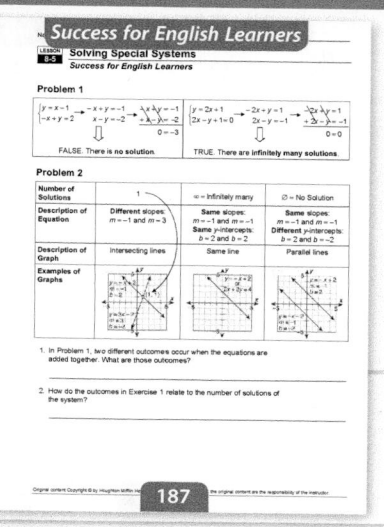

Personal Math Trainer
Daily Intervention
8.5 Homework

Pages shown are from *Differentiated Instruction*.
Also available online.

⏱ **Pressed for Time**

8.5 Differentiated Homework Assignments

AL **Approaching Level**	6–14, 16–17
OL **On Level**	10–17, 20
BL **Beyond Level**	14–20

*For **Below Level** students, assign Personal Math Trainer, Daily Intervention 8.5 Homework.*

Mathematical Processes	Exercises
MP.2 Reasoning	6–14
MP.3 Logic	15, 18–19
MP.4 Modeling	16–17
MP.7 Using Structure	20

Focus on Higher Order Thinking

Depth of Knowledge	Exercises
1 Recall of Information	6–7
2 Skills/Concepts	8–14
3 Strategic Thinking H.O.T.\	15–20

Name _____ Class _____ Date _____

8.5 Independent Practice

Personal Math Trainer
Online Assessment and Intervention
my.hrw.com

Solve each system by graphing. Check your answer algebraically.

6. $\begin{cases} -2x + 6y = 12 \\ x - 3y = 3 \end{cases}$

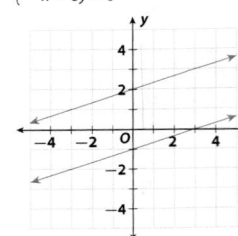

7. $\begin{cases} 15x + 5y = 5 \\ 3x + y = 1 \end{cases}$

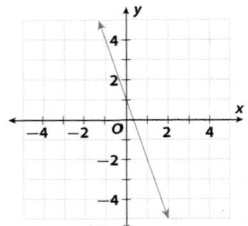

Solution: _____ no solution _____

Solution: _____ infinitely many solutions _____

For Exs. 8–14, state the number of solutions for each system of linear equations.

8. a system whose graphs have the same slope but different y-intercepts

_____ no solution _____

9. a system whose graphs have the same y-intercepts but different slopes

_____ one solution _____

10. a system whose graphs have the same y-intercepts and the same slopes

_____ infinitely many solutions _____

11. a system whose graphs have different y-intercepts and different slopes

_____ one solution _____

12. the system $\begin{cases} y = 2 \\ y = -3 \end{cases}$ _____ no solution _____

13. the system $\begin{cases} x = 2 \\ y = -3 \end{cases}$ _____ one solution _____

14. the system whose graphs were drawn using these tables of values:

Equation 1

x	0	1	2	3
y	1	3	5	7

Equation 2

x	0	1	2	3
y	3	5	7	9

_____ no solution _____

15. **Draw Conclusions** The graph of a linear system appears in a textbook. You can see that the lines do not intersect on the graph, but also they do not appear to be parallel. Can you conclude that the system has no solution? Explain.

No; although the lines do not intersect on the graph, they intersect at a point that is not on the graph. To prove that a system has no solution, you must do so algebraically.

© Houghton Mifflin Harcourt Publishing Company

DIFFERENTIATE INSTRUCTION *Leveled Homework/Practice*

Personal Math Trainer
• 8.5 Homework

Pages shown are from *Differentiated Instruction*. **Also available online.**

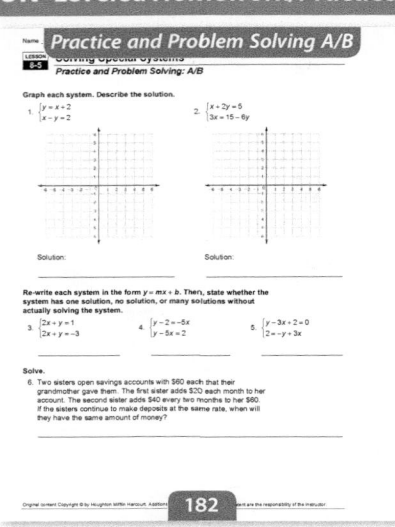

Practice and Problem Solving A/B

182

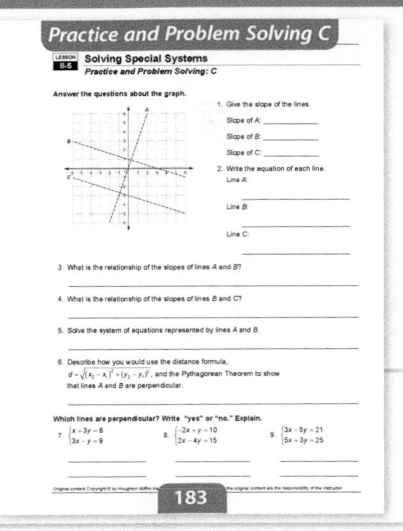

Practice and Problem Solving C

183

Practice and Problem Solving D

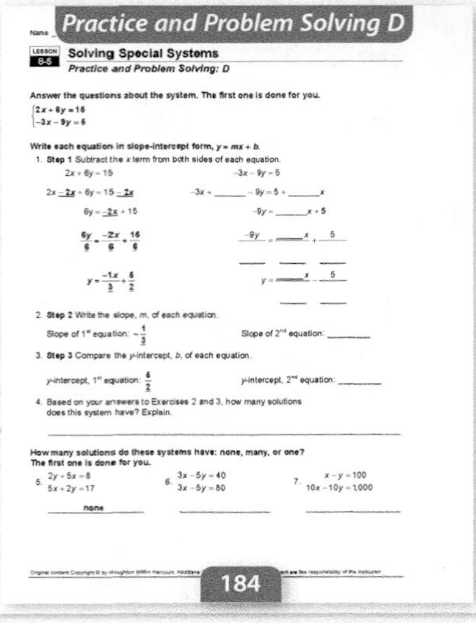

184

16. Represent Real-World Problems Two school groups go to a roller skating rink. One group pays $243 for 36 admissions and 21 skate rentals. The other group pays $81 for 12 admissions and 7 skate rentals. Let x represent the cost of admission and let y represent the cost of a skate rental. Is there enough information to find values for x and y? Explain.

No; there are infinitely many solutions to the system.

17. Represent Real-World Problems Juan and Tory are practicing for a track meet. They start their practice runs at the same point, but Tory starts 1 minute after Juan. Both run at a speed of 704 feet per minute. Does Tory catch up to Juan? Explain.

No; both Juan and Tory run at the same rate, so the lines representing the distances each has run are parallel.

There is no solution to the system.

 **FOCUS ON HIGHER ORDER THINKING**

18. Justify Reasoning A linear system with no solution consists of the equation $y = 4x - 3$ and a second equation of the form $y = mx + b$. What can you say about the values of m and b? Explain your reasoning.

$m = 4$ and $b \neq -3$; The graphs of the lines must be parallel and thus must have the same slope, so $m = 4$. The y-intercepts must be different because two equations with the same slope and the same y-intercept are the same line, so $b \neq -3$.

19. Justify Reasoning A linear system with infinitely many solutions consists of the equation $3x + 5 = 8$ and a second equation of the form $Ax + By = C$. What can you say about the values of A, B, and C? Explain your reasoning.

A, B, and C must all be the same multiple of 3, 5, and 8, respectively. The two equations represent a single line, so the coefficients and constants of one equation must be a multiple of the other.

20. Draw Conclusions Both the points $(2, -2)$ and $(4, -4)$ are solutions of a system of linear equations. What conclusions can you make about the equations and their graphs?

The linear system has more than one solution, so the lines coincide. There are infinitely many solutions.

Work Area

© Houghton Mifflin Harcourt Publishing Company • Image Credits: ©Bill Brooks/Alamy Images

264 Unit 3

8.5 Lesson Quiz

Solve each system. Tell how many solutions each system has.

1. $\begin{cases} x + 3y = 1 \\ 2x + 6y = 2 \end{cases}$ infinitely many solutions

2. $\begin{cases} 3x - 2y = 7 \\ -2x - 4y = 6 \end{cases}$ $(1, -2)$; one solution

3. $\begin{cases} 5x + 3y = -2 \\ -15x - 9y = 5 \end{cases}$ no solution

Solve each system. Tell how many solutions each system has. Describe the graph of each system.

4. $\begin{cases} 5x + 2y = 3 \\ -5x - 2y = 3 \end{cases}$ no solution; parallel lines

5. $\begin{cases} 3x + 6y = 3 \\ -x - 2y = -1 \end{cases}$ infinitely many solutions; one line

6. $\begin{cases} x - 7y = 15 \\ -2x - 5y = -11 \end{cases}$ $(8, -1)$; intersecting lines

Differentiate Instruction

IF a student misses more than one question, THEN

Differentiate Instruction:
• 8.5 Reteach
• Personal Math Trainer

Interactive Whiteboard
Interactive Lesson quiz available online

DIFFERENTIATE INSTRUCTION *Extend-the-Math Activity* **PRE-AP**

Activity For each of the following systems, find the value or values for a and b that make the system have no solution.

1. $\begin{cases} 3x - y = -4 \\ y = ax + b \end{cases}$ a must have a value of 3; b can have any value except 4.

2. $\begin{cases} -x + ay = 0 \\ -2x + 8y = b \end{cases}$ a must have a value of 4; b can have any value except 0.

3. $\begin{cases} x = a \\ y = b \end{cases}$ This system will have exactly one solution for any possible values of a and b.

Ready to Go On?

Assess Mastery

Access *Ready to Go On?* assessment online, and receive instant scoring, feedback, and customized intervention or enrichment.

Personal Math Trainer

Online Assessment and Intervention
• Module 8 Posttest

Additional Resources

Digital Teacher Resources

Go online for module-level resources.

Assessment Resources
• Module 8 Quiz: B, p.43
• Module 8 Quiz: D, p.45

Ready to Go On?

Personal Math Trainer
Online Assessment and Intervention
my.hrw.com

8.1 Solving Systems of Linear Equations by Graphing

Solve each system by graphing.

1. $\begin{cases} y = x - 1 \\ y = 2x - 3 \end{cases}$

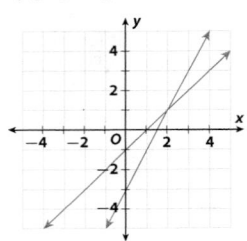

(2, 1)

2. $\begin{cases} x + 2y = 1 \\ -x + y = 2 \end{cases}$

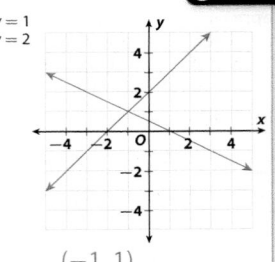

(−1, 1)

8.2 Solving Systems by Substitution

Solve each system of equations by substitution.

3. $\begin{cases} y = 2x \\ x + y = -9 \end{cases}$ _____ (−3, −6)

4. $\begin{cases} 3x - 2y = 11 \\ x + 2y = 9 \end{cases}$ _____ (5, 2)

8.3 Solving Systems by Elimination

Solve each system of equations by adding or subtracting.

5. $\begin{cases} 3x + y = 9 \\ 2x + y = 5 \end{cases}$ _____ (4, −3)

6. $\begin{cases} -x - 2y = 4 \\ 3x + 2y = 4 \end{cases}$ _____ (4, −4)

8.4 Solving Systems by Elimination with Multiplication

Solve each system of equations by multiplying first.

7. $\begin{cases} x + 3y = -2 \\ 3x + 4y = -1 \end{cases}$ _____ (1, −1)

8. $\begin{cases} 2x + 8y = 22 \\ 3x - 2y = 5 \end{cases}$ _____ (3, 2)

8.5 Solving Special Systems

Solve each system. Tell how many solutions each system has.

9. $\begin{cases} -2x + 8y = 5 \\ x - 4y = -3 \end{cases}$ _____ no solution

10. $\begin{cases} 6x + 18y = -12 \\ x + 3y = -2 \end{cases}$ _____ infinitely many

 ESSENTIAL QUESTION

11. What are the possible solutions to a system of linear equations, and what do they represent graphically?

No solution: parallel lines; one solution: intersecting lines;

infinitely many solutions: same line

© Houghton Mifflin Harcourt Publishing Company

Module 8 **265**

READY TO GO ON? *Diagnostic Assessment*

 **RtI** Response to Intervention

Use to determine if students have mastered the concepts covered in this module.

Lesson	Exercises	Content Focus	Review with *Differentiated Instruction*
8.1	1–2	Solving Systems of Linear Equations by Graphing	8.1 Reteach, Reading Strategies, Success for English Learners
8.2	3–4	Solving Systems by Substitution	8.2 Reteach, Reading Strategies, Success for English Learners
8.3	5–6	Solving Systems by Elimination	8.3 Reteach, Reading Strategies, Success for English Learners
8.4	7–8	Solving Systems by Elimination with Multiplication	8.4 Reteach, Reading Strategies, Success for English Learners
8.5	9–10	Solving Special Systems	8.5 Reteach, Reading Strategies, Success for English Learners

Personal Math Trainer

my.hrw.com
Online Assessment and Intervention

Selected Response

1. The graph of which equation is shown?

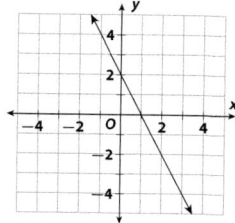

(A) $y = -2x + 2$ (C) $y = 2x + 2$

(B) $y = -x + 2$ (D) $y = 2x + 1$

2. Which best describes the solutions to the system $\begin{cases} x + y = -4 \\ -2x - 2y = 0 \end{cases}$?

(A) one solution   (C) infinitely many

(B) no solution   (D) $(0, 0)$

3. Which of the following represents 0.000056023 written in scientific notation?

(A) 5.6023×10^5 (C) 5.6023×10^{-4}

(B) 5.6023×10^4 (D) 5.6023×10^{-5}

4. Which is the solution to $\begin{cases} 2x - y = 1 \\ 4x + y = 11 \end{cases}$?

(A) $(2, 3)$ (C) $(-2, 3)$

(B) $(3, 2)$ (D) $(3, -2)$

5. Which expression can you substitute in the indicated equation to solve $\begin{cases} 3x - y = 5 \\ x + 2y = 4 \end{cases}$?

(A) $2y - 4$ for x in $3x - y = 5$

(B) $4 - x$ for y in $3x - y = 5$

(C) $3x - 5$ for y in $3x - y = 5$

(D) $3x - 5$ for y in $x + 2y = 4$

6. What is the solution to the system of linear equations shown on the graph?

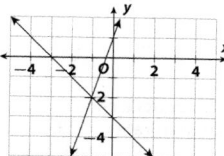

(A) -1 (C) $(-1, -2)$

(B) -2 (D) $(-2, -1)$

7. Which step could you use to start solving $\begin{cases} x - 6y = 8 \\ 2x - 5y = 3 \end{cases}$?

(A) Add $2x - 5y = 3$ to $x - 6y = 8$.

(B) Multiply $x - 6y = 8$ by 2 and add it to $2x - 5y = 3$.

(C) Multiply $x - 6y = 8$ by 2 and subtract it from $2x - 5y = 3$.

(D) Substitute $x = 6y - 8$ for x in $2x - 5y = 3$.

Mini-Task

8. A hot-air balloon begins rising from the ground at 4 meters per second at the same time a parachutist's chute opens at a height of 200 meters. The parachutist descends at 6 meters per second.

a. Define the variables and write a system that represents the situation.

y is the height in meters and x is the time in seconds; $\begin{cases} y = 4x \\ y = 200 - 6x \end{cases}$

b. Find the solution. What does it mean?

20 s, 80 m; the time when the balloon and parachutist are the same height

© Houghton Mifflin Harcourt Publishing Company

Preparing for High Stakes Tests

Assessment Readiness Tip

Some items are only solvable by examining the answer choices in turn and eliminating incorrect choices.

- **Item 5** Several different substitutions are possible. Rather than trying to identify every possible substitution, it is quicker and easier to examine each answer choice and eliminate the choices that are incorrect. Students will be left with answer choice D as the only correct substitution.

- **Item 7** A variety of first steps are possible—there are several different substitutions as well as a few different ways to set up the equations for elimination. Students should examine the answer choices and use the process of elimination rather than trying to identify all possible first steps.

Avoid Common Errors

- **Item 2** Students may notice that the coefficients of the variables are different in the two equations, and therefore assume that they represent lines with different slopes that intersect in one place. Remind them that the slope is not equal to either of the coefficients unless the equations are in slope-intercept form.

- **Item 8** Students are likely to write the equations representing the situation in slope-intercept form, and may be uncertain how to proceed. Point out that with both equations in slope-intercept form, they can immediately substitute for y in one equation without any further manipulation of the equations.

Items	Grade 8 Lessons	Mathematical Processes
1*	5.1	MP.4
2	8.5	MP.2
3*	2.3	MP.2
4	8.3	MP.2
5	8.2	MP.2
6	8.1	MP.2
7	8.4	MP.2
8	8.1	MP.4

*Item integrates mixed review concepts from previous modules or a previous course.

DIFFERENTIATE ASSESSMENT

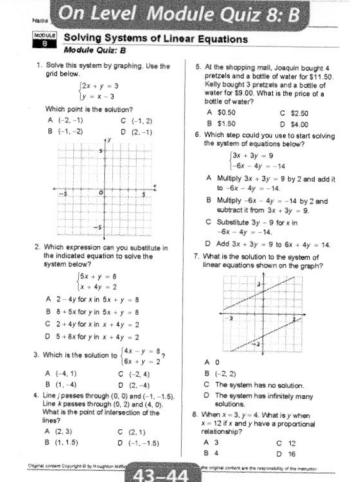

Below Level Module Quiz 8: D

MODULE 8
Solving Systems of Linear Equations
Module Quiz: D

On Level Module Quiz 8: B

MODULE 8
Solving Systems of Linear Equations
Module Quiz: B

Personal Math Trainer

Module 8 Assessment Readiness

Pages shown are from _Assessment Resources_. **Also available online.**

3

Solving Equations and Systems of Equations

Study Guide Review

Vocabulary Development

Integrating Language Arts

Encourage students to practice using the unit vocabulary as they talk and write about mathematics. Understanding vocabulary will aid their understanding of the concepts.

MODULE 7

Solving Linear Equations

Key Concepts

- To solve an equation or inequality with the same variable on both sides of the equal sign, add or subtract to eliminate the variable term from one side of the equation or inequality. *(Lesson 7.1)*

- To eliminate fractions from an equation or inequality, multiply every term by the least common multiple of the denominators to create an equivalent equation or inequality. *(Lesson 7.2)*

- To eliminate decimals from an equation or inequality, multiply every term by a power of 10 to eliminate the decimals and create an equivalent equation or inequality. *(Lesson 7.2)*

- To solve an equation containing an expression in parentheses multiplied by a factor, use the Distributive Property to distribute the factor and eliminate the parentheses. *(Lesson 7.3)*

- Linear equations can have one solution, infinitely many solutions, or, if there is no value of x that makes the equation true, no solution. *(Lesson 7.4)*

MODULE 7 Solving Linear Equations

? ESSENTIAL QUESTION

How can you use equations with variables on both sides to solve real-world problems?

EXAMPLE 1

A tutor gives students a choice of how to pay: a base rate of \$20 plus \$8 per hour, or a set rate of \$13 per hour. Find the number of hours of tutoring for which the cost is the same for either choice.

Plan 1 cost: $20 + 8x$ Plan 2 cost: $13x$

$20 + 8x = 13x$	Write the equation.
$\underline{-8x \qquad -8x}$	Subtract 8x from both sides.
$20 = 5x$	Divide both sides by 5.
$x = 4$	

The cost is the same for 4 hours of tutoring.

EXAMPLE 2

Solve $-2.4(3x + 5) = 0.8(x + 3.5)$.

$-2.4(3x + 5) = 0.8(x + 3.5)$	
$10(-2.4)(3x + 5) = 10(0.8)(x + 3.5)$	Multiply each side by 10 to clear some decimals.
$-24(3x + 5) = 8(x + 3.5)$	
$-24(3x) - 24(5) = 8(x) + 8(3.5)$	Apply the Distributive Property.
$-72x - 120 = 8x + 28$	
$\underline{-8x \qquad\qquad -8x}$	Subtract 8x from both sides of the equation.
$-80x - 120 = 28$	
$\underline{+ 120 \quad + 120}$	Add 120 to both sides of the equation.
$-80x = 148$	
$\frac{-80x}{-80} = \frac{148}{-80}$	Divide both sides of the equation by −80.
$x = -1.85$	

© Houghton Mifflin Harcourt Publishing Company

EXAMPLE 3

Solve 4(3x − 6) = 2(6x − 5).

$$4(3x - 6) = 2(6x - 5)$$

$12x - 24 = 12x - 10$	Apply the Distributive Property.
$\underline{-12x \qquad -12x}$	Subtract 8x from both sides of the equation.
$-24 = -10$	The statement is false.

There is no value of x that makes a true statement. Therefore, this equation has no solution.

EXERCISES

Solve. (Lessons 7.1, 7.2, 7.3, 7.4)

1. $13.02 - 6y = 8y$ _____ $y = 0.93$

2. $\frac{1}{5}x + 5 = 19 - \frac{1}{2}x$ _____ $x = 20$

3. $7.3t + 22 = 2.1t - 22.2$ _____ $t = -8.5$

4. $1.4 + \frac{2}{5}e = \frac{3}{15}e - 0.8$ _____ $e = -11$

5. $5(x - 4) = 2(x + 5)$ _____ $x = 10$

6. $-7(3 + t) = 4(2t + 6)$ _____ $t = -3$

7. $\frac{3}{4}(x + 8) = \frac{1}{3}(x + 27)$ _____ $x = 7\frac{1}{5}$

8. $3(4x - 8) = \frac{1}{5}(35x + 30)$ _____ $x = 6$

9. $-1.6(2y + 15) = -1.2(2y - 10)$

_____ $y = -45$ _____

10. $9(4a - 2) = 12(3a + 8)$

_____ no solution _____

11. $6(x - \frac{1}{3}) = -2(x + 23)$

_____ $x = -5\frac{1}{2}$ _____

12. $8(p - 0.25) = 4(2p - 0.5)$

_____ infinitely many solutions _____

13. Write a real-world situation that could be modeled by the equation $650 + 10m = 60m + 400$. (Lesson 7.1)

Sample answer: Jill and Sam are both putting money in their savings accounts. Jill starts with $650 and puts in $10 a month. Sam starts with $400 and puts in $60 a month. After how many months will Jill and Sam have the same amount in their accounts?

© Houghton Mifflin Harcourt Publishing Company

Solving Systems of Linear Equations

Key Concepts

- To solve a system of equations by graphing, find the point of intersection. *(Lesson 8.1)*

- To solve a system of equations by substitution, rewrite one equation as an expression that represents one variable and substitute this expression into the other equation. *(Lesson 8.2)*

- To solve a system of equations by elimination, begin by adding or subtracting the equations in such a way that a variable is eliminated. The equations can first be multiplied by a constant. *(Lessons 8.3, 8.4)*

- Some systems of equations may have no solution or an infinite number of solutions. *(Lesson 8.5)*

 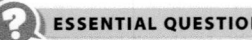

Solving Systems of Linear Equations

Key Vocabulary

solution of a system of equations *(solución de un sistema de ecuaciones)*

system of equations *(sistema de ecuaciones)*

? ESSENTIAL QUESTION

How can you use systems of equations to solve real-world problems?

EXAMPLE 1 Solve the system of equations by substitution.

$$\begin{cases} 3x + y = 7 \\ x + y = 3 \end{cases}$$

Step 1 Solve an equation for one variable.

$$3x + y = 7$$
$$y = -3x + 7$$

Step 2 Substitute the expression for y in the other equation and solve.

$$x + y = 3$$
$$x + (-3x + 7) = 3$$
$$-2x + 7 = 3$$
$$-2x = -4$$
$$x = 2$$

Step 3 Substitute the value of x into one of the equations and solve for the other variable, y.

$$x + y = 3$$
$$2 + y = 3$$
$$y = 1$$

$(2, 1)$ is the solution of the system.

EXAMPLE 2 Solve the system of equations by elimination.

$$\begin{cases} x + y = 8 \\ 2x - 3y = 1 \end{cases}$$

Step 1 Multiply the first equation by 3 and add this new equation to the second equation.

$$3(x + y = 8) = 3x + 3y = 24$$
$$3x + 3y = 24$$
$$\underline{2x - 3y = 1}$$
$$5x + 0y = 25$$
$$5x = 25$$
$$x = 5$$

Step 2 Substitute the solution into one of the original equations and solve for y.

$$x + y = 8$$
$$5 + y = 8$$
$$y = 3$$

$(5, 3)$ is the solution of the system.

© Houghton Mifflin Harcourt Publishing Company

EXERCISES

Solve each system of linear equations. (Lessons 8.1, 8.2, 8.3, 8.4, and 8.5)

14. $\begin{cases} x + y = -2 \\ 2x - y = 5 \end{cases}$

$(1, -3)$

15. $\begin{cases} y = 2x + 1 \\ x + 2y = 17 \end{cases}$

$(3, 7)$

16. $\begin{cases} y = -2x - 3 \\ 2x + y = 9 \end{cases}$

no solution

17. $\begin{cases} y = 5 - x \\ 2x + 2y = 10 \end{cases}$

infinitely many solutions

18. $\begin{cases} 2x - y = 26 \\ 3x - 2y = 42 \end{cases}$

$(10, -6)$

19. $\begin{cases} 2x + 3y = 11 \\ 5x - 2y = 18 \end{cases}$

$(4, 1)$

20. Last week Andrew bought 3 pounds of zucchini and 2 pounds of tomatoes for $7.05 at a farm stand. This week he bought 4 pounds of zucchini and 3 pounds of tomatoes, at the same prices, for $9.83. What is the cost of 1 pound of zucchini and 1 pound of tomatoes at the farm stand?

Zucchini: $1.49 per pound, tomatoes: $1.29 per pound

Unit 3 Performance Tasks

1. **CAREERS IN MATH** | Hydraulic Engineer A hydraulic engineer is studying the pressure in a particular fluid. The pressure is equal to the atmospheric pressure 101 kN/m plus 8 kN/m for every meter below the surface, where kN/m is kilonewtons per meter, a unit of pressure.

a. Write an expression for the pressure at a depth of d_1 meters below the liquid surface.

$101 + 8d_1$

b. Write and solve an equation to find the depth at which the pressure is 200 kN/m.

$200 = 101 + 8d_1$, $99 = 8d_1$, $d_1 = \dfrac{99}{8} = 12.375$; $d_1 = 12.375$ m

c. The hydraulic engineer alters the density of the fluid so that the pressure at depth d_2 below the surface is atmospheric pressure 101 kN/m plus 9 kN/m for every meter below the surface. Write an expression for the pressure at depth d_2.

$101 + 9d_2$

d. If the pressure at depth d_1 in the first fluid is equal to the pressure at depth d_2 in the second fluid, what is the relationship between d_1 and d_2? Explain how you found your answer.

Since the pressures are equal, set the two expressions equal to each other: $101 + 8d_1 = 101 + 9d_2$. Then solve for d_1: $d_1 = \dfrac{9}{8} d_2$.

This means that d_1 is $\dfrac{9}{8}$ times d_2.

© Houghton Mifflin Harcourt Publishing Company

Performance Tasks

The Performance Tasks provide students with the opportunity to apply concepts from this unit in real-world problem situations.

CAREERS IN MATH

Hydraulic Engineer

In Performance Task Item 1, students can see how a hydraulic engineer uses mathematics on the job.

Scoring Guides for Performance Tasks

1. **Mathematical Processes**

MP.2, MP.3, MP.4

Task	Possible Points (Total: 6)
a	**1 point** for a correct expression: $101 + 8d_2$
b	**1 point** for the equation $200 = 101 + 8d_1$ and **1 point** for the correct answer $d_1 = 12.375$ m
c	**1 point** for the correct expression: $101 + 9d_2$
d	**1 point** for an explanation, for example, since the pressures are equal, set the two expressions equal to each other; and **1 point** for the answer: $d_1 = \frac{9}{8} d_2$; d_1 is $\frac{9}{8}$ times d_2, or $d_2 = \frac{8}{9} d_1$

Assessment Readiness

Assessment Readiness Tip
Students can work backwards by using the answer choices to solve problems.

- **Item 5** After reading the problem, students know that Alana bought a total of 5 rolls of streamers and 3 packages of balloons for a total of $16.25. Using the answer choices, students can multiply the number of streamers by the cost, then the number of balloons by the cost, combining them to see which will give a total of $16.25.

Avoid Common Errors

- **Item 6** Some students will forget to consider the sides not labeled in the rectangle when finding the perimeter. Remind students that there are two bases and two heights, so the expressions $2x - 1$ and $x + 7$ will each be used twice when writing an expression for the perimeter of the rectangle.

Items	Grade 8 Lessons	Mathematical Processes
1*	5.1, 7.1	MP.4
2	7.2	MP.4
3*	4.2	MP.2
4	8.1, 8.2	MP.4
5	8.3	MP.2
6	7.1	MP.7
7	7.1	MP.2
8*	1.1	MP.4
9	8.4	MP.2
10	8.5	MP.3
11	7.1, 7.2, 7.3	MP.4

* Item integrates mixed review concepts from previous modules or a previous course.

Assessment Readiness

Personal Math Trainer
Online Assessment and Intervention
my.hrw.com

Selected Response

1. Ricardo and John start swimming from the same location. Ricardo starts 15 seconds before John and swims at a rate of 3 feet per second. John swims at a rate of 4 feet per second in the same direction as Ricardo. Which equation could you solve to find how long it will take John to catch up with Ricardo?

- (A) $4t + 3 = 3t$
- (B) $4t + 60 = 3t$
- (C) $3t + 3 = 4t$
- (D) $3t + 45 = 4t$

2. Gina and Rhonda work for different real estate agencies. Gina earns a monthly salary of $5,000 plus a 6% commission on her sales. Rhonda earns a monthly salary of $6,500 plus a 4% commission on her sales. How much must each sell to earn the same amount in a month?

- (A) $1,500
- (B) $15,000
- (C) $75,000
- (D) $750,000

3. What is the slope of the line?

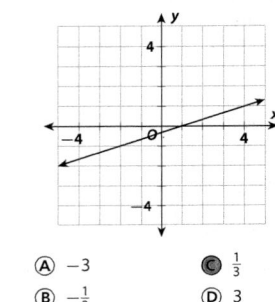

- (A) -3
- (B) $-\frac{1}{3}$
- (C) $\frac{1}{3}$
- (D) 3

4. What is the solution of the system of equations?
$$\begin{cases} y = 2x - 3 \\ 5x + y = 11 \end{cases}$$

- (A) $(2, 1)$
- (B) $(1, 2)$
- (C) $(3, -4)$
- (D) $(1, -1)$

5. Alana is having a party. She bought 3 rolls of streamers and 2 packages of balloons for $10.00. She realized she needed more supplies and went back to the store and bought 2 more rolls of streamers and 1 more package of balloons for $6.25. How much did each roll of streamers and each package of balloons cost?

- (A) streamers: $3.00, balloons: $2.00
- (B) streamers: $2.00, balloons: $1.00
- (C) streamers: $1.25, balloons: $2.50
- (D) streamers: $2.50, balloons: $1.25

6. The triangle and the rectangle have the same perimeter.

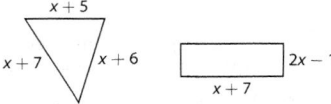

Find the value of x.

- (A) 2
- (B) 10
- (C) 18
- (D) 24

Unit 3 **271**

DIFFERENTIATE ASSESSMENT

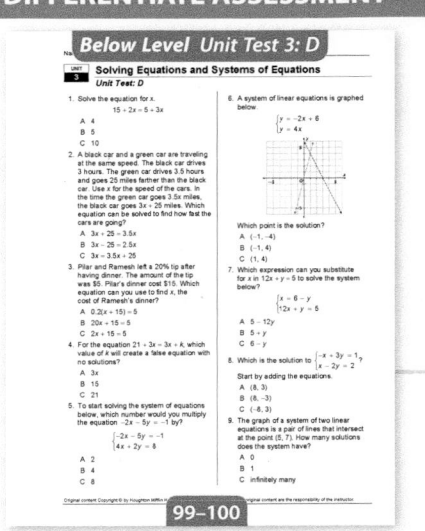

99–100

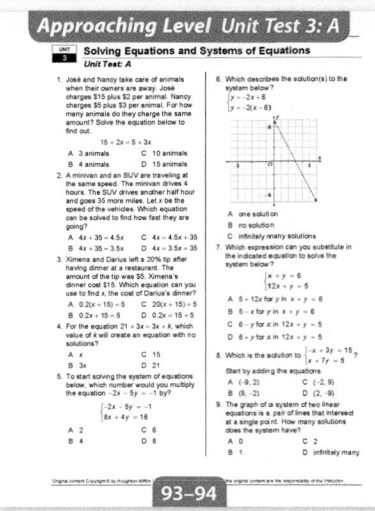

93–94

7. What is the solution of the equation $8(3x + 4) = 2(12x - 8)$?

Ⓐ $x = -2$

Ⓑ $x = 2$

Ⓒ no solution

Ⓓ infinitely many solutions

8. A square wall tile has an area of 58,800 square millimeters. Between which two measurements is the length of one side?

Ⓐ between 24 and 25 millimeters

Ⓑ between 76 and 77 millimeters

Ⓒ between 242 and 243 millimeters

Ⓓ between 766 and 767 millimeters

Mini-Task

9. Lily and Alex went to a Mexican restaurant. Lily paid $9 for 2 tacos and 3 enchiladas, and Alex paid $12.50 for 3 tacos and 4 enchiladas.

a. Write a system of equations that represents this situation.

$2t + 3e = 9$

$3t + 4e = 12.50$

b. Use the system of equations to find how much the restaurant charges for a taco and for an enchilada.

enchilada: $2, taco: $1.50

c. Describe the method you used to solve the system of equations.

Sample answer: Multiply the first equation by 3 and the second by −2, then add. Solve for e, then substitute and solve for t.

Solutions of a system of two equations must make both equations true. Check solutions in both equations.

10. Use the system of equations to answer the questions below.

$$\begin{cases} 4x + 2y = -8 \\ 2x + y = 4 \end{cases}$$

a. Graph the equations on the grid.

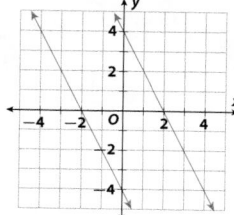

b. How many solutions does the system of equations have? Explain your answer.

The system of equations has no solution. The lines never intersect.

11. Isaac wants to join a gym. He checked out the membership fees at two gyms.

Gym A charges a new member fee of $65 and $20 per month.

Gym B charges a new member fee of $25 and $35 per month, but Isaac will get a discount of 20% on the monthly fee.

a. Write an equation you can use to find the number of months for which the total costs at the gyms are the same.

$65 + 20m = 25 + (1 - 0.20)35m$

b. Solve the equation to find the number of months for which the total costs of the gyms are the same.

$m = 5$, so at 5 months, the total costs of the two gyms are the same.

© Houghton Mifflin Harcourt Publishing Company

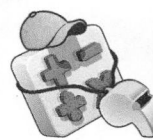
Personal Math Trainer

Online Assessment and Intervention

Additional Resources

Digital Teacher Resources

Go online for unit-level resources.

Assessment Resources

- Leveled Unit Tests: A, B, C, D
- Unit Performance Task

⏻ my.hrw.com

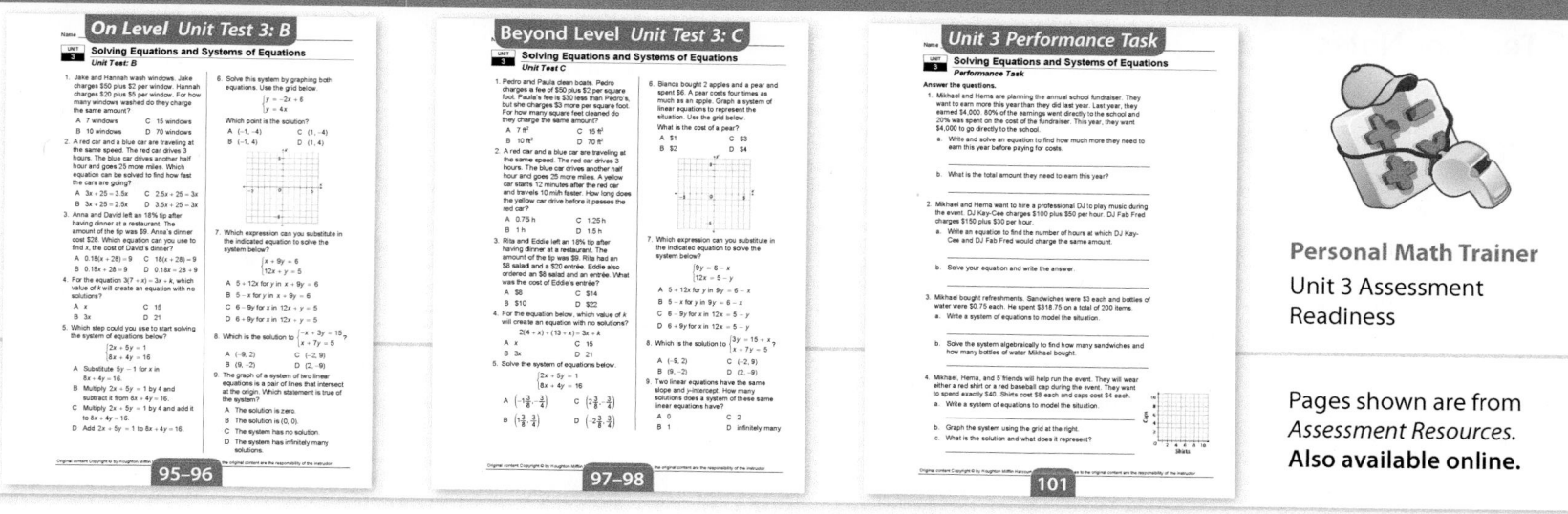

Personal Math Trainer

Unit 3 Assessment Readiness

Pages shown are from *Assessment Resources*.
Also available online.

Transformational Geometry

Contents

Teacher Notes

PLANNING AND PACING GUIDE
Instructional Path

Lesson	Lesson Objectives	Pacing*
UNIT 4 | Transformational Geometry		
Progress Tracker 1 2 3 **4** 5 6		
MODULE 9 | Transformations and Congruence		1 day
9.1 Properties of Translations	Students will describe the properties of translation and their effect on the congruence and orientation of figures.	2 days
9.2 Properties of Reflections	Students will describe the properties of reflection and their effect on the congruence and orientation of figures.	2 days
9.3 Properties of Rotations	Students will describe the properties of rotation and their effect on the congruence and orientation of figures.	2 days
9.4 Algebraic Representations of Transformations	Students will describe the effect of a translation, rotation, or reflection on coordinates using an algebraic representation.	3 days
9.5 Congruent Figures	Students will determine the connection between transformations and figures that have the same shape and size.	2 days
Ready to Go On? **Module 9 Assessment Readiness**		1 day
MODULE 10 | Transformations and Similarity		1 day
10.1 Properties of Dilations	Students will describe the properties of dilations.	3 days
10.2 Algebraic Representations of Dilations	Students will describe the effect of a dilation on coordinates using an algebraic representation.	3 days
10.3 Similar Figures	Students will determine the connection between transformations and similar figures.	3 days
Activity 10.3 Copy-Cat	Students will use properties of similar figures to reproduce a dilation.	
Ready to Go On? **Module 10 Assessment Readiness**		1 day
Study Guide Review **Unit 4 Assessment Readiness**		2 days

* Based on a 45-minute class period.

Teaching for Depth

Translations, Reflections, Rotations

Translations, reflections, and rotations are examples of rigid transformations. A rigid transformation preserves the size and shape of a figure.

- Translation: a transformation that *slides* a figure
- Reflection: a transformation that *flips* a figure
- Rotation: a transformation that *turns* a figure

To rotate a figure you must be given or know three things: the center of rotation, the magnitude (number of degrees), and direction (clockwise or counterclockwise) of the rotation.

Algebraic Representations of Transformations

Algebraic representations of transformations tells us how the coordinates change when a figure is transformed. Using algebra to represent transformations on a coordinate plane allows us to express and analyze the relationships between image and preimage.

Translations

Shift right or left:	$(x, y) \rightarrow (x \pm a, y)$
Shift up or down:	$(x, y) \rightarrow (x, y \pm b)$
Shift right/left and up/down:	$(x, y) \rightarrow (x, y \pm b)$

Reflections

Across the *x*-axis:	$(x, y) \rightarrow (-x, y)$
Across the *y*-axis:	$(x, y) \rightarrow (x, -y)$

Rotations

90° clockwise:	$(x, y) \rightarrow (y, -x)$
90° counterclockwise:	$(x, y) \rightarrow (-y, x)$
180°:	$(x, y) \rightarrow (-x, -y)$

Notice that when (x, y) is reflected across the *x*-axis and the image is reflected across the *y*-axis, we have $(x, y) \rightarrow (-x, y) \rightarrow (-x, -y)$, so that the final image is the same as the image of (x, y) under a 180° rotation. Therefore, we can conclude that two successive reflections across the two axes are equivalent to a single 180° rotation about the origin.

Rigid Transformations and Congruence

Congruence: Two figures are congruent if they have exactly the same size and shape.

- Two line segments are congruent if they have the same length.
- Two angles are congruent if they have the same measure.

Rigid transformations: Transformations can also be used to define congruence. That is, two figures are congruent if one figure can be transformed into the other through a sequence of translations, reflections, and rotations. This matches our intuitive notion of congruence: given two congruent paper triangles, one triangle may be made to fit exactly on top of the other by sliding (translating), flipping (reflecting), and turning (rotating) the paper. These rigid transformations preserve the size and shape of the figure, and are also known as isometries.

Reflections are sometimes called *improper rigid motions* as they can cause shapes to flip into a new orientation. However, applying the same reflection twice results in the original orientation. Translations and rotations are sometimes called *proper rigid motions* as they never cause the shape to flip.

Go Math *provides a strong framework for teaching mathematics with focus and coherence by aligning content in meaningful ways. Units focus on key aspects of major mathematical strands. Modules focus on key concepts within each grade.* **Go Math** *also provides coherence through the Progressions within and across each grade level.*

MATT LARSON on Focus and Coherence

Dilations

A dilation is a transformation in which the lines connecting every point P with its image P' all intersect at a point C known as the center of dilation. Also, the ratio $\frac{CP'}{CP}$ is the same for all points P. In the figure below, for example, $\triangle D'E'F'$ is a dilation of $\triangle DEF$.

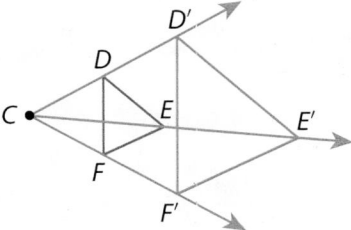

A dilation must be described by two pieces of information: the *scale factor* and the *center* of dilation. If the center of dilation is at vertex A of the original figure, then the corresponding vertex on the dilation image has the same coordinates as vertex A. In Grade 8, students study dilations in the coordinate plane with centers located at the origin.

Professional Development Videos

Module 9: Transformations and Congruence

Algebraic Representations of Dilations

For each preimage point $P(x, y)$ of a figure, its image after dilation with scale factor k is $P'(kx, ky)$.

Dilations are unique among the transformations because they have a scale factor k that describes whether the image is a reduction or enlargement of the preimage.

- If $0 < k < 1$, the dilation is a **reduction**.
- If $k > 1$, the dilation is an **enlargement**.

Though uncommon, the scale factor k can equal 1. In this case, the image is congruent to the preimage. The scale factor is sometimes called the **magnitude** of the dilation.

Similar Figures

Similar figures have the same shape but not necessarily the same size. One way to create similar figures is to perform a sequence of dilations on a figure.

A dilation is often called a *similarity transformation*. Unlike rigid transformations (translations, reflections, and rotations), dilations may change the size of the preimage.

Transformational Geometry

Transformational Geometry

MODULE 9
Transformations and Congruence

MODULE 10
Transformations and Similarity

CAREERS IN MATH

Contractor

In addition to a hammer and saw, a contractor needs mathematical tools to figure out the amount of materials needed for a job and their cost, to compute areas and volumes, and to determine wages and other expenses. You will learn more about working as a contractor in the Performance Tasks at the end of the unit.

For more information about careers in mathematics as well as various mathematics appreciation topics, visit the American Mathematical Society at www.ams.org.

CAREERS IN MATH

Contractor A contractor is engaged in the construction, repair, and dismantling of structures such as buildings, bridges, and roads. Contractors use math when researching and implementing building codes, making measurements and scaling models, and in financial management.

If you are interested in a career as a contractor, you should study the following mathematical subjects:
- Business Math
- Geometry
- Algebra
- Trigonometry

Research other careers that require the use of business math and scaling.

Unit 4 Performance Task

At the end of the unit, check out how **contractors** use math.

UNIT 4
Vocabulary Preview

Use the puzzle to preview key vocabulary from this unit. Unscramble the circled letters within found words to answer the riddle at the bottom of the page.

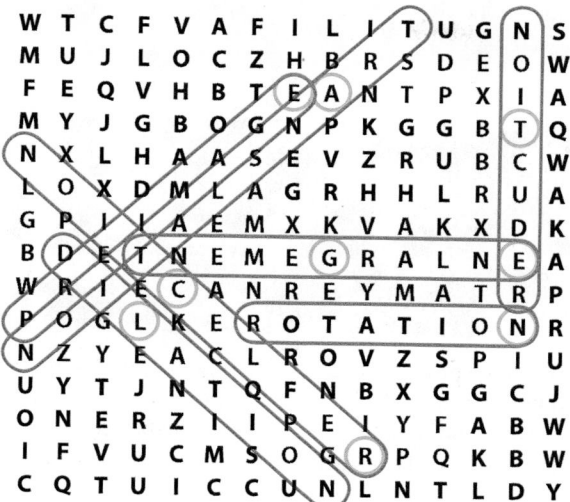

The input of a transformation. (Lesson 9.1) **preimage**

A transformation that flips a figure across a line. (Lesson 9.2) **reflection**

A transformation that slides a figure along a straight line. (Lesson 9.1) **translation**

A transformation that turns a figure around a given point. (Lesson 9.3) **rotation**

The product of a figure made larger by dilation. (Lesson 10.1) **enlargement**

The product of a figure made smaller by dilation. (Lesson 10.1) **reduction**

Scaled replicas that change the size but not the shape of a figure. (Lesson 10.1) **dilation**

© Houghton Mifflin Harcourt Publishing Company

Q: What do you call an angle that's broken?

A: A _R_ _E_ _C_ _T_ _A_ _N_ _G_ _L_ _E_ !

274 Vocabulary Preview

Vocabulary Preview

Use the puzzle to give students a preview of important concepts in this unit. Students may work individually, in pairs, or in groups.

Digital Teacher Resources

Go online for unit-level resources.

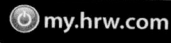

my.hrw.com

LEARNING PROGRESSIONS AND STANDARDS ACROSS THE GRADES

Before	In this Unit	After
Students understand:	Students will learn about:	Students will connect:
• how to classify and draw plane figures	• effects of transformations	• transformations and dilations with graphic design, art, photography, and scale drawings
• how to graph plane figures on the coordinate plane	• translations	• transformations and congruence
• congruence and similarity	• reflections	• dilation and similarity
	• rotations	
	• dilations	
	• transformations in the coordinate plane	

Transformational Geometry **274**

Module At A Glance

MODULE 9 | Transformations and Congruence

Lessons at A Glance	Lesson 9.1 Properties of Translations	Lesson 9.2 Properties of Reflections	Lesson 9.3 Properties of Rotations
	Pg. T279A	Pg. T285A	Pg. T291A
Essential Question	How do you describe the properties of translation and their effect on the congruence and orientation of figures?	How do you describe the properties of reflection and their effect on the congruence and orientation of figures?	How do you describe the properties of rotation and their effect on the congruence and orientation of figures?
Objective	Students will describe the properties of translation and their effect on the congruence and orientation of figures.	Students will describe the properties of reflection and their effect on the congruence and orientation of figures.	Students will describe the properties of rotation and their effect on the congruence and orientation of figures.
Vocabulary	image, preimage, transformation, translation	line of reflection, reflection	center of rotation, rotation
Go online for all your module resources my.hrw.com	9.1 *i*Student Edition 9.1 *i*Teacher Edition 9.1 *e*Student Edition 🐿 Personal Math Trainer 📺 Math on the Spot Videos	9.2 *i*Student Edition 9.2 *i*Teacher Edition 9.2 *e*Student Edition 🐿 Personal Math Trainer 📺 Math on the Spot Videos	9.3 *i*Student Edition 9.3 *i*Teacher Edition 9.3 *e*Student Edition 🐿 Personal Math Trainer 📺 Math on the Spot Videos 🎞 Animated Math
Print Resources	**9.1 Student Edition:** Lesson *Differentiated Instruction* 9.1 Practice and Problem Solving A/B, C, and D 9.1 Reteach 9.1 Reading Strategies 9.1 Success for English Learners	**9.2 Student Edition:** Lesson *Differentiated Instruction* 9.2 Practice and Problem Solving A/B, C, and D 9.2 Reteach 9.2 Reading Strategies 9.2 Success for English Learners	**9.3 Student Edition:** Lesson *Differentiated Instruction* 9.3 Practice and Problem Solving A/B, C, and D 9.3 Reteach 9.3 Reading Strategies 9.3 Success for English Learners

RtI Response to Intervention

Before the Module	During the Lesson	After the Module
Are You Ready	**Guided/Independent Practice**	**Ready to Go On?**
• Prerequisite Skills Activities • Personal Math Trainer	• Reteach • Personal Math Trainer • Practice and Problem Solving D	• Reteach • Personal Math Trainer

Module Pacing Chart			
Introduction	Instruction	Assessment	Total
1 day	11 days	1 day	13 days

Lesson 9.4 Algebraic Representations of Transformations	Lesson 9.5 Congruent Figures
Pg. T297A	Pg. T303A
How can you describe the effect of a translation, rotation, or reflection on coordinates using an algebraic representation? Students will describe the effect of a translation, rotation, or reflection on coordinates using an algebraic representation.	What is the connection between transformations and figures that have the same shape and size? Students will understand the connection between transformations and figures that have the same shape and size. congruent
9.4 *i*Student Edition 9.4 *i*Teacher Edition 9.4 *e*Student Edition Personal Math Trainer Math on the Spot Videos	9.5 *i*Student Edition 9.5 *i*Teacher Edition 9.5 *e*Student Edition Personal Math Trainer Math on the Spot Videos
9.4 Student Edition: Lesson *Differentiated Instruction* 9.4 Practice and Problem Solving A/B, C, and D 9.4 Reteach 9.4 Reading Strategies 9.4 Success for English Learners	**9.5 Student Edition:** Lesson *Differentiated Instruction* 9.5 Practice and Problem Solving A/B, C, and D 9.5 Reteach 9.5 Reading Strategies 9.5 Success for English Learners

Teacher Notes

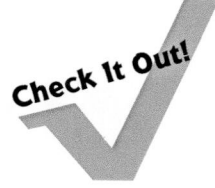

Check It Out!

Math on the Spot Videos	Animated Math
One for every Example in every Lesson	During Lesson 9.3

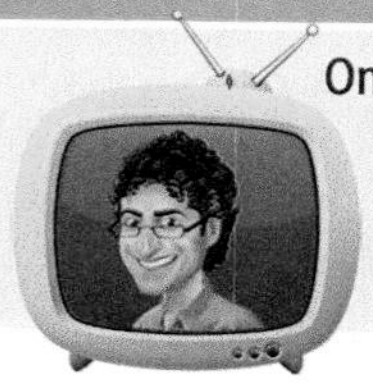

Transformations and Congruence

Real-World Video Viewing Guide

After students have watched the video, discuss the following:

- What are some ways mentioned in the video that transformations are used in the real world?
- How do you move the band formation by using a transformation? Move each person the same number of steps up or down and left or right.

Professional Development Video

Author Juli Dixon models successful teaching practices as she explores the concept of transformations and congruence in an actual eighth-grade classroom.

Transformations and Congruence

? ESSENTIAL QUESTION

How can you use transformations and congruence to solve real-world problems?

You can analyze how real-world objects are affected when they undergo reflections, translations, rotations, and dilations.

Real-World Video
When a marching band lines up and marches across the field, they are modeling a translation. As they march, they maintain size and orientation. A translation is one type of transformation.

my.hrw.com

© Houghton Mifflin Harcourt Publishing Company • Image Credits:
© Gregory K. Scott/Getty Images

GO DIGITAL
my.hrw.com

my.hrw.com
Go digital with your write-in student edition, accessible on any device.

Math On the Spot
Scan with your smart phone to jump directly to the online edition, video tutor, and more.

Animated Math
Interactively explore key concepts to see how math works.

Personal Math Trainer
Get immediate feedback and help as you work through practice sets.

TEACHER ONLINE RESOURCES

 ONLINE TEACHER EDITION Access a full suite of teaching resources online—plan, present, and manage classes and assignments.

 INTERACTIVE WHITEBOARDS Engage students with interactive whiteboard-ready examples and a lesson quiz for each lesson.

 MY SMART PLANNER Easily plan your classes and access all your resources online.

 PERSONAL MATH TRAINER: Online Assessment and Intervention Assign automatically graded homework, quizzes, tests, and intervention activities. Prepare your students for standardized tests in short-answer and multiple-choice formats.

Reading **Start-Up**

Visualize Vocabulary

Use the ✔ words to complete the graphic organizer. You will put one word in each oval.

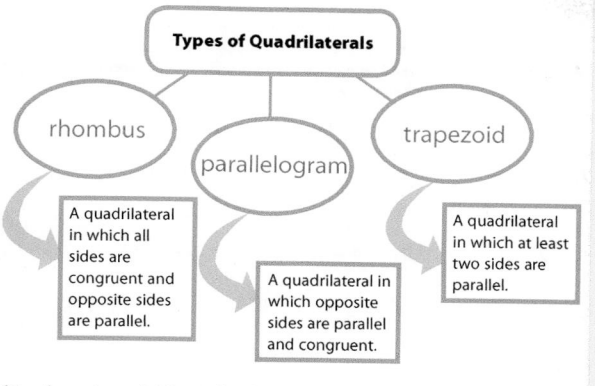

Types of Quadrilaterals

- rhombus
- parallelogram
- trapezoid

A quadrilateral in which all sides are congruent and opposite sides are parallel.

A quadrilateral in which opposite sides are parallel and congruent.

A quadrilateral in which at least two sides are parallel.

© Houghton Mifflin Harcourt Publishing Company

Vocabulary

Review Words
- coordinate plane *(plano cartesiano)*
- ✔ parallelogram *(paralelogramo)*
- quadrilateral *(cuadrilátero)*
- ✔ rhombus *(rombo)*
- ✔ trapezoid *(trapecio)*

Preview Words
- center of rotation *(centro de rotación)*
- congruent *(congruente)*
- image *(imagen)*
- line of reflection *(línea de reflexión)*
- preimage *(imagen original)*
- reflection *(reflexión)*
- rotation *(rotación)*
- transformation *(transformación)*
- translation *(traslación)*

Understand Vocabulary

Match the term on the left to the correct expression on the right.

1. transformation → **A.** A function that describes a change in the position, size, or shape of a figure.

2. reflection **B.** A function that slides a figure along a straight line.

3. translation **C.** A transformation that flips a figure across a line.

Active Reading

Booklet Before beginning the module, create a booklet to help you learn the concepts in this module. Write the main idea of each lesson on each page of the booklet. As you study each lesson, write important details that support the main idea, such as vocabulary and formulas. Refer to your finished booklet as you work on assignments and study for tests.

Reading Start-Up

Visualize Vocabulary
The case diagram helps students review types of quadrilaterals to prepare them to complete the exercises on transformations in this module. Students should write one review word in each oval. If time allows, brainstorm additional shapes and properties as a class and add them to the diagram.

Understand Vocabulary
Use the following explanation to help students learn the preview words.

The word transformation *means "change." In math,* **transformation** *means changes to points or figures. Figures can change in several ways. They can slide in straight lines, called a* **translation**. *Figures can also flip across a line, called a* **reflection**. *A* **rotation** *turns a figure around a point.*

Active Reading

Integrating Language Arts
Students can use these reading and note-taking strategies to help them organize and understand new concepts and vocabulary.

Additional Resources
Differentiated Instruction
- Reading Strategies **ELL**
- Interactive multilingual glossary

LEARNING PROGRESSIONS ACROSS THE GRADES

Before	In this Module	After
Students understand: • how to classify and draw plane figures • how to graph plane figures on the coordinate plane • congruence	Students use transformational geometry to represent: • properties of orientation and congruence of translations in a coordinate plane • properties of orientation and congruence of reflections in a coordinate plane • properties of orientation and congruence of rotations in a coordinate plane • the effect of translations, reflections, and rotations in a coordinate plane using an algebraic representation	Students will connect: • transformations and congruence • reflections over an axis and symmetry • algebra and coordinate geometry

Are You Ready?

Assess Readiness

Access *Are You Ready?* assessment online, and receive instant scoring, feedback, and customized intervention or enrichment.

Personal Math Trainer

Online Assessment and Intervention

Additional Resources

Digital Teacher Resources

Go online for module-level resources.

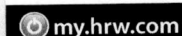
my.hrw.com

Are YOU Ready?

Complete these exercises to review skills you will need for this module.

Personal Math Trainer
Online Assessment and Intervention
my.hrw.com

Integer Operations

EXAMPLE $-3 - (-6) = -3 + 6$

$\quad\quad\quad\quad = |-3| - |6|$

$\quad\quad\quad\quad = 3$

To subtract an integer, add its opposite. The signs are different, so find the difference of the absolute values: $6 - 3 = 3$. Use the sign of the number with the greater absolute value.

Find each difference.

1. $5 - (-9)$
   14

2. $-6 - 8$
   -14

3. $2 - 9$
   -7

4. $-10 - (-6)$
   -4

5. $3 - (-11)$
   14

6. $12 - 7$
   5

7. $-4 - 11$
   -15

8. $0 - (-12)$
   12

Measure Angles

EXAMPLE

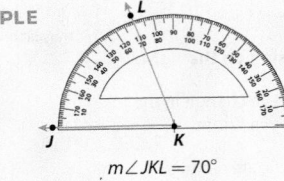

$m\angle JKL = 70°$

Place the center point of the protractor on the angle's vertex.

Align one ray with the base of the protractor.

Read the angle measure where the other ray intersects the semicircle.

Use a protractor to measure each angle.

9.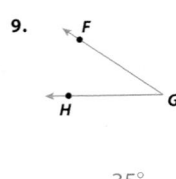

   35°

10.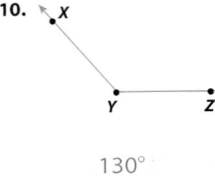

    130°

11.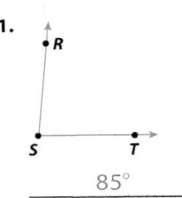

    85°

© Houghton Mifflin Harcourt Publishing Company

ARE YOU READY? *Diagnostic Assessment*

RtI Response to Intervention

Use to determine if students need intervention for the module's prerequisite skills.

Skill	Missed More Than . . .	Intervene With *Skills Intervention* worksheets (available online)	For Enrichment *Differentiated Instruction* (available in print and online)
Integer Operations	2 questions	**Skill 47** Integer Operations	**Module 9 Challenge** Extend-the-Math Lesson Activities in TE
Measure Angles	1 question	**Skill 89** Measure Angles	**Module 9 Challenge** Extend-the-Math Lesson Activities in TE

Are YOU Ready? *(cont'd)*

Complete these exercises to review skills you will need for this module.

Integer Operations

12. Explain how to find the difference 6 − 8.

> To subtract an integer, add its opposite, so add 6 + (−8). Since the signs of these two numbers are different, add them by finding the difference of their absolute values: $|-8| - |6| = 8 - 6 = 2$. Use the sign of the number with the greater absolute value, −8. The answer is −2.

13. The number line graph represents the difference of two integers. Interpret the graph to find the difference expression, and then give the solution.

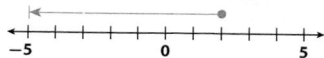

> The graph represents the difference 2 − 7. The solution is −5.

Measure Angles

14. Explain how to measure an angle using a protractor. What is the measure of the angle shown?

> Place the center point of the protractor on the angle's vertex. Align the base of the protractor with one ray. Read the angle measure where the other ray intersects the semicircle. Use the larger number on the protractor for an obtuse angle and the smaller number for an acute angle. The angle measures 120°.

15. Marco used a protractor to measure the angles shown. He concluded that the angle on the left measures 95° and the angle on the right measures 50°. What was Marco's error? Give the correct angle measures.

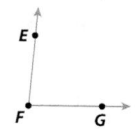 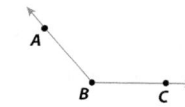

> For each angle, Marco used the wrong scale on the protractor. The angle on the left is 85° and the angle on the right is 130°.

© Houghton Mifflin Harcourt Publishing Company

Integer Operations

Exercise 12 Remind students to rewrite subtraction as addition of the opposite, and then use addition rules.

Exercise 13 Students may have difficulty reading the graph. Help the students understand which point on the graph represents the first number in the expression and which point represents the solution.

Measure Angles

Exercise 14 The center point of the protractor may vary with different protractors. Caution students to line up the vertex of the angle carefully.

Exercise 15 Help students understand how to choose a reasonable angle measure when using a protractor. If the angle is greater than a right angle (the corner of a piece of paper), then they should use the larger number on the scale of the protractor.

Use to determine if students are able to apply the module's prerequisite skills.

Skill	Exercise	Depth of Knowledge (D.O.K.)	Mathematical Processes
Integer Operations	12	**3** Strategic Thinking	**MP.6** Use Precise Mathematical Language
	13	**2** Skills/Concepts	**MP.4** Mathematical Modeling
Measure Angles	14	**3** Strategic Thinking	**MP.5** Use Mathematical Tools
	15	**2** Skills/Concepts	**MP.5** Use Mathematical Tools

Lesson Support

Content Objective Students will learn how to describe the properties of translations and their effect on the congruence and orientation of figures.

Professional Development

Integrate Mathematical Processes MP.6

This lesson provides an opportunity to address this Mathematical Processes standard. It calls for students to communicate precisely. Students translate a figure on a coordinate grid following a given translation rule. Then, students measure the lengths of the sides and the degrees of the angles to show that the corresponding sides and angles are congruent. Finally, students make a conjecture about the preservation of the size and shape of a figure.

FOCUS

Building Background

Eliciting Prior Knowledge Review what it means for two polygons to have corresponding sides and corresponding angles. Then ask students to create a definition and example chart for congruent figures. Transition into the lesson by asking whether two congruent figures remain congruent if one of the figures is moved up or down or to the right or left.

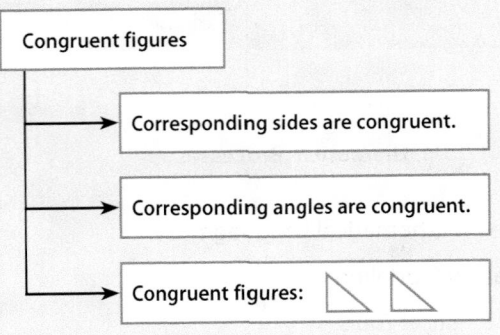

COHERENCE

Learning Progressions

In this lesson, students verify experimentally the properties of translations by translating polygons in the coordinate plane. Important understandings for students include the following:

- **Investigate the properties of translations.**
- **Graph translations.**

Students are familiar with translations from earlier grades. This lesson provides a review of the properties of translations, which students have likely encountered before. They verify the properties by translating figures on a coordinate plane. They begin to connect the geometry of the translation to the algebraic concept of a translation as a function with an input (the preimage) and the output (the image).

RIGOR

Cluster Connections

This lesson provides an excellent opportunity to connect ideas in the cluster:

Understand congruence and similarity using physical models, transparencies, or geometry software.

Tell students that line segment AB has endpoints $A(2, 1)$ and $B(5, 3)$. Ask them to describe how each translation changes the coordinates of the endpoints of the preimage to create the coordinates of the endpoints of the image:

   (1) translate $\overline{AB}$ 4 units to the right;
   (2) translate $\overline{AB}$ 4 units to the left;
   (3) translate $\overline{AB}$ 4 units up;
   (4) translate $\overline{AB}$ 4 units down

Sample answer: (1) add 4 to the x-coordinate; y-coordinate stays same; (2) subtract 4 from the x-coordinate; y-coordinate stays same; (3) x-coordinate stays same; add 4 to the y-coordinate; (4) x-coordinate stays same; subtract 4 from the y-coordinate.

Language Support ELL

Language Objective Students will describe the properties of translation and their effect on the congruence and orientation of figures.

Leveled Strategies for English Learners ELL

Emerging
Have students at this level of English proficiency work in pairs to review and copy on graph paper the translations in Explore Activities 1 & 2. If possible, have them discuss in their primary language the steps to take to accomplish the translations.

Expanding
Have students at this level of English proficiency work in pairs to redraw the translations in Explore Activities 1 & 2. Then have them list the steps they took to accomplish the translations.

Bridging
Have students at this level of English proficiency work in pairs to redraw the translations in Explore Activities 1 & 2. Then have them describe for each other the steps they took to accomplish these translations.

 **Math Talk**

Write out and model for students a sentence frame to begin their answer.

Yes, the figures are congruent because_____.

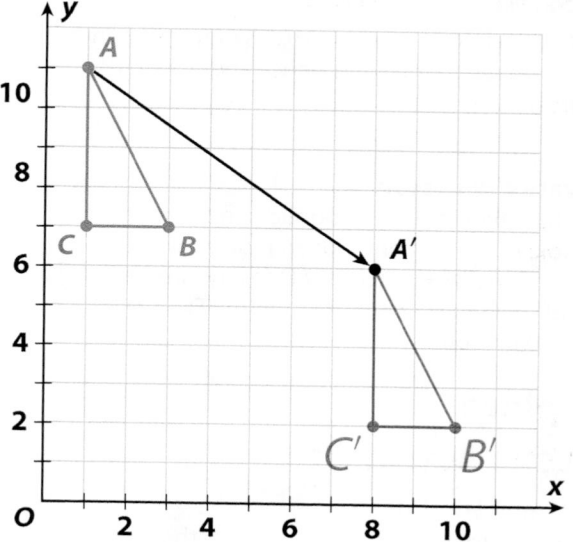

Linguistic Support ELL

Academic/Content Vocabulary
This lesson on properties of translations relies on students' understanding of the meaning of several words as they are used in mathematics: *transformation*, *preimage*, *image*, and *translation*. While English learners at the expanding and bridging levels of English proficiency might have encountered these words in other classes, they may be new to them in mathematics. Even with the definition in the lesson, students may benefit from adding an illustration along with the word to their word journals.

Background Knowledge
pre- The term *preimage* is introduced in this lesson. *Pre-* is a prefix meaning "before, earlier, or in front of." Other useful words beginning with the prefix *pre-* are *precook*, *predict*, and *precaution*.

-tion The terms *transformation* and *translation* are also introduced in this lesson. The suffix *-tion* means "action." Other words ending in *-tion* are *competition*, *exploration*, and *organization*.

Properties of Translations

1 Engage

❓ ESSENTIAL QUESTION

How do you describe the properties of translation and their effect on the congruence and orientation of figures? Sample answer: Translations preserve size, shape, and orientation.

Motivate the Lesson

Ask: What changes when you slide an object, such as a book, from one corner of your desk to different corners of your desk? Does the size or shape of the object change? Begin the Explore Activity to find out.

2 Explore

EXPLORE ACTIVITY 1

Focus on Modeling

Ask students to move the triangle from the image position back to the preimage position and describe the movement. 7 units left and 5 units up How does the description of the movement change? How does the description stay the same? Students should see that the magnitude of the movement stays the same, but the direction changes.

LESSON 9.1 Properties of Translations

8.4.9.1
Students will describe the properties of translation and their effect on the congruence and orientation of figures.

❓ ESSENTIAL QUESTION
How do you describe the properties of translation and their effect on the congruence and orientation of figures?

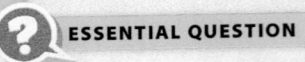

EXPLORE ACTIVITY 1

Exploring Translations

You learned that a function is a rule that assigns exactly one output to each input. A **transformation** is a function that describes a change in the position, size, or shape of a figure. The input of a transformation is the **preimage**, and the output of a transformation is the **image**.

A **translation** is a transformation that slides a figure along a straight line.

The triangle shown on the grid is the preimage (input). The arrow shows the motion of a translation and how point A is translated to point A'.

A Trace triangle ABC onto a piece of paper. Cut out your traced triangle.

B Slide your triangle along the arrow to model the translation that maps point A to point A'.

C The image of the translation is the triangle produced by the translation. Sketch the image of the translation.

D The vertices of the image are labeled using prime notation. For example, the image of A is A'. Label the images of points B and C.

E Describe the motion modeled by the translation.

Move _____7_____ units right and _____5_____ units down.

F Check that the motion you described in part **E** is the same motion that maps point A onto A', point B onto B', and point C onto C'.

Reflect

1. How is the orientation of the triangle affected by the translation?
   It is not affected. The orientation stays the same.

Lesson 9.1 **279**

© Houghton Mifflin Harcourt Publishing Company • Image Credits: ©Brand X Pictures/Alamy Images

DIFFERENTIATE INSTRUCTION *Leveled Questions*

	EXPLORE ACTIVITY 1
(AL) DOK 1 *Recall*	If triangle ABC is the preimage, what is the image triangle called? A'B'C'
(OL) DOK 2 *Skills/Concepts*	Does a translation change the size of a figure? No, the figure changes location but not orientation or size.
(BL) DOK 3 *Strategic Thinking*	Describe the types of motions that are translations of triangle ABC. Any movement of x units right or left and y units up or down is a translation, as long as all points are moved the same way so the shape doesn't change.

LEVELED QUESTIONS: (AL) Approaching Level | (OL) On Level | (BL) Beyond Level

Properties of Translations

Use trapezoid *TRAP* to investigate the properties of translations.

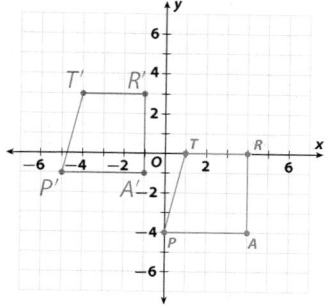

A Trace the trapezoid onto a piece of paper. Cut out your traced trapezoid.

B Place your trapezoid on top of the trapezoid in the figure. Then translate your trapezoid 5 units to the left and 3 units up. Sketch the image of the translation by tracing your trapezoid in this new location. Label the vertices of the image *T'*, *R'*, *A'*, and *P'*.

C Use a ruler to measure the sides of trapezoid *TRAP* in centimeters.

$TR =$ __1.3 cm__ $RA =$ __1.7 cm__ $AP =$ __1.7 cm__ $TP =$ __1.75 cm__

D Use a ruler to measure the sides of trapezoid *T'R'A'P'* in centimeters.

$T'R' =$ __1.3 cm__ $R'A' =$ __1.7 cm__ $A'P' =$ __1.7 cm__ $T'P' =$ __1.75 cm__

E What do you notice about the lengths of corresponding sides of the two figures?

__The lengths of corresponding sides are the same.__

F Use a protractor to measure the angles of trapezoid *TRAP*.

$m\angle T =$ __104°__ $m\angle R =$ __90°__ $m\angle A =$ __90°__ $m\angle P =$ __76°__

G Use a protractor to measure the angles of trapezoid *T'R'A'P'*.

$m\angle T' =$ __104°__ $m\angle R' =$ __90°__ $m\angle A' =$ __90°__ $m\angle P' =$ __76°__

H What do you notice about the measures of corresponding angles of the two figures?

__The measures of corresponding angles are the same.__

I Which sides of trapezoid *TRAP* are parallel? How do you know?

__$\overline{TR}$ and $\overline{AP}$; They both lie along horizontal grid lines.__

Which sides of trapezoid *T'R'A'P'* are parallel? __$\overline{T'R'}$ and $\overline{A'P'}$__

What do you notice? __The sides that were parallel in the preimage remain parallel in the image.__

© Houghton Mifflin Harcourt Publishing Company

3 Explain

Talk About It

Connect Vocabulary ELL

Emphasize that a *transformation* is a function that describes a change in the position, size, or shape of a figure, and a *translation* is a *type* of transformation in which a shape changes position but not size or orientation. Students often mix up these two terms.

EXPLORE ACTIVITY 2

Engage with the Whiteboard

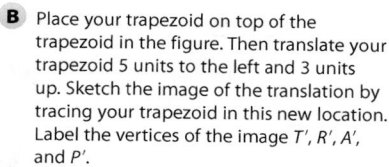 You may wish to have students measure the actual side lengths of the projected image and preimage on the whiteboard. Point out to students that although the lengths of the sides in centimeters on the projected image will not match the lengths in their books, the angle measurements will be the same.

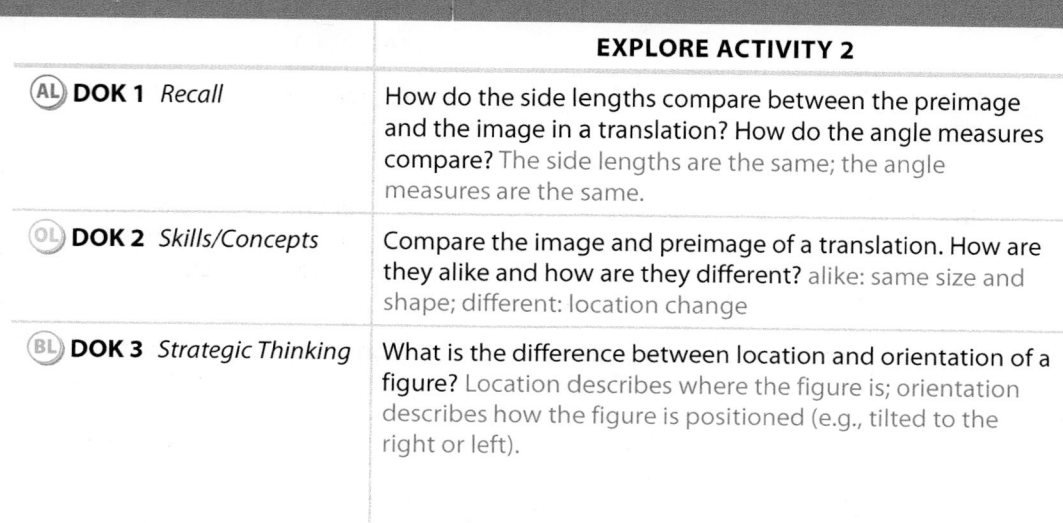

	EXPLORE ACTIVITY 2
AL **DOK 1** *Recall*	How do the side lengths compare between the preimage and the image in a translation? How do the angle measures compare? The side lengths are the same; the angle measures are the same.
OL **DOK 2** *Skills/Concepts*	Compare the image and preimage of a translation. How are they alike and how are they different? alike: same size and shape; different: location change
BL **DOK 3** *Strategic Thinking*	What is the difference between location and orientation of a figure? Location describes where the figure is; orientation describes how the figure is positioned (e.g., tilted to the right or left).

TEACHER TO TEACHER

Modeling Have groups of students make up a pattern of dance steps formed by translating shapes, which represent dancers' feet, on a grid. Then have students show the class their "dance" using the tiles on the floor as an enlarged grid.

EXAMPLE 1

ADDITIONAL EXAMPLE 1 The figure shows triangle *PQR*. Graph the image of the triangle after a translation of 7 units to the right and 2 units up.

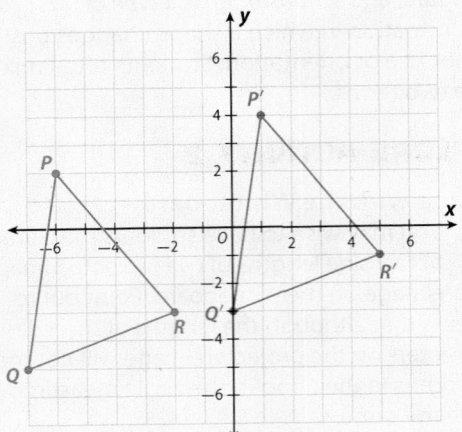

 Interactive Whiteboard
Interactive example available online

 **Digital Teacher Resources**

Go online to access all your lesson-level resources.

Differentiated Instruction
- Reteach
- Reading Strategies
- Success for English Learners
- Practice and Problem Solving A/B, C, D

Math on the Spot Videos

Reflect

2. **Make a Conjecture** Use your results from parts **E**, **H**, and **I** to make a conjecture about translations.

   Sample answer: Translations preserve the size and shape of a figure, as well as its orientation.

3. Two figures that have the same size and shape are called *congruent*. What can you say about translations and congruence?

   A translation produces a figure that is congruent to the original figure.

Graphing Translations

To translate a figure in the coordinate plane, translate each of its vertices. Then connect the vertices to form the image.

Math On the Spot
my.hrw.com

EXAMPLE 1

The figure shows triangle *XYZ*. Graph the image of the triangle after a translation of 4 units to the right and 1 unit up.

STEP 1 Translate point *X*.

Count right 4 units and up 1 unit and plot point *X'*.

STEP 2 Translate point *Y*.

Count right 4 units and up 1 unit and plot point *Y'*.

STEP 3 Translate point *Z*.

Count right 4 units and up 1 unit and plot point *Z'*.

STEP 4 Connect *X'*, *Y'*, and *Z'* to form triangle *X'Y'Z'*.

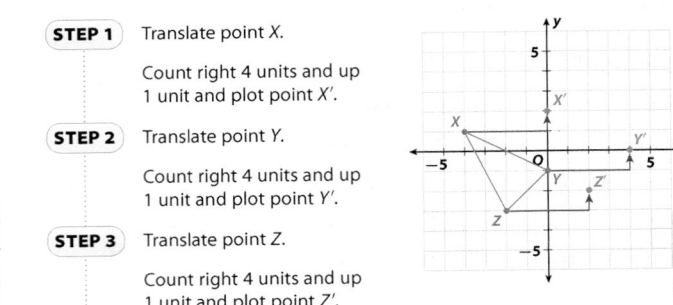

Each vertex is moved 4 units right and 1 unit up.

Math Talk
Mathematical Processes

Is the image congruent to the preimage? How do you know?

Yes, the figures are congruent. Translations preserve size and shape.

Lesson 9.1 **281**

© Houghton Mifflin Harcourt Publishing Company

DIFFERENTIATE INSTRUCTION *Leveled Questions*

	EXAMPLE 1
(AL) DOK 1 *Recall*	How do you know where to plot each vertex of the image *X'Y'Z'*? Move each vertex one at a time 4 units to the right and 1 unit up.
(OL) DOK 2 *Skills/Concepts*	Suppose you drew a line segment from each preimage vertex to its corresponding image vertex in a translation. Describe how the line segments would be related. They would be parallel line segments.
(BL) DOK 3 *Strategic Thinking*	What is the inverse translation of the translation in this example? The inverse translation of 4 units to the right and 1 unit up is 4 units to the left and 1 unit down. The translation would move the image back to the preimage location.

LEVELED QUESTIONS: **(AL)** Approaching Level | **(OL)** On Level | **(BL)** Beyond Level

Personal Math Trainer
Online Assessment and Intervention
my.hrw.com

YOUR TURN

4. The figure shows parallelogram *ABCD*. Graph the image of the parallelogram after a translation of 5 units to the left and 2 units down.

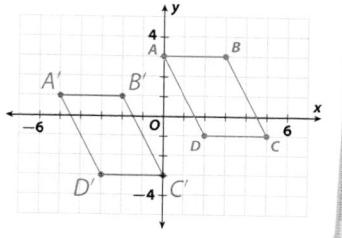

Guided Practice

1. **Vocabulary** A __transformation__ is a change in the position, size, or shape of a figure.

2. **Vocabulary** When you perform a transformation of a figure on the coordinate plane, the input of the transformation is called the __preimage__, and the output of the transformation is called the __image__.

3. Joni translates a right triangle 2 units down and 4 units to the right. How does the orientation of the image of the triangle compare with the orientation of the preimage? (Explore Activity 1)

   The orientation will be the same.

4. Rashid drew rectangle *PQRS* on a coordinate plane. He then translated the rectangle 3 units up and 3 units to the left and labeled the image *P'Q'R'S'*. How do rectangle *PQRS* and rectangle *P'Q'R'S'* compare? (Explore Activity 2)

   They are congruent.

5. The figure shows trapezoid *WXYZ*. Graph the image of the trapezoid after a translation of 4 units up and 2 units to the left. (Example 1)

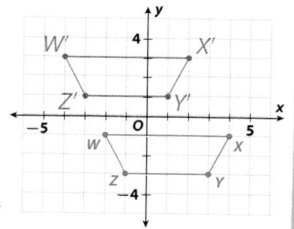

? ESSENTIAL QUESTION CHECK-IN

6. What are the properties of translations?

   Sample answer: Translations preserve the size, shape, and orientation of a figure.

© Houghton Mifflin Harcourt Publishing Company

YOUR TURN MP.4

Avoid Common Errors
Students can check that they have not miscounted units in the translation of any one point by checking that the image and preimage have the same size, shape, and orientation.

4 Elaborate

Talk About It

Summarize the Lesson

Ask: How do you know when a transformation is a translation? The image will have the same size, shape, and orientation as the preimage.

Guided Practice

Engage with the Whiteboard
To help students visualize **Exercises 3–4**, have volunteers sketch the images and preimages on a coordinate grid. In **Exercise 3**, have students assign letters to the vertices.

Avoid Common Errors

- **Exercises 3–5** Remind students that a translation is a type of transformation. A translation only causes a change in the position of the figure; everything else remains the same.

- **Exercise 5** Remind students that the image will have its vertices labeled with the same letters as the corresponding preimage vertices, along with the *prime* symbol (').

DIFFERENTIATE INSTRUCTION *Intervention and Additional Support*

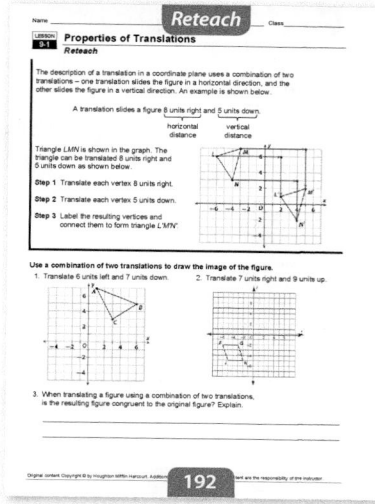

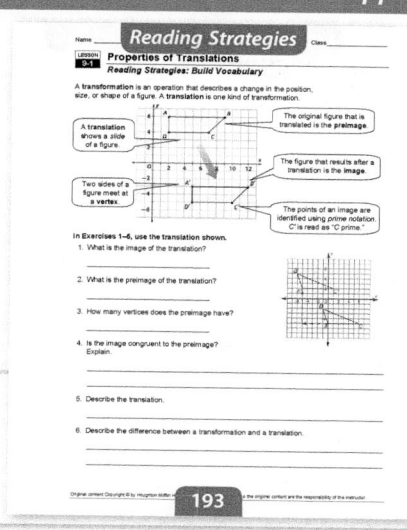

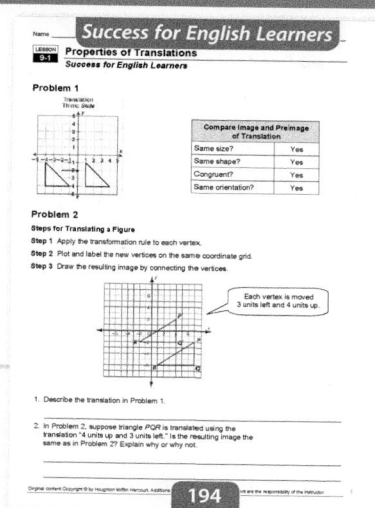

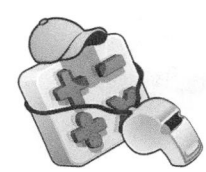

Personal Math Trainer
Daily Intervention
9.1 Homework

Pages shown are from *Differentiated Instruction*.
Also available online.

Pressed for Time

9.1 Differentiated Homework Assignments

(AL) **Approaching Level** — 7–11, 14

(OL) **On Level** — 8–13

(BL) **Beyond Level** — 11–15

*For **Below Level** students, assign Personal Math Trainer, Daily Intervention 9.1 Homework.*

Mathematical Processes	Exercises
MP.3 Logic	12, 15
MP.4 Modeling	11
MP.6 Precision	7, 13
MP.7 Using Structure	8
MP.8 Patterns	9–10, 14

Focus on Higher Order Thinking

Depth of Knowledge	Exercises
2 Skills/Concepts	7–12
3 Strategic Thinking H.O.T.	13–15

Name _____ Class _____ Date _____

9.1 Independent Practice

Personal Math Trainer
Online Assessment and Intervention
my.hrw.com

7. The figure shows triangle *DEF*.

   a. Graph the image of the triangle after the translation that maps point *D* to point *D'*.

   b. How would you describe the translation?

   The translation moved the triangle 2 units to the left and 4 units down.

   c. How does the image of triangle *DEF* compare with the preimage?

   They are congruent.

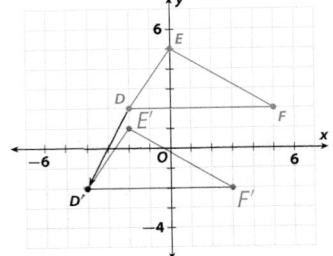

8. a. Graph quadrilateral *KLMN* with vertices $K(-3, 2)$, $L(2, 2)$, $M(0, -3)$, and $N(-4, 0)$ on the coordinate grid.

   b. On the same coordinate grid, graph the image of quadrilateral *KLMN* after a translation of 3 units to the right and 4 units up.

   c. Which side of the image is congruent to side $\overline{LM}$?

   $\overline{L'M'}$

   Name three other pairs of congruent sides.

   $\overline{KL}$ and $\overline{K'L'}$, $\overline{MN}$ and $\overline{M'N'}$, $\overline{KN}$ and $\overline{K'N'}$

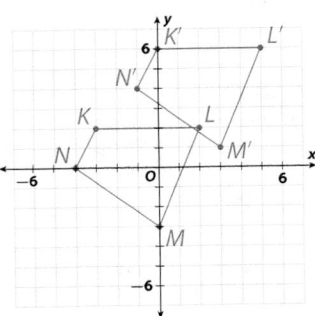

Draw the image of the figure after each translation.

9. 4 units left and 2 units down

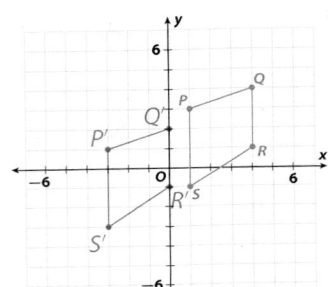

10. 5 units right and 3 units up

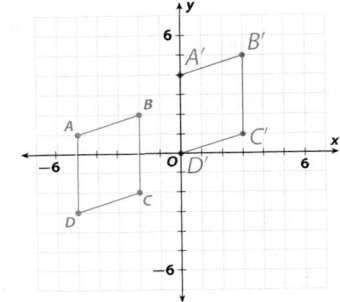

© Houghton Mifflin Harcourt Publishing Company

Lesson 9.1 **283**

DIFFERENTIATE INSTRUCTION *Leveled Homework/Practice*

Personal Math Trainer
- 9.1 Homework

Pages shown are from *Differentiated Instruction*. **Also available online.**

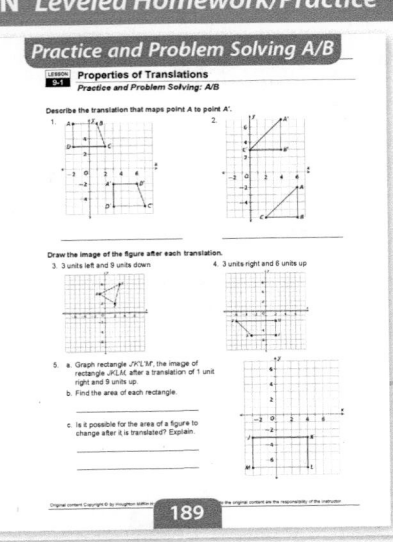

Practice and Problem Solving A/B

189

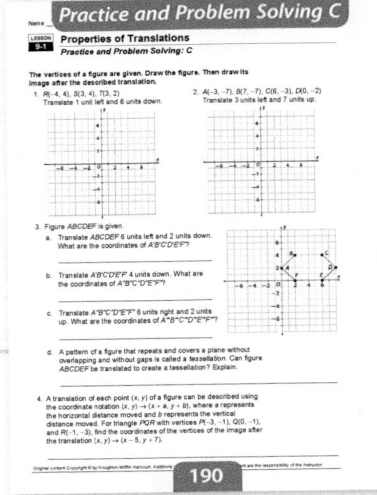

Practice and Problem Solving C

190

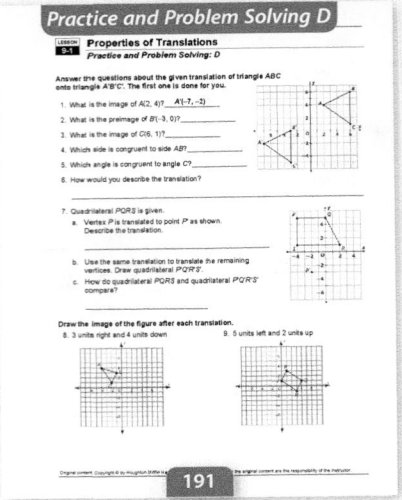

Practice and Problem Solving D

191

11. The figure shows the ascent of a hot air balloon. How would you describe the translation?

The hot air balloon was translated 4 units to the right and 5 units up.

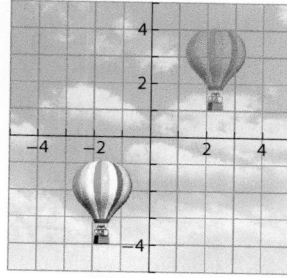

12. Critical Thinking Is it possible that the orientation of a figure could change after it is translated? Explain.

No; when a figure is translated, it is slid to a new location. Since it is not turned or flipped, the orientation will remain the same.

 **FOCUS ON HIGHER ORDER THINKING**

13. a. Multistep Graph triangle *XYZ* with vertices *X*(−2, −5), *Y*(2, −2), and *Z*(4, −4) on the coordinate grid.

b. On the same coordinate grid, graph and label triangle *X'Y'Z'*, the image of triangle *XYZ* after a translation of 3 units to the left and 6 units up.

c. Now graph and label triangle *X"Y"Z"*, the image of triangle *X'Y'Z'* after a translation of 1 unit to the left and 2 units down.

d. Analyze Relationships How would you describe the translation that maps triangle *XYZ* onto triangle *X"Y"Z"*?

Sample answer: The original triangle was translated 4 units up and 4 units to the left.

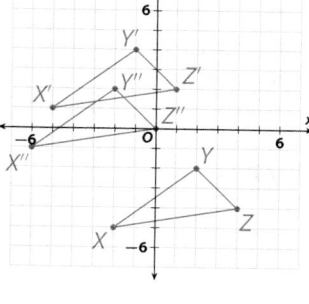

14. Critical Thinking The figure shows rectangle *P'Q'R'S'*, the image of rectangle *PQRS* after a translation of 5 units to the right and 7 units up. Graph and label the preimage *PQRS*.

15. Communicate Mathematical Ideas Explain why the image of a figure after a translation is congruent to its preimage.

Sample answer: Since every point of the original figure is translated the same number of units up/down and left/right, the image is exactly the same size and shape as the preimage. Only the location is different.

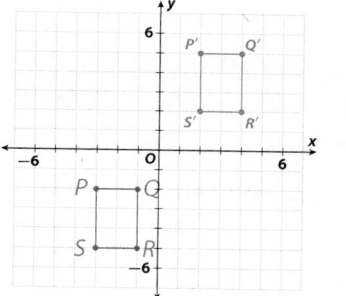

© Houghton Mifflin Harcourt Publishing Company

9.1 Lesson Quiz

Graph triangle *ABC* with vertices *A*(−3, 4), *B*(0, 2), and *C*(−2, 1) on a coordinate grid.

1. Graph the image of triangle *ABC* after a translation of 4 units right and 3 units down.

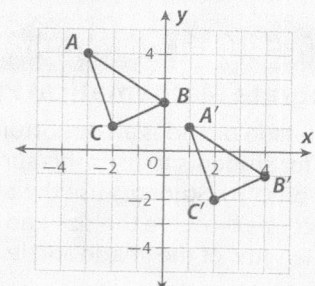

2. Which side of the image is congruent to side $\overline{AB}$? $\overline{A'B'}$

3. Which angle in the image is congruent to angle *B*? angle *B'*

4. Angle *G* in quadrilateral *FGHJ* measures 135°. Brent translates the quadrilateral 3 units right and 1 unit up. What is the measure of the image of angle *G*? 135°

Differentiate Instruction

IF a student misses more than one question, THEN

Differentiate Instruction:
- 9.1 Reteach
- Personal Math Trainer

 Interactive Whiteboard
Interactive Lesson quiz available online

DIFFERENTIATE INSTRUCTION *Extend-the-Math Activity* **PRE-AP**

Activity A strip pattern is a design that repeats itself along a straight line. Some strip patterns, like the one shown, are examples of translations. On a strip of paper, create a design. Then repeat the design by translating it along a straight line to create your own strip pattern.

Lesson Support

Content Objective Students will learn how to describe the properties of reflections and their effect on the congruence and orientation of figures.

Professional Development

Integrate Mathematical Processes MP.5

This lesson provides an opportunity to address this Mathematical Processes standard. It calls for students to use tools such as models, rulers, and pencil and paper to analyze relationships. Students use the results of the Explore Activities to make a conjecture that reflections preserve the size and shape of a figure. They find the measures of the angles and side lengths of the image and its preimage and use them to justify their conjecture.

FOCUS

Building Background

Eliciting Prior Knowledge Ask students to work with a partner or in small groups to create a concept map based on reflections. The map should include both real-life connections and whatever geometrical concepts students can recall about reflections.

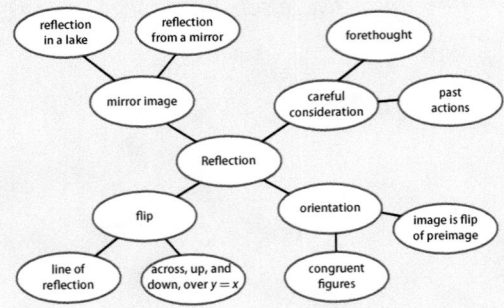

COHERENCE

Learning Progressions

In this lesson, students verify experimentally the properties of reflections by reflecting polygons in the coordinate plane across the axes. Important understandings for students include the following:

- **Investigate the properties of reflections.**
- **Graph reflections.**

Students are familiar with reflections, or flips, from earlier grades. This lesson provides an examination of the properties of reflections by having students measure and compare lengths and angles of corresponding parts of preimages and images. Students apply their understanding by graphing reflections of polygons in the coordinate plane.

RIGOR

Cluster Connections

This lesson provides an excellent opportunity to connect ideas in the cluster:

Understand congruence and similarity using physical models, transparencies, or geometry software.

Tell students that triangle ABC has vertices $A(1, 1)$, $B(3, 1)$, and $C(2, 4)$. Ask them to describe how each reflection changes the coordinates of the vertices of the preimage to create the coordinates of the vertices of the image:

- across the x-axis
- across the y-axis

Sample answer: (1) the x-coordinates stay the same and the y-coordinates have opposite signs from the original; (2) the x-coordinates have opposite signs from the original and the y-coordinates stay the same.

Language Support ELL

Language Objective Students will explain how to describe the properties of reflections and their effect on the congruence and orientation of figures.

Leveled Strategies for English Learners ELL

Emerging
Have students at this level of English proficiency work in pairs to illustrate and label on graph paper a translation and reflection of the same size and shape. Ask them to show or point to how they are similar and how they are different.

Expanding
Have students at this level of English proficiency work in pairs to define and illustrate on graph paper a translation and reflection of the same size and shape. Have students write down how the two are different.

Bridging
Have students at this level of English proficiency work in pairs to discuss, illustrate, and label the differences between translation and reflection of the same size and shape.

Write out and model for students a sentence frame to begin their answer.

A reflection produces a figure that is congruent _____.

Linguistic Support ELL

Academic/Content Vocabulary
This lesson relies on students' understanding of the meanings of *reflection* and *line of reflection*. Point out that these terms are defined in the context of the sentence in which they are introduced. Also, have students turn to the glossary to see the new word defined. Often there is a visual diagram or other support, including a Spanish-language explanation, in the glossary. For a glossary resource in 13 world languages, be sure to take students to the Online Multilingual Glossary.

Building Background
Help English learners figure out the meaning of unknown words in the lesson by pointing out patterns in words. In Explore Activity 1 of this lesson, students are instructed to "fold" and "unfold" a piece of paper. The prefix *un-* means "to do the opposite of" or "not." So, *unfold* means "to remove from a folded position." Other examples of words that use this prefix are *able/unable, do/undo, fair/unfair,* and *decided/undecided.* Suggest that students add this information to their math journals.

1 Engage

ESSENTIAL QUESTION

How do you describe the properties of reflection and their effect on the congruence and orientation of figures? Sample answer: Reflections preserve size and shape but not orientation.

Motivate the Lesson
Ask: What changes when you flip an object, such as a book, in any direction? Does the size or shape of the object change? Begin the Explore Activity to find out.

2 Explore

EXPLORE ACTIVITY 1

Focus on Modeling
After students have folded their paper across the axes and drawn both reflections, have them fold their papers over both axes at the same time, folding the paper into quarters. If they have drawn the reflections correctly, all three figures should match up exactly.

LESSON
9.2

**Properties of
Reflections**

8.4.9.2
Students will describe the properties of reflection and their effect on the congruence and orientation of figures.

? ESSENTIAL QUESTION

How do you describe the properties of reflection and their effect on the congruence and orientation of figures?

EXPLORE ACTIVITY 1

Exploring Reflections

A **reflection** is a transformation that flips a figure across a line. The line is called the **line of reflection**. Each point and its image are the same distance from the line of reflection.

The triangle shown on the grid is the preimage. You will explore reflections across the x- and y-axes.

A Trace triangle *ABC* and the x- and y-axes onto a piece of paper.

B Fold your paper along the x-axis and trace the image of the triangle on the opposite side of the x-axis. Unfold your paper and label the vertices of the image *A'*, *B'*, and *C'*.

C What is the line of reflection for this transformation?
the x-axis

D Find the perpendicular distance from each point to the line of reflection.
Point A __5 units__   Point B __2 units__   Point C __2 units__

E Find the perpendicular distance from each point to the line of reflection.
Point A' __5 units__   Point B' __2 units__   Point C' __2 units__

F What do you notice about the distances you found in **D** and **E**?
They are the same for a point and its reflection.

Reflect

1. Fold your paper from **A** along the y-axis and trace the image of triangle *ABC* on the opposite side. Label the vertices of the image *A''*, *B''*, and *C''*. What is the line of reflection for this transformation? ____the y-axis____

2. How does each image in your drawings compare with its preimage?
Sample answer: △A'B'C' is △ABC flipped across the x-axis. △A''B''C'' is △ABC flipped across the y-axis.

Lesson 9.2 **285**

© Houghton Mifflin Harcourt Publishing Company • Image Credits: ©Getty Images/Photodisc

---

DIFFERENTIATE INSTRUCTION *Leveled Questions*

	EXPLORE ACTIVITY 1
AL DOK 1 *Recall*	In what quadrant is the reflection of triangle *ABC* across the x-axis? across the y-axis? Quadrant IV; Quadrant II
OL DOK 2 *Skills/Concepts*	How far away from the line of reflection is a vertex of the image if the corresponding vertex of the preimage is 3 units from the line of reflection? 3 units
BL DOK 3 *Strategic Thinking*	Compare the preimage triangle *ABC* with one of the reflections. How are they alike and how are they different? The preimage *ABC* and image *A'B'C'* are the same size and shape, but they are in different locations and have different orientations.

LEVELED QUESTIONS: **AL** Approaching Level | **OL** On Level | **BL** Beyond Level

Properties of Reflections

Use trapezoid *TRAP* to investigate the properties of reflections.

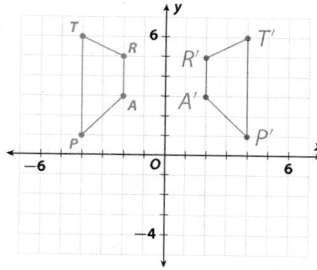

A Trace the trapezoid onto a piece of paper. Cut out your traced trapezoid.

B Place your trapezoid on top of the trapezoid in the figure. Then reflect your trapezoid across the *y*-axis. Sketch the image of the reflection by tracing your trapezoid in this new location. Label the vertices of the image *T'*, *R'*, *A'*, and *P'*.

C Use a ruler to measure the sides of trapezoid *TRAP* in centimeters.

$TR =$ __0.9 cm__ $RA =$ __0.8 cm__ $AP =$ __1.2 cm__ $TP =$ __2.1 cm__

D Use a ruler to measure the sides of trapezoid *T'R'A'P'* in centimeters.

$T'R' =$ __0.9 cm__ $R'A' =$ __0.8 cm__ $A'P' =$ __1.2 cm__ $T'P' =$ __2.1 cm__

E What do you notice about the lengths of corresponding sides of the two figures?

The lengths of corresponding sides are the same.

F Use a protractor to measure the angles of trapezoid *TRAP*.

$m\angle T =$ __63°__ $m\angle R =$ __117°__ $m\angle A =$ __135°__ $m\angle P =$ __45°__

G Use a protractor to measure the angles of trapezoid *T'R'A'P'*.

$m\angle T' =$ __63°__ $m\angle R' =$ __117°__ $m\angle A' =$ __135°__ $m\angle P' =$ __45°__

H What do you notice about the measures of corresponding angles of the two figures?

The measures of corresponding angles are the same.

I Which sides of trapezoid *TRAP* are parallel? __$\overline{TP}$ and $\overline{RA}$__

Which sides of trapezoid *T'R'A'P'* are parallel? __$\overline{T'P'}$ and $\overline{R'A'}$__
What do you notice?

The sides that were parallel in the preimage remain

parallel in the image.

© Houghton Mifflin Harcourt Publishing Company

	EXPLORE ACTIVITY 2
(AL) DOK 1 *Recall*	How do the side lengths compare between the preimage and the image in a reflection? How do the angle measures compare? The side lengths are the same; the angle measures are the same.
(OL) DOK 2 *Skills/Concepts*	How many different ways could trapezoid *TRAP* be reflected? Justify your answer. It can be reflected an infinite number of ways. Any line can be a line of reflection, and there are an infinite number of lines.
(BL) DOK 3 *Strategic Thinking*	If you are shown a preimage and the image of its reflection, how could you determine the line of reflection? Draw a line segment connecting the corresponding vertices between the preimage and the image. Then connect the points that divide each line segment in half.

3 Explain

Connect Vocabulary ELL

Point out that translations and *reflections* are both types of transformations. While a translation does not change the orientation of a figure, a reflection does. Emphasize that a *line of reflection* is often one of the axes, but it can be any line, including lines that are not horizontal or vertical.

EXPLORE ACTIVITY 2

Engage with the Whiteboard

Have students draw the reflection of trapezoid *TRAP* across the *x*-axis. Name the new image *T"R"A"P"*. Students can also draw the reflection of *T'R'A'P'* across the *x*-axis and name the new image *T"'R"'A"'P"'*.

TEACHER TO TEACHER

Cooperative Learning Give each student a full sheet of grid paper. Have the students fold the paper into quarters along grid lines, and mark the fold lines as the *x*- and *y*-axes. Each student should draw half of a face or design to the left of the *y*-axis. The right edge of the face or design should touch the *y*-axis. Students then trade with another student to complete the face or design by drawing a reflection of the drawing across the *y*-axis.

EXAMPLE 1

ADDITIONAL EXAMPLE 1 The figure shows triangle *PQR*. Graph the image of the triangle after a reflection across the *x*-axis.

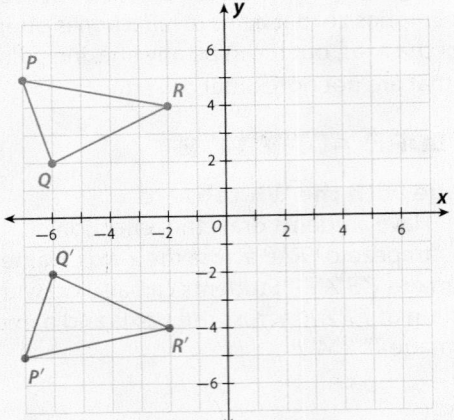

 Interactive Whiteboard
Interactive example available online

 my.hrw.com

Digital Teacher Resources

Go online to access all your lesson-level resources.

Differentiated Instruction
• Reteach
• Reading Strategies
• Success for English Learners
• Practice and Problem Solving A/B, C, D

Math on the Spot Videos

Reflect

3. **Make a Conjecture** Use your results from **E**, **H**, and **I** to make a conjecture about reflections.

Sample answer: Reflections preserve the size and shape of a figure, but the orientation changes to a mirror image of the original.

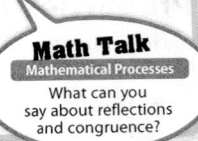

Math Talk
Mathematical Processes

What can you say about reflections and congruence?

Math Talk Anno: A reflection produces a figure that is congruent to the original figure.

Graphing Reflections

To reflect a figure across a line of reflection, reflect each of its vertices. Then connect the vertices to form the image. Remember that each point and its image are the same distance from the line of reflection.

Math On the Spot
my.hrw.com

EXAMPLE 1

The figure shows triangle *XYZ*. Graph the image of the triangle after a reflection across the *x*-axis.

STEP 1 Reflect point *X*.

Point *X* is 3 units below the *x*-axis. Count 3 units above the *x*-axis and plot point *X'*.

STEP 2 Reflect point *Y*.

Point *Y* is 1 unit below the *x*-axis. Count 1 unit above the *x*-axis and plot point *Y'*.

STEP 3 Reflect point *Z*.

Point *Z* is 5 units below the *x*-axis. Count 5 units above the *x*-axis and plot point *Z'*.

STEP 4 Connect *X'*, *Y'*, and *Z'* to form triangle *X'Y'Z'*.

Each vertex of the image is the same distance from the *x*-axis as the corresponding vertex in the original figure.

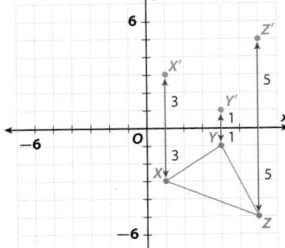
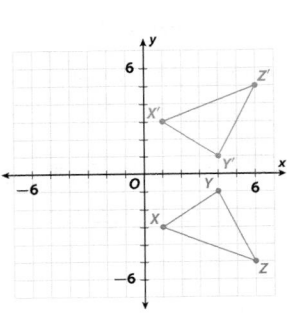

My Notes

© Houghton Mifflin Harcourt Publishing Company

Lesson 9.2 **287**

DIFFERENTIATE INSTRUCTION *Leveled Questions*

	EXAMPLE 1
AL **DOK 1** *Recall*	Are you moving the vertices horizontally or vertically when you reflect an image across the *x*-axis? across the *y*-axis? vertically; horizontally
OL **DOK 2** *Skills/Concepts*	Is triangle *X'Y'Z'* also considered a translation of preimage *XYZ*? Why or why not? No, the orientation is different between the preimage and the image, so the transformation cannot be a translation.
BL **DOK 3** *Strategic Thinking*	Is there a sequence of four reflections that will result in the same image as the preimage? Explain. Yes; you could reflect *XYZ* across the *x*-axis as shown, then across the *y*-axis, then the *x*-axis, and finally across the *y*-axis. The resulting image will be identical to the preimage.

LEVELED QUESTIONS: **AL** Approaching Level | **OL** On Level | **BL** Beyond Level

Personal
Math Trainer
Online Assessment
and Intervention

my.hrw.com

YOUR TURN

4. The figure shows pentagon *ABCDE*. Graph the image of the pentagon after a reflection across the *y*-axis.

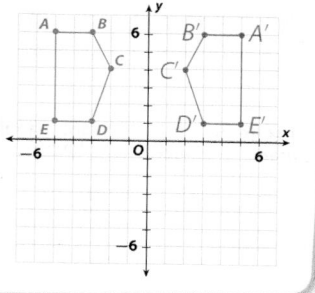

Guided Practice

1. **Vocabulary** A reflection is a transformation that flips a figure across a line called the <u>line of reflection</u>.

2. The figure shows trapezoid *ABCD*. (Explore Activities 1 and 2 and Example 1)

   a. Graph the image of the trapezoid after a reflection across the *x*-axis. Label the vertices of the image.

   b. How do trapezoid *ABCD* and trapezoid *A'B'C'D'* compare?

      <u>They are congruent.</u>

   c. **What If?** Suppose you reflected trapezoid *ABCD* across the *y*-axis. How would the orientation of the image of the trapezoid compare with the orientation of the preimage?

      <u>The orientation would be reversed</u>
      <u>horizontally. That is, the figure from</u>
      <u>left to right in the preimage would match the figure</u>
      <u>from right to left in the image.</u>

ESSENTIAL QUESTION CHECK-IN

3. What are the properties of reflections?

   <u>Sample answer: Reflections preserve size and shape but</u>
   <u>not orientation.</u>

288 Unit 4

© Houghton Mifflin Harcourt Publishing Company

Talk About It

Check for Understanding

 Ask: How do the coordinates of the image differ from the coordinates of the preimage when a figure is reflected across the *y*-axis? The *x*-values are the opposite of the preimage's *x*-values, but the *y*-values remain the same.

4 Elaborate

Talk About It

Summarize the Lesson

 Ask: How do you know when a transformation is a reflection? The image will have the same size and shape as the preimage, but the orientation will not be the same. There will be a line of reflection such that each image point will be the same distance from that line as its corresponding preimage point.

Guided Practice

Engage with the Whiteboard

For **Exercise 2,** have students graph the reflections of trapezoid *ABCD* across both the *x*-axis and the *y*-axis on the coordinate grid. Label the images *A'B'C'D'* and *A"B"C"D"*.

Avoid Common Errors

Exercise 2a Remind students that the image will have its vertices labeled with the same letters as the corresponding preimage vertices, along with the *prime* symbol (').

DIFFERENTIATE INSTRUCTION *Intervention and Additional Support*

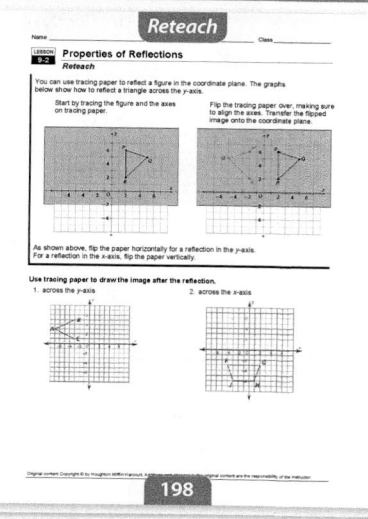

Reteach

198

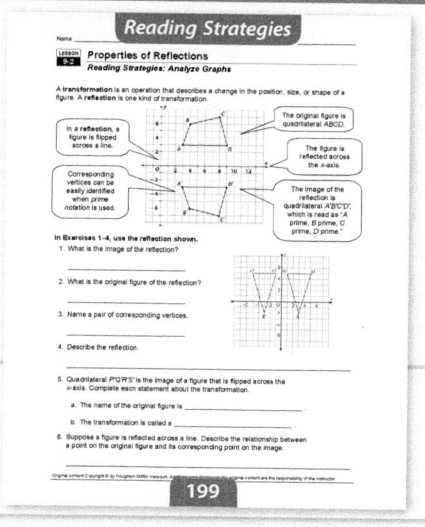

Reading Strategies

199

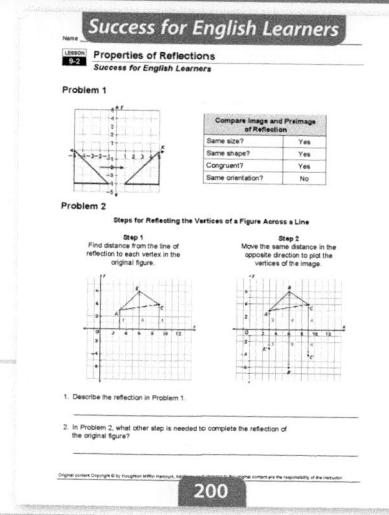

Success for English Learners

200

Personal Math Trainer
Daily Intervention
9.2 Homework

Pages shown are from *Differentiated Instruction.*
Also available online.

Pressed for Time

9.2 Differentiated Homework Assignments

(AL) **Approaching Level**   4–9

(OL) **On Level**   4–8, 11

(BL) **Beyond Level**   8–11

For **Below Level** students, assign Personal Math Trainer, Daily Intervention 9.2 Homework.

Mathematical Processes	Exercises
MP.2 Reasoning	4–5
MP.3 Logic	7, 9
MP.6 Precision	6, 8, 10–11

Focus on Higher Order Thinking

Depth of Knowledge	Exercises
1 Recall of Information	4–5, 7
2 Skills/Concepts	6, 8
3 Strategic Thinking H.O.T.	9–11

The graph shows four right triangles. Use the graph for Exercises 4–7.

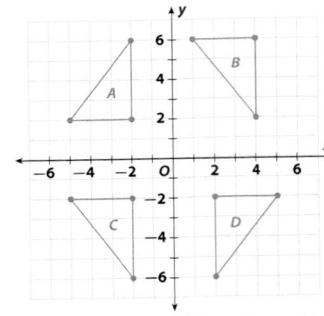

4. Which two triangles are reflections of each other across the x-axis?

A and C

5. For which two triangles is the line of reflection the y-axis?

C and D

6. Which triangle is a translation of triangle C? How would you describe the translation?

triangle B; a translation of 8 units

up and 6 units right

7. Which triangles are congruent? How do you know?

Sample answer: Since each

triangle is either a reflection or

translation of triangle C, they are

all congruent.

8. a. Graph quadrilateral WXYZ with vertices W(−2, −2), X(3, 1), Y(5, −1), and Z(4, −6) on the coordinate grid.

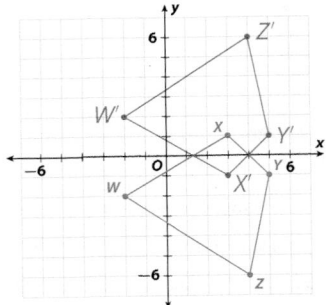

b. On the same coordinate grid, graph quadrilateral W'X'Y'Z', the image of quadrilateral WXYZ after a reflection across the x-axis.

c. Which side of the image is congruent to side $\overline{YZ}$?

$\overline{Y'Z'}$

Name three other pairs of congruent sides.

$\overline{WX}$ and $\overline{W'X'}$, $\overline{XY}$ and $\overline{X'Y'}$,

$\overline{WZ}$ and $\overline{W'Z'}$

d. Which angle of the image is congruent to ∠X?

_∠X'_

Name three other pairs of congruent angles.

∠W and ∠W', ∠Y and ∠Y',

∠Z and ∠Z'

Lesson 9.2   **289**

© Houghton Mifflin Harcourt Publishing Company

DIFFERENTIATE INSTRUCTION *Leveled Homework/Practice*

Personal Math Trainer
• 9.2 Homework

Pages shown are from *Differentiated Instruction.*
Also available online.

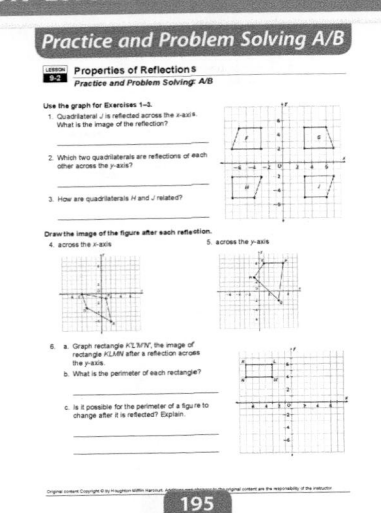

Practice and Problem Solving A/B

195

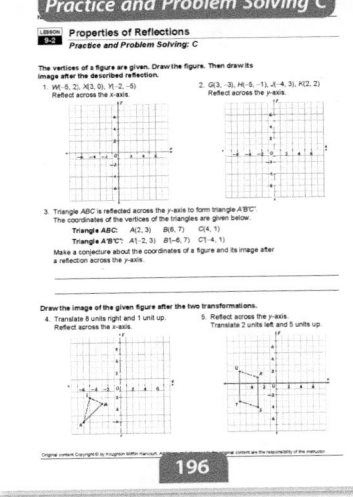

Practice and Problem Solving C

196

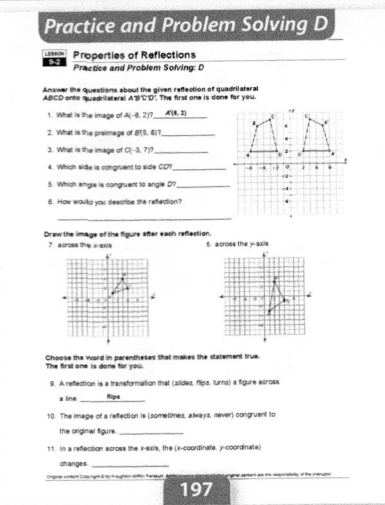

Practice and Problem Solving D

197

9. **Critical Thinking** Is it possible that the image of a point after a reflection could be the same point as the preimage? Explain.

Yes; if the point lies on the line of reflection, then the image and the preimage will be the same point.

 **FOCUS ON HIGHER ORDER THINKING**

10. a. Graph the image of the figure shown after a reflection across the y-axis.

b. On the same coordinate grid, graph the image of the figure you drew in part **a** after a reflection across the x-axis.

c. **Make a Conjecture** What other sequence of transformations would produce the same final image from the original preimage? Check your answer by performing the transformations. Then make a conjecture that generalizes your findings.

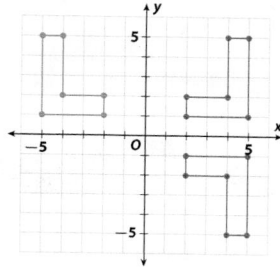

The same image can be obtained by reflecting first across the x-axis and then across the y-axis. In general, reflecting a figure first across the y-axis and then across the x-axis produces the same result as reflecting first across the x-axis and then across the y-axis.

11. a. Graph triangle DEF with vertices D(2, 6), E(5, 6), and F(5, 1) on the coordinate grid.

b. Next graph triangle D′E′F′, the image of triangle DEF after a reflection across the y-axis.

c. On the same coordinate grid, graph triangle D″E″F″, the image of triangle D′E′F′ after a translation of 7 units down and 2 units to the right.

d. **Analyze Relationships** Find a different sequence of transformations that will transform triangle DEF to triangle D″E″F″.

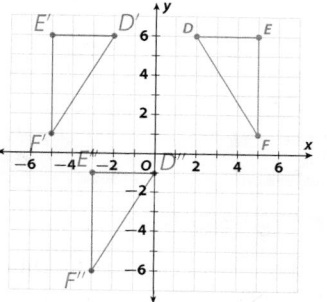

Sample answer: Translate triangle DEF 7 units down and 2 units to the left. Then reflect the image across the y-axis.

© Houghton Mifflin Harcourt Publishing Company

DIFFERENTIATE INSTRUCTION *Extend-the-Math Activity* **PRE-AP**

Activity Reflect triangle ABC across line ℓ. Label the image triangle A′B′C′. Then reflect triangle A′B′C′ across line m, where ℓ ∥ m. Label the image triangle A″B″C″. What other transformation could you have performed on triangle ABC to get triangle A″B″C″? Do you think this would be true of any shape that goes through the same process?

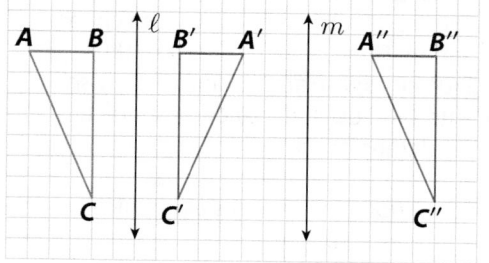

Sample answer: A translation of triangle ABC could have produced A″B″C″. Yes, any shape would be reversed after one reflection, then reversed again to the original figure after the second reflection only if the lines of reflection are parallel.

✔ **Quick Check**

9.2 Lesson Quiz

Graph triangle ABC with vertices A(−4, 1), B(−2, 1), and C(−1, −2) on a coordinate grid.

1. Graph the image of triangle ABC after a reflection across the y-axis.

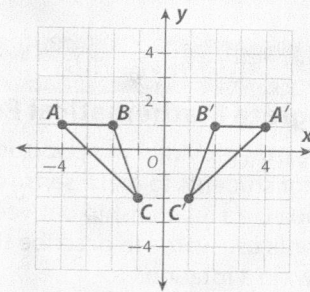

2. Which side of the image is congruent to side $\overline{AB}$? $\overline{A'B'}$

3. Which angle in the image is congruent to angle B? angle B′

4. If a point M, 5 units from the x-axis, is reflected across the x-axis, how far is the image of the point M′ from the x-axis? 5 units

5. Angle G in trapezoid FGHJ measures 135°. Jasmine reflects the trapezoid over the x-axis. What is the measure of the image of angle G? 135°

Differentiate Instruction

IF a student misses more than one question, THEN

Differentiate Instruction:
- 9.2 Reteach
- Personal Math Trainer

 Interactive Whiteboard
Interactive Lesson quiz available online

Lesson Support

Content Objective Students will learn how to describe the properties of rotations and their effects on the congruence and orientation of figures.

Professional Development

Integrate Mathematical Processes MP.2

This lesson provides an opportunity to address this Mathematical Processes standard. It calls for students to make sense of relationships in a problem. Students use coordinate grids to visualize a relationship between a preimage and a rotation that results in an image. Then students use words to describe the relationship between the preimage and the image following a rotation.

FOCUS

Building Background

Connecting to Everyday Life Ask students to explain what a rotation means in their own words. Then have them describe examples of rotations with which they are familiar. Possible examples include an analog clock, gears, wind and water mills, Ferris wheels, tires, planetary orbits, and Earth's rotation. Elicit the observation that all of the examples rotate about a center point, the center of rotation.

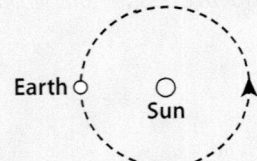

COHERENCE

Learning Progressions

In this lesson, students verify experimentally the properties of reflections by rotating polygons in the coordinate plane around a given center of rotation. Important understandings for students include the following:

- **Investigate the properties of rotations.**
- **Graph rotations.**

Like the other rigid transformations, students learn that a rotation preserves congruence and, like reflections, can change orientation. They rotate figures 90°, 180°, and 270°, clockwise and counterclockwise. Students wind up their review and practice with rigid transformations in this lesson in preparation for analyzing these transformations as functions algebraically in the next lesson.

RIGOR

Cluster Connections

This lesson provides an excellent opportunity to connect ideas in the cluster:

Understand congruence and similarity using physical models, transparencies, or geometry software.

The center of rotation of a polygon can be inside the polygon. Have students graph an octagon with vertices $A(1, 3)$, $B(1, 1)$, $C(2, 0)$, $D(2, -2)$, $E(-2, -2)$, $F(-2, 0)$, $G(-1, 1)$, and $H(-1, 3)$. Ask students to rotate the octagon about the origin clockwise 90°, 180°, and 270°. Have them record the coordinates of preimage vertex A and the corresponding rotation images of A', A'', and A'''.

$A(2, 3)$, $A'(3, -2)$, $A''(-2, -3)$, $A'''(-3, 2)$

Language Support ELL

Language Objective Students will describe the properties of rotations and their effects on the congruence and orientation of figures.

Leveled Strategies for English Learners ELL

Emerging
When proficiency in English is limited, having students use their primary language in peer-to-peer discussion encourages higher-level thinking.

Expanding
Have students at this level of English proficiency work in small groups of mixed language proficiency to list the properties of rotations.

Bridging
To make sure that the nuances of language have not prevented students from understanding the concepts, have them separate the parts of the essential question to help them answer it.

 **Math Talk**
Write out and model for students a sentence frame to begin their answer.

The orientation of the triangle is affected by _____.

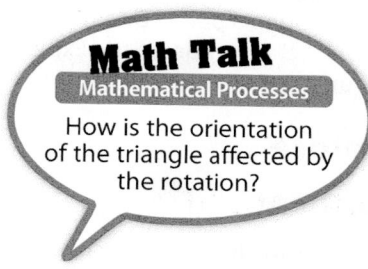

Math Talk
Mathematical Processes
How is the orientation of the triangle affected by the rotation?

Image Credits: ©Tom Grill/Media Bakery

Linguistic Support ELL

Academic/Content Vocabulary
This lesson relies on students' understanding of the meanings of *rotation* and *center of rotation*. These terms are defined in the context of the sentence in which they are introduced. Have students also turn to the glossary to see the new word defined as well as a visual diagram. For a glossary resource for 13 world languages, including Spanish, be sure to take students to the Online Multilingual Glossary.

Building Background
The words *rotate* and *rotation* are found throughout this lesson. Many English verbs can be turned into nouns by adding the suffix *-tion* to them. Words that end in *-tion* in English are often cognates in Spanish (*rotación, reflexión*).

counter- The prefix *counter-* is also found in this lesson in the word *counterclockwise*. Provide a demonstration of *clockwise* first. Then point out that *counter* is like *contra*, meaning "against."

Properties of Rotations

1 Engage

? ESSENTIAL QUESTION

How do you describe the properties of rotation and their effect on the congruence and orientation of figures? Sample answer: Rotations preserve size and shape but change orientation.

Motivate the Lesson

Ask: What changes when you turn an object, such as a book, around a point? Does the size or shape of the object change? Begin the Explore Activity to find out.

2 Explore

EXPLORE ACTIVITY 1

Focus on Modeling
Make sure students understand that point A is the same as point A´ because A lies at the center of rotation. The next Explore Activity shows a rotation where none of the vertices lie at the center of rotation, and therefore all of the vertices change position.

LESSON
9.3 **Properties of Rotations**

8.4.9.3
Students will describe the properties of rotation and their effect on the congruence and orientation of figures.

? ESSENTIAL QUESTION

How do you describe the properties of rotation and their effect on the congruence and orientation of figures?

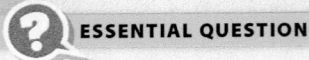

EXPLORE ACTIVITY 1

Exploring Rotations

A **rotation** is a transformation that turns a figure around a given point called the **center of rotation**. The image has the same size and shape as the preimage.

The triangle shown on the grid is the preimage. You will use the origin as the center of rotation.

A Trace triangle *ABC* onto a piece of paper. Cut out your traced triangle.

B Rotate your triangle 90° counterclockwise about the origin. The side of the triangle that lies along the *x*-axis should now lie along the *y*-axis.

C Sketch the image of the rotation. Label the images of points *A*, *B*, and *C* as *A'*, *B'*, and *C'*.

D Describe the motion modeled by the rotation.

Rotate _____90_____ degrees ___counterclockwise___ about the origin.

E Check that the motion you described in **D** is the same motion that maps point *A* onto *A'*, point *B* onto *B'*, and point *C* onto *C'*.

Reflect

1. **Communicate Mathematical Ideas** How are the size and the orientation of the triangle affected by the rotation?

   The size stays the same, but the orientation changes in that the triangle is turned or tilted left – what was "up" is now "left".

2. Rotate triangle *ABC* 90° clockwise about the origin. Sketch the result on the coordinate grid above. Label the image vertices *A''*, *B''*, and *C''*.

© Houghton Mifflin Harcourt Publishing Company • Image Credits: ©IKO/Fotolia

---

DIFFERENTIATE INSTRUCTION *Leveled Questions*

	EXPLORE ACTIVITY 1
AL DOK 1 *Recall*	How do the side lengths compare between the preimage and the image in a rotation? How do the angle measures compare? The side lengths are the same; the angle measures are the same.
OL DOK 2 *Skills/Concepts*	To read the vertices of triangle *ABC* in alphabetical order, you read them counterclockwise. After you rotate triangle *ABC*, do the image vertices still read in a counterclockwise direction? Yes
BL DOK 3 *Strategic Thinking*	What if you rotate the preimage in a clockwise direction, will the vertices of the image still be read in a counterclockwise direction? Explain. Yes; it doesn't matter which way the preimage is rotated, the vertices of the image will be read in the same direction as they are read on the preimage.

LEVELED QUESTIONS: **AL** Approaching Level | **OL** On Level | **BL** Beyond Level

Properties of Rotations

Use trapezoid *TRAP* to investigate the properties of rotations.

A Trace the trapezoid onto a piece of paper. Include the portion of the *x*- and *y*-axes bordering the third quadrant. Cut out your tracing.

B Place your trapezoid and axes on top of those in the figure. Then use the axes to help rotate your trapezoid 180° counterclockwise about the origin. Sketch the image of the rotation of your trapezoid in this new location. Label the vertices of the image *T'*, *R'*, *A'*, and *P'*.

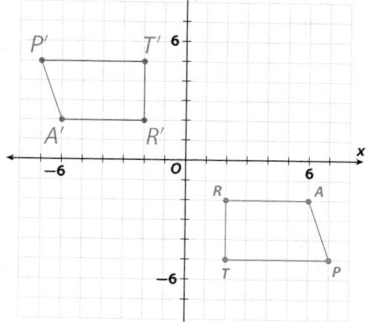

C Use a ruler to measure the sides of trapezoid *TRAP* in centimeters.

$TR =$ __1.3 cm__ $RA =$ __1.7 cm__

$AP =$ __1.5 cm__ $TP =$ __2.2 cm__

D Use a ruler to measure the sides of trapezoid *T'R'A'P'* in centimeters.

$T'R' =$ __1.3 cm__ $R'A' =$ __1.7 cm__

$A'P' =$ __1.5 cm__ $T'P' =$ __2.2 cm__

E What do you notice about the lengths of corresponding sides of the two figures?

The lengths of corresponding sides are the same.

F Use a protractor to measure the angles of trapezoid *TRAP*.

$m\angle T =$ __90°__ $m\angle R =$ __90°__ $m\angle A =$ __108°__ $m\angle P =$ __72°__

G Use a protractor to measure the angles of trapezoid *T'R'A'P'*.

$m\angle T' =$ __90°__ $m\angle R' =$ __90°__ $m\angle A' =$ __108°__ $m\angle P' =$ __72°__

H What do you notice about the measures of corresponding angles of the two figures?

The measures of corresponding angles are the same.

I Which sides of trapezoid *TRAP* are parallel? __$\overline{TP}$ and $\overline{RA}$__

Which sides of trapezoid *T'R'A'P'* are parallel? __$\overline{T'P'}$ and $\overline{R'A'}$__

What do you notice? The sides that were parallel in the preimage remain parallel in the image.

© Houghton Mifflin Harcourt Publishing Company

3 Explain

Connect Vocabulary ELL

Emphasize that a *transformation* is a function that describes a change in the position, size, or shape of a figure, and a *rotation* is a *type* of transformation. The measures of the figure's sides and angles do not ever change in a rotation. In most rotations, the figure's position and orientation change.

EXPLORE ACTIVITY 2

Focus on Critical Thinking

Point out to students that a clockwise rotation of 270° results in the same image as a counterclockwise rotation of 90°. Ask students to examine this claim, discuss why it is true, and justify it with a logical argument. Sample answer: Since 270° + 90° = 360°, and a full rotation is 360°, then rotating 270° in one direction is the same as rotating 90° in the opposite direction.

		EXPLORE ACTIVITY 2
AL	**DOK 1** *Recall*	The preimage trapezoid is in Quadrant IV. What quadrant is the image of the trapezoid after a 180° rotation about the origin? Quadrant II
OL	**DOK 2** *Skills/Concepts*	How does the distance from the origin to *T* compare to the distance from the origin to *T'*? It is the same.
BL	**DOK 3** *Strategic Thinking*	If you drew segments from *T* to the origin and from *T'* to the origin, what angle would the two segments form? Is this true for the segments to the origin from any vertex and its image? a 180° angle, or straight angle; yes

TEACHER TO TEACHER

Teaching Tip Tell students that a rotation is a mathematical model of the motion of turning. To rotate a figure you must know three things: the center of rotation, the magnitude (number of degrees), and the direction (clockwise or counterclockwise) of the rotation.

EXAMPLE 1

ADDITIONAL EXAMPLE 1 The figure shows triangle *PQR*. Graph the image of the triangle after a clockwise rotation of 90° about the origin.

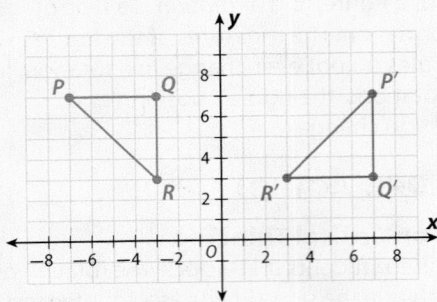

 Interactive Whiteboard
Interactive example available online

YOUR TURN MP.7

Talk About It

Check for Understanding

Ask: Looking at your answer to **Exercise 6**, what indicates that quadrilateral *ABCD* was not translated to get quadrilateral *A′B′C′D′*? The size and shape of the figures are the same, but the orientation is different.

Digital Teacher Resources

Go online to access all your lesson-level resources.

Differentiated Instruction
• Reteach
• Reading Strategies
• Success for English Learners
• Practice and Problem Solving A/B, C, D

Math on the Spot Videos

🔘 my.hrw.com

Reflect

3. **Make a Conjecture** Use your results from **E**, **H**, and **I** to make a conjecture about rotations.

Sample answer: Rotations preserve size and shape, or congruence, but change a figure's orientation by turning it.

4. Place your tracing back in its original position. Then perform a 180° *clockwise* rotation about the origin. Compare the result with the result of the transformation in **B**.

A 180° clockwise rotation gives the same image as a 180° counterclockwise rotation.

Graphing Rotations

To rotate a figure in the coordinate plane, rotate each of its vertices. Then connect the vertices to form the image.

EXAMPLE 1

Math On the Spot
🔘 my.hrw.com

Animated Math
🔘 my.hrw.com

The figure shows triangle *ABC*. Graph the image of triangle *ABC* after a rotation of 90° clockwise.

STEP 1 Rotate the figure clockwise from the *y*-axis to the *x*-axis. Point *A* will still be at (0, 0).

Point *B* is 2 units to the left of the *y*-axis, so point *B′* is 2 units above the *x*-axis.

Point *C* is 2 units to the right of the *y*-axis, so point *C′* is 2 units below the *x*-axis.

STEP 2 Connect *A′*, *B′*, and *C′* to form the image triangle *A′B′C′*.

Reflect

5. Is the image congruent to the preimage? How do you know?

Sample answer: Yes, you can see from the grid squares that the side lengths and angle measures are the same.

Math Talk
Mathematical Processes

How is the orientation of the triangle affected by the rotation?

Sample answer: The triangle is turned to the right about the origin by the angle of rotation.

Lesson 9.3 **293**

DIFFERENTIATE INSTRUCTION *Leveled Questions*

	EXAMPLE 1
AL **DOK 1** *Recall*	About what point are you rotating triangle *ABC*? the origin, which is the location of point *A*
OL **DOK 2** *Skills/Concepts*	What counterclockwise rotation of triangle *ABC* can you make so that its image is in Quadrants I and IV? 270°
BL **DOK 3** *Strategic Thinking*	What would be the vertices of the image if you rotated triangle *ABC* clockwise 90° about point *B*? *A′*(−5, 1), *B′*(−2, 3), *C′*(−2, −1)

LEVELED QUESTIONS: **AL** Approaching Level | **OL** On Level | **BL** Beyond Level

Personal Math Trainer
Online Assessment and Intervention
my.hrw.com

YOUR TURN

Graph the image of quadrilateral *ABCD* after each rotation.

6. 180°

7. 270° clockwise

8. Find the coordinates of Point *C* after a 90° counterclockwise rotation followed by a 180° rotation.

_____ (2, −4)

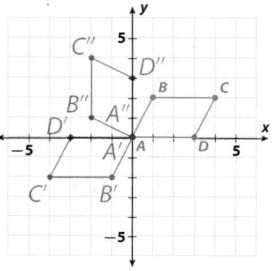

Guided Practice

1. **Vocabulary** A rotation is a transformation that turns a figure around a given _____ point _____ called the center of rotation.

Siobhan rotates a right triangle 90° counterclockwise about the origin.

2. How does the orientation of the image of the triangle compare with the orientation of the preimage? (Explore Activity 1)

   The triangle is turned 90° to the left.

3. Is the image of the triangle congruent to the preimage? (Explore Activity 2)

   Yes, the figures are congruent.

Draw the image of the figure after the given rotation about the origin. (Example 1)

4. 90° counterclockwise

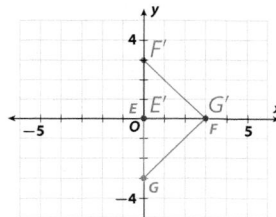

5. 180°

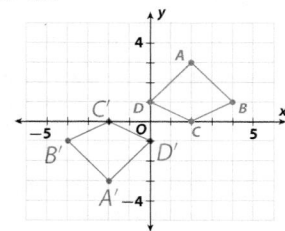

 ESSENTIAL QUESTION CHECK-IN

6. What are the properties of rotations?

   Sample answer: Rotations preserve size and shape but change orientation.

294 Unit 4

© Houghton Mifflin Harcourt Publishing Company

4 Elaborate

Talk About It

Summarize the Lesson

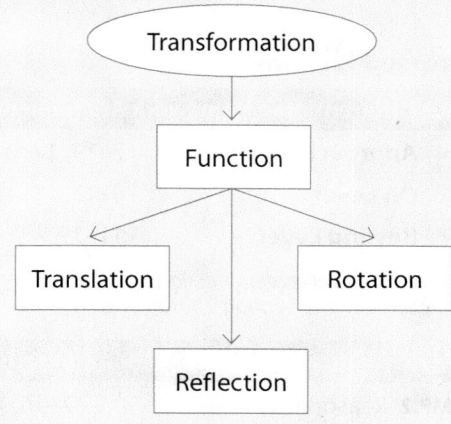

Guided Practice

Engage with the Whiteboard

For **Exercises 2–5,** have volunteers circle the degree, direction, and center of rotation of the figures. In **Exercises 4–5,** draw curved arrows in the direction of rotation.

Avoid Common Errors

Exercise 5 Make sure students label the image correctly. Some students may swap *B'* and *D'* out of carelessness or thinking the order of the labels doesn't matter.

DIFFERENTIATE INSTRUCTION *Intervention and Additional Support*

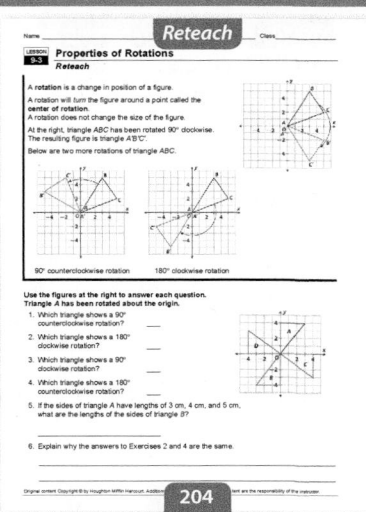

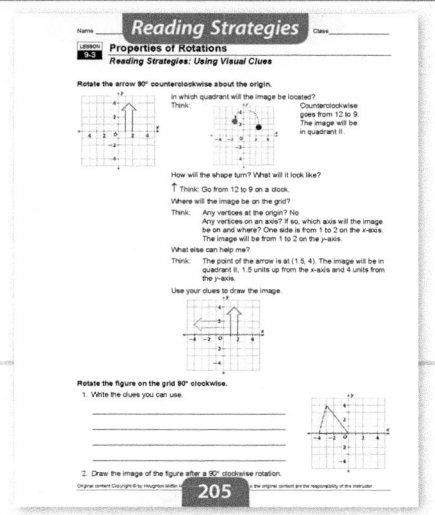

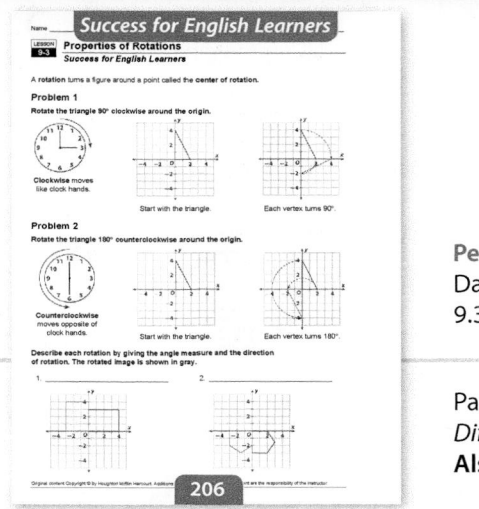

Personal Math Trainer
Daily Intervention
9.3 Homework

Pages shown are from *Differentiated Instruction.*
Also available online.

⏱ Pressed for Time

9.3 Differentiated Homework Assignments

AL Approaching Level		7–14, 17
OL On Level		8–13, 15–17
BL Beyond Level		11–19

*For **Below Level** students, assign Personal Math Trainer, Daily Intervention 9.3 Homework.*

Mathematical Processes	Exercises
MP.2 Reasoning	7–16, 18
MP.3 Logic	17
MP.4 Modeling	19

Focus on Higher Order Thinking

Depth of Knowledge	Exercises
2 Skills/Concepts	7–16
3 Strategic Thinking H.O.T.\	17–19

Name_____ Class_____ Date_____

9.3 Independent Practice

📱 my.hrw.com Personal Math Trainer Online Assessment and Intervention

7. The figure shows triangle *ABC* and a rotation of the triangle about the origin.

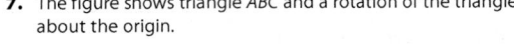

 a. How would you describe the rotation?

 ABC was rotated 90° counterclockwise.

 _____

 b. What are the coordinates of the image?

 A′ (3, 1) , *B′* (2, 3) , *C′* (−1, 4)

8. The graph shows a figure and its image after a transformation.

 a. How would you describe this as a rotation?

 The figure was rotated 180° about the

 origin.

 b. Can you describe this as a transformation other than a rotation? Explain.

 Yes, you can also describe it as a reflection

 across the *y*-axis.

9. What type of rotation will preserve the orientation of the H-shaped figure in the grid?

 180° rotation

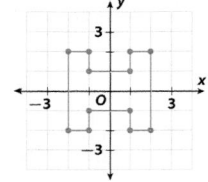

10. A point with coordinates (−2, −3) is rotated 90° clockwise about the origin. What are the coordinates of its image?

 (−3, 2)

Complete the table with rotations of 180° or 90°. Include the direction of rotation for rotations of 90°.

	Shape in quadrant	Image in quadrant	Rotation
11.	I	IV	90° clockwise
12.	III	I	180°
13.	IV	III	90° clockwise

© Houghton Mifflin Harcourt Publishing Company

DIFFERENTIATE INSTRUCTION *Leveled Homework/Practice*

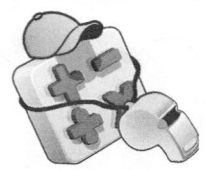

Personal Math Trainer
• 9.3 Homework

Pages shown are from *Differentiated Instruction.* **Also available online.**

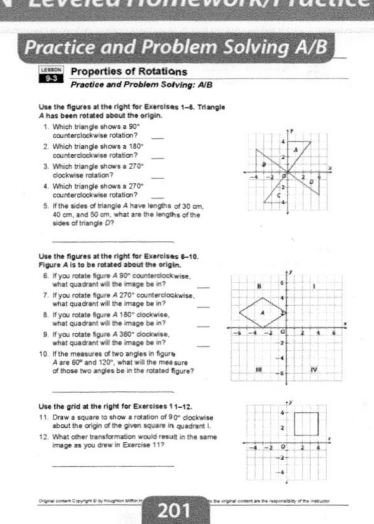

Practice and Problem Solving A/B

201

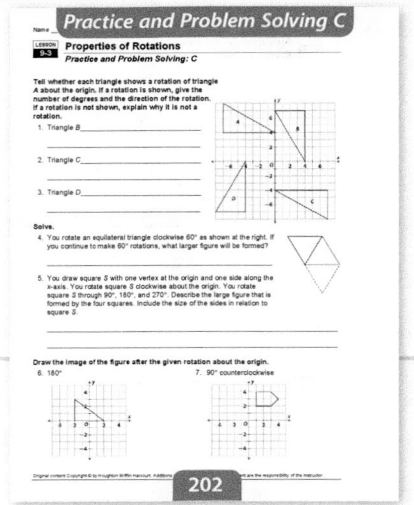

Practice and Problem Solving C

202

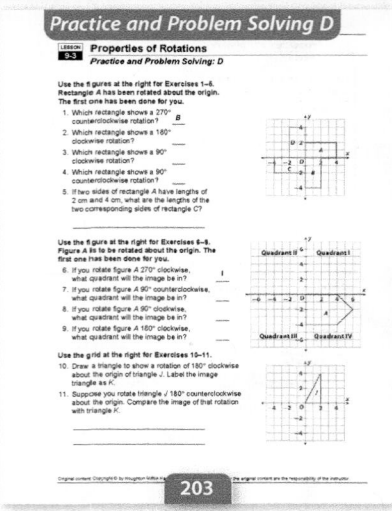

Practice and Problem Solving D

203

Draw the image of the figure after the given rotation about the origin.

14. 180°

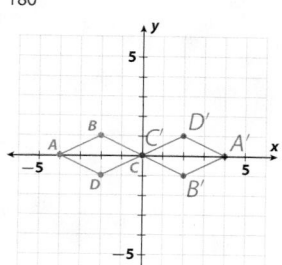

15. 270° counterclockwise

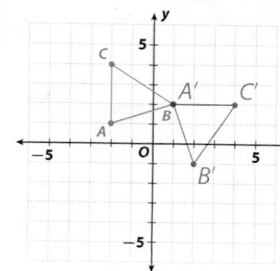

16. Is there a rotation for which the orientation of the image is always the same as that of the preimage? If so, what?

_____ Yes, a 360° rotation _____

 **FOCUS ON HIGHER ORDER THINKING**

17. **Problem Solving** Lucas is playing a game where he has to rotate a figure for it to fit in an open space. Every time he clicks a button, the figure rotates 90 degrees clockwise. How many times does he need to click the button so that each figure returns to its original orientation?

Figure A ___2 times___

Figure B ___1 time___

Figure C ___4 times___

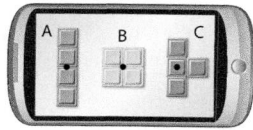

18. **Make a Conjecture** Triangle *ABC* is reflected across the *y*-axis to form the image *A'B'C'*. Triangle *A'B'C'* is then reflected across the *x*-axis to form the image *A"B"C"*. What type of rotation can be used to describe the relationship between triangle *A"B"C"* and triangle *ABC*?

Triangle *A"B"C"* is a 180° rotation of triangle *ABC*.

19. **Communicate Mathematical Ideas** Point *A* is on the *y*-axis. Describe all possible locations of image *A'* for rotations of 90°, 180°, and 270°. Include the origin as a possible location for *A*.

Sample answer: If *A* is at the origin, *A'* for any rotation

about the origin is at the origin. Otherwise, *A'* is on the

x-axis for 90° and 270° rotations and on the *y*-axis for a

180° rotation.

296 Unit 4

© Houghton Mifflin Harcourt Publishing Company

Work Area

9.3 Lesson Quiz

Graph triangle *ABC* with vertices *A*(−4, 1), *B*(−2, 1), and *C*(−1, −2) on a coordinate grid.

1. Graph the image of triangle *ABC* after a 180° clockwise rotation about the origin.

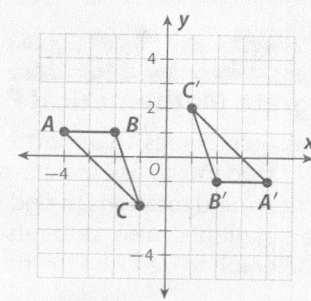

2. Which side of the image is congruent to side $\overline{AB}$? $\overline{A'B'}$

3. Which angle in the image is congruent to angle *B*? angle *B'*

4. If a point *M*, located at (3, −2), is rotated clockwise 90° about the origin, what are the coordinates of its image, *M'*? (−2, −3)

5. Angle *G* in trapezoid *FGHJ* measures 135°. If Lee rotates the trapezoid 270° counterclockwise about the origin, what will be the measure of angle *G'* in the image? 135°

Differentiate Instruction

IF a student misses more than one question, THEN

Differentiate Instruction:

• 9.3 Reteach

• Personal Math Trainer

 Interactive Whiteboard

Interactive Lesson quiz available online

DIFFERENTIATE INSTRUCTION *Extend-the-Math Activity* PRE-AP

Activity The transformed image of point *A* located at (3, 3) is point *A'* located at (−3, −3). Explain how this image could be produced by a translation, a rotation, and by one or more reflections.

By a translation: move 6 units left and 6 units down.

By a rotation: rotate 180° about the origin.

By a reflection or reflections: the point is reflected across the line *y* = −*x*, or is reflected across the *x*-axis and the *y*-axis sequentially in either order.

Lesson Support

Content Objective Students will learn how to describe the effect of a translation, rotation, or reflection on coordinates using an algebraic representation.

Professional Development

Integrate Mathematical Processes MP.3

This lesson provides an opportunity to address this Mathematical Processes standard. It calls for students to use logic to analyze situations. Students use the rules for translations, reflections, and rotations to find the vertices of the image using an algebraic representation instead of graphs. Also, students use an algebraic rule to create a graph of an image, then use the graph to describe the transformation.

FOCUS	COHERENCE	RIGOR

FOCUS

Building Background

Visualizing Math Have students work in pairs. Ask them to use triangle *ABC* and perform the following transformations: translate the triangle 1 unit left and 3 units down; reflect the triangle across the *y*-axis; rotate the triangle 180°. As they perform the transformations, ask them to look for patterns in how the coordinates of each vertex in the preimage change to create the coordinates of the corresponding vertices in the image. Discuss the patterns students observe.

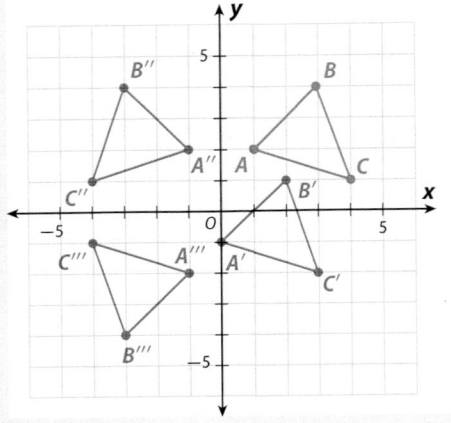

COHERENCE

Learning Progressions

In this lesson, students are introduced to the rules that describe how coordinates change when a figure is transformed by a rigid transformation. Important understandings for students include the following:

- **Describe the effect of a translation on the coordinates of the vertices of a geometric figure.**
- **Describe the effect of a reflection on the coordinates of the vertices of a geometric figure.**
- **Describe the effect of a rotation on the coordinates of the vertices of a geometric figure.**

In earlier lessons, students may have noticed patterns in the way the coordinates of vertices change in rigid transformations. In this lesson they learn the formal rules for the transformations and apply the rules to perform given transformations. They continue to graph the preimage and image to both check and visualize the transformations.

RIGOR

Cluster Connections

This lesson provides an excellent opportunity to connect ideas in the cluster:

Understand congruence and similarity using physical models, transparencies, or geometry software.

Triangle *QRS* has vertices $Q(2, 2)$, $R(-2, 3)$, and $S(-2, -2)$. Ask students to perform the following series of transformations, in order, on triangle *QRS*.

Rule 1: $(x, y) \rightarrow (x, -y)$
Rule 2: $(x, y) \rightarrow (-x, y)$
Rule 3: $(x, y) \rightarrow (x, -y)$
Rule 4: $(x, y) \rightarrow (-x, y)$

What is the final result of the transformations? Encourage students to verify their result by graphing the transformations.

The final result is the original triangle *QRS*.

Language Support ELL

Language Objective Students will demonstrate how to describe the effect of a translation, rotation, or reflection on coordinates using an algebraic representation.

Leveled Strategies for English Learners ELL

Emerging
When proficiency in English is limited, having students use their primary language in peer-to-peer discussion encourages higher-level thinking. Have students illustrate rotating a triangle and labeling the vertices.

Expanding
Working in small groups is an excellent way for English learners to deepen concept knowledge and practice the academic language and vocabulary. Have students work together to illustrate rotating a triangle and label the new x- and y-coordinates.

Bridging
Have students discuss and illustrate rotating a triangle and labeling the new x- and y-coordinates and then take turns explaining how they did it.

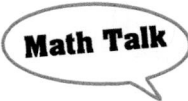

In Explore Actiivity Example 1, ask students which coordinate is changed when translating to the left or right. Write out and model for students a sentence frame to begin their answer.

When you translate a figure to the left, you add to or subtract from the

_____.

Rotations	
90° clockwise	Multiply each x-coordinate by -1; then switch the x- and y-coordinates: $(x, y) \rightarrow (y, -x)$
90° counterclockwise	Multiply each y-coordinate by -1; then switch the x- and y-coordinates: $(x, y) \rightarrow (-y, x)$
180°	Multiply both coordinates by -1: $(x, y) \rightarrow (-x, -y)$

Linguistic Support ELL

Academic/Content Vocabulary
Following Example 2 in the lesson, there is a table that points to the coordinates of the vertices of an image when points are rotated about the origin. English learners may find this especially helpful to tab in their book or to copy into their math journals.

Building Background
Words that are spelled the same yet have different pronunciations and meanings are called homographs. While the word *coordinate* in this lesson refers to one of the values in an ordered pair (x-coordinate or y-coordinate), it also has another meaning and pronunciation as a verb. Discuss these different meanings, and have students add them to their word journals.

Algebraic Representations of Transformations

1 Engage

? ESSENTIAL QUESTION

How can you describe the effect of a translation, rotation, or reflection on coordinates using an algebraic representation? Sample answer: For a given transformation, the change in the coordinates can be described algebraically following specific rules for that transformation.

Motivate the Lesson

Ask: How can you find the coordinates of the vertices of an image after a translation, rotation, or reflection without graphing? Begin the lesson to find out.

2 Explore

EXPLORE ACTIVITY | EXAMPLE 1

ADDITIONAL EXAMPLE 1 Triangle *PQR* has vertices *P* (3, 3), *Q* (5, −1), and *R* (1, −2). Find the vertices of triangle *P'Q'R'* after a translation of 3 units to the left and 1 unit up. Then graph the triangle and its image.

P'(0, 4), *Q'*(2, 0), and *R'*(−2, −1)

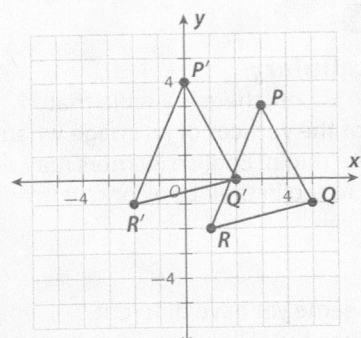

Interactive Whiteboard
Interactive example available online

LESSON 9.4 **Algebraic Representations of Transformations**

8.4.9.4
Students will describe the effect of a translation, rotation, or reflection on coordinates using an algebraic representation.

? ESSENTIAL QUESTION

How can you describe the effect of a translation, rotation, or reflection on coordinates using an algebraic representation?

EXPLORE ACTIVITY

Algebraic Representations of Translations

The rules shown in the table describe how coordinates change when a figure is translated up, down, right, and left on the coordinate plane.

Translations	
Right *a* units	Add *a* to the *x*-coordinate: $(x, y) \rightarrow (x + a, y)$
Left *a* units	Subtract *a* from the *x*-coordinate: $(x, y) \rightarrow (x − a, y)$
Up *b* units	Add *b* to the *y*-coordinate: $(x, y) \rightarrow (x, y + b)$
Down *b* units	Subtract *b* from the *y*-coordinate: $(x, y) \rightarrow (x, y − b)$

EXAMPLE 1 Triangle *XYZ* has vertices *X*(0, 0), *Y*(2, 3), and *Z*(4, −1). Find the vertices of triangle *X'Y'Z'* after a translation of 3 units to the right and 1 unit down. Then graph the triangle and its image.

> Add 3 to the *x*-coordinate of each vertex, and subtract 1 from the *y*-coordinate of each vertex.

STEP 1 Apply the rule to find the vertices of the image.

Vertices of △*XYZ*	Rule: $(x + 3, y − 1)$	Vertices of △*X'Y'Z'*
X(0, 0)	(0 + 3, 0 − 1)	*X'*(3 , −1)
Y(2, 3)	(2 + 3, 3 − 1)	*Y'*(5 , 2)
Z(4, −1)	(4 + 3 , −1 − 1)	*Z'*(7 , −2)

STEP 2 Graph the image with triangle *XYZ* on the coordinate plane.

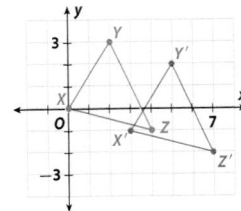

DIFFERENTIATE INSTRUCTION *Leveled Questions*

	EXPLORE ACTIVITY EXAMPLE 1
(AL) DOK 1 *Recall*	When you translate triangle *XYZ* 3 units to the right and 1 unit down, how do the *x*- and *y*-coordinates change? *x* increases by 3, *y* decreases by 1.
(OL) DOK 2 *Skills/Concepts*	What is the slope of each line that connects a preimage vertex to its image vertex? $-\frac{1}{3}$
(BL) DOK 3 *Strategic Thinking*	To translate triangle *X'Y'Z'* back to the position of its preimage, how can you modify the operations in the algebraic rule from those in the original translation? Use the inverse operations. Instead of adding 3 to *x*, subtract 3 from *x*. Instead of subtracting 1 from *y*, add 1 to *y*.

LEVELED QUESTIONS: (AL) Approaching Level | (OL) On Level | (BL) Beyond Level

© Houghton Mifflin Harcourt Publishing Company

YOUR TURN

1. A rectangle has vertices at (0, −2), (0, 3), (3, −2), and (3, 3). What are the coordinates of the vertices of the image after the translation $(x, y) \rightarrow (x − 6, y − 3)$? Describe the translation.

   (−6, −5), (−6, 0), (−3, −5), and (−3, 0); the rectangle is translated 6 units to the left and 3 units down.

Personal
Math Trainer

Online Assessment
and Intervention

my.hrw.com

Math On the Spot
my.hrw.com

Algebraic Representations of Reflections

The signs of the coordinates of a figure change when the figure is reflected across the *x*-axis and *y*-axis. The table shows the rules for changing the signs of the coordinates after a reflection.

Reflections	
Across the *x*-axis	Multiply each *y*-coordinate by −1: $(x, y) \rightarrow (x, −y)$
Across the *y*-axis	Multiply each *x*-coordinate by −1: $(x, y) \rightarrow (−x, y)$

EXAMPLE 2

My Notes

Rectangle *RSTU* has vertices $R(−4, −1)$, $S(−1, −1)$, $T(−1, −3)$, and $U(−4, −3)$. Find the vertices of rectangle $R'S'T'U'$ after a reflection across the *y*-axis. Then graph the rectangle and its image.

Multiply the *x*-coordinate of each vertex by −1.

STEP 1 Apply the rule to find the vertices of the image.

Vertices of *RSTU*	Rule: $(−1 \cdot x, y)$	Vertices of $R'S'T'U'$
$R(−4, −1)$	$(−1 \cdot (−4), −1)$	$R'(4, −1)$
$S(−1, −1)$	$(−1 \cdot (−1), −1)$	$S'(1, −1)$
$T(−1, −3)$	$(−1 \cdot (−1), −3)$	$T'(1, −3)$
$U(−4, −3)$	$(−1 \cdot (−4), −3)$	$U'(4, −3)$

STEP 2 Graph rectangle *RSTU* and its image.

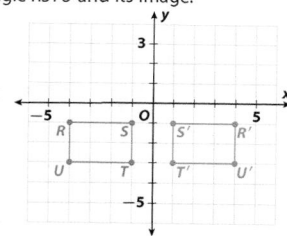

© Houghton Mifflin Harcourt Publishing Company

Avoid Common Errors
Students may make changes to the wrong coordinate. Help them understand that a change to the left or right affects the *x*-coordinate, and a change up or down affects the *y*-coordinate.

3 Explain

EXAMPLE 2

ADDITIONAL EXAMPLE 2 Triangle *PQR* has vertices *P* (3, 3), *Q* (5, −1), and *R* (1, −3). Find the vertices of triangle *P'Q'R'* after a reflection across the *y*-axis. Then graph the triangle and its image.

$P'(−3, 3)$, $Q'(−5, −1)$, and $R'(−1, −3)$

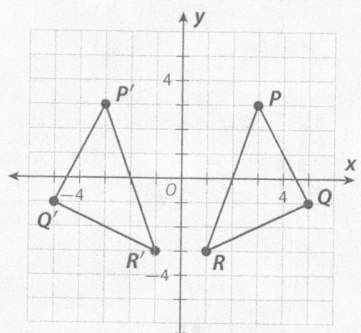

Interactive Whiteboard
Interactive example available online

	EXAMPLE 2
AL **DOK 1** *Recall*	How do the coordinates change when you reflect a figure over the *x*-axis? over the *y*-axis? The *y*-coordinate is multiplied by −1; the *x*-coordinate is multiplied by −1.
OL **DOK 2** *Skills/Concepts*	Does translating quadrilateral *RSTU* right 5 units produce the same image as the reflection shown? Explain. No; the orientation of a reflection is different than the orientation of an image after a translation. The corresponding vertices of the image after reflection and the image after translation are in different positions.
BL **DOK 3** *Strategic Thinking*	What is the algebraic representation of a reflection of *RSTU* across the line $y = −x$? $(x, y) \rightarrow (−y, −x)$

TEACHER TO TEACHER

Communicating Math Have students work in pairs. One student provides a transformation. The other describes how the ordered pairs change using an algebraic representation.

Student 1: Translate right 3 units and up 2 units.

Student 2: Add 3 to the *x*-value and add 2 to the *y*-value: $(x, y) \rightarrow (x + 3, y + 2)$.

Algebraic Representations of Transformations   **298**

Avoid Common Errors
Make sure that students understand they do not just make the y-value a negative number. The y-value of the image must have a sign opposite that of the preimage's y-value.

EXAMPLE 3

ADDITIONAL EXAMPLE 3 Triangle PQR has vertices $P(3, 3)$, $Q(5, -1)$, and $R(1, -3)$. Find the vertices of triangle $P'Q'R'$ after a 90° counterclockwise rotation about the origin. Then graph the triangle and its image.

$P'(-3, 3)$, $Q'(1, 5)$, and $R'(3, 1)$

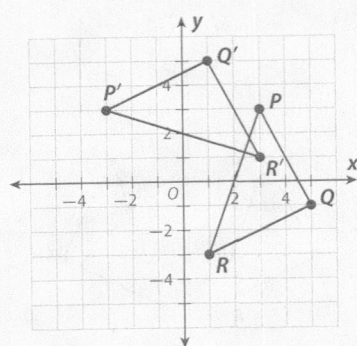

Interactive Whiteboard
Interactive example available online

Digital Teacher Resources

Go online to access all your lesson-level resources.

Differentiated Instruction
• Reteach
• Reading Strategies
• Success for English Learners
• Practice and Problem Solving A/B, C, D

Math on the Spot Videos

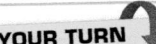
YOUR TURN

2. Triangle ABC has vertices $A(-2, 6)$, $B(0, 5)$, and $C(3, -1)$. Find the vertices of triangle $A'B'C'$ after a reflection across the x-axis.

$A'(-2, -6)$, $B'(0, -5)$, and $C'(3, 1)$

Personal Math Trainer
Online Assessment and Intervention
my.hrw.com

Math On the Spot
my.hrw.com

Algebraic Representations of Rotations

When points are rotated about the origin, the coordinates of the image can be found using the rules shown in the table.

Rotations	
90° clockwise	Multiply each x-coordinate by -1; then switch the x- and y-coordinates: $(x, y) \rightarrow (y, -x)$
90° counterclockwise	Multiply each y-coordinate by -1; then switch the x- and y-coordinates: $(x, y) \rightarrow (-y, x)$
180°	Multiply both coordinates by -1: $(x, y) \rightarrow (-x, -y)$

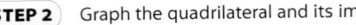
EXAMPLE 3

Quadrilateral $ABCD$ has vertices at $A(-4, 2)$, $B(-3, 4)$, $C(2, 3)$, and $D(0, 0)$. Find the vertices of quadrilateral $A'B'C'D'$ after a 90° clockwise rotation. Then graph the quadrilateral and its image.

STEP 1 Apply the rule to find the vertices of the image.

> Multiply the x-coordinate of each vertex by -1, and then switch the x- and y-coordinates.

Vertices of $ABCD$	Rule: $(y, -x)$	Vertices of $A'B'C'D'$
$A(-4, 2)$	$(2, -1 \cdot (-4))$	$A'(2, 4)$
$B(-3, 4)$	$(4, -1 \cdot (-3))$	$B'(4, 3)$
$C(2, 3)$	$(3, -1 \cdot 2)$	$C'(3, -2)$
$D(0, 0)$	$(0, -1 \cdot 0)$	$D'(0, 0)$

STEP 2 Graph the quadrilateral and its image.

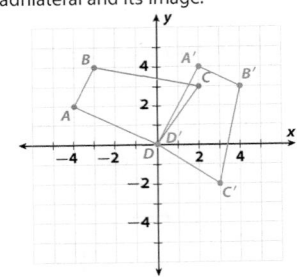

© Houghton Mifflin Harcourt Publishing Company

DIFFERENTIATE INSTRUCTION *Leveled Questions*

		EXAMPLE 3
AL	DOK 1 *Recall*	What is the transformation performed on quadrilateral $ABCD$? 90° rotation clockwise
OL	DOK 2 *Skills/Concepts*	In what quadrants would the image of quadrilateral $ABCD$ be in after a 90° rotation counterclockwise? Quadrants II and III
BL	DOK 3 *Strategic Thinking*	Is a 180° rotation the same as two 90° clockwise rotations? Is it the same as two 90° counterclockwise rotations? Justify your answer. Yes; two 90° clockwise rotations: $(x, y) \rightarrow (y, -x) \rightarrow (-x, -y)$; yes, two 90° counterclockwise rotations: $(x, y) \rightarrow (-y, x) \rightarrow (-x, -y)$.

LEVELED QUESTIONS: AL Approaching Level | **OL** On Level | **BL** Beyond Level

Reflect

3. **Communicate Mathematical Ideas** How would you find the vertices of an image if a figure were rotated 270° clockwise? Explain.

A 270° clockwise rotation is the same as a 90° counterclockwise rotation. Change the sign of the y-coordinate and switch the coordinates.

YOUR TURN

4. A triangle has vertices at $J(-2, -4)$, $K(1, 5)$, and $L(2, 2)$. What are the coordinates of the vertices of the image after the triangle is rotated 90° counterclockwise?

$J'(4, -2)$, $K'(-5, 1)$, and $L'(-2, 2)$

Personal Math Trainer
Online Assessment and Intervention
my.hrw.com

Guided Practice

1. Triangle XYZ has vertices $X(-3, -2)$, $Y(-1, 0)$, and $Z(1, -6)$. Find the vertices of triangle $X'Y'Z'$ after a translation of 6 units to the right. Then graph the triangle and its image. (Explore Activity Example 1)

$X'(3, -2)$, $Y'(5, 0)$, and $Z'(7, -6)$

2. Describe what happens to the x- and y-coordinates after a point is reflected across the x-axis. (Example 2)

The x-coordinate remains the same, while the y-coordinate changes sign.

3. Use the rule $(x, y) \rightarrow (y, -x)$ to graph the image of the triangle at right. Then describe the transformation. (Example 3)

The triangle is rotated 90° clockwise.

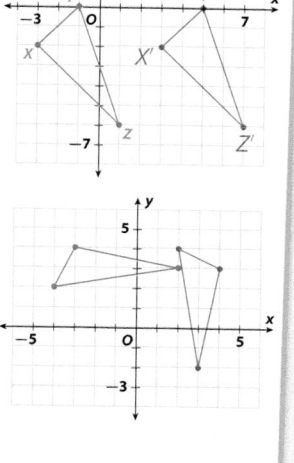

ESSENTIAL QUESTION CHECK-IN

4. How do the x- and y-coordinates change when a figure is translated right a units and down b units?

The x-coordinates increase by a, and the y-coordinates decrease by b.

© Houghton Mifflin Harcourt Publishing Company

Avoid Common Errors

It does not matter if students multiply the y-values by −1 before or after the coordinates are switched in **Exercise 4**, but multiplying by −1 first may prevent errors.

4 Elaborate

Talk About It

Summarize the Lesson

Ask: Is it possible to determine if a translation, reflection, or rotation occurred by examining the coordinates of the image and preimage? The rules for translations, reflections, and rotations affect coordinates of the ordered pair in distinct ways, so it is often possible to determine which transformation occurred.

Guided Practice

Engage with the Whiteboard

For **Exercise 2**, graph a point such as (2, 2) and reflect it across the x-axis on the grid for **Exercise 1**.

Avoid Common Errors

Exercise 3 Remind students that they must state the number of degrees, point of rotation, and the direction of the rotation.

DIFFERENTIATE INSTRUCTION *Intervention and Additional Support*

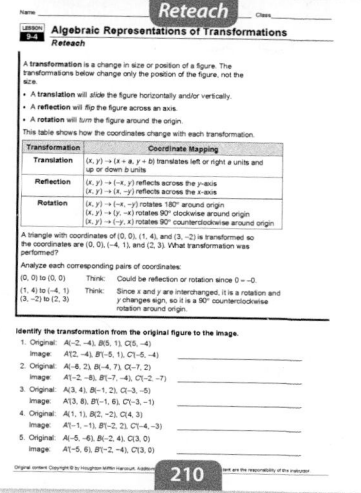

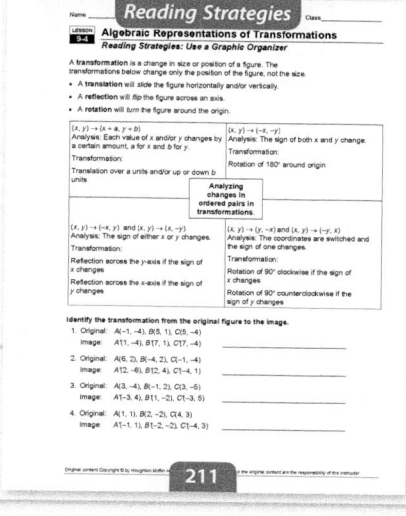

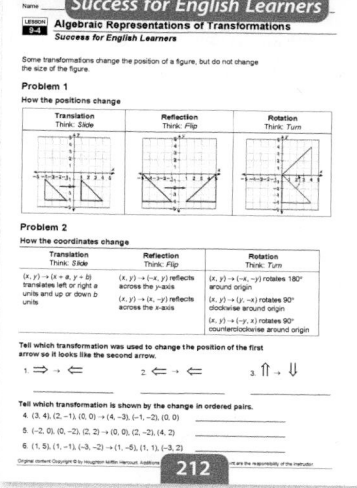

Personal Math Trainer
Daily Intervention
9.4 Homework

Pages shown are from *Differentiated Instruction*.
Also available online.

⏱ Pressed for Time

9.4 Differentiated Homework Assignments

AL Approaching Level	5–11, 14
OL On Level	7–12, 14
BL Beyond Level	11–15

*For **Below Level** students, assign Personal Math Trainer, Daily Intervention 9.4 Homework.*

Mathematical Processes	Exercises
MP.2 Reasoning	13, 15
MP.3 Logic	14
MP.6 Precision	5–9, 11–12
MP.7 Using Structure	10

Focus on Higher Order Thinking

Depth of Knowledge	Exercises
2 Skills/Concepts	5–12
3 Strategic Thinking H.O.T.	13–15

Write an algebraic rule to describe each transformation. Then describe the transformation.

5.

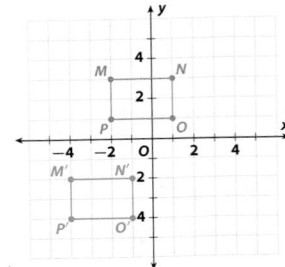

$(x, y) \rightarrow (x - 2, y - 5)$; translation of 2 units to the left and 5 units down

6.

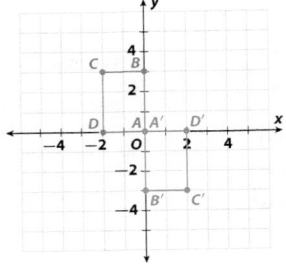

$(x, y) \rightarrow (-x, -y)$; rotation of 180°

7. Triangle *XYZ* has vertices *X*(6, −2.3), *Y*(7.5, 5), and *Z*(8, 4). When translated, *X′* has coordinates (2.8, −1.3). Write a rule to describe this transformation. Then find the coordinates of *Y′* and *Z′*.

$(x, y) \rightarrow (x - 3.2, y + 1)$; *Y′*(4.3, 6), *Z′*(4.8, 5)

8. Point *L* has coordinates (3, −5). The coordinates of point *L′* after a reflection are (−3, −5). Without graphing, tell which axis point *L* was reflected across. Explain your answer.

y-axis; when you reflect a point across the *y*-axis, the sign of the *x*-coordinate changes and the sign of the *y*-coordinate remains the same.

9. Use the rule $(x, y) \rightarrow (x - 2, y - 4)$ to graph the image of the rectangle. Then describe the transformation.

The rectangle is translated 2 units to the left and 4 units down.

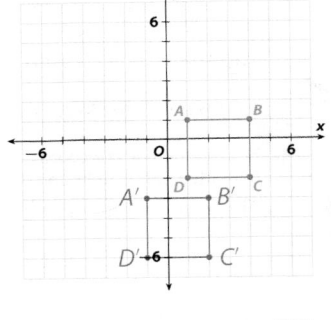

10. Parallelogram *ABCD* has vertices *A*(−2, −5½), *B*(−4, −5½), *C*(−3, −2), and *D*(−1, −2). Find the vertices of parallelogram *A′B′C′D′* after a translation of 2½ units down.

$A'(-2, -8)$, $B'(-4, -8)$, $C'\left(-3, -4\frac{1}{2}\right)$, and $D'\left(-1, -4\frac{1}{2}\right)$

© Houghton Mifflin Harcourt Publishing Company

DIFFERENTIATE INSTRUCTION *Leveled Homework/Practice*

Personal Math Trainer
• 9.4 Homework

Pages shown are from *Differentiated Instruction*. **Also available online.**

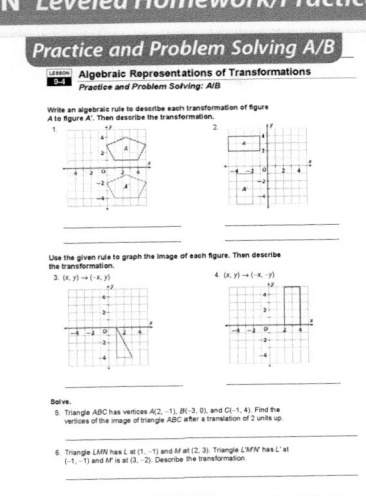

Practice and Problem Solving A/B

207

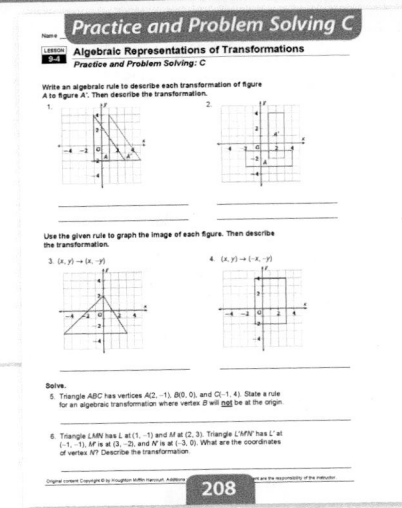

Practice and Problem Solving C

208

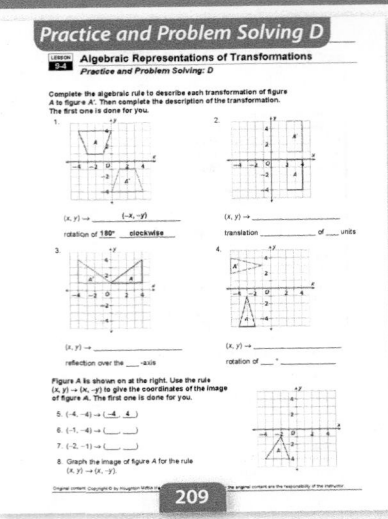

Practice and Problem Solving D

209

11. Alexandra drew the logo shown on half-inch graph paper. Write a rule that describes the translation Alexandra used to create the shadow on the letter A.

$$(x, y) \rightarrow (x + 0.5, y - 0.25)$$

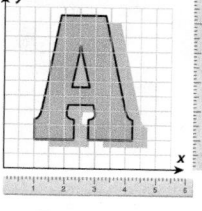

12. Kite *KLMN* has vertices at *K*(1, 3), *L*(2, 4), *M*(3, 3), and *N*(2, 0). After the kite is rotated, *K'* has coordinates (−3, 1). Describe the rotation, and include a rule in your description. Then find the coordinates of *L'*, *M'*, and *N'*.

90° counterclockwise; $(x, y) \rightarrow (-y, x)$; *L'*(−4, 2),

M'(−3, 3), and *N'*(0, 2)

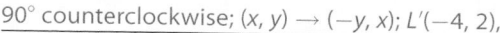 **H.O.T.** FOCUS ON HIGHER ORDER THINKING

13. **Make a Conjecture** Graph the triangle with vertices (−3, 4), (3, 4), and (−5, −5). Use the transformation (*y*, *x*) to graph its image.

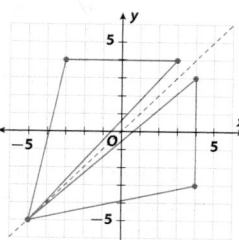

a. Which vertex of the image has the same coordinates as a vertex of the original figure? Explain why this is true.

(−5, −5); *x* and *y* are equal, so switching *x* and *y*

has no effect on the coordinates.

b. What is the equation of a line through the origin and this point?

$$y = x$$

c. Describe the transformation of the triangle.

The triangle is reflected across the line $y = x$.

14. **Critical Thinking** Mitchell says the point (0, 0) does not change when reflected across the *x*- or *y*-axis or when rotated about the origin. Do you agree with Mitchell? Explain why or why not.

Yes; reflecting across the *x*- or *y*-axis changes the sign of

the *y*- or *x*-coordinate; 0 cannot change signs. Rotating

about the origin doesn't change the origin, (0, 0).

15. **Analyze Relationships** Triangle *ABC* with vertices *A*(−2, −2), *B*(−3, 1), and *C*(1, 1) is translated by $(x, y) \rightarrow (x - 1, y + 3)$. Then the image, triangle *A'B'C'*, is translated by $(x, y) \rightarrow (x + 4, y - 1)$, resulting in *A"B"C"*.

a. Find the coordinates for the vertices of triangle *A"B"C"*.

A"(1, 0), *B"*(0, 3), and *C"*(4, 3)

b. Write a rule for one translation that maps triangle *ABC* to triangle *A"B"C"*.

$$(x, y) \rightarrow (x + 3, y + 2)$$

302 Unit 4

© Houghton Mifflin Harcourt Publishing Company

Work Area

✔ Quick Check

9.4 Lesson Quiz

Triangle *ABC* has vertices *A*(−4, 1), *B*(−2, 1), and *C*(−1, −2).

1. Find the coordinates of the vertices of triangle *A'B'C'* after a 90° clockwise rotation about the origin. *A'*(1, 4), *B'*(1, 2), and *C'*(−2, 1)

2. Find the coordinates of the vertices of triangle *A'B'C'* after triangle *ABC* is reflected across the *y*-axis. *A'*(4, 1), *B'*(2, 1), and *C'*(1, −2)

3. Find the coordinates of the vertices of triangle *A'B'C'* after triangle *ABC* is translated using the rule $(x, y) \rightarrow (x + 5, y - 3)$. Then describe the translation. *A'*(1, −2), *B'*(3, −2), and *C'*(4, −5); The triangle is translated 5 units to the right and 3 units down.

4. Point *M* has coordinates (3, −2). The coordinates of point *M'* after a single transformation are (−3, 2). Name a transformation that could have done this. Sample answers: translation 6 units left and 4 units up; rotation of 180°; reflection across the line $y = x$

Differentiate Instruction

IF a student misses more than one question, THEN

Differentiate Instruction:

• 9.4 Reteach

• Personal Math Trainer

Interactive Whiteboard
Interactive Lesson quiz available online

DIFFERENTIATE INSTRUCTION *Extend-the-Math Activity* PRE-AP

Activity Transform the square shown into five smaller, but equal squares, with only four cuts. The sum of the areas of the five smaller squares must total the area of the larger square. Pieces of the larger square, produced when the four cuts are made, can be rotated, reflected, or translated and combined to form the five smaller squares.

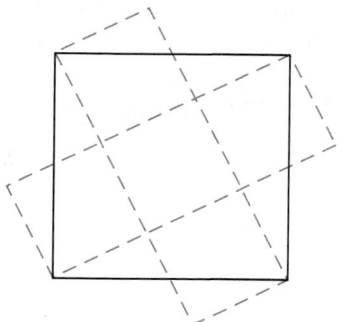

Lesson Support

Content Objective Students will learn how transformations can be used to verify that two figures have the same shape and size.

Professional Development

Integrate Mathematical Processes MP.6

This lesson provides an opportunity to address this Mathematical Process standard. It calls for students to attend to precision. Students pay close attention to the coordinates of the vertices of a figure in order to apply a given sequence of transformations and graph the resulting image. Each transformation must be carefully and precisely applied to obtain the desired outcome. Students also must pay close attention to the coordinates of the vertices of a figure and its images when determining the sequence of transformations that result in a figure being transformed into a particular image.

FOCUS

Building Background

Visualizing Math Have students create a pattern by using a series of rigid transformations. Ask them to draw a simple geometric figure, such as a triangle, quadrilateral, or pentagon. Then ask them to translate, reflect, or rotate the figure several times to create a pattern. It may be helpful to have students use graph paper. Encourage them to combine transformations. For example, they can create a slide image by reflecting and translating the figure successively. Discuss whether the figures in the pattern are congruent and why or why not.

COHERENCE

Learning Progressions

In this lesson, students are introduced to a formal definition of *congruence in the coordinate plane*. Important understandings for students include the following:

- **Combine transformations to create a congruent figure.**
- **Identify a sequence of transformations that create a congruent figure.**

Students conclude the work with rigid transformations that they have been studying throughout this module with this lesson. They understand that two figures in the plane are congruent if one can be transformed into the other using a series of rigid transformations. They also apply their experience with the transformations to describe a sequence that will transform one figure into the other in the coordinate plane.

RIGOR

Cluster Connections

This lesson provides an excellent opportunity to connect ideas in the cluster:

Understand congruence and similarity using physical models, transparencies, or geometry software.

Have students graph triangle *ABC* with vertices $A(-1, 1)$, $B(-3, 2)$, and $C(-3, 1)$. Then ask them to perform the following series of transformations, in order, on triangle *ABC*.

(1) Rotate the triangle 90° clockwise.

(2) Reflect the rotated triangle over the *x*-axis.

(3) Translate the reflected triangle 3 units left and 1 unit up.

What are the coordinates of the vertices of the final image?

$(-2, 0), (-1, -2), (-2, -3)$

Language Support ELL

Language Objective Students will show how transformations can be used to verify that two figures have the same shape and size.

Leveled Strategies for English Learners ELL

Emerging
When proficiency in English is limited, having students use their primary language in peer-to-peer discussion encourages higher-level thinking. Have students check the glossary, review the definition of *congruent figures*, and then illustrate and label an example on graph paper.

Expanding
Have students at this level of English proficiency work in pairs to review the definition of *congruent figures* and then illustrate examples of congruent figures with different transformations on graph paper.

Bridging
Have students at this level of English proficiency work in pairs to review and rephrase the definition of *congruent figures* and then illustrate examples of congruent figures with different transformations on graph paper.

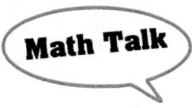

Write out and model for students a sentence frame to begin their answer.

The sequence of transformations must include a rotation when _____.

EXPLORE ACTIVITY

Combining Transformations

Apply the indicated series of transformations to the triangle. Each transformation is applied to the image of the previous transformation, not the original figure. Label each image with the letter of the transformation applied.

A Reflection across the *x*-axis

B $(x, y) \rightarrow (x - 3, y)$

C Reflection across the *y*-axis

D $(x, y) \rightarrow (x, y + 4)$

E Rotation 90° clockwise around the origin

F Compare the size and shape of the final image to that of the original figure.

They have the same size and shape, just a different

orientation.

Linguistic Support ELL

Academic/Content Vocabulary
This lesson opens with an Explore Activity in which students are provided instructions for combining transformations. Understanding detailed instructions like these requires a high level of English proficiency. To assure that English learners understand the details described, you may want to form groups of students of mixed English proficiency levels to solve problems. Provide them with sentence frames to support their responses. Encourage students to use visuals and check each step as information is shared.

Rules and Patterns
When English learners read the instructions on tests and in textbooks, they encounter the imperative form, or command form. For example, the instructions might use the word *complete*, which is a command prompting them to finish out the exercise. Among the verbs in the imperative form in this lesson are *apply, label, compare, identify, graph*, and *describe*. Have English learners add these to their word journals for future reference.

Congruent Figures

1 Engage

? ESSENTIAL QUESTION

What is the connection between transformations and figures that have the same shape and size?

Sample answer: After a sequence of translations, reflections, and rotations, the image is always the same shape and size as the preimage. (The image and preimage are congruent.)

Motivate the Lesson
Ask: What effect will a combination of rotations, translations, and/or reflections have on a triangle's size and shape? Begin the Explore Activity to find out.

2 Explore

EXPLORE ACTIVITY

Engage with the Whiteboard
Color coding the corresponding sides or labeling the vertices of the triangle and its images will help students better visualize the movement of the triangle.

LESSON
9.5 Congruent Figures

8.4.9.5
Students will determine the connection between transformations and figures that have the same shape and size.

? ESSENTIAL QUESTION 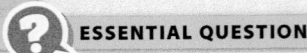 What is the connection between transformations and figures that have the same shape and size?

EXPLORE ACTIVITY

Combining Transformations

Apply the indicated series of transformations to the triangle. Each transformation is applied to the image of the previous transformation, not the original figure. Label each image with the letter of the transformation applied.

A Reflection across the x-axis

B $(x, y) \rightarrow (x - 3, y)$

C Reflection across the y-axis

D $(x, y) \rightarrow (x, y + 4)$

E Rotation 90° clockwise around the origin

F Compare the size and shape of the final image to that of the original figure.

They have the same size and shape, just a different orientation.

Reflect

1. Which transformation(s) change the orientation of figures? Which do not?

Reflections and rotations; translations

2. **Make a Conjecture** Two figures have the same size and shape. What does this indicate about the figures?

One figure is the image of the other, and there is a sequence of transformations that will transform one figure into the other.

© Houghton Mifflin Harcourt Publishing Company

Lesson 9.5 **303**

DIFFERENTIATE INSTRUCTION *Leveled Questions*

	EXPLORE ACTIVITY
AL **DOK 1** *Recall*	In Steps A–E, which steps do change and which do not change the orientation? Steps A, C, E do; Steps B, D do not change the orientation.
OL **DOK 2** *Skills/Concepts*	What one transformation is the same as a reflection across the x- and y-axis? a rotation of 180°
BL **DOK 3** *Strategic Thinking*	Is a reflection across the line $y = -x$ always equivalent to a rotation of 180° about the origin? Explain. No; consider *ABCD*, with vertices $A(1, 2)$, $B(5, 2)$, $C(5, 1)$ and $D(1, 1)$. A rotation of 180° about the origin has image vertices $A'(-1, -2)$, $B'(-5, -2)$, $C'(-5, -1)$, $D'(-1, -1)$ but a reflection across the line $y = -x$ has image vertices $A'(-2, -1)$, $B'(-2, -5)$, $C'(-1, -5)$, and $D'(-1, -1)$.

LEVELED QUESTIONS: **AL** Approaching Level | **OL** On Level | **BL** Beyond Level

Math On the Spot
my.hrw.com

Congruent Figures

Recall that segments and their images have the same length and angles and their images have the same measure under a translation, reflection, or rotation. Two figures are said to be **congruent** if one can be obtained from the other by a sequence of translations, reflections, and rotations. Congruent figures have the same size and shape.

When you are told that two figures are congruent, there must be a sequence of translations, reflections, and/or rotations that transforms one into the other.

EXAMPLE 1

A Identify a sequence of transformations that will transform figure A into figure B.

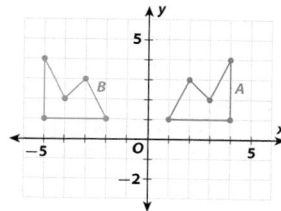

To transform figure A into figure B, you need to reflect it over the y-axis and translate one unit to the left. A sequence of transformations that will accomplish this is $(x, y) \rightarrow (-x, y)$ and $(x, y) \rightarrow (x - 1, y)$.

B Identify a sequence of transformations that will transform figure B into figure C.

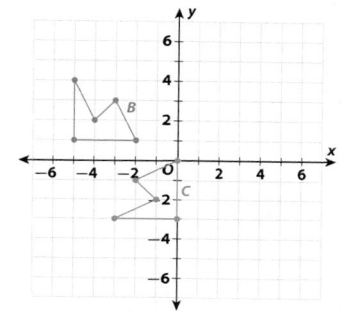

Any sequence of transformations that changes figure B into figure C will need to include a rotation. A 90° counterclockwise rotation around the origin would result in the figure being oriented as figure C.

However, the rotated figure would be 2 units below and 1 unit to the left of where figure C is. You would need to translate the rotated figure up 2 units and right 1 unit.

In both cases, the image is turned sideways from the original figure. Only a rotation will do this.

Math Talk
Mathematical Processes

How do you know that the sequence of transformations in Parts B and C must include a rotation?

304 Unit 4

© Houghton Mifflin Harcourt Publishing Company

Animated Math

Explore Transformations
Using an interactive model, students explore the effect of translations, reflections, and rotations.

my.hrw.com

3 Explain

EXAMPLE 1

Focus on Communication
In Part C, encourage students to suggest other approaches that might map figure D on to figure E. For example, figure D could have been reflected over the x-axis, rotated 90° clockwise about the origin, and translated 1 unit down. The algebraic sequence of transformations is $(x, y) \rightarrow (-x, y)$, $(x, y) \rightarrow (y, -x)$, $(x, y) \rightarrow (x, y - 1)$.

ADDITIONAL EXAMPLE 1

A Identify a sequence of transformations that will transform figure G into figure H.

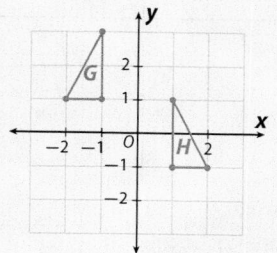

Sample answer: $(x, y) \rightarrow (-x, y)$, $(x, y) \rightarrow (x, y - 2)$

(Continued on page 305)

Interactive Whiteboard
Interactive example available online

	EXAMPLE 1
AL **DOK 1** *Recall*	What two transformations are performed in Part A? in Part B? Reflection over the y-axis and translation; rotation 90°counterclockwise and translation
OL **DOK 2** *Skills/Concepts*	Is there a sequence of transformations that will transform Figure A into Figure B if you perform the translation first? Explain. Yes, a translation of 1 unit to the right and then reflection across the y-axis
BL **DOK 3** *Strategic Thinking*	Does it matter which transformation is done first in the sequence of transformations in Part C? No; a translation 6 units down, followed by a 90° clockwise rotation about the origin will have the same result.

TEACHER TO TEACHER

Multiple Representations Provide students with 6 congruent equilateral triangles. Have students arrange the triangles to form a hexagon. Students should then draw a simple but colorful design on one of the triangles and then reflect that design around the hexagon 5 times onto the other triangles. Explain that their final design will be a kaleidoscope image.

EXAMPLE 1 (continued)

ADDITIONAL EXAMPLE 1 *continued*

B Identify a sequence of transformations that will transform figure *J* into figure *K*.

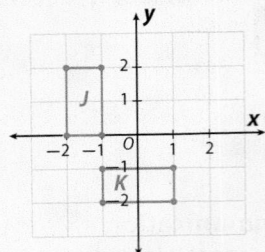

Sample answer: $(x, y) \rightarrow (-y, x)$, $(x, y) \rightarrow (x + 1, y)$

C Identify a sequence of transformations that will transform figure *L* into figure *M*.

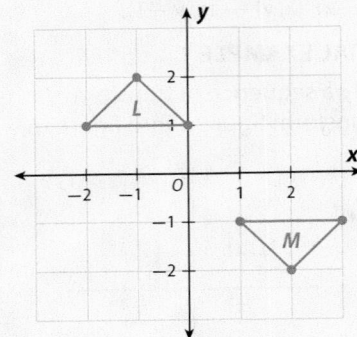

Sample answer: $(x, y) \rightarrow (-x, y)$, $(x, y) \rightarrow (x, -y)$, $(x, y) \rightarrow (x + 1, y)$

 Interactive Whiteboard
Interactive example available online

YOUR TURN   MP.5

Avoid Common Errors
If students cannot visualize the sequence of transformations, suggest they use a cut-out paper triangle the same size and shape as figure *A* that they can rotate and translate on the coordinate grid.

Digital Teacher Resources

Go online to access all your lesson-level resources.

Differentiated Instruction
- Reteach
- Reading Strategies
- Success for English Learners
- Practice and Problem Solving A/B, C, D

Math on the Spot Videos

The sequence of transformations is a 90° counterclockwise rotation about the origin, $(x, y) \rightarrow (-y, x)$, followed by $(x, y) \rightarrow (x + 1, y + 2)$.

C Identify a sequence of transformations that will transform figure *D* into figure *E*.

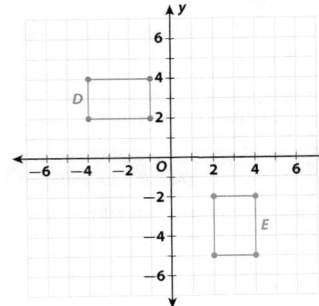

A sequence of transformations that changes figure *D* to figure *E* will need to include a rotation. A 90° clockwise rotation around the origin would result in the figure being oriented as figure *E*.

However, the rotated figure would be 6 units above where figure *E* is. You would need to translate the rotated figure down 6 units.

The sequence of transformations is a 90° clockwise rotation about the origin, $(x, y) \rightarrow (y, -x)$, followed by $(x, y) \rightarrow (x, y - 6)$.

YOUR TURN

3. Identify a sequence of transformations that will transform figure *A* into figure *B*.

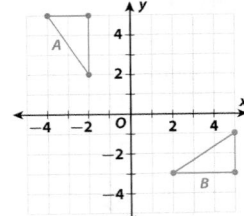

Rotation 90° clockwise about origin, translation 5 units down; $(x, y) \rightarrow (y, -x)$, $(x, y) \rightarrow (x, y - 5)$

Personal Math Trainer
Online Assessment and Intervention
my.hrw.com

© Houghton Mifflin Harcourt Publishing Company

1. Apply the indicated series of transformations to the rectangle. Each transformation is applied to the image of the previous transformation, not the original figure. Label each image with the letter of the transformation applied. *(Explore Activity)*

   a. Reflection across the *y*-axis

   b. Rotation 90° clockwise around the origin

   c. $(x, y) \rightarrow (x - 2, y)$

   d. Rotation 90° counterclockwise around the origin

   e. $(x, y) \rightarrow (x - 7, y - 2)$

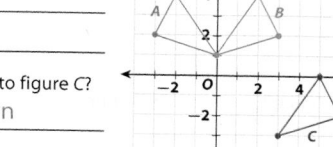

Identify a sequence of transformations that will transform figure *A* into figure *C*. *(Example 1)*

2. What transformation is used to transform figure *A* into figure *B*?

   reflection across the *y*-axis
   _____

3. What transformation is used to transform figure *B* into figure *C*?

   translation 3 units right and 4 units down
   _____

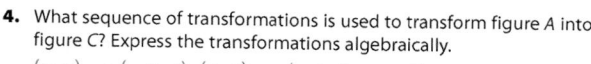

4. What sequence of transformations is used to transform figure *A* into figure *C*? Express the transformations algebraically.

   $(x, y) \rightarrow (-x, y), (x, y) \rightarrow (x + 3, y - 4)$
   _____

5. **Vocabulary** What does it mean for two figures to be congruent?

   The figures have the same size and the same shape.
   _____

? ESSENTIAL QUESTION CHECK-IN

6. After a sequence of translations, reflections, and rotations, what is true about the first figure and the final figure?

   They have the same size and the same shape. (They are congruent.)
   _____

© Houghton Mifflin Harcourt Publishing Company

4 Elaborate

Talk About It

Summarize the Lesson

Ask: When two figures have different orientations, what clues help you decide which transformations were performed in the sequence of transformations? In order to get a turned image, a rotation must have occurred. In order to get a mirror image, a reflection must have occurred.

Guided Practice

Engage with the Whiteboard

For **Exercise 1**, have five volunteers take turns drawing the indicated series of transformations on the coordinate grid provided.

Avoid Common Errors

• **Exercise 2** Students might think a rotation was used to transform figure *A* into figure *B*. Suggest students use a paper cut-out of triangle *A* and actually rotate it about point (0, 2) to see that the orientation of figure *B* is not right for the transformation to have been a rotation.

• **Exercise 4** Before trying to write the algebraic sequence of transformations used, suggest that students label figures *A*, *B*, and *C* with the ordered pairs for each of the vertices. Then, analyze the pairs to understand the changes to the *x* and *y* values.

DIFFERENTIATE INSTRUCTION *Intervention and Additional Support*

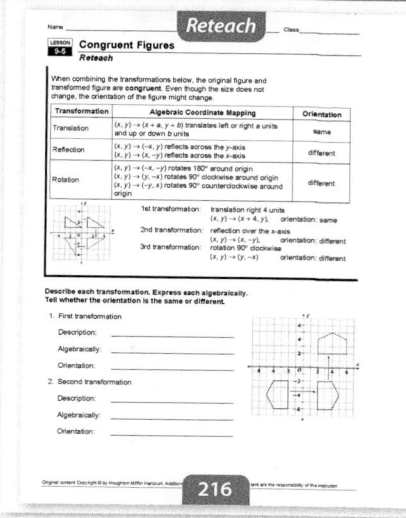

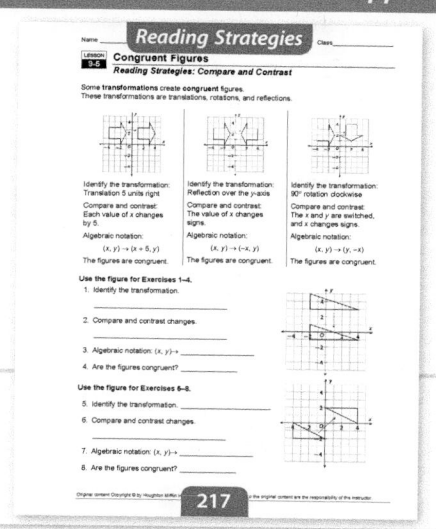

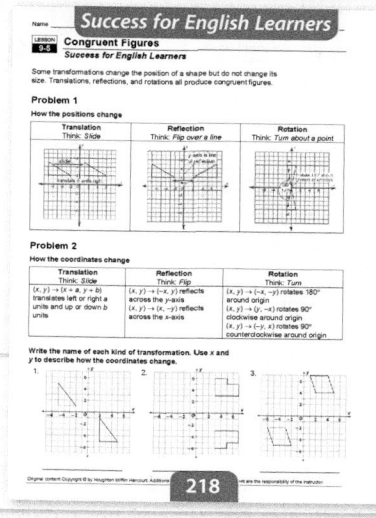

Personal Math Trainer
Daily Intervention
9.5 Homework

Pages shown are from *Differentiated Instruction*. **Also available online.**

5 Evaluate

Independent Practice

⏱ **Pressed for Time**

9.5 Differentiated Homework Assignments

(AL) **Approaching Level** 7–11, 13

(OL) **On Level** 9–12, 13

(BL) **Beyond Level** 11–14

*For **Below Level** students, assign Personal Math Trainer, Daily Intervention 9.5 Homework.*

Mathematical Processes	Exercises
MP.2 Reasoning	14
MP.3 Logic	12–13
MP.4 Modeling	7–11

Focus on Higher Order Thinking

Depth of Knowledge	Exercises
1 Recall of Information	7–10
2 Skills/Concepts	11–12
3 Strategic Thinking H.O.T.	13–14

9.5 Independent Practice

Personal Math Trainer
Online Assessment and Intervention
my.hrw.com

For each given figure *A*, graph figures *B* and *C* using the given sequence of transformations. State whether figures *A* and *C* have the same or different orientation.

7.

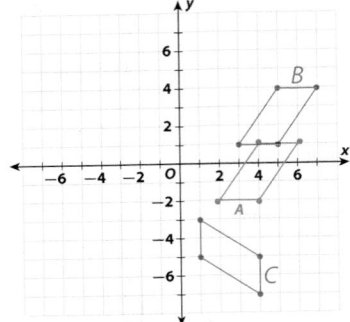

Figure *B*: a translation of 1 unit to the right and 3 units up

Figure *C*: a 90° clockwise rotation around the origin

Different orientation

8.

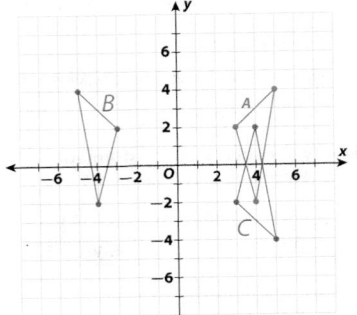

Figure *B*: a reflection across the *y*-axis

Figure *C*: a 180° rotation around the origin

Different orientation

9.

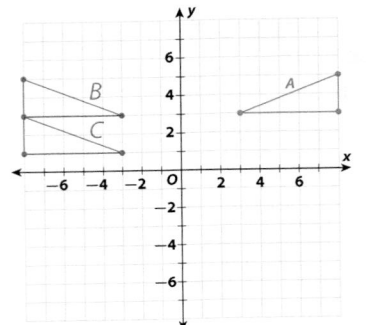

Figure *B*: a reflection across the *y*-axis

Figure *C*: a translation 2 units down

Different orientation

10.

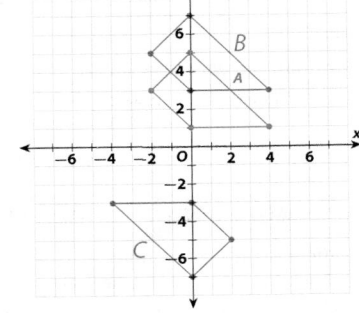

Figure *B*: a translation 2 units up

Figure *C*: a rotation of 180° around the origin

Different orientation

© Houghton Mifflin Harcourt Publishing Company

Lesson 9.5 **307**

DIFFERENTIATE INSTRUCTION *Leveled Homework/Practice*

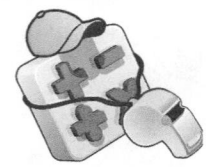

Personal Math Trainer
• 9.5 Homework

Pages shown are from *Differentiated Instruction.* **Also available online.**

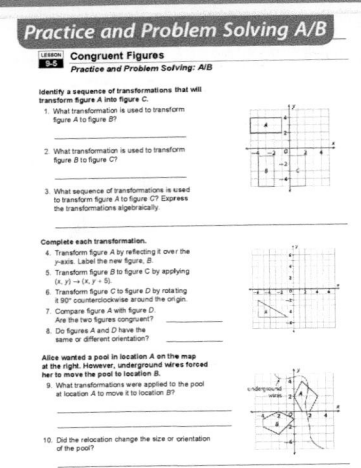

Practice and Problem Solving A/B

213

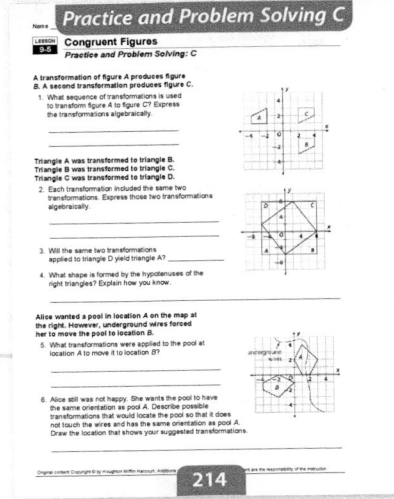

Practice and Problem Solving C

214

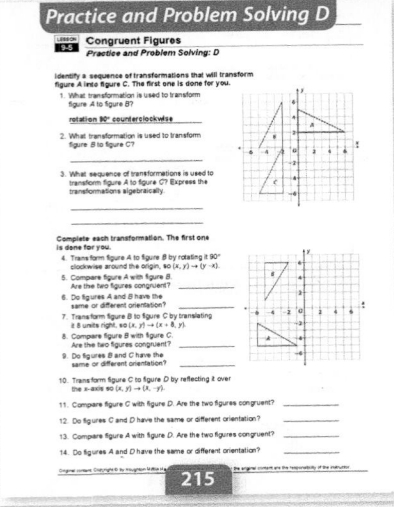

Practice and Problem Solving D

215

11. Represent Real-World Problems A city planner wanted to place the new town library at site *A*. The mayor thought that it would be better at site *B*. What transformations were applied to the building at site *A* to relocate the building to site *B*? Did the mayor change the size or orientation of the library?

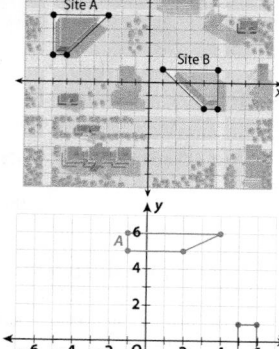

Sample answer: translation 2 units right and

4 units down, reflection across *y*-axis; size: no;

orientation: yes

12. Persevere in Problem Solving Find a sequence of three transformations that can be used to obtain figure *D* from figure *A*. Graph the figures *B* and *C* that are created by the transformations.

Sample answer: Figure *B*: rotation 90° clockwise

around origin; figure *C*: translation 4 units left

and 2 units down; figure *D*: reflection across

y-axis

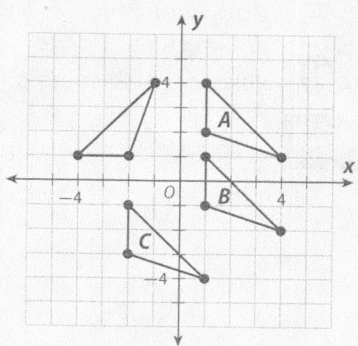

H.O.T. FOCUS ON HIGHER ORDER THINKING

13. Counterexamples The Commutative Properties for Addition and Multiplication state that the order of two numbers being added or multiplied does not change the sum or product. Are translations and rotations commutative? If not, give a counterexample.

No; the point (1, 2), translated 2 units to the right,

becomes (3, 2), then rotated 90° around the origin it

becomes (2, −3). The point (1, 2) rotated 90° around the

origin becomes (2, −1), then translated 2 units to the

right it becomes (4, −1), which is not the same.

14. Multiple Representations For each representation, describe a possible sequence of transformations.

a. $(x, y) \rightarrow (-x - 2, y + 1)$

Sample answer: translation 2 units right and 1 unit

up, reflection across *y*-axis

b. $(x, y) \rightarrow (y, -x - 3)$

Sample answer: rotation 90° clockwise around the

origin, translation 3 units down

308 Unit 4

Work Area

© Houghton Mifflin Harcourt Publishing Company

DIFFERENTIATE INSTRUCTION *Extend-the-Math Activity* **PRE-AP**

Activity A translation followed by a reflection about a line that is parallel to the line of translation is called a glide reflection. The heart shown below has been glided and reflected twice.

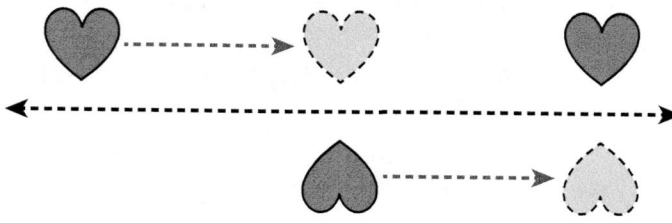

Draw a horizontal line on a piece of paper, choose a shape, and make a glide reflection pattern.

 Quick Check

9.5 Lesson Quiz

1. On a coordinate grid, graph a triangle with its vertices at $(-2, 1)$, $(-4, 1)$, and $(-1, 4)$. Then apply the indicated series of transformations to the triangle. Each transformation is applied to the image of the previous transformation. Label each image with the letter of the transformation applied.

   A Rotation 90° clockwise around the origin

   B $(x, y) \rightarrow (x, y - 3)$

   C $(x, y) \rightarrow (x - 3, y - 2)$

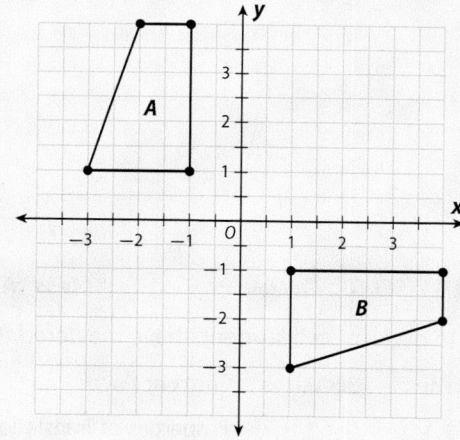

2. Identify a sequence of transformations that will transform figure *A* into figure *B*.

Reflection across the *y*-axis, rotation 90° clockwise about the origin; $(x, y) \rightarrow (-x, y)$, $(x, y) \rightarrow (y, -x)$

Differentiate Instruction

IF a student misses more than one question, THEN

Differentiate Instruction:

• 9.5 Reteach

• Personal Math Trainer

Interactive Whiteboard

Interactive Lesson quiz available online

Congruent Figures **308**

Ready to Go On?

Assess Mastery

Access *Ready to Go On?* assessment online, and receive instant scoring, feedback, and customized intervention or enrichment.

Personal Math Trainer

Online Assessment and Intervention

• Module 9 Posttest

Additional Resources

Digital Teacher Resources

Go online for module-level resources.

Assessment Resources
• Module 9 Quiz: B, p.47
• Module 9 Quiz: D, p.49

my.hrw.com

Ready to Go On?

Personal Math Trainer
Online Assessment and Intervention
my.hrw.com

9.1–9.3 Properties of Translations, Reflections, and Rotations

1. Graph the image of triangle ABC after a translation of 6 units to the right and 4 units down. Label the vertices of the image A′, B′, and C′.

2. On the same coordinate grid, graph the image of triangle ABC after a reflection across the x-axis. Label the vertices of the image A″, B″, and C″.

3. Graph the image of HIJK after it is rotated 180° about the origin. Label the vertices of the image H′I′J′K′.

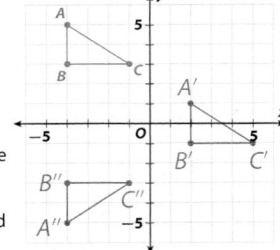

9.4 Algebraic Representations of Transformations

4. A triangle has vertices at (2, 3), (−2, 2), and (−3, 5). What are the coordinates of the vertices of the image after the translation $(x, y) \rightarrow (x + 4, y − 3)$?

   <u>(6, 0), (2, −1), and (1, 2)</u>

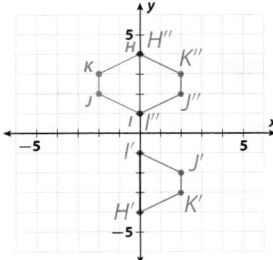

9.5 Congruent Figures

5. **Vocabulary** Translations, reflections, and rotations produce a figure that is <u> congruent </u> to the original figure.

6. Use the coordinate grid for Exercise 3. Reflect H′I′J′K′ over the y-axis, then rotate it 180° about the origin. Label the new figure H″I″J″K″.

? ESSENTIAL QUESTION

7. How can you use transformations to solve real-world problems?

   <u>Sample answer: You can use transformations to</u>
   <u>determine movement from one location to another.</u>

© Houghton Mifflin Harcourt Publishing Company

READY TO GO ON? *Diagnostic Assessment*

RtI Response to Intervention

Use to determine if students have mastered the concepts covered in this module.

Lesson	Exercises	Content Focus	Review with *Differentiated Instruction*
9.1	1	Properties of Translations	9.1 Reteach, Reading Strategies, Success for English Learners
9.2	2	Properties of Reflections	9.2 Reteach, Reading Strategies, Success for English Learners
9.3	3	Properties of Rotations	9.3 Reteach, Reading Strategies, Success for English Learners
9.4	4	Algebraic Representations of Transformations	9.4 Reteach, Reading Strategies, Success for English Learners
9.5	5–6	Congruent Figures	9.5 Reteach, Reading Strategies, Success for English Learners

Personal Math Trainer
Online Assessment and Intervention
my.hrw.com

Selected Response

1. What would be the orientation of the figure L after a translation of 8 units to the right and 3 units up?

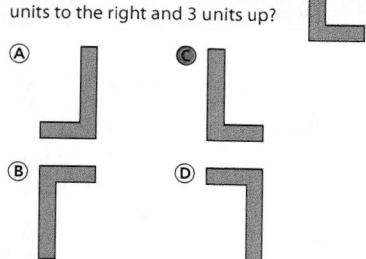

Ⓐ   Ⓒ

Ⓑ   Ⓓ

2. Figure A is reflected over the *y*-axis and then lowered 6 units. Which sequence describes these transformations?

Ⓐ $(x, y) \rightarrow (x, -y)$ and $(x, y) \rightarrow (x, y - 6)$

Ⓑ $(x, y) \rightarrow (-x, y)$ and $(x, y) \rightarrow (x, y - 6)$

Ⓒ $(x, y) \rightarrow (x, -y)$ and $(x, y) \rightarrow (x - 6, y)$

Ⓓ $(x, y) \rightarrow (-x, y)$ and $(x, y) \rightarrow (x - 6, y)$

3. What quadrant would the triangle be in after a rotation of 90° counterclockwise about the origin?

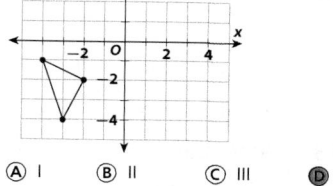

Ⓐ I   Ⓑ II   Ⓒ III   Ⓓ IV

4. Which rational number is greater than $-3\frac{1}{3}$ but less than $-\frac{4}{5}$?

Ⓐ -0.4 Ⓒ -0.19

Ⓑ $-\frac{9}{7}$ Ⓓ $-\frac{22}{5}$

5. Which of the following is **not** true of a trapezoid that has been reflected across the *x*-axis?

Ⓐ The new trapezoid is the same size as the original trapezoid.

Ⓑ The new trapezoid is the same shape as the original trapezoid.

Ⓒ The new trapezoid is in the same orientation as the original trapezoid.

Ⓓ The *x*-coordinates of the new trapezoid are the same as the *x*-coordinates of the original trapezoid.

6. A triangle with coordinates (6, 4), (2, −1), and (−3, 5) is translated 4 units left and rotated 180° about the origin. What are the coordinates of its image?

Ⓐ (2, 4), (−2, −1), (−7, 5)

Ⓑ (4, 6), (−1, 2), (5, −3)

Ⓒ (4, −2), (−1, 2), (5, 7)

Ⓓ (−2, −4), (2, 1), (7, −5)

Mini-Task

7. A rectangle with vertices (3, −2), (3, −4), (7, −2), (7, −4) is reflected across the *x*-axis and then rotated 90° counterclockwise.

a. In what quadrant does the image lie?

II

b. What are the vertices of the image?

(−2, 3), (−4, 3), (−2, 7), (−4, 7)

c. What other transformations produce the same image?

Reflect over *y*-axis, then rotate 90° clockwise about origin

310 Unit 4

© Houghton Mifflin Harcourt Publishing Company

Preparing for High Stakes Tests

Assessment Readiness Tip

Students can sketch a diagram to help represent information from a problem.

- **Item 5** Students can sketch a trapezoid with a pair of coordinate axes and then reflect the trapezoid across the *x*-axis to help them visualize the problem.

- **Item 6** Students can use a coordinate plane to plot the points in item 6. It will help them to visualize the initial orientation of the triangle and predict where the image will be located.

Avoid Common Errors

- **Item 3** Some students have difficulty determining which way is clockwise and which is counterclockwise. Remind the students to glance at an analog clock, if one is available in the room, to remind them which way is which by following the numbers forward for clockwise, or backward for counterclockwise. They should also label the four quadrants of the coordinate plane before answering the question.

- **Item 5** Students may miss the word not in this question, and instead pick the first thing they see as true instead of looking for the false statement. Remind the students to read carefully, and highlight, underline, or circle key words like *not*, so they can better approach the question.

Items	Grade 8 Lessons	Mathematical Processes
1	9.1	MP.7
2	9.2	MP.4
3	9.3	MP.4
4*	1.3	MP.2
5	9.5	MP.7
6	9.4	MP.4
7	9.4	MP.4

* Item integrates mixed review concepts from previous modules or a previous course.

DIFFERENTIATE ASSESSMENT

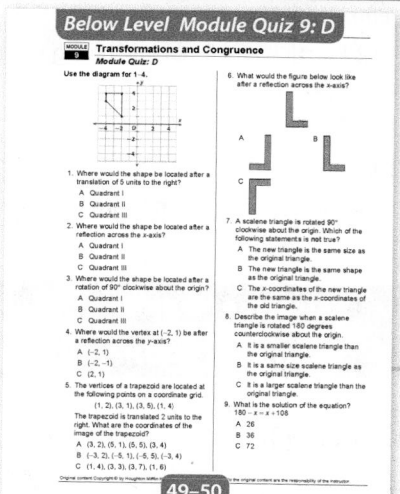

Below Level Module Quiz 9: D

49–50

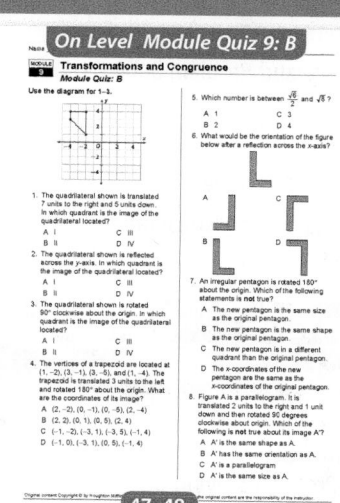

On Level Module Quiz 9: B

47–48

Personal Math Trainer
Module 9 Assessment Readiness

Pages shown are from *Assessment Resources.* **Also available online.**

Module At A Glance

Module Essential Question: How can you use dilations and similarity to solve real-world problems?

MODULE 10 | Transformations and Similarity

Lessons at A Glance	Lesson 10.1 Properties of Dilations	Lesson 10.2 Algebraic Representations of Dilations	Lesson 10.3 Similar Figures
	Pg. T315A	Pg. T321A	Pg. T327A
Essential Question	How do you describe the properties of dilations?	How can you describe the effect of a dilation on coordinates using an algebraic representation?	What is the connection between transformations and the orientations of similar figures?
Objective	Students will describe the properties of dilations.	Students will describe the effect of a dilation on coordinates using an algebraic representation.	Students will describe the connection between transformations and the orientations of similar figures.
Vocabulary	center of dilation, dilation, enlargement, reduction, scale factor		similar
Go online for all your module resources my.hrw.com	10.1 *i*Student Edition 10.1 *i*Teacher Edition 10.1 *e*Student Edition 🐾 Personal Math Trainer 📺 Math on the Spot Videos 🖩 Animated Math	10.2 *i*Student Edition 10.2 *i*Teacher Edition 10.2 *e*Student Edition 🐾 Personal Math Trainer 📺 Math on the Spot Videos	10.3 *i*Student Edition 10.3 *i*Teacher Edition 10.3 *e*Student Edition 🐾 Personal Math Trainer 📺 Math on the Spot Videos
Print Resources	**10.1 Student Edition:** Lesson *Differentiated Instruction* 10.1 Practice and Problem Solving A/B, C, and D 10.1 Reteach 10.1 Reading Strategies 10.1 Success for English Learners	**10.2 Student Edition:** Lesson *Differentiated Instruction* 10.2 Practice and Problem Solving A/B, C, and D 10.2 Reteach 10.2 Reading Strategies 10.2 Success for English Learners	**10.3 Student Edition:** Lesson *Differentiated Instruction* 10.3 Practice and Problem Solving A/B, C, and D 10.3 Reteach 10.3 Reading Strategies 10.3 Success for English Learners

RtI

Response to Intervention

Before the Module	During the Lesson	After the Module
Are You Ready	**Guided/Independent Practice**	**Ready to Go On?**
• Prerequisite Skills Activities • Personal Math Trainer	• Reteach • Personal Math Trainer • Practice and Problem Solving D	• Reteach • Personal Math Trainer

Teacher Notes

Check It Out!

Activity	Math on the Spot Videos	Animated Math
Copy-Cat After Lesson 10.3	One for every Example in every Lesson	During Lesson 10.1

Transformations and Similarity

Real-World Video Viewing Guide

After students have watched the video, discuss the following:

- How are dilations used to create murals?
- How do the distances and sizes change in the image Luis is creating? They increase proportionally.

Professional Development Video

Author Juli Dixon models successful teaching practices as she explores the concept of transformations and similarity in an actual eighth-grade classroom.

Transformations and Similarity

 ESSENTIAL QUESTION

How can you use dilations and similarity to solve real-world problems?

You can use similarity to analyze how real-world objects are affected when they undergo dilations.

LESSON 10.1
Properties of Dilations

LESSON 10.2
Algebraic Representations of Dilations

LESSON 10.3
Similar Figures

© Houghton Mifflin Harcourt Publishing Company

Real-World Video

To plan a mural, the artist first makes a smaller drawing showing what the mural will look like. Then the image is enlarged by a scale factor on the mural canvas. This enlargement is called a dilation.

my.hrw.com

GO DIGITAL
my.hrw.com

my.hrw.com	**Math On the Spot**	**Animated Math**	**Personal Math Trainer**
Go digital with your write-in student edition, accessible on any device.	Scan with your smart phone to jump directly to the online edition, video tutor, and more.	Interactively explore key concepts to see how math works.	Get immediate feedback and help as you work through practice sets.

311

TEACHER ONLINE RESOURCES

 ONLINE TEACHER EDITION Access a full suite of teaching resources online—plan, present, and manage classes and assignments.

 INTERACTIVE WHITEBOARDS Engage students with interactive whiteboard-ready examples and a lesson quiz for each lesson.

 MY SMART PLANNER Easily plan your classes and access all your resources online.

 PERSONAL MATH TRAINER: Online Assessment and Intervention Assign automatically graded homework, quizzes, tests, and intervention activities. Prepare your students for standardized tests in short-answer and multiple-choice formats.

Reading Start-Up

Visualize Vocabulary

Use the ✔ words to complete the graphic organizer.
You will put one word in each rectangle.

```
┌──────────────────┐        ┌──────────────────┐
│ The four regions │        │ The point where  │
│ on a coordinate  │        │ the axes inter-  │
│ plane.           │        │ sect to form the │
│                  │        │ coordinate plane.│
│   quadrants      │        │    origin        │
└──────────────────┘        └──────────────────┘
         ╲                      ╱
          ┌─────────────────────┐
          │  Reviewing the      │
          │  Coordinate Plane   │
          └─────────────────────┘
         ╱                      ╲
┌──────────────────┐        ┌──────────────────┐
│ The horizontal   │        │ The vertical axis│
│ axis of a coord- │        │ of a coordinate  │
│ inate plane.     │        │ plane.           │
│                  │        │                  │
│    x-axis        │        │    y-axis        │
└──────────────────┘        └──────────────────┘
```

Understand Vocabulary

Complete the sentences using the preview words.

1. A figure larger than the original, produced through dilation, is
   an ___enlargement___.

2. A figure smaller than the original, produced through dilation, is
   a ___reduction___.

Vocabulary

Review Words
coordinate plane *(plano cartesiano)*
image *(imagen)*
✔ origin *(origen)*
preimage *(imagen original)*
✔ quadrants *(cuadrante)*
ratio *(razón)*
scale *(escala)*
✔ x-axis *(eje x)*
✔ y-axis *(eje y)*

Preview Words
center of dilation *(centro de dilatación)*
dilation *(dilatación)*
enlargement *(agrandamiento)*
reduction *(reducción)*
scale factor *(factor de escala)*
similar *(similar)*

Active Reading

Key-Term Fold Before beginning the module, create a key-term fold to help you learn the vocabulary in this module. Write the highlighted vocabulary words on one side of the flap. Write the definition for each word on the other side of the flap. Use the key-term fold to quiz yourself on the definitions used in this module.

© Houghton Mifflin Harcourt Publishing Company

Reading Start-Up

Visualize Vocabulary
The main idea web helps students review the coordinate plane. Students should write one review word in each rectangle. If time allows, brainstorm additional terms as a class to add to the diagram.

Understand Vocabulary
Use the following explanation to help students learn the preview words.

> An **enlargement** is when something has been made larger. If you increase the size of a photo on your computer, you have enlarged it.
>
> A **reduction** is when something has been made smaller. In a dollhouse, the furniture is reduced to scale so that it resembles actual furniture but is small.
>
> **Dilations** include both enlargements and reductions.

Active Reading

Integrating Language Arts
Students can use these reading and note-taking strategies to help them organize and understand new concepts and vocabulary.

Additional Resources
Differentiated Instruction
- Reading Strategies **ELL**
- Interactive multilingual glossary

LEARNING PROGRESSIONS ACROSS THE GRADES

Before	In this Module	After
Students understand: • ratios • similar triangles	Students use transformational geometry to: • compare and contrast the attributes of a shape and its dilation(s) on a coordinate plane • represent algebraically the effect of a scale factor applied to two-dimensional figures on a coordinate plane with the origin as the center of dilation • explore how transformations can be used to obtain similar figures	Students will connect: • dilations and similarity

Are You Ready?

Assess Readiness

Access *Are You Ready?* assessment online, and receive instant scoring, feedback, and customized intervention or enrichment.

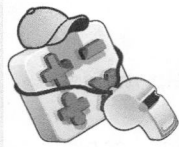

Personal Math Trainer

Online Assessment and Intervention

Additional Resources

Digital Teacher Resources

Go online for module-level resources.

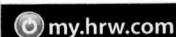

my.hrw.com

Complete these exercises to review skills you will need for this module.

Personal Math Trainer
Online Assessment and Intervention
my.hrw.com

Simplify Ratios

EXAMPLE
$$\frac{35}{21} = \frac{35 \div 7}{21 \div 7}$$
$$= \frac{5}{3}$$

To write a ratio in simplest form, find the greatest common factor of the numerator and denominator. Divide the numerator and denominator by the GCF.

Write each ratio in simplest form.

1. $\frac{6}{15}$ ___ $\frac{2}{5}$
2. $\frac{8}{20}$ ___ $\frac{2}{5}$
3. $\frac{30}{18}$ ___ $\frac{5}{3}$
4. $\frac{36}{30}$ ___ $\frac{6}{5}$

Multiply with Fractions and Decimals

EXAMPLE
$2\frac{3}{5} \times 20$

$= \frac{13 \times 20}{5 \times 1}$

$= \frac{13 \times \overset{4}{20}}{\underset{1}{5} \times 1}$

$= 52$

Write numbers as fractions and multiply.

Simplify.

$$\begin{array}{r} 68 \\ \times 4.5 \\ \hline 340 \\ +272 \\ \hline 306.0 \end{array}$$

Multiply as you would with whole numbers.

Place the decimal point in the answer based on the total number of decimal places in the two factors.

Multiply.

5. $60 \times \frac{25}{100}$ ___ 15
6. 3.5×40 ___ 140
7. 4.4×44 ___ 193.6
8. $24 \times \frac{8}{9}$ ___ $21\frac{1}{3}$

Graph Ordered Pairs (First Quadrant)

EXAMPLE

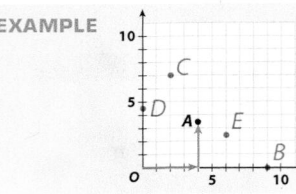

Graph the point A(4, 3.5).
Start at the origin.
Move 4 units right.
Then move 3.5 units up.
Graph point A(4, 3.5).

Graph each point on the coordinate grid above.

9. $B(9, 0)$
10. $C(2, 7)$
11. $D(0, 4.5)$
12. $E(6, 2.5)$

ARE YOU READY? *Diagnostic Assessment*

RtI Response to Intervention

Use to determine if students need intervention for the module's prerequisite skills.

Skill	Missed More Than . . .	Intervene With *Skills Intervention* worksheets (available online)	For Enrichment *Differentiated Instruction* (available in print and online)
Simplify Ratios	1 question	**Skill 28** Simplify Ratios	**Module 10 Challenge** Extend-the-Math Lesson Activities in TE
Multiply with Fractions and Decimals	1 question	**Skill 45** Multiply with Fractions and Decimals	**Module 10 Challenge** Extend-the-Math Lesson Activities in TE
Graph Ordered Pairs (First Quadrant)	1 question	**Skill 69** Graph Ordered Pairs (First Quadrant)	**Module 10 Challenge** Extend-the-Math Lesson Activities in TE

© Houghton Mifflin Harcourt Publishing Company

Complete these exercises to review skills you will need for this module.

Simplify Ratios

13. a. Explain how to find the simplest form of a ratio.

b. Describe what these ratios have in common.

$$\frac{75}{100}, \frac{24}{32}, \frac{15}{20}, \frac{9}{12}$$

> **a.** Find the greatest common factor (GCF) of the numerator and denominator. Divide both the numerator and denominator by the GCF.
>
> **b.** Each ratio in simplest form is $\frac{3}{4}$.

Multiply with Fractions and Decimals

14. To find $32 \times 1\frac{3}{4}$, Jose rewrote $1\frac{3}{4}$ as $\frac{6}{4}$ and multiplied to get 48. Find and correct Jose's error.

> Jose wrote the mixed number $1\frac{3}{4}$ as $\frac{6}{4}$, but it should be $\frac{7}{4}$ because $1\frac{3}{4} = \frac{4}{4} + \frac{3}{4} = \frac{7}{4}$.
> So, the correct answer is $32 \times \frac{7}{4} = \frac{^8 32 \times 7}{1 \times 4_1} = 8 \times 7 = 56$.

Graph Ordered Pairs (First Quadrant)

15. If the x- and y-coordinates of each of the points shown are doubled, what are the coordinates of the resulting points? Can they be graphed on the same grid? Explain.

> The coordinates of the points shown are (0, 2), (3, 4), (6, 6), and (9, 8), so the new points are (0, 4), (6, 8), (12, 12), and (18, 16). The first two points can be graphed on the same grid, but the last two points cannot, because the scales of the x- and y-axes only go to 11.

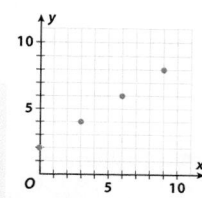

16. Adam drew a graph by plotting the value of a car each year after purchase. The x-axis label was "Time (years)" and the y-axis label was "Value (thousands of dollars)." The car's value was $5,749 after 4 years. Explain how he graphed this point.

> The x-coordinate was the time in years, or 4. The y-coordinate was the value, in thousands of dollars, so he divided 5,749 by 1,000 to get 5.749, which is about 5.75, or $5\frac{3}{4}$. Starting at the origin, he moved right 4 units and up $5\frac{3}{4}$ units to plot the point.

© Houghton Mifflin Harcourt Publishing Company

Simplify Ratios

Exercise 13 Some students may make errors when finding the simplest form of a ratio. Point out that the numerator and denominator cannot have any factors in common for the ratio to be in simplest form.

Multiply with Fractions and Decimals

Exercise 14 Point out that students can simplify the fractions before multiplying the whole number by the improper fraction. Verify that various methods can lead to the same product.

Graph Ordered Pairs (First Quadrant)

Exercise 15 Students may confuse the coordinates if they interpret units to the right or left as a change in the y-coordinate instead of a change in the x-coordinate. Caution students to locate the points carefully and to check whether the coordinates have a pattern.

Exercise 16 Encourage students to make a sketch of the graph to help them describe how to plot the point. Remind students that the y-axis should be in intervals of $1,000.

Use to determine if students are able to apply the module's prerequisite skills.

Skill	Exercise	Depth of Knowledge (D.O.K.)	Mathematical Processes
Simplify Ratios	13	**3** Strategic Thinking	**MP.2** Abstract and Quantitative Reasoning
Multiply with Fractions and Decimals	14	**2** Skills/Concepts	**MP.3** Use and Evaluate Logical Reasoning
Graph Ordered Pairs (First Quadrant)	15	**3** Strategic Thinking	**MP.7** See Structure
	16	**3** Strategic Thinking	**MP.6** Use Precise Mathematical Language

Lesson Support

Content Objective Students will learn how to describe the properties of dilations.

Professional Development

Integrate Mathematical Processes MP.5

This lesson provides an opportunity to address this Mathematical Processes standard. It calls for students to consider available tools when solving a problem. Students use tables and a diagram to model a relationship between a figure and its dilation. Then students use graphs on a coordinate plane to generalize the language of dilations and the scale factor. Finally, students use mathematical language to describe, contrast, and compare dilations with other transformations.

FOCUS	COHERENCE	RIGOR

FOCUS

Building Background

Connecting to Everyday Life Ask students to describe examples of scale models and scale drawings with which they are familiar. Then have them explain what a scale model/drawing is in their own words. After discussing the definitions, call attention to the word *scale*. Invite students to explain what the scale refers to in the context of scale models and scale drawings.

COHERENCE

Learning Progressions

In this lesson, students are introduced to the properties of dilations. They recognize that a figure and a dilation of the figure are similar. Important understandings for students include the following:

- **Define a dilation and the center of dilation.**
- **Recognize a dilation on a coordinate plane.**
- **Find a scale factor.**

Students are familiar with similar figures and scale factors from earlier grades. This lesson introduces them to similar figures created by dilations on the coordinate plane. They compare corresponding sides of a figure and its dilation to find the scale factor. This prepares them to connect the geometry of a dilation to its algebraic representation in the next lesson.

RIGOR

Cluster Connections

This lesson provides an excellent opportunity to connect ideas in the cluster:

Understand congruence and similarity using physical models, transparencies, or geometry software.

Have students look back at the quadrilaterals in Explore Activity 2. Ask them to make a conjecture about the relationship of the slopes of the corresponding sides of a figure and its dilation. Then have them test their conjecture by finding the slopes of the corresponding line segments.

Slopes of corresponding line segments are the same. Slopes: $\overline{AB}, \overline{A'B'}$: $-\frac{1}{2}$; $\overline{BC}, \overline{B'C'}$: no slope; $\overline{CD}, \overline{C'D'}$: 0; $\overline{AD}, \overline{A'D'}$: $\frac{9}{2}$

Language Support ELL

Language Objective Students will list the properties of dilations.

Leveled Strategies for English Learners ELL

Emerging
When proficiency in English is limited, having students use their primary language in peer-to-peer discussion encourages higher-level thinking. Have students tab, review, and copy the table in the Independent Practice to be sure they understand the effects of different transformations.

Expanding
Have students at this level of English proficiency work in pairs to review and copy the table in the Independent Practice to be sure they understand the effects of different transformations. Then have them illustrate each transformation on graph paper.

Bridging
Have students at this level of English proficiency work in pairs to copy the table in the Independent Practice to be sure they understand the effects of the different transformations. Then have them discuss and illustrate each transformation on graph paper.

Math Talk Write out and model for students a sentence frame to begin their answer to Math Talk for Your Turn Exercise 5.

Scale factors greater than 1 lead to enlargements. Scale factors between _____ lead to reductions.

	Image Compared to Original Figure		
	Orientation	Size	Shape
Translation	same	same	same
Reflection	changed	same	same
Rotation	changed	same	same
Dilation	same	changed	same

Image Credits: ©NASA/Bill Ingalls

Linguistic Support ELL

Academic/Content Vocabulary
This lesson introduces students to several new vocabulary words: *dilation, center of dilation, enlargement, reduction,* and *scale factor.* Explore Activity 1 involves the development of scaled-down models of rockets used by the Johnson Space Center in Houston. This should be explained to students. To assure that English learners better grasp the concept of dilation, you may want to form teams of mixed English proficiency to solve problems. You may also want to provide sentence frames to support student responses.

Building Background
-ment Word parts, like prefixes and suffixes, are the building blocks of the English language, and knowing their meanings will help students understand many new words. The suffix *-ment* means "action or process." So, the word *enlargement* means "the action of enlarging." The suffix *-ment* is the same as *-mento* in Spanish.

Properties of Dilations

1 Engage

ESSENTIAL QUESTION

How do you describe the properties of dilations?
Sample answer: Dilations change the size of figures but not their orientation or shape.

Motivate the Lesson
Ask: Have you ever made an enlarged or reduced copy of a document or photograph on a copying machine? What is the math behind changing the size of an image? Begin the Explore Activity to find out.

2 Explore

EXPLORE ACTIVITY 1

Focus on Communication
In discussing Reflect Exercise 2, you may wish to point out that the orientation of a figure and its dilation remain the same only if the scale factor is positive. See *Extend-the-Math*.

LESSON 10.1 **Properties of Dilations**

8.4.10.1
Students will describe the properties of dilations.

ESSENTIAL QUESTION

How do you describe the properties of dilations?

EXPLORE ACTIVITY 1

Exploring Dilations

The missions that placed 12 astronauts on the moon were controlled at the Johnson Space Center in Houston. The toy models at the right are scaled-down replicas of the Saturn V rocket that powered the moon flights. Each replica is a transformation called a **dilation**. Unlike the other transformations you have studied—translations, rotations, and reflections—dilations change the size (but not the shape) of a figure.

Every dilation has a fixed point called the **center of dilation** located where the lines connecting corresponding parts of figures intersect.

Triangle R'S'T' is a dilation of triangle RST. Point C is the center of dilation.

A Use a ruler to measure segments $\overline{CR}$, $\overline{CR'}$, $\overline{CS}$, $\overline{CS'}$, $\overline{CT}$, and $\overline{CT'}$ to the nearest millimeter. Record the measurements and ratios in the table.

CR'	CR	$\frac{CR'}{CR}$	CS'	CS	$\frac{CS'}{CS}$	CT'	CT	$\frac{CT'}{CT}$
5 cm	2.5 cm	2	4 cm	2 cm	2	6 cm	3 cm	2

B Write a conjecture based on the ratios in the table.
The ratios all equal 2. The distances are proportional.

C Measure and record the corresponding side lengths of the triangles.

R'S'	RS	$\frac{R'S'}{RS}$	S'T'	ST	$\frac{S'T'}{ST}$	R'T'	RT	$\frac{R'T'}{RT}$
2 cm	1 cm	2	2 cm	1 cm	2	2.8 cm	1.4 cm	2

D Write a conjecture based on the ratios in the table.
The ratios all equal 2. The side lengths are proportional.

E Measure the corresponding angles and describe your results.
The corresponding angles are congruent.

Lesson 10.1 **315**

© Houghton Mifflin Harcourt Publishing Company

DIFFERENTIATE INSTRUCTION *Leveled Questions*

	EXPLORE ACTIVITY 1
AL DOK 1 *Recall*	What is the main difference when dilations are compared to translations, reflections, or rotations? It is the only transformation that changes the size of the figure.
OL DOK 2 *Skills/Concepts*	What is the relationship of the perimeter of △R'S'T' to the perimeter of △RST? Explain. The perimeter of △R'S'T' is twice that of △RST.
BL DOK 3 *Strategic Thinking*	There is a dilation of △R'S'T' whose image is the same as △RST. How will the ratios for this dilation of △R'S'T' compare to the ratios in the original dilation of △RST? Explain. The ratios will be $\frac{1}{2}$ instead of 2 (reciprocals); the second dilation undoes the original dilation.

LEVELED QUESTIONS: **AL** Approaching Level | **OL** On Level | **BL** Beyond Level

Reflect

1. Two figures that have the same shape but different sizes are called *similar*. Are triangles *RST* and *R'S'T'* similar? Why or why not?

   Yes; their corresponding sides are proportional, and
   their corresponding angles are congruent.

2. Compare the orientation of a figure with the orientation of its dilation.

   A figure and its dilation have the same orientation.

Exploring Dilations on a Coordinate Plane

In this activity you will explore how the coordinates of a figure on a coordinate plane are affected by a dilation.

A Complete the table. Record the *x*- and *y*-coordinates of the points in the two figures and the ratios of the *x*-coordinates and the *y*-coordinates.

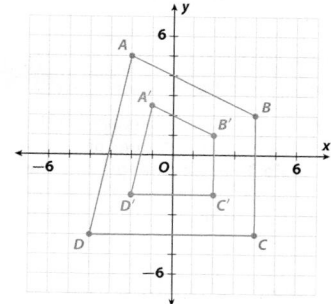

Vertex	x	y	Vertex	x	y	Ratio of x-coordinates (A'B'C'D' ÷ ABCD)	Ratio of y-coordinates (A'B'C'D' ÷ ABCD)
A'	−1	2.5	A	−2	5	0.5	0.5
B'	2	1	B	4	2	0.5	0.5
C'	2	−2	C	4	−4	0.5	0.5
D'	−2	−2	D	−4	−4	0.5	0.5

B Write a conjecture about the ratios of the coordinates of a dilation image to the coordinates of the original figure.

   Sample answer: The ratios all equal 0.5.

   The ratios are in proportion.

© Houghton Mifflin Harcourt Publishing Company

---

3 Explain

Connect Vocabulary ELL

Help students remember *dilation* by asking if anyone has had an eye exam where their pupils were dilated (made larger) for the exam. Use blocks, models, or pictures to demonstrate the two kinds of dilations: enlargements and reductions. Help students find the *large* in *enlargement* and relate the *reduc* in *reduction* to *reduce*.

EXPLORE ACTIVITY 2

Engage with the Whiteboard

Have a student measure and label the lengths of the line segments and compare the ratios of these lengths. Have another student draw lines that join the corresponding points of the two figures to see where these lines intersect.

EXPLORE ACTIVITY 2

(AL) DOK 1 *Recall*	What stays the same as the preimage and what changes for a dilated figure? The shape and orientation stay the same; the size changes.
(OL) DOK 2 *Skills/Concepts*	Find the slope of each side of quadrilateral *ABCD* and its corresponding image side in *A'B'C'D'*. How do the corresponding slopes compare? Slopes of $\overline{AB}$ and $\overline{A'B'}$ are $-\frac{1}{2}$; slopes of $\overline{BC}$ and $\overline{B'C'}$ are undefined; slopes of $\overline{CD}$ and $\overline{C'D'}$ are 0; slopes of $\overline{AD}$ and $\overline{A'D'}$ are $\frac{9}{2}$; the corresponding slopes are the same.
(BL) DOK 3 *Strategic Thinking*	In Part A, what would be the coordinates of the vertices of *A'B'C'D'* if all the ratios of *x*-coordinates and all the ratios of *y*-coordinates were 2? *A'*(−4, 10), *B'*(8, 4), *C'*(8, −8), *D'*(−8, −8)

TEACHER TO TEACHER

Communicating Math Tell students that in order to make a dilation, you need to know the point that is the center of dilation. If no center of dilation is given, it is usually assumed that the center of dilation is the origin of the coordinate plane. The scale factor is sometimes called the magnitude of the dilation. One notation that is used to specify a dilation is $D_{O,k}$, which means a dilation with center *O* (at the origin) and a scale factor (or magnitude) of *k*.

EXAMPLE 1

Animated Math

Explore Dilations and Similar Figures

Students explore the effect of dilations on an interactive figure and discover how side length changes.

my.hrw.com

ADDITIONAL EXAMPLE 1 An office supply store sells index cards in two different sizes. The large size is a dilation of the small size. Both sizes are shown. Find the scale factor of the dilation. The scale factor is 3.

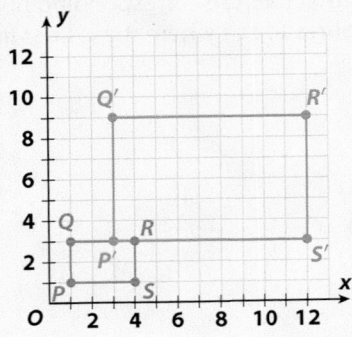

Interactive Whiteboard

Interactive example available online

Digital Teacher Resources

Go online to access all your lesson-level resources.

Differentiated Instruction
• Reteach
• Reading Strategies
• Success for English Learners
• Practice and Problem Solving A/B, C, D

Math on the Spot Videos

my.hrw.com

Dilations do not preserve size, whereas the others do.

Math Talk
Mathematical Processes

How are dilations different from the other transformations you have learned about?

Reflect

3. In Explore Activity 1, triangle *R'S'T'* was larger than triangle *RST*. How is the relationship between quadrilateral *A'B'C'D'* and quadrilateral *ABCD* different?

Quad. *A'B'C'D'* is smaller than quad. *ABCD*.

Finding a Scale Factor

As you have seen in the two activities, a dilation can produce a larger figure (an **enlargement**) or a smaller figure (a **reduction**). The **scale factor** describes how much the figure is enlarged or reduced. The scale factor is the ratio of a length of the image to the corresponding length on the original figure.

In Explore Activity 1, the side lengths of triangle *R'S'T'* were twice the length of those of triangle *RST*, so the scale factor was 2. In Explore Activity 2, the side lengths of quadrilateral *A'B'C'D'* were half those of quadrilateral *ABCD*, so the scale factor was 0.5.

Math On the Spot
my.hrw.com

EXAMPLE 1

An art supply store sells several sizes of drawing triangles. All are dilations of a single basic triangle. The basic triangle and one of its dilations are shown on the grid. Find the scale factor of the dilation.

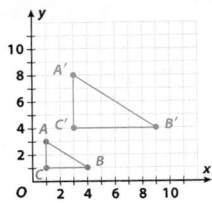

STEP 1 Use the coordinates to find the lengths of the sides of each triangle.

Triangle *ABC*: $AC = 2$ $CB = 3$

Triangle *A'B'C'*: $A'C' = 4$ $C'B' = 6$

Since the scale factor is the same for all corresponding sides, you can record just two pairs of side lengths. Use one pair as a check on the other.

STEP 2 Find the ratios of the corresponding sides.

$$\frac{A'C'}{AC} = \frac{4}{2} = 2 \qquad \frac{C'B'}{CB} = \frac{6}{3} = 2$$

The scale factor of the dilation is 2.

Animated Math
my.hrw.com

Reflect

4. Is the dilation an enlargement or a reduction? How can you tell?

An enlargement; sample answer: Triangle *A'B'C'* is larger than triangle *ABC*, and the scale factor is greater than 1.

© Houghton Mifflin Harcourt Publishing Company

DIFFERENTIATE INSTRUCTION *Leveled Questions*

	EXAMPLE 1
AL DOK 1 *Recall*	In the figure, the line that joins corresponding vertices *A* and *A'* doesn't go through the origin. What can you conclude about the center of dilation? The center of dilation is not the origin.
OL DOK 2 *Skills/Concepts*	If the length of side $\overline{AB}$ of triangle *ABC* is about 3.6, what is the length of side $\overline{A'B'}$ of triangle *A'B'C'*? Explain. It is about 7.2; $\overline{AB}$ and $\overline{A'B'}$ are corresponding sides, and the ratio of corresponding sides is 2.
BL DOK 3 *Strategic Thinking*	The center of dilation in Example 1 is the origin. Suppose you translate △*A'B'C'* down and left so that *C'* has the same coordinates as *C*. What is the center of dilation now? Support your answer. (1, 1), the coordinates of both *C* and *C'*; $\frac{C'A'}{CA} = \frac{4}{2} = 2$ and $\frac{C'B'}{CB} = \frac{6}{3} = 2$.

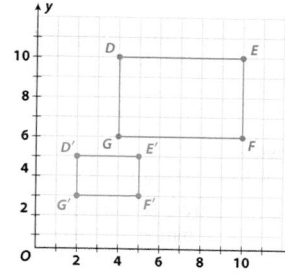

Personal Math Trainer
Online Assessment and Intervention
my.hrw.com

YOUR TURN

5. Find the scale factor of the dilation.

The scale factor is 0.5.

Math Talk
Mathematical Processes

Which scale factors lead to enlargements? Which scale factors lead to reductions?

If the scale factor is greater than 1, the dilation is an enlargement. If it is between 0 and 1, the dilation is a reduction.

Guided Practice

Use triangles ABC and A'B'C' for 1–5. (Explore Activities 1 and 2, Example 1)

1. For each pair of corresponding vertices, find the ratio of the x-coordinates and the ratio of the y-coordinates.

   ratio of x-coordinates = ___2___

   ratio of y-coordinates = ___2___

2. I know that triangle A'B'C' is a dilation of triangle ABC because the ratios of the corresponding

   x-coordinates are ___equal___ and the ratios of the corresponding y-coordinates are ___equal___.

3. The ratio of the lengths of the corresponding sides of triangle A'B'C' and triangle ABC equals ___2___.

4. The corresponding angles of triangle ABC and triangle A'B'C' are ___congruent___.

5. The scale factor of the dilation is ___2___.

? ESSENTIAL QUESTION CHECK-IN

6. How can you find the scale factor of a dilation?

   Sample answer: Divide a side length of the dilated figure by the corresponding side length of the original figure.

318 Unit 4

© Houghton Mifflin Harcourt Publishing Company

YOUR TURN MP.5

Focus on Critical Thinking

Have students discuss whether the dilated image can overlap, or be inside, the original figure. Refer them to all the illustrations in the lesson as they decide on their answer.

4 Elaborate

Talk About It

Summarize the Lesson

Ask: You are given a graph of a dilation and asked to identify its scale factor and whether it is an enlargement or a reduction. What do you look for? Look for the prime marks to indicate the image; if the image is larger than the original, it is an enlargement and the scale factor will be greater than one. Find the ratio of the new side lengths to the original to find the scale factor.

Guided Practice

Engage with the Whiteboard

Have a student label each of the six points of the image and preimage with its ordered pair. Have another student measure the side lengths and confirm that corresponding sides are proportional.

Avoid Common Errors

- **Exercises 1, 3** Remind students that there will be three ratios in each case and that all three must be equal.

- **Exercise 4** Remind students that the angles, not the sides, of similar figures are congruent.

DIFFERENTIATE INSTRUCTION *Intervention and Additional Support*

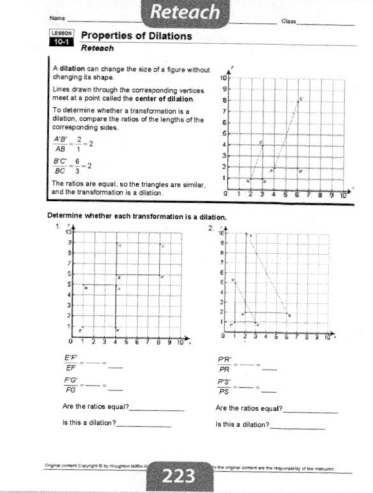

Reteach

223

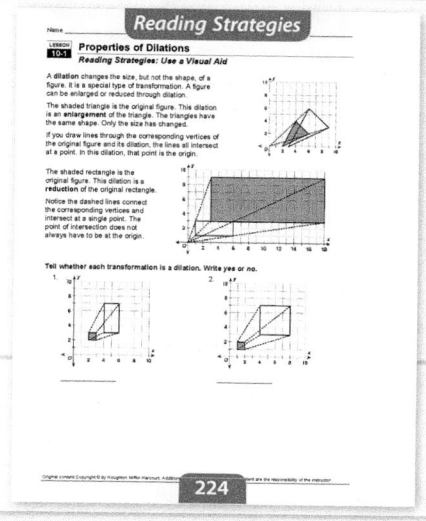

Reading Strategies

224

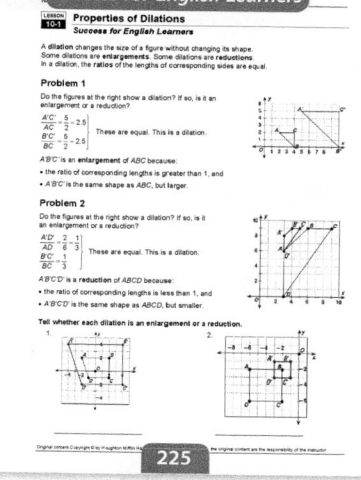

Success for English Learners

225

Personal Math Trainer
Daily Intervention
10.1 Homework

Pages shown are from *Differentiated Instruction.*
Also available online.

5 Evaluate

 **Pressed for Time**

10.1 Differentiated Homework Assignments

(AL) **Approaching Level** 7–9, 12–15, 17–19

(OL) **On Level** 10–18, 20

(BL) **Beyond Level** 11, 16–20

*For **Below Level** students, assign Personal Math Trainer, Daily Intervention 10.1 Homework.*

Mathematical Processes	Exercises
MP.2 Reasoning	12–15, 20
MP.3 Logic	7–11, 19
MP.5 Using Tools	17–18
MP.6 Precision	16

Focus on Higher Order Thinking

Depth of Knowledge	Exercises
1 Recall of Information	12–15
2 Skills/Concepts	7–11, 16–18
3 Strategic Thinking H.O.T.	19–20

Name_____ Class_____ Date_____

Personal Math Trainer
Online Assessment and Intervention
my.hrw.com

For 7–11, tell whether one figure is a dilation of the other or not. Explain your reasoning.

7. Quadrilateral *MNPQ* has side lengths of 15 mm, 24 mm, 21 mm, and 18 mm. Quadrilateral *M'N'P'Q'* has side lengths of 5 mm, 8 mm, 7 mm, and 4 mm.

No; the ratios of the lengths of the corresponding sides are not equal.

8. Triangle *RST* has angles measuring 38° and 75°. Triangle *R'S'T'* has angles measuring 67° and 38°. The sides are proportional.

Yes; both triangles have angles of measure 38°, 75°, and 67°, so the corresponding angles are congruent.

9. Two triangles, Triangle 1 and Triangle 2, are similar.

Yes; a dilation produces an image similar to the original figure.

10. Quadrilateral *MNPQ* is the same shape but a different size than quadrilateral *M'N'P'Q'*.

Yes; if figures are the same shape but a different size, they are similar. Therefore, one is a dilation of the other.

11. On a coordinate plane, triangle *UVW* has coordinates *U*(20, −12), *V*(8, 6), and *W*(−24, −4). Triangle *U'V'W'* has coordinates *U'*(15, −9), *V'*(6, 4.5), and *W'*(−18, −3).

Yes; each coordinate of triangle *U'V'W'* is $\frac{3}{4}$ times the corresponding coordinate of triangle *UVW*. So, the scale factor of the dilation is $\frac{3}{4}$.

Complete the table by writing "same" or "changed" to compare the image with the original figure in the given transformation.

	Image Compared to Original Figure		
	Orientation	Size	Shape
12. Translation	same	same	same
13. Reflection	changed	same	same
14. Rotation	changed	same	same
15. Dilation	same	changed	same

16. Describe the image of a dilation with a scale factor of 1.

The image is congruent to the original figure.

© Houghton Mifflin Harcourt Publishing Company

DIFFERENTIATE INSTRUCTION *Leveled Homework/Practice*

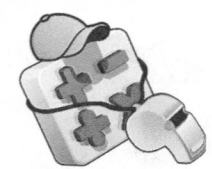

Personal Math Trainer
• 10.1 Homework

Pages shown are from *Differentiated Instruction.* **Also available online.**

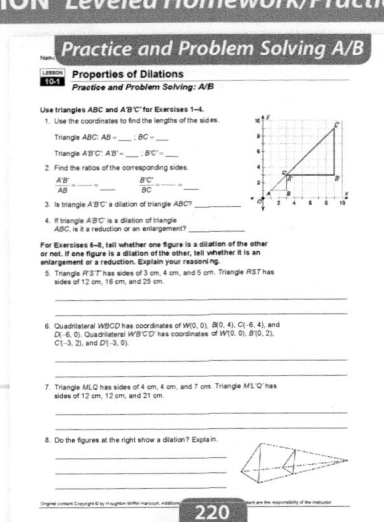

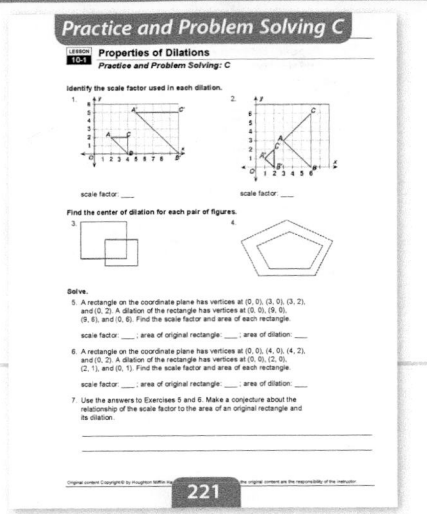

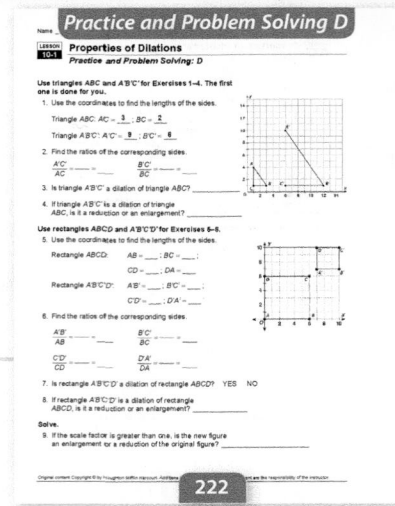

Identify the scale factor used in each dilation.

17.

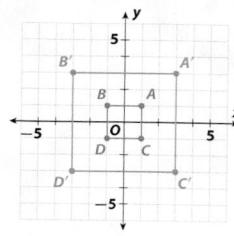

_____
3

18.

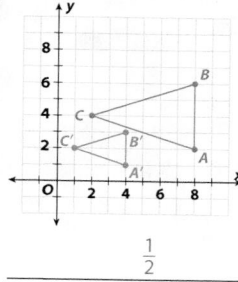

_____
$\frac{1}{2}$

H.O.T. **FOCUS ON HIGHER ORDER THINKING**

19. Critical Thinking Explain how you can find the center of dilation of a triangle and its dilation.

Sample answer: Locate the corresponding vertices of the

triangles and draw lines connecting each pair. The lines

will intersect at the center of dilation.

20. Make a Conjecture

a. A square on the coordinate plane has vertices at $(-2, 2)$, $(2, 2)$, $(2, -2)$, and $(-2, -2)$. A dilation of the square has vertices at $(-4, 4)$, $(4, 4)$, $(4, -4)$, and $(-4, -4)$. Find the scale factor and the perimeter of each square.

scale factor: 2; perimeter of original square: 16;

perimeter of image: 32

b. A square on the coordinate plane has vertices at $(-3, 3)$, $(3, 3)$, $(3, -3)$, and $(-3, -3)$. A dilation of the square has vertices at $(-6, 6)$, $(6, 6)$, $(6, -6)$, and $(-6, -6)$. Find the scale factor and the perimeter of each square.

scale factor: 2; perimeter of original square: 24;

perimeter of image: 48

c. Make a conjecture about the relationship of the scale factor to the perimeter of a square and its image.

Sample answer: The perimeter of the image is the

perimeter of the original figure times the scale factor.

Work Area

© Houghton Mifflin Harcourt Publishing Company

✔ Quick Check

10.1 Lesson Quiz

Use triangles _RST_ and _R'S'T'_ to answer the questions.

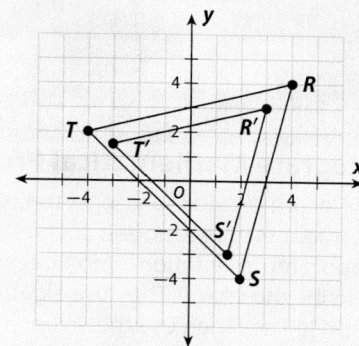

1. For each pair of corresponding vertices, find the ratio of the _x_-coordinates.
$\frac{3}{4} = \frac{1.5}{2} = \frac{-3}{-4} = 0.75$

2. For each pair of corresponding vertices, find the ratio of the _y_-coordinates.
$\frac{3}{4} = \frac{-3}{-4} = \frac{1.5}{2} = 0.75$

3. What is the ratio of the lengths of the corresponding sides of triangle _RST_ and _R'S'T'_? Explain how you know. 0.75; Sample answer: Because the corresponding _x_- and _y_-coordinates are in the same ratio, the figure shows a dilation. Therefore, the side lengths must be in the same ratio as the coordinates.

4. What is the scale factor of the dilation? Is it an enlargement or a reduction? 0.75; reduction

Differentiate Instruction

IF a student misses more than one question, THEN

Differentiate Instruction:
- 10.1 Reteach
- Personal Math Trainer

 Interactive Whiteboard
Interactive Lesson quiz available online

DIFFERENTIATE INSTRUCTION _Extend-the-Math Activity_ **PRE-AP**

Activity Have students graph a dilation with the origin as the center of dilation but with a negative scale factor. For example, have them graph the triangle with vertices at $A(1, 5)$, $B(2, 1)$, and $C(2, 4)$, using a scale factor of -2. Ask them to describe the location and orientation of the original (in QI with the shortest side at the top) and the image (in QIII with the shortest side at the bottom).

Then have them graph the triangle with vertices at $A(10, 4)$, $B(2, 6)$, and $C(6, 2)$, using a scale factor of $-\frac{1}{2}$. Have them compare the orientation of the figure with that of the dilation. Lead students to conclude that the orientation is opposite when the scale factor is less than zero. Point out that this is similar to a dilation with a positive scale factor followed by a reflection in which both coordinates are multiplied by -1.

Lesson Support

Content Objective Students will learn how to describe the effect of a dilation on coordinates using an algebraic representation.

Professional Development

Integrate Mathematical Processes MP.4

This lesson provides an opportunity to address this Mathematical Processes standard. It calls for students to use models such as diagrams, tables, graphs, and formulas. Students change graphic representations into tables, back into a graph of a dilation, and then use words to describe the image. They use algebraic methods to find the new coordinates for a dilation and graph it. They then use these representations to solve problems involving blueprints. Finally, they generalize the effect of transformations in words.

FOCUS

Building Background

Visualizing Math Tell students that a square on the coordinate plane has vertices $A(1, 1)$, $B(-1, 1)$, $C(-1, -1)$, and $D(1, -1)$. A dilation of the square has vertices $A'(4, 4)$ and $B'(-4, 4)$. Ask students to identify the scale factor. 4 Then have them find the coordinates of vertices C and D and graph the dilation. Discuss how they found the coordinates of the vertices.

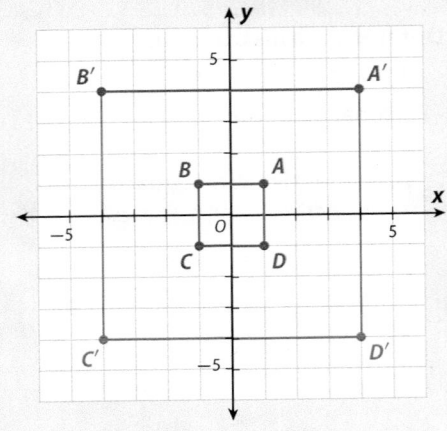

COHERENCE

Learning Progressions

In this lesson, students graph dilations in the coordinate plane to observe the effect of a dilation on the coordinates. Important understandings for students include the following:

- **Graph enlargements.**
- **Graph reductions.**
- **Graph a dilation with the center of dilation outside the image.**

Students know how to represent rigid transformations using algebraic representations. In this lesson they connect the scale factor to the algebraic representation of a dilation. They also learn that the center of dilation can be anywhere on the coordinate plane.

This lesson prepares students for the final lesson of the module, in which students combine rigid transformations and dilations to describe the motion of similar figures in the plane both graphically and algebraically.

RIGOR

Cluster Connections

This lesson provides an excellent opportunity to connect ideas in the cluster:

Understand congruence and similarity using physical models, transparencies, or geometry software.

Present students with the following problem: A triangle has vertices $A(1, 2)$, $B(1, 4)$, and $C(4, 2)$. The triangle is transformed using the rule $(2x, 0.5y)$. Is the transformation a dilation? Is the image similar to the preimage? Explain your thinking.

Sample answer: The transformation is not a dilation since there is no scale factor. The transformation stretches horizontally and shrinks vertically, so the image is not similar to the preimage.

Language Support ELL

Leveled Strategies for English Learners ELL

Emerging
Have students at this level of English proficiency work in pairs to draw on graph paper the preimage and image from a set of coordinates. Have them label the coordinates, specifying which is the preimage and which is the image.

Expanding
Have students at this level of English proficiency work in pairs to draw on graph paper the preimage and image from a set of coordinates. Have them label the coordinates and then list the differences between the preimage and image from the dilation.

Bridging
Have students at this level of English proficiency work in pairs to draw on graph paper the preimage and image from a set of coordinates. Have them label the coordinates and then describe the effect of the dilation on the coordinates.

Math Talk Write out and model for students a sentence frame to begin their answer to Math Talk for Explore Activity 1.

The radius of the dilated circle will be _____ because _____.

Image Credits: ©Lane Oatey/Blue Jean Images/Getty Images

Linguistic Support ELL

Academic/Content Vocabulary
To assure that English learners fully grasp the concept of dilation, have students of mixed language proficiency work together. Have students research to find images or video of other examples of scaled-down models to solidify their understanding of the concept.

Building Background
opposites One of the concepts in this lesson that students need to understand is the location of the center of dilation, whether the dilated image is inside or outside the original image. Point out to English learners that *inside* and *outside* are opposites.

1 Engage

? ESSENTIAL QUESTION

How can you describe the effect of a dilation on coordinates using an algebraic representation?
Sample answer: For scale factor k, the algebraic representation of the dilation, with center at the origin, is $(x, y) \rightarrow (kx, ky)$.

Motivate the Lesson

Ask: Have you ever drawn a picture or diagram, and then enlarged it to, for example, paint a mural or make a poster? How could you describe and specify such an enlargement using the language of mathematics? Begin the Explore Activity to find out.

2 Explore

EXPLORE ACTIVITY 1

Connect Vocabulary **ELL**

Have a student read the opening paragraph aloud. Have students practice and discuss the pronunciation and meaning of the math terms. Make sure students understand the meaning of the arrow, and that they read it as "becomes" or "is transformed into."

LESSON
10.2 **Algebraic Representations of Dilations**

8.4.10.2
Students will describe the effect of a dilation on coordinates using an algebraic representation.

? ESSENTIAL QUESTION

How can you describe the effect of a dilation on coordinates using an algebraic representation?

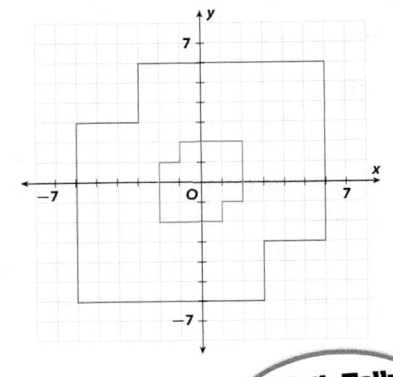

EXPLORE ACTIVITY 1

Graphing Enlargements

When a dilation in the coordinate plane has the origin as the center of dilation, you can find points on the dilated image by multiplying the x- and y-coordinates of the original figure by the scale factor. For scale factor k, the algebraic representation of the dilation is $(x, y) \rightarrow (kx, ky)$. For enlargements, $k > 1$.

The figure shown on the grid is the preimage. The center of dilation is the origin.

A List the coordinates of the vertices of the preimage in the first column of the table.

Preimage (x, y)	Image $(3x, 3y)$
(2, 2)	(6, 6)
(2, −1)	(6, −3)
(1, −1)	(3, −3)
(1, −2)	(3, −6)
(−2, −2)	(−6, −6)
(−2, 1)	(−6, 3)
(−1, 1)	(−3, 3)
(−1, 2)	(−3, 6)

B What is the scale factor for the dilation? ___3___

C Apply the dilation to the preimage and write the coordinates of the vertices of the image in the second column of the table.

D Sketch the image after the dilation on the coordinate grid.
The radius of the dilated circle will be 4 times as long as the radius of the original circle.

Math Talk
Mathematical Processes

What effect would the dilation $(x, y) \rightarrow (4x, 4y)$ have on the radius of a circle?

Lesson 10.2 **321**

© Houghton Mifflin Harcourt Publishing Company

DIFFERENTIATE INSTRUCTION *Leveled Questions*

	EXPLORE ACTIVITY 1
(AL) DOK 1 *Recall*	How are the coordinates of points in the image column related to the coordinates of points in the preimage column? multiplied by 3
(OL) DOK 2 *Skills/Concepts*	How is the distance from the origin to a point in the image related to the distance from the origin to the corresponding point in the preimage? A point in the image is 3 times the distance from the origin as the corresponding point in the preimage.
(BL) DOK 3 *Strategic Thinking*	Suppose you apply the dilation $(x, y) \rightarrow (0.5x, 0.5y)$ to the image that you drew. What is the relationship between the new figure and the original figure in the Explore Activity? Explain. It is a dilation of the original figure by a factor of 1.5; first by 3, then by 0.5, so $3 \cdot 0.5 = 1.5$.

LEVELED QUESTIONS: (AL) Approaching Level | (OL) On Level | (BL) Beyond Level

Reflect

1. How does the dilation affect the length of line segments?

Each line segment in the image is three times longer than the corresponding line segment in the preimage.

2. How does the dilation affect angle measures?

The dilation does not change the angle measures.

EXPLORE ACTIVITY 2

Graphing Reductions

For scale factors between 0 and 1, the image is smaller than the preimage. This is called a reduction.

The arrow shown is the preimage. The center of dilation is the origin.

A List the coordinates of the vertices of the preimage in the first column of the table.

B What is the scale factor for the dilation? $\frac{1}{2}$

C Apply the dilation to the preimage and write the coordinates of the vertices of the image in the second column of the table.

Preimage (x, y)	Image ($\frac{1}{2}x, \frac{1}{2}y$)
(4, 2)	(2, 1)
(0, 5)	(0, 2.5)
(−4, 2)	(−2, 1)
(−2, 2)	(−1, 1)
(−2, −4)	(−1, −2)
(2, −4)	(1, −2)
(2, 2)	(1, 1)

D Sketch the image after the dilation on the coordinate grid.

Reflect

3. How does the dilation affect the length of line segments?

The image length is $\frac{1}{2}$ that of the preimage.

4. How would a dilation with scale factor 1 affect the preimage?

The image and preimage would be the same.

© Houghton Mifflin Harcourt Publishing Company

3 Explain

EXPLORE ACTIVITY 2

Engage with the Whiteboard

Have a student write the coordinates for the vertices on both figures. Ask a student to label the lengths of the vertical and horizontal segments and then to compare the ratios of these lengths. Have a student draw lines to join the corresponding vertices of the two figures to demonstrate these lines intersect at the origin, or center of dilation.

TEACHER TO TEACHER

Graphic Organizers Ask students to create a table or diagram, which they can use for reference, that lists the various transformations they have learned about (translations, reflections, rotations, and dilations). For each transformation, have them write an ordered pair and then rewrite the ordered pair after the transformation. Next, have them write an algebraic representation of the transformation and a sentence describing the transformation.

EXPLORE ACTIVITY 2

AL) DOK 1 *Recall*	What value of scale factor produces a reduction? between 0 and 1
OL) DOK 2 *Skills/Concepts*	How is the distance from the origin to a point in the image related to the distance from the origin to the corresponding point in the preimage? A point in the image is $\frac{1}{2}$ the distance from the origin as the corresponding point in the preimage.
BL) DOK 3 *Strategic Thinking*	What are the areas of the image and preimage? How is the ratio of their areas related to the scale factor? 9 square units and 36 square units; it is the square of the scale factor: $\frac{1}{4} = \left(\frac{1}{2}\right)^2$.

EXAMPLE 1

ADDITIONAL EXAMPLE 1 Graph the image of rectangle *JKLM* after a dilation with the origin as its center and a scale factor of 2. What are the vertices of the image?

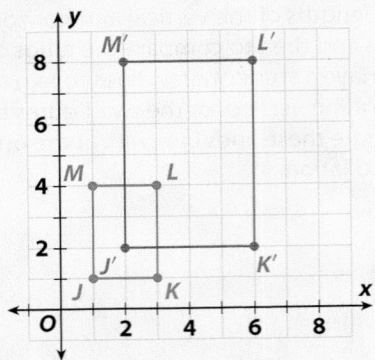

The vertices of the dilated image are *J'* (2, 2), *K'* (6, 2), *L'* (6, 8), and *M'* (2, 8).

 Interactive Whiteboard
Interactive example available online

YOUR TURN MP.4

Avoid Common Errors
Have students check their images by confirming that they are the same shape as the preimage and the corresponding side lengths are proportional.

 **Digital Teacher Resources**

Go online to access all your lesson-level resources.

Differentiated Instruction
• Reteach
• Reading Strategies
• Success for English Learners
• Practice and Problem Solving A/B, C, D

Math on the Spot Videos

my.hrw.com

Center of Dilation Outside the Image

The center of dilation can be inside *or* outside the original image and the dilated image. The center of dilation can be anywhere on the coordinate plane as long as the lines that connect each pair of corresponding vertices between the original and dilated image intersect at the center of dilation.

Math On the Spot
my.hrw.com

EXAMPLE 1

Graph the image of △*ABC* after a dilation with the origin as its center and a scale factor of 3. What are the vertices of the image?

STEP 1 Multiply each coordinate of the vertices of △*ABC* by 3 to find the vertices of the dilated image.

△*ABC* $(x, y) \rightarrow (3x, 3y)$ △*A'B'C'*

$A(1, 1) \rightarrow A'(1 \cdot 3, 1 \cdot 3) \rightarrow A'(3, 3)$

$B(3, 1) \rightarrow B'(3 \cdot 3, 1 \cdot 3) \rightarrow B'(9, 3)$

$C(1, 3) \rightarrow C'(1 \cdot 3, 3 \cdot 3) \rightarrow C'(3, 9)$

The vertices of the dilated image are *A'*(3, 3), *B'*(9, 3), and *C'*(3, 9).

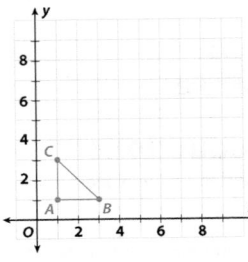

STEP 2 Graph the dilated image.

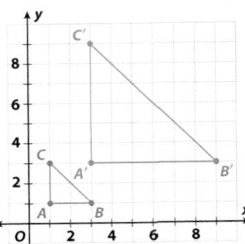

Math Talk
Mathematical Processes

Describe how you can check graphically that you have drawn the image triangle correctly.

Draw segments from the center of dilation through the vertices of the preimage to make sure they pass through the image vertices. Then check the length of 1 side of the image.

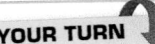

YOUR TURN

5. Graph the image of △*XYZ* after a dilation with a scale factor of $\frac{1}{3}$ and the origin as its center. Then write an algebraic rule to describe the dilation.

$(x, y) \rightarrow \left(\frac{1}{3}x, \frac{1}{3}y\right)$

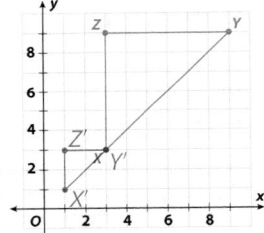

Personal Math Trainer
Online Assessment and Intervention
my.hrw.com

Lesson 10.2 **323**

© Houghton Mifflin Harcourt Publishing Company

DIFFERENTIATE INSTRUCTION *Leveled Questions*

	EXAMPLE 1
(AL) DOK 1 *Recall*	What is the center of dilation for this dilation? Explain. Origin; the lines containing corresponding vertices all intersect at the origin.
(OL) DOK 2 *Skills/Concepts*	The point (2.3, 1) is on triangle *ABC*. What are the coordinates of its image point on triangle *A'B'C'*? (6.9, 3)
(BL) DOK 3 *Strategic Thinking*	For a dilation $(x, y) \rightarrow (kx, ky)$, where $k > 0$ and $k \neq 1$, is the dilation image the same size as its preimage? Is it the same shape? Make a conjecture about how the two are related. It will not be the same size but it will be the same shape; the dilation image will be an enlargement of the preimage.

LEVELED QUESTIONS: (AL) Approaching Level | (OL) On Level | (BL) Beyond Level

1. The grid shows a diamond-shaped preimage. Write the coordinates of the vertices of the preimage in the first column of the table. Then apply the dilation $(x, y) \rightarrow \left(\frac{3}{2}x, \frac{3}{2}y\right)$ and write the coordinates of the vertices of the image in the second column. Sketch the image of the figure after the dilation. (Explore Activities 1 and 2)

Preimage	Image
(2, 0)	(3, 0)
(0, 2)	(0, 3)
(−2, 0)	(−3, 0)
(0, −2)	(0, −3)

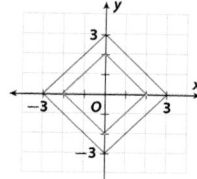

Graph the image of each figure after a dilation with the origin as its center and the given scale factor. Then write an algebraic rule to describe the dilation. (Example 1)

2. scale factor of 1.5

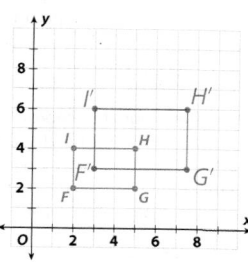

$(x, y) \rightarrow (1.5x, 1.5y)$

3. scale factor of $\frac{1}{3}$

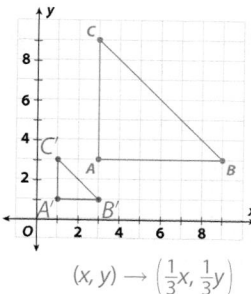

$(x, y) \rightarrow \left(\frac{1}{3}x, \frac{1}{3}y\right)$

ESSENTIAL QUESTION CHECK-IN

4. A dilation of $(x, y) \rightarrow (kx, ky)$ when $0 < k < 1$ has what effect on the figure? What is the effect on the figure when $k > 1$?

When k is between 0 and 1, the dilation is a reduction by the scale factor k. When k is greater than 1, the dilation is an enlargement by the scale factor k.

© Houghton Mifflin Harcourt Publishing Company

4 Elaborate

Talk About It

Summarize the Lesson

Ask: Describe the mathematical notation used to write the algebraic representation of a dilation. It begins with the ordered pair (x, y) and then has an arrow pointing right to another ordered pair that shows both x and y multiplied by the scale factor.

Guided Practice

Engage with the Whiteboard

Have a student label each of the vertices with the ordered pair that names the point. Have a student draw lines to join the corresponding vertices of the two figures to demonstrate these lines intersect at the origin, or center of dilation.

Avoid Common Errors

- **Exercise 1** Point out that when the center of dilation is not explicitly mentioned, students should assume that it is the origin.

- **Exercises 2–3** Students may try to draw enlargements so that they enclose the original figure and reductions so that they are enclosed within the original figure. Remind students that this will occur only in certain cases, such as **Exercise 1**, when the original figure is centered on the origin.

DIFFERENTIATE INSTRUCTION *Intervention and Additional Support*

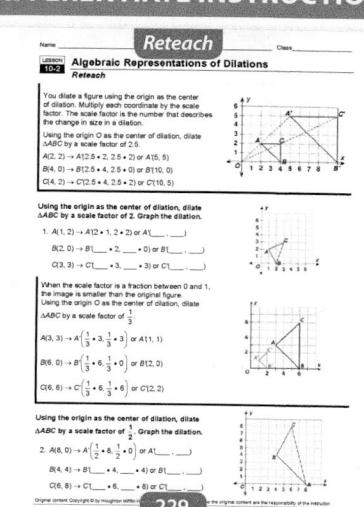

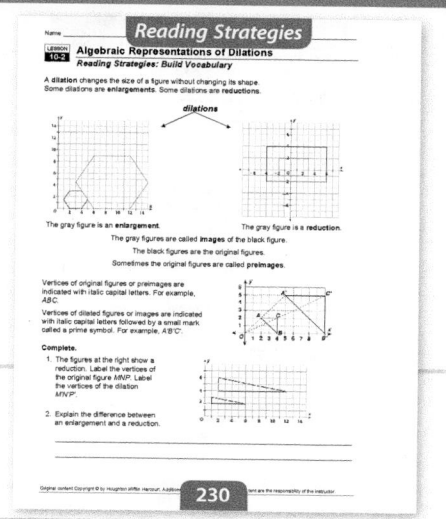

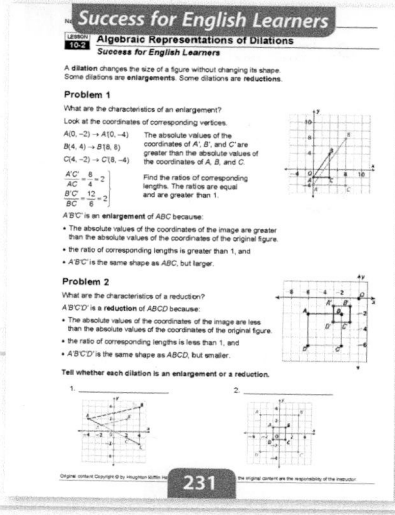

Personal Math Trainer
Daily Intervention
10.2 Homework

Pages shown are from *Differentiated Instruction*.
Also available online.

5 Evaluate

Independent Practice

🕐 **Pressed for Time**

10.2 Differentiated Homework Assignments

(AL) **Approaching Level** 5–7, 9–10

(OL) **On Level** 8–11

(BL) **Beyond Level** 7, 11–13

*For **Below Level** students, assign Personal Math Trainer, Daily Intervention 10.2 Homework.*

Mathematical Processes	Exercises
MP.2 Reasoning	5–8, 12–13
MP.3 Logic	11
MP.4 Modeling	9
MP.5 Using Tools	10

Focus on Higher Order Thinking

Depth of Knowledge	Exercises
2 Skills/Concepts	5–7, 10
3 Strategic Thinking **H.O.T.**	8–9, 11–13

10.2 Independent Practice

5. The blue square is the preimage. Write two algebraic representations, one for the dilation to the green square and one for the dilation to the purple square.

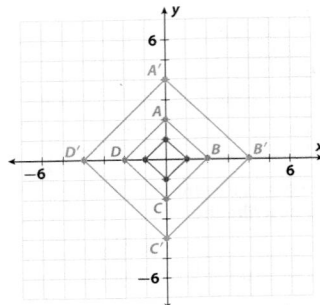

Green square: $(x, y) \rightarrow (2x, 2y)$

Purple square: $(x, y) \rightarrow \left(\frac{1}{2}x, \frac{1}{2}y\right)$

6. Critical Thinking A triangle has vertices $A(-5, -4)$, $B(2, 6)$, and $C(4, -3)$. The center of dilation is the origin and $(x, y) \rightarrow (3x, 3y)$. What are the vertices of the dilated image?

$A'(-15, -12)$, $B'(6, 18)$,

and $C'(12, -9)$

7. Critical Thinking $M'N'O'P'$ has vertices at $M'(3, 4)$, $N'(6, 4)$, $O'(6, 7)$, and $P'(3, 7)$. The center of dilation is the origin. $MNOP$ has vertices at $M(4.5, 6)$, $N(9, 6)$, $O(9, 10.5)$, and $P(4.5, 10.5)$. What is the algebraic representation of this dilation?

$(x, y) \rightarrow \left(\frac{2}{3}x, \frac{2}{3}y\right)$

8. Critical Thinking A dilation with center $(0,0)$ and scale factor k is applied to a polygon. What dilation can you apply to the image to return it to the original preimage?

a dilation with scale factor $\frac{1}{k}$

9. Represent Real-World Problems The blueprints for a new house are scaled so that $\frac{1}{4}$ inch equals 1 foot. The blueprint is the preimage and the house is the dilated image. The blueprints are plotted on a coordinate plane.

a. What is the scale factor in terms of inches to inches?

The scale factor is 48.

b. One inch on the blueprint represents how many inches in the actual house? How many feet?

48 inches or 4 feet

c. Write the algebraic representation of the dilation from the blueprint to the house.

$(x, y) \rightarrow (48x, 48y)$

d. A rectangular room has coordinates $Q(2, 2)$, $R(7, 2)$, $S(7, 5)$, and $T(2, 5)$ on the blueprint. The homeowner wants this room to be 25% larger. What are the coordinates of the new room?

$Q'(2.5, 2.5)$, $R'(8.75, 2.5)$,

$S'(8.75, 6.25)$, and $T'(2.5, 6.25)$

e. What are the dimensions of the new room, in inches, on the blueprint? What will the dimensions of the new room be, in feet, in the new house?

Dimensions on blueprint:

6.25 in. by 3.75 in.

Dimensions in house: 25 ft

by 15 ft

© Houghton Mifflin Harcourt Publishing Company

DIFFERENTIATE INSTRUCTION *Leveled Homework/Practice*

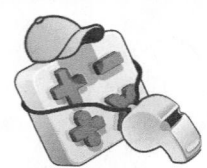

Personal Math Trainer

• 10.2 Homework

Pages shown are from *Differentiated Instruction.* **Also available online.**

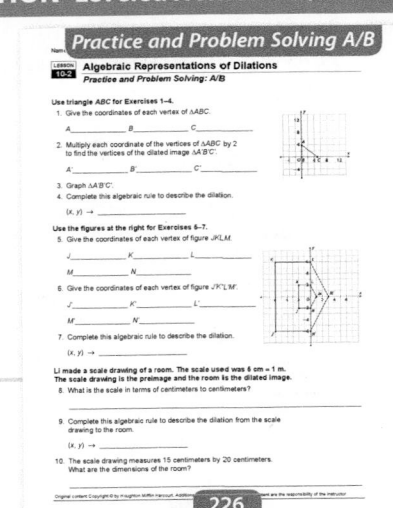

Practice and Problem Solving A/B

226

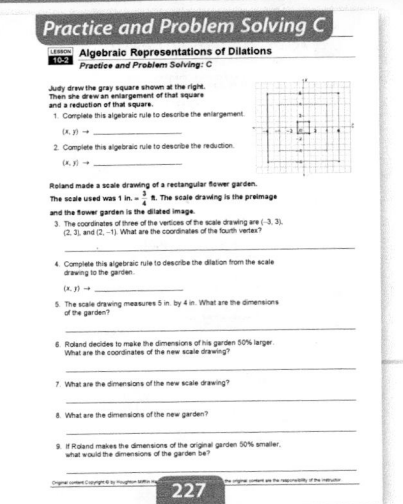

Practice and Problem Solving C

227

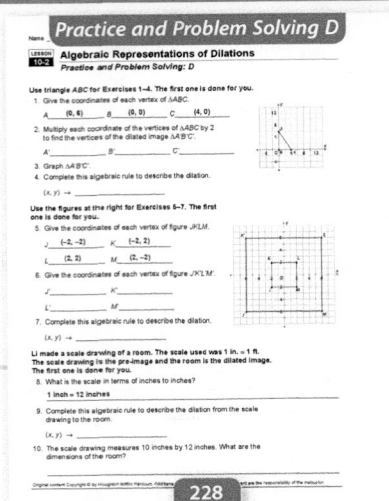

Practice and Problem Solving D

228

10. Write the algebraic representation of the dilation shown.

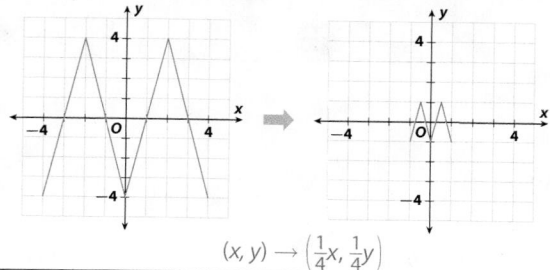

$$(x, y) \rightarrow \left(\tfrac{1}{4}x, \tfrac{1}{4}y\right)$$

 **FOCUS ON HIGHER ORDER THINKING**

11. Critique Reasoning The set for a school play needs a replica of a historic building painted on a backdrop that is 20 feet long and 16 feet high. The actual building measures 400 feet long and 320 feet high. A stage crewmember writes $(x, y) \rightarrow \left(\tfrac{1}{12}x, \tfrac{1}{12}y\right)$ to represent the dilation. Is the crewmember's calculation correct if the painted replica is to cover the entire backdrop? Explain.

The stage crewmember's calculation is incorrect.

The scale factor for the backdrop is $\tfrac{1}{20}$, not $\tfrac{1}{12}$.

12. Communicate Mathematical Ideas Explain what each of these algebraic transformations does to a figure.

a. $(x, y) \rightarrow (y, -x)$ rotates the figure 90° clockwise

b. $(x, y) \rightarrow (-x, -y)$ rotates the figure 180°

c. $(x, y) \rightarrow (x, 2y)$ stretches the figure vertically by a factor of 2

d. $(x, y) \rightarrow \left(\tfrac{2}{3}x, y\right)$ shrinks the figure horizontally by a factor of $\tfrac{2}{3}$

e. $(x, y) \rightarrow (0.5x, 1.5y)$ shrinks the figure horizontally by a factor of 0.5 and stretches it vertically by a factor of 1.5

13. Communicate Mathematical Ideas Triangle ABC has coordinates $A(1, 5)$, $B(-2, 1)$, and $C(-2, 4)$. Sketch triangle ABC and $A'B'C'$ for the dilation $(x, y) \rightarrow (-2x, -2y)$. What is the effect of a negative scale factor?

The figure is dilated by a factor of 2, but the orientation of the figure in the coordinate plane is rotated 180°.

© Houghton Mifflin Harcourt Publishing Company

Work Area

10.2 Lesson Quiz

1. A rectangle has vertices at $P(6, 6)$, $Q(6, -6)$, $R(-6, -6)$, and $S(-6, 6)$. The origin is the center of dilation, and $(x, y) \rightarrow \left(\tfrac{1}{3}x, \tfrac{1}{3}y\right)$. What are the vertices of the dilated image? $P'(2, 2)$, $Q'(2, -2)$, $R'(-2, -2)$, $S'(-2, 2)$

2. Write an algebraic representation of a dilation that has a scale factor of 0.45.
$(x, y) \rightarrow (0.45x, 0.45y)$

3. Triangle JKL is the preimage. Write two algebraic representations: one for the dilation from the preimage to triangle $J'K'L'$, and one for the dilation from the preimage to triangle $J''K''L''$. Triangle $J'K'L'$: $(x, y) \rightarrow (0.5x, 0.5y)$ Triangle $J''K''L''$: $(x, y) \rightarrow (1.5x, 1.5y)$

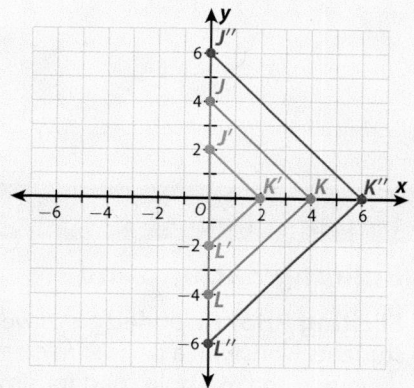

Differentiate Instruction

IF a student misses more than one question, THEN

Differentiate Instruction:

- 10.2 Reteach
- Personal Math Trainer

 Interactive Whiteboard
Interactive Lesson quiz available online

Activity Have students discuss various ways they have seen shrinking and stretching in their daily lives. Remind them that they may have seen movies, cartoons, or other entertainment that used this basic principle, as well as read about it in books such as *Gulliver's Travels*. Ask them what models they have seen, such as toy cars, action figures, and dolls. Then show them a figure, such as a model car or doll (or have them bring one in), and ask them to calculate (or estimate) the scale compared to the real thing. For example, they can compare their own heights to that of the action figure, and measure other dimensions of the figure to see if they are realistic or exaggerated.

Ask them to make a conjecture whether the model could realistically exist as an actual person or car, given the dimensions of the toy, and what those measurements would be if enlarged.

Lesson Support

Content Objective Students will learn the connection between transformations and the orientations of similar figures.

Professional Development

Integrate Mathematical Processes MP.6

This lesson provides an opportunity to address this Mathematical Process standard that calls for students to attend to precision. It is important that students pay close attention to the coordinates of the vertices as they apply transformations and graph the results. Each transformation must be applied carefully and precisely to obtain the desired outcome. For example, the magnitude, direction, and center of a rotation must be stated precisely. The scale factor of a dilation must be calculated precisely to have the algebraic rule be accurate.

FOCUS	COHERENCE	RIGOR

Building Background

Eliciting Prior Knowledge Have students work with a partner to create a definition and example chart for similar figures. In particular ask them to include descriptions of real-life examples of similar figures.

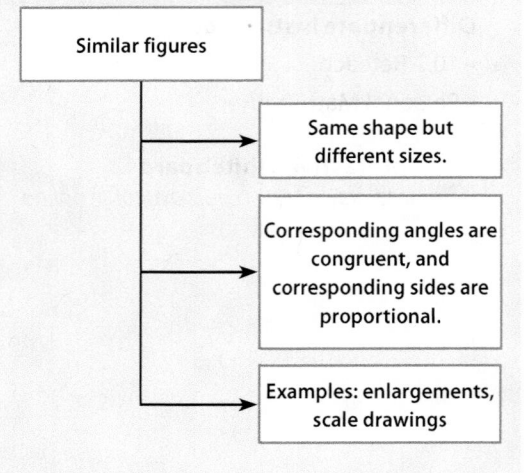

Learning Progressions

In this lesson, students are introduced to a formal definition of *similarity in the coordinate plane*. Important understandings for students include the following:

- **Combine rigid transformations with dilations.**
- **Understand that two figures are similar if one can be obtained from the other using a sequence of transformations in the plane.**

Students conclude the work with rigid transformations and dilations they have been studying throughout this unit. They understand that two figures in the plane are similar if one can be transformed into the other using a series of rigid transformations and dilations. They also apply their knowledge to describe algebraically how to transform one figure into a similar figure using coordinates.

Cluster Connections

This lesson provides an excellent opportunity to connect ideas in this cluster:

Understand congruence and similarity using physical models, transparencies, or geometry software.

Have students graph triangle *ABC* with vertices $A(1, 2)$, $B(1, 4)$, and $C(4, 1)$. Then ask them to identify and perform the following series of transformations, in order, on triangle *ABC*.

- $(x, y) \rightarrow (2x, 2y)$ dilation by a factor of 2
- $(x, y) \rightarrow (-x, -y)$ rotation 180°
- $(x, y) \rightarrow (-x, y)$ reflection across *y*-axis
- $(x, y) \rightarrow (x - 3, y + 3)$ translation 3 units left and 3 units up

What are the coordinates of the vertices of the final transformation?

$(-1, -1), (-1, -5), (5, 1)$

Language Support ELL

Leveled Strategies for English Learners ELL

Emerging

Have students at this level of English proficiency work in pairs to illustrate on graph paper similar figures and describe the sequence of transformations that transformed one to the other.

Expanding

Have students at this level of English proficiency work in pairs to illustrate on graph paper similar figures. On one sheet of graph paper, have them illustrate similar figures transformed by rotation. On the second sheet of graph paper, have them illustrate similar figures transformed by reflection. Label each one.

Bridging

Have students at this level of English proficiency work in pairs to illustrate on graph paper similar figures transformed by translation, reflection, rotation, and dilation. Then have students discuss which of the four transformations they think would be most useful for animation.

Math Talk

Write out and model for students a sentence frame to begin their answer.

In order to generate an image that is of a different size and orientation than the original, the sequence must contain _____.

Linguistic Support ELL

Academic/Content Vocabulary

This lesson on similar figures relies on students' understanding that, in this instance, the word *similar* has a very specific mathematical definition. Although English learners may know the meaning of *similar* in other contexts, point out to them that here it is related to translations, reflections, rotations, and dilations. Have students read the definition in the glossary and then add the word *similar* and its definition to their word journals.

Building Background

visuals In this lesson on similar figures, the opening activity shows students how combining transformations with dilations is used in creating animation. Point out to students that this is an area in which they can apply math concepts while in the process of acquiring English. They can show how they would apply these math concepts through animation.

Image Credits: ©TWPhoto/Corbis

Similar Figures

1 Engage

❓ ESSENTIAL QUESTION

What is the connection between transformations and the orientations of similar figures? Sample answer: If two figures are similar, then there exists a sequence of translations, reflections, rotations, and/or dilations that transforms one figure into the other.

Motivate the Lesson

Ask: What kinds of changes can be made to a shape while keeping the new shape similar to the original? Begin the Explore Activity to find out.

2 Explore

EXPLORE ACTIVITY

Engage with the Whiteboard

Invite a volunteer to label the coordinates of the vertices of the green figure and of figure *A*. Compare those values to the rule given in Part A. Repeat for Parts B–E.

10.3 Similar Figures

❓ ESSENTIAL QUESTION

What is the connection between transformations and similar figures?

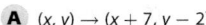

EXPLORE ACTIVITY

Combining Transformations with Dilations

When creating an animation, figures need to be translated, reflected, rotated, and sometimes dilated. As an example of this, apply the indicated sequence of transformations to the rectangle. Each transformation is applied to the image of the previous transformation, not to the original figure. Label each image with the letter of the transformation applied.

A $(x, y) \rightarrow (x + 7, y - 2)$

B $(x, y) \rightarrow (x, -y)$

C rotation 90° clockwise around the origin

D $(x, y) \rightarrow (x + 5, y + 3)$

E $(x, y) \rightarrow (3x, 3y)$

F List the coordinates of the vertices of rectangle *E*.
$(3, 6), (3, -6), (-3, -6), (-3, 6)$

G Compare the following attributes of rectangle *E* to those of the original figure.

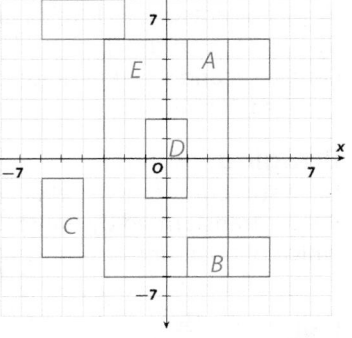

Shape	Same shape
Size	The sides of rectangle *E* are three times the lengths of the sides of the original figure.
Angle Measures	Same angle measures

© Houghton Mifflin Harcourt Publishing Company • Image Credits: ©TWPhoto/Corbis

Lesson 10.3 **327**

DIFFERENTIATE INSTRUCTION *Leveled Questions*

	EXPLORE ACTIVITY
AL **DOK 1** *Recall*	Which transformations in Parts A through E change the size of the rectangle? Which change the shape? Only the dilation in Part E changes the size; none change the shape.
OL **DOK 2** *Skills/Concepts*	What are the vertices of the original image and the vertices of the final image in their corresponding order? Sample answer: original: $(-6, 8), (-2, 8), (-2, 6), (-6, 6)$; final image: $(-3, -6), (-3, 6), (3, 6), (3, -6)$
BL **DOK 3** *Strategic Thinking*	Suppose the preimage rectangle is labeled *VWXY*, read clockwise from top left. Tell whether the corresponding image vertices after the transformation in each part (Parts A–E) are read clockwise or counterclockwise. A: clockwise; B: counterclockwise; C: counterclockwise; D: counterclockwise; E: counterclockwise

LEVELED QUESTIONS: **AL** Approaching Level | **OL** On Level | **BL** Beyond Level

Reflect

1. Which transformation represents the dilation? How can you tell?

   $(x, y) \rightarrow (3x, 3y)$; the algebraic form of a dilation is

   $(x, y) \rightarrow (kx, ky)$; in this case, $k = 3$.

2. A sequence of transformations containing a single dilation is applied to a figure. Are the original figure and its final image congruent? Explain.

   No; the dilation would shrink or expand the figure so

   that it and its final image would not be the same size.

Math On the Spot
my.hrw.com

Similar Figures

Two figures are **similar** if one can be obtained from the other by a sequence of translations, reflections, rotations, and dilations. Similar figures have the same shape but may be different sizes.

When you are told that two figures are similar, there must be a sequence of translations, reflections, rotations, and/or dilations that can transform one to the other.

EXAMPLE 1

A Identify a sequence of transformations that will transform figure *A* into figure *B*. Tell whether the figures are congruent. Tell whether they are similar.

My Notes

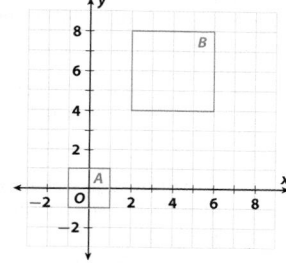

Both figures are squares whose orientations are the same, so no reflection or rotation is needed. Figure *B* has sides twice as long as figure *A*, so a dilation with a scale factor of 2 is needed. Figure *B* is moved to the right and above figure *A*, so a translation is needed. A sequence of transformations that will accomplish this is a dilation by a scale factor of 2 centered at the origin followed by the translation $(x, y) \rightarrow (x + 4, y + 6)$. The figures are not congruent, but they are similar.

328 Unit 4

© Houghton Mifflin Harcourt Publishing Company

3 Explain

EXAMPLE 1

ADDITIONAL EXAMPLE 1

A Identify a sequence of transformations that will transform figure *A* into figure *B*.

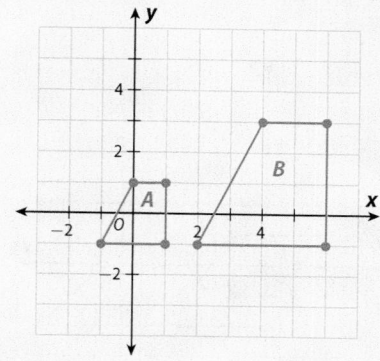

$(x, y) \rightarrow (2x, 2y), (x, y) \rightarrow (x + 4, y + 1)$

(Continued on page 329)

 Interactive Whiteboard
Interactive example available online

	EXAMPLE 1
(AL) DOK 1 *Recall*	Which transformation produces a similar image but not necessarily a congruent image? dilation
(OL) DOK 2 *Skills/Concepts*	What is a sequence of transformations that will transform figure *B* back into figure *A*? Perform the translation $(x, y) \rightarrow (x - 4, y - 6)$, followed by a dilation centered at the origin with a scale factor of 0.5.
(BL) DOK 3 *Strategic Thinking*	In Part B, describe the image of reflecting figure *C* across the *x*-axis. How are the corresponding vertices affected? Figure *C* would look the same after a reflection across the *x*-axis because the top and bottom halves are the same, but the corresponding vertices would be in different locations.

TEACHER TO TEACHER

Cooperative Learning Have students work in groups of four. Have one student draw a simple shape on a coordinate grid. Have two of the students come up with an algebraic sequence (include a dilation and at least two other transformations) that the fourth student will apply to the shape. Students should change roles and repeat this activity as much as time permits.

EXAMPLE 1 (continued)

ADDITIONAL EXAMPLE 1 *continued*

B Identify a sequence of transformations that will transform figure *C* into figure *D*. Include a reflection.

$(x, y) \rightarrow (-x, y), (x, y) \rightarrow (x + 1, y),$
$(x, y) \rightarrow (2x, 2y)$

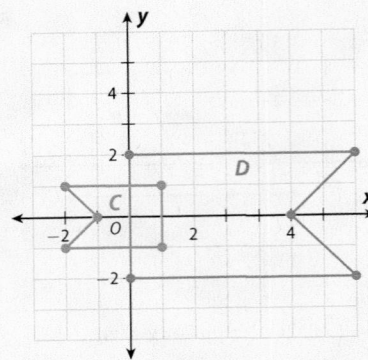

C Identify a sequence of transformations that will transform figure *C* into figure *D* in the figure in Part B. Include a rotation.

$(x, y) \rightarrow (-x, -y), (x, y) \rightarrow (x + 1, y),$
$(x, y) \rightarrow (2x, 2y)$

 Interactive Whiteboard
Interactive example available online

YOUR TURN   MP.5

Avoid Common Errors

If students cannot visualize the sequence of transformations, suggest they use a paper cut-out rectangle the same size and shape as the green rectangle that they can rotate and translate on a coordinate grid. Once the rectangle is centered on the origin in the proper orientation, it is ready for the dilation into figure *E*.

Digital Teacher Resources

Go online to access all your lesson-level resources.

Differentiated Instruction
• Reteach
• Reading Strategies
• Success for English Learners
• Practice and Problem Solving A/B, C, D
Math on the Spot Videos

my.hrw.com

B Identify a sequence of transformations that will transform figure *C* into figure *D*. Include a reflection. Tell whether the figures are congruent. Tell whether they are similar.

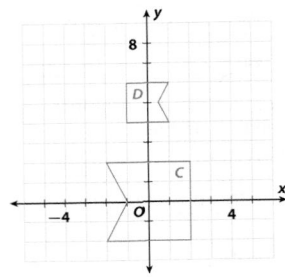

The orientation of figure *D* is reversed from that of figure *C*, so a reflection over the *y*-axis is needed. Figure *D* has sides that are half as long as figure *C*, so a dilation with a scale factor of $\frac{1}{2}$ is needed. Figure *D* is moved above figure *C*, so a translation is needed. A sequence of transformations that will accomplish this is a dilation by a scale factor of $\frac{1}{2}$ centered at the origin, followed by the reflection $(x, y) \rightarrow (-x, y)$, followed by the translation $(x, y) \rightarrow (x, y + 5)$. The figures are not congruent, but they are similar.

C Identify a sequence of transformations that will transform figure *C* into figure *D*. Include a rotation.

The orientation of figure *D* is reversed from that of figure *C*, so a rotation of 180° is needed. Figure *D* has sides that are half as long as figure *C*, so a dilation with a scale factor of $\frac{1}{2}$ is needed. Figure *D* is moved above figure *C*, so a translation is needed. A sequence of transformations that will accomplish this is a rotation of 180° about the origin, followed by a dilation by a scale factor of $\frac{1}{2}$ centered at the origin, followed by the translation $(x, y) \rightarrow (x, y + 5)$.

Math Talk
Mathematical Processes

A figure and its image have different sizes and orientations. What do you know about the sequence of transformations that generated the image?

The sequence must contain a dilation and at least one reflection or rotation.

YOUR TURN

3. Look again at the Explore Activity. Start with the original figure. Create a new sequence of transformations that will yield figure *E*, the final image. Your transformations do not need to produce the images in the same order in which they originally appeared.

Sample answer: $(x, y) \rightarrow (x + 7, y - 12)$; rotation 90° clockwise about the origin; $(x, y) \rightarrow (x + 5, y + 3)$; $(x, y) \rightarrow (3x, 3y)$

Personal
Math Trainer

Online Assessment
and Intervention

my.hrw.com

© Houghton Mifflin Harcourt Publishing Company

1. Apply the indicated sequence of transformations to the square. Apply each transformation to the image of the previous transformation. Label each image with the letter of the transformation applied. *(Explore Activity)*

    A $(x, y) \rightarrow (-x, y)$

    B Rotate the square 180° around the origin.

    C $(x, y) \rightarrow (x - 5, y - 6)$

    D $(x, y) \rightarrow \left(\frac{1}{2}x, \frac{1}{2}y\right)$

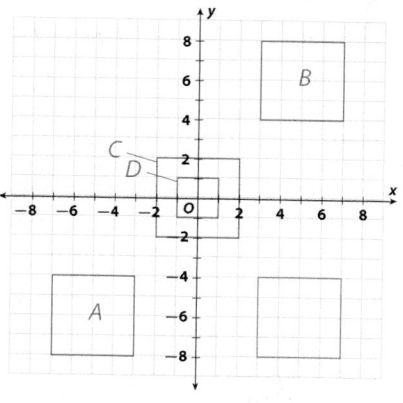

Identify a sequence of two transformations that will transform figure A into the given figure. *(Example 1)* Sample answers are given.

2. figure B

    $(x, y) \rightarrow (x, -y)$

    $(x, y) \rightarrow (x + 5, y - 6)$

3. figure C

    $(x, y) \rightarrow (x, y + 6)$

    rotate 90° counterclockwise

4. figure D

    $(x, y) \rightarrow (1.5x, 1.5y)$

    $(x, y) \rightarrow (x + 3, y + 5)$

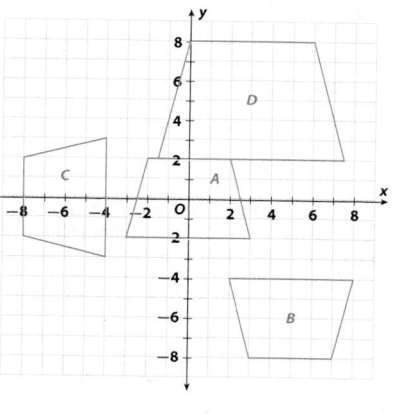

? ESSENTIAL QUESTION CHECK-IN

5. If two figures are similar but not congruent, what do you know about the sequence of transformations used to create one from the other?

    At least one transformation must be a dilation with a

    scale factor other than 1.

© Houghton Mifflin Harcourt Publishing Company

---

4 Elaborate

Talk About It

Summarize the Lesson

Ask: How do you know when a dilation has occurred? The image is either larger or smaller than the original figure, and the original figure and image are similar.

Guided Practice

Engage with the Whiteboard

For **Exercise 1**, have four volunteers take turns drawing the indicated series of transformations (A–D) to the blue square on the coordinate grid provided.

Avoid Common Errors

- **Exercises 2–3** Suggest students use a paper cut-out of trapezoid A and actually slide, turn, and flip it around until they can see the same orientation that figures B and C have.

- **Exercise 4** Suggest students use the length of the top base or the length of the height to determine the scale factor. The vertices of the bottom base of the enlarged trapezoid do not have whole number x-coordinate values.

DIFFERENTIATE INSTRUCTION *Intervention and Additional Support*

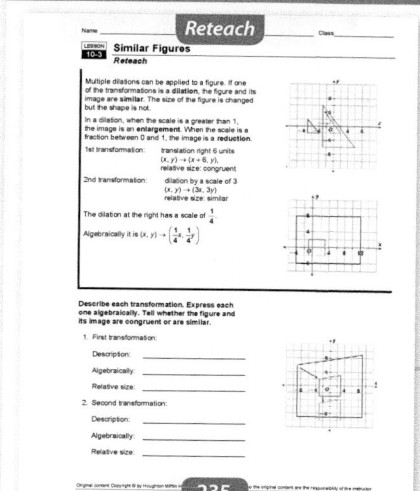

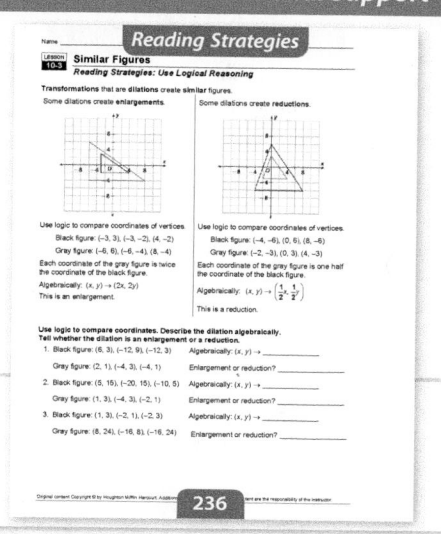

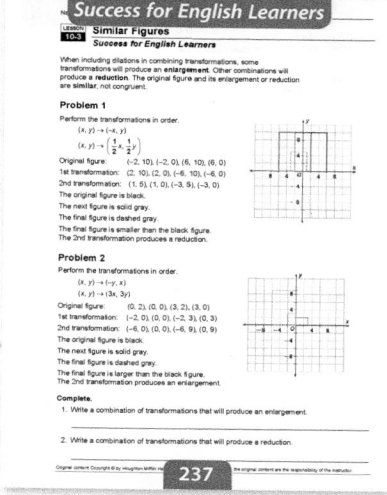

Personal Math Trainer
Daily Intervention
10.3 Homework

Pages shown are from *Differentiated Instruction*.
Also available online.

🕐 **Pressed for Time**

10.3 Differentiated Homework Assignments

(AL) **Approaching Level**	6–8, 10–11
(OL) **On Level**	7–11
(BL) **Beyond Level**	10–13

*For **Below Level** students, assign Personal Math Trainer, Daily Intervention 10.3 Homework.*

Mathematical Processes	Exercises
MP.2 Reasoning	13
MP.3 Logic	11
MP.4 Modeling	6–10, 12

Focus on Higher Order Thinking

Depth of Knowledge	Exercises
2 Skills/Concepts	6–10
3 Strategic Thinking **H.O.T.**	11–13

Name_____ Class_____ Date_____

Personal
Math Trainer

Online
Assessment and
Intervention
my.hrw.com

6. A designer creates a drawing of a triangular sign on centimeter grid paper for a new business. The drawing has sides measuring 6 cm, 8 cm, and 10 cm, and angles measuring 37°, 53°, and 90°. To create the actual sign shown, the drawing must be dilated using a scale factor of 40.

Jan's Café

a. Find the lengths of the sides of the actual sign.

240 cm, 320 cm, 400 cm

b. Find the angle measures of the actual sign.

37°, 53°, 90°

c. The drawing has the hypotenuse on the bottom. The business owner would like it on the top. Describe two transformations that will do this.

Reflect the drawing over the x-axis; rotate the drawing 180° around the origin.

d. The shorter leg of the drawing is currently on the left. The business owner wants it to remain on the left after the hypotenuse goes to the top. Which transformation in part c will accomplish this?

Reflecting over the x-axis

In Exercises 7–10, the transformation of a figure into its image is described. Describe the transformations that will transform the image back into the original figure. Then write them algebraically.

7. The figure is reflected across the x-axis and dilated by a scale factor of 3. Dilate the image by a scale factor of $\frac{1}{3}$ and reflect it back across the x-axis; $(x, y) \rightarrow (\frac{1}{3}x, \frac{1}{3}y)$, $(x, y) \rightarrow (x, -y)$.

8. The figure is dilated by a scale factor of 0.5 and translated 6 units left and 3 units up. Translate the image 3 units down and 6 units right and dilate it by a factor of 2; $(x, y) \rightarrow (x + 6, y - 3)$, $(x, y) \rightarrow (2x, 2y)$.

9. The figure is dilated by a scale factor of 5 and rotated 90° clockwise. Rotate the image 90° counterclockwise and dilate it by a factor of $\frac{1}{5}$; $(x, y) \rightarrow (-y, x)$, $(x, y) \rightarrow (\frac{1}{5}x, \frac{1}{5}y)$.

© Houghton Mifflin Harcourt Publishing Company

DIFFERENTIATE INSTRUCTION *Leveled Homework/Practice*

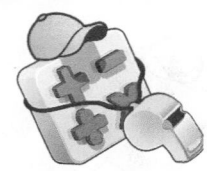

Personal Math Trainer
• 10.3 Homework

Pages shown are from *Differentiated Instruction*. **Also available online.**

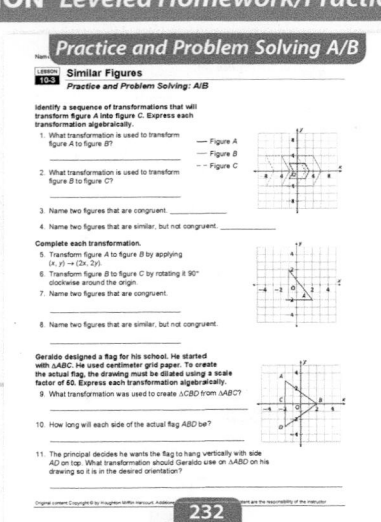

Practice and Problem Solving A/B

232

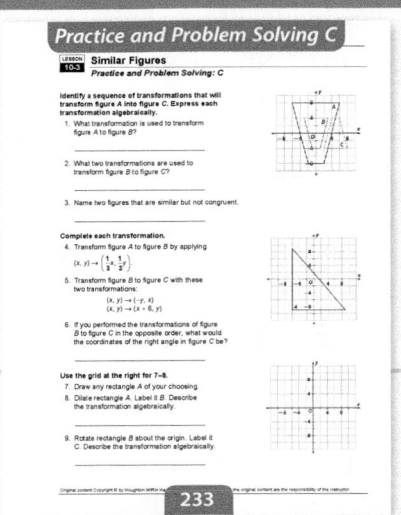

Practice and Problem Solving C

233

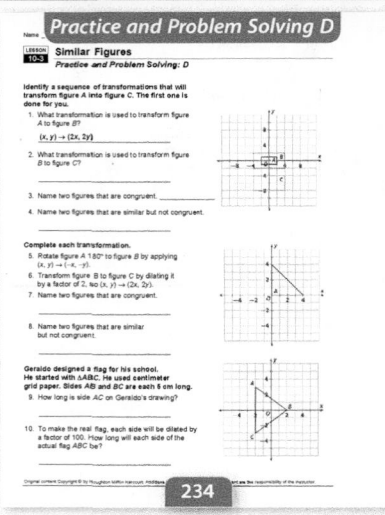

Practice and Problem Solving D

234

10. The figure is reflected across the y-axis and dilated by a scale factor of 4.

Dilate the image by a factor of $\frac{1}{4}$ and reflect it back

across the y-axis; $(x, y) \rightarrow (\frac{1}{4}x, \frac{1}{4}y)$, $(x, y) \rightarrow (-x, y)$.

 **FOCUS ON HIGHER ORDER THINKING**

11. Draw Conclusions A figure undergoes a sequence of transformations that include dilations. The figure and its final image are congruent. Explain how this can happen.

There can be an even number of dilations in pairs

where each has the opposite effect.

12. Multistep As with geometric figures, graphs can be transformed through translations, reflections, rotations, and dilations. Describe how the graph of $y = x$ shown at the right is changed through each of the following transformations.

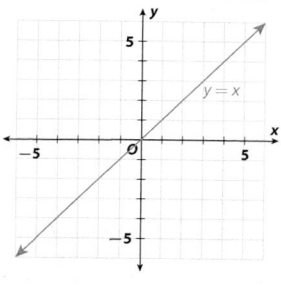

a. a dilation by a scale factor of 4

The transformed graph is

the same line, $y = x$, since

each transformed point is still on the line: $(0, 0) \rightarrow$

$(0, 0), (-1, -1) \rightarrow (-4, -4), (1, 1) \rightarrow (4, 4)$, and so on.

b. a translation down 3 units

The y-intercept moves from 0 to -3, but the slope

stays the same. The new equation is $y = x - 3$.

c. a reflection across the y-axis

The graph still goes through $(0, 0)$, but $(1, 1) \rightarrow (-1, 1)$,

so the new slope is -1. The new equation is $y = -x$.

13. Justify Reasoning The graph of the line $y = x$ is dilated by a scale factor of 3 and then translated up 5 units. Is this the same as translating the graph up 5 units and then dilating by a scale factor of 3? Explain.

No; dilate first: $(0, 0) \rightarrow (0, 0) \rightarrow (0, 5)$ and $(1, 1) \rightarrow (3, 3)$

$\rightarrow (3, 8)$, so $y = x + 5$; translate first: $(0, 0) \rightarrow (0, 5) \rightarrow$

$(0, 15)$ and $(1, 1) \rightarrow (1, 6) \rightarrow (3, 18)$, so $y = x + 15$.

Work Area

© Houghton Mifflin Harcourt Publishing Company

DIFFERENTIATE INSTRUCTION *Extend-the-Math Activity* **PRE-AP**

Activity Similar figures can be created by using a flashlight and a cardboard figure. The projection point (center of dilation) is the flashlight, and each point on the cardboard figure is mapped to exactly one point on the shadow created. The scale factor of the dilation is the distance a point on the shadow is from the projection point divided by the distance the corresponding point on the rectangle is from the projection point. Have one person hold a cardboard rectangle 36 inches from a wall and another person hold the flashlight 12 inches from the cardboard rectangle. Measure the lengths of the sides of the shadow and the cardboard rectangle. What is the scale factor of the dilation? 4

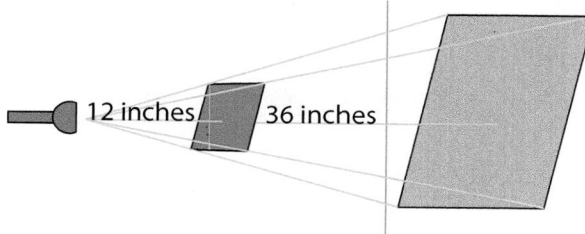
12 inches   36 inches

✓ Quick Check

10.3 Lesson Quiz

1. On a coordinate grid, graph a triangle with its vertices at $(-2, 0)$, $(-2, 6)$, and $(-8, 0)$. Then apply the indicated series of transformations to the triangle. The transformations in **b.** and **c.** are applied to the image of the previous transformation, not the original figure. Label each image with the letter of the transformation applied.

A $(x, y) \rightarrow (-x, y)$

B Rotation 90° clockwise about the origin

C $(x, y) \rightarrow (0.5x, 0.5y)$

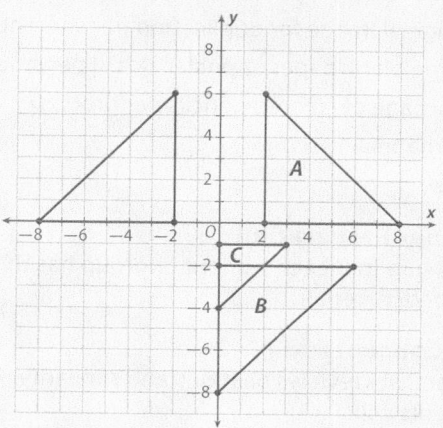

2. Identify a sequence of transformations that will transform figure A into figure B.

$(x, y) \rightarrow (0.5x, 0.5y)$, $(x, y) \rightarrow (x + 3, y - 2)$

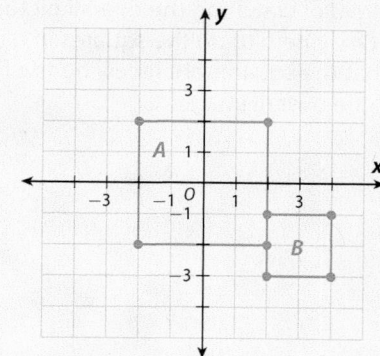

Differentiate Instruction

IF a student misses more than one question, THEN

Differentiate Instruction:

• 10.3 Reteach

• Personal Math Trainer

 Interactive Whiteboard
Interactive Lesson quiz available online

Copy-Cat

Objective
Students will use properties of similar figures to reproduce a dilation.

Grouping
2 students per group (optional)

Materials
- 1 piece of tracing paper per student
- 1 original image for duplication per student
- 1 large blank paper or poster board per student
- 1 package of colored pencils per group
- grid paper
- tape

Teacher Preparation
Make sure that each student or group has the required materials.

Key Concepts
This activity reviews dilations and similarity. Students will:
- divide an image into parts
- create dilations of all the parts to create a dilation of the whole

Encourage students to focus only on one square at a time instead of watching the overall picture develop. It may help to do the squares in random order so that the squares are receiving the focus instead of the overall image.

© Houghton Mifflin Harcourt Publishing Company · Photo credit: © Getty Images

WARM-UP EXERCISES

1. A photo is 12 inches wide by 18 inches tall. If the width is scaled down to 9 inches, how tall should the similar photo be? 13.5 inches

2. A picture of a school's mascot is 18 inches wide and 24 inches long. It is enlarged proportionally to banner size. If the width is enlarged to 63 inches, what is the length of the banner? 84 inches

STEP 3 Create a blank grid on your large blank piece of paper or poster board. The blank grid should have the same number of squares as the grid on the tracing paper over the original image. The squares do not need to be the same size as those on the tracing paper.

STEP 4 Copy exactly the appearance of each square from the original image onto the corresponding square of the blank grid on the large piece of paper or poster board.

Be careful not to focus on the overall picture, only focus on one square at a time. It may help to do the squares in random order so that the squares are receiving the focus instead of the overall image.

© Houghton Mifflin Harcourt Publishing Company

STEP 5 When you have copied all of the squares, the drawing on your finished grid should look like a dilation or copy of the original image.

Instructions

STEP 1 Students should use tape to secure the tracing paper on the grid, and trace the grid lines onto the tracing paper.

STEP 2 Students should remove the tracing paper from the grid paper and securely tape the tracing paper over the image that will be copied. Remind students to leave the tracing paper attached to the original image when submitting their work.

STEP 3 Students should create a blank grid on the large blank piece of paper or poster board. Make sure the blank grid has the same number of squares as the grid drawn on tracing paper. The squares do not need to be the same size as those on the tracing paper.

STEP 4 Have students copy exactly the appearance of *each square* from the original image onto the corresponding square of the blank grid on the large piece of paper or poster board.

TEACHER NOTES

• **Extension** Let students explore how an overhead projector can be used to create similar figures. Have them use an overhead projector to enlarge a drawing or picture for display in the classroom.

Ready to Go On?

Assess Mastery

Access *Ready to Go On?* assessment online, and receive instant scoring, feedback, and customized intervention or enrichment.

Personal Math Trainer

Online Assessment and Intervention
- Module 10 Posttest

Additional Resources

Digital Teacher Resources

Go online for module-level resources.

Assessment Resources
- Module 10 Quiz: B, p.51
- Module 10 Quiz: D, p.53

my.hrw.com

Ready to Go On?

Personal Math Trainer
Online Assessment and Intervention
my.hrw.com

10.1 Properties of Dilations

Determine whether one figure is a dilation of the other. Justify your answer.

1. Triangle *XYZ* has angles measuring 54° and 29°. Triangle *X′Y′Z′* has angles measuring 29° and 92°.

   No; the triangles have only one pair of congruent angles.

2. Quadrilateral *DEFG* has sides measuring 16 m, 28 m, 24 m, and 20 m. Quadrilateral *D′E′F′G′* has sides measuring 20 m, 35 m, 30 m, and 25 m.

   Yes; each side of the second figure is 1.25 times the

   corresponding side of the original figure.

10.2 Algebraic Representations of Dilations

Dilate each figure with the origin as the center of dilation.

3. $(x, y) \rightarrow (0.8x, 0.8y)$

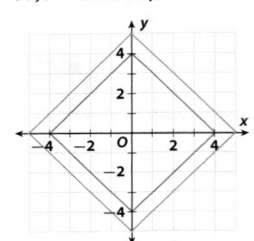

4. $(x, y) \rightarrow (2.5x, 2.5y)$

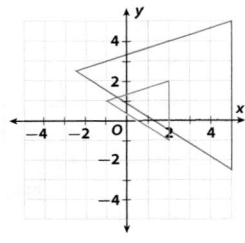

10.3 Similar Figures

5. Describe what happens to a figure when the given sequence of transformations is applied to it: $(x, y) \rightarrow (-x, y)$; $(x, y) \rightarrow (0.5x, 0.5y)$; $(x, y) \rightarrow (x - 2, y + 2)$

   reflection over the *y*-axis; dilation with a scale factor of

   0.5; translation 2 units left and 2 units up

 **ESSENTIAL QUESTION**

6. How can you use dilations to solve real-world problems?

   You can use dilations when drawing blueprints.

Module 10 **333**

© Houghton Mifflin Harcourt Publishing Company

READY TO GO ON? *Diagnostic Assessment*

RtI Response to Intervention

Use to determine if students have mastered the concepts covered in this module.

Lesson	Exercises	Content Focus	Review with *Differentiated Instruction*
10.1	1–2	Properties of Dilations	**10.1** Reteach **10.1** Reading Strategies **10.1** Success for English Learners
10.2	3–4	Algebraic Representations of Dilations	**10.2** Reteach **10.2** Reading Strategies **10.2** Success for English Learners
10.3	5	Similar Figures	**10.3** Reteach **10.3** Reading Strategies **10.3** Success for English Learners

Assessment Readiness

Personal
Math Trainer

Online
Assessment and
Intervention

my.hrw.com

Selected Response

1. A rectangle has vertices (6, 4), (2, 4), (6, −2), and (2, −2). What are the coordinates of the vertices of the image after a dilation with the origin as its center and a scale factor of 1.5?

Ⓐ (9, 6), (3, 6), (9, −3), (3, −3)

Ⓑ (3, 2), (1, 2), (3, −1), (1, −1)

Ⓒ (12, 8), (4, 8), (12, −4), (4, −4)

Ⓓ (15, 10), (5, 10), (15, −5), (5, −5)

2. Which represents the dilation shown where the black figure is the preimage?

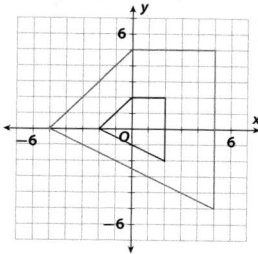

Ⓐ $(x, y) \rightarrow (1.5x, 1.5y)$

Ⓑ $(x, y) \rightarrow (2.5x, 2.5y)$

Ⓒ $(x, y) \rightarrow (3x, 3y)$

Ⓓ $(x, y) \rightarrow (6x, 6y)$

3. Identify the sequence of transformations that will reflect a figure over the x-axis and then dilate it by a scale factor of 3.

Ⓐ $(x, y) \rightarrow (−x, y); (x, y) \rightarrow (3x, 3y)$

Ⓑ $(x, y) \rightarrow (−x, y); (x, y) \rightarrow (x, 3y)$

Ⓒ $(x, y) \rightarrow (x, −y); (x, y) \rightarrow (3x, y)$

Ⓓ $(x, y) \rightarrow (x, −y); (x, y) \rightarrow (3x, 3y)$

4. Solve $−a + 7 = 2a − 8$.

Ⓐ $a = −3$

Ⓑ $a = −\frac{1}{3}$

Ⓒ $a = 5$

Ⓓ $a = 15$

5. Which equation does **not** represent a line with an x-intercept of 3?

Ⓐ $y = −2x + 6$

Ⓑ $y = −\frac{1}{3}x + 1$

Ⓒ $y = \frac{2}{3}x − 2$

Ⓓ $y = 3x − 1$

Mini-Task

6. The square is dilated under the dilation $(x, y) \rightarrow (0.25x, 0.25y)$.

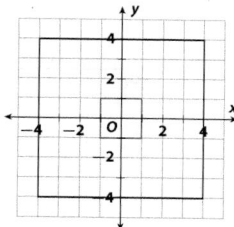

a. Graph the image. What are the coordinates?

$(−1, 1), (1, 1), (1, −1), (−1, −1)$

b. What is the length of a side of the image?

2 units

c. What are the perimeter and area of the preimage?

32 units; 64 square units

d. What are the perimeter and area of the image?

8 units; 4 square units

© Houghton Mifflin Harcourt Publishing Company

Preparing for High Stakes Tests

Assessment Readiness Tip

Students should distinguish problems where they can quickly solve the problem and match their answer to the correct answer choice from context-based items where it is impossible to find the answer by reading the stem in isolation.

- **Item 1** Students should multiply the given coordinates by 1.5 and find the corresponding answer choice. There is no need to determine the scale factor of each answer choice.

- **Item 5** Here, it is impossible to find the correct answer without examining the answer choices, but straightforward if the answer choices are looked at in turn, substituting 0 for y and solving for x.

Avoid Common Errors

- **Item 2** Encourage students to actually calculate the ratio between the coordinates of one pair of corresponding vertices rather than trying to identify the ratio by estimating the relative sizes of the figures. Answer choices A, B, and C are all reasonable estimates, but only B is correct.

- **Item 3** Encourage students to test their answer with sample coordinates, especially for the first step. They may be confused about which coordinate has the sign change when reflected over the x-axis.

Items	Grade 8 Lessons	Mathematical Processes
1	10.1, 10.2	MP.4
2	10.2	MP.4
3	10.2, 10.3	MP.4
4*	7.1	MP.2
5*	4.2	MP.2
6	10.1, 10.2	MP.4

Item integrates mixed review concepts from previous modules or a previous course.

DIFFERENTIATE ASSESSMENT

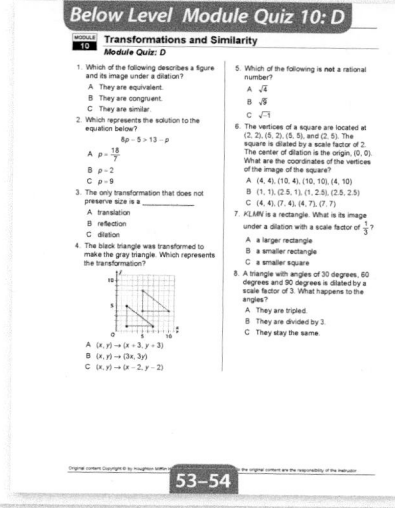

Below Level Module Quiz 10: D

53–54

On Level Module Quiz 10: B

51–52

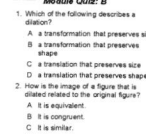

Personal Math Trainer
Module 10
Assessment Readiness

Pages shown are from *Assessment Resources*. **Also available online.**

UNIT 4

Transformational Geometry

Study Guide Review

Vocabulary Development

Integrating Language Arts

Encourage students to practice using the unit vocabulary as they talk and write about mathematics. Understanding vocabulary will aid their understanding of the concepts.

MODULE 9

Transformations and Congruence

Key Concepts

- A transformation is a function that changes the position, size, or shape of a figure. *(Lesson 9.1)*
- Translations, reflections, and rotations are transformations that preserve the size and shape of the preimage. *(Lessons 9.1, 9.2, 9.3)*
- A translation is a transformation that slides a figure along a straight line. *(Lesson 9.1)*
- A reflection is a transformation that flips a figure across a line. Each point and its image are the same distance from the line of reflection. *(Lesson 9.2)*
- A rotation is a transformation that turns a figure around a point called the center of rotation. *(Lesson 9.3)*

MODULE 9 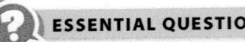 **Transformations and Congruence**

© Houghton Mifflin Harcourt Publishing Company

Key Vocabulary

center of rotation *(centro de rotación)*
congruent *(congruente)*
image *(imagen)*
line of reflection *(línea de reflexión)*
preimage *(imagen original)*
reflection *(reflexión)*
rotation *(rotación)*
transformation *(transformación)*
translation *(traslación)*

? ESSENTIAL QUESTION

How can you use transformations and congruence to solve real-world problems?

EXAMPLE

Translate triangle *XYZ* left 4 units and down 2 units. Graph the image and label the vertices.

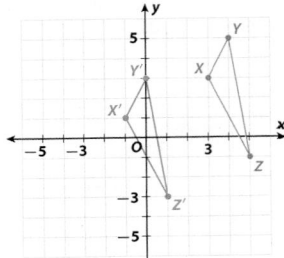

Translate the vertices by subtracting 4 from each *x*-coordinate and 2 from each *y*-coordinate. The new vertices are $X'(-1, 1)$, $Y'(0, 3)$, and $Z'(1, -3)$.

Connect the vertices to draw triangle $X'Y'Z'$.

EXERCISES

Perform the transformation shown. (Lessons 9.1, 9.2, 9.3)

1. Reflection over the *x*-axis

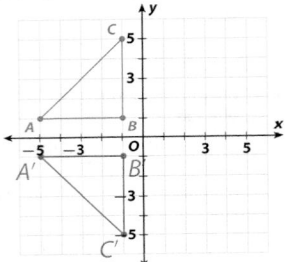

2. Translation 5 units right

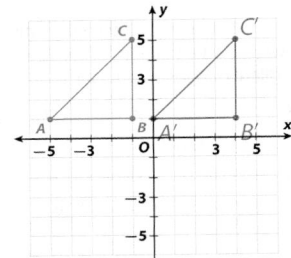

3. Rotation 90° counterclockwise about the origin

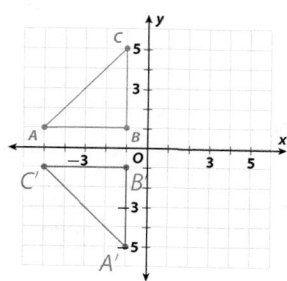

4. Translation 4 units right and 4 units down

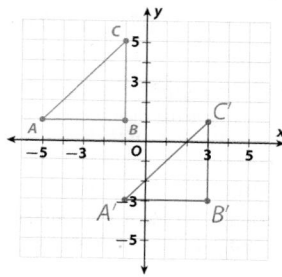

5. Quadrilateral *ABCD* with vertices *A*(4, 4), *B*(5, 1), *C*(5, −1) and *D*(4, −2) is translated left 2 units and down 3 units. Graph the preimage and the image. (Lesson 9.4)

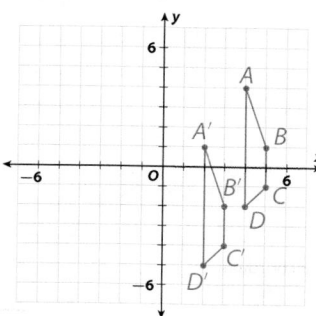

6. Triangle *ABC* with vertices *A*(1, 2), *B*(1, 4), and *C*(3, 3) is translated by $(x, y) \rightarrow (x - 4, y)$, and the result is reflected by $(x, y) \rightarrow (x, -y)$. Graph the preimage and the image. (Lesson 9.5)

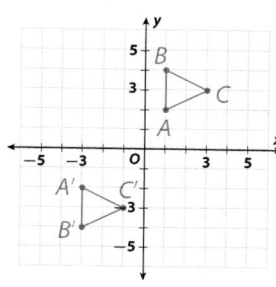

7. Triangle *RST* has vertices at (−8, 2), (−4, 0), and (−12, 8). Find the vertices after the triangle has been reflected over the *y*-axis. (Lesson 9.4)

(8, 2), (4, 0), (12, 8)

8. Triangle *XYZ* has vertices at (3, 7), (9, 14), and (12, −1). Find the vertices after the triangle has been rotated 180° about the origin. (Lesson 9.4)

(−3, −7), (−9, −14), (−12, 1)

9. Triangle *MNP* has its vertices located at (−1, −4), (−2, −5), and (−3, −3). Find the vertices after the triangle has been reflected by $(x, y) \rightarrow (x, -y)$ and translated by $(x, y) \rightarrow (x + 6, y)$. (Lesson 9.5)

(5, 4), (4, 5), (3, 3)

© Houghton Mifflin Harcourt Publishing Company

Key Concepts

- To reflect an image over the *x*-axis, change the sign of the *y*-coordinates, and to reflect an image over the *y*-axis, change the sign of the *x*-coordinates. **(Lesson 9.4)**

- After translations, reflections, and rotations, the image is always the same shape and size as the preimage. These transformations result in a congruent image from the preimage. **(Lesson 9.5)**

Transformations and Similarity

Key Concepts

- A dilation is a transformation that changes the position and size but not the shape of a figure. *(Lesson 10.1)*

- The scale factor of a dilation describes how much the figure is enlarged or reduced and is the ratio of a length of the image to the corresponding length of the preimage. *(Lesson 10.1)*

- To find the coordinates of a dilated image with the origin as the center, multiply the *x*- and *y*-coordinates of the vertices by the scale factor. *(Lesson 10.2)*

- If two figures are similar, then there exists a sequence of translations, reflections, rotations, and/or dilations that transforms one figure into the other. *(Lesson 10.3)*

MODULE 10 Transformations and Similarity

Key Vocabulary
center of dilation *(centro de dilatación)*
dilation *(dilatación)*
enlargement *(agrandamiento)*
reduction *(reducción)*
scale factor *(factor de escala)*
similar *(semejantes)*

? ESSENTIAL QUESTION

How can you use dilations, similarity, and proportionality to solve real-world problems?

EXAMPLE

Dilate triangle *ABC* with the origin as the center of dilation and scale factor $\frac{1}{2}$. Graph the dilated image.

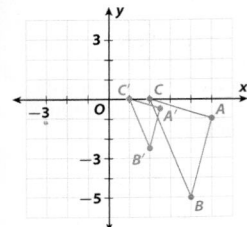

Multiply each coordinate of the vertices of *ABC* by $\frac{1}{2}$ to find the vertices of the dilated image.

$A(5, -1) \rightarrow A'\left(5 \cdot \frac{1}{2}, -1 \cdot \frac{1}{2}\right) \rightarrow A'\left(2\frac{1}{2}, -\frac{1}{2}\right)$

$B(4, -5) \rightarrow B'\left(4 \cdot \frac{1}{2}, -5 \cdot \frac{1}{2}\right) \rightarrow B'\left(2, -2\frac{1}{2}\right)$

$C(2, 0) \rightarrow C'\left(2 \cdot \frac{1}{2}, 0 \cdot \frac{1}{2}\right) \rightarrow C'(1, 0)$

EXERCISES

1. For each pair of corresponding vertices, find the ratio of the *x*-coordinates and the ratio of the *y*-coordinates. (Lesson 10.1)

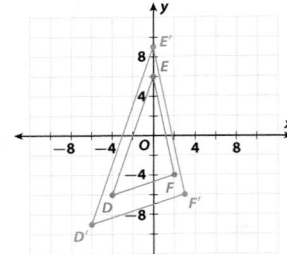

Ratio of *x*-coordinates: _____1.5_____

Ratio of *y*-coordinates: _____1.5_____

What is the scale factor of the dilation? _____1.5_____

2. Rectangle *WXYZ* has vertices at $(-2, -1)$, $(-2, 1)$, $(2, -1)$, and $(2, 1)$. It is first dilated by $(x, y) \rightarrow (2x, 2y)$, and then translated by $(x, y) \rightarrow (x, y + 3)$. (Lesson 10.3)

   a. What are the vertices of the image? _____$(-4, 1), (-4, 5), (4, 1), (4, 5)$_____

   b. Are the preimage and image congruent? Are they similar? Explain.

   They are not congruent because the lengths of the corresponding sides of the image and preimage are not equal; they are similar because they have the same shape.

© Houghton Mifflin Harcourt Publishing Company

Dilate each figure with the origin as the center of the dilation. List the vertices of the dilated figure then graph the figure. (Lesson 10.2)

3. $(x, y) \rightarrow \left(\frac{1}{4}x, \frac{1}{4}y\right)$
  X'(−2, 1); Y'(−1, 1); Z'(1, 2)

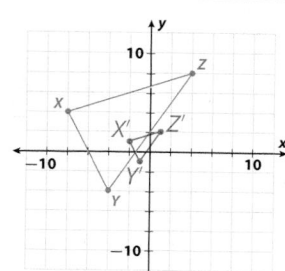

4. $(x, y) \rightarrow (2x, 2y)$
  A'(−2, 4); B'(4, 4); C'(6, −2); D'(0, −2)

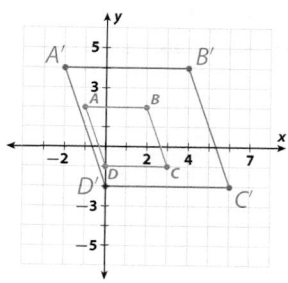

Unit 4 Performance Tasks

1. **CAREERS IN MATH** Contractor Fernando is expanding his dog's play yard. The original yard has a fence represented by rectangle *LMNO* on the coordinate plane. Fernando hires a contractor to construct a new fence that should enclose 6 times as much area as the current fence. The shape of the fence must remain the same. The contractor constructs the fence shown by rectangle *L'M'N'O'*.

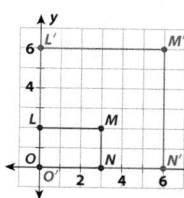

  a. Did the contractor increase the area by the amount Fernando wanted? Explain.

  Yes; the original area was 2 · 3 = 6 square units, and the new area is

  6 · 6 = 36 square units, and 6 · 6 = 36.

  b. Does the new fence maintain the shape of the old fence? How do you know?

  No; the corresponding side lengths are not in proportion. The ratio

  of the width is 2, and the ratio of the height is 3.

2. A sail for a sailboat is represented by a triangle on the coordinate plane with vertices (0, 0), (5, 0), and (5, 4). The triangle is dilated by a scale factor of 1.5 with the origin as the center of dilation. Find the coordinates of the dilated triangle. Are the triangles similar? Explain.

  (0, 0), (7.5, 0), and (7.5, 6); Yes; the angle measures are the same in both,

  and the ratio of corresponding side lengths is 1.5 (the scale factor).

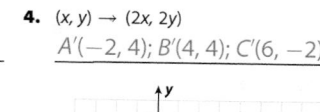

© Houghton Mifflin Harcourt Publishing Company

Performance Tasks

The Performance Tasks provide students with the opportunity to apply concepts from this unit in real-world problem situations.

CAREERS IN MATH

Contractor
In Performance Task Item 1, students can see how a contractor uses mathematics on the job.

Scoring Guides For Performance Tasks

1. **Mathematical Processes**

   MP.3, MP.4, MP.6

Task	Possible Points (Total: 6)
a	**1 point** for the correct answer yes, and **2 points** for correctly explaining that the area increased by a factor of 6, from 6 square units to 36 square units.
b	**1 point** for the correct answer no, and **2 points** for a correct explanation, for example: One side length increased by a factor of 2, and the other side length increased by a factor of 3.

2. **Mathematical Processes**

   MP.3, MP.4, MP.7

Possible Points   (Total: 6)
2 points for the correct points (0, 0), (7.5, 0), and (7.5, 6)
2 points for the correct answer yes, and **2 points** for correctly explaining that the angle measures are the same in both triangles, and the ratio of corresponding side lengths increase by the scale factor.

Assessment Readiness

Assessment Readiness Tip

Students can make a graph to help them understand questions for which graphs are not given.

- **Items 2 and 8** Students can make a graph, plot the points of the original image, and then perform the transformations on the figure. They can find the answer by looking at the coordinates of the vertices of the image they create.

- **Item 5** Students can quickly sketch a graph of a trapezoid and then translate it 8 units down. This allows them to check each statement using a concrete model of the situation.

Avoid Common Errors

- **Item 4** Some students will only check the first pair of values in the table to see if they work in the equations. In this case, three of the given equations are fulfilled by the first pair of values in the table. Remind them that they need to check multiple pairs of values to make sure the table and equation match each other.

- **Item 6** Some students will choose answer choice C because *x* and *y* are multiplied by coefficients less than one. Remind students that in a reduction, both variables must be multiplied by the same value.

Items	Grade 8 Lessons	Mathematical Processes
1	9.2	MP.2
2	9.4	MP.2
3	10.1	MP.1
4*	5.2	MP.2
5	9.1	MP.6
6	10.2	MP.2
7*	7.3	MP.2
8	10.2	MP.2
9*	8.2	MP.1
10*	1.2	MP.7
11*	8.3	MP.2
12	9.5	MP.4
13	10.2, 10.3	MP.1

* Item integrates mixed review concepts from previous modules or a previous course.

339 Unit 4

UNIT 4 MIXED REVIEW
Assessment Readiness

Personal Math Trainer
Online Assessment and Intervention
my.hrw.com

Selected Response

1. What would be the orientation of the figure below after a reflection over the *x*-axis?

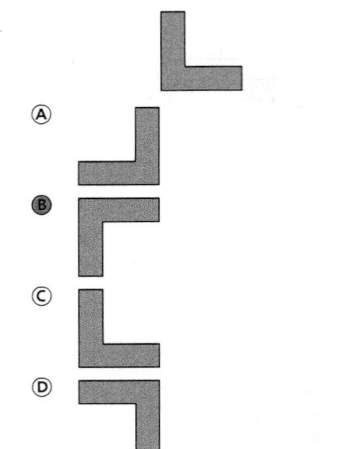

Ⓐ
Ⓑ
Ⓒ
Ⓓ

2. A triangle with coordinates (4, 2), (0, −3), and (−5, 3) is translated 5 units right and rotated 180° about the origin. What are the coordinates of its image?

Ⓐ (9, 2), (−1, −2), (5, −7)

Ⓑ (−10, 3), (−1, 2), (−5, −3)

Ⓒ (2, −1), (−3, −5), (3, −10)

Ⓓ (−9, −2), (−5, 3), (0, −3)

3. Quadrilateral *LMNP* has sides measuring 16, 28, 12, and 32. Which could be the side lengths of a dilation of *LMNP*?

Ⓐ 24, 40, 18, 90

Ⓑ 32, 60, 24, 65

Ⓒ 20, 35, 15, 40

Ⓓ 40, 70, 30, 75

4. The table below represents which equation?

x	−1	0	1	2
y	1	−2	−5	−8

Ⓐ $y = x + 2$

Ⓑ $y = -x$

Ⓒ $y = 3x + 6$

Ⓓ $y = -3x - 2$

5. Which of the following is **not** true of a trapezoid that has been translated 8 units down?

Ⓐ The new trapezoid is the same size as the original trapezoid.

Ⓑ The new trapezoid is the same shape as the original trapezoid.

Ⓒ The new trapezoid is in the same orientation as the original trapezoid.

Ⓓ The y-coordinates of the new trapezoid are the same as the y-coordinates of the original trapezoid.

6. Which represents a reduction?

Ⓐ $(x, y) \to (0.9x, 0.9y)$

Ⓑ $(x, y) \to (1.4x, 1.4y)$

Ⓒ $(x, y) \to (0.7x, 0.3y)$

Ⓓ $(x, y) \to (2.5x, 2.5y)$

7. Which is the solution for $4(x + 1) = 2(3x - 2)$?

Ⓐ $x = -4$

Ⓑ $x = -1$

Ⓒ $x = 0$

Ⓓ $x = 4$

DIFFERENTIATE ASSESSMENT

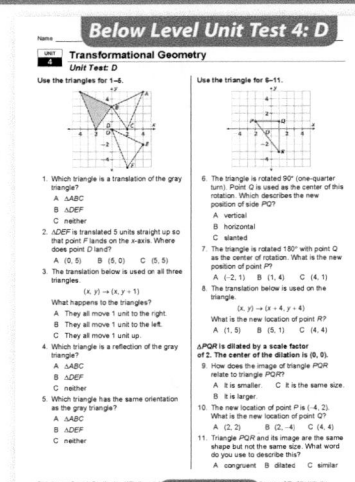

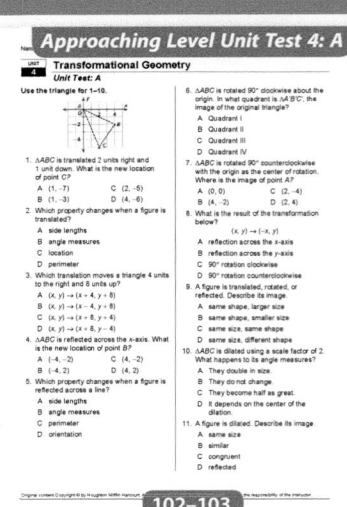

8. A rectangle has vertices (8, 6), (4, 6), (8, −4), and (4, −4). What are the coordinates after dilating from the origin by a scale factor of 1.5?

Ⓐ (9, 6), (3, 6), (9, −3), (3, −3)

Ⓑ (10, 8), (5, 8), (10, −5), (5, −5)

Ⓒ (16, 12), (8, 12), (16, −8), (8, −8)

Ⓓ (12, 9), (6, 9), (12, −6), (6, −6)

 Make sure you look at all answer choices before making your decision. Try substituting each answer choice into the problem if you are unsure of the answer.

9. Two apples plus four bananas cost $2.00. An apple costs twice as much as a banana. Using the equations $2a + 4b = 2.00$ and $a = 2b$, where a is the cost of one apple and b is the cost of one banana, what are a and b?

Ⓐ $a = \$0.25$; $b = \$0.25$

Ⓑ $a = \$0.25$; $b = \$0.50$

Ⓒ $a = \$0.50$; $b = \$0.25$

Ⓓ $a = \$0.50$; $b = \$0.50$

10. Which statement is false?

Ⓐ No integers are irrational numbers.

Ⓑ All whole numbers are integers.

Ⓒ No real numbers are rational numbers.

Ⓓ All integers greater than or equal to 0 are whole numbers.

11. Consider the system of equations $3x + 4y = 2$ and $2x − 4y = 8$. Which is its solution?

Ⓐ $x = −1, y = −2$

Ⓑ $x = 1, y = 2$

Ⓒ $x = −2, y = 1$

Ⓓ $x = 2, y = −1$

12. A triangle with vertices (−2, −3), (−4, 0), and (0, 0) is congruent to a second triangle located in quadrant I with two of its vertices at (3, 2) and (1, 5).

a. Graph the two triangles on the same coordinate grid.

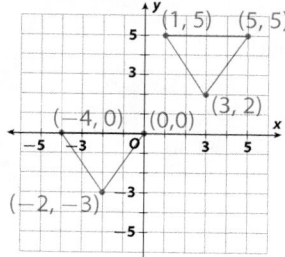

b. What are the coordinates of the third vertex of the second triangle?

(5, 5)

13. Tamiko is planning a stone wall shaped like a triangle, with vertices at (−1, −2), (2, 2), and (−2, 2) on a coordinate grid. She plans to add a second wall, in the same shape, enclosing the first wall, with the origin as the center of dilation. The vertices of the second wall are (−3, −6), (6, 6), and (−6, 6).

a. What scale factor did Tamiko use for the second wall?

3

b. Are the two walls similar? Explain.

Yes. Two figures are similar if one can be obtained from the other by dilation.

© Houghton Mifflin Harcourt Publishing Company

Additional Resources

 **Digital Teacher Resources**

Go online for unit-level resources.

Assessment Resources

• Leveled Unit Tests: A, B, C, D

• Unit Performance Task

my.hrw.com

On Level Unit Test 4: B

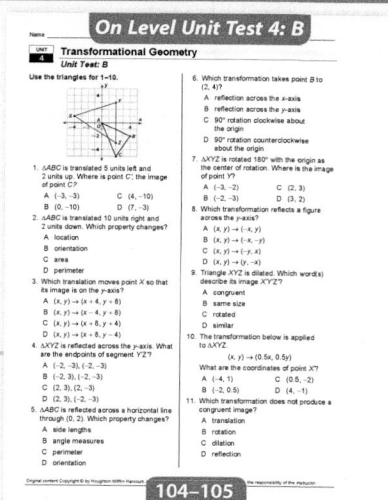

104–105

Beyond Level Unit Test 4: C

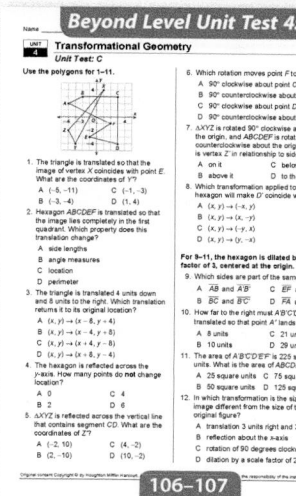

106–107

Unit 4 Performance Task

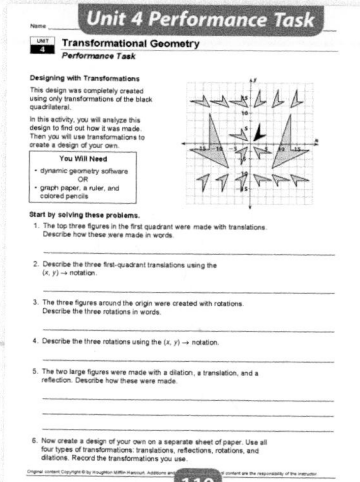

110

 **Personal Math Trainer**

Unit 4 Assessment Readiness

Pages shown are from *Assessment Resources*. **Also available online.**

Measurement Geometry

Contents

Teacher Notes

PLANNING AND PACING GUIDE
Instructional Path

Lesson	Lesson Objectives	Pacing*
UNIT 5	**Measurement Geometry**	
Progress Tracker 1 2 3 4 5 6		
MODULE 11	**Angle Relationships in Parallel Lines and Triangles**	1 day
11.1 Parallel Lines Cut by a Transversal	Students will make conclusions about the angles formed by parallel lines that are cut by a transversal.	3 days
11.2 Angle Theorems for Triangles	Students will make conclusions about the measures of the angles of a triangle.	3 days
11.3 Angle-Angle Similarity **Going Further 11.3** Similar Triangles and Slope	Students will determine how two triangles are similar. Students will apply the concept of similar triangles to prove that the slope of a line is constant between any two points on the line.	3 days
Ready to Go On? **Module 11 Assessment Readiness**		1 day
MODULE 12	**The Pythagorean Theorem**	1 day
12.1 The Pythagorean Theorem	Students will use the Pythagorean Theorem to solve problems.	2 days
12.2 Converse of the Pythagorean Theorem **Game 12.2** Triple Concentration	Students will test the converse of the Pythagorean Theorem and use it to solve problems. Students will form a list of Pythagorean triples and use the list in a game of concentration.	3 days
12.3 Distance Between Two Points	Students will use the Pythagorean Theorem to find the distance between two points on a coordinate plane.	2 days
Ready to Go On? **Module 12 Assessment Readiness**		1 day
MODULE 13	**Volume**	1 day
13.1 Volume of Cylinders	Students will find the volume of a cylinder.	2 days
13.2 Volume of Cones	Students will find the volume of a cone.	2 days
13.3 Volume of Spheres	Students will find the volume of a sphere.	2 days
Ready to Go On? **Module 13 Assessment Readiness**		1 day
Study Guide Review **Unit 5 Assessment Readiness**		2 days

* Based on a 45-minute class period

Teaching for Depth

Nonintersecting Lines

Two lines that do not intersect are parallel if they are in the same plane. Two lines that do not intersect and are not in the same line are called skew lines. In the figure below, $\overleftrightarrow{AB}$ and $\overleftrightarrow{CD}$ are skew lines.

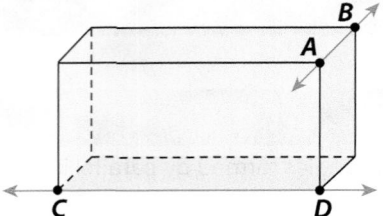

Sum of Interior Angles

The sum of the measures of the interior angles of a triangle is always 180°. This is true for any triangle. In polygons with more than three sides, the sum of the interior angles can be determined by drawing diagonals to divide the polygon into triangles. The number of triangles multiplied by 180° gives the sum of the interior angles. This leads to the general formula for the sum of the measures of the interior angles of any convex polygon with n sides: $(n - 2)180°$.

The Converse of the Pythagorean Theorem

Previously, students learned that if a triangle is a right triangle, then $a^2 + b^2 = c^2$, where a, b, and c are side lengths and c is the longest side. In this lesson, students learn that the converse of this statement is also true. When a conditional statement and its converse are both true, then the two statements can be combined to form a *biconditional* statement. For the Pythagorean Theorem and its converse, the biconditional statement can be stated this way: a triangle is a right triangle if and only if $a^2 + b^2 = c^2$, where a, b, and c are side lengths and c is the longest side.

The Pythagorean Theorem

The proof of the Pythagorean Theorem in the Explore Activity involves using physical objects to demonstrate that the theorem is true.

The Pythagorean Theorem can also be proved algebraically as follows:

The area of the outer square in the diagram below is $(a + b)^2$. The area of each triangle is $\frac{1}{2}ab$.

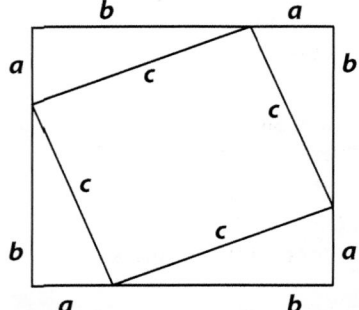

To find the area of the inner square in terms of a and b, subtract the area of the four triangles from the area of the outer square.

$$c^2 = (a + b)^2 - 4\left(\frac{1}{2}ab\right)$$
$$= a^2 + 2ab + b^2 - 2ab$$
$$= a^2 + b^2$$

Therefore, $c^2 = a^2 + b^2$.

> **Go Math** *integrates mathematical thinking, habits of mind, and processes into both the student and teacher materials so that they support instruction on a daily basis. In addition, Professional Development videos model successful ways to bring the mathematical practices and processes to life in your classroom.*

JULI DIXON on Integrating Mathematical Practices and Processes

Volume of Cylinders

The general formula $V = Bh$ can be applied to all prisms and cylinders. However, the formula used to calculate B, the area of the base, will differ due to the shape of the base.

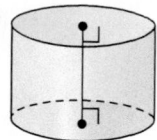 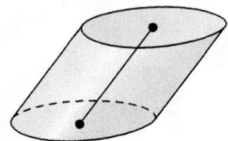

Right cylinder   Oblique cylinder

The cylinders in this lesson are *right cylinders* (with an axis perpendicular to the base) with circular bases. However, the same formula applies to *oblique* prisms and cylinders, based on Cavalieri's Principle: if two three-dimensional figures have the same height and the same cross-sectional area at every level, then they have the same volume.

Professional Development Videos

Module 12: The Pythagorean Theorem

Volume of Cones

A cone has two aspects that are referred to as *height*.

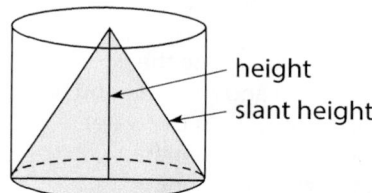

height
slant height

The *height* of the cone is the length of the segment from the vertex perpendicular to the center of the base. For a right circular cone, this height joins the vertex and the center of the base.

The *slant height* is the length of the segment from the vertex to any point on the circumference of the circular base. The slant height is used to find the lateral surface area of a cone.

Volume of Spheres

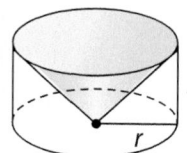 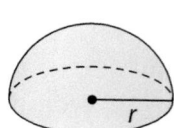

Archimedes derived the formula for the volume of a sphere by showing that a hemisphere with radius r and the solid remaining when the cone is removed from a cylinder with radius and height r have equal volumes.

$$(\pi r^2)r - \tfrac{1}{3}(\pi r^2)r = \tfrac{2}{3}(\pi r^2)r = \tfrac{2}{3}\pi r^3.$$

The volume of the sphere is thus twice that of the hemisphere, or $2(\tfrac{2}{3}\pi r^3) = \tfrac{4}{3}\pi r^3$.

MODULE 11
Angle Relationships in Parallel Lines and Triangles

MODULE 12
The Pythagorean Theorem

MODULE 13
Volume

CAREERS IN MATH

Hydrologist

A hydrologist uses math to determine the availability of water for urban and rural use and to understand and predict processes in the water cycle. You will learn more about this in the Performance Tasks at the end of the unit.

For more information about careers in mathematics as well as various mathematics appreciation topics, visit the American Mathematical Society at www.ams.org.

CAREERS IN MATH

Hydrologist A hydrologist is a scientist who studies and solves water-related issues. A hydrologist might work to prevent or clean up polluted water sources, locate water supplies for urban or rural needs, or control flooding and erosion. A hydrologist uses math to assess water resources and mathematical models to understand water systems, as well as statistics to analyze phenomena such as rainfall patterns. If you are interested in a career as a hydrologist, you should study the following mathematical subjects:
- Algebra
- Trigonometry
- Calculus
- Statistics

Research other careers that require creating and using mathematical models to understand physical phenomena.

Unit 5 Performance Task

At the end of the unit, check out how **hydrologists** use math.

Unit 5 **341**

Vocabulary Preview

Use the puzzle to preview key vocabulary from this unit. Unscramble the circled letters to answer the riddle at the bottom of the page.

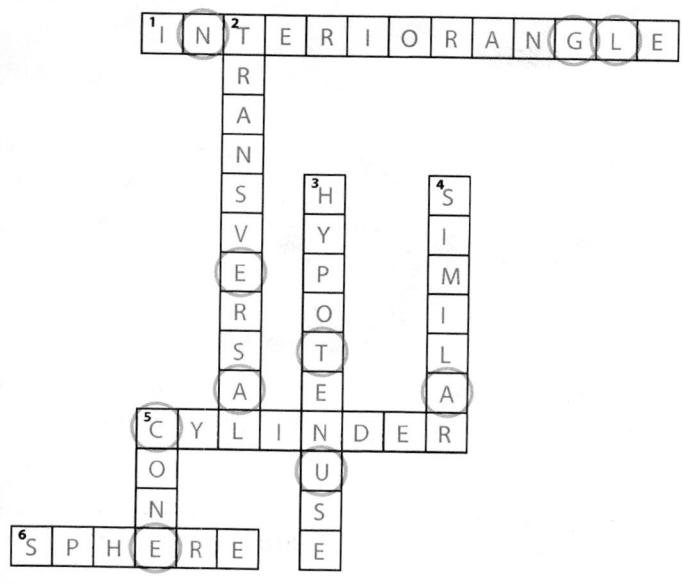

Across

1. The angle formed by two sides of a triangle (2 words) (Lesson 11.2)

5. A three-dimensional figure that has two congruent circular bases. (Lesson 13.1)

6. A three-dimensional figure with all points the same distance from the center. (Lesson 13.3)

Down

2. The line that intersects two or more lines. (Lesson 11.1)

3. The side opposite the right angle in a right triangle. (Lesson 12.1)

4. Figures with the same shape but not necessarily the same size. (Lesson 11.3)

5. A three-dimensional figure that has one vertex and one circular base. (Lesson 13.2)

Q: What do you call an angle that is adorable?

A: A C U T E   A N G L E !

© Houghton Mifflin Harcourt Publishing Company

Vocabulary Preview

Use the puzzle to give students a preview of important concepts in this unit. Students may work individually, in pairs, or in groups.

Digital Teacher Resources

Go online for unit-level resources.

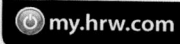

my.hrw.com

LEARNING PROGRESSIONS AND STANDARDS ACROSS THE GRADES

Before	In this Unit	After
Students understand: • angle pair relationships • volume of prisms	Students will learn about: • angle relationships of parallel lines and transversals • sum of the measures of the angles of a triangle • exterior angles of a triangle • similarity of triangles • the Pythagorean Theorem and its converse • the Distance Formula • volume of cylinders, cones, and spheres	Students will connect: • angle relationships and transversals of parallel lines • interior and exterior angles of a triangle • similar and congruent triangles • volume of a cylinder, a cone, and a sphere

Module At A Glance

MODULE 11 | Angle Relationships in Parallel Lines and Triangles

Lessons at A Glance	Lesson 11.1 Parallel Lines Cut by a Transversal	Lesson 11.2 Angle Theorems for Triangles	Lesson 11.3 Angle-Angle Similarity
	Pg. T347A	Pg. T353A	Pg. T361A
Essential Question	What can you conclude about the angles formed by parallel lines that are cut by a transversal?	What can you conclude about the measures of the angles of a triangle?	How can you determine when two triangles are similar?
Objective	Students will make conclusions about parallel lines that are cut by a transversal.	Students will make conclusions about the measures of the angles of a triangle.	Students will determine when two triangles are similar.
Vocabulary	alternate exterior angles, alternate interior angles, corresponding angles, same-side interior angles, transversal	exterior angle, interior angle, remote interior angle	similar figures, similar
Go online for all your module resources my.hrw.com	11.1 *i*Student Edition 11.1 *i*Teacher Edition 11.1 *e*Student Edition Personal Math Trainer Math on the Spot Videos Animated Math	11.2 *i*Student Edition 11.2 *i*Teacher Edition 11.2 *e*Student Edition Personal Math Trainer Math on the Spot Videos	11.3 *i*Student Edition 11.3 *i*Teacher Edition 11.3 *e*Student Edition Personal Math Trainer Math on the Spot Videos
Print Resources	**11.1 Student Edition:** Lesson *Differentiated Instruction* 11.1 Practice and Problem Solving A/B, C, and D 11.1 Reteach 11.1 Reading Strategies 11.1 Success for English Learners	**11.2 Student Edition:** Lesson *Differentiated Instruction* 11.2 Practice and Problem Solving A/B, C, and D 11.2 Reteach 11.2 Reading Strategies 11.2 Success for English Learners	**11.3 Student Edition:** Lesson **11.3 Student Edition:** Going Further *Differentiated Instruction* 11.3 Practice and Problem Solving A/B, C, and D 11.3 Reteach 11.3 Reading Strategies 11.3 Success for English Learners

RtI

Response to Intervention

	Before the Module	During the Lesson	After the Module
	Are You Ready	**Guided/Independent Practice**	**Ready to Go On?**
	• Prerequisite Skills Activities • Personal Math Trainer	• Reteach • Personal Math Trainer • Practice and Problem Solving D	• Reteach • Personal Math Trainer

Teacher Notes

Check It Out!

Math on the Spot Videos	Animated Math
One for every Example in every Lesson	During Lesson 11.1

Angle Relationships in Parallel Lines and Triangles

Real-World Video Viewing Guide

After students have watched the video, discuss the following:

- According to the video, what feature of Washington D.C. makes it easy to get around? Most of the streets of the city are laid out like a grid.

- What kind of line does Pennsylvania Avenue represent in the video? a transversal

Professional Development Video

Author Juli Dixon models successful teaching practices as she explores the concept of angle relationships in intersecting lines and triangles in an actual eighth-grade classroom.

© Houghton Mifflin Harcourt Publishing Company • Image Credits: ©Nifro Travel Images/Alamy Images

Angle Relationships in Parallel Lines and Triangles

MODULE 11

LESSON 11.1
Parallel Lines Cut by a Transversal

LESSON 11.2
Angle Theorems for Triangles

LESSON 11.3
Angle-Angle Similarity

 ESSENTIAL QUESTION

How can you use angle relationships in parallel lines and triangles to solve real-world problems?

You can use the relationships to find the measures of unknown angles in real-world situations.

Real-World Video

Many cities are designed on a grid with parallel streets. If another street runs across the parallel lines, it is a transversal. Special relationships exist between parallel lines and transversals.

my.hrw.com

GO DIGITAL
my.hrw.com

my.hrw.com
Go digital with your write-in student edition, accessible on any device.

Math On the Spot
Scan with your smart phone to jump directly to the online edition, video tutor, and more.

Animated Math
Interactively explore key concepts to see how math works.

Personal Math Trainer
Get immediate feedback and help as you work through practice sets.

343

TEACHER ONLINE RESOURCES

 ONLINE TEACHER EDITION Access a full suite of teaching resources online—plan, present, and manage classes and assignments.

 MY SMART PLANNER Easily plan your classes and access all your resources online.

 INTERACTIVE WHITEBOARDS Engage students with interactive whiteboard-ready examples and a lesson quiz for each lesson.

 PERSONAL MATH TRAINER: Online Assessment and Intervention Assign automatically graded homework, quizzes, tests, and intervention activities. Prepare your studentsfor standardized tests in short-answer and multiple-choice formats.

Reading Start-Up

Visualize Vocabulary

Use the ✔ words to complete the graphic. You can put more than one word in each section of the triangle.

Reviewing Angles

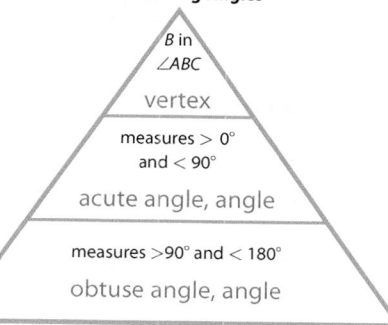

B in ∠*ABC*

vertex

measures > 0° and < 90°

acute angle, angle

measures >90° and < 180°

obtuse angle, angle

Understand Vocabulary

Complete the sentences using preview words.

1. A line that intersects two or more lines is a ___transversal___.

2. Figures with the same shape but not necessarily the same size are ___similar___.

3. An ___exterior angle___ is an angle formed by one side of the triangle and the extension of an adjacent side.

Active Reading

Pyramid Before beginning the module, create a pyramid to help you organize what you learn. Label each side with one of the lesson titles from this module. As you study each lesson, write important ideas like vocabulary, properties, and formulas on the appropriate side.

Vocabulary

Review Words

✔ acute angle *(ángulo agudo)*
✔ angle *(ángulo)*
   congruent *(congruente)*
✔ obtuse angle *(ángulo obtuso)*
   parallel lines *(líneas paralelas)*
✔ vertex *(vértice)*

Preview Words

alternate exterior angles *(ángulos alternos externos)*
alternate interior angles *(ángulos alternos internos)*
corresponding angles *(ángulos correspondientes (para líneas)*
exterior angle *(ángulo externo de un polígono)*
interior angle *(ángulos internos)*
remote interior angle *(ángulo interno remoto)*
same-side interior angles *(ángulos internos del mismo lado)*
similar *(semejantes)*
transversal *(transversal)*

© Houghton Mifflin Harcourt Publishing Company

Reading Start-Up

Visualize Vocabulary

The summary triangle helps students review the concepts related to angles and will help prepare them for the exercises in this module. Students should write one or more review words in each section of the triangle.

Understand Vocabulary

Use the following explanation to help students learn the preview words.

Angles are all around us. For example, streets that intersect form different angles. If one street crosses two parallel streets, it is a **transversal** *and creates special angles.* **Corresponding angles** *and* **same-side interior angles** *are formed on the same side of the transversal. Across the transversal from each other are the* **alternate interior** *and* **alternate exterior angles**.

Active Reading

Integrating Language Arts

Students can use these reading and note-taking strategies to help them organize and understand new concepts and vocabulary.

Additional Resources

Differentiated Instruction

- Reading Strategies **ELL**
- Interactive multilingual glossary

LEARNING PROGRESSIONS ACROSS THE GRADES

Before	In this Module	After
Students understand: • angle pair relationships • the sum of the angles of a triangle • similar shapes	Students represent and determine angle relationships: • angles formed by parallel lines that are cut by a transversal • the sum of the measures of the angles of a triangle • similarity of triangles	Students will connect: • classifying triangles by their angles and their sides • similar and congruent triangles

Are You Ready?

Assess Readiness

Access *Are You Ready?* assessment online, and receive instant scoring, feedback, and customized intervention or enrichment.

Personal Math Trainer

Online Assessment and Intervention

Additional Resources

Digital Teacher Resources

Go online for module-level resources.

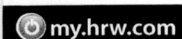
my.hrw.com

Are YOU Ready?

Complete these exercises to review skills you will need for this module.

Personal Math Trainer
Online Assessment and Intervention
my.hrw.com

Solve Two-Step Equations

EXAMPLE

$7x + 9 = 30$	Write the equation.
$7x + 9 - 9 = 30 - 9$	Subtract 9 from both sides.
$7x = 21$	Simplify.
$\frac{7x}{7} = \frac{21}{7}$	Divide both sides by 7.
$x = 3$	Simplify.

Solve for x.

1. $6x + 10 = 46$ **6**

2. $7x - 6 = 36$ **6**

3. $3x + 26 = 59$ **11**

4. $2x + 5 = -25$ **−15**

5. $6x - 7 = 41$ **8**

6. $\frac{1}{2}x + 9 = 30$ **42**

7. $\frac{1}{3}x - 7 = 15$ **66**

8. $0.5x - 0.6 = 8.4$ **18**

Name Angles

EXAMPLE

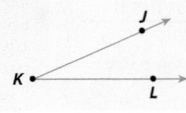

Use three points of an angle, including the vertex, to name the angle. Write the vertex between the other two points: $\angle JKL$ or $\angle LKJ$. You can also use just the vertex letter to name the angle if there is no danger of confusing the angle with another. This is also $\angle K$.

Give two names for the angle formed by the dashed rays.

9. $\angle MHR$ or $\angle RHM$

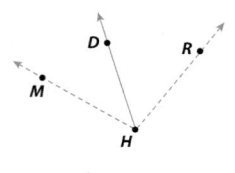

10. $\angle SGK$ or $\angle KGS$

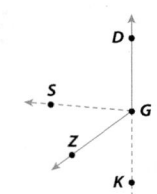

11. $\angle BTF$ or $\angle FTB$

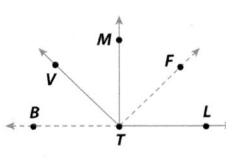

Module 11 **345**

ARE YOU READY? *Diagnostic Assessment*

RtI   Response to Intervention

Use to determine if students need intervention for the module's prerequisite skills.

Skill	Missed More Than . . .	Intervene With *Skills Intervention* worksheets (available online)	For Enrichment *Differentiated Instruction* (available in print and online)
Solve Two-Step Equations	3 questions	**Skill 60** Solve Two-Step Equations	**Module 11 Challenge** Extend-the-Math Lesson Activities in TE
Name Angles	1 question	**Skill 75** Name Angles	**Module 11 Challenge** Extend-the-Math Lesson Activities in TE

Complete these exercises to review skills you will need for this module.

Solve Two-Step Equations

12. a. Describe a plan to solve the equation $4x - 8 = 32$.

 b. Use your plan to solve the equation.

 a. Use the inverse of subtraction by adding 8 to both sides. Simplify both sides. Use the inverse of multiplication by dividing both sides by 4. Simplify.

 b.
$$4x - 8 = 32$$
$$4x - 8 + 8 = 32 + 8$$
$$4x = 40$$
$$\frac{4x}{4} = \frac{40}{4}$$
$$x = 10$$

13. Aisha solved the equation below as shown. What was her error?

$$\frac{1}{2}x + 4 = 18$$
$$\frac{1}{2}x + 4 - 4 = 18 - 4$$
$$\frac{1}{2}x = 14$$
$$\frac{1}{2} \cdot \frac{1}{2}x = \frac{1}{2} \cdot 14$$
$$x = 7$$

The inverse operation used to simplify $\frac{1}{2}x = 14$ should have been to multiply both sides by 2, not by $\frac{1}{2}$. Multiplying by 2 at this step gives the solution $x = 28$.

Name Angles

14. Enid says that the angle formed by ray SM and ray SN can be named as either $\angle MSN$ or $\angle NSM$. Andrew says it can be named as either $\angle SMN$ or $\angle SNM$. Who is correct? Explain.

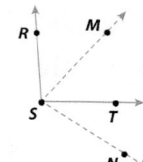

Enid is correct. When you use three points to name an angle, the vertex is always the point in the middle.

© Houghton Mifflin Harcourt Publishing Company

Solve Two-Step Equations

Exercise 12 Some students make the common error of subtracting 8 from both sides instead of adding 8. Suggest that they check their work carefully so that they can spot errors in the calculations.

Exercise 13 Point out that $\frac{1}{2}x$ represents $\frac{x}{2}$, so the correct inverse operation is to multiply both sides by 2.

Name Angles

Exercise 14 Have students identify the vertex of the angle. Check that students understand how to properly name an angle with the vertex in the middle.

Use to determine if students are able to apply the module's prerequisite skills.

Skill	Exercise	Depth of Knowledge (D.O.K.)	Mathematical Processes
Solve Two-Step Equations	12	**2** Skills/Concepts	**MP.7** See Structure
	13	**3** Strategic Thinking	**MP.3** Use and Evaluate Logical Reasoning
Name Angles	14	**3** Strategic Thinking	**MP.6** Use Precise Mathematical Language

Lesson Support

Content Objective Students will draw conclusions about the angles formed by parallel lines that are cut by a transversal.

Professional Development

Integrate Mathematical Processes MP.6

This lesson provides an opportunity to address this Mathematical Processes standard. It calls for students to communicate mathematical ideas and arguments using precise mathematical language. Students learn to recognize the relationships among the angles formed when two parallel lines intersect a transversal. Students learn the precise terms used to characterize these angles and describe their mathematical relationship.

FOCUS

Building Background

Visualizing Math Ask students to provide definitions of *supplementary angles* and *vertical angles*. Then have them use what they know about special angle relationships to find the missing angle measures of the intersecting lines. Discuss how they found the angle measures.

$m\angle A = 70°$; $m\angle B = 110°$; $m\angle C = 70°$

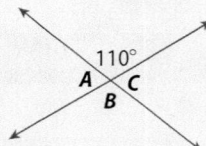

COHERENCE

Learning Progressions

In this lesson, students are introduced to the special angle relationships that occur when parallel lines are cut by a transversal. Important understandings for students include the following:

- **Identify angle pairs formed by a transversal.**
- **Justify angle relationships.**
- **Find unknown angle measures when two parallel lines are cut by a transversal.**

From earlier grades students are familiar with complementary, supplementary, and vertical angles. This lesson introduces students to the properties of the angle pairs formed by a transversal that intersects parallel lines. They use informal arguments to establish these special relationships, which students will continue to encounter as they explore geometry more formally in higher grades.

RIGOR

Cluster Connections

This lesson provides an excellent opportunity to connect ideas in the cluster:

Understand congruence and similarity using physical models, transparencies, or geometry software.

Show students the following figure:

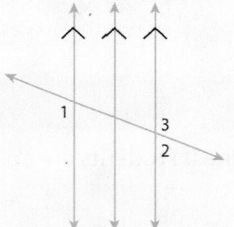

Ask them to find the measures of angles 1, 2, and 3, if $m\angle 1 = 8x°$ and $m\angle 2 = (5x° - 2)$. Have them justify their answers.

$m\angle 1 = 112°$; $m\angle 2 = 68°$; $m\angle 3 = 112°$; sample answer: The first line is parallel to the third line since all the lines are parallel. So, angles 1 and 2 are supplementary and angles 1 and 3 are congruent.

Language Support **ELL**

Language Objective Students will justify their conclusions about the angles formed by parallel lines that are cut by a transversal.

Leveled Strategies for English Learners **ELL**

Emerging
Have students at this level of English proficiency work in pairs to illustrate and label on graph paper examples of the four types of angle pairs formed from cutting parallel lines by a transversal.

Expanding
Have students work in pairs to illustrate on graph paper examples of the four types of angle pairs formed from cutting parallel lines by a transversal. Then have them list the names and descriptions of the angle pairs.

Bridging
Have students work with a partner to illustrate on graph paper the four types of angle pairs formed by a transversal. Then have them discuss and describe similarities and differences in the angle pairs.

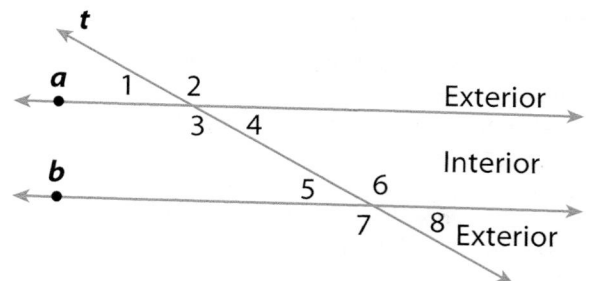

Math Talk To help students answer, use sentence frames and let the students work together.

_____ angles have the same measure, so they are _____.

Linguistic Support **ELL**

Academic/Content Vocabulary
This lesson relies on students' knowing and understanding the names of the angle pairs: *corresponding, alternate interior, alternate exterior,* and *same-side interior*. Point out to Spanish-speaking English learners that these angle pairs, except for same-side interior angles, are cognates with Spanish.

Building Background
ordinal numbers Ordinal numbers are numbers that show place or position. Point out to English learners that, except for *first (1 st), second (2 nd),* and *third (3 rd)* and numbers ending with the digit 1, 2, or 3, the rule for ordering numbers is consistent for all other numbers (for example, 4th, 80th, 1000th, $500,000^{th}$). Have English learners add this rule to their word journals for future reference.

Image Credits: ©Stockbyte/Getty Images

Parallel Lines Cut by a Transversal

1 Engage

ESSENTIAL QUESTION

What can you conclude about the angles formed by parallel lines that are cut by a transversal?
Sample answer: Eight angles are created by the intersection of two parallel lines and a transversal. Corresponding angles are congruent, alternate interior angles are congruent, alternate exterior angles are congruent, and same-side interior angles are supplementary.

Motivate the Lesson

Ask: Which angles are congruent when you draw two parallel lines and a third line that intersects both of the parallel lines? Begin the Explore Activity to find out.

2 Explore

EXPLORE ACTIVITY 1

Connect Vocabulary ELL

Explain that even though *corresponding angles* and *same-side interior angles* are both found on the same side of the transversal, they are not the same pair of angles. Corresponding angles have one angle on the exterior and one on the interior and are congruent, while same-side interior angles are both on the interior and are supplementary.

Parallel Lines Cut by a Transversal

8.5.11.1
Students will make conclusions about the angles formed by parallel lines that are cut by a transversal.

? ESSENTIAL QUESTION

What can you conclude about the angles formed by parallel lines that are cut by a transversal?

EXPLORE ACTIVITY 1

Parallel Lines and Transversals

A **transversal** is a line that intersects two lines in the same plane at two different points. Transversal *t* and lines *a* and *b* form eight angles.

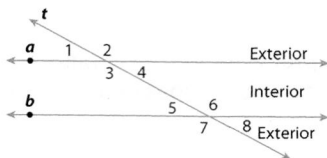

Angle Pairs Formed by a Transversal

Term	Example
Corresponding angles lie on the same side of the transversal *t*, on the same side of lines *a* and *b*.	∠1 and ∠5
Alternate interior angles are nonadjacent angles that lie on opposite sides of the transversal *t*, between lines *a* and *b*.	∠3 and ∠6
Alternate exterior angles lie on opposite sides of the transversal *t*, outside lines *a* and *b*.	∠1 and ∠8
Same-side interior angles lie on the same side of the transversal *t*, between lines *a* and *b*.	∠3 and ∠5

Use geometry software to explore the angles formed when a transversal intersects parallel lines.

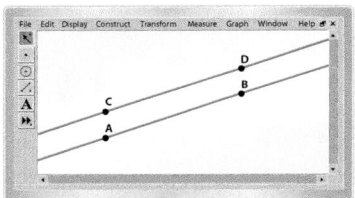

A Construct a line and label two points on the line A and B.

B Create point C not on $\overleftrightarrow{AB}$. Then construct a line parallel to $\overleftrightarrow{AB}$ through point C. Create another point on this line and label it D.

Lesson 11.1 **347**

DIFFERENTIATE INSTRUCTION *Leveled Questions*

	EXPLORE ACTIVITY 1
AL DOK 1 *Recall*	Can you name another example of each type of angle pair? Sample answer: corresponding ∠s 3, 7; alternate interior ∠s 4, 5; alternate exterior ∠s 2, 7; same-side interior ∠s 4, 6
OL DOK 2 *Skills/Concepts*	Which of the angle pairs formed by a transversal appear to form supplementary angles when the lines are parallel? same-side interior angles
BL DOK 3 *Strategic Thinking*	If two parallel lines intersect two other parallel lines at four different points, how many pairs of alternate interior angles are formed in all? Explain. 8; each of the four lines is a transversal to a pair of parallel lines, and each intersection of a transversal and parallel lines forms two pairs of alternate interior angles.

© Houghton Mifflin Harcourt Publishing Company

C Create two points outside the two parallel lines and label them *E* and *F*. Construct transversal $\overleftrightarrow{EF}$. Label the points of intersection *G* and *H*.

D Measure the angles formed by the parallel lines and the transversal. Write the angle measures in the table below.

E Drag point *E* or point *F* to a different position. Record the new angle measures in the table.

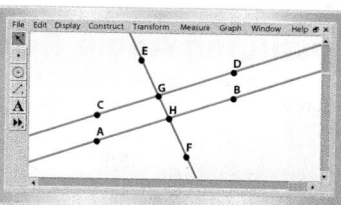

Answers will vary.

Angle	∠CGE	∠DGE	∠CGH	∠DGH	∠AHG	∠BHG	∠AHF	∠BHF
Measure								
Measure								

Reflect

Make a Conjecture **Identify the pairs of angles in the diagram. Then make a conjecture about their angle measures. Drag a point in the diagram to confirm your conjecture.**

1. corresponding angles
   ∠CGE and ∠AHG, ∠DGE and ∠BHG, ∠CGH and ∠AHF, ∠DGH and ∠BHF; congruent.

2. alternate interior angles
   ∠CGH and ∠BHG, ∠DGH and ∠AHG; congruent.

3. alternate exterior angles
   ∠CGE and ∠BHF, ∠DGE and ∠AHF; congruent.

4. same-side interior angles
   ∠CGH and ∠AHG, ∠DGH and ∠BHG; supplementary.

© Houghton Mifflin Harcourt Publishing Company

3 Explain

EXPLORE ACTIVITY 2

Engage with the Whiteboard

Have a student circle the number of an angle on the diagram. Then have another student circle the numbers of the angles that are congruent to that first angle.

EXPLORE ACTIVITY 2

AL **DOK 1** *Recall*	What symbols on lines *a* and *b* indicate that those lines are parallel? the black arrows
OL **DOK 2** *Skills/Concepts*	From the diagram, ∠2 ≅ ∠3 because they are vertical angles. Likewise, ∠6 ≅ ∠7. Also, ∠3 ≅ ∠6 because they are alternate interior angles. How does this tell you that ∠2 ≅ ∠7? ∠2 ≅ ∠3 ≅ ∠6 ≅ ∠7, so by transitivity, ∠2 ≅ ∠7.
BL **DOK 3** *Strategic Thinking*	What can you say about the eight angles formed when line *t* is perpendicular to line *a*? Explain. They are all congruent, right angles; lines *a* and *b* are parallel, so all the corresponding angle pairs that the transversal forms with lines *a* and *b* are congruent, and so are also right angles.

TEACHER TO TEACHER

Kinesthetic Experience Have students look around the classroom to find structures or drawings that show parallel lines cut by a transversal. Examples may appear on bookcases, windowpanes, floor patterns, posters on walls, and photos on book covers. Have students identify the corresponding angles, alternate interior angles, alternate exterior angles, and same-side interior angles in each example that they discover. In many of the examples, the transversal will form right angles with the parallel lines.

EXAMPLE 1

ADDITIONAL EXAMPLE 1

A Find m∠1 when m∠5 = 65°.

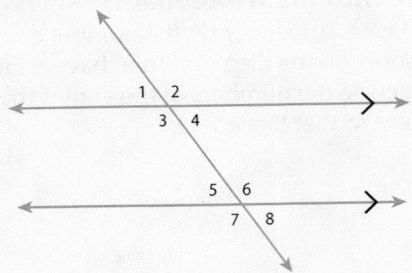

m∠1 = 65°

B Find m∠ADE.

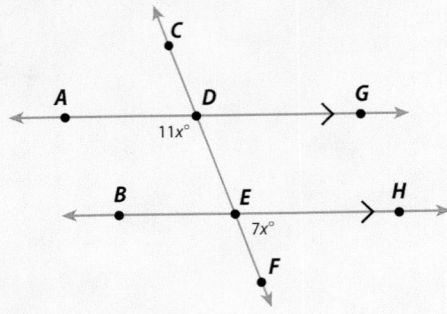

m∠ADE = 110°

 Interactive Whiteboard
Interactive example available online

Animated Math

Parallel Lines Cut by
a Transversal
Students explore an interactive
model of a transversal intersecting parallel lines.

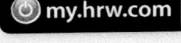 my.hrw.com

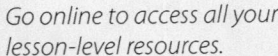 my.hrw.com

Digital Teacher Resources

*Go online to access all your
lesson-level resources.*

Differentiated Instruction
• Reteach
• Reading Strategies
• Success for English Learners
• Practice and Problem Solving
A/B, C, D

Math on the Spot Videos

EXPLORE ACTIVITY 2

Justifying Angle Relationships

You can use tracing paper to informally
justify your conclusions from the first
Explore Activity.

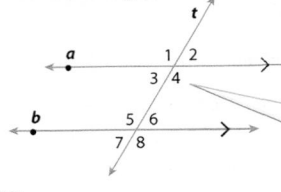

**Lines a and b are parallel. (The black
arrows on the diagram indicate
parallel lines.)**

> Recall that vertical
> angles are the opposite
> angles formed by two
> intersecting lines.
> ∠1 and ∠4 are vertical
> angles.

A Trace the diagram onto tracing paper.

B Position the tracing paper over the original diagram so that ∠1 on
the tracing is over ∠5 on the original diagram. Compare the two
angles. Do they appear to be congruent?

∠1 of the traced diagram coincides with ∠5 of the

original diagram; yes, they appear to be congruent.

C Use the tracing paper to compare all eight angles in the
diagram to each other. List all of the congruent angle pairs.

∠1 and ∠5, ∠1 and ∠8, ∠1 and ∠4, ∠2 and ∠6, ∠2

and ∠7, ∠2 and ∠3, ∠3 and ∠6, ∠3 and ∠7, ∠4 and

∠5, ∠4 and ∠8, ∠5 and ∠8, ∠6 and ∠7

Math Talk
Mathematical Processes

What do you notice
about the special angle
pairs formed by the
transversal?

Corresponding
angles are
congruent,
alternate
interior angles
are congruent,
and alternate
exterior angles
are congruent.

Math On the Spot
my.hrw.com

Finding Unknown Angle Measures

You can find any unknown angle measure when two parallel lines are cut by
a transversal if you are given at least one other angle measure.

EXAMPLE 1

A Find m∠2 when m∠7 = 125°.

∠2 is congruent to ∠7 because they
are alternate exterior angles.

Therefore, m∠2 = 125°.

B Find m∠VWZ.

∠VWZ is supplementary to
∠YVW because they are
same-side interior angles.
m∠VWZ + m∠YVW = 180°

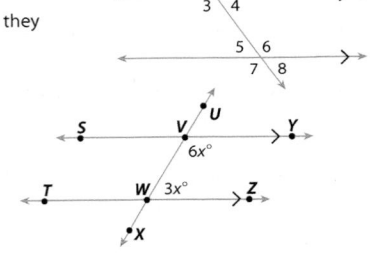

Animated
Math
my.hrw.com

© Houghton Mifflin Harcourt Publishing Company

Lesson 11.1 **349**

DIFFERENTIATE INSTRUCTION *Leveled Questions*

	EXAMPLE 1
AL DOK 1 *Recall*	What angle relationship is used to find m∠2 in Part A? Alternate exterior angles
OL DOK 2 *Skills/Concepts*	Once you know x and m∠VWZ in Part B, what are two ways to find m∠YVW? Substitute 20 for x in 6x°; subtract m∠VWZ from 180°.
BL DOK 3 *Strategic Thinking*	Is there another way you can find m∠VWZ in Part B without using the fact that same-side interior angles are supplementary? Justify your answer. Yes; ∠VWZ ≅ ∠WVS because they are alternate interior angles, so m∠WVS = 3x°. Then m∠WVY + m∠WVS = 6x° + 3x° = 180° because they are a linear pair, and you can solve as before.

LEVELED QUESTIONS: **AL** Approaching Level | **OL** On Level | **BL** Beyond Level

From the previous page, m∠VWZ + m∠YVW = 180°, m∠VWZ = 3x°, and m∠YVW = 6x°.

$$m\angle VWZ + m\angle YVW = 180°$$

$3x° + 6x° = 180°$ Replace m∠VWZ with 3x° and m∠YVW with 6x°.

$9x = 180$ Combine like terms.

$\dfrac{9x}{9} = \dfrac{180}{9}$ Divide both sides by 9.

$x = 20$ Simplify.

$m\angle VWZ = 3x° = (3 \cdot 20)° = 60°$

Personal Math Trainer
Online Assessment and Intervention
my.hrw.com

YOUR TURN

Find each angle measure.

5. m∠GDE = ___72°___
6. m∠BEF = ___108°___
7. m∠CDG = ___108°___

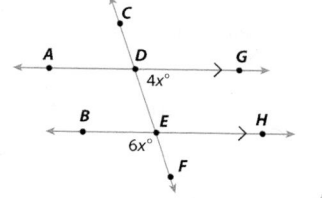

Guided Practice

Use the figure for Exercises 1–4. (Explore Activity 1 and Example 1)

1. ∠UVY and _∠VWZ_ are a pair of corresponding angles.

2. ∠WVY and ∠VWT are ___alternate interior___ angles.

3. Find m∠SVW. ___80°___

4. Find m∠VWT. ___100°___

5. **Vocabulary** When two parallel lines are cut by a transversal, ___same-side interior___ angles are supplementary. (Explore Activity 1)

ESSENTIAL QUESTION CHECK-IN

6. What can you conclude about the interior angles formed when two parallel lines are cut by a transversal?

   Each pair of alternate interior angles is congruent.

   Each pair of same-side interior angles is supplementary.

© Houghton Mifflin Harcourt Publishing Company

Focus on Reasoning

Make sure students know that they should not make any assumptions about the measures of the angles in a diagram based on their appearance.

4 Elaborate

Talk About It

Summarize the Lesson

Ask: How many *different* angle measures can be found among the eight angles formed when two parallel lines are cut by a transversal? Two; the intersection of the transversal and the parallel lines forms angles with two different measures.

Guided Practice

Engage with the Whiteboard

After completing **Exercise 5**, invite a student to circle each pair of same-side interior angles in the diagram for **Exercises 1–4**.

Avoid Common Errors

Exercises 3–4 Some students will give the value of x as the angle measure. Stress that m∠SVW = 4x° and m∠VWT = 5x°, and that once the value of x is known students must find the values of these two expressions.

DIFFERENTIATE INSTRUCTION *Intervention and Additional Support*

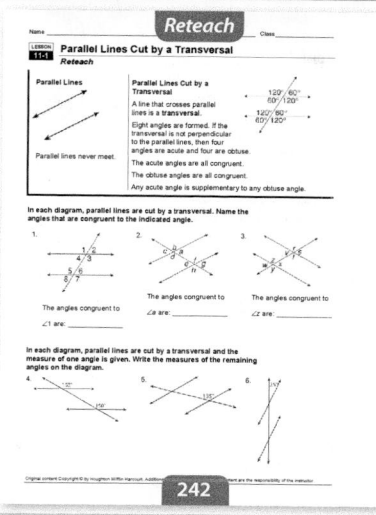

Reteach
242

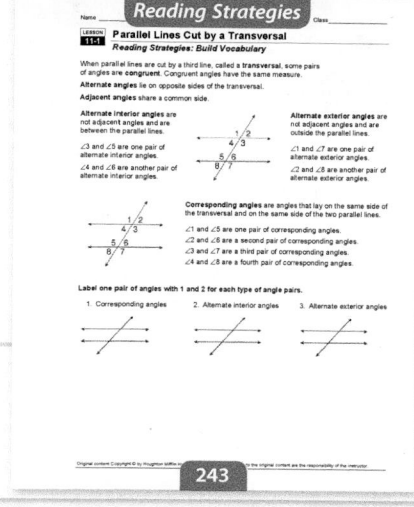

Reading Strategies
243

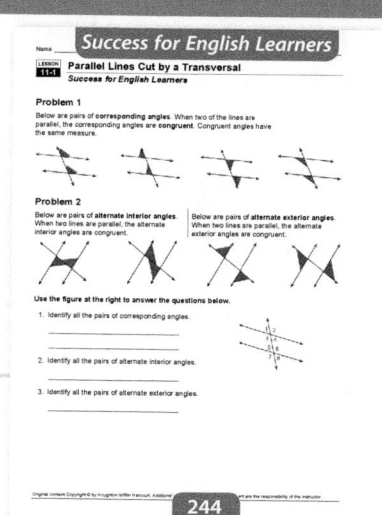

Success for English Learners
244

Personal Math Trainer
Daily Intervention
11.1 Homework

Pages shown are from *Differentiated Instruction.*
Also available online.

Pressed for Time

11.1 Differentiated Homework Assignments

AL Approaching Level	7–12, 15–18
OL On Level	11–17, 19
BL Beyond Level	18–22

*For **Below Level** students, assign Personal Math Trainer, Daily Intervention 11.1 Homework.*

Mathematical Processes	Exercises
MP.2 Reasoning	15–16, 18–19
MP.3 Logic	17, 20–22
MP.6 Precision	7–14

Focus on Higher Order Thinking

Depth of Knowledge	Exercises
1 Recall of Information	7–14
2 Skills/Concepts	15–17, 19
3 Strategic Thinking H.O.T.	18, 20–22

Name_____ Class_____ Date_____

11.1 Independent Practice

Personal Math Trainer
Online Assessment and Intervention
my.hrw.com

Vocabulary Use the figure for Exercises 7–10.

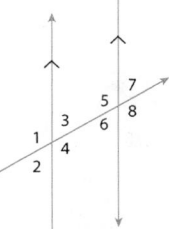

7. Name all pairs of corresponding angles.
∠1 and ∠5, ∠2 and ∠6, ∠3 and ∠7, ∠4 and ∠8

8. Name both pairs of alternate exterior angles.
∠1 and ∠8, ∠2 and ∠7

9. Name the relationship between ∠3 and ∠6.
alternate interior angles

10. Name the relationship between ∠4 and ∠6.
same-side interior angles

Find each angle measure.

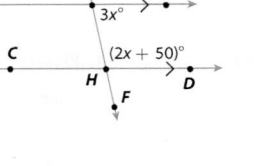

11. m∠AGE when m∠FHD = 30° __30°__

12. m∠AGH when m∠CHF = 150° __150°__

13. m∠CHF when m∠BGE = 110° __110°__

14. m∠CHG when m∠HGA = 120° __60°__

15. m∠BGH = __78°__

16. m∠GHD = __102°__

17. The Cross Country Bike Trail follows a straight line where it crosses 350th and 360th Streets. The two streets are parallel to each other. What is the measure of the larger angle formed at the intersection of the bike trail and 360th Street? Explain.

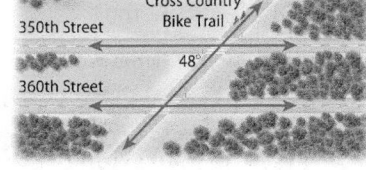

132°; the 48° angle is supplementary to the larger angle because the two angles are same-side interior angles.

18. **Critical Thinking** How many different angles would be formed by a transversal intersecting three parallel lines? How many different angle measures would there be?

12 angles; at most two different angle measures (one if the transversal is perpendicular)

Lesson 11.1 **351**

© Houghton Mifflin Harcourt Publishing Company

DIFFERENTIATE INSTRUCTION *Leveled Homework/Practice*

Personal Math Trainer
• 11.1 Homework

Pages shown are from *Differentiated Instruction.*
Also available online.

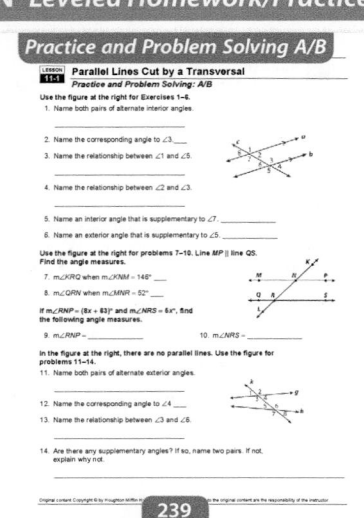

Practice and Problem Solving: A/B

239

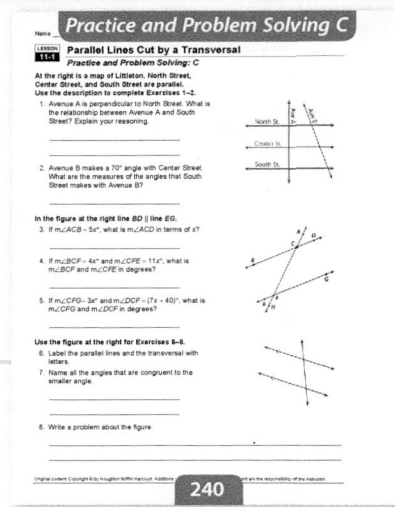

Practice and Problem Solving: C

240

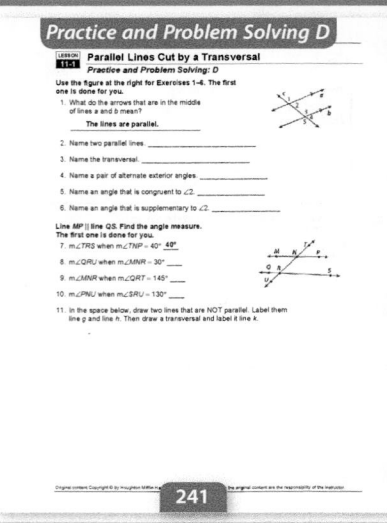

Practice and Problem Solving: D

241

19. Communicate Mathematical Ideas In the diagram at the right, suppose m∠6 = 125°. Explain how to find the measures of each of the other seven numbered angles.

∠6 and ∠2 are corr., so m∠2 = 125°. ∠6 and ∠3 are alt. int., so m∠3 = 125°. ∠3 and ∠7 are corr., so m∠7 = 125°. ∠6 and ∠4 are same-side int., so m∠4 = 180° − 125°, or 55°. ∠4 and ∠8 are corr., so m∠8 = 55°. ∠4 and ∠5 are alt. int., so m∠5 = 55°. ∠1 and ∠5 are corr., so m∠1 = 55°.

H.O.T. FOCUS ON HIGHER ORDER THINKING

20. Draw Conclusions In a diagram showing two parallel lines cut by a transversal, the measures of two same-side interior angles are both given as 3x°. Without writing and solving an equation, can you determine the measures of both angles? Explain. Then write and solve an equation to find the measures.

Yes. Since the angles are supplementary and have the same measure, each angle measure is one-half of 180°, or 90°; $3x° + 3x° = 180°$, $6x = 180$, $x = 30$, so $3x° = (3 · 30)° = 90°$.

21. Make a Conjecture Draw two parallel lines and a transversal. Choose one of the eight angles that are formed. How many of the other seven angles are congruent to the angle you selected? How many of the other seven angles are supplementary to your angle? Will your answer change if you select a different angle?

3 angles; 4 angles; no

22. Critique Reasoning In the diagram at the right, ∠2, ∠3, ∠5, and ∠8 are all congruent, and ∠1, ∠4, ∠6, and ∠7 are all congruent. Aiden says that this is enough information to conclude that the diagram shows two parallel lines cut by a transversal. Is he correct? Justify your answer.

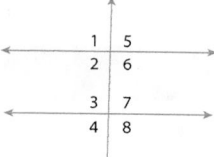

No. For the lines to be parallel, ∠2 must be supplementary to ∠3. Since it is only known that these angles are congruent, the only possibility for them to also be supplementary is if they both measure 90°.

352 Unit 5

© Houghton Mifflin Harcourt Publishing Company

DIFFERENTIATE INSTRUCTION *Extend-the-Math Activity* PRE-AP

Activity The figure shows parallelogram *ABCD* with its diagonal $\overline{AC}$ drawn. If m∠1 = 80° and m∠2 = 40°, what are the measures of ∠*DAB*, ∠*B*, ∠*BCD*, and ∠*D*? Explain how you found your answers.

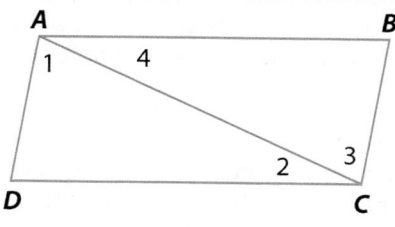

By definition, each pair of opposite sides of the parallelogram is parallel. The diagonal is a transversal to both pairs of parallel sides. If m∠1 = 80°, then m∠3 = 80° since they are alternate interior angles. If m∠2 = 40°, then m∠4 = 40° since they are alternate interior angles. So, m∠*DAB* = 80° + 40° = 120°. Also, m∠*B* = 180° − 120° = 60° since m∠*DAB* and m∠*B* are supplementary same-side interior angles. So, m∠*BCD* = 80° + 40° = 120°. Finally, m∠*D* = 180° − 120° = 60° since m∠*BCD* and m∠*D* are supplementary same-side interior angles.

✔ **Quick Check**

11.1 Lesson Quiz
Use the figure for 1–3.

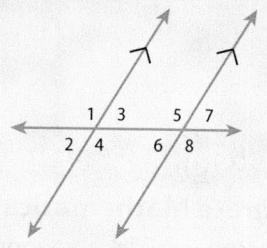

1. Name both pairs of alternate interior angles. ∠3 and ∠6, ∠4 and ∠5

2. Name all pairs of corresponding angles. ∠1 and ∠5, ∠2 and ∠6, ∠3 and ∠7, ∠4 and ∠8

3. Name the relationship between ∠2 and ∠7. alternate exterior angles

Find each angle measure.

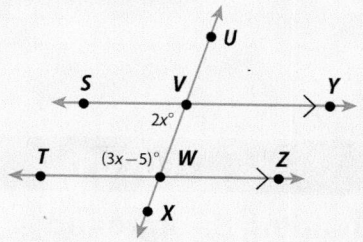

4. m∠*UVY* if m∠*TWX* = 84° 84°

5. m∠*SVW* 74°

6. m∠*TWV* 106°

Differentiate Instruction

IF a student misses more than one question, THEN

Differentiate Instruction:
• 11.1 Reteach
• Personal Math Trainer

Interactive Whiteboard
Interactive Lesson quiz available online

Lesson Support

Content Objective Students will draw conclusions about the measures of the angles of a triangle.

Professional Development

Integrate Mathematical Processes MP.5

This lesson provides an opportunity to address this Mathematical Process standard. It calls for students to use appropriate tools strategically to solve problems. Students use a paper triangle to model the relationship between the measures of the interior angles of a triangle. They can then use paper and pencil to solve equations to find the measures of the interior angles of a triangle or the measure of an exterior angle of a triangle.

FOCUS

Building Background

Visualizing Math Ask students to draw examples of acute, right, and obtuse triangles. Then review the definition of each type of triangle. In particular, note that a right triangle has one right angle and an obtuse triangle has one obtuse angle. Challenge students to draw a triangle with two right, two obtuse, or an obtuse and a right angle. Then discuss why this is not possible and why a triangle can have only one right or obtuse angle.

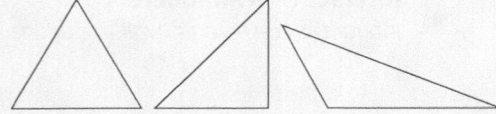

COHERENCE

Learning Progressions

In this lesson, students establish and apply the Triangle Sum Theorem. Important understandings for students include the following:

- **Informally establish the sum of the angle measures in a triangle.**
- **Justify the Triangle Sum Theorem.**
- **Find missing angle measures in triangles.**
- **Establish the relationship between the measures of an exterior angle and its remote interior angles.**
- **Use the Exterior Angle Theorem.**

Students apply the special angle relationships from the previous lesson to informally justify the Triangle Sum Theorem. Then they use the Triangle Sum Theorem to establish the Exterior Angle Theorem. An understanding of the relationship among the angles of a triangle prepares students for the Angle-Angle Similarity Postulate in the next lesson.

RIGOR

Cluster Connections

This lesson provides an excellent opportunity to connect ideas in the cluster:

Understand congruence and similarity using physical models, transparencies, or geometry software.

Display the figure below and tell students that it is a trapezoid. Have them find the measures of ∠ABC, ∠CBD, and ∠D. Ask them to justify their answers.

Sample answer: m∠ABC = 105° by the Triangle Sum Theorem. m∠CBD = 25° because it forms alternate interior angles with ∠ACB. m∠D = 125° by the Triangle Sum Theorem.

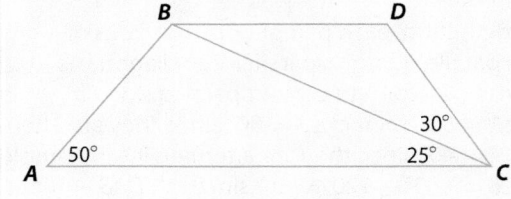

Language Support ELL

Language Objective Students will summarize their conclusions about the measures of the angles of a triangle.

Leveled Strategies for English Learners ELL

Emerging
Have students at this level of English proficiency work in pairs to review the exercises in the Guided Practice to verify that the sum of the measures of the interior angles of each triangle is 180°. For English learners who speak Spanish, point out that *interior* and *exterior* are cognates.

Expanding
Have students review the Triangle Sum Theorem by reviewing the exercises in the Guided Practice to verify that the sum of the measures of the interior angles of each triangle is 180°. Provide a sentence frame:
I know the sum of the interior angles is 180° because _____.

Bridging
Have students at this level of English proficiency work in pairs to review the Triangle Sum Theorem by reviewing the exercises in the Guided Practice to verify that the sum of the measures of the interior angles of each triangle is 180°. Then have students discuss which angles are exterior and which are interior.

 **Math Talk**
Write out and model for students a sentence frame to begin their answer.

The two ways to find $m\angle ACB$ are _____ and _____.

Linguistic Support ELL

Academic/Content Vocabulary
justify reasoning Students are asked to justify their reasoning, which requires a high level of English proficiency. Have students of mixed language proficiency work together to justify their reasoning. Provide sentence frames to support student responses, if needed.

A triangle _____ (can/cannot) have two right angles because _____.

A triangle _____ (can/cannot) have two obtuse angles because _____.

Building Background
theorem/theory This is a lesson on angle theorems for triangles. Although students may already know the word *theory*, or the Spanish cognate *teoría*, the word *theorem* may be new to them. The word *theory* is most often used in general science and refers to an idea or ideas that try to explain something. On the other hand, *theorem* is used in mathematics and refers to a rule or principal that can be shown to be true. Point out to English learners that these are different words.

Image Credits: ©13/Inti St. Clair/Ocean/Corbis

Angle Theorems for Triangles

1 Engage

? ESSENTIAL QUESTION

What can you conclude about the measures of the angles of a triangle? Sample answer: The sum of the measures of the interior angles of a triangle is always 180°. The measure of an exterior angle is equal to the sum of its remote interior angles.

Motivate the Lesson

Ask: How can tearing a triangle apart help you illustrate the Triangle Sum Theorem? Begin the Explore Activity to find out.

2 Explore

EXPLORE ACTIVITY 1

Focus on Modeling

Students will use a paper triangle to model the Triangle Sum Theorem. Point out that no matter what type of triangle is used, the three torn "corners" will form a straight angle. Have students try the activity using a variety of triangle types.

LESSON
11.2 **Angle Theorems for Triangles**

8.5.11.2
Students will make conclusions about the measures of the angles of a triangle.

? ESSENTIAL QUESTION

What can you conclude about the measures of the angles of a triangle?

EXPLORE ACTIVITY 1

Sum of the Angle Measures in a Triangle

There is a special relationship between the measures of the interior angles of a triangle.

A Draw a triangle and cut it out. Label the angles *A*, *B*, and *C*.

B Tear off each "corner" of the triangle. Each corner includes the vertex of one angle of the triangle.

C Arrange the vertices of the triangle around a point so that none of your corners overlap and there are no gaps between them.

D What do you notice about how the angles fit together around a point?
Sample answer: The angles form a straight angle.

E What is the measure of a straight angle? ____180°____

F Describe the relationship among the measures of the angles of △*ABC*.
The sum of the angle measures is 180°.

The Triangle Sum Theorem states that for △*ABC*, $m\angle A + m\angle B + m\angle C = $ ___180°___.

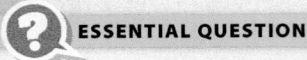

Reflect

1. **Justify Reasoning** Can a triangle have two right angles? Explain.
No; the sum of the measures of two right angles is 180°. That means the measure of the third angle would be 180° − 180° = 0°, which is impossible.

2. **Analyze Relationships** Describe the relationship between the two acute angles in a right triangle. Explain your reasoning.
They are complementary; sample answer: the sum of their measures must be 180° − (measure of the right angle) = 180° − 90° = 90°.

© Houghton Mifflin Harcourt Publishing Company

Lesson 11.2 **353**

DIFFERENTIATE INSTRUCTION *Leveled Questions*

	EXPLORE ACTIVITY 1
AL) DOK 1 *Recall*	Where do the angles that are used to form a 180° angle come from? the angles come from the three corners of a triangle.
OL) DOK 2 *Skills/Concepts*	What type of triangle will have vertices that fit together to form a 180° angle? Explain. Any type of triangle, because the measures of the interior angles of a triangle is always 180°.
BL) DOK 3 *Strategic Thinking*	Every trapezoid can be divided into two nonoverlapping triangles. Can you use this fact and the results of Explore Activity 1 to draw any conclusions about the sum of the angle measures in a trapezoid? Explain. Yes; it must be 360° by angle addition because the sum of the measures of the angles making up the trapezoid's angles is 180° + 180° = 360°.

LEVELED QUESTIONS: (AL) Approaching Level | (OL) On Level | (BL) Beyond Level

Justifying the Triangle Sum Theorem

You can use your knowledge of parallel lines intersected by a transversal to informally justify the Triangle Sum Theorem.

Follow the steps to informally prove the Triangle Sum Theorem. You should draw each step on your own paper. The figures below are provided for you to check your work.

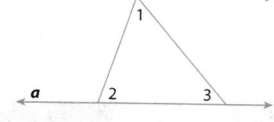

A Draw a triangle and label the angles as ∠1, ∠2, and ∠3 as shown.

B Draw line *a* through the base of the triangle.

C The Parallel Postulate states that through a point not on a line ℓ, there is exactly one line parallel to line ℓ. Draw line *b* parallel to line *a*, through the vertex opposite the base of the triangle.

D Extend each of the non-base sides of the triangle to form transversal *s* and transversal *t*. Transversals *s* and *t* intersect parallel lines *a* and *b*.

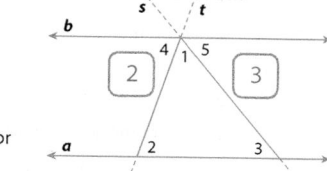

E Label the angles formed by line *b* and the transversals as ∠4 and ∠5.

F Because ∠4 and _____∠2_____ are alternate interior

angles, they are ___congruent___.

Label ∠4 with the number of the angle to which it is congruent.

G Because ∠5 and _____∠3_____ are alternate interior angles,

they are ___congruent___.

Label ∠5 with the number of the angle to which it is congruent.

H The three angles that lie along line *b* at the vertex of the triangle are ∠1, ∠4, and ∠5. Notice that these three angles lie along a line.

So, m∠1 + m∠4 + m∠5 = _____180°_____.

Because angles 2 and 4 are congruent and angles 3 and 5 are congruent, you can substitute m∠2 for m∠4 and m∠3 for m∠5 in the equation above.

So, m∠1 + m∠2 + m∠3 = _____180°_____.

This shows that the sum of the angle measures in a triangle is

always _____180°_____.

© Houghton Mifflin Harcourt Publishing Company

3 Explain

EXPLORE ACTIVITY 2

Talk About It

Check for Understanding

Ask: Why is it important that line *b* be drawn parallel to line *a* in Step C of the activity? In order for the angle pairs in steps F (∠2 and ∠4) and G (∠3 and ∠5) to be congruent, lines *a* and *b* must be parallel.

	EXPLORE ACTIVITY 2
(AL) DOK 1 *Recall*	What angle pairs are used to justify the Triangle Sum Theorem in this activity? alternate interior angles
(OL) DOK 2 *Skills/Concepts*	If the triangle is a right triangle with right angle ∠2, what can you say about m ∠1 + m∠5? 90°
(BL) DOK 3 *Strategic Thinking*	Let ∠6 be the acute angle formed by *s* and *b* adjacent to ∠4. Consider the angle between *s* and *t* formed by combining ∠6 and ∠4. Can you tell the relationship between this angle and the base angles of the triangle? Explain. Yes; its measure is their sum because ∠6 ≅ ∠3 (corres. angles) and ∠4 ≅ ∠2 (alt. int. angles), so m∠6 + m∠4 = m∠3 + m∠2 by substitution.

TEACHER TO TEACHER

Curriculum Connection Tell students that the sum of the interior angles of a triangle is always 180°, and it is true for any triangle. In polygons with more than 3 sides, the sum of the interior angles can be determined by drawing diagonals to divide the polygon into triangles. The number of triangles formed multiplied by 180° gives the sum of the interior angles. Have students draw a convex polygon and find the sum of the measures of the interior angles.

EXAMPLE 1

ADDITIONAL EXAMPLE 1

Find the missing angle measure. 75°

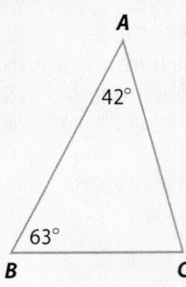

 Interactive Whiteboard
Interactive example available online

YOUR TURN   MP.8

Focus on Reasoning
The triangles in **Example 1** and **Exercises 4–5** should lead students to see that if a triangle has two acute angles, then the third angle could be acute, right, or obtuse. Ask students if a triangle can have two obtuse angles or two right angles.

Reflect

3. Analyze Relationships How can you use the fact that $m\angle 4 + m\angle 1 + m\angle 5 = 180°$ to show that $m\angle 2 + m\angle 1 + m\angle 3 = 180°$?

$\underline{m\angle 2 = m\angle 4 \text{ and } m\angle 3 = m\angle 5. \text{ Substituting } m\angle 2 \text{ for}}$

$\underline{m\angle 4 \text{ and } m\angle 3 \text{ for } m\angle 5 \text{ in the equation } m\angle 4 + m\angle 1}$

$\underline{+ m\angle 5 = 180° \text{ gives } m\angle 2 + m\angle 1 + m\angle 3 = 180°.}$

Math On the Spot
my.hrw.com

Finding Missing Angle Measures in Triangles

If you know the measures of two angles in a triangle, you can use the Triangle Sum Theorem to find the measure of the third angle.

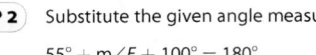

Find the missing angle measure.

STEP 1 Write the Triangle Sum Theorem for this triangle.

$m\angle D + m\angle E + m\angle F = 180°$

STEP 2 Substitute the given angle measures.

$55° + m\angle E + 100° = 180°$

STEP 3 Solve the equation for $m\angle E$.

$55° + m\angle E + 100° = 180°$

$155° + m\angle E = 180°$

$\underline{-155° \qquad\qquad -155°}$ Subtract 155° from both sides.

$m\angle E = \quad 25°$ Simplify.

So, $m\angle E = 25°$.

My Notes

YOUR TURN

Find the missing angle measure.

4.

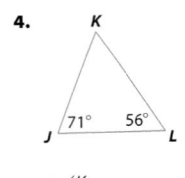

$m\angle K = \underline{\qquad 53° \qquad}$

5.

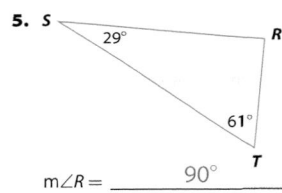

$m\angle R = \underline{\qquad 90° \qquad}$

Personal Math Trainer
Online Assessment and Intervention
my.hrw.com

© Houghton Mifflin Harcourt Publishing Company

Lesson 11.2 **355**

DIFFERENTIATE INSTRUCTION *Leveled Questions*

	EXAMPLE 1
AL DOK 1 *Recall*	What statement using the Triangle Sum Theorem can be made about this triangle? Sample answer: $m\angle D + m\angle E + m\angle F = 180°$
OL DOK 2 *Skills/Concepts*	In a triangle, all the measures of the angles are multiples of 20 degrees. One of the angles has a measure of 60°. What are the possible measures of the other two angles? 60° and 60°, 40° and 80°, or 20° and 100°
BL DOK 3 *Strategic Thinking*	An isosceles triangle has two congruent angles. If you are given the measure of one of the congruent angles, how could you find the measures of all three angles in the triangle? You could subtract the measures of the two congruent angles from 180° to find the measure of the third angle.

LEVELED QUESTIONS: **AL** Approaching Level | **OL** On Level | **BL** Beyond Level

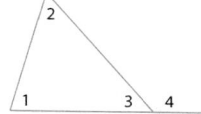

EXPLORE ACTIVITY 3

Exterior Angles and Remote Interior Angles

An **interior angle** of a triangle is formed by two sides of the triangle. An **exterior angle** is formed by one side of the triangle and the extension of an adjacent side. Each exterior angle has two remote interior angles. A **remote interior angle** is an interior angle that is not adjacent to the exterior angle.

- ∠1, ∠2, and ∠3 are interior angles.
- ∠4 is an exterior angle.
- ∠1 and ∠2 are remote interior angles to ∠4.

There is a special relationship between the measure of an exterior angle and the measures of its remote interior angles.

A Extend the base of the triangle and label the exterior angle as ∠4.

B The Triangle Sum Theorem states:

m∠1 + m∠2 + m∠3 = ___180°___.

C ∠3 and ∠4 form a ___linear pair or straight angle___,

so m∠3 + m∠4 = ___180°___.

D Use the equations in **B** and **C** to complete the following equation:

m∠1 + m∠2 + ___m∠3___ = ___m∠3___ + m∠4

E Use properties of equality to simplify the equation in **D**:

___m∠1 + m∠2 = m∠4___

The Exterior Angle Theorem states that the measure of an ___exterior___ angle

is equal to the sum of its ___remote interior___ angles.

Reflect

6. Sketch a triangle and draw all of its exterior angles. How many exterior angles does a triangle have at each vertex?

___2___

7. How many total exterior angles does a triangle have?

___6___

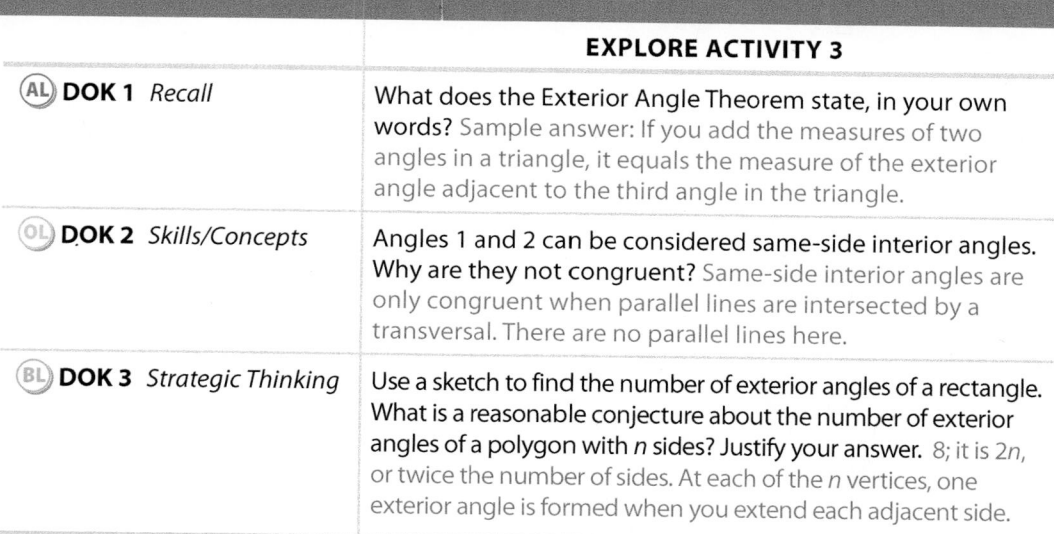

 (diagram with angles 1, 2, 3, 4, 5, 6)

© Houghton Mifflin Harcourt Publishing Company

	EXPLORE ACTIVITY 3
AL) DOK 1 *Recall*	What does the Exterior Angle Theorem state, in your own words? Sample answer: If you add the measures of two angles in a triangle, it equals the measure of the exterior angle adjacent to the third angle in the triangle.
OL) DOK 2 *Skills/Concepts*	Angles 1 and 2 can be considered same-side interior angles. Why are they not congruent? Same-side interior angles are only congruent when parallel lines are intersected by a transversal. There are no parallel lines here.
BL) DOK 3 *Strategic Thinking*	Use a sketch to find the number of exterior angles of a rectangle. What is a reasonable conjecture about the number of exterior angles of a polygon with *n* sides? Justify your answer. 8; it is 2*n*, or twice the number of sides. At each of the *n* vertices, one exterior angle is formed when you extend each adjacent side.

Talk About It

Check for Understanding

Ask: How can you find the measure of an exterior angle if its two remote interior angles have measures 75° and 50°? The measure of an exterior angle is equal to the sum of the measures of its remote interior angles. So this exterior angle would have a measure of 75° + 50° = 125°.

TEACHER TO TEACHER

Manipulatives Have students draw a large scalene triangle *ABC* on a piece of construction paper and label the interior angles 1, 2, and 3. Then have them draw all six of the exterior angles and label those angles 4–9. Have students trace triangle *ABC* on another sheet of paper and label its angles 1–3. Now have students cut out the triangle they traced and tear off the three corners (including the numbers). Ask them to place two of the torn corners over the exterior angle for which they are the remote interior angles. A sample is shown below.

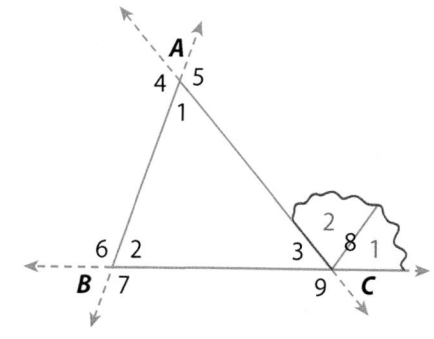

EXAMPLE 2

ADDITIONAL EXAMPLE 2

Find m∠A and m∠B.

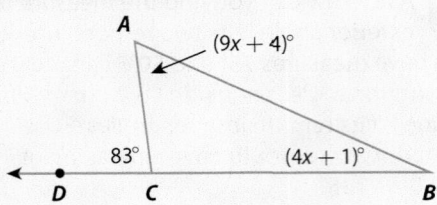

$m\angle A = 58°$ and $m\angle B = 25°$

 Interactive Whiteboard
Interactive example available online

YOUR TURN   MP.6

Talk About It

Check for Understanding

 **Ask:** To check that your answers are correct, is it enough to check that the sum of the angle measures equals the measure of the exterior angle? Explain how you know. No, the answers must also satisfy the expressions given for the unknown angle measures.

Digital Teacher Resources

Go online to access all your lesson-level resources.

Differentiated Instruction
• Reteach
• Reading Strategies
• Success for English Learners
• Practice and Problem Solving
  A/B, C, D

Math on the Spot Videos

my.hrw.com

Using the Exterior Angle Theorem

You can use the Exterior Angle Theorem to find the measures of the interior angles of a triangle.

Math On the Spot
my.hrw.com

EXAMPLE 2

Find m∠A and m∠B.

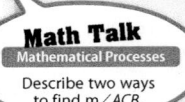

STEP 1   Write the Exterior Angle Theorem as it applies to this triangle.

$m\angle A + m\angle B = m\angle ACD$

STEP 2   Substitute the given angle measures.

$(4y - 4)° + 3y° = 52°$

STEP 3   Solve the equation for y.

$(4y - 4)° + 3y° = 52°$

$4y° - 4° + 3y° = 52°$ Remove parentheses.

$7y° - 4° = 52°$ Simplify.

$\underline{+4°\qquad +4°}$ Add 4° to both sides.

$7y° = 56°$ Simplify.

$\dfrac{7y°}{7} = \dfrac{56°}{7}$ Divide both sides by 7.

$y = 8$ Simplify.

STEP 4   Use the value of y to find m∠A and m∠B.

$m\angle A = 4y - 4$ $m\angle B = 3y$
$\quad = 4(8) - 4$ $\quad = 3(8)$
$\quad = 32 - 4$ $\quad = 24$
$\quad = 28$

So, $m\angle A = 28°$ and $m\angle B = 24°$.

YOUR TURN

8. Find m∠M and m∠N.

   $m\angle M = \underline{\quad 78° \quad}$

   $m\angle N = \underline{\quad 68° \quad}$

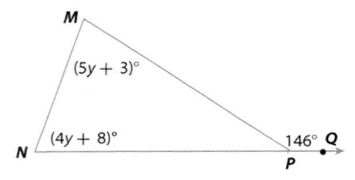

© Houghton Mifflin Harcourt Publishing Company

Math Talk
Mathematical Processes

Describe two ways to find m∠ACB.

Use the Triangle Sum Theorem and subtract the sum of the measures of angles A and B from 180°. Use the fact that an exterior angle and its adjacent interior angle are supplementary and subtract 52° from 180°.

Personal Math Trainer
Online Assessment and Intervention
my.hrw.com

Find each missing angle measure. (Explore Activity 1 and Example 1)

1.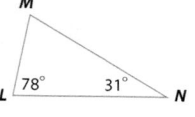

$m\angle M = \underline{\quad 71° \quad}$

2.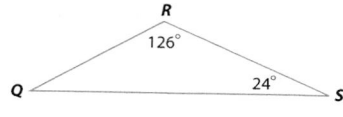

$m\angle Q = \underline{\quad 30° \quad}$

Use the Triangle Sum Theorem to find the measure of each angle in degrees. (Explore Activity 2 and Example 1)

3.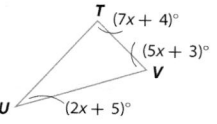

$m\angle T = \underline{\quad 88° \quad}$, $m\angle U = \underline{\quad 29° \quad}$,

$m\angle V = \underline{\quad 63° \quad}$

4.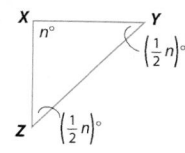

$m\angle X = \underline{\quad 90° \quad}$, $m\angle Y = \underline{\quad 45° \quad}$,

$m\angle Z = \underline{\quad 45° \quad}$

Use the Exterior Angle Theorem to find the measure of each angle in degrees. (Explore Activity 3 and Example 2)

5.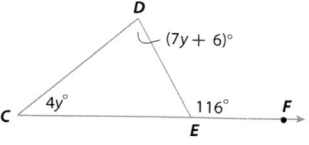

$m\angle C = \underline{\quad 40° \quad}$, $m\angle D = \underline{\quad 76° \quad}$,

$m\angle DEC = \underline{\quad 64° \quad}$

6.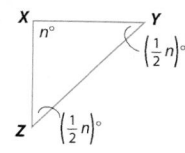

$m\angle L = \underline{\quad 129° \quad}$, $m\angle M = \underline{\quad 32° \quad}$,

$m\angle LKM = \underline{\quad 19° \quad}$

? **ESSENTIAL QUESTION CHECK-IN**

7. Describe the relationships among the measures of the angles of a triangle.

The sum of the interior angles is 180°. The measure of an
exterior angle equals the sum of the measures of its two
remote interior angles.

© Houghton Mifflin Harcourt Publishing Company

4 Elaborate

Talk About It

Summarize the Lesson

Ask: How can you find the measure of the third angle of a triangle if the other two measures are known? How can you find the measure of one remote interior angle of a triangle if the measures of an exterior angle and its other related remote interior angle are known?
The sum of the measures of the angles of a triangle is 180°, so subtract the sum of the two known measures from 180°. The sum of the measures of the remote interior angles is equal to the measure of the related exterior angle, so subtract the known measure of one interior angle from the measure of the related exterior angle.

Guided Practice

Engage with the Whiteboard

Next to each figure in **Exercises 1–6**, write an equation using either the Triangle Sum Theorem or the Exterior Angle Theorem to find the angle measure.

Avoid Common Errors

Exercises 5–6 Students may set the sum of the expressions for the interior angles or the sum of all three given expressions equal to 180°. Reteach the definition of an exterior angle and then remind these students that the sum of the measures of the two remote interior angles is equal to the measure of the related exterior angle.

DIFFERENTIATE INSTRUCTION *Intervention and Additional Support*

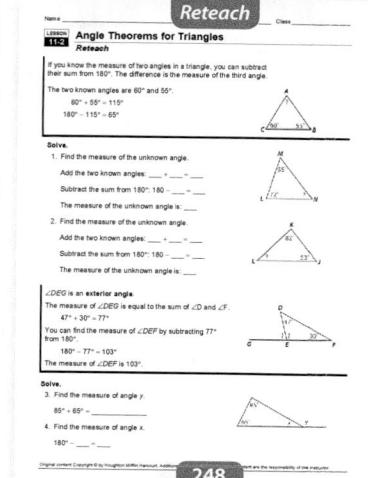

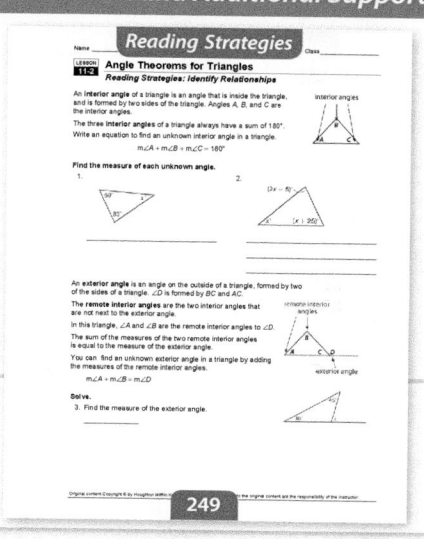

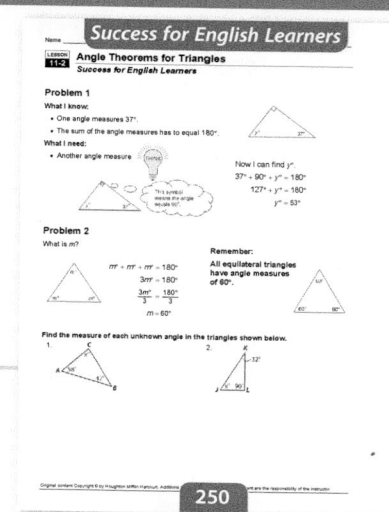

Personal Math Trainer
Daily Intervention
11.2 Homework

Pages shown are from
Differentiated Instruction.
Also available online.

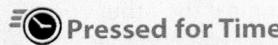

⏱ **Pressed for Time**

11.2 Differentiated Homework Assignments

AL Approaching Level	8–15
OL On Level	10–16
BL Beyond Level	13–14, 15–18

*For **Below Level** students, assign Personal Math Trainer, Daily Intervention 11.2 Homework.*

Mathematical Processes	Exercises
MP.2 Reasoning	15, 17
MP.3 Logic	16
MP.5 Using Tools	8-14
MP.6 Precision	18

Focus on Higher Order Thinking

Depth of Knowledge	Exercises
2 Skills/Concepts	8–15
3 Strategic Thinking **H.O.T.**	16–18

11.2 Independent Practice

Personal Math Trainer
Online Assessment and Intervention
my.hrw.com

Find the measure of each angle.

8.

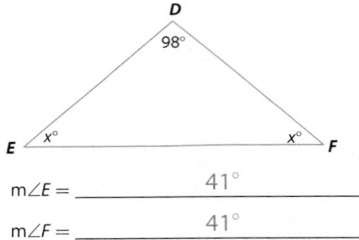

$m\angle E =$ _____ 41°

$m\angle F =$ _____ 41°

9.

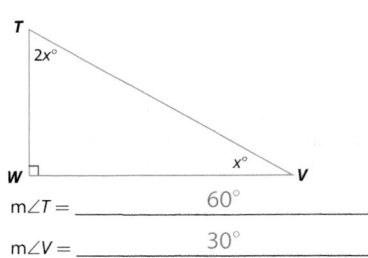

$m\angle T =$ _____ 60°

$m\angle V =$ _____ 30°

10.

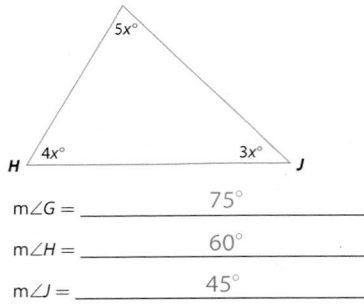

$m\angle G =$ _____ 75°

$m\angle H =$ _____ 60°

$m\angle J =$ _____ 45°

11.

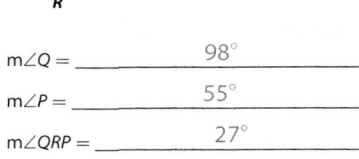

$m\angle Q =$ _____ 98°

$m\angle P =$ _____ 55°

$m\angle QRP =$ _____ 27°

12.

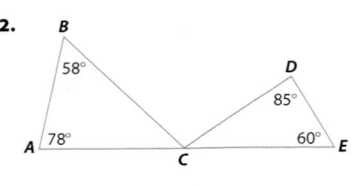

$m\angle ACB =$ _____ 44°

$m\angle BCD =$ _____ 101°

$m\angle DCE =$ _____ 35°

13.

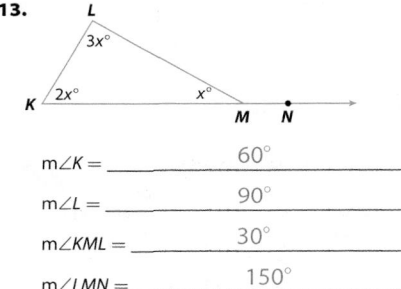

$m\angle K =$ _____ 60°

$m\angle L =$ _____ 90°

$m\angle KML =$ _____ 30°

$m\angle LMN =$ _____ 150°

14. **Multistep** The second angle in a triangle is five times as large as the first. The third angle is two-thirds as large as the first. Find the angle measures. _____ 27°, 135°, 18°

DIFFERENTIATE INSTRUCTION *Leveled Homework/Practice*

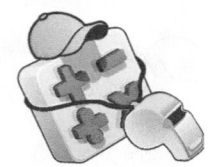

Personal Math Trainer
• 11.2 Homework

Pages shown are from *Differentiated Instruction.*
Also available online.

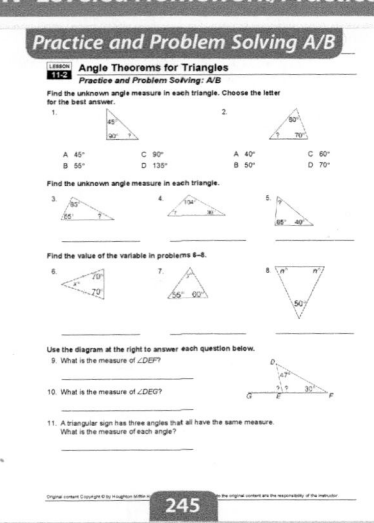

Practice and Problem Solving A/B

245

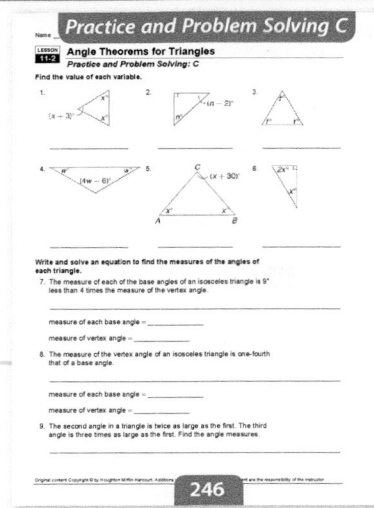

Practice and Problem Solving C

246

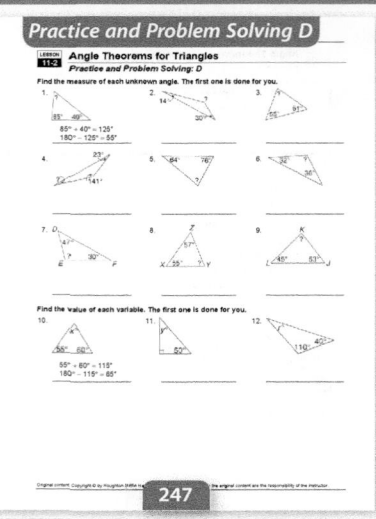

Practice and Problem Solving D

247

15. Analyze Relationships Can a triangle have two obtuse angles? Explain.

No; the measure of an obtuse angle is greater than 90°.
If a triangle had two obtuse angles, the sum of their
measures would be greater than 180°, the sum of the
angle measures of a triangle.

 **FOCUS ON HIGHER ORDER THINKING**

16. Critical Thinking Explain how you can use the Triangle Sum Theorem to find the measures of the angles of an equilateral triangle.

The angles of an equilateral triangle are congruent. Let
the measure of each angle equal x. Then, by the Triangle
Sum Theorem, $x + x + x = 180$. So, $3x = 180$. Solving for
x gives $x = 60$. So the measure of each angle is 60°.

17. a. Draw Conclusions Find the sum of the measures of the angles in quadrilateral *ABCD*. (Hint: Draw diagonal $\overline{AC}$. How can you use the figures you have formed to find the sum?)

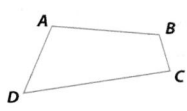

Sum = _____ 360°

b. Make a Conjecture Write a "Quadrilateral Sum Theorem." Explain why you think it is true.

The sum of the angle measures of a quadrilateral
is 360°. Sample answer: Any quadrilateral can be
divided into two triangles. So, the sum of the angle
measures of a quadrilateral is twice the sum of the
angle measures of a triangle; 2 × 180° = 360°

18. Communicate Mathematical Ideas Describe two ways that an exterior angle of a triangle is related to one or more of the interior angles.

(1) The measure of an exterior angle is equal to the sum
of the measures of its two remote interior angles. (2) An
exterior angle is supplementary to the interior angle
adjacent to it.

 Work Area

© Houghton Mifflin Harcourt Publishing Company

DIFFERENTIATE INSTRUCTION *Extend-the-Math Activity* **PRE-AP**

Activity Use inductive reasoning to make a conjecture about the sum of the measures of the exterior angles of any triangle, one at each vertex. Draw three different large triangles and extend each side in one direction to create one exterior angle at each vertex. For each triangle, measure and label the three exterior angles, and then find the sum of these measures.

Next, following the same method as you did for triangles, find the sum of the measures of the exterior angles of any convex quadrilateral, pentagon, and hexagon. Make a conjecture about the sum of the measures of the exterior angles of any convex polygon. Compare your results with those of other students.

The sum of the exterior angles of any triangle is 360°. The sum of the exterior angles (one at each vertex) of any convex polygon is 360°.

✔ **Quick Check**

11.2 Lesson Quiz
Find the missing angle measure.
1.

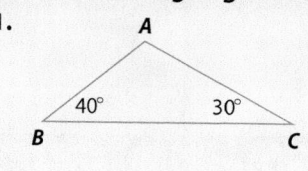

$m\angle A = 110°$

2.

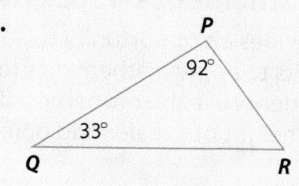

$m\angle R = 55°$

Use the Triangle Sum Theorem to find the measure of each angle in degrees.

3.

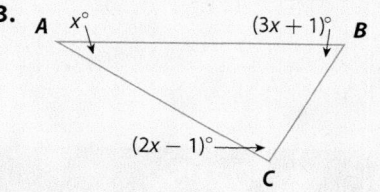

$m\angle A = 30°$, $m\angle B = 91°$, $m\angle C = 59°$

4.

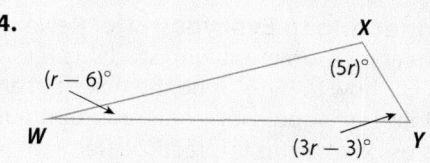

$m\angle W = 15°$, $m\angle X = 105°$, $m\angle Y = 60°$

5. Use the Exterior Angle Theorem to find the measures of $\angle A$, $\angle B$, and $\angle ACB$. $m\angle A = 20°$, $m\angle B = 90°$, $m\angle ACB = 70°$

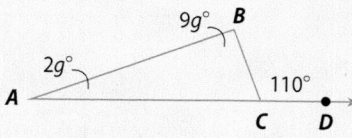

Differentiate Instruction

IF a student misses more than one question, THEN

Differentiate Instruction:
• 11.2 Reteach
• Personal Math Trainer

 Interactive Whiteboard
Interactive Lesson quiz available online

Lesson Support

Content Objective Students will determine when two triangles are similar.

Professional Development

Integrate Mathematical Processes MP.4

This lesson provides an opportunity to address this Mathematical Processes standard. It calls for students to apply mathematics to problems arising in everyday life, society, and the workplace. Students use the properties of similar triangles to write proportions and determine the height of a real-world object that would be difficult to measure directly.

FOCUS	COHERENCE	RIGOR

Building Background

Connecting to Everyday Life Review indirect measurement with students. Discuss how to determine the height of a building, a flagpole, or a tall tree. Point out that using a ruler is impractical. Remind students about similar figures. Discuss how similar figures can be used to measure things that are too tall, long, or wide to measure with a ruler.

Learning Progressions

In this lesson, students establish and apply the Angle-Angle (AA) Similarity Postulate. Important understandings for students include the following:

- **Informally establish the AA Similarity Postulate.**
- **Apply the AA Similarity Postulate to decide if two triangles are similar.**
- **Find missing angle measures in similar triangles.**
- **Use similar triangles to show that the slope of a line is constant.**

This lesson provides students with an opportunity to understand the connections and overlap between geometry and algebra by providing them with additional ways to establish similarity and the slope of a line. They also use similar figures and indirect measurement to solve real-life problems.

Cluster Connections

This lesson provides an excellent opportunity to connect ideas in the cluster:

Understand congruence and similarity using physical models, transparencies, or geometry software.

Tell students that in an isosceles triangle, the two equal sides are called legs and the third side is called the base. The angle formed by the two congruent sides is called the vertex angle. The other two angles are called base angles. The base angles of an isosceles triangle are congruent. Then ask, "If the vertex angles of two isosceles triangles are congruent, are the triangles necessarily similar?" Have students explain their thinking.

The two triangles must be similar. Sample explanation: Both pairs of base angles must be congruent since each angle will measure one-half of the difference of 180° minus the measure of the vertex angle. So, the triangles are similar by AA.

Language Support ELL

Leveled Strategies for English Learners ELL

Emerging
Have students at this level of English proficiency work in pairs to take turns drawing triangles and measuring the angles to see if their triangles are similar. Have them write *yes* on those that are similar and *no* on those that are not.

Expanding
Have students at this level of English proficiency work in pairs to take turns drawing sample triangles on graph paper and then exchange papers to measure the angles in each other's triangles. Have them note whether or not the triangles' corresponding angles are congruent.

Bridging
Have students at this level of English proficiency work in pairs to draw sample triangles and then measure their angles using a protractor. Have them discuss whether or not any of their triangles are similar and explain why or why not.

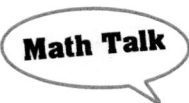
Math Talk

Write out and model for students a sentence frame to begin their answer.

All right triangles _____ (are/are not) similar because _____.

Image Credits: ©VStock/Alamy Images

Linguistic Support ELL

Academic/Content Vocabulary
postulate and theorem This introduces students to the Angle-Angle Similarity Postulate. The previous lesson introduced students to angle theorems for triangles. Point out to students the difference in the meanings of *postulate* and *theorem*. A *postulate* is a statement that is assumed true without proof, while a *theorem* is a true statement that can be proven. Therefore, the Angle-Angle Similarity Postulate is assumed to be true without proof.

Rules and Patterns
Compound words are made when two words are joined to form a new word. Most of the time, knowing the meaning of each word will help English learners figure out the meaning of the new word. For example, some compound words are *skateboard, basketball*, and *moonlight*. In this lesson, the compound words *wheelchair, earrings*, and *flagpole* are used in exercises. Suggest that students start a list of compound words they find and add them to their word journals.

Angle-Angle Similarity

1 Engage

? ESSENTIAL QUESTION

How can you determine when two triangles are similar? Sample answer: Two triangles are similar if it can be shown that two angles of one triangle are congruent to two angles of the other triangle.

Motivate the Lesson

Ask: How many different triangles can be drawn that have one angle measuring 45° and another measuring 60°? Begin the Explore Activity to find out.

2 Explore

EXPLORE ACTIVITY 1

Connect Vocabulary **ELL**

Discuss the various meanings of *similar*. In nonmathematical situations, *similar* can be used to mean *likeness* or *resemblance* in a general way. In mathematical terms, *similar* figures are similar in a specific way: the corresponding angles are congruent. The lengths of their corresponding sides are not necessarily congruent but are proportional.

LESSON 11.3 Angle-Angle Similarity

8.5.11.3
Students will determine how two triangles are similar.

? ESSENTIAL QUESTION

How can you determine when two triangles are similar?

EXPLORE ACTIVITY 1

Discovering Angle-Angle Similarity

Similar figures have the same shape but may have different sizes. Two triangles are **similar** if their corresponding angles are congruent and the lengths of their corresponding sides are proportional.

A Use your protractor and a straightedge to draw a triangle. Make one angle measure 45° and another angle measure 60°.

B Compare your triangle to those drawn by your classmates. How are the triangles the same?

They all have the same shape.

How are they different?

They are different sizes.

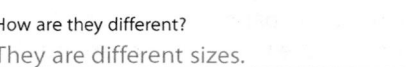

C Use the Triangle Sum Theorem to find the measure of the third angle of your triangle.

$180° − (45° + 60°) = 180° − 105° = 75°$

Reflect

1. If two angles in one triangle are congruent to two angles in another triangle, what do you know about the third pair of angles?

They must also be congruent.

2. **Make a Conjecture** Are two pairs of congruent angles enough information to conclude that two triangles are similar? Explain.

Yes; by the Triangle Sum Theorem, the third pair of angles must have the same angle measure and thus are congruent, so the triangles must be similar.

DIFFERENTIATE INSTRUCTION *Leveled Questions*

	EXPLORE ACTIVITY 1
AL DOK 1 *Recall*	How are two triangles related when all of their angle measures are congruent? similar; same shape, not necessarily same size
OL DOK 2 *Skills/Concepts*	Why do you only need to know that two pairs of angle measures are congruent in order to state that all three pairs of angle measures are congruent? If you know the measures of two angles in a triangle, then you can find the third measure by subtracting from 180°. Subtracting the same two measures from 180° will result in the same third angle measure.
BL DOK 3 *Strategic Thinking*	A right triangle contains a 27° angle. A second right triangle contains a 63° angle. Are the triangles similar? Explain. Yes; the third angle in the first triangle must measure $180° − 90° − 27° = 63°$, and the third angle in the second triangle must measure $180° − 90° − 63° = 27°$.

LEVELED QUESTIONS: **AL** Approaching Level | **OL** On Level | **BL** Beyond Level

Math On the Spot
my.hrw.com

Using the AA Similarity Postulate

Angle-Angle (AA) Similarity Postulate

If two angles of one triangle are congruent to two angles of another triangle, then the triangles are similar.

No; a right triangle has one right angle and two acute angles. The measures of the acute angles can be any number of degrees that add to 90°.

EXAMPLE 1

Explain whether the triangles are similar.

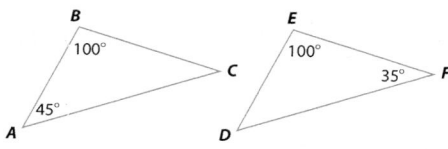

The figure shows only one pair of congruent angles. Find the measure of the third angle in each triangle.

$45° + 100° + m\angle C = 180°$　　　$100° + 35° + m\angle D = 180°$

$145° + m\angle C = 180°$　　　　　$135° + m\angle D = 180°$

$145° + m\angle C - 145° = 180° - 145°$　$135° + m\angle D - 135° = 180° - 135°$

$m\angle C = 35°$　　　　　　　　$m\angle D = 45°$

Because two angles in one triangle are congruent to two angles in the other triangle, the triangles are similar.

Math Talk

Mathematical Processes

Are all right triangles similar? Why or why not?

YOUR TURN

3. **Explain whether the triangles are similar.**

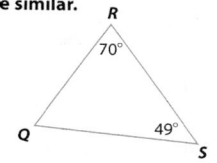

The triangles are not similar, because only one angle is congruent. The angle measures of the triangles are 70°, 58°, and 52° and 70°, 61°, and 49°.

Personal Math Trainer
Online Assessment and Intervention
my.hrw.com

③ Explain

EXAMPLE 1

ADDITIONAL EXAMPLE 1 Explain whether the triangles are similar.

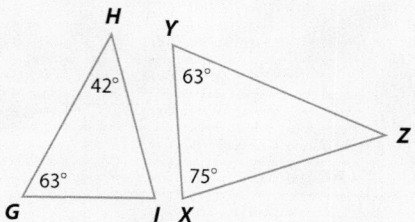

The triangles are similar by the AA Similarity Postulate. The missing angles are 42° in one triangle and 75° in the other. All corresponding angle pairs are congruent.

Interactive Whiteboard
Interactive example available online

YOUR TURN

Avoid Common Errors

In **Exercise 3**, students may assume the triangles are not similar because the triangles are rotated with respect to each other. Remind students that visual inspection is not sufficient to prove or disprove similarity.

© Houghton Mifflin Harcourt Publishing Company

	EXAMPLE 1
AL DOK 1 *Recall*	Why is it important to find the measure of the third angle? Before finding the measure of the third angle, there is only one pair of angles that is known to be congruent. There must be at least two pairs of congruent angles to state similar triangles.
OL DOK 2 *Skills/Concepts*	One triangle has angles that measure 30° and 77°. A second triangle has angles that measure 30° and 83°. Are the triangles similar? Explain. No; the angle measures in the first triangle are 30°, 77°, and 73°, while in the second they are 30°, 67°, and 83°.
BL DOK 3 *Strategic Thinking*	Isosceles triangles have two congruent angles. Are all isosceles triangles similar? No; an isosceles triangle with measures 30°, 30°, and 120° is not similar to an isosceles triangle with measures 40°, 40°, and 100°.

TEACHER TO TEACHER

Modeling Sierpinski's Triangle is a *fractal* made from similar triangles. To make this fractal, begin with a large equilateral triangle. Connect the midpoints of each side to create four smaller triangles similar to the original. Inside each of the four smaller triangles, connect the midpoints of each side to form four even smaller equilateral triangles. Repeat to make more and more smaller similar triangles.

EXAMPLE 2

ADDITIONAL EXAMPLE 2 A flagpole casts a shadow that is 30 feet long. A signpost near the flagpole is 4 feet tall, and it casts a shadow that is 6 feet long. How tall is the flagpole? 20 ft

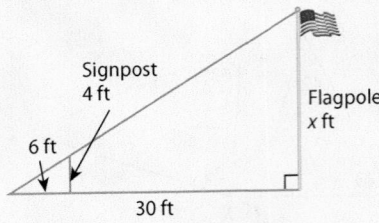

Signpost
4 ft

Flagpole
x ft

6 ft

30 ft

Interactive Whiteboard
Interactive example available online

Math On the Spot
my.hrw.com

Finding Missing Measures in Similar Triangles

Because corresponding angles are congruent and corresponding sides are proportional in similar triangles, you can use similar triangles to solve real-world problems.

EXAMPLE 2 Real World

While playing tennis, Matt is 12 meters from the net, which is 0.9 meter high. He needs to hit the ball so that it just clears the net and lands 6 meters beyond the base of the net. At what height should Matt hit the tennis ball?

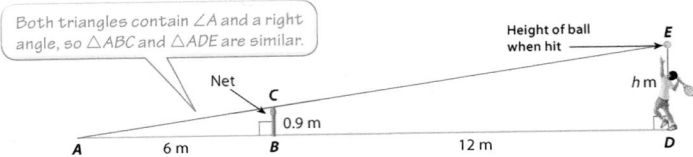

Both triangles contain $\angle A$ and a right angle, so $\triangle ABC$ and $\triangle ADE$ are similar.

Height of ball when hit

Net

C

0.9 m

h m

A   6 m   *B*   12 m   *D*

E

In similar triangles, corresponding side lengths are proportional.

$$\frac{AD}{AB} = \frac{DE}{BC} \longrightarrow \frac{6+12}{6} = \frac{h}{0.9}$$ Substitute the lengths from the figure.

$$0.9 \times \frac{18}{6} = \frac{h}{0.9} \times 0.9$$ Use properties of equality to get *h* by itself.

$$0.9 \times 3 = h$$ Simplify.

$$2.7 = h$$ Multiply.

Matt should hit the ball at a height of 2.7 meters.

Reflect

4. **What If?** Suppose you set up a proportion so that each ratio compares parts of one triangle, as shown below.

height of $\triangle ABC$ ⟶ $\frac{BC}{AB} = \frac{DE}{AD}$ ⟵ height of $\triangle ADE$
base of $\triangle ABC$ ⟶   ⟵ base of $\triangle ADE$

Show that this proportion leads to the same value for *h* as in Example 2.

$$\frac{0.9}{6} = \frac{h}{18}$$
$$18 \times 0.15 = h$$
$$2.7 = h$$

© Houghton Mifflin Harcourt Publishing Company

Lesson 11.3 **363**

DIFFERENTIATE INSTRUCTION *Leveled Questions*

	EXAMPLE 2
AL **DOK 1** *Recall*	What does point *A* in the diagram represent? point *E*? the point where the ball lands; the point where the ball is hit
OL **DOK 2** *Skills/Concepts*	Suppose Matt runs 6 meters toward the net and hits another shot along the same path as the first shot. At what height does he hit the ball this time? 1.8 m
BL **DOK 3** *Strategic Thinking*	The triangles in the diagram are dilations. How can you find the scale factor, and how can you use it to find the height *h* at which Matt should hit the ball? $\frac{AD}{AB} = \frac{12+6}{6} = \frac{18}{6} = 3$; $h = 3 \cdot BC = 3 \cdot 0.9 = 2.7$ meters

LEVELED QUESTIONS: **AL** Approaching Level | **OL** On Level | **BL** Beyond Level

Personal Math Trainer Online Assessment and Intervention
my.hrw.com

5. Rosie is building a wheelchair ramp that is 24 feet long and 2 feet high. She needs to install a vertical support piece 8 feet from the end of the ramp. What is the length of the support piece in inches?

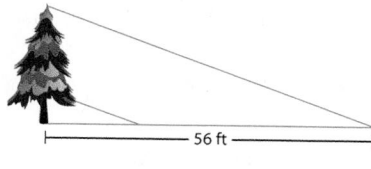

8 inches

6. The lower cable meets the tree at a height of 6 feet and extends out 16 feet from the base of the tree. If the triangles are similar, how tall is the tree?

21 ft

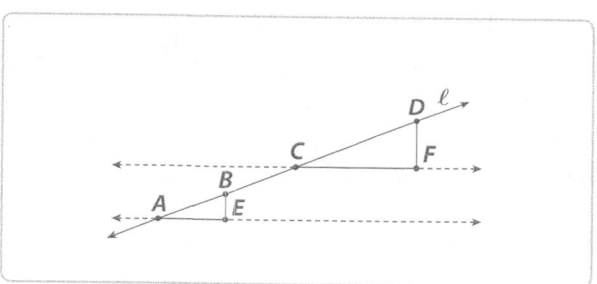

EXPLORE ACTIVITY 2

Using Similar Triangles to Explain Slope

You can use similar triangles to show that the slope of a line is constant.

A Draw a line ℓ that is not a horizontal line. Label four points on the line as A, B, C, and D.

You need to show that the slope between points A and B is the same as the slope between points C and D.

© Houghton Mifflin Harcourt Publishing Company

Focus on Math Connections

Tell students to think of the wheelchair ramp as the graph of a line with the origin at the left end of the ramp. Label the right end of the ramp with the coordinates (24, 2). Ask students what the rise and run are between the origin and the point (24, 2), and what the slope of the line is (rise = 2, run = 24, slope = $\frac{1}{12}$). Label the point (8, h). Ask what the rise and run are between the origin and the point (8, h) (rise = h, run = 8). Ask students if they can find h when they know the slope and the run. This will prepare students for the next Explore Activity.

EXPLORE ACTIVITY 2

Focus on Modeling

In Explore Activity 2, be sure students are clear on what the diagram looks like after steps A and B. If necessary, consider adding an x-axis and y-axis to the diagram or drawing the diagram on a grid to help students understand the diagram.

TEACHER TO TEACHER

Multiple Representations Have students graph a line, such as y = 2x, on graph paper. Then have students draw right triangles, with the base of the triangles on the x-axis and a vertex at (0, 0), as shown in the example below. Discuss with students that all the right triangles are similar. Have students compare the slope of the line with the ratio of the leg lengths of the triangles. Point out to students that the similar triangles show that the slope of the line is constant.

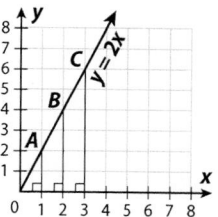

		EXPLORE ACTIVITY 2
(AL)	**DOK 1** *Recall*	In Part B, which segments represent the rise and which segments represent the run? rise: $\overline{BE}$ and $\overline{DF}$; run: $\overline{AE}$ and $\overline{CF}$
(OL)	**DOK 2** *Skills/Concepts*	Are all the triangles formed with parallel lines along line ℓ similar to each other? How do you know? Yes; if the lines are parallel, then the corresponding angles will be congruent and the triangles formed will be similar.
(BL)	**DOK 3** *Strategic Thinking*	Can you show that the slope between points A and B is the same as the slope between points C and D using two angles other than ∠BAE and ∠DCF? Explain. Yes, ∠ABE and ∠CDF; because $\overline{BE}$ and $\overline{DF}$ are both vertical, the lines containing them are parallel. Line ℓ is still a transversal, but this time to $\overleftrightarrow{BE}$ and $\overleftrightarrow{DF}$, so the corresponding angles are now ∠ABE and ∠CDF.

Angle-Angle Similarity   **364**

Digital Teacher Resources

Go online to access all your lesson-level resources.

my.hrw.com

Differentiated Instruction
• Reteach
• Reading Strategies
• Success for English Learners
• Practice and Problem Solving A/B, C, D

Math on the Spot Videos

B Draw the rise and run for the slope between points *A* and *B*. Label the intersection as point *E*. Draw the rise and run for the slope between points *C* and *D*. Label the intersection as point *F*.

C Write expressions for the slope between *A* and *B* and between *C* and *D*.

Slope between *A* and *B*: $\dfrac{BE}{AE}$ Slope between *C* and *D*: $\dfrac{DF}{CF}$

D Extend $\overleftrightarrow{AE}$ and $\overleftrightarrow{CF}$ across your drawing. $\overleftrightarrow{AE}$ and $\overleftrightarrow{CF}$ are both horizontal lines, so they are parallel.

Line ℓ is a _transversal_ that intersects parallel lines.

E Complete the following statements:

∠*BAE* and ∠*DCF* are corresponding angles and are _congruent_.

∠*BEA* and ∠*DFC* are right angles and are _congruent_.

F By Angle–Angle Similarity, △*ABE* and △*CDF* are similar triangles.

G Use the fact that the lengths of corresponding sides of similar triangles are proportional to complete the following ratios: $\dfrac{BE}{DF} = \dfrac{AE}{CF}$

H Recall that you can also write the proportion so that the ratios compare parts of the same triangle: $\dfrac{BE}{AE} = \dfrac{DF}{CF}$.

I The proportion you wrote in step **H** shows that the ratios you wrote in **C** are equal. So, the slope of line ℓ is constant.

Reflect

7. **What If?** Suppose that you label two other points on line ℓ as *G* and *H*. Would the slope between these two points be different than the slope you found in the Explore Activity? Explain.

No; the slope of the line is constant, so the slope

between the points would be the same.

© Houghton Mifflin Harcourt Publishing Company

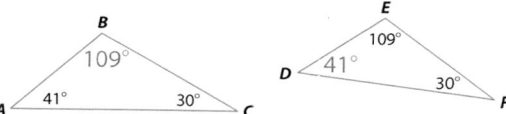

1. Explain whether the triangles are similar. Label the angle measures in the figure. (Explore Activity 1 and Example 1)

△ABC has angle measures __41°, 109°, and 30°__ and △DEF has angle

measures __41°, 109°, and 30°__. Because __two angles__ in one

triangle are congruent to __two angles__ in the other triangle, the

triangles are __similar__.

2. A flagpole casts a shadow 23.5 feet long. At the same time of day, Mrs. Gilbert, who is 5.5 feet tall, casts a shadow that is 7.5 feet long. How tall in feet is the flagpole? Round your answer to the nearest tenth. (Example 2)

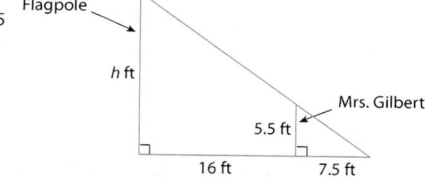

$$\frac{5.5}{\boxed{7.5}} = \frac{h}{\boxed{23.5}}$$

$h = \underline{17.2}$ feet

3. Two transversals intersect two parallel lines as shown. Explain whether △ABC and △DEC are similar. (Example 1)

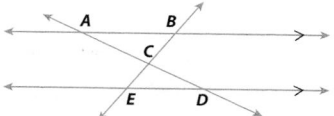

∠BAC and ∠EDC are __congruent__ since they are __alternate interior angles__.

∠ABC and ∠DEC are __congruent__ since they are __alternate interior angles__.

By __AA Similarity__, △ABC and △DEC are __similar__.

 ESSENTIAL QUESTION CHECK-IN

4. How can you determine when two triangles are similar?

__If two angles of one triangle are congruent to two__
__angles of the other triangle, the triangles are similar by__
__the angle–angle similarity postulate.__

© Houghton Mifflin Harcourt Publishing Company

4 Elaborate

Talk About It

Summarize the Lesson

Ask: What do you need to show in order to prove that two triangles are similar?

To prove two triangles are similar, you need to prove that at least two angles in one triangle are congruent to two angles in the other triangle. Or, you can show that the lengths of all three of their corresponding sides are proportional.

Guided Practice

Engage with the Whiteboard

For **Exercise 2**, use color markers to outline the two similar triangles and to mark pairs of corresponding angles.

Avoid Common Errors

- **Exercise 2** Some students may forget to add the two measures along the bottom of the figure and simply use the three values in the diagram in their proportion. Have students draw separate sketches of the two triangles shown in the figure, one large and one small. This should help students see that the length of the horizontal leg of the large triangle is 16 + 7.5, or 23.5 feet.

- **Exercise 3** If students have difficulty identifying that ∠BAC and ∠CDE are alternate interior angles, have students cover $\overleftrightarrow{EB}$ to help them identify this angle relationship. Likewise, have them cover $\overleftrightarrow{AD}$ to help them identify the angle relationship between ∠ABC and ∠CED.

DIFFERENTIATE INSTRUCTION *Intervention and Additional Support*

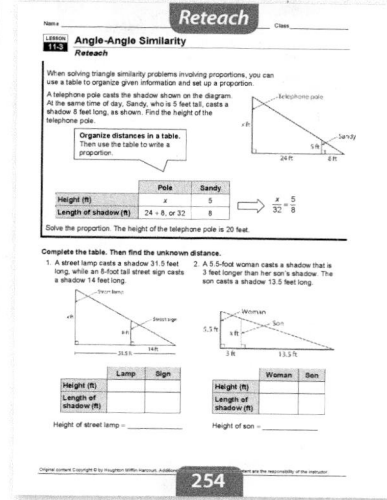

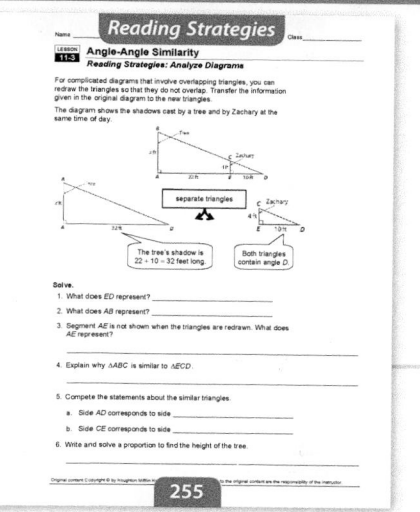

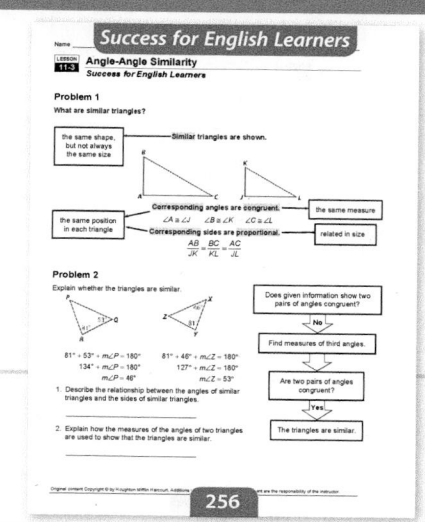

Personal Math Trainer
Daily Intervention
11.3 Homework

Pages shown are from *Differentiated Instruction.*
Also available online.

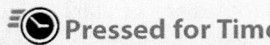

⏱ **Pressed for Time**

11.3 Differentiated Homework Assignments

AL Approaching Level	5–9, 11
OL On Level	8–12
BL Beyond Level	9, 11–14

*For **Below Level** students, assign Personal Math Trainer, Daily Intervention 11.3 Homework.*

Mathematical Processes	Exercises
MP.1 Problem Solving	8–9
MP.2 Reasoning	5–7, 10, 13
MP.3 Logic	11, 14
MP.6 Precision	12

Focus on Higher Order Thinking

Depth of Knowledge	Exercises
2 Skills/Concepts	5–10
3 Strategic Thinking H.O.T.	11–14

11.3 Independent Practice

Use the diagrams for Exercises 5–7.

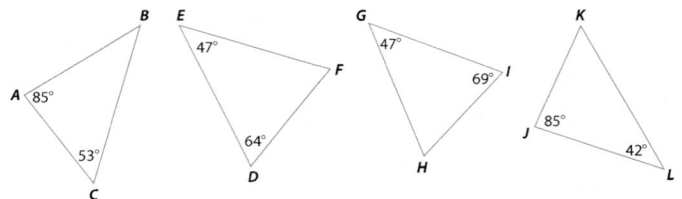

5. Find the missing angle measures in the triangles.

   m∠B = 42°, m∠F = 69°, m∠H = 64°, m∠K = 53°

6. Which triangles are similar?

   △ABC and △JLK are similar. △DEF and △HGI are similar.

7. **Analyze Relationships** Determine which angles are congruent to the angles in △ABC.

   ∠J ≅ ∠A, ∠L ≅ ∠B, and ∠K ≅ ∠C

8. **Multistep** A tree casts a shadow that is 20 feet long. Frank is 6 feet tall, and while standing next to the tree he casts a shadow that is 4 feet long.

   a. How tall is the tree? _____30 ft_____

   b. How much taller is the tree than Frank? _____24 ft_____

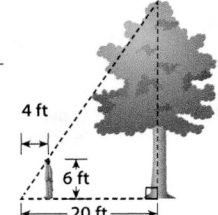

9. **Represent Real-World Problems** Sheila is climbing on a ladder that is attached against the side of a jungle gym wall. She is 5 feet off the ground and 3 feet from the base of the ladder, which is 15 feet from the wall. Draw a diagram to help you solve the problem. How high up the wall is the top of the ladder?

   _____25 feet_____

10. **Justify Reasoning** Are two equilateral triangles always similar? Explain.

    Yes; each angle of an equilateral triangle measures 60°, so all three angles of one equilateral triangle are congruent to all three angles of any other equilateral triangle.

© Houghton Mifflin Harcourt Publishing Company

DIFFERENTIATE INSTRUCTION *Leveled Homework/Practice*

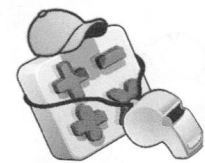

Personal Math Trainer
• 11.3 Homework

Pages shown are from *Differentiated Instruction*. **Also available online.**

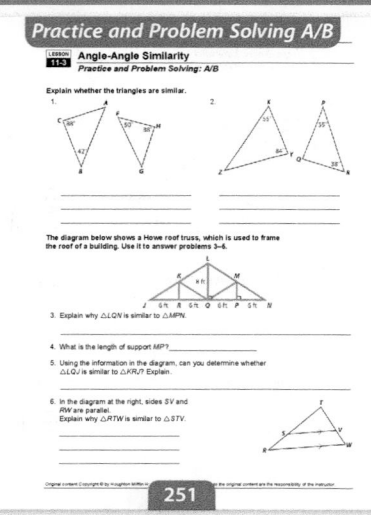

Practice and Problem Solving A/B

251

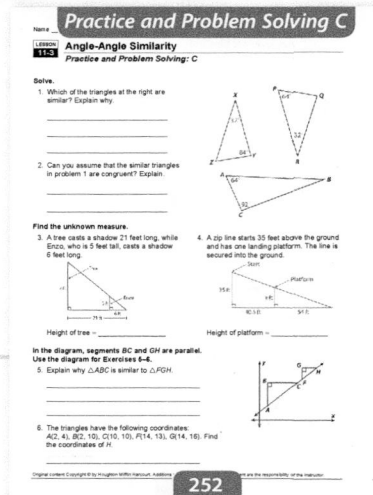

Practice and Problem Solving C

252

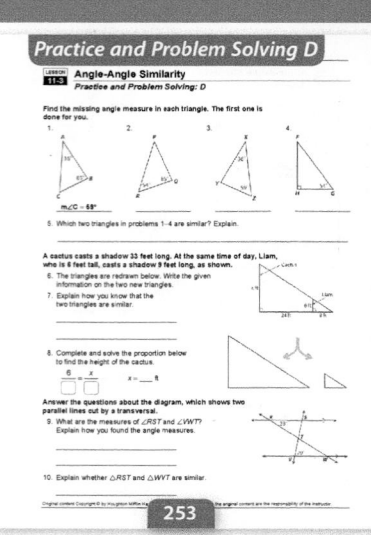

Practice and Problem Solving D

253

11. Critique Reasoning Ryan calculated the missing measure in the diagram shown. What was his mistake?

$$\frac{3.4}{6.5} = \frac{h}{19.5}$$

$$19.5 \times \frac{3.4}{6.5} = \frac{h}{19.5} \times 19.5$$

$$\frac{66.3}{6.5} = h$$

$$10.2 \text{ cm} = h$$

In the first line, Ryan should have added 19.5 and 6.5 to get a denominator of 26 for the expression on the right side. Doing so gives the correct value of 13.6 cm for h.

 **FOCUS ON HIGHER ORDER THINKING**

12. Communicate Mathematical Ideas For a pair of triangular earrings, how can you tell if they are similar? How can you tell if they are congruent?

The earrings are similar if two angle measures of one are equal to two angle measures of the other. They are congruent if they are similar and if the side lengths of one are equal to the side lengths of the other.

13. Critical Thinking When does it make sense to use similar triangles to measure the height and length of objects in real life?

Sample answer: If the item is too tall or too large to measure with a tape measure or other measuring device, or if a straight–line path is not accessible

14. Justify Reasoning Two right triangles on a coordinate plane are similar but not congruent. Each of the legs of both triangles are extended by 1 unit, creating two new right triangles. Are the resulting triangles similar? Explain using an example.

No; Unless the original triangle was isosceles, the side lengths will no longer be proportional. A right triangle with side lengths 3, 4, and 5 is similar to a right triangle with side lengths 6, 8, and 10. If the legs of both triangles are extended by 1 unit, the leg lengths become 4 and 5 and 7 and 9, and $\frac{7}{4} \neq \frac{9}{5}$.

368 Unit 5

Work Area

© Houghton Mifflin Harcourt Publishing Company

DIFFERENTIATE INSTRUCTION *Extend-the-Math Activity* **PRE-AP**

Activity Triangle *AGD*, shown here, is an isosceles triangle with sides *AG* and *DG* congruent. Two line segments, segments *EB* and *FC*, have been drawn perpendicular to side *AD*. Use what you have learned about the AA Similarity Postulate and finding missing measures in similar triangles to describe how you would find the length of line segment *CD*.

Perpendicular segments form right angles, so angle *ABE* and angle *DCF* are congruent. Angles *A* and *D* are congruent because the base angles of an isosceles triangle are congruent. Therefore, triangles *AEB* and *DFC* are similar triangles by the AA Similarity Postulate. This means that their corresponding sides are proportional. So, $\frac{25 \text{ in.}}{15 \text{ in.}} = \frac{10 \text{ in.}}{x \text{ in.}}$ and $x = 6$. Therefore, segment *CD* is 6 inches long.

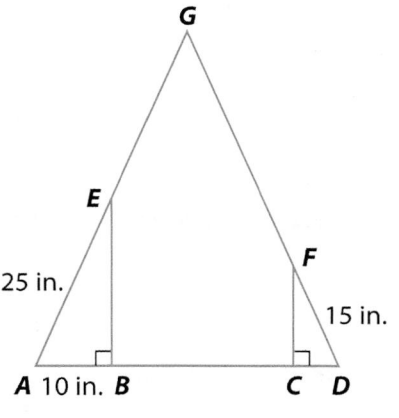

11.3 Lesson Quiz

1. Explain whether the triangles are similar.

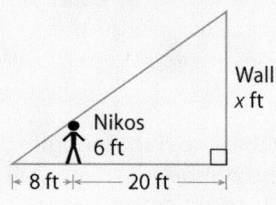

The triangles are similar by the AA Similarity Postulate. The missing angle measure in the triangle on the left is 33°. The missing angle measure in the triangle on the right is 37°. All pairs of corresponding angles are congruent.

2. Nikos is 6 ft tall and his shadow is 8 ft long. A wall casts a shadow that is 28 ft long. How tall in feet is the wall?

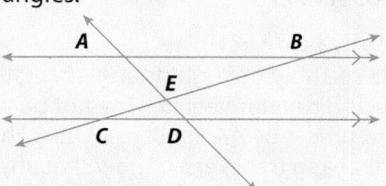

21 ft

3. Two transversals intersect two parallel lines as shown. Explain whether △*ABE* and △*DCE* are similar and list the corresponding pairs of angles.

∠*EAB* and ∠*EDC* are congruent since they are alternate interior angles. ∠*ABE* and ∠*DCE* are congruent since they are also alternate interior angles. By the AA Similarity Postulate, △*ABE* and △*DCE* are similar. The pairs of corresponding angles are ∠*EAB* and ∠*EDC*, ∠*ABE* and ∠*DCE*, and ∠*AEB* and ∠*DEC*.

Differentiate Instruction

IF a student misses more than one question, THEN

Differentiate Instruction:
• 11.3 Reteach
• Personal Math Trainer

Interactive Whiteboard
Interactive Lesson quiz available online

Similar Triangles and Slope

1 Engage

? ESSENTIAL QUESTION

How can you use the concept of similar triangles to prove that the slope of a line is constant between any two points on the line? By AA Similarity, any two pairs of points on a line in the coordinate plane result in similar right triangles using the rise and run segments. Therefore, the corresponding side lengths, rise-to-run, are proportional, so the slopes are equal.

Motivate the Lesson

Ask: How do you know that the right triangles formed using the rise and run between any pair of points on a line are similar right triangles? Begin the Explore Activity to find out.

2 Explore

EXPLORE ACTIVITY

Focus on Math Connections

Help students see how the right triangles created using the rise and run between any pair of points on the line are similar by AA Similarity. Using the graph of the line as a transversal, show that any two horizontal lines, which are parallel, form congruent corresponding angles with the graph of the line. Likewise, any two vertical lines, which are parallel, also form congruent corresponding angles with the graph of the line. Because all the angles are congruent, the right triangles formed along the line are all similar.

TEACHER TO TEACHER

Critical Thinking Direct students' attention to the graph for **Exercises 3–8**. Suppose the right angle at C is drawn above $\overleftrightarrow{AD}$ instead of below it. How does this change the pairs of congruent angles and the similarity statement? How does it change the slope calculation?

$\angle C \cong \angle F$ is still true, but $\angle CAB \cong \angle FED$ and $\triangle ABC \sim \triangle EDF$; the slope becomes $\frac{-2}{4}$ instead of $\frac{-2}{4}$, but both are equal to $-\frac{1}{2}$.

Similar Triangles and Slope

8.5.GF11.3
Students will apply the concept of similar triangles to prove that the slope of a line is constant between any two points on the line.

? ESSENTIAL QUESTION

How can you apply the concept of similar triangles to prove that the slope of a line is constant between any two points on the line?

EXPLORE ACTIVITY

Using Similar Triangles to Prove a Constant Slope

The R-value of insulation gives the material's resistance to heat flow. The graph shows the proportional relationship between the R-value and the thickness of fiberglass insulation.

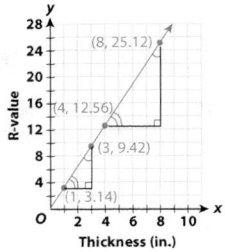

A The graph shows four points on the line and the triangles resulting from sketching the rise and run from one point to the next. Viewing the graph of R-value as a transversal to the rise and run segments, are the two pairs of corresponding angles along the transversal congruent? Explain.

Yes, because the two horizontal lines are parallel and the two vertical lines are parallel. Corresponding angles formed by a transversal and parallel lines are congruent.

B What is the relationship between the two resulting triangles? Explain your answer.

The triangles are similar because of AA Similarity.

C Use the relationship from Part B to state the relationship between corresponding sides of the resulting triangles.

Because the triangles are similar, the corresponding sides are proportional.

D Use the properties of similar triangles to explain why the slope, or rise-to-run ratio, is constant between any two points on the line.

Any two pairs of points on the line result in similar right triangles, which have proportional side lengths. So the rise-to-run ratios are equal, and the slopes are equal.

E Use any two points to find the unit rate for this proportional relationship. Show your work.

Using (0, 0) and (1, 3.14): $m = \frac{3.14 - 0}{1 - 0} = 3.14$.

The unit rate is the R-value, 3.14/in.

Going Further 11.3 **368A**

DIFFERENTIATE INSTRUCTION *Leveled Questions*

	EXPLORE ACTIVITY
AL DOK 1 *Recall*	The angles at (1, 3.14) and (4, 12.56) and the angles at (3, 9.42) and (8, 25.12) are corresponding angles for what pairs of lines in the coordinate plane? (1, 3.14) and (4, 12.56): $y = 3.14$ and $y = 12.56$; (3, 9.42) and (8, 25.12): $x = 3$ and $x = 8$
OL DOK 2 *Skills/Concepts*	Use the slope formula to show that the slopes of the side of each triangle that lies on the R-value graph are equal. for (1, 3.14) and (3, 9.42): $m = \frac{9.42 - 3.14}{3 - 1} = \frac{6.28}{2} = 3.14$; for (4, 12.56) and (8, 25.12): $m = \frac{25.12 - 12.56}{8 - 4} = \frac{12.56}{4} = 3.14$
BL DOK 3 *Strategic Thinking*	Can you find the unit rate for any linear relationship that passes through the line $x = 1$ by using the point (1, y)? Explain. No; only for a proportional relationship. Otherwise, you must find the difference of y-values for an x-value change of 1.

LEVELED QUESTIONS: **AL** Approaching Level | **OL** On Level | **BL** Beyond Level

© Houghton Mifflin Harcourt Publishing Company

Reflect

1. **Communicate Mathematical Ideas** How can you use properties of similar triangles to show that the unit rate of a real-world proportional relationship is the same as the slope of its graph?

   The graph of a proportional relationship is a line through the origin. The slope for any two points on that line is the same, so finding the slope by using the origin and the point on the line with an x-coordinate of 1 will give the unit rate.

2. **Critical Thinking** What can you say about the y-value of the point $(1, y)$ on the graph of a proportional relationship?

   The y-value of the point $(1, y)$ gives the unit rate.

Practice

The graph shows two pairs of points on a line and similar right triangles formed by drawing the rise and run segments for each pair of points.

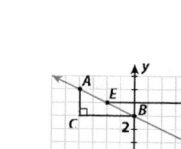

1. List the pairs of congruent angles and the similar triangles.

   $\angle A$ and $\angle D$; $\angle E$ and $\angle C$; $\angle ABC$ and $\angle DBE$;

   $\triangle ABC \sim \triangle DBE$

2. Use proportional corresponding side lengths to show that the slope of $\overline{AB}$ is equal to the slope of $\overline{BD}$.

   slope $\overline{AB} = \dfrac{BC}{AC} = \dfrac{2}{3}$; slope $\overline{BD} = \dfrac{BE}{DE} = \dfrac{4}{6} = \dfrac{2}{3}$

Use the graph at right for Exercises 3–8.

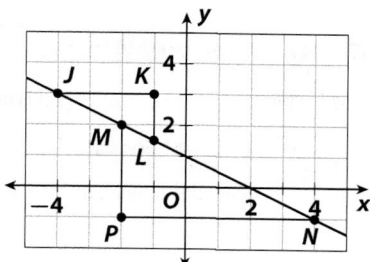

3. Name the pairs of congruent angles and similar triangles from the line containing A and D.

   $\angle CAB \cong \angle FDE$; $\angle C \cong \angle F$; $\angle CBA \cong \angle FED$;

   $\triangle ABC \sim \triangle DEF$

4. Name the pairs of congruent angles and similar triangles from the line containing P and Q.

   $\angle RPQ \cong \angle TQS$; $\angle R \cong \angle T$; $\angle RQP \cong \angle TSQ$; $\triangle PQR \sim \triangle QST$

Complete each ratio.

5. $\dfrac{AC}{CB} = \dfrac{\boxed{DF}}{FE}$

6. $\dfrac{AB}{\boxed{DE}} = \dfrac{CB}{FE}$

7. $\dfrac{\boxed{QR}}{\blacksquare} = \dfrac{ST}{\blacksquare}$

8. $\dfrac{PQ}{QS} = \dfrac{PR}{\boxed{QT}}$

© Houghton Mifflin Harcourt Publishing Company

3 Explain

Avoid Common Errors

In the exercises, students may list the angle correspondences incorrectly. Make sure that students understand that the order of the vertices is important when naming angles and triangles, and to indicate the correct correspondence. For example, in **Exercise 1,** $\angle DBE$ corresponds to $\angle ABC$, with the vertices listed in that order because they are listed in order of correspondence: $\angle D \cong \angle A$ and $\angle E \cong \angle C$.

4 Elaborate

Summarize the Lesson

💬 **Ask:** How can you use properties of similar triangles to show that the slope of a line is constant between any two pairs of points on a non-vertical line? Sample answer: Using any two pairs of points on a line, form two right triangles along the line. Use corresponding angles formed by a transversal and two parallel lines to show that the triangles are similar by AA Similarity. Then use properties of similar triangles to show that the ratios of rise to run for both triangles are equal, so that the slopes are equal.

5 Evaluate

Practice

Focus on Math Connections

In **Exercises 5–8**, have students identify which ratios are slope ratios. Only the ratios in Exercise 5 are rise/run ratios.

LESSON QUIZ

Use the graph for Items 1–3.

1. Name the pairs of congruent angles and the similar triangles. $\angle KJL \cong \angle PNM$; $\angle KLJ \cong \angle PMN$; $\angle LKJ \cong \angle MPN$; $\triangle JKL \sim \triangle NPM$

2. Use proportional corresponding lengths to show that the slope of $\overline{JL}$ is equal to the slope of $\overline{MN}$.

   slope $\overline{JL} = \dfrac{KL}{JK} = \dfrac{-1.5}{3} = -\dfrac{1}{2}$;

   slope $\overline{MN} = \dfrac{MP}{PN} = \dfrac{-3}{6} = -\dfrac{1}{2}$

3. What ratio is equivalent to the ratio $\dfrac{MP}{NM}$? $\dfrac{LK}{JL}$

Ready to Go On?

Assess Mastery

Access *Ready to Go On?* assessment online, and receive instant scoring, feedback, and customized intervention or enrichment.

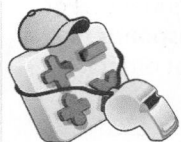

Personal Math Trainer

Online Assessment and Intervention
• Module 11 Posttest

Additional Resources

Digital Teacher Resources

Go online for module-level resources.

Assessment Resources
• Module 11 Quiz: B, p.55
• Module 11 Quiz: D, p.57

my.hrw.com

Ready to Go On?

Personal Math Trainer
Online Assessment and Intervention
my.hrw.com

11.1 Parallel Lines Cut by a Transversal

In the figure, line $p \parallel$ line q. Find the measure of each angle if $m\angle 8 = 115°$.

1. $m\angle 7 = $ ___65°___

2. $m\angle 6 = $ ___115°___

3. $m\angle 1 = $ ___115°___

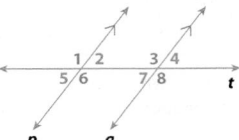

11.2 Angle Theorems for Triangles

Find the measure of each angle.

4. $m\angle A = $ ___48°___

5. $m\angle B = $ ___58°___

6. $m\angle BCA = $ ___74°___

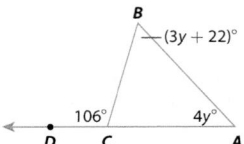

11.3 Angle-Angle Similarity

Triangle *FEG* is similar to triangle *IHJ*. Find the missing values.

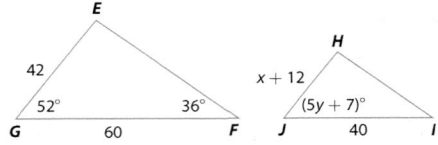

7. $x = $ ___16___   **8.** $y = $ ___9___   **9.** $m\angle H = $ ___92°___

 ESSENTIAL QUESTION

10. How can you use similar triangles to solve real-world problems?

Sample answer: You can find lengths that you can't measure directly.

© Houghton Mifflin Harcourt Publishing Company

READY TO GO ON? *Diagnostic Assessment*

 RtI Response to Intervention

Use to determine if students have mastered the concepts covered in this module.

Lesson	Exercises	Content Focus	Review with *Differentiated Instruction*
11.1	1–3	Parallel Lines Cut by a Transversal	**11.1** Reteach **11.1** Reading Strategies **11.1** Success for English Learners
11.2	4–6	Angle Theorems for Triangles	**11.2** Reteach **11.2** Reading Strategies **11.2** Success for English Learners
11.3	7–9	Angle-Angle Similarity	**11.3** Reteach **11.3** Reading Strategies **11.3** Success for English Learners

Assessment Readiness

Personal Math Trainer

Online Assessment and Intervention

my.hrw.com

Preparing for High Stakes Tests

Assessment Readiness Tip

Students should underline or highlight the final sentence of the word problem to make sure they have finished the problem, especially in problems with multiple steps.

- **Item 3** Students might stop after solving for x, which would give them answer choice A. If they underline the last sentence in the problem, they will realize that while they have found x, they have not yet found the measure of the smallest angle.

Avoid Common Errors

- **Item 2** Some students may miss the word *not* in the question and instead select an angle that is congruent. Remind students to look diligently for words that indicate opposites, like *not*.

- **Item 4** Students should remember that the exterior angle must be larger than either of the remote interior angles.

Selected Response

Use the figure for Exercises 1 and 2.

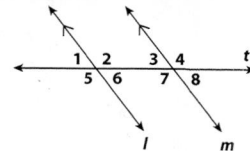

1. Which angle pair is a pair of alternate exterior angles?

Ⓐ ∠5 and ∠6 Ⓒ ∠5 and ∠4

Ⓑ ∠6 and ∠7 Ⓓ ∠5 and ∠2

2. Which of the following angles is **not** congruent to ∠3?

Ⓐ ∠1 Ⓒ ∠6

Ⓑ ∠2 Ⓓ ∠8

3. The measures, in degrees, of the three angles of a triangle are given by $2x + 1$, $3x - 3$, and $9x$. What is the measure of the smallest angle?

Ⓐ 13° Ⓒ 36°

Ⓑ 27° Ⓓ 117°

4. Which is a possible measure of ∠DCA in the triangle below?

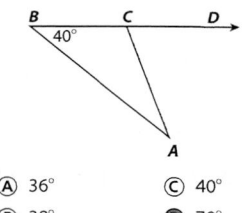

Ⓐ 36° Ⓒ 40°

Ⓑ 38° Ⓓ 70°

5. Kaylee wrote in her dinosaur report that the Jurassic period was 1.75×10^8 years ago. What is this number written in standard form?

Ⓐ 1,750,000

Ⓑ 17,500,000

Ⓒ 175,000,000

Ⓓ 17,500,000,000

6. Given that y is proportional to x, what linear equation can you write if y is 16 when x is 20?

Ⓐ $y = 20x$ Ⓒ $y = \frac{4}{5}x$

Ⓑ $y = \frac{5}{4}x$ Ⓓ $y = 0.6x$

Mini-Task

7. Two transversals intersect two parallel lines as shown.

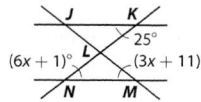

a. What is the value of x?

4

b. What is the measure of ∠LMN?

23°

c. What is the measure of ∠KLM?

48°

d. Which two triangles are similar? How do you know?

Triangle KLJ is similar to triangle NLM because they have two congruent angles.

© Houghton Mifflin Harcourt Publishing Company

Items	Grade 8 Lessons	Mathematical Processes
1	11.1	MP.6
2	11.1	MP.7
3	11.2	MP.2
4	11.2	MP.4
5*	2.2	MP.4
6*	3.1	MP.4
7	11.1, 11.3	MP.4, MP.7

* Item integrates mixed review concepts from previous modules or a previous course.

DIFFERENTIATE ASSESSMENT

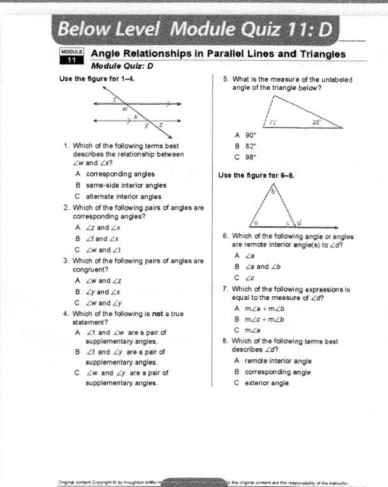

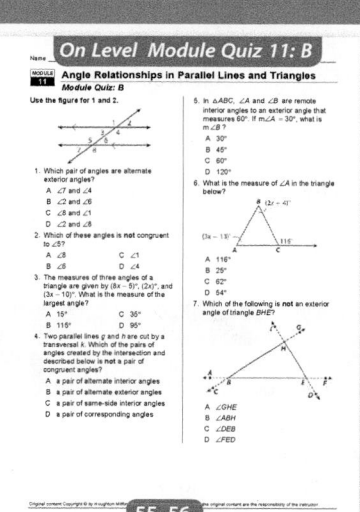

Personal Math Trainer

Module 11 Assessment Readiness

Pages shown are from *Assessment Resources*. **Also available online.**

Module At A Glance

Module Essential Question: How can you use the Pythagorean Theorem to solve real-world problems?

MODULE 12 | The Pythagorean Theorem

Lessons at A Glance	Lesson 12.1 The Pythagorean Theorem	Lesson 12.2 Converse of the Pythagorean Theorem	Lesson 12.3 Distance Between Two Points
	Pg. T375A	Pg. T381A	Pg. T387A
Essential Question	How can you prove the Pythagorean Theorem and use it to solve problems?	How can you test the converse of the Pythagorean Theorem and use it to solve problems?	How can you use the Pythagorean Theorem to find the distance between two points on a coordinate plane?
Objective	Students will prove the Pythagorean Theorem and use it to solve problems.	Students will test the converse of the Pythagorean Theorem and use it to solve problems.	Students will use the Pythagorean Theorem to find the distance between two points on a coordinate plane.
Vocabulary	hypotenuse, legs		
Go online for all your module resources my.hrw.com 	12.1 *i*Student Edition 12.1 *i*Teacher Edition 12.1 *e*Student Edition 🐾 Personal Math Trainer 📺 Math on the Spot Videos ✕ Animated Math	12.2 *i*Student Edition 12.2 *i*Teacher Edition 12.2 *e*Student Edition 🐾 Personal Math Trainer 📺 Math on the Spot Videos	12.3 *i*Student Edition 12.3 *i*Teacher Edition 12.3 *e*Student Edition 🐾 Personal Math Trainer 📺 Math on the Spot Videos
Print Resources	**12.1 Student Edition:** Lesson *Differentiated Instruction* 12.1 Practice and Problem Solving A/B, C, and D 12.1 Reteach 12.1 Reading Strategies 12.1 Success for English Learners	**12.2 Student Edition:** Lesson *Differentiated Instruction* 12.2 Practice and Problem Solving A/B, C, and D 12.2 Reteach 12.2 Reading Strategies 12.2 Success for English Learners	**12.3 Student Edition:** Lesson *Differentiated Instruction* 12.3 Practice and Problem Solving A/B, C, and D 12.3 Reteach 12.3 Reading Strategies 12.3 Success for English Learners

RtI — Response to Intervention

Before the Module	During the Lesson	After the Module
Are You Ready	**Guided/Independent Practice**	**Ready to Go On?**
• Prerequisite Skills Activities • Personal Math Trainer	• Reteach • Personal Math Trainer • Practice and Problem Solving D	• Reteach • Personal Math Trainer

Teacher Notes

Check It Out!

Game	Math on the Spot Videos	Animated Math
 **Triple Concentration** After Lesson 12.2	 One for every Example in every Lesson	x^2 During Lesson 12.1

The Pythagorean Theorem

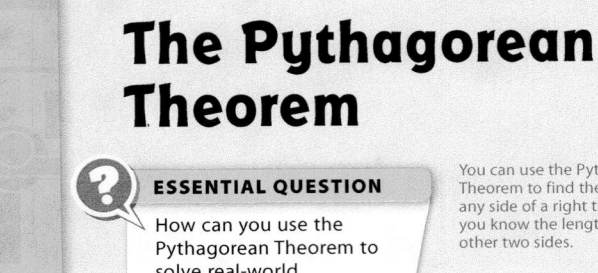

🔵 **Real-World Video Viewing Guide**

After students have watched the video, discuss the following:

- How can you use the length of the diagonal of a television to find its height and width?

- What does the variable *c* represent in the Pythagorean Theorem? the length of the diagonal

Professional Development Video

Author Juli Dixon models successful teaching practices as she explores the Pythagorean Theorem in an actual eighth-grade classroom.

? ESSENTIAL QUESTION

How can you use the Pythagorean Theorem to solve real-world problems?

You can use the Pythagorean Theorem to find the length of any side of a right triangle if you know the lengths of the other two sides.

LESSON 12.1
The Pythagorean Theorem

LESSON 12.2
Converse of the Pythagorean Theorem

LESSON 12.3
Distance Between Two Points

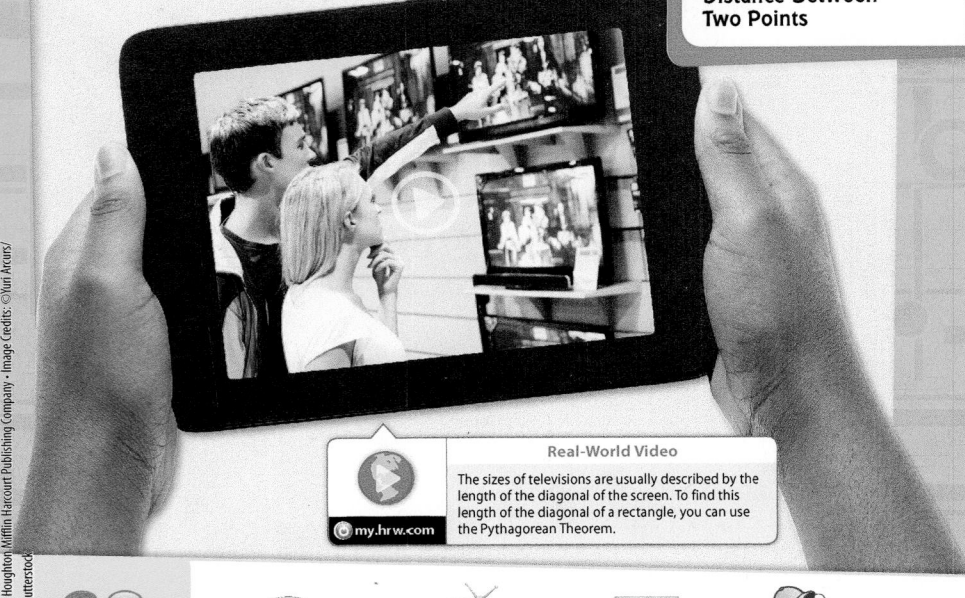

Real-World Video

The sizes of televisions are usually described by the length of the diagonal of the screen. To find this length of the diagonal of a rectangle, you can use the Pythagorean Theorem.

🔵 my.hrw.com

© Houghton Mifflin Harcourt Publishing Company • Image Credits: ©Yuri Arcurs/Shutterstock

GO DIGITAL
my.hrw.com

my.hrw.com

Go digital with your write-in student edition, accessible on any device.

Math On the Spot

Scan with your smart phone to jump directly to the online edition, video tutor, and more.

Animated Math

Interactively explore key concepts to see how math works.

Personal Math Trainer

Get immediate feedback and help as you work through practice sets.

371

TEACHER ONLINE RESOURCES

 ONLINE TEACHER EDITION Access a full suite of teaching resources online—plan, present, and manage classes and assignments.

 MY SMART PLANNER Easily plan your classes and access all your resources online.

 INTERACTIVE WHITEBOARDS Engage students with interactive whiteboard-ready examples and a lesson quiz for each lesson.

 PERSONAL MATH TRAINER: Online Assessment and Intervention Assign automatically graded homework, quizzes, tests, and intervention activities. Prepare your students for standardized tests in short-answer and multiple-choice formats.

Reading Start-Up

Visualize Vocabulary

Use the ✔ words to complete the graphic.

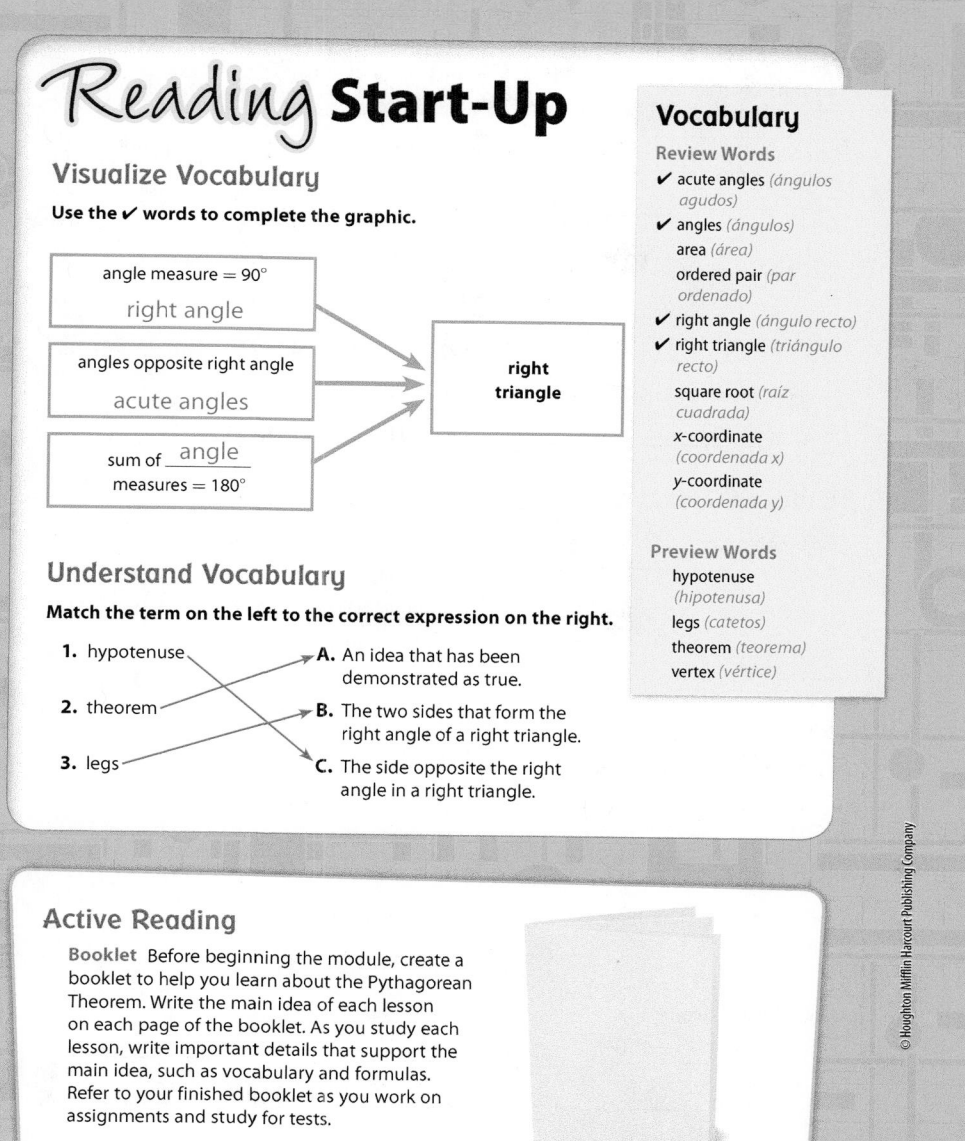

angle measure = 90°
right angle

angles opposite right angle
acute angles

→ **right triangle**

sum of ___angle___
measures = 180°

Understand Vocabulary

Match the term on the left to the correct expression on the right.

1. hypotenuse

2. theorem

3. legs

A. An idea that has been demonstrated as true.

B. The two sides that form the right angle of a right triangle.

C. The side opposite the right angle in a right triangle.

Vocabulary

Review Words
✔ acute angles (*ángulos agudos*)
✔ angles (*ángulos*)
area (*área*)
ordered pair (*par ordenado*)
✔ right angle (*ángulo recto*)
✔ right triangle (*triángulo recto*)
square root (*raíz cuadrada*)
x-coordinate (*coordenada x*)
y-coordinate (*coordenada y*)

Preview Words
hypotenuse (*hipotenusa*)
legs (*catetos*)
theorem (*teorema*)
vertex (*vértice*)

Active Reading

Booklet Before beginning the module, create a booklet to help you learn about the Pythagorean Theorem. Write the main idea of each lesson on each page of the booklet. As you study each lesson, write important details that support the main idea, such as vocabulary and formulas. Refer to your finished booklet as you work on assignments and study for tests.

© Houghton Mifflin Harcourt Publishing Company

Reading Start-Up

Visualize Vocabulary
The decision tree helps students review vocabulary associated with right triangles. Students should write one review word in each box.

Understand Vocabulary
Use the following explanation to help students learn the preview words.

> *Right triangles have special properties. One angle in a right triangle always measures 90°, which is a right angle.*
>
> *The side of a right triangle that is opposite the right angle, is called the* **hypotenuse**. *The two sides that form the right angle are called the* **legs**. *Naming these sides of the triangle can help us understand and talk about a triangle and its properties.*

Active Reading

Integrating Language Arts
Students can use these reading and note-taking strategies to help them organize and understand new concepts and vocabulary.

Additional Resources
Differentiated Instruction
- Reading Strategies **ELL**
- Interactive multilingual glossary

LEARNING PROGRESSIONS ACROSS THE GRADES

Before	In this Module	After
Students understand: • how to write and solve an equation • how to use exponents and the order of operations • how to graph points on the coordinate plane	Students represent and solve right triangles using the Pythagorean Theorem: • use models and diagrams to explain the Pythagorean Theorem • use the Pythagorean Theorem and its converse to solve problems • determine the distance between two points on a coordinate plane using the Pythagorean Theorem	Students will connect: • right triangles and the Pythagorean triples • sum of the interior angles of a triangle and sum of the interior angles of a polygon

Are You Ready?

Assess Readiness

Access *Are You Ready?* assessment online, and receive instant scoring, feedback, and customized intervention or enrichment.

Personal Math Trainer

Online Assessment and Intervention

Additional Resources

Digital Teacher Resources

Go online for module-level resources.

my.hrw.com

Are YOU Ready?

Complete these exercises to review skills you will need for this module.

Personal Math Trainer

Online Assessment and Intervention
my.hrw.com

Find the Square of a Number

EXAMPLE Find the square of 2.7.

$$\begin{array}{r} 2.7 \\ \times\, 2.7 \\ \hline 189 \\ 54 \\ \hline 7.29 \end{array}$$

Multiply the number by itself.

So, $2.7^2 = 7.29$.

Find the square of each number.

1. 5 __25__
2. 16 __256__
3. −11 __121__
4. $\frac{2}{7}$ __$\frac{4}{49}$__

Order of Operations

EXAMPLE

$$\sqrt{(5-2)^2 + (8-4)^2}$$ First, operate within parentheses.

$$\sqrt{(3)^2 + (4)^2}$$ Next, simplify exponents.

$$\sqrt{9 + 16}$$ Then add and subtract left to right.

$$\sqrt{25}$$ Finally, take the square root.

$$5$$

Evaluate each expression.

5. $\sqrt{(6+2)^2 + (3+3)^2}$ __10__
6. $\sqrt{(9-4)^2 + (5+7)^2}$ __13__
7. $\sqrt{(10-6)^2 + (15-12)^2}$ __5__
8. $\sqrt{(6+9)^2 + (10-2)^2}$ __17__

Simplify Numerical Expressions

EXAMPLE $\frac{1}{2}(2.5)^2(4) = \frac{1}{2}(6.25)(4)$ Simplify the exponent.

$= 12.5$ Multiply from left to right.

Simplify each expression.

9. 5(8)(10) __400__
10. $\frac{1}{2}(6)(12)$ __36__
11. $\frac{1}{3}(3)(12)$ __12__
12. $\frac{1}{2}(8)^2(4)$ __128__
13. $\frac{1}{4}(10)^2(15)$ __375__
14. $\frac{1}{3}(9)^2(6)$ __162__

© Houghton Mifflin Harcourt Publishing Company

Module 12 **373**

RtI Response to Intervention

Use to determine if students need intervention for the module's prerequisite skills.

Skill	Missed More Than . . .	Intervene With *Skills Intervention* worksheets (available online)	For Enrichment *Differentiated Instruction* (available in print and online)
Find the Square of a Number	1 question	**Skill 11** Find the Square of a Number	**Module 12 Challenge** Extend-the-Math Lesson Activities in TE
Order of Operations	1 question	**Skill 51** Order of Operations	**Module 12 Challenge** Extend-the-Math Lesson Activities in TE
Simplify Numerical Expressions	1 question	**Skill 52** Simplify Numerical Expressions	**Module 12 Challenge** Extend-the-Math Lesson Activities in TE

Complete these exercises to review skills you will need for this module.

Find the Square of a Number

15. A checkerboard is a square board that is divided into smaller squares, with eight squares along each side. Describe how to find the number of small squares on a checkerboard without counting.

Find the square of 8, or multiply 8 by itself, to get 64.

16. Describe how to find the square of -12.

Multiply the number by itself. $-12 \times (-12) = 144$

Order of Operations

17. Simplify the expression $\sqrt{(4-1)^2 + (3+1)^2}$ using the order of operations. Show your work, and justify each step.

$\sqrt{(4-1)^2 + (3+1)^2}$	First, operate within parentheses.
$\sqrt{(3)^2 + (4)^2}$	Next, simplify exponents.
$\sqrt{9 + 16}$	Add.
$\sqrt{25}$	Finally, take the square root.
5	

Simplify Numerical Expressions

18. To simplify $\frac{1}{4}(8)^2(12)$, Remy wrote $2^2 \cdot 12 = 48$. Find and correct Remy's error.

Instead of multiplying $\frac{1}{4}$ by 8, Remy should have simplified the exponent first to get $\frac{1}{4}(64)(12)$. The correct value for the expression is 192.

© Houghton Mifflin Harcourt Publishing Company

Find the Square of a Number

Exercise 15 Students may want to multiply a number by 2 when squaring, instead of correctly multiplying the number by itself. Caution them to check their answers within the context of the problem.

Exercise 16 Caution students to use the rules of integer multiplication when squaring signed numbers.

Order of Operations

Exercise 17 Students may have difficulty performing the order of operations correctly. Help them with the mnemonic "Please Excuse My Dear Aunt Sally" (PEMDAS).

Simplify Numerical Expressions

Exercise 18 Students may always work from left to right and forget to consider the exponents. Have students state the order in which they will do the operations, and make sure that they see the exponent.

Use to determine if students are able to apply the module's prerequisite skills.

Skill	Exercise	Depth of Knowledge (D.O.K.)	Mathematical Processes
Find the Square of a Number	15	**2** Skills/Concepts	**MP.2** Abstract and Quantitative Reasoning
	16	**2** Skills/Concepts	**MP.2** Abstract and Quantitative Reasoning
Order of Operations	17	**3** Strategic Thinking	**MP.3** Use and Evaluate Logical Reasoning
Simplify Numerical Expressions	18	**3** Strategic Thinking	**MP.3** Use and Evaluate Logical Reasoning

Lesson Support

Content Objective Students will learn how to prove the Pythagorean Theorem and use it to solve problems.

Professional Development

Integrate Mathematical Processes MP.5

This lesson provides an opportunity to address this Mathematical Processes standard. It calls for students to use appropriate tools strategically to solve problems. Students use paper and pencil to create models to prove the Pythagorean Theorem. They go on to solve problems using the Pythagorean Theorem with the aid of number sense to recognize reasonable answers and calculators to determine squares and square roots. They then find the diagonal of a box, an exercise which will be aided by examining a real box.

FOCUS	COHERENCE	RIGOR

Building Background

Connecting to Everyday Life Draw or ask students to draw several right triangles that are different sizes and shapes. Then ask students to suggest real-life settings or situations in which they might encounter right triangles or objects arranged as right triangles. If necessary, suggest a ladder leaning against a building, a ramp, part of a trellis, or a bridge support.

Learning Progressions

In this lesson, students are introduced to the Pythagorean Theorem. They apply the theorem to determine unknown side lengths to solve problems in both two and three dimensions. Important understandings for students include the following:

- **Prove the Pythagorean Theorem.**
- **Use the Pythagorean Theorem to find a missing side length.**
- **Use the Pythagorean Theorem to solve problems in three dimensions.**

The Pythagorean Theorem is a very important theorem in Euclidean geometry. It is the building block for many special relationships that students will explore as they continue to study geometry and trigonometry in high school mathematics classes. This lesson provides a solid foundation for starting this exploration, which continues with the converse of the Pythagorean Theorem in the next lesson.

Cluster Connections

This lesson provides an excellent opportunity to connect ideas in the cluster:

Understand and apply the Pythagorean Theorem.

Tell students that a Pythagorean triple is a set of positive integers a, b, and c such that $a^2 + b^2 = c^2$. The smallest Pythagorean triple is 3, 4, 5. Ask students to verify that those three integers form a Pythagorean triple. Then ask them to find a third integer that will combine with each of the following pairs to form a Pythagorean triple: 5 and 12; 7 and 25; 15 and 17. Encourage students to think of the two given integers as side lengths of a right triangle, and point out that they need to determine if the missing side is a leg or the hypotenuse.

Triples: 5, 12, 13; 7, 24, 25; and 8, 15, 17

Language Support ELL

Language Objective Students will model how to prove the Pythagorean Theorem and to use it to solve problems.

Leveled Strategies for English Learners ELL

Emerging
Have students work in pairs and listen while a partner reads aloud the steps for using the Pythagorean Theorem in Example 1 and then work together to solve the problems in Your Turn.

Expanding
Have students at this level of English proficiency work in pairs to list the steps for using the Pythagorean Theorem in Example 1 and then do the exercises in the Guided Practice together.

Bridging
Have students at this level of English proficiency work in pairs to list the steps for using the Pythagorean Theorem in Example 1 and then do the exercises in the Guided Practice together.

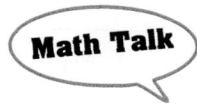

Math Talk Write out and model for students a sentence frame to begin their answer to Math Talk in Example 1.

No, it does not matter because the length of the leg _____.

Linguistic Support ELL

Academic/Content Vocabulary
Pythagorean theorem This lesson relies on students' understanding of the words *hypotenuse* and *leg* in this context. Point out that in this instance, *leg* does not refer to a body part but to one of the sides that makes the right angle in a right triangle. Also remind students that the word *right* in *right triangle* does not mean the opposite of *wrong*. Instead it refers to a triangle with a 90° angle. Refer students to the Online Multilingual Glossary.

Building Background
Several exercises in this lesson ask students to apply the Pythagorean Theorem to figure out the biggest, longest, or greatest item that will fit in a box. *Biggest, longest,* and *nearest* are superlative forms of an adjective. For English learners, post a chart in the classroom to show comparatives and superlatives from the lesson.

Adjective	Comparative	Superlative
big	bigger	biggest
near	nearer	nearest
long	longer	longest

Image Credits: ©Goodluz/Shutterstock

The Pythagorean Theorem

1 Engage

? ESSENTIAL QUESTION

How can you prove the Pythagorean Theorem and use it to solve problems? Sample answer: You can use the formulas for the area of squares and triangles to prove the Pythagorean Theorem. You can use the Pythagorean Theorem to find the missing lengths of sides of right triangles and to solve real-world problems.

Motivate the Lesson

Ask: If you draw a triangle on a coordinate grid with horizontal and vertical legs and with the vertices at the intersection of grid lines, it is easy to count grid lines to find the length of the legs. How do you find the length of the hypotenuse? Begin the Explore Activity to find out.

2 Explore

EXPLORE ACTIVITY

Focus on Reasoning

Guide students through the reasoning to see why the unshaded regions of the two congruent squares have the same area. Then guide them to see why $a^2 + b^2 = c^2$.

LESSON **12.1** 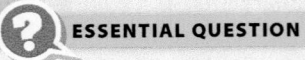 **The Pythagorean Theorem**

8.5.12.1
Students will use the Pythagorean Theorem to solve problems.

? ESSENTIAL QUESTION

How can you prove the Pythagorean Theorem and use it to solve problems?

EXPLORE ACTIVITY

Proving the Pythagorean Theorem

In a right triangle, the two sides that form the right angle are the **legs**. The side opposite the right angle is the **hypotenuse**.

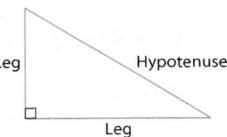

> **The Pythagorean Theorem**
>
> In a right triangle, the sum of the squares of the lengths of the legs is equal to the square of the length of the hypotenuse.
>
> If a and b are legs and c is the hypotenuse, $a^2 + b^2 = c^2$.

A Draw a right triangle on a piece of paper and cut it out. Make one leg shorter than the other.

B Trace your triangle onto another piece of paper four times, arranging them as shown. For each triangle, label the shorter leg a, the longer leg b, and the hypotenuse c.

C What is the area of the unshaded square?

c^2 square units

Label the unshaded square with its area.

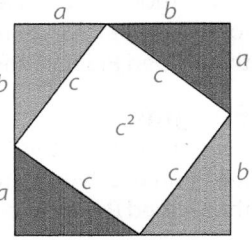

D Trace your original triangle onto a piece of paper four times again, arranging them as shown. Draw a line outlining a larger square that is the same size as the figure you made in **B**.

E What is the area of the unshaded square at the top right of the figure in **D**? at the top left?

a^2 square units; b^2 square units

Label the unshaded squares with their areas.

F What is the total area of the unshaded regions in **D**?

$a^2 + b^2$ square units

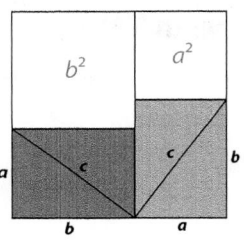

© Houghton Mifflin Harcourt Publishing Company

Lesson 12.1 **375**

DIFFERENTIATE INSTRUCTION *Leveled Questions*

	EXPLORE ACTIVITY
AL DOK 1 *Recall*	Is the total shaded area in the first figure the same as the total shaded area in the second figure? How do you know? Yes; they are the same shaded triangles traced again.
OL DOK 2 *Skills/Concepts*	The area of the large square is $(a + b)^2$. From the bottom diagram, how can you tell that $(a + b)^2 = a^2 + 2ab + b^2$? As noted in Part E, the small squares in the bottom diagram have areas of a^2 and b^2. Each of the two rectangles has an area of ab. So, the total area is $a^2 + 2ab + b^2$.
BL DOK 3 *Strategic Thinking*	How do you know that the area of the unshaded quadrilateral in the first figure is equal to the area of the unshaded regions in the second figure? The respective shaded figures are congruent, so their cumulative areas are the same. The resulting unshaded areas are also equal.

LEVELED QUESTIONS: AL Approaching Level | OL On Level | BL Beyond Level

Reflect

1. Explain whether the figures in **B** and **D** have the same area.

   Yes, the outlines of the figures are the same size.

2. Explain whether the unshaded regions of the figures in **B** and **D** have the same area.

   Yes, the shaded regions have the same area. Subtracting the area of the shaded region from the total area gives the same area for the unshaded region in each figure.

3. **Analyze Relationships** Write an equation relating the area of the unshaded region in step **B** to the unshaded region in **D**.

   $$a^2 + b^2 = c^2$$

Math On the Spot
my.hrw.com

Animated Math
my.hrw.com

Using the Pythagorean Theorem

You can use the Pythagorean Theorem to find the length of a side of a right triangle when you know the lengths of the other two sides.

EXAMPLE 1

Find the length of the missing side.

A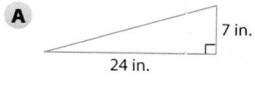

$$a^2 + b^2 = c^2$$
$$24^2 + 7^2 = c^2 \quad \text{Substitute into the formula.}$$
$$576 + 49 = c^2 \quad \text{Simplify.}$$
$$625 = c^2 \quad \text{Add.}$$
$$25 = c \quad \text{Take the square root of both sides.}$$

The length of the hypotenuse is 25 inches.

B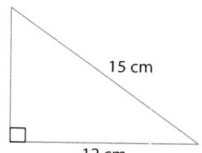

$$a^2 + b^2 = c^2$$
$$a^2 + 12^2 = 15^2 \quad \text{Substitute into the formula.}$$
$$a^2 + 144 = 225 \quad \text{Simplify.}$$
$$a^2 = 81 \quad \text{Use properties of equality to get } a^2 \text{ by itself.}$$
$$a = 9 \quad \text{Take the square root of both sides.}$$

The length of the leg is 9 centimeters.

Math Talk
Mathematical Processes

If you are given the length of the hypotenuse and one leg, does it matter whether you solve for a or b? Explain.

No, the length of the leg can be substituted for either a or b since both a and b represent the lengths of legs.

376 Unit 5

© Houghton Mifflin Harcourt Publishing Company

---

3 Explain

EXAMPLE 1

ADDITIONAL EXAMPLE 1

Find the length of the missing side.

A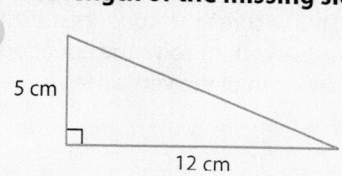

13 cm

B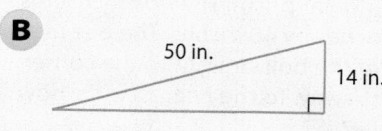

48 in.

 Interactive Whiteboard
Interactive example available online

Animated Math

The Pythagorean Theorem
Students explore an interactive model of a dynamic proof of the Pythagorean Theorem.

my.hrw.com

	EXAMPLE 1
AL **DOK 1** *Recall*	The hypotenuse of a right triangle is always opposite which angle? the right angle
OL **DOK 2** *Skills/Concepts*	When you take the square root of both sides, why don't you state both positive and negative roots? The relationship stated in the Pythagorean Theorem involves the side lengths of a triangle, which are always positive.
BL **DOK 3** *Strategic Thinking*	A right triangle has a hypotenuse of 20 centimeters. Are there possible leg lengths that are both integers? If so, what are they? yes; 12 cm and 16 cm

TEACHER TO TEACHER

Manipulatives Have each student draw a right triangle, using a protractor or angle template to draw the right angle. Have students measure the lengths of the sides to the nearest millimeter. Then have them use a calculator to verify the Pythagorean relationship between the side lengths of the right triangles. (Because the measurements are approximate, $a^2 + b^2$ may be close to but not exactly c^2 in some cases.)

Avoid Common Errors

Make sure students correctly identify the hypotenuse before applying the Pythagorean Theorem. Students may assume that the two given side lengths are the legs. In **Exercise 5,** make sure that students substitute 41 for c in $a^2 + b^2 = c^2$ and then solve the equation correctly to find the length of the vertical leg.

EXAMPLE 2

ADDITIONAL EXAMPLE 2 A bee is in a box shaped as a rectangular prism. The box measures 30 inches by 14 inches by 40 inches. The bee flies from one corner of the box straight to the corner that is the farthest away. To the nearest inch, how far does the bee fly?   52 in.

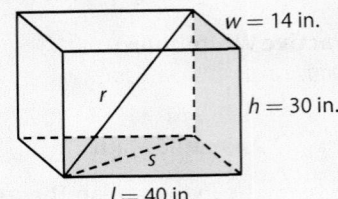

$w = 14$ in.
r
$h = 30$ in.
s
$l = 40$ in.

 Interactive Whiteboard
Interactive example available online

Digital Teacher Resources

Go online to access all your lesson-level resources.

Differentiated Instruction
• Reteach
• Reading Strategies
• Success for English Learners
• Practice and Problem Solving A/B, C, D

Math on the Spot Videos

my.hrw.com

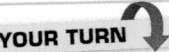 **YOUR TURN**

Find the length of the missing side.

4.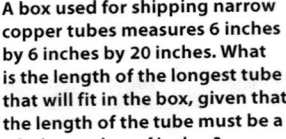
30 ft
40 ft
50 ft

5.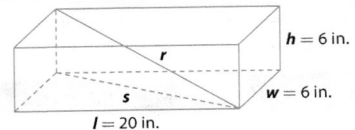
41 in.
40 in.
9 in.

Personal Math Trainer
Online Assessment and Intervention
my.hrw.com

Pythagorean Theorem in Three Dimensions

You can use the Pythagorean Theorem to solve problems in three dimensions.

EXAMPLE 2   Real World

A box used for shipping narrow copper tubes measures 6 inches by 6 inches by 20 inches. What is the length of the longest tube that will fit in the box, given that the length of the tube must be a whole number of inches?

$h = 6$ in.
r
s
$w = 6$ in.
$l = 20$ in.

STEP 1   You want to find r, the length from a bottom corner to the opposite top corner. First, find s, the length of the diagonal across the bottom of the box.

$w^2 + l^2 = s^2$

$6^2 + 20^2 = s^2$ Substitute into the formula.

$36 + 400 = s^2$ Simplify.

$436 = s^2$ Add.

STEP 2   Use your expression for s to find r.

$h^2 + s^2 = r^2$

$6^2 + 436 = r^2$ Substitute into the formula.

$472 = r^2$ Add.

$\sqrt{472} = r$ Take the square root of both sides.

$21.7 \approx r$ Use a calculator to round to the nearest tenth.

The length of the longest tube that will fit in the box is 21 inches.

Math Talk
Mathematical Processes

Looking at Step 2, why did the calculations in Step 1 stop before taking the square root of both sides of the final equation?

By stopping with an expression for s^2, it could be substituted directly into the formula for r^2.

Lesson 12.1 **377**

DIFFERENTIATE INSTRUCTION *Leveled Questions*

	EXAMPLE 2
AL **DOK 1** *Recall*	How can a box hold an object that is longer than the length of the box? by positioning the object along a diagonal of the box
OL **DOK 2** *Skills/Concepts*	Why do you need to find the length of the diagonal of the bottom before finding the diagonal from a top corner to the opposite bottom corner? The diagonal connecting the farthest corners is the hypotenuse of a right triangle with only one leg being the diagonal across the bottom of the box.
BL **DOK 3** *Strategic Thinking*	Make a conjecture about the dimensions of the shape that will produce the shortest distance from a bottom corner to the opposite top corner. A square will have the shortest diagonal. So, for a cube with dimensions of 10 in., the shortest distance will be about 17 in.

LEVELED QUESTIONS: **AL** Approaching Level | **OL** On Level | **BL** Beyond Level

Personal Math Trainer
Online Assessment and Intervention
my.hrw.com

YOUR TURN

6. Tina ordered a replacement part for her desk. It was shipped in a box that measures 4 in. by 4 in. by 14 in. What is the greatest length in whole inches that the part could have been?

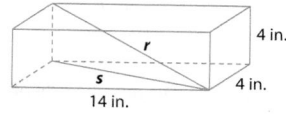

$$4^2 + 14^2 = s^2 \qquad 4^2 + 212 = r^2$$

$$16 + 196 = s^2 \qquad 228 = r^2$$

$$212 = s^2 \qquad \sqrt{228} = r$$

$$15.1 \approx r$$

The greatest length is 15 in.

Guided Practice

1. Find the length of the missing side of the triangle. (Explore Activity 1 and Example 1)

$$a^2 + b^2 = c^2 \rightarrow 24^2 + \boxed{10^2} = c^2 \rightarrow \boxed{676} = c^2$$

The length of the hypotenuse is $\boxed{26}$ feet.

10 ft

24 ft

2. Mr. Woo wants to ship a fishing rod that is 42 inches long to his son. He has a box with the dimensions shown. (Example 2)

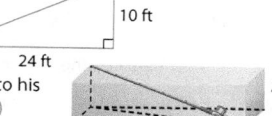

$h = 10$ in.
$w = 10$ in.
$l = 40$ in.

   a. Find the square of the length of the diagonal across the bottom of the box.

   _____1700_____

   b. Find the length from a bottom corner to the opposite top corner to the nearest tenth. Will the fishing rod fit?

   _____42.4 in.; yes_____

 ESSENTIAL QUESTION CHECK-IN

3. State the Pythagorean Theorem and tell how you can use it to solve problems.

   Sample answer: For a right triangle with legs of lengths
   a and b and hypotenuse of length c, $a^2 + b^2 = c^2$. You
   can use it to find the length of a side of a right triangle
   when the lengths of the other two sides are known.

378 Unit 5

© Houghton Mifflin Harcourt Publishing Company

YOUR TURN   MP.1

Focus on Communication

Students may object that an object such as a part for a desk may be too thick to be able to fit into the corner of a box. Point out that **Exercise 6** asks what is the greatest length the part could be and that students have to treat this as a theoretical maximum.

4 Elaborate

Talk About It

Summarize the Lesson

Have students complete the graphic organizer below. Let a, b, and c be the side lengths of a right triangle, with c the length of its hypotenuse.

a	b	c
3	4	5
5	12	13
7	24	25
8	15	17
9	40	41

Guided Practice

Engage with the Whiteboard

In **Exercise 1**, label the sides of the triangle a, b, and c. Either leg can be labeled a or b. After completing the problem, write the missing side length on the triangle.

Avoid Common Errors

Exercise 1 Students may forget to find the square root of c^2. Remind them that the hypotenuse is the longest side of the triangle and that $a + b$ must be greater than c.

DIFFERENTIATE INSTRUCTION *Intervention and Additional Support*

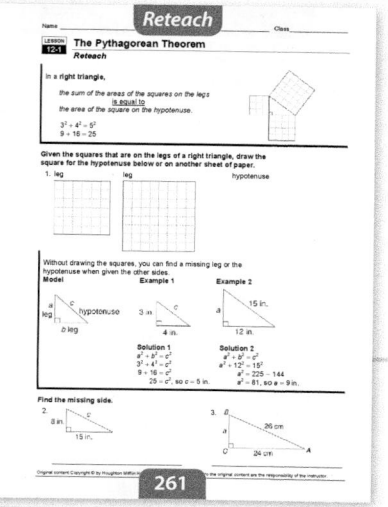

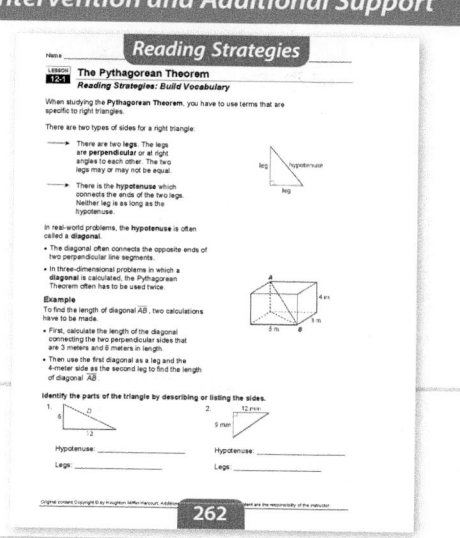

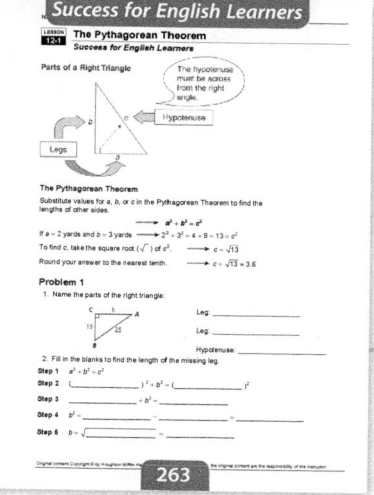

Personal Math Trainer
Daily Intervention
12.1 Homework

Pages shown are from *Differentiated Instruction*.
Also available online.

The Pythagorean Theorem   **378**

Pressed for Time

12.1 Differentiated Homework Assignments

(AL) **Approaching Level**	4–11
(OL) **On Level**	6–12
(BL) **Beyond Level**	9–10, 12–14

*For **Below Level** students, assign Personal Math Trainer, Daily Intervention 12.1 Homework.*

Mathematical Processes	Exercises
MP.1 Problem Solving	14
MP.3 Logic	13
MP.4 Modeling	6–12
MP.5 Using Tools	4–5

Focus on Higher Order Thinking

Depth of Knowledge	Exercises
2 Skills/Concepts	4–10
3 Strategic Thinking H.O.T.	11–14

12.1 Independent Practice

Find the length of the missing side of each triangle. Round your answers to the nearest tenth.

4.

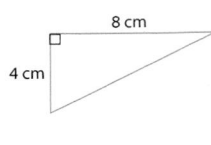

8 cm
4 cm

_____8.9 cm_____

5.

14 in.
8 in.

_____11.5 in._____

6. The diagonal of a rectangular big-screen TV screen measures 152 cm. The length measures 132 cm. What is the height of the screen?

_____75.4 cm_____

7. Dylan has a square piece of metal that measures 10 inches on each side. He cuts the metal along the diagonal, forming two right triangles. What is the length of the hypotenuse of each right triangle to the nearest tenth of an inch?

_____14.1 in._____

8. **Represent Real-World Problems** A painter has a 24-foot ladder that he is using to paint a house. For safety reasons, the ladder must be placed at least 8 feet from the base of the side of the house. To the nearest tenth of a foot, how high can the ladder safely reach?

_____22.6 ft_____

9. What is the longest flagpole (in whole feet) that could be shipped in a box that measures 2 ft by 2 ft by 12 ft? _12 feet_

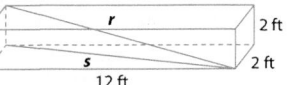

r
s
12 ft
2 ft
2 ft

10. **Sports** American football fields measure 100 yards long between the end zones, and are $53\frac{1}{3}$ yards wide. Is the length of the diagonal across this field more or less than 120 yards? Explain.

Less than; $\sqrt{12844} \cong 113$

11. **Justify Reasoning** A tree struck by lightning broke at a point 12 ft above the ground as shown. What was the height of the tree to the nearest tenth of a foot? Explain your reasoning.

12 ft
39 ft

52.8 ft; $12^2 + 39^2 = c^2$, so $144 + 1521 = c^2$, $1665 = c^2$, and $40.8 \approx c$. Add this length to the height of the bottom of the tree: $40.8 + 12 = 52.8$ ft.

© Houghton Mifflin Harcourt Publishing Company

DIFFERENTIATE INSTRUCTION *Leveled Homework/Practice*

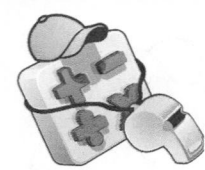

Personal Math Trainer
• 12.1 Homework

Pages shown are from *Differentiated Instruction.* **Also available online.**

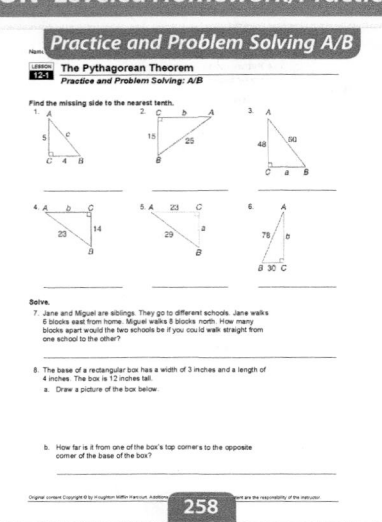

Practice and Problem Solving A/B

258

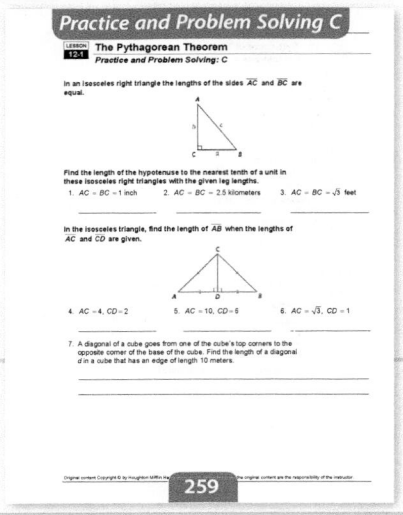

Practice and Problem Solving C

259

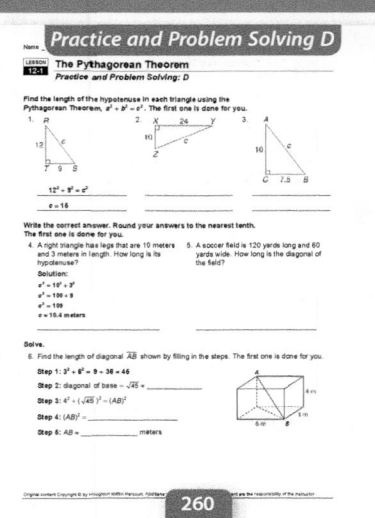

Practice and Problem Solving D

260

H.O.T. FOCUS ON HIGHER ORDER THINKING

12. Multistep Main Street and Washington Avenue meet at a right angle. A large park begins at this corner. Joe's school lies at the opposite corner of the park. Usually Joe walks 1.2 miles along Main Street and then 0.9 miles up Washington Avenue to get to school. Today he walked in a straight path across the park and returned home along the same path. What is the difference in distance between the two round trips? Explain.

1.2 mi; today Joe walked $\sqrt{1.2^2 + 0.9^2} = 1.5$ mi each way.

He usually walks $1.2 + 0.9 = 2.1$ mi each way. So the

difference is $2.1 - 1.5 = 0.6$ mi each way, or 1.2 mi.

13. Analyze Relationships An isosceles right triangle is a right triangle with congruent legs. If the length of each leg is represented by x, what algebraic expression can be used to represent the length of the hypotenuse? Explain your reasoning.

$\sqrt{x^2 + x^2}$ (or $\sqrt{2x^2}$ or $x\sqrt{2}$); if $a = x$ and $b = x$, then

$x^2 + x^2 = c^2$. Thus, $c = \sqrt{x^2 + x^2}$.

14. Persevere in Problem Solving A square hamburger is centered on a circular bun. Both the bun and the burger have an area of 16 square inches.

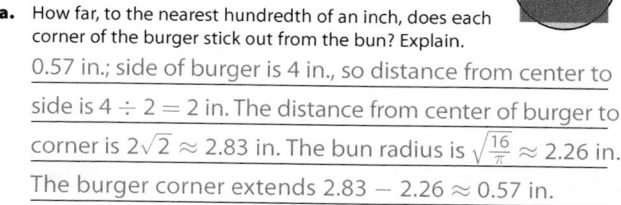

a. How far, to the nearest hundredth of an inch, does each corner of the burger stick out from the bun? Explain.

0.57 in.; side of burger is 4 in., so distance from center to

side is $4 \div 2 = 2$ in. The distance from center of burger to

corner is $2\sqrt{2} \approx 2.83$ in. The bun radius is $\sqrt{\frac{16}{\pi}} \approx 2.26$ in.

The burger corner extends $2.83 - 2.26 \approx 0.57$ in.

b. How far does each bun stick out from the center of each side of the burger?

about $2.26 - 2 = 0.26$ in.

c. Are the distances in part **a** and part **b** equal? If not, which sticks out more, the burger or the bun? Explain.

No; the burger sticks out a little more than a half

inch, and the bun sticks out about a quarter inch, so

the corners of the burger stick out more.

380 Unit 5

© Houghton Mifflin Harcourt Publishing Company

Work Area

✓ Quick Check

12.1 Lesson Quiz

Find the length of the missing side of each triangle.

1.

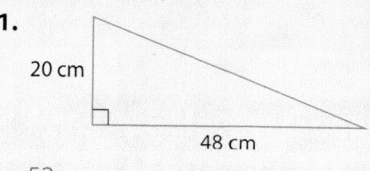

52 cm

2.

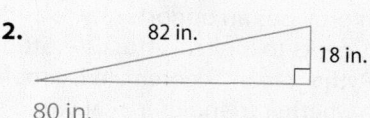

80 in.

3. A box used for shipping a volleyball set measures 10 inches by 20 inches by 40 inches. What is the longest length of support pole that will fit into the box, rounded to a tenth of an inch?

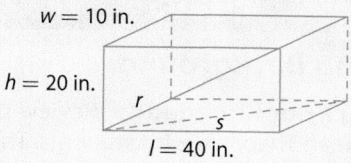

45.8 in.

Differentiate Instruction

IF a student misses more than one question, THEN

Differentiate Instruction:

- 12.1 Reteach
- Personal Math Trainer

 Interactive Whiteboard
Interactive Lesson quiz available online

DIFFERENTIATE INSTRUCTION *Extend-the-Math Activity* PRE-AP

Activity A common right triangle is called the "3–4–5 triangle." This set of numbers is called a "primitive Pythagorean triple" because the side lengths have no factors other than 1 in common. If you multiply each length in a Pythagorean triple by a whole number like 2, 3, or 4, you will get another Pythagorean triple. So, 6–8–10, 9–12–15, and 12–16–20 are also Pythagorean triples. Find as many Pythagorean triples as you can. Remember—once you find a primitive triple, find whole-number multiples of the triple to get other triples! Hint: There are 50 Pythagorean triples where each length is less than 100, with 16 of them primitive triples.

Primitive Pythagorean Triples Less Than 100	
3–4–5	16–63–65
5–12–13	20–21–29
8–15–17	28–45–53
7–24–25	33–56–65
9–40–41	36–77–85
11–60–61	39–80–89
12–35–37	48–55–73
13–84–85	65–72–97

Lesson Support

Content Objective Students will learn how to test the converse of the Pythagorean Theorem and use it to solve problems.

Professional Development

Integrate Mathematical Processes MP.7

This lesson provides an opportunity to address this Mathematical Processes standard. It calls for students to look for structure. Students determine whether triangle side lengths fulfill the Pythagorean Theorem. In Example 2 and in many of the exercises, students determine whether triangles in real-world situations are right triangles.

FOCUS

Building Background

Eliciting Prior Knowledge Review the Pythagorean Theorem with students. Then ask them to apply the theorem to find the missing side lengths of the following two right triangles: a right triangle with legs measuring 9 and 12 units and a right triangle with a hypotenuse measuring 26 units and a leg measuring 24 units.

hypotenuse: 15 units; leg: 10 units

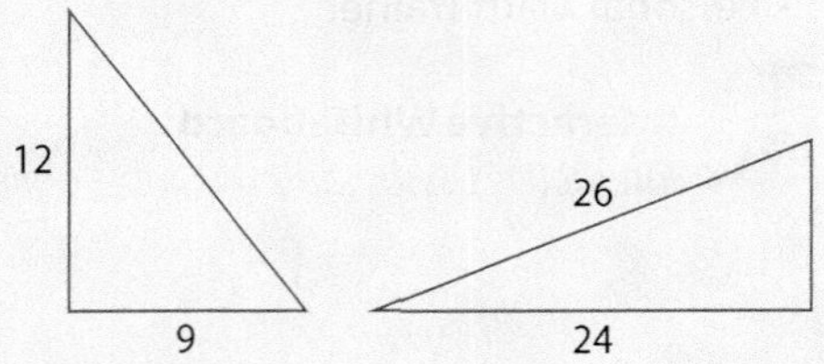

COHERENCE

Learning Progressions

In this lesson, students use the converse of the Pythagorean Theorem to test right triangles. Important understandings for students include the following:

- **Test the converse of the Pythagorean Theorem.**
- **Identify whether a triangle is a right triangle.**
- **Use the converse of the Pythagorean Theorem to solve real-world problems.**

The converse of the Pythagorean Theorem has many important real-life applications. In particular, it is often used to construct or verify a right angle or square corner. This lesson introduces students to the *converse* of a theorem. It is important to note that the converse of a theorem is not always true. The converse must be proved to be established as a theorem on its own.

RIGOR

Cluster Connections

This lesson provides an excellent opportunity to connect ideas in the cluster:

Understand and apply the Pythagorean Theorem.

Ask students to solve the following problem: A triangle with a base of 8 meters has an area of 60 square meters. The longest side of the triangle is 17 meters. Is the triangle a right triangle? Explain.

Yes; $A = \frac{1}{2}bh$, so $60 = \frac{1}{2}(8)h$, which means $h = 15$. The three sides are 8, 15, and 17. Since $8^2 + 15^2 = 17^2$, the triangle is a right triangle.

Language Support **ELL**

Language Objective Students will show how to test the converse of the Pythagorean Theorem and use it to solve problems.

Leveled Strategies for English Learners **ELL**

Emerging
Have students of mixed language proficiency work together. Have them do the Your Turn exercises after Example 1 to test the converse of the Pythagorean Theorem.

Expanding
Have students work with a partner and copy the table from Explore Activity 1. Then have them complete the table to test the converse of the Pythagorean Theorem.

Bridging
Have students at this level of English proficiency work in pairs to describe the difference between the Pythagorean Theorem and the converse of the Pythagorean Theorem. Then have them rework the Your Turn exercises following Example 2.

 Write out and model for students a sentence frame to begin their answer.

In order to form a right triangle, Katya must trim _____.

Math Talk
Mathematical Processes

To what length, to the nearest tenth, can Katya trim the longest piece of edging to form a right triangle?

Linguistic Support **ELL**

Academic/Content Vocabulary
Pythagorean Theorem This lesson on the converse of the Pythagorean Theorem relies on students' understanding of the word *converse* in this context. Point out to students in this lesson, *converse* means "*reverse*." Therefore, in this lesson, students are learning about the reverse of the Pythagorean Theorem.

Rules and Patterns
One of the best ways to help English learners get better at word problems is to build their vocabulary. English has some confusing words that sound and look alike, such as *then* and *than*. They sound similar, but they are spelled differently. In this lesson, the word *then* is used in an *if/then* structure: If a triangle is a right triangle, then…. *Then* is also used when giving instructions: First… , then….

LESSON 12.2

Converse of the Pythagorean Theorem

1 Engage

❓ ESSENTIAL QUESTION

How can you test the converse of the Pythagorean Theorem and use it to solve problems?
Sample answer: Test whether triangles whose side lengths are a, b, and c satisfy $a^2 + b^2 = c^2$. You can use the converse of the Pythagorean Theorem to help you determine whether real-world triangles are right triangles.

Motivate the Lesson
Ask: How can you tell whether a triangle is a right triangle? Begin the Explore Activity to find out.

2 Explore

EXPLORE ACTIVITY

Talk About It

Check for Understanding

💬 **Ask:** How do you know if a triangle is a right triangle? If the sum of the squares of the lengths of the two shorter sides of a triangle is equal to the square of the length of the longest side, then the triangle is a right triangle.

LESSON **12.2** **Converse of the Pythagorean Theorem**

8.5.12.2
Students will test the converse of the Pythagorean Theorem and use it to solve problems.

❓ ESSENTIAL QUESTION
How can you test the converse of the Pythagorean Theorem and use it to solve problems?

EXPLORE ACTIVITY

Testing the Converse of the Pythagorean Theorem

The Pythagorean Theorem states that if a triangle is a right triangle, then $a^2 + b^2 = c^2$.

The *converse* of the Pythagorean Theorem states that if $a^2 + b^2 = c^2$, then the triangle is a right triangle.

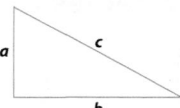

Decide whether the converse of the Pythagorean Theorem is true.

A Verify that the following sets of lengths make the equation $a^2 + b^2 = c^2$ true. Record your results in the table.

a	b	c	Is $a^2 + b^2 = c^2$ true?	Makes a right triangle?
3	4	5	yes	yes
5	12	13	yes	yes
7	24	25	yes	yes
8	15	17	yes	yes
20	21	29	yes	yes

B For each set of lengths in the table, cut strips of grid paper with a width of one square and lengths that correspond to the values of a, b, and c.

C For each set of lengths, use the strips of grid paper to try to form a right triangle. An example using the first set of lengths is shown. Record your findings in the table.

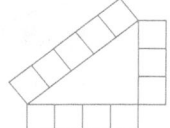

Reflect

1. **Draw Conclusions** Based on your observations, explain whether you think the converse of the Pythagorean Theorem is true.

   Students should note that each set of lengths satisfies $a^2 + b^2 = c^2$ and

   forms a right triangle, and conclude that the converse is true.

Lesson 12.2 **381**

© Houghton Mifflin Harcourt Publishing Company

DIFFERENTIATE INSTRUCTION *Leveled Questions*

	EXPLORE ACTIVITY
(AL) DOK 1 *Recall*	State the converse of the Pythagorean Theorem. If the sum of the squares of two side lengths of a triangle equals the square of the third side length, then the triangle is a right triangle.
(OL) DOK 2 *Skills/Concepts*	A 24-foot length of rope has knots 6 feet and 14 feet from one end. Can you use the rope to form a right triangle where the knots are at vertices? Explain. Yes; the sections of the rope are 6 ft, 8 ft, and 10 ft, and $6^2 + 8^2 = 36 + 64 = 10^2$.
(BL) DOK 3 *Strategic Thinking*	Part C shows strips of grid paper forming a right triangle. How can you find side lengths for other right triangles similar to this one? Explain. Sample answer: Multiply all the side lengths by the same number to form a dilation. The angles stay the same, and corresponding sides will be proportional.

LEVELED QUESTIONS: (AL) Approaching Level | (OL) On Level | (BL) Beyond Level

Math On the Spot
my.hrw.com

Identifying a Right Triangle

The converse of the Pythagorean Theorem gives you a way to tell if a triangle is a right triangle when you know the side lengths.

EXAMPLE 1

Tell whether each triangle with the given side lengths is a right triangle.

A 9 inches, 40 inches, and 41 inches

Let $a = 9$, $b = 40$, and $c = 41$.

$$a^2 + b^2 = c^2$$
$$9^2 + 40^2 \stackrel{?}{=} 41^2 \qquad \text{Substitute into the formula.}$$
$$81 + 1600 \stackrel{?}{=} 1681 \qquad \text{Simplify.}$$
$$1681 = 1681 \qquad \text{Add.}$$

Since $9^2 + 40^2 = 41^2$, the triangle is a right triangle by the converse of the Pythagorean Theorem.

B 8 meters, 10 meters, and 12 meters

Let $a = 8$, $b = 10$, and $c = 12$.

$$a^2 + b^2 = c^2$$
$$8^2 + 10^2 \stackrel{?}{=} 12^2 \qquad \text{Substitute into the formula.}$$
$$64 + 100 \stackrel{?}{=} 144 \qquad \text{Simpify.}$$
$$164 \neq 144 \qquad \text{Add.}$$

Since $8^2 + 10^2 \neq 12^2$, the triangle is not a right triangle by the converse of the Pythagorean Theorem.

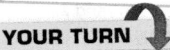
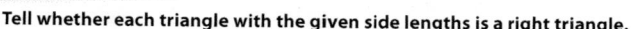

YOUR TURN

Tell whether each triangle with the given side lengths is a right triangle.

2. 14 cm, 23 cm, and 25 cm

not a right triangle

3. 16 in., 30 in., and 34 in.

a right triangle

4. 27 ft, 36 ft, 45 ft

right triangle

5. 11 mm, 18 mm, 21 mm

not a right triangle

Personal Math Trainer
Online Assessment and Intervention
my.hrw.com

© Houghton Mifflin Harcourt Publishing Company

3 Explain

Avoid Common Errors

Students may be confused about when to use the Pythagorean Theorem and when to use its converse. Make sure that students understand that if they want to determine whether a triangle is a right triangle and have all three side lengths, they should use the converse of the Pythagorean Theorem. If they want to find a missing side length of a right triangle, they should use the Pythagorean Theorem.

EXAMPLE 1

ADDITIONAL EXAMPLE 1

Tell whether each triangle with the given side lengths is a right triangle.

A 16 inches, 30 inches, 34 inches   yes

B 14 feet, 49 feet, 51 feet   no

 Interactive Whiteboard
Interactive example available online

YOUR TURN   MP.7

Focus on Math Connections

Since the side lengths of the triangle in **Exercise 3** have a common factor of 2, $16^2 + 30^2 = 34^2$ can be rewritten as $(2 \cdot 8)^2 + (2 \cdot 15)^2 = (2 \cdot 17)^2$. The converse of the Pythagorean Theorem shows that side lengths of 8 in., 15 in., and 17 in. also form a right triangle.

		EXAMPLE 1
AL DOK 1 *Recall*		In Part A, how do you know which length should be the value of c in the equation $a^2 + b^2 = c^2$? The longest side length is always the value of c.
OL DOK 2 *Skills/Concepts*		You have 8-inch, 10-inch, and 14-inch straws. Can you form a right triangle from the three straws? no; $8^2 + 10^2 \neq 14^2$
BL DOK 3 *Strategic Thinking*		The converse of the Pythagorean Theorem also applies to triangles with irrational number side lengths. What is an example of a right triangle with irrational number side lengths? Sample answer: $\sqrt{3}$, $\sqrt{7}$, $\sqrt{10}$

TEACHER TO TEACHER

Manipulatives Have students make two triangles (one a right triangle, and the other not a right triangle) on a geometry board. Then have them measure the lengths of the sides of each triangle to the nearest millimeter. Ask them to use the converse of the Pythagorean Theorem to verify that the right triangle is indeed a right triangle and the other triangle is not a right triangle. (Because the measurements are approximate, for the right triangle, $a^2 + b^2$ and c^2 may be close but not exactly the same.)

EXAMPLE 2

ADDITIONAL EXAMPLE 2 A small triangular park at the intersection of 3 streets has side lengths 19 feet, 80 feet, and 82 feet. Does the park have the shape of a right triangle? Explain. No; $19^2 + 80^2 \neq 82^2$, and since $a^2 + b^2 \neq c^2$, the park is not the shape of a right triangle.

Interactive Whiteboard
Interactive example available online

YOUR TURN MP.5

Focus on Technology
Use geometry software to create the triangles in **Exercises 6–7**. Use the measurement tools of the software to find out if the triangle has an angle of 90°.

Digital Teacher Resources

Go online to access all your lesson-level resources.

Differentiated Instruction
- Reteach
- Reading Strategies
- Success for English Learners
- Practice and Problem Solving A/B, C, D

Math on the Spot Videos

@ my.hrw.com

Math On the Spot
@ my.hrw.com

Using the Converse of the Pythagorean Theorem

You can use the converse of the Pythagorean Theorem to solve real-world problems.

EXAMPLE 2

Katya is buying edging for a triangular flower garden she plans to build in her backyard. If the lengths of the three pieces of edging that she purchases are 13 feet, 10 feet, and 7 feet, will the flower garden be in the shape of a right triangle?

Use the converse of the Pythagorean Theorem. Remember to use the longest length for c.

Let $a = 7$, $b = 10$, and $c = 13$.

$$a^2 + b^2 = c^2$$

$$7^2 + 10^2 \stackrel{?}{=} 13^2 \quad \text{Substitute into the formula.}$$

$$49 + 100 \stackrel{?}{=} 169 \quad \text{Simpify.}$$

$$149 \neq 169 \quad \text{Add.}$$

Since $7^2 + 10^2 \neq 13^2$, the garden will not be in the shape of a right triangle.

Math Talk
Mathematical Processes

To what length, to the nearest tenth, can Katya trim the longest piece of edging to form a right triangle?

approximately 12.2 feet

YOUR TURN

6. A blueprint for a new triangular playground shows that the sides measure 480 ft, 140 ft, and 500 ft. Is the playground in the shape of a right triangle? Explain.

Yes; $140^2 + 480^2 = 250{,}000$; $500^2 = 250{,}000$;

$250{,}000 = 250{,}000$

7. A triangular piece of glass has sides that measure 18 in., 19 in., and 25 in. Is the piece of glass in the shape of a right triangle? Explain.

No; $18^2 + 19^2 = 685$, $25^2 = 625$, $685 \neq 625$

8. A corner of a fenced yard forms a right angle. Can you place a 12 foot long board across the corner to form a right triangle for which the leg lengths are whole numbers? Explain.

No; there are no pairs of whole numbers whose

squares add to $12^2 = 144$.

Personal Math Trainer
Online Assessment and Intervention
@ my.hrw.com

© Houghton Mifflin Harcourt Publishing Company

DIFFERENTIATE INSTRUCTION *Leveled Questions*

	EXAMPLE 2
(AL) DOK 1 *Recall*	If the longest side of the garden must be 13 feet and the shape must be a right triangle, what lengths for the other two sides can you find from the table in the activity at the beginning of the lesson? 5 ft and 12 ft
(OL) DOK 2 *Skills/Concepts*	If the shortest sides of the garden must be 10 feet and 7 feet and the shape must be a right triangle, how long will the longest side be? 12.2 inches
(BL) DOK 3 *Strategic Thinking*	A large bulletin board at school has a checkerboard pattern of 6-inch squares. You have a $7\frac{1}{2}$-foot piece of ribbon. Can you tack the ribbon on the board so that its ends are at corners of grid squares? Explain. Yes; the ribbon is 15 square lengths, so the legs would be 12 and 9 square lengths: $12^2 + 9^2 = 225 = 15^2$.

LEVELED QUESTIONS: (AL) Approaching Level | (OL) On Level | (BL) Beyond Level

1. Lashandra used grid paper to construct the triangle shown. (Explore Activity)

   a. What are the lengths of the sides of Lashandra's triangle?

      __6__ units, __8__ units, __10__ units

   b. Use the converse of the Pythagorean Theorem to determine whether the triangle is a right triangle.

   $$a^2 + b^2 = c^2$$

   $$\boxed{6}^2 + \boxed{8}^2 \overset{?}{=} \boxed{10}^2$$

   $$\boxed{36} + \boxed{64} \overset{?}{=} \boxed{100}$$

   $$\boxed{100} \overset{?}{=} \boxed{100}$$

   The triangle that Lashandra constructed ⟨**is**/ is not⟩ a right triangle.

2. A triangle has side lengths 9 cm, 12 cm, and 16 cm. Tell whether the triangle is a right triangle. (Example 1)

   Let $a = $ __9__, $b = $ __12__, and $c = $ __16__.

   $$a^2 + b^2 = c^2$$

   $$\boxed{9}^2 + \boxed{12}^2 \overset{?}{=} \boxed{16}^2$$

   $$\boxed{81} + \boxed{144} \overset{?}{=} \boxed{256}$$

   $$\boxed{225} \overset{?}{=} \boxed{256}$$

   By the converse of the Pythagorean Theorem, the triangle ⟨is /**is not**⟩ a right triangle.

3. The marketing team at a new electronics company is designing a logo that contains a circle and a triangle. On one design, the triangle's side lengths are 2.5 in., 6 in., and 6.5 in. Is the triangle a right triangle? Explain. (Example 2)

   Yes; $2.5^2 + 6^2 = 42.25$, $6.5^2 = 42.25$, $42.25 = 42.25$

? ESSENTIAL QUESTION CHECK-IN

4. How can you use the converse of the Pythagorean Theorem to tell if a triangle is a right triangle?

   Test the side lengths in $a^2 + b^2 = c^2$, using the longest side for c.

   If the equation is true, the triangle is a right triangle. Otherwise, it isn't.

© Houghton Mifflin Harcourt Publishing Company

4 Elaborate

Talk About It

Summarize the Lesson

Ask: How can you use the converse of the Pythagorean Theorem to classify a triangle as a right triangle or not a right triangle? Find the sum of the squares of the two shortest sides of a triangle. If the sum is equal to the square of the longest side, the triangle must be a right triangle. Otherwise, it is not.

Guided Practice

Engage with the Whiteboard

Have students sketch the triangles described in **Exercises 2–3** in the margin and then label the sides with the side lengths. Then have them label the sides a, b, and c.

Avoid Common Errors

Exercises 1–3 Remind students to let c be the length of the longest side of the triangle. Also remind students to square the side lengths before adding.

DIFFERENTIATE INSTRUCTION *Intervention and Additional Support*

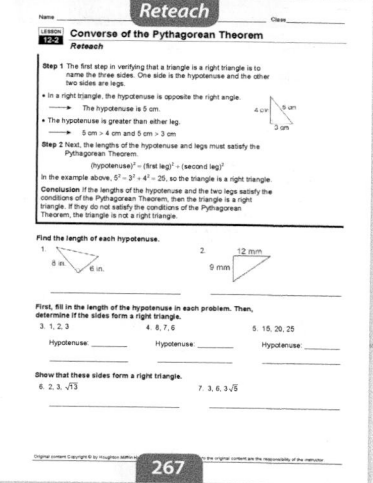

267

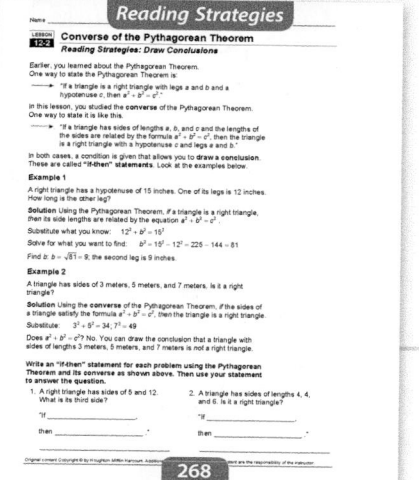

268

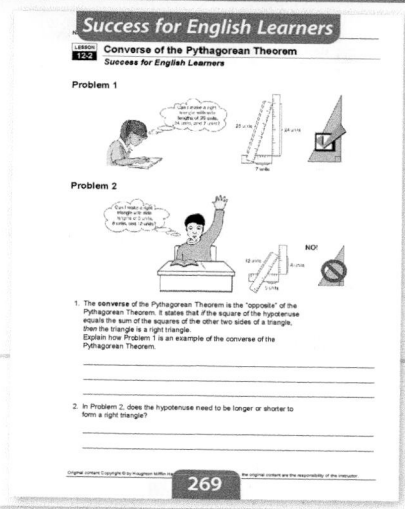

269

Personal Math Trainer
Daily Intervention
12.2 Homework

Pages shown are from *Differentiated Instruction.* **Also available online.**

Converse of the Pythagorean Theorem **384**

Pressed for Time

12.2 Differentiated Homework Assignments

(AL) **Approaching Level**	5–12, 17, 19
(OL) **On Level**	12–20, 21
(BL) **Beyond Level**	15–16, 18–23

*For **Below Level** students, assign Personal Math Trainer, Daily Intervention 12.2 Homework.*

Mathematical Processes	Exercises
MP.2 Reasoning	18–19, 22
MP.3 Logic	20–21
MP.4 Modeling	15–17
MP.5 Using Tools	5–14
MP.6 Precision	23

Focus on Higher Order Thinking

Depth of Knowledge	Exercises
2 Skills/Concepts	5–17
3 Strategic Thinking H.O.T.\	18–23

Name _____ Class _____ Date _____

12.2 Independent Practice

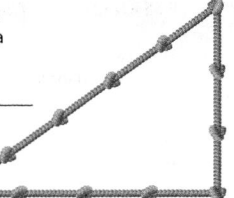

Personal Math Trainer
Online Assessment and Intervention
my.hrw.com

Tell whether each triangle with the given side lengths is a right triangle.

5. 11 cm, 60 cm, 61 cm
right triangle

6. 5 ft, 12 ft, 15 ft
not a right triangle

7. 9 in., 15 in., 17 in.
not a right triangle

8. 15 m, 36 m, 39 m
right triangle

9. 20 mm, 30 mm, 40 mm
not a right triangle

10. 20 cm, 48 cm, 52 cm
right triangle

11. 18.5 ft, 6 ft, 17.5 ft
right triangle

12. 2 mi, 1.5 mi, 2.5 mi
right triangle

13. 35 in., 45 in., 55 in.
not a right triangle

14. 25 cm, 14 cm, 23 cm
not a right triangle

15. The emblem on a college banner consists of the face of a tiger inside a triangle. The lengths of the sides of the triangle are 13 cm, 14 cm, and 15 cm. Is the triangle a right triangle? Explain.
No; $13^2 + 14^2 = 365$, $15^2 = 225$, and $365 \neq 225$.

16. Kerry has a large triangular piece of fabric that she wants to attach to the ceiling in her bedroom. The sides of the piece of fabric measure 4.8 ft, 6.4 ft, and 8 ft. Is the fabric in the shape of a right triangle? Explain.
Yes; $4.8^2 + 6.4^2 = 64$, and $8^2 = 64$.

17. A mosaic consists of triangular tiles. The smallest tiles have side lengths 6 cm, 10 cm, and 12 cm. Are these tiles in the shape of right triangles? Explain.
No; $6^2 + 10^2 = 136$, $12^2 = 144$, and $136 \neq 144$.

18. **History** In ancient Egypt, surveyors made right angles by stretching a rope with evenly spaced knots as shown. Explain why the rope forms a right angle.
Sample answer: The knots are evenly spaced, so the side lengths are 3 units, 4 units, and 5 units. Since $3^2 + 4^2 = 5^2$, the sides form a right triangle.

© Houghton Mifflin Harcourt Publishing Company

DIFFERENTIATE INSTRUCTION *Leveled Homework/Practice*

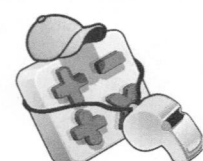

Personal Math Trainer
• 12.2 Homework

Pages shown are from *Differentiated Instruction.* Also available online.

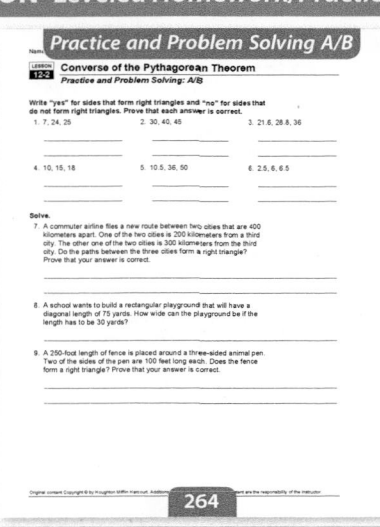

Practice and Problem Solving A/B

LESSON 12-2 **Converse of the Pythagorean Theorem**
Practice and Problem Solving: A/B

Write "yes" for sides that form right triangles and "no" for sides that do not form right triangles. Prove that each answer is correct.

1. 7, 24, 25   2. 30, 40, 45   3. 21.6, 28.8, 36

4. 10, 15, 18   5. 10.5, 36, 50   6. 2.5, 6, 6.5

Solve.

7. A commuter airline flies a new route between two cities that are 400 kilometers apart. One of the two cities is 200 kilometers from a third city. The other one of the two cities is 300 kilometers from the third city. Do the paths between the three cities form a right triangle? Prove that your answer is correct.

8. A school wants to build a rectangular playground that will have a diagonal length of 75 yards. How wide can the playground be if the length has to be 30 yards?

9. A 250-foot length of fence is placed around a three-sided animal pen. Two of the sides of the pen are 100 feet long each. Does the fence form a right triangle? Prove that your answer is correct.

264

Practice and Problem Solving C

LESSON 12-2 **Converse of the Pythagorean Theorem**
Practice and Problem Solving: C

Problems 1–3 give the dimensions of isosceles triangles. Which triangles are right triangles? Prove your answer is correct.
1. Sides: 10   2. Sides: 2   3. Sides: 300
   Hypotenuse: 15   Hypotenuse: 2√2   Hypotenuse: 700

Solve.

4. Can an equilateral triangle be a right triangle? Explain your answer.

5. A quadrilateral has two pair of opposite parallel sides. Each of one pair of parallel sides is 4 yards long. Each of the second pair of sides is 8 yards long. A diagonal connecting two corners of the quadrilateral is 9 yards long. Is the quadrilateral a rectangle? Prove that your answer is correct.

6. A clear plastic prism has six faces, each of which is a parallelogram of side length 1 meter. A diagonal made of nylon filament line connecting two opposite vertices of the solid has a length of 4 meters. Is the solid a cube? Prove that your answer is correct.

A prism has a diagonal, d, connecting its opposite vertices. Give the lengths of the sides of the prism in each problem that will make the solid described.
7. d = 6 meters; a cube

8. d = √8 feet; a rectangular solid with a pair of opposite square faces and two pair of rectangular faces in which the length is twice the width.

265

Practice and Problem Solving D

LESSON 12-2 **Converse of the Pythagorean Theorem**
Practice and Problem Solving: D

Problems 1–3 give the sides of a right triangle. In each case, which of the three sides is the hypotenuse? The first one is done for you.
1. 3, 4, 5   2. 5, 12, 13   3. 1, 1, √2   4. 2, 3, √13
   5

Do the sides given in 5–8 form a right triangle? Prove your answer is correct using the Pythagorean Theorem, $a^2 + b^2 = c^2$. The first one is done for you.
5. 8, 9, 10   6. 12, 14, 15
   no; $8^2 + 9^2 \neq 10^2$
7. 10, 24, 26   8. 14, 15, 21

A parking lot has four sides. One pair of opposite sides is 100 yards long. The other two sides are 60 yards long. The distance from one end of the longer side to the opposite end of the shorter side is 120 yards. Is the parking lot a rectangle? Answer the questions below to find out.
9. If the distances given form a right triangle, which number is the hypotenuse, and why?

10. Which numbers are the two sides?

11. Fill in the numbers in the Pythagorean Theorem for this problem. Does $a^2 + b^2 = c^2$?
    ____² + ____² ? ____²

12. Simplify the numbers from problem 11.
    Does ____ + ____ ? ____
    Does ____ ? ____

13. Are the two sides of the equation equal? ____

14. Is the parking lot a rectangle? Explain.

266

---

19. Justify Reasoning Yoshi has two identical triangular boards as shown. Can he use these two boards to form a rectangle? Explain.

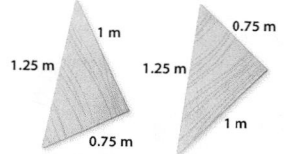

Yes; since $0.75^2 + 1^2 = 1.25^2$, the triangles are right triangles. Adjoining them at their hypotenuses will form a rectangle with sides 1 m and 0.75 m.

20. Critique Reasoning Shoshanna says that a triangle with side lengths 17 m, 8 m, and 15 m is not a right triangle because $17^2 + 8^2 = 353$, $15^2 = 225$, and $353 \neq 225$. Is she correct? Explain.

No, she did not use the longest length for c.

$8^2 + 15^2 = 17^2$, so it is a right triangle.

H.O.T. FOCUS ON HIGHER ORDER THINKING

21. Make a Conjecture Diondre says that he can take any right triangle and make a new right triangle just by doubling the side lengths. Is Diondre's conjecture true? Test his conjecture using three different right triangles.

Yes. His conjecture is true. Students' work will vary but should show that they've used the converse of the Pythagorean Theorem to test whether the new triangles are right triangles.

22. Draw Conclusions A diagonal of a parallelogram measures 37 inches. The sides measure 35 inches and 1 foot. Is the parallelogram a rectangle? Explain your reasoning.

Yes; 1 ft = 12 in. Since $12^2 + 35^2 = 37^2$, each half of the parallelogram is a right triangle. Therefore, the sides of the parallelogram meet at right angles, making the parallelogram a rectangle.

23. Represent Real-World Problems A soccer coach is marking the lines for a soccer field on a large recreation field. The dimensions of the field are to be 90 yards by 48 yards. Describe a procedure she could use to confirm that the sides of the field meet at right angles.

She could measure the diagonal of the field to see if the sides of the field and the diagonal form a right triangle. The diagonal should measure 102 yards if the sides of the field meet at right angles.

Work Area

© Houghton Mifflin Harcourt Publishing Company

✔ Quick Check

12.2 Lesson Quiz

Tell whether each triangle with the given side lengths is a right triangle.

1. 36 cm, 48 cm, 60 cm right triangle

2. 12 ft, 35 ft, 37 ft right triangle

3. 60.5 ft, 63 ft, 87.5 ft not a right triangle

4. A club at school designed a banner consisting of two congruent triangles surrounded by stripes. The lengths of the sides of each of the triangles were 1.5 feet, 2.0 feet, and 2.5 feet. Are the triangles right triangles? Explain.
yes; $1.5^2 + 2.0^2 = 6.25 = 2.5^2$

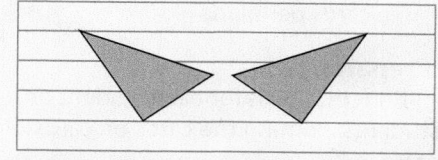

Differentiate Instruction

IF a student misses more than one question, THEN

Differentiate Instruction:

• 12.2 Reteach

• Personal Math Trainer

 Interactive Whiteboard
Interactive Lesson quiz available online

DIFFERENTIATE INSTRUCTION *Extend-the-Math Activity* PRE-AP

Activity Draw three different acute triangles (triangles with all three angles less than 90°) and three different obtuse triangles (triangles with one angle greater than 90°). Label the longest side of each triangle c and the other two sides a and b. Measure each side of each triangle to the nearest millimeter and record the results in a table like the one shown here. Calculate a^2, b^2, and c^2 for each triangle. Compare c^2 to $a^2 + b^2$ for each triangle. Make a conjecture about the type of triangle that has $a^2 + b^2 > c^2$ and about the type of triangle that has $a^2 + b^2 < c^2$. Use your conjecture to predict whether a triangle with side lengths 12 cm, 60 cm, and 61 cm is acute, right, or obtuse.

Type of triangle	a	b	$a^2 + b^2$	c	c^2	$a^2 + b^2$ greater than or less than c^2
acute						
acute						
acute						
obtuse						
obtuse						
obtuse						

If the triangle is acute, then $a^2 + b^2 > c^2$. If the triangle is obtuse, then $a^2 + b^2 < c^2$; acute.

Triple Concentration

Objective
Students will form a list of Pythagorean triples and use the list in a game of concentration.

Number of Players
2–4 players per game (recommended)

Materials
- 1 Pythagorean Triples Worksheet per player
- 1 set of game cards per game

Teacher Preparation
Print and cut out materials for each student or group of students. Printing the cards on cardstock is recommended.

Game Resources
Go online to access all your game resources.

my.hrw.com

- Pythagorean Triples Worksheets A and B
- Pythagorean Triples Worksheets (with answers)
- *Triple Concentration* game cards

Key Concepts
This game reviews Pythagorean triples. Students will:
- calculate Pythagorean triples
- form Pythagorean triples
- recognize Pythagorean triples

Encourage students to use the completed worksheet to form Pythagorean triples during the *Triple Concentration* game.

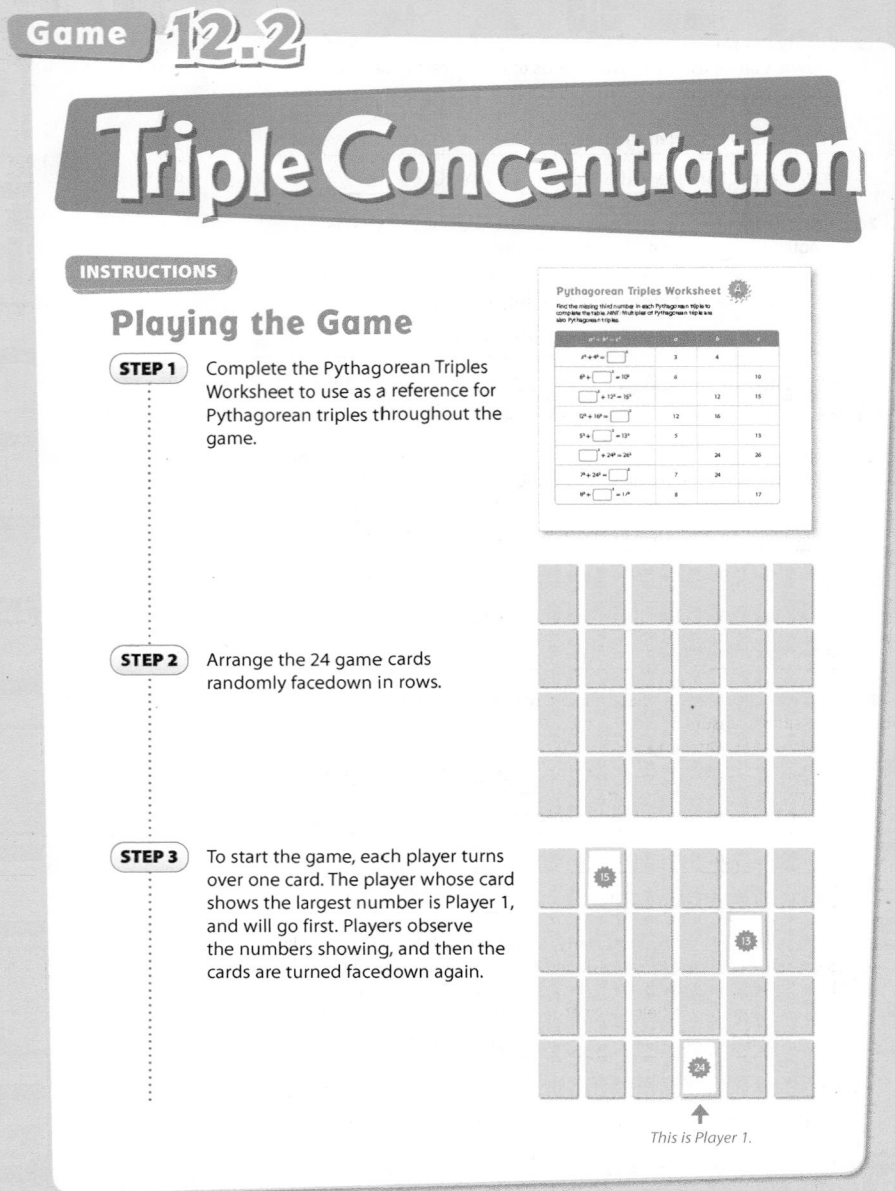

Game 12.2

Triple Concentration

INSTRUCTIONS

Playing the Game

STEP 1 Complete the Pythagorean Triples Worksheet to use as a reference for Pythagorean triples throughout the game.

STEP 2 Arrange the 24 game cards randomly facedown in rows.

STEP 3 To start the game, each player turns over one card. The player whose card shows the largest number is Player 1, and will go first. Players observe the numbers showing, and then the cards are turned facedown again.

This is Player 1.

WARM-UP EXERCISES

Find the third number in the given Pythagorean triple.

1. 6, 8, <u>10</u>
2. 15, <u>20</u>, 25
3. <u>7</u>, 24, 25

© Houghton Mifflin Harcourt Publishing Company

STEP 4 Players take turns moving clockwise.

When it is your turn, flip over any three cards, one at a time. Make sure that all players observe the cards. If the numbers shown form a Pythagorean triple, then pick up the cards, keep them, and take another turn. If they do not form a Pythagorean triple, then turn the cards facedown again in their original positions, and continue playing the game.

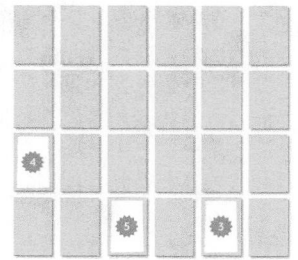

Is this a Pythagorean Triple?

STEP 5 Continue until all of the cards are removed.

 ## Winning the Game

The player with the most triples at the end of the game wins.

386B Unit 5

© Houghton Mifflin Harcourt Publishing Company

Playing the Game

STEP 1 Each player completes his/her own worksheet. This will serve as a reference for Pythagorean triples throughout the game.

STEP 2 Students should arrange the game cards randomly face-down in rows.

STEP 3 To start, each player turns over one card. The player whose card shows the largest number is Player 1 and will go first. Players observe the numbers showing, and then the cards are turned face-down again.

STEP 4 Player 1 turns over any three cards, one at a time. If the numbers on the cards form a Pythagorean triple, Player 1 keeps the cards and takes another turn. If the cards do not form a Pythagorean triple, they are turned face-down in their original positions, and play continues clockwise.

STEP 5 Play continues until all of the cards are removed from the table.

Winning the Game

The player or team with the most triples at the end of the game wins.

TEACHER NOTES

- **Discussion** Discuss with students how they know when they turn over three cards which numbers to substitute for the variables in the Pythagorean theorem. Lead them to see that the greatest length is always c, the hypotenuse. The lengths of a and b, the legs, are interchangeable.

- **Extension** Have students find as many triples as they can.

- **Differentiation** Reserve the last three rows of cards containing Pythagorean Triples 9, 40, 41; 11, 60, 61; and 20, 21, 29 for advanced students. Worksheet B includes these Pythagorean Triples, but Worksheet A does not include them.

Lesson Support

Content Objective Students will learn how to use the Pythagorean Theorem to find the distance between two points on a coordinate plane.

Professional Development

Integrate Mathematical Processes MP.2

This lesson provides an opportunity to address this Mathematical Processes standard. It calls for students to reason abstractly and quantitatively. Students connect the Pythagorean Theorem with finding the distance between two points in the coordinate plane and then derive the Distance Formula.

FOCUS	COHERENCE	RIGOR

Building Background

Eliciting Prior Knowledge Review how to find the distance between any two points in the coordinate plane with the same x-coordinate or the same y-coordinate. Ask students to find the distance between (3, 5) and (3, 18). Then ask them to find the distance between (−6, −2) and (9, −2).

13 units; 15 units

Elicit the observation that the first pair of coordinates are the end points of a vertical line and the second pair are the end points of a horizontal line. Review how this observation can be used to find the distance between each pair of points.

Learning Progressions

In this lesson, students use the Pythagorean Theorem to find the distance between points in the coordinate plane. Important understandings for students include the following:

- **Use the Pythagorean Theorem in the coordinate plane.**
- **Use the Distance Formula to find the distance between any two points.**
- **Use the Pythagorean Theorem to find the distance between two points in a real-world situation.**

This lesson concludes students' work with the Pythagorean Theorem. It introduces them to a very useful application of the theorem in coordinate geometry and provides practical real-life examples.

Cluster Connections

This lesson provides an excellent opportunity to connect ideas in the cluster:

Understand and apply the Pythagorean Theorem.

Tell students that the coordinates (−4, 1), (−4, 5), and (8, 1) form the vertices of a right triangle. Ask them to find the lengths of each side of the right triangle. Discuss how students found the lengths. Is it necessary to graph the coordinates to find the lengths of the sides of the right triangle?

The side lengths are 5, 12, and 13 units. Sample answer: It is not necessary to plot the points if you notice that two pairs of coordinates form vertical and horizontal segments. Find the lengths of the vertical and horizontal legs of the right triangle and then apply the Pythagorean Theorem to find the length of the hypotenuse.

Language Support ELL

Leveled Strategies for English Learners ELL

Emerging
Have students at this level of English proficiency work in pairs to copy the steps in Explore Activity Example 1 and do the Your Turn exercise to practice using the Pythagorean Theorem to find distance.

Expanding
Have students at this level of English proficiency work in pairs to review the steps in Explore Activity 2, check answers with each other, and then answer the Reflect question.

Bridging
Have students at this level of English proficiency work in pairs to review the Activities and Examples before discussing the problems in the Guided Practice as they calculate the answers.

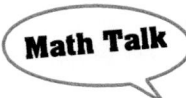 **Math Talk** Write out and model for students a sentence frame to begin their answer to Math Talk for Explore Activity 2.

In the context of the Pythagorean Theorem, they represent _____.

Distance Formula

In a coordinate plane, the distance d between two points (x_1, y_1) and (x_2, y_2) is
$$d = \sqrt{(x_2 - x_1)^2 + (y_2 - y_1)^2}.$$

Linguistic Support ELL

Academic/Content Vocabulary

distance formula This lesson on finding the distance between any two points relies on students' understanding of the Distance Formula, which is derived from the Pythagorean Theorem. English learners may find it especially helpful to copy both the Pythagorean Theorem and the Distance Formula into their math journals. Also, point out that *derive/derivar* are English-Spanish cognates.

Multiple-Meaning Words

English learners grow their vocabulary by learning new words and using them daily. In this lesson, the directional words *due north* and *due south* are used in an exercise. English learners may know the meaning of the word *due* as in *due date* but not when it is used with a direction. Point out to English learners that when *due* is used with a direction, it means "directly," as in *directly north* or *directly south*.

Distance Between Two Points

1 Engage

? ESSENTIAL QUESTION

How can you use the Pythagorean Theorem to find the distance between two points on a coordinate plane? Sample answer: Draw a segment connecting the two points and a right triangle with that segment as the hypotenuse. Then use the Pythagorean Theorem to find the length of the hypotenuse.

Motivate the Lesson
Ask: How would you verify, without measuring, that three points on a coordinate plane form a right triangle? Begin the lesson to find out.

2 Explore

EXPLORE ACTIVITY EXAMPLE 1

ADDITIONAL EXAMPLE 1 The figure shows a right triangle. Approximate the length of the hypotenuse to the nearest tenth using a calculator. about 5.8 units

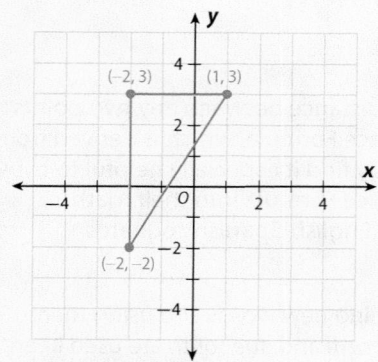

Interactive Whiteboard
Interactive example available online

YOUR TURN MP.6

Engage with the Whiteboard
Label the lengths of the legs. Label one leg *a* and the other leg *b* before substituting the values into the Pythagorean Theorem.

LESSON 12.3 **Distance Between Two Points**

8.5.12.3
Students will use the Pythagorean Theorem to find the distance between two points on a coordinate plane.

? ESSENTIAL QUESTION
How can you use the Pythagorean Theorem to find the distance between two points on a coordinate plane?

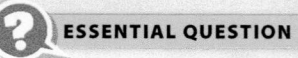

EXPLORE ACTIVITY

Pythagorean Theorem in the Coordinate Plane

Math On the Spot
my.hrw.com

EXAMPLE 1 The figure shows a right triangle. Approximate the length of the hypotenuse to the nearest tenth using a calculator.

STEP 1 Find the length of each leg.

The length of the vertical leg is __4__ units.

The length of the horizontal leg is __2__ units.

STEP 2 Let $a = 4$ and $b = 2$. Let c represent the length of the hypotenuse.

Use the Pythagorean Theorem to find c.　　$a^2 + b^2 = c^2$

Substitute into the formula.　　$\boxed{4}^2 + \boxed{2}^2 = c^2$

Simplify.　　$\boxed{20} = c^2$

Take the square root of both sides.　　$\sqrt{\boxed{20}} = c$

Use a calculator. Round to the nearest tenth.　　$\boxed{4.5} \approx c$

STEP 3 Check for reasonableness by finding perfect squares close to 20.

$\sqrt{20}$ is between $\sqrt{16}$ and $\sqrt{25}$.　　$\sqrt{16} < \boxed{\sqrt{20}} < \sqrt{25}$

Simplify.　　$\boxed{4} < \boxed{\sqrt{20}} < 5$

Because 4.5 is between __4__ and __5__, the answer is reasonable.

The hypotenuse is about 4.5 units long.

YOUR TURN

1. Approximate the length of the hypotenuse to the nearest tenth using a calculator.

6.4 units

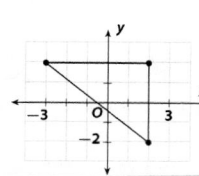

Personal Math Trainer
Online Assessment and Intervention
my.hrw.com

Lesson 12.3 **387**

DIFFERENTIATE INSTRUCTION *Leveled Questions*

	EXPLORE ACTIVITY EXAMPLE 1
AL DOK 1 *Recall*	How are you able to find the leg lengths of the triangle? Count using grid lines because they are horizontal and vertical segments.
OL DOK 2 *Skills/Concepts*	A triangle on a coordinate grid has vertices at $(-5, 0)$, $(0, 0)$, and $(0, -7)$. What is the length of its hypotenuse to the nearest tenth? 8.6 units
BL DOK 3 *Strategic Thinking*	If you increase the horizontal leg length by 2 units, does the hypotenuse increase by more or less than 2 units? Explain. Less; the equation becomes $4^2 + 4^2 = c^2$, which gives $c = \sqrt{32} \approx 5.7$. This is less than a 2-unit increase.

LEVELED QUESTIONS:　AL Approaching Level | OL On Level | BL Beyond Level

© Houghton Mifflin Harcourt Publishing Company

Finding the Distance Between Any Two Points

The Pythagorean Theorem can be used to find the distance between any two points (x_1, y_1) and (x_2, y_2) in the coordinate plane. The resulting expression is called the Distance Formula.

> **Distance Formula**
>
> In a coordinate plane, the distance d between two points (x_1, y_1) and (x_2, y_2) is
> $$d = \sqrt{(x_2 - x_1)^2 + (y_2 - y_1)^2}.$$

Use the Pythagorean Theorem to derive the Distance Formula.

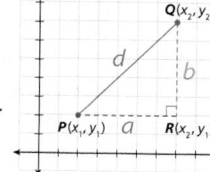

A To find the distance between points P and Q, draw segment $\overline{PQ}$ and label its length d. Then draw horizontal segment $\overline{PR}$ and vertical segment $\overline{QR}$. Label the lengths of these segments a and b. Triangle PQR is a ___right___ triangle, with hypotenuse ___$\overline{PQ}$___.

B Since $\overline{PR}$ is a horizontal segment, its length, a, is the difference between its x-coordinates. Therefore, $a = x_2 - \underline{x_1}$.

C Since $\overline{QR}$ is a vertical segment, its length, b, is the difference between its y-coordinates. Therefore, $b = y_2 - \underline{y_1}$.

D Use the Pythagorean Theorem to find d, the length of segment $\overline{PQ}$. Substitute the expressions from **B** and **C** for a and b.

$$d^2 = a^2 + b^2$$
$$d = \sqrt{a^2 + b^2}$$
$$d = \sqrt{\left(\boxed{x_2} - \boxed{x_1}\right)^2 + \left(\boxed{y_2} - \boxed{y_1}\right)^2}$$

Math Talk
Mathematical Processes

What do $x_2 - x_1$ and $y_2 - y_1$ represent in terms of the Pythagorean Theorem?

They represent the lengths of the legs of the right triangle formed by P, Q, and R.

Reflect

2. Why are the coordinates of point R the ordered pair (x_2, y_1)?

Since R lies on the same vertical line as Q, their x-coordinates are the same. Since R lies on the same horizontal line as P, their y-coordinates are the same.

© Houghton Mifflin Harcourt Publishing Company

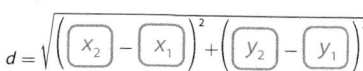

	EXPLORE ACTIVITY 2
(AL) DOK 1 *Recall*	The variable c in the Pythagorean Theorem is represented by what variable or expression in the Distance Formula? d
(OL) DOK 2 *Skills/Concepts*	In the Distance Formula, do $x_2 - x_1$ and $y_2 - y_1$ have to be positive? Explain. No; they are squared before they are added, so the sum $(x_2 - x_1)^2 + (y_2 - y_1)^2$ is always positive.
(BL) DOK 3 *Strategic Thinking*	Every point on a circle with its center at the origin is the same distance, the radius r, from the origin. Show that $r = \sqrt{x^2 + y^2}$ is true for any point (x, y) on a circle with its center at the origin. By the Distance Formula, the distance r from a point (x, y) to the origin, $(0, 0)$, is $r = \sqrt{(x - 0)^2 + (y - 0)^2} = \sqrt{x^2 + y^2}$.

---

3 Explain

EXPLORE ACTIVITY 2

Focus on Math Connections

Point out to students that finding the length of the hypotenuse of a right triangle is the same as finding the distance between the endpoints of the hypotenuse in the coordinate plane.

TEACHER TO TEACHER

Visual Cues Use the diagram of triangle ABC below to lead students through the derivation of the Distance Formula, $\sqrt{(x_2 - x_1)^2 + (y_2 - y_1)^2} = d$. To start, ask students: What are the coordinates of point C? What are the lengths of the legs? Answers are shown on the graph.

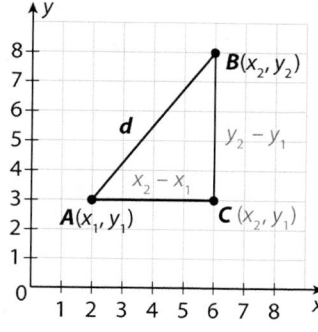

EXAMPLE 2

ADDITIONAL EXAMPLE 2 Dominic wants to find the distance between his house on one side of the park and his school on the other side. He marks off a third point forming a right triangle, as shown in the diagram. The distances in the diagram are measured in yards. Use the Pythagorean Theorem to find the distance from Dominic's house to the school. 500 yd

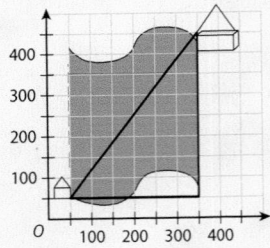

 Interactive Whiteboard
Interactive example available online

Digital Teacher Resources

Go online to access all your lesson-level resources.

Differentiated Instruction
- Reteach
- Reading Strategies
- Success for English Learners
- Practice and Problem Solving A/B, C, D

Math on the Spot Videos

Finding the Distance Between Two Points

Math On the Spot
my.hrw.com

The Pythagorean Theorem can be used to find the distance between two points in a real-world situation. You can do this by using a coordinate grid that overlays a diagram of the real-world situation.

EXAMPLE 2

Francesca wants to find the distance between her house on one side of a lake and the beach on the other side. She marks off a third point forming a right triangle, as shown. The distances in the diagram are measured in meters.

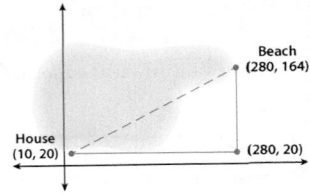
Beach (280, 164)
House (10, 20)
(280, 20)

Use the Pythagorean Theorem to find the straight-line distance from Francesca's house to the beach.

STEP 1 Find the length of the horizontal leg.

The length of the horizontal leg is the absolute value of the difference between the x-coordinates of the points (280, 20) and (10, 20).

$$|280 - 10| = 270$$

The length of the horizontal leg is 270 meters.

STEP 2 Find the length of the vertical leg.

The length of the vertical leg is the absolute value of the difference between the y-coordinates of the points (280, 164) and (280, 20).

$$|164 - 20| = 144$$

The length of the vertical leg is 144 meters.

STEP 3 Let $a = 270$ and $b = 144$. Let c represent the length of the hypotenuse. Use the Pythagorean Theorem to find c.

$$a^2 + b^2 = c^2$$
$$270^2 + 144^2 = c^2 \quad \text{Substitute into the formula.}$$
$$72{,}900 + 20{,}736 = c^2 \quad \text{Simplify.}$$
$$93{,}636 = c^2 \quad \text{Add.}$$
$$\sqrt{93{,}636} = c \quad \text{Take the square root of both sides.}$$
$$306 = c \quad \text{Simplify.}$$

The distance from Francesca's house to the beach is 306 meters.

> **Math Talk**
> Mathematical Processes
>
> Why is it necessary to take the absolute value of the coordinates when finding the length of a segment?
>
> Sample answer: You take the absolute value because the length of a segment cannot be a negative number.

Lesson 12.3 **389**

DIFFERENTIATE INSTRUCTION *Leveled Questions*

	EXAMPLE 2
(AL) DOK 1 *Recall*	What distances do you find before using the Pythagorean Theorem? Find the horizontal distance and the vertical distance first.
(OL) DOK 2 *Skills/Concepts*	In Steps 1 and 2, why are absolute value symbols used? The difference is used to describe a distance in the real world, which is always non-negative.
(BL) DOK 3 *Strategic Thinking*	How can Francesca use a translation of the triangle in the diagram to make a simpler version of the problem for a student who is struggling with the concept? Use the transformation $(x, y) \rightarrow (x - 10, y - 20)$ to redraw the diagram with vertices at (0, 0), (270, 0), and (270, 144) so that the leg lengths are immediately apparent to the other student.

LEVELED QUESTIONS: (AL) Approaching Level | (OL) On Level | (BL) Beyond Level

© Houghton Mifflin Harcourt Publishing Company

Reflect

3. Show how you could use the Distance Formula to find the distance from Francesca's house to the beach.

Let $(x_1, y_1) = (10, 20)$ and $(x_2, y_2) = (280, 164)$.

$d = \sqrt{(280 - 10)^2 + (164 - 20)^2} = \sqrt{(270)^2 + (144)^2}$

$d = \sqrt{72{,}900 + 20{,}736} = \sqrt{93{,}636} = 306$

Personal Math Trainer
Online Assessment and Intervention
my.hrw.com

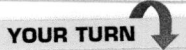

YOUR TURN

4. Camp Sunshine is also on the lake. Use the Pythagorean Theorem to find the distance between Francesca's house and Camp Sunshine to the nearest tenth of a meter.

approximately 214.7 meters

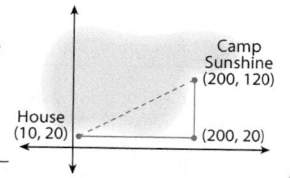

Camp Sunshine (200, 120)

House (10, 20)   (200, 20)

Guided Practice

1. Approximate the length of the hypotenuse of the right triangle to the nearest tenth using a calculator. (Explore Activity Example 1)

5.8 units

2. Find the distance between the points (3, 7) and (15, 12) on the coordinate plane. (Explore Activity 2)

13 units

3. A plane leaves an airport and flies due north. Two minutes later, a second plane leaves the same airport flying due east. The flight plan shows the coordinates of the two planes 10 minutes later. The distances in the graph are measured in miles. Use the Pythagorean Theorem to find the distance shown between the two planes.

(Example 2)   103.6 miles

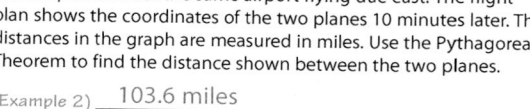

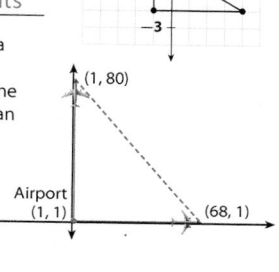

(1, 80)

Airport (1, 1)   (68, 1)

ESSENTIAL QUESTION CHECK-IN

4. Describe two ways to find the distance between two points on a coordinate plane.

Sample answer: Draw a right triangle whose hypotenuse is the segment connecting the two points and then use the Pythagorean Theorem to find the length of that segment, or use the Distance Formula.

© Houghton Mifflin Harcourt Publishing Company

Connect to Daily Life

Discuss with students why the distance across water might be measured using distances on land instead of directly. Remind students that they have already learned another method to measure the length of inaccessible areas using similar triangles.

4 Elaborate

Talk About It

Summarize the Lesson

Ask: What are two ways you can find the distance between points (x_1, y_1) and (x_2, y_2) in the coordinate plane? Draw a segment connecting the two points and complete a right triangle with the segment as the hypotenuse. Then use the Pythagorean Theorem to find the length of the hypotenuse. You can also use the Distance Formula.

Guided Practice

Engage with the Whiteboard

Sketch a graph for **Exercise 2**. Label the points, and then add vertical and horizontal segments that connect at (15, 7). Label the legs of the triangle with their length (horizontal leg is 12 units long; vertical leg is 5 units long).

Avoid Common Errors

- **Exercise 2** Watch for students who confuse the x- and y-coordinates. Have them write (x_1, y_1) and (x_2, y_2) over the given coordinates to help them substitute the correct values into the Distance Formula.

- **Exercise 3** Some students may be unsure what is meant by north and east. Help them to interpret the diagram.

DIFFERENTIATE INSTRUCTION *Intervention and Additional Support*

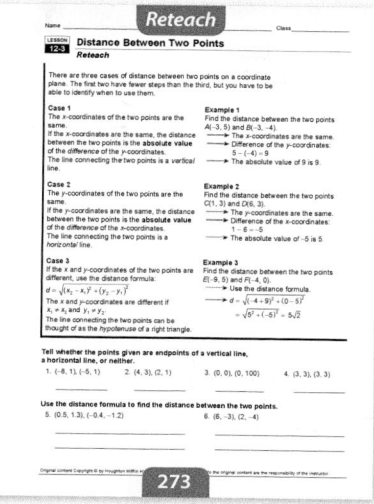

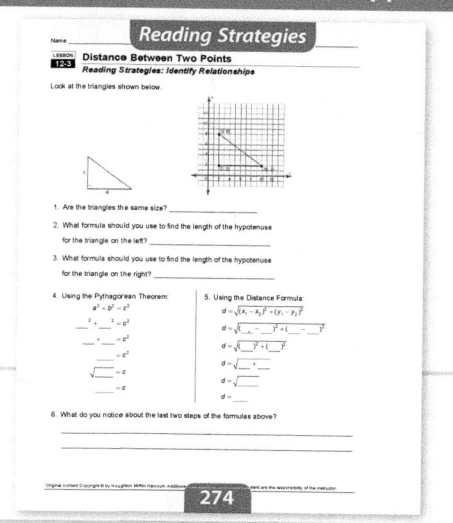

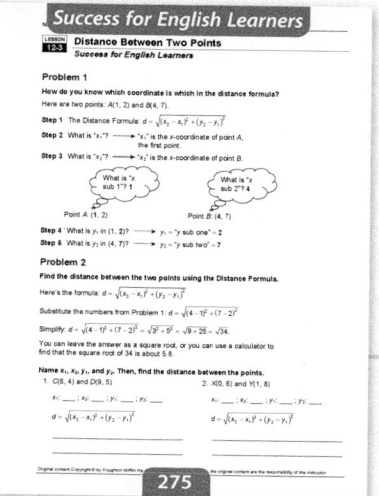

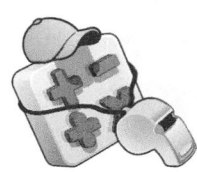

Personal Math Trainer
Daily Intervention
12.3 Homework

Pages shown are from *Differentiated Instruction.* **Also available online.**

5 Evaluate

⏱ **Pressed for Time**

12.3 Differentiated Homework Assignments

AL Approaching Level	5–10
OL On Level	7–11
BL Beyond Level	8–12

*For **Below Level** students, assign Personal Math Trainer, Daily Intervention 12.3 Homework.*

Mathematical Processes	Exercises
MP.1 Problem Solving	8
MP.2 Reasoning	10
MP.4 Modeling	5–6, 12
MP.5 Using Tools	7, 11
MP.8 Patterns	9

Focus on Higher Order Thinking

Depth of Knowledge	Exercises
2 Skills/Concepts	5–8, 10
3 Strategic Thinking **H.O.T.**	9, 11–12

12.3 Independent Practice

5. A metal worker traced a triangular piece of sheet metal on a coordinate plane, as shown. The units represent inches. What is the length of the longest side of the metal triangle? Approximate the length to the nearest tenth of an inch using a calculator. Check that your answer is reasonable.

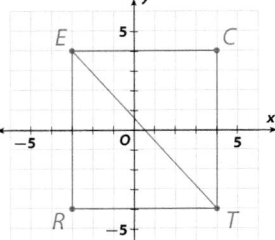

$$7.8 \text{ in.; } 49 < \sqrt{61} < 64$$

6. When a coordinate grid is superimposed on a map of Harrisburg, the high school is located at (17, 21) and the town park is located at (28, 13). If each unit represents 1 mile, how many miles apart are the high school and the town park? Round your answer to the nearest tenth.

$$13.6 \text{ miles}$$

7. The coordinates of the vertices of a rectangle are given by $R(-3, -4)$, $E(-3, 4)$, $C(4, 4)$, and $T(4, -4)$. Plot these points on the coordinate plane at the right and connect them to draw the rectangle. Then connect points E and T to form diagonal $\overline{ET}$.

a. Use the Pythagorean Theorem to find the exact length of $\overline{ET}$.

$$ET = \sqrt{113} \text{ units}$$

b. How can you use the Distance Formula to find the length of $\overline{ET}$? Show that the Distance Formula gives the same answer.

Let $(x_1, y_1) = (-3, 4)$ and $(x_2, y_2) = (4, -4)$ and then substitute the coordinates into the Distance Formula.

$$d = \sqrt{(x_2 - x_1)^2 + (y_2 - y_1)^2}$$
$$d = \sqrt{(4 - (-3))^2 + (-4 - 4)^2}$$
$$d = \sqrt{(7)^2 + (-8)^2} = \sqrt{49 + 64} = \sqrt{113}$$

8. **Multistep** The locations of three ships are represented on a coordinate grid by the following points: $P(-2, 5)$, $Q(-7, -5)$, and $R(2, -3)$. Which ships are farthest apart?

the ships at points P and Q

© Houghton Mifflin Harcourt Publishing Company

DIFFERENTIATE INSTRUCTION *Leveled Homework/Practice*

Personal Math Trainer
- 12.3 Homework

Pages shown are from *Differentiated Instruction.*
Also available online.

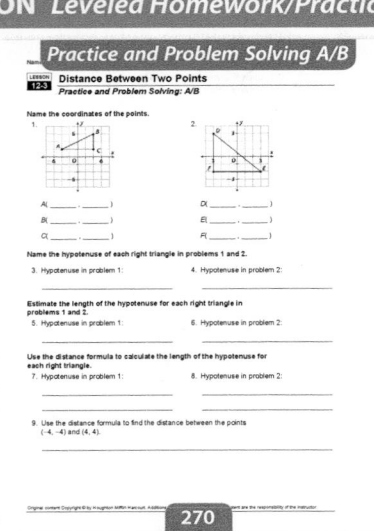

Practice and Problem Solving A/B

270

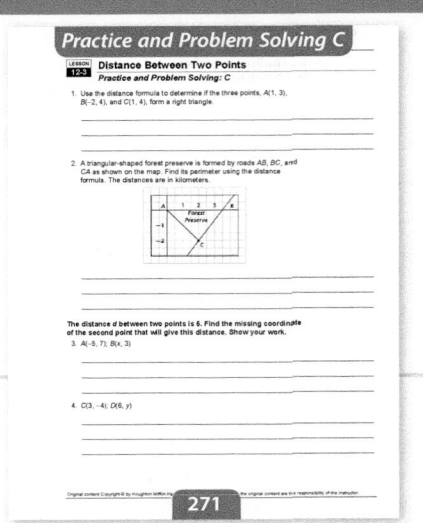

Practice and Problem Solving C

271

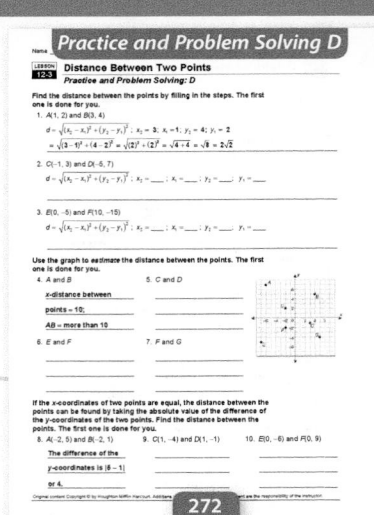

Practice and Problem Solving D

272

9. Make a Conjecture Find as many points as you can that are 5 units from the origin. Make a conjecture about the shape formed if all the points 5 units from the origin were connected.

$(5, 0), (4, 3), (3, 4), (0, 5), (-3, 4), (-4, 3), (-5, 0), (-4, -3),$
$(-3, -4), (0, -5), (3, -4), (4, -3);$ The points would form
a circle.

10. Justify Reasoning The graph shows the location of a motion detector that has a maximum range of 34 feet. A peacock at point P displays its tail feathers. Will the motion detector sense this motion? Explain.

Yes; the distance from the motion detector to the

peacock is $\sqrt{30^2 + 15^2} \approx 33.5$ ft, which is less than 34 ft.

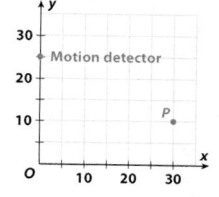

 **FOCUS ON HIGHER ORDER THINKING**

11. Persevere in Problem Solving One leg of an isosceles right triangle has endpoints (1, 1) and (6, 1). The other leg passes through the point (6, 2). Draw the triangle on the coordinate plane. Then show how you can use the Distance Formula to find the length of the hypotenuse. Round your answer to the nearest tenth.

Let $(x_1, y_1) = (6, 6)$, and $(x_2, y_2) = (1, 1)$.

$d = \sqrt{(x_2 - x_1)^2 + (y_2 - y_1)^2} = \sqrt{(6 - 1)^2 + (6 - 1)^2}$

$d = \sqrt{(5)^2 + (5)^2} = \sqrt{25 + 25} = \sqrt{50}; d \approx 7.1$

12. Represent Real-World Problems The figure shows a representation of a football field. The units represent yards. A sports analyst marks the locations of the football from where it was thrown (point A) and where it was caught (point B). Explain how you can use the Pythagorean Theorem to find the distance the ball was thrown. Then find the distance.

Create a right triangle with hypotenuse $\overline{AB}$. The vertex

at the right angle is either (40, 14) or (75, 26), and the

lengths of the legs of the triangle are 12 yards and

35 yards. The distance between A and B is about

37 yards.

© Houghton Mifflin Harcourt Publishing Company

392 Unit 5

12.3 Lesson Quiz

1. Approximate the length of the hypotenuse of the right triangle to the nearest tenth of a unit. 7.2 units

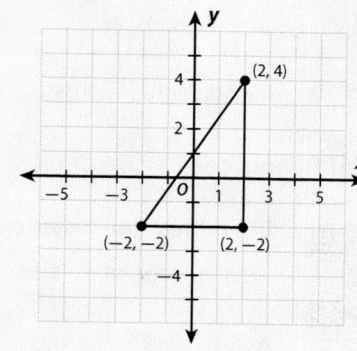

2. Find the distance between points (1, 3) and (9, 18) on the coordinate plane. 17 units

3. The coordinates of the vertices of a rectangle are $A(-4, 2)$, $B(2, 2)$, $C(2, -3)$, and $D(-4, -3)$. Plot these points on the coordinate plane and connect them to draw a rectangle. Connect points A and C. Find the exact length of the diagonal $\overline{AC}$. $\sqrt{61}$ units

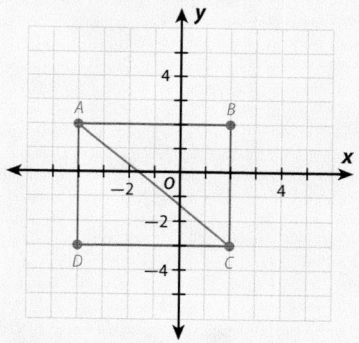

Differentiate Instruction

IF a student misses more than one question, THEN

Differentiate Instruction:

- 12.3 Reteach
- Personal Math Trainer

 Interactive Whiteboard
Interactive Lesson quiz available online

DIFFERENTIATE INSTRUCTION *Extend-the-Math Activity* **PRE-AP**

Activity Draw and label a line segment from $A(0, 0)$ to $B(1, 1)$. Use the Pythagorean Theorem to find the length of $\overline{AB}$. Use a protractor with the compass point on A and the opening of the compass set to $\overline{AB}$. With the point of the compass on A, rotate the pencil point from B to a point on the x-axis. Label the point C. What are the exact coordinates of C? What is the length of $\overline{AC}$? What kind of number did you graph?

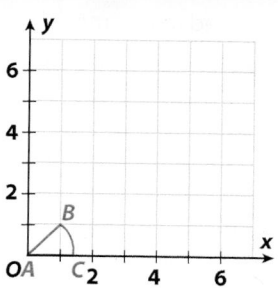

$AB = \sqrt{2}; C = (\sqrt{2}, 0); AC = \sqrt{2};$ irrational number

Ready to Go On?

Assess Mastery

Access *Ready to Go On?* assessment online, and receive instant scoring, feedback, and customized intervention or enrichment.

Personal Math Trainer

Online Assessment and Intervention
- Module 12 Posttest

Additional Resources

my.hrw.com

Digital Teacher Resources

Go online for module-level resources.

Assessment Resources
- Module 12 Quiz: B, p.59
- Module 12 Quiz: D, p.61

Ready to Go On?

Personal Math Trainer
Online Assessment and Intervention
my.hrw.com

12.1 The Pythagorean Theorem

Find the length of the missing side.

1.
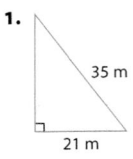
35 m
21 m

_____ 28 m _____

2.
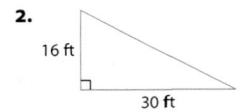
16 ft
30 ft

_____ 34 ft _____

12.2 Converse of the Pythagorean Theorem

Tell whether each triangle with the given side lengths is a right triangle.

3. 11, 60, 61 _____ yes _____   **4.** 9, 37, 40 _____ no _____

5. 15, 35, 38 _____ no _____   **6.** 28, 45, 53 _____ yes _____

7. Keelie has a triangular-shaped card. The lengths of its sides are 4.5 cm, 6 cm, and 7.5 cm. Is the card a right triangle? _____ yes _____

12.3 Distance Between Two Points

Find the distance between the given points. Round to the nearest tenth.

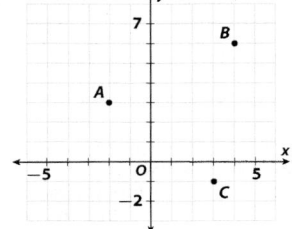

8. *A* and *B* _____ 6.7 _____

9. *B* and *C* _____ 7.1 _____

10. *A* and *C* _____ 6.4 _____

 ESSENTIAL QUESTION

11. How can you use the Pythagorean Theorem to solve real-world problems?

Sample answer: You can use the Pythagorean Theorem to find missing lengths in objects that are right triangles.

© Houghton Mifflin Harcourt Publishing Company

READY TO GO ON? *Diagnostic Assessment*

RtI Response to Intervention

Use to determine if students have mastered the concepts covered in this module.

Lesson	Exercises	Content Focus	Review with *Differentiated Instruction*
12.1	1–2	The Pythagorean Theorem	**12.1** Reteach **12.1** Reading Strategies **12.1** Success for English Learners
12.2	3–7	Converse of the Pythagorean Theorem	**12.2** Reteach **12.2** Reading Strategies **12.2** Success for English Learners
12.3	8–10	Distance Between Two Points	**12.3** Reteach **12.3** Reading Strategies **12.3** Success for English Learners

Personal Math Trainer
Online Assessment and Intervention
my.hrw.com

Selected Response

1. What is the missing length of the side?

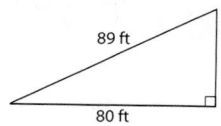

89 ft

80 ft

- (A) 9 ft
- (C) 39 ft
- (B) 30 ft
- (D) 120 ft

2. Which relation does **not** represent a function?

- (A) (0, 8), (3, 8), (1, 6)
- (B) (4, 2), (6, 1), (8, 9)
- (C) (1, 20), (2, 23), (9, 26)
- (D) (0, 3), (2, 3), (2, 0)

3. Two sides of a right triangle have lengths of 72 cm and 97 cm. The third side is **not** the hypotenuse. How long is the third side?

- (A) 25 cm
- (C) 65 cm
- (B) 45 cm
- (D) 121 cm

4. To the nearest tenth, what is the distance between point F and point G?

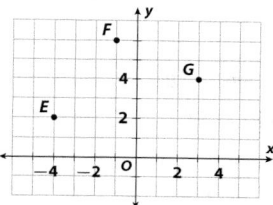

- (A) 4.5 units
- (C) 7.3 units
- (B) 5.0 units
- (D) 20 units

5. A flagpole is 53 feet tall. A rope is tied to the top of the flagpole and secured to the ground 28 feet from the base of the flagpole. What is the length of the rope?

- (A) 25 feet
- (C) 53 feet
- (B) 45 feet
- (D) 60 feet

6. Which set of lengths are **not** the side lengths of a right triangle?

- (A) 36, 77, 85
- (C) 27, 120, 123
- (B) 20, 99, 101
- (D) 24, 33, 42

7. A triangle has one right angle. What could the measures of the other two angles be?

- (A) 25° and 65°
- (C) 55° and 125°
- (B) 30° and 15°
- (D) 90° and 100°

Mini-Task

8. A fallen tree is shown on the coordinate grid below. Each unit represents 1 meter.

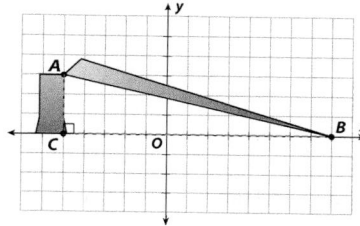

a. What is the distance from A to B?

13.3 meters

b. What was the height of the tree before it fell?

16.3 meters

© Houghton Mifflin Harcourt Publishing Company

Preparing for High Stakes Tests

Assessment Readiness Tip

Quickly sketching the problem situation can help students to organize information and solve correctly.

- **Item 3** Sketching the triangle and labeling the sides a, b, and c can help students to correctly use the Pythagorean Theorem to find the answer.

- **Item 5** Drawing a sketch of the flagpole, rope, and ground and labeling it with the given measurements can help students to see that they are finding the hypotenuse of a right triangle.

Avoid Common Errors

Item 4 Remind students to use the Distance Formula to find the distance between two points. Some students may try to count the boxes between F and G. Remind them that counting the boxes only works when a line is horizontal or vertical. If it is angled in any way, the Distance Formula must be used.

Items	Grade 8 Lessons	Mathematical Processes
1	12.1	MP.4
2*	6.1	MP.6
3	12.1	MP.2
4	12.3	MP.2
5	12.1	MP.4
6	12.2	MP.4
7*	11.2	MP.2
8	12.1, 12.3	MP.4

Item integrates mixed review concepts from previous modules or a previous course.

DIFFERENTIATE ASSESSMENT

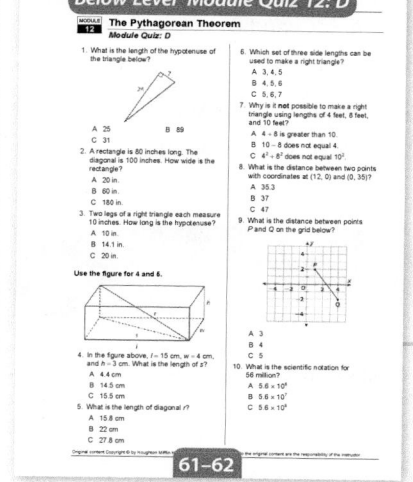

Below Level Module Quiz 12: D

61–62

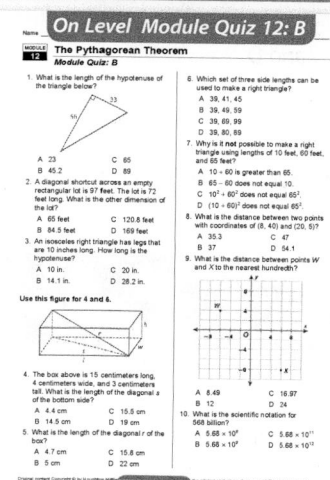

On Level Module Quiz 12: B

59–60

Personal Math Trainer

Module 12 Assessment Readiness

Pages shown are from *Assessment Resources*. **Also available online.**

The Pythagorean Theorem **394**

Module At A Glance

Module Essential Question: How can you use volume to solve real-world problems?

MODULE 13 | Volume

Lessons at A Glance	Lesson 13.1 Volume of Cylinders	Lesson 13.2 Volume of Cones	Lesson 13.3 Volume of Spheres
	Pg. T399A	Pg. T405A	Pg. T411A
Essential Question	How do you find the volume of a cylinder?	How do you find the volume of a cone?	How do you find the volume of a sphere?
Objective	Students will find the volume of a cylinder.	Students will find the volume of a cone.	Students will find the volume of a sphere.
Vocabulary	cylinder	cone	radius of a sphere, sphere
Go online for all your module resources my.hrw.com 	13.1 *i*Student Edition 13.1 *i*Teacher Edition 13.1 *e*Student Edition Personal Math Trainer Math on the Spot Videos Animated Math	13.2 *i*Student Edition 13.2 *i*Teacher Edition 13.2 *e*Student Edition Personal Math Trainer Math on the Spot Videos	13.3 *i*Student Edition 13.3 *i*Teacher Edition 13.3 *e*Student Edition Personal Math Trainer Math on the Spot Videos
Print Resources	**13.1 Student Edition**: Lesson *Differentiated Instruction* 13.1 Practice and Problem Solving A/B, C, and D 13.1 Reteach 13.1 Reading Strategies 13.1 Success for English Learners	**13.2 Student Edition**: Lesson *Differentiated Instruction* 13.2 Practice and Problem Solving A/B, C, and D 13.2 Reteach 13.2 Reading Strategies 13.2 Success for English Learners	**13.3 Student Edition**: Lesson *Differentiated Instruction* 13.3 Practice and Problem Solving A/B, C, and D 13.3 Reteach 13.3 Reading Strategies 13.3 Success for English Learners

RtI

Response to Intervention

Before the Module	During the Lesson	After the Module
Are You Ready	**Guided/Independent Practice**	**Ready to Go On?**
• Prerequisite Skills Activities • Personal Math Trainer	• Reteach • Personal Math Trainer • Practice and Problem Solving D	• Reteach • Personal Math Trainer

Teacher Notes

Check It Out!

Math on the Spot Videos	Animated Math
One for every Example in every Lesson	During Lesson 13.1

Volume

Real-World Video Viewing Guide

After students have watched the video, discuss the following:

- What three-dimensional figures did you see in the video?

- How is volume used to solve problems in the real world?

Professional Development Video

Author Juli Dixon models successful teaching practices as she explores the concept of volume of curved-surface solids in an actual eighth-grade classroom.

Volume

ESSENTIAL QUESTION

How can you use volume to solve real-world problems?

You can use formulas to find the volumes of real-world objects shaped like cylinders, cones, and spheres.

LESSON 13.1
Volume of Cylinders

LESSON 13.2
Volume of Cones

LESSON 13.3
Volume of Spheres

© Houghton Mifflin Harcourt Publishing Company

Real-World Video

Many foods are in the shape of cylinders, cones, and spheres. To find out how much of the food you are eating, you can use formulas for volume.

my.hrw.com

GO DIGITAL
my.hrw.com

my.hrw.com	Math On the Spot	Animated Math	Personal Math Trainer
Go digital with your write-in student edition, accessible on any device.	Scan with your smart phone to jump directly to the online edition, video tutor, and more.	Interactively explore key concepts to see how math works.	Get immediate feedback and help as you work through practice sets.

395

TEACHER ONLINE RESOURCES

 ONLINE TEACHER EDITION Access a full suite of teaching resources online—plan, present, and manage classes and assignments.

 MY SMART PLANNER Easily plan your classes and access all your resources online.

 INTERACTIVE WHITEBOARDS Engage students with interactive whiteboard-ready examples and a lesson quiz for each lesson.

 PERSONAL MATH TRAINER: Online Assessment and Intervention Assign automatically graded homework, quizzes, tests, and intervention activities. Prepare your students for standardized tests in short-answer and multiple-choice formats.

Reading Start-Up

Visualize Vocabulary

Use the ✔ words to complete the empty columns in the chart. You may use words more than once.

Shape	Distance Around	Attributes	Associated Review Words
circle	circumference	r, d	radius, diameter
square	perimeter	90° corner, sides	right angle, length, width
rectangle	perimeter	90° corner, sides	right angle, length, width

Understand Vocabulary

Complete the sentences using the preview words.

1. A three-dimensional figure that has one vertex and one circular base is a _____cone_____.

2. A three-dimensional figure with all points the same distance from the center is a _____sphere_____.

3. A three-dimensional figure that has two congruent circular bases is a _____cylinder_____.

© Houghton Mifflin Harcourt Publishing Company

Vocabulary

Review Words
- area *(área)*
- base *(base, en numeración)*
- ✔ circumference *(circunferencia)*
- ✔ diameter *(diámetro)*
- height *(altura)*
- ✔ length *(longitud)*
- ✔ perimeter *(perímetro)*
- ✔ radius *(radio)*
- ✔ right angle *(ángulo recto)*
- ✔ width *(ancho)*

Preview Words
- cone *(cono)*
- cylinder *(cilindro)*
- sphere *(esfera)*

Active Reading

Three-Panel Flip Chart Before beginning the module, create a three-panel flip chart to help you organize what you learn. Label each flap with one of the lesson titles from this module. As you study each lesson, write important ideas like vocabulary, properties, and formulas under the appropriate flap.

Reading Start-Up

Visualize Vocabulary
The chart helps students review the terms related to volume of three-dimensional figures. Students should write one or more review words in each box.

Understand Vocabulary
Use the following explanation to help students learn the preview words.

> A birthday hat with a pointed top is similar to a **cone**. A can of vegetables is a **cylinder**, and a basketball is a **sphere**. In this module, you will learn how to find the volume of all of these shapes.

Active Reading
Integrating Language Arts
Students can use these reading and note-taking strategies to help them organize and understand new concepts and vocabulary.

Additional Resources
Differentiated Instruction
- Reading Strategies **ELL**
- Interactive multilingual glossary

LEARNING PROGRESSIONS ACROSS THE GRADES

Before

Students understand how to use formulas:
- find the circumference of a circle
- find the area of a circle
- find the volume of rectangular prisms and pyramids, and of triangular prisms and pyramids

In this Module

Students represent and solve for the volumes of three-dimensional curved figures:
- describe the volume formula $V = Bh$ of a cylinder in terms of its base area and height
- model the relationship between the volume of a cylinder and a cone having both congruent bases and the same height and connect that relationship to their volume formulas
- solve problems involving the volume of cylinders, cones, and spheres

After

Students will connect:
- the effect on volume when the dimensions of a solid change proportionally
- capacity and volume

Are You Ready?

Assess Readiness

Access *Are You Ready?* assessment online, and receive instant scoring, feedback, and customized intervention or enrichment.

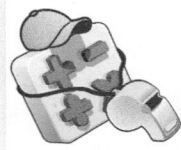

Personal Math Trainer

Online Assessment and Intervention

Additional Resources

Digital Teacher Resources

Go online for module-level resources.

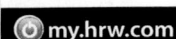
my.hrw.com

Are YOU Ready?

Complete these exercises to review skills you will need for this module.

Personal Math Trainer
Online Assessment and Intervention
my.hrw.com

Exponents

EXAMPLE $6^3 = 6 \times 6 \times 6$ Multiply the base (6) by itself the number of times indicated by the exponent (3).

$= 36 \times 6$ Find the product of the first two terms.

$= 216$ Find the product of all the terms.

Evaluate each exponential expression.

1. 11^2 __121__
2. 2^5 __32__
3. $\left(\frac{1}{5}\right)^3$ __$\frac{1}{125}$__
4. $(0.3)^2$ __0.09__

5. 2.1^3 __9.261__
6. 0.1^3 __0.001__
7. $\left(\frac{9.6}{3}\right)^2$ __10.24__
8. 100^3 __1,000,000__

Round Decimals

EXAMPLE   Round 43.2685 to the underlined place.

$43.2685 \rightarrow 43.27$

The digit to be rounded: 6
The digit to its right is 8.
8 is *5 or greater*, so round *up*.
The rounded number is 43.27.

Round to the underlined place.

9. 2.374   __2.37__
10. 126.399   __126__
11. 13.9577   __14.0__
12. 42.690   __42.69__

13. 134.95   __135.0__
14. 2.0486   __2.0__
15. 63.6352   __63.64__
16. 98.9499   __98.9__

Simplify Numerical Expressions

EXAMPLE $\frac{1}{3}(3.14)(4)^2(3) = \frac{1}{3}(3.14)(16)(3)$ Simplify the exponent.

$= 50.24$ Multiply from left to right.

Simplify each expression.

17. $3.14(5)^2(10)$ __785__
18. $\frac{1}{3}(3.14)(3)^2(5)$ __47.1__
19. $\frac{4}{3}(3.14)(3)^3$ __113.04__

20. $\frac{4}{3}(3.14)(6)^3$ __904.32__
21. $3.14(4)^2(9)$ __452.16__
22. $\frac{1}{3}(3.14)(9)^2\left(\frac{2}{3}\right)$ __56.52__

ARE YOU READY? *Diagnostic Assessment*

RtI   Response to Intervention

Use to determine if students need intervention for the module's prerequisite skills.

Skill	Missed More Than . . .	Intervene With *Skills Intervention* worksheets (available online)	For Enrichment *Differentiated Instruction* (available in print and online)
Exponents	2 questions	**Skill 12** Integer Operations	**Module 13 Challenge** Extend-the-Math Lesson Activities in TE
Round Decimals	2 questions	**Skill 16** Graph Ordered Pairs (First Quadrant)	**Module 13 Challenge** Extend-the-Math Lesson Activities in TE
Simplify Numerical Expressions	2 questions	**Skill 52** Graph Ordered Pairs (First Quadrant)	**Module 13 Challenge** Extend-the-Math Lesson Activities in TE

© Houghton Mifflin Harcourt Publishing Company

Are YOU Ready? (cont'd)

Complete these exercises to review skills you will need for this module.

Exponents

23. Explain how to evaluate $\left(\frac{1}{2}\right)^4$.

Multiply the base, $\frac{1}{2}$, by itself the number of times indicated by the exponent, 4: $\frac{1}{2} \times \frac{1}{2} \times \frac{1}{2} \times \frac{1}{2}$.
Find the product: $\left(\frac{1}{2} \times \frac{1}{2}\right) \times \frac{1}{2} \times \frac{1}{2} = \left(\frac{1}{4} \times \frac{1}{2}\right) \times \frac{1}{2} = \frac{1}{8} \times \frac{1}{2} = \frac{1}{16}$.

24. a. Describe the pattern in the values of 0.1, 0.1^2, 0.1^3, 0.1^4, and 0.1^5.

b. Use the pattern to predict the value of 0.1^{12}.

a. Each number after the first is 0.1 times the previous number, so the values of the expressions are 0.1, 0.01, 0.001, 0.0001, and 0.00001. The number of zeros to the right of the decimal point is one less than the exponent.

b. In 0.1^{12}, the number of zeros to the right of the decimal point is 11. The value is 0.000000000001.

Round Decimals

25. To find the value of her bank balance with interest, Carla multiplied her starting balance by 1.0425 and calculated that she should have $1,099.8375 in her account. Explain how to round $1,099.8375 to the nearest hundredth.

Identify the digit in the hundredths place, 3. The digit to the right of this place is 7. Since 7 is *5 or greater*, round up. The rounded number is $1,099.84.

Simplify Numerical Expressions

26. Kendra could not decide what to do first when simplifying $\frac{1}{2}(3.14)(10)^3(4)$. How should she complete the problem?

Her first step should be to simplify the exponent to get $\frac{1}{2}(3.14)(1,000)(4)$. Then she should multiply from left to right to get 6,280.

Houghton Mifflin Harcourt Publishing Company

Exponents

Exercise 23 Remind students that the laws of exponents work for all numbers. Make sure they don't make the error of multiplying $\frac{1}{2}$ by 4 instead of multiplying $\frac{1}{2}$ by itself four times.

Exercise 24 Some students may find it helpful to use technology to help them see a pattern and make a prediction.

Round Decimals

Exercise 25 Point out that many banks do not actually round up when calculating the interest on an account. Instead, they drop the digits after the hundredths place.

Simplify Numerical Expressions

Exercise 26 Remind students to use the order of operations when they are simplifying any mathematical expression.

Use to determine if students are able to apply the module's prerequisite skills.

Skill	Exercise	Depth of Knowledge (D.O.K.)	Mathematical Processes
Exponents	23	2 Skills/Concepts	MP.2 Abstract and Quantitative Reasoning
	24	3 Strategic Thinking	MP.8 Generalize
Round Decimals	25	2 Skills/Concepts	MP.6 Use Precise Mathematical Language
Simplify Numerical Expressions	26	2 Skills/Concepts	MP.2 Abstract and Quantitative Reasoning

Volume **398**

Lesson Support

Content Objective Students will learn how to find the volume of a cylinder.

Professional Development

Integrate Mathematical Processes MP.3

This lesson provides an opportunity to address this Mathematical Processes standard. It calls for students to construct viable arguments by making conjectures and building a logical progression of statements. Students explore ways to find the volume of a cylinder, working from descriptions or diagrams. Students then represent the volume in symbolic form as an equation.

FOCUS

Building Background

Eliciting Prior Knowledge Ask students to work with a partner or in small groups to create a main idea web that shows what they recall about volume. Have them include a definition and the type of units used to measure volume, as well as any formulas they remember.

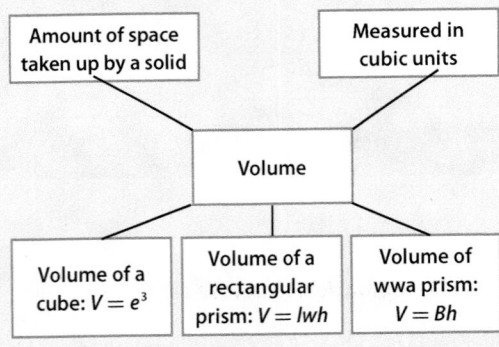

COHERENCE

Learning Progressions

In this lesson, students find the volume of a cylinder. They model the volume with cubes and then generalize their findings to develop a formula for the volume of a cylinder. Important understandings for students include the following:

- **Model the volume of a cylinder.**
- **Find the volume of a cylinder using a formula.**
- **Find the volume of a cylinder in a real-world context.**

From previous grades students are familiar with finding the volumes of cubes and rectangular and triangular prisms. The volume of a cylinder is closely related to the volume of a prism. For both solids, the volume formula is the same. The difference lies in computing the area of the base. Students make this connection and are ready to move on to volumes of cones and cylinders in the remaining lessons in this module.

RIGOR

Cluster Connections

This lesson provides an excellent opportunity to connect ideas in this cluster:

Solve real-world and mathematical problems involving volumes of cylinders, cones, and spheres.

Tell students that a pipe is made from 3 cylinders. The smaller cylinders are each 8 centimeters tall and have a diameter of 6 centimeters. The larger cylinder is 12 centimeters tall and has a diameter of 10 centimeters. Ask students to find the volume of the pipe to the nearest tenth.

1394.2 cm^3

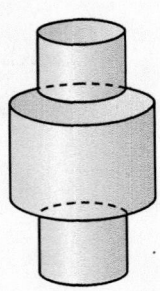

Language Support ELL

Language Objective Students will create a set of instructions for how to find the volume of a cylinder.

Leveled Strategies for English Learners ELL

Emerging

Have students at this level of English proficiency work in pairs to copy the formula for the volume of a cylinder and then use the formula to calculate the volume in the first four Independent Practice exercises.

Expanding

Have students at this level of English proficiency work in pairs to copy the formula for the volume of a cylinder on paper, list what each variable stands for (V = volume, Bh = base times height), and then use the formula to calculate the volume in the first four Independent Practice exercises.

Bridging

Have students at this level of English proficiency work in pairs to review the formula for the volume of a cylinder. Then have them discuss as they use the formula to calculate the volume in the first four Independent Practice exercises.

Math Talk Provide a sentence frame to help students answer the Reflect question in Example 1.

Because the diameter d is equal to _____, the formula can be rewritten as V = _____ .

> ### Volume of a Cylinder
>
> The volume V of a cylinder with radius r is the area of the base B times the height h.
>
>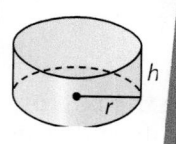
>
> $V = Bh$ or $V = \pi r^2 h$

Linguistic Support ELL

Academic/Content Vocabulary

cylinder This lesson on the volumes of cylinders relies on students' understanding of the definition of a cylinder, a three-dimensional figure with two congruent circular bases that are in parallel planes. It might help students to remember that most soup cans are in the shape of a cylinder.

Also point out that *circular* and *cylinder* are English-Spanish cognates with *circular* and *cilindro*, respectively. Have English learners add these terms to their word journals.

Building Background

Homographs are words that are spelled the same but have different pronunciations and meanings. While the word *bass* in this lesson refers to a type of drum, it also has another meaning and pronunciation when referring to a type of fish. Point this out to English learners and have them add both uses of the word *bass* to their word journals.

Image Credits: ©Roman Samokhin/Shutterstock

Volume of Cylinders

1 Engage

ESSENTIAL QUESTION

How do you find the volume of a cylinder? Sample answer: You multiply the area of the base by the height.

Motivate the Lesson

Ask: What three-dimensional objects with two congruent circular bases do you see around you in the classroom? What examples of this shape might you find in a kitchen? How could you find out how much food an object like this might hold? Begin the Explore Activity to find out.

2 Explore

EXPLORE ACTIVITY

Connect to Daily Life

Ask students to think of a circular pancake or cookie (*B*), and then to think of stacking up enough of these pancakes (*h*) to fill the cylinder. Relate this to the formula $V = Bh$.

ESSENTIAL QUESTION

How do you find the volume of a cylinder?

EXPLORE ACTIVITY

Modeling the Volume of a Cylinder

A **cylinder** is a three-dimensional figure that has two congruent circular bases that lie in parallel planes. The volume of any three-dimensional figure is the number of cubic units needed to fill the space taken up by the solid figure.

One cube represents one cubic unit of volume. You can develop the formula for the volume of a cylinder using an empty soup can or other cylindrical container. First, remove one of the bases.

A Arrange centimeter cubes in a single layer at the bottom of the cylinder. Fit as many cubes into the layer as possible. How many cubes are in this layer?

Answers will vary. Check students' work.

B To find how many layers of cubes fit in the cylinder, make a stack of cubes along the inside of the cylinder. How many layers fit in the cylinder?

Answers will vary. Check students' work.

C How can you use what you know to find the approximate number of cubes that would fit in the cylinder?

Sample answer: Multiply the number of cubes in the bottom layer times the number of layers.

Reflect

1. **Make a Conjecture** Suppose you know the area of the base of a cylinder and the height of the cylinder. How can you find the cylinder's volume?

Multiply the area of the base times the height.

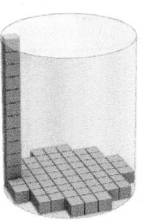

2. Let the area of the base of a cylinder be *B* and the height of the cylinder be *h*. Write a formula for the cylinder's volume *V*. $V = Bh$

© Houghton Mifflin Harcourt Publishing Company

Lesson 13.1 **399**

DIFFERENTIATE INSTRUCTION *Leveled Questions*

	EXPLORE ACTIVITY
AL **DOK 1** *Recall*	How are cubes used to estimate the volume of the cylindrical can? Cover the bottom with cubes, and multiply that number of cubes by the number of cubes high that the can is.
OL **DOK 2** *Skills/Concepts*	How are prisms and cylinders alike? How are they different? Both have parallel and congruent bases. Prisms have bases that are polygons, and cylinders have bases that are circles.
BL **DOK 3** *Strategic Thinking*	For which shape can you get a better estimate of volume using cubes—cylinder or prism? Justify your response. Prism. Both estimates using cubes will consist of the base area multiplied by height. A prism base is a polygon, so it will be better estimated with cubes than the cylinder base, a circle.

LEVELED QUESTIONS: **AL** Approaching Level | **OL** On Level | **BL** Beyond Level

Math On the Spot
my.hrw.com

Finding the Volume of a Cylinder Using a Formula

Finding volumes of cylinders is similar to finding volumes of prisms. You find the volume V of both a prism and a cylinder by multiplying the height h by the area of the base B, so $V = Bh$.

The base of a cylinder is a circle, so for a cylinder, $B = \pi r^2$.

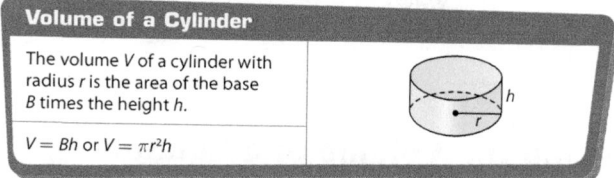

Volume of a Cylinder

The volume V of a cylinder with radius r is the area of the base B times the height h.	
$V = Bh$ or $V = \pi r^2 h$	

Animated Math
my.hrw.com

My Notes

EXAMPLE 1

Find the volume of each cylinder. Round your answers to the nearest tenth if necessary. Use 3.14 for π.

A

10 in.

3 in.

$V = \pi r^2 h$

$\approx 3.14 \cdot 3^2 \cdot 10$ Substitute.

$\approx 3.14 \cdot 9 \cdot 10$ Simplify.

≈ 282.6 Multiply.

The volume is about 282.6 in³.

B 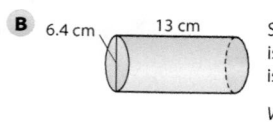 6.4 cm   13 cm

Since the diameter is 6.4 cm, the radius is 3.2 cm.

> Recall that the diameter of a circle is twice the radius, so $2r = d$ and $r = \frac{d}{2}$.

$V = \pi r^2 h$

$\approx 3.14 \cdot 3.2^2 \cdot 13$ Substitute.

$\approx 3.14 \cdot 10.24 \cdot 13$ Simplify.

≈ 418 Multiply.

The volume is about 418 cm³.

Reflect

3. **What If?** If you want a formula for the volume of a cylinder that involves the diameter d instead of the radius r, how can you rewrite it?

Write $\frac{d}{2}$ in place of r, so $V = \pi \left(\frac{d}{2}\right)^2 h$.

© Houghton Mifflin Harcourt Publishing Company

3 Explain

EXAMPLE 1

ADDITIONAL EXAMPLE 1

Find the volume of each cylinder. Round your answers to the nearest tenth if necessary. Use 3.14 for π.

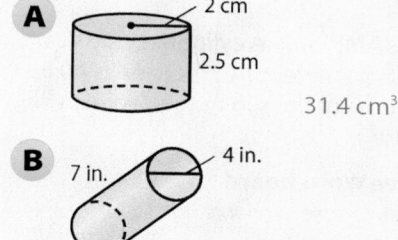

A 2 cm   2.5 cm

31.4 cm³

B 7 in.   4 in.

87.9 in³

Interactive Whiteboard

Interactive example available online

my.hrw.com

Animated Math

Volume of Cylinders

Students explore the effect of radius and height on the volume of a cylinder using a dynamic model.

	EXAMPLE 1
AL DOK 1 *Recall*	In Example 1, why use the symbol "≈" instead of "=" after values are substituted in the formula? 3.14 is an approximate value for π.
OL DOK 2 *Skills/Concepts*	A cylinder has both a diameter and a height of 10 inches. Is the volume $\pi \cdot 10^2 \cdot 10$ cubic inches? Explain. No; it is $\pi \cdot 5^2 \cdot 10$ cubic inches; you must halve the diameter to find the radius before squaring.
BL DOK 3 *Strategic Thinking*	Which increases the volume more, doubling the radius or doubling the height? Explain. Doubling the radius; the radius is squared in the volume formula, so doubling it increases the volume $2^2 = 4$ times; doubling the height only doubles the volume.

TEACHER TO TEACHER

Cognitive Strategies Show students that a cylinder is constructed very much like a prism. A prism has two congruent *polygon* bases, and a cylinder has two congruent *circular* bases. Both the volume of a prism and the volume of a cylinder are found by multiplying the base area and the height.

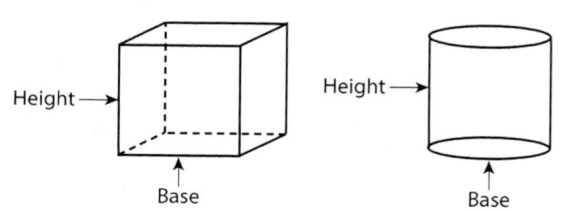

Height →   Height →

Base   Base

Avoid Common Errors

Remind students to always consider the question, "Do I know the radius, r, or only the diameter?" In **Exercise 4**, students may try to use the diameter instead of the radius in the formula.

EXAMPLE 2

ADDITIONAL EXAMPLE 2 A cylindrical silo that stores grain has a diameter of 16 feet and is 40 feet tall. Find the volume of the silo to the nearest tenth. Use 3.14 for π. 8038.4 ft³

 Interactive Whiteboard
Interactive example available online

YOUR TURN   MP.7

Focus on Critical Thinking

To calculate the answer for **Exercise 6**, Elsa multiplied 6² by 3.14 and then multiplied that product by 4. Tommie multiplied 6² by 4 and then multiplied that product by 3.14. Which process gives the correct answer? Explain. Both; factors can be multiplied in any order.

Digital Teacher Resources

Go online to access all your lesson-level resources.

Differentiated Instruction
• Reteach
• Reading Strategies
• Success for English Learners
• Practice and Problem Solving A/B, C, D

Math on the Spot Videos

my.hrw.com

 **YOUR TURN**

Find the volume of each cylinder. Round your answers to the nearest tenth if necessary. Use 3.14 for π.

Personal Math Trainer
Online Assessment and Intervention
my.hrw.com

4.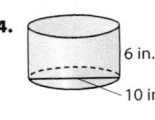
6 in.
10 in.
471 in³

5.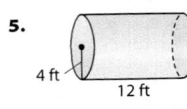
4 ft
12 ft
602.9 ft³

Math On the Spot
my.hrw.com

Finding the Volume of a Cylinder in a Real-World Context

The Longhorn Band at the University of Texas at Austin has one of the world's largest bass drums, known as Big Bertha.

EXAMPLE 2 Real World

Big Bertha has a diameter of 8 feet and is 4.5 feet deep. Find the volume of the drum to the nearest tenth. Use 3.14 for π.

STEP 1   Find the radius of the drum.

$$r = \frac{d}{2} = \frac{8}{2} = 4 \text{ ft}$$

STEP 2   Find the volume of the drum.

$V = \pi r^2 h$

$\approx 3.14 \cdot 4^2 \cdot 4.5$ Substitute.

$\approx 3.14 \cdot 16 \cdot 4.5$ Simplify the exponent.

≈ 226.08 Multiply.

The volume of the drum is about 226.1 ft³.

The Univ. of Texas
Big Bertha
Longhorn Band

 YOUR TURN

6. A drum company advertises a snare drum that is 4 inches high and 12 inches in diameter. Find the volume of the drum to the nearest tenth. Use 3.14 for π.

452.2 in³

Personal Math Trainer
Online Assessment and Intervention
my.hrw.com

© Houghton Mifflin Harcourt Publishing Company • Image Credits: ©Brian Bahr/ Getty Images

---

DIFFERENTIATE INSTRUCTION *Leveled Questions*

	EXAMPLE 2
AL DOK 1 *Recall*	In Step 1, why is 8 divided by 2? Because 8 is the diameter, and the formula uses the radius.
OL DOK 2 *Skills/Concepts*	A Japanese odaiko drum has a diameter of 7 feet and is 8 feet deep. How would its volume compare with Big Bertha's? It's about $3.14 \cdot 3.5^2 \cdot 8 \approx 308$ cubic feet, or about 80 cubic feet more than Big Bertha's.
BL DOK 3 *Strategic Thinking*	Suppose Big Bertha is shipped in the smallest possible box-shaped crate. How does the amount of empty space between Big Bertha and the crate compare to Big Bertha's volume? Explain. It is about 27% of the drum's volume because the volume of the smallest possible crate is $8 \cdot 8 \cdot 4.5 = 288$ cubic feet, and $288 - 226.1 = 61.9$ is about 27% of 226.1.

LEVELED QUESTIONS: AL Approaching Level | OL On Level | BL Beyond Level

1. **Vocabulary** Describe the bases of a cylinder. (Explore Activity)

   two congruent circles that lie in parallel planes

2. Figure 1 shows a view from above of inch cubes on the bottom of a cylinder. Figure 2 shows the highest stack of cubes that will fit inside the cylinder. Estimate the volume of the cylinder. Explain your reasoning. (Explore Activity)

   Sample answer: 427 in³; there are 61 cubes on

   the bottom of the cylinder. The height is 7 cubes.

   $V = 61 \times 7 = 427$ in³

   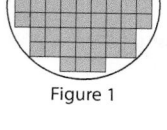

   Figure 1   Figure 2

3. Find the volume of the cylinder to the nearest tenth. Use 3.14 for π. (Example 1)

   $V = \pi r^2 h$

   $V = \pi \cdot \boxed{6}^{\,2} \cdot \boxed{15}$

   $\approx 3.14 \cdot \boxed{36} \cdot \boxed{15}$

   $\approx \boxed{1695.6}$

    6 m

   15 m

   The volume of the cylinder is approximately $\underline{1695.6}$ m³.

4. A Japanese odaiko is a very large drum that is made by hollowing out a section of a tree trunk. A museum in Takayama City has three odaikos of similar size carved from a single tree trunk. The largest measures about 2.7 meters in both diameter and length, and weighs about 4.5 metric tons. Using the volume formula for a cylinder, approximate the volume of the drum to the nearest tenth. (Example 2)

   The radius of the drum is about $\underline{1.35}$ m.

   The volume of the drum is about $\underline{15.5}$ m³.

   ESSENTIAL QUESTION CHECK-IN

5. How do you find the volume of a cylinder? Describe which measurements of a cylinder you need to know.

   You need to know the height and know or be able to

   calculate the radius of the base. Then you can substitute

   into the volume formula $V = \pi r^2 h$.

© Houghton Mifflin Harcourt Publishing Company

4 Elaborate

Talk About It

Summarize the Lesson

Ask: What measurements do you need to know in order to find the volume of a cylinder? What formula will you use? You need to know either the radius or the diameter of the bases and the height of the cylinder. $V = Bh$

Guided Practice

Avoid Common Errors

- **Exercises 2–4** Ask students to predict the units they will write for the final answer before they begin the problem. Make sure students remember that volume requires cubic units.

- **Exercises 3–4** Have students circle the key words *radius* and *diameter* before they begin to substitute values into the volume formula. Students may carelessly use the diameter for the radius in Exercise 4.

Engage with the Whiteboard

In **Exercise 3**, have a student write the variables for the radius *r* and the height *h* next to the measurements on the cylinder. In **Exercise 4**, have a student draw and label a cylinder next to the statement of the problem.

DIFFERENTIATE INSTRUCTION *Intervention and Additional Support*

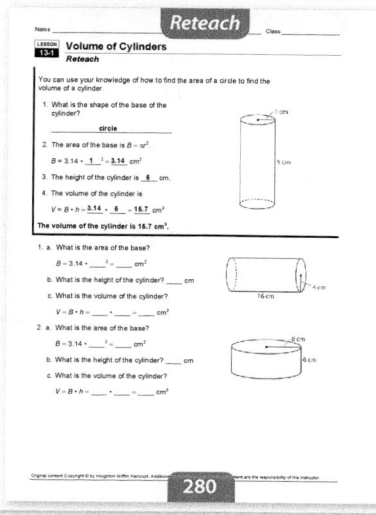

280

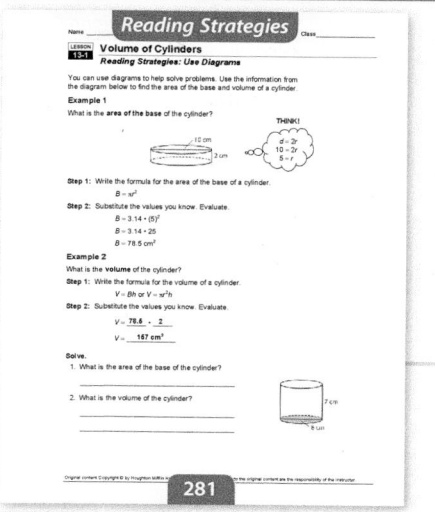

281

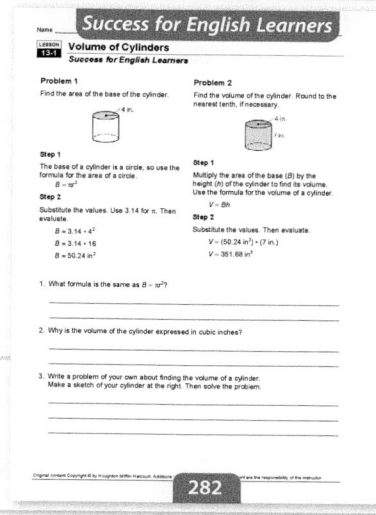

282

Personal Math Trainer
Daily Intervention
13.1 Homework

Pages shown are from *Differentiated Instruction*. **Also available online.**

Pressed for Time

13.1 Differentiated Homework Assignments

(AL) **Approaching Level**	6–13, 17–18	
(OL) **On Level**	10–17, 19	
(BL) **Beyond Level**	14–20	

*For **Below Level** students, assign Personal Math Trainer, Daily Intervention 13.1 Homework.*

Mathematical Processes	Exercises
MP.3 Logic	18, 20
MP.4 Modeling	12–17
MP.5 Using Tools	6–11
MP.6 Precision	19

Focus on Higher Order Thinking

Depth of Knowledge	Exercises
2 Skills/Concepts	6–17
3 Strategic Thinking H.O.T.	18–20

Name_____ Class_____ Date_____

13.1 Independent Practice

Personal Math Trainer
Online Assessment and Intervention
my.hrw.com

Find the volume of each figure. Round your answers to the nearest tenth if necessary. Use 3.14 for π.

6.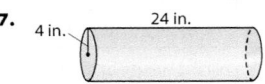
1.5 cm — 11 cm

569.9 cm³

7. 4 in. — 24 in.

1205.8 in³

8.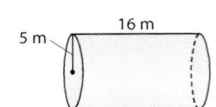
5 m — 16 m

1256 m³

9.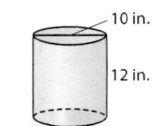
10 in. — 12 in.

942 in³

10. A cylinder has a radius of 4 centimeters and a height of 40 centimeters.

2009.6 cm³

11. A cylinder has a radius of 8 meters and a height of 4 meters.

803.8 m³

Round your answer to the nearest tenth, if necessary. Use 3.14 for π.

12. The cylindrical Giant Ocean Tank at the New England Aquarium in Boston is 24 feet deep and has a radius of 18.8 feet. Find the volume of the tank.

26,635.2 ft³

13. A standard-size bass drum has a diameter of 22 inches and is 18 inches deep. Find the volume of this drum.

6838.9 in³

14. Grain is stored in cylindrical structures called silos. Find the volume of a silo with a diameter of 11.1 feet and a height of 20 feet.

1934.4 ft³

15. The Frank Erwin Center, or "The Drum," at the University of Texas in Austin can be approximated by a cylinder that is 120 meters in diameter and 30 meters in height. Find its volume.

339,120 m³

© Houghton Mifflin Harcourt Publishing Company • Image Credits: ©Tim Laman / National Geographic/Getty Images

Lesson 13.1 **403**

DIFFERENTIATE INSTRUCTION *Leveled Homework/Practice*

Personal Math Trainer
• 13.1 Homework

Pages shown are from *Differentiated Instruction.* **Also available online.**

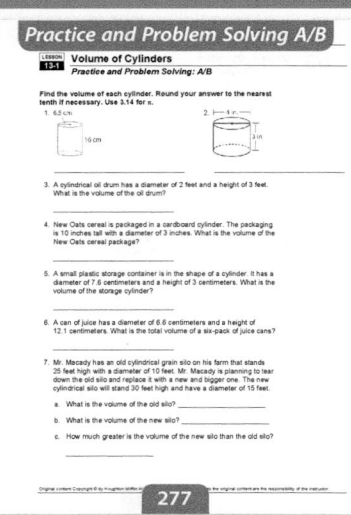

Practice and Problem Solving: A/B

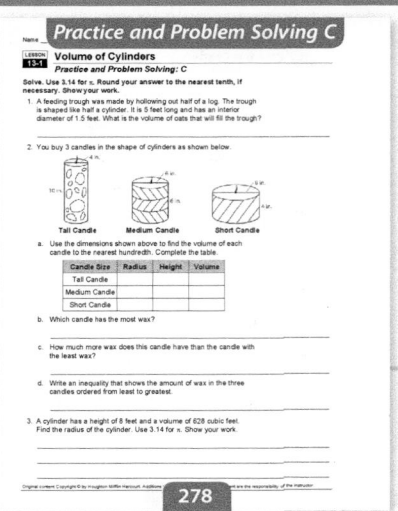

Practice and Problem Solving: C

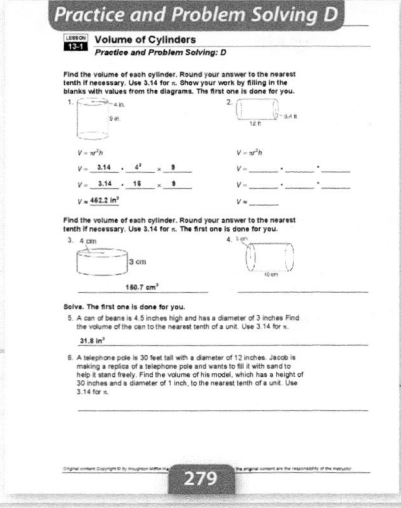

Practice and Problem Solving: D

16. A barrel of crude oil contains about 5.61 cubic feet of oil. How many barrels of oil are contained in 1 mile (5280 feet) of a pipeline that has an inside diameter of 6 inches and is completely filled with oil? How much is "1 mile" of oil in this pipeline worth at a price of $100 per barrel?

184.7 barrels; $18,470

17. A pan for baking French bread is shaped like half a cylinder. It is 12 inches long and 3.5 inches in diameter. What is the volume of uncooked dough that would fill this pan?

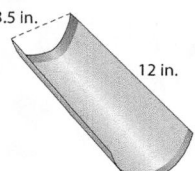
3.5 in.
12 in.

57.7 in³

 **FOCUS ON HIGHER ORDER THINKING**

18. **Explain the Error** A student said the volume of a cylinder with a 3-inch diameter is two times the volume of a cylinder with the same height and a 1.5-inch radius. What is the error?

Sample answer: The volumes are equal because a
cylinder with a 3-inch diameter has a 1.5-inch radius.

19. **Communicate Mathematical Ideas** Explain how you can find the height of a cylinder if you know the diameter and the volume. Include an example with your explanation.

Divide the diameter by 2 to find the radius. Then
substitute the volume and radius in $V = \pi r^2 h$ and
solve for h. Sample example: For a cylinder with
volume 72 m³ and a diameter of 6 m, $72 = \pi \cdot 3^2 h$,
so $h = \frac{72}{9\pi} = \frac{8}{\pi} \approx 2.5$ m.

20. **Analyze Relationships** Cylinder A has a radius of 6 centimeters. Cylinder B has the same height and a radius half as long as cylinder A. What fraction of the volume of cylinder A is the volume of cylinder B? Explain.

$\frac{1}{4}$; for any height h, cylinder A has a volume of $36\pi \cdot h$.
Cylinder B has a volume of $9\pi \cdot h$. Since 9 is $\frac{1}{4}$ of 36, the
volume of cylinder B is $\frac{1}{4}$ the volume of cylinder A.

Work Area

© Houghton Mifflin Harcourt Publishing Company

 Quick Check

13.1 Lesson Quiz

Use 3.14 for π. Round answers to the nearest tenth if necessary.

1. A can of chili has a radius of 5.25 cm and a height of 13 cm. Find the volume. 1125.1 cm³

2. A cylindrical carton of oatmeal has a diameter of 13 cm and is 24 cm tall. Find the volume. 3184.0 cm³

3. Which has a greater volume?
    Cylinder A: $r = 3$ m, $h = 1.2$ m
    Cylinder B: $d = 4$ m, $h = 2.5$ m Cylinder A

4. Daren uses rice to fill a cylindrical glass measuring 6 inches high with a radius of 2.5 inches. He pours this rice into a cardboard cylinder that is 3.5 inches high with a diameter of 8 inches. Will he have enough rice to fill the cardboard cylinder? Explain. The glass has a volume of 117.75 in³. The cardboard cylinder has a volume of 175.84 in³. He will not have enough rice to fill the cardboard cylinder, since 117.75 in³ is less than 175.84 in³.

Differentiate Instruction

IF a student misses more than one question, THEN

Differentiate Instruction:
- 13.1 Reteach
- Personal Math Trainer

Interactive Whiteboard
Interactive Lesson quiz available online

DIFFERENTIATE INSTRUCTION *Extend-the-Math Activity* **PRE-AP**

Activity When a three-dimensional figure and a plane intersect, the intersection is called a cross section. A three-dimensional figure can have many different cross sections. For example, when you cut a cylinder in half, the cross section that is exposed depends on the direction of the cut. Have students explore the cross sections of a right circular cylinder, either by using drawings or making a cylinder of clay or plastic foam, and cutting it in various ways to form a rectangle, a circle, or an ellipse (oval). Students may also obtain a partial ellipse if the cut enters the side and exits through a base.

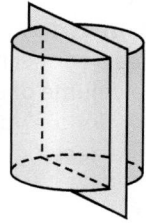

Lesson Support

Content Objective Students will learn how to find the volume of a cone.

Professional Development

Integrate Mathematical Processes MP.4

This lesson provides an opportunity to address this Mathematical Processes standard. It calls for students to model with mathematics. Students use models to explore the relationship between the volume of a cone and a cylinder with congruent bases and heights. They use this activity to write a rule for the volume of a cone.

FOCUS

Building Background

Connecting to Everyday Life Ask students to describe what comes to mind when they hear the word *cone*. Many students may first think of an ice cream cone. Encourage students to list as many other examples of cones as possible. Examples include volcanoes, traffic cones, and cones used in sports drills. Discuss properties of the shapes that allow students to identify them as cones.

COHERENCE

Learning Progressions

In this lesson, students find the volume of a cone. They explore volume of a cone with popcorn kernels and then generalize their findings to develop a formula for the volume of a cone. Important understandings for students include the following:

- **Model the volume of a cone.**
- **Find the volume of a cone using a formula.**
- **Find the volume of a cone in a real-world context.**

Cones follow in a logical progression after cylinders in the mathematical study of solids with curved surfaces. While the relationship may not be intuitive, students may see a connection between the formula for the volume of a cone and the formula not only for the volume of a cylinder but also for a rectangular prism.

RIGOR

Cluster Connections

This lesson provides an excellent opportunity to connect ideas in this cluster:

Solve real-world and mathematical problems involving volumes of cylinders, cones, and spheres.

Tell students that a party favor is made by joining two cones to the bases of a cylinder. The cylinder is 6 centimeters long and has a diameter of 4 centimeters. Each cone has a height of 3 centimeters. Ask students to find the volume of the party favor to the nearest tenth.

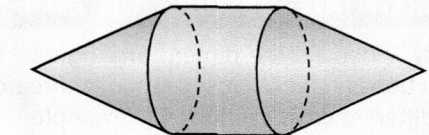

100.5 cm³

Language Support ELL

Language Objective Students will demonstrate how to find the volume of a cone.

Leveled Strategies for English Learners ELL

Emerging
Have students at this level of English proficiency work in pairs to copy the formula for the volume of a cone and then complete the Your Turn exercises for Example 1 together.

Expanding
Have students at this level of English proficiency work in pairs to copy the formula for the volume of a cone and then complete the first four exercises in the Guided Practice together.

Bridging
Have students at this level of English proficiency work in pairs to copy the formula for the volume of a cone and then discuss and solve exercises in the Independent Practice.

 **Math Talk**

Provide a sentence frame to help students answer the Reflect question in Example 1.

Because the diameter d is equal to _____, the formula can be rewritten as V = _____ .

Volume of a Cone

The volume V of a cone with radius r is one third the area of the base B times the height h.

$$V = \frac{1}{3} Bh \text{ or } V = \frac{1}{3} \pi r^2 h$$

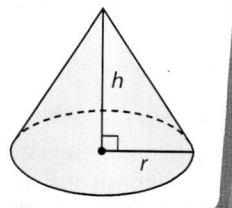

Linguistic Support ELL

Academic/Content Vocabulary
This lesson on the volume of cones relies on students' understanding of the definition of a cone—a three-dimensional figure that has one vertex and one circular base. It might help students to remember that the vertex is the point at the top of the cone. For Spanish-speaking English learners, it may help to know that the words *circular* and *cone* are cognates: *circular* and *cono*. Have students add these terms to their word journals.

Building Background
In the Guided Practice, a building is described as *cone-shaped*. Adding *-shaped* to the end of a word provides information about its form. For example, *a U-shaped driveway* provides a clear visual of what the driveway looks like. Everyday examples students may recognize are *heart-shaped*, *crescent-shaped*, and *pear-shaped*.

One of the exercises in the Guided Practice refers to waffle cones. Point out to English learners that, in addition to the breakfast item, the word *waffle* can also be a verb that means "to act evasively."

Image Credits: ©Jane Cocoa/Fotolia

Volume of Cones

1 Engage

ESSENTIAL QUESTION

How do you find the volume of a cone? Sample answer: Find one-third of the product of the area of the circular base and the height of the cone.

Motivate the Lesson

Ask: If you had a paper cone and paper cylinder with the same base and height, which would hold more popcorn? How much more? Begin the Explore Activity to find out.

2 Explore

EXPLORE ACTIVITY

Avoid Common Errors
Some students may try to measure the height of a cone from the vertex to a point on the circumference of the base, which is the slant height. Point out that the height is a segment perpendicular to the base from the vertex to the center of the circular base.

ESSENTIAL QUESTION

How do you find the volume of a cone?

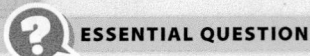

EXPLORE ACTIVITY

Modeling the Volume of a Cone

A **cone** is a three-dimensional figure that has one vertex and one circular base.

To explore the volume of a cone, Sandi does an experiment with a cone and a cylinder that have congruent bases and heights. She fills the cone with popcorn kernels and then pours the kernels into the cylinder. She repeats this until the cylinder is full.

Sandi finds that it takes 3 cones to fill the volume of the cylinder.

STEP 1 What is the formula for the volume V of a cylinder with base area B and height h? ____$V = Bh$____

STEP 2 What is the area of the base of the cone? ____B, or πr^2____

STEP 3 Sandi found that, when the bases and height are the same,

____3____ times $V_{cone} = V_{cylinder}$.

STEP 4 How does the volume of the cone compare to the volume of the cylinder?

Volume of the cone: $V_{cone} = \dfrac{1}{3} \cdot V_{cylinder}$

Reflect

1. Use the conclusion from this experiment to write a formula for the volume of a cone in terms of the height and the radius. Explain.
$V_{cylinder} = \pi r^2 h$, so $V_{cone} = \frac{1}{3}\pi r^2 h$

2. How do you think the formula for the volume of a cone is similar to the formula for the volume of a pyramid?
Both are one third the area of the base times the height.

Lesson 13.2 **405**

© Houghton Mifflin Harcourt Publishing Company

DIFFERENTIATE INSTRUCTION *Leveled Questions*

	EXPLORE ACTIVITY
AL DOK 1 *Recall*	Compare the volume of a cylinder and a cone with congruent bases and heights. Which is greater? the volume of the cylinder
OL DOK 2 *Skills/Concepts*	Is the distance along the surface of the cone from its base to its tip the height of the cone? Explain. No; the height is the perpendicular distance from the tip of the cone to its base.
BL DOK 3 *Strategic Thinking*	In the Activity, if you used a cone with a base congruent to that of the cylinder, how tall would the cone need to be in order to fill the entire cylinder? Explain. 3 times the cylinder's height; in the formula for the volume of the cone, if you replace the height h by 3 times the height, or $3h$, and simplify, you get the formula for the cylinder's volume.

LEVELED QUESTIONS: AL Approaching Level | OL On Level | BL Beyond Level

Math On the Spot
my.hrw.com

Finding the Volume of a Cone Using a Formula

The formulas for the volume of a prism and the volume of a cylinder are the same: multiply the height h by the area of the base B, so $V = Bh$.

In the **Explore Activity**, you saw that the volume of a cone is one third the volume of a cylinder with the same base and height.

Volume of a Cone

The volume V of a cone with radius r is one third the area of the base B times the height h.

$V = \frac{1}{3}Bh$ or $V = \frac{1}{3}\pi r^2 h$

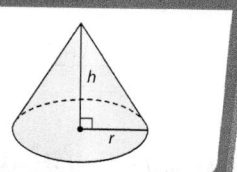

My Notes

EXAMPLE 1

Find the volume of each cone. Round your answers to the nearest tenth. Use 3.14 for π.

A

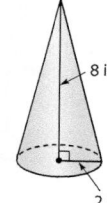

8 in.

2 in.

$V = \frac{1}{3}\pi r^2 h$

$\approx \frac{1}{3} \cdot 3.14 \cdot 2^2 \cdot 8$ Substitute.

$\approx \frac{1}{3} \cdot 3.14 \cdot 4 \cdot 8$ Simplify.

≈ 33.5 Multiply.

The volume is about 33.5 in³.

B Since the diameter is 8 ft, the radius is 4 ft.

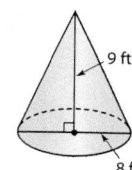

9 ft

8 ft

$V = \frac{1}{3}\pi r^2 h$

$\approx \frac{1}{3} \cdot 3.14 \cdot 4^2 \cdot 9$ Substitute.

$\approx \frac{1}{3} \cdot 3.14 \cdot 16 \cdot 9$ Simplify.

≈ 150.7 Multiply.

The volume is about 150.7 ft³.

Reflect

3. How can you rewrite the formula for the volume of a cone using the diameter d instead of the radius r?

$V = \frac{1}{3}\pi\left(\frac{d}{2}\right)^2 h$

© Houghton Mifflin Harcourt Publishing Company

	EXAMPLE 1
AL **DOK 1** *Recall*	In the formula for the volume of a cone, what is the approximate value of the product of constant (not variable) factors? The constant factors in $V = \frac{1}{3}\pi r^2 h$ are $\frac{1}{3}$ and π, and $\frac{1}{3} \cdot \pi = \frac{\pi}{3} \approx 1.047$ or about 1.
OL **DOK 2** *Skills/Concepts*	In Part B, how would the volume change if you switched the diameter and the height measurements? It would increase from about 151 ft³ to about 170 ft³.
BL **DOK 3** *Strategic Thinking*	Tripling the radius of a cylinder increases its volume by a factor of $3^2 = 9$. Is this same relationship true for a cone? Explain. Yes, for a cone, like a cylinder, the factor for the radius in the formula is r^2. Since changing the radius doesn't change anything else in the formula, the result of tripling the radius is the same.

3 Explain

EXAMPLE 1

ADDITIONAL EXAMPLE 1
Find the volume of each cone. Round your answers to the nearest tenth. Use 3.14 for π.

A

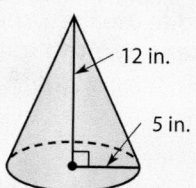

12 in.

5 in.

314 in³

B

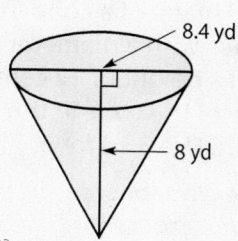

8.4 yd

8 yd

147.7 yd³

Interactive Whiteboard
Interactive example available online

Avoid Common Errors
If students use a calculator, remind them to enter 3.14 instead of using the π key.

TEACHER TO TEACHER

Cognitive Strategies Show students that a cone is constructed very much like a pyramid. A pyramid has a *polygon* base, and a cylinder has a *circular* base. Both the height of a pyramid and the height of a cone are measured from the center of the base to its vertex. Both the volume of a pyramid and the volume of a cone are found by multiplying $\frac{1}{3}$ the base area and the height.

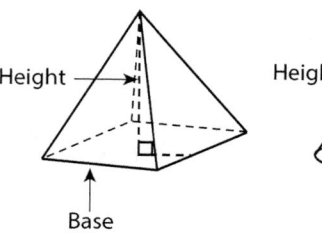

Height   Height

Base   Base

Focus on Technology

Discuss the use of the π key if the instruction to use 3.14 were not given. Have students consider how much error is introduced by using 3.14 for π. Remind students that π is irrational, and even the value used by the calculator is inexact. When students are expected to use the π key, they will still need to round the answer to a specified precision.

EXAMPLE 2

ADDITIONAL EXAMPLE 2 A model of a volcano is in the shape of a cone. The model has a circular base with a diameter of 48 centimeters and a height of 12 centimeters. Find the volume of the cone in the model to the nearest tenth. Use 3.14 for π. 7234.6 cm³

 Interactive Whiteboard
Interactive example available online

YOUR TURN MP.6

Avoid Common Errors

Students may get arithmetic errors when calculating with large numbers. Before they solve the problem, have them estimate the answer. The radius is about 200 meters, so the radius squared is about 40,000 m². Multiplying this value by the height, which is about 400 meters, gives 16,000,000 m³. Multiplying by π and then multiplying by $\frac{1}{3}$ roughly cancel out. Since all the measurements in this estimate were rounded down, the volume should be larger than but within two-fold of 16,000,000 m³.

Digital Teacher Resources

Go online to access all your lesson-level resources.

Differentiated Instruction
• Reteach
• Reading Strategies
• Success for English Learners
• Practice and Problem Solving A/B, C, D

Math on the Spot Videos

my.hrw.com

YOUR TURN

Find the volume of each cone. Round your answers to the nearest tenth. Use 3.14 for π.

4.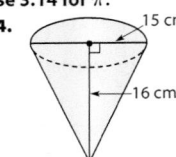
15 cm
16 cm

5.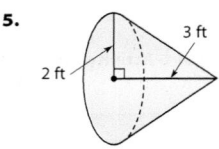
3 ft
2 ft

942 cm³ _____   12.6 ft³ _____

Personal Math Trainer
Online Assessment and Intervention
my.hrw.com

Finding the Volume of a Volcano

The mountain created by a volcano is often cone-shaped.

 EXAMPLE 2 Real World

For her geography project, Karen built a clay model of a volcano in the shape of a cone. Her model has a diameter of 12 inches and a height of 8 inches. Find the volume of clay in her model to the nearest tenth. Use 3.14 for π.

STEP 1 Find the radius.
$$r = \frac{12}{2} = 6 \text{ in.}$$

STEP 2 Find the volume of clay.
$$V = \frac{1}{3}\pi r^2 h$$
$$\approx \frac{1}{3} \cdot 3.14 \cdot 6^2 \cdot 8 \qquad \text{Substitute.}$$
$$\approx \frac{1}{3} \cdot 3.14 \cdot 36 \cdot 8 \qquad \text{Simplify.}$$
$$\approx 301.44 \qquad \text{Multiply.}$$

The volume of the clay is about 301.4 in³.

© Houghton Mifflin Harcourt Publishing Company • Image Credits: ©Marco Regalia Sell/Alamy Images

YOUR TURN

6. The cone of the volcano Parícutin in Mexico had a height of 410 meters and a diameter of 424 meters. Approximate the volume of the cone.
about 19,286,968.5 m³ _____

Personal Math Trainer
Online Assessment and Intervention
my.hrw.com

DIFFERENTIATE INSTRUCTION *Leveled Questions*

	EXAMPLE 2
AL DOK 1 *Recall*	What is the first step? Why? Divide 12 by 2; to get the radius
OL DOK 2 *Skills/Concepts*	Mayon Volcano in the Philippines has a base diameter of about 12 miles and a height of about $1\frac{1}{2}$ miles. What is its volume to the nearest 10 cubic miles? 60 cubic miles
BL DOK 3 *Strategic Thinking*	If Karen's model were scaled down by a factor of $\frac{1}{2}$, how would its volume compare to the one in the example? Explain. It would have $\frac{1}{8}$ the volume. If it is scaled down by a scale factor of $\frac{1}{2}$, then both h and r are divided by 2: $V_{\text{smaller}} = \frac{1}{3}\pi\left(\frac{r}{2}\right)^2\left(\frac{h}{2}\right) = \frac{1}{24}\pi r^2 h$

LEVELED QUESTIONS: AL Approaching Level | OL On Level | BL Beyond Level

1. The area of the base of a cylinder is 45 square inches and its height is 10 inches. A cone has the same area for its base and the same height. What is the volume of the cone? (Explore Activity)

$$V_{cylinder} = Bh = \boxed{45} \cdot \boxed{10} = \boxed{450}$$

$$V_{cone} = \frac{1}{3} V_{cylinder}$$

$$= \frac{1}{3} \boxed{450}$$

$$= \boxed{150}$$

The volume of the cone is ___150___ in³.

2. A cone and a cylinder have congruent height and bases. The volume of the cone is 18 m³. What is the volume of the cylinder? Explain. (Explore Activity)

54 m³; the volume of a cylinder is 3 times the volume of a cone with a congruent base and height.

Find the volume of each cone. Round your answer to the nearest tenth if necessary. Use 3.14 for π. (Example 1)

3.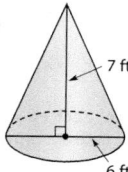

7 ft
6 ft

___65.9 ft³___

4.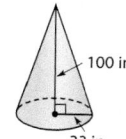

100 in.
33 in.

___113,982 in³___

5. Gretchen made a paper cone to hold a gift for a friend. The paper cone was 15 inches high and had a radius of 3 inches. Find the volume of the paper cone to the nearest tenth. Use 3.14 for π. (Example 2)

___141.3 in³___

6. A cone-shaped building is commonly used to store sand. What would be the volume of a cone-shaped building with a diameter of 50 meters and a height of 20 meters? Round your answer to the nearest tenth. Use 3.14 for π. (Example 2)

___13,083.3 m³___

 ESSENTIAL QUESTION CHECK-IN

7. How do you find the volume of a cone?

You can find one third of the volume of a cylinder with the same base and height, or you can use the formula $V = \frac{1}{3}\pi r^2 h$.

© Houghton Mifflin Harcourt Publishing Company

---

4 Elaborate

Talk About It

Summarize the Lesson

Ask: What step is similar when you find the volume of a cone, a cylinder, or a prism? You have to find the area of the base and multiply by the height. What do you think is the most important difference between a cone and a cylinder or prism when you need to find the volume? The volume for a cone is one-third of the product of the base area and height.

Guided Practice

Engage with the Whiteboard

Exercise 1 Have students draw both figures and label them. Note that they do not need to know the radius of the base for each figure because the base area is given.

Avoid Common Errors

Exercises 3–4 Have students, before they substitute or calculate, write the formula and write the value of the radius. This will help students who may use the diameter instead of the radius or who may forget to include the $\frac{1}{3}$ in the formula.

DIFFERENTIATE INSTRUCTION *Intervention and Additional Support*

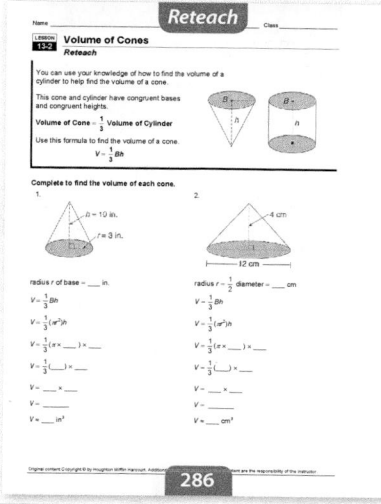

286

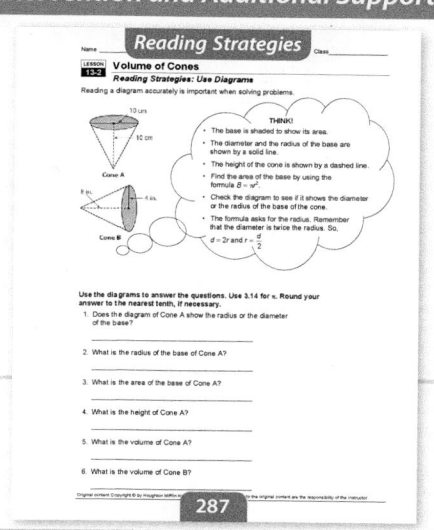

287

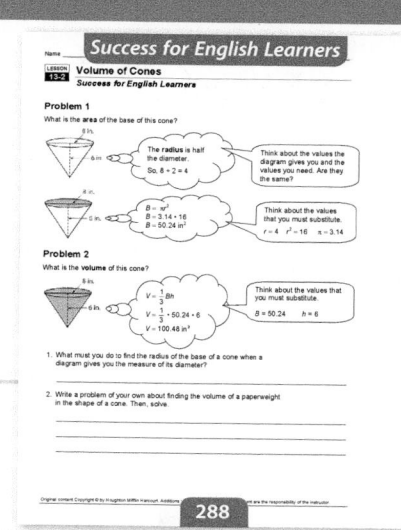

288

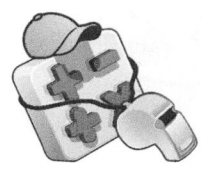

Personal Math Trainer
Daily Intervention
13.2 Homework

Pages shown are from *Differentiated Instruction.*
Also available online.

⏱ Pressed for Time

13.2 Differentiated Homework Assignments

AL Approaching Level	8–17, 20
OL On Level	12–18, 20–21
BL Beyond Level	14–17, 19–22

*For **Below Level** students, assign Personal Math Trainer, Daily Intervention 13.2 Homework.*

Mathematical Processes	Exercises
MP.2 Reasoning	16–18, 20
MP.3 Logic	19, 21–22
MP.4 Modeling	12–15
MP.5 Using Tools	8–11

Focus on Higher Order Thinking

Depth of Knowledge	Exercises
2 Skills/Concepts	8–18
3 Strategic Thinking H.O.T.	19–22

Personal Math Trainer
Online Assessment and Intervention
my.hrw.com

13.2 Independent Practice

Find the volume of each cone. Round your answers to the nearest tenth if necessary. Use 3.14 for π.

8.

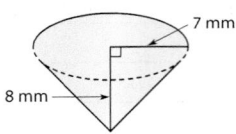

7 mm

8 mm

_____410.3 mm³_____

9.

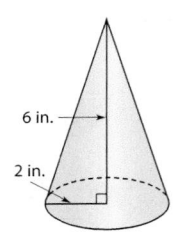

6 in.

2 in.

_____25.1 in³_____

10. A cone has a diameter of 6 centimeters and a height of 11.5 centimeters.

_____108.3 cm³_____

11. A cone has a radius of 3 meters and a height of 10 meters.

_____94.2 m³_____

Round your answers to the nearest tenth if necessary. Use 3.14 for π.

12. Antonio is making mini waffle cones. Each waffle cone is 3 inches high and has a radius of $\frac{3}{4}$ inch. What is the volume of a waffle cone?

_____1.8 in³_____

13. A snack bar sells popcorn in cone-shaped containers. One container has a diameter of 8 inches and a height of 10 inches. How many cubic inches of popcorn does the container hold?

_____167.5 in³_____

14. A volcanic cone has a diameter of 300 meters and a height of 150 meters. What is the volume of the cone?

_____3,532,500 m³_____

15. **Multistep** Orange traffic cones come in a variety of sizes. Approximate the volume, in cubic inches, of a traffic cone that has a height of 2 feet and a diameter of 10 inches. Use 3.14 for π.

_____628 in³_____

Find the missing measure for each cone. Round your answers to the nearest tenth if necessary. Use 3.14 for π.

16. radius = _____4 in._____

height = 6 in.

volume = 100.48 in³

17. diameter = 6 cm

height = _____6 cm_____

volume = 56.52 cm³

18. The diameter of a cone-shaped container is 4 inches, and its height is 6 inches. How much greater is the volume of a cylinder-shaped container with the same diameter and height? Round your answer to the nearest hundredth. Use 3.14 for π.

_____50.24 in³_____

© Houghton Mifflin Harcourt Publishing Company

DIFFERENTIATE INSTRUCTION *Leveled Homework/Practice*

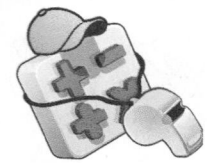

Personal Math Trainer
• 13.2 Homework

Pages shown are from *Differentiated Instruction.* **Also available online.**

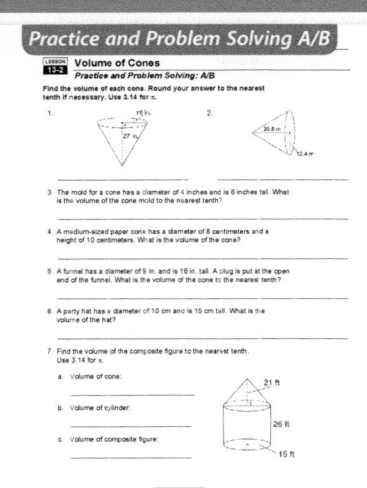
Practice and Problem Solving A/B — 283

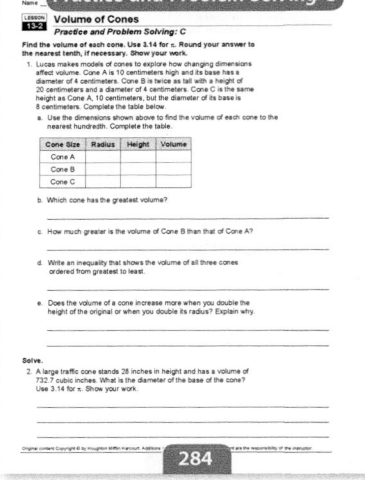
Practice and Problem Solving C — 284

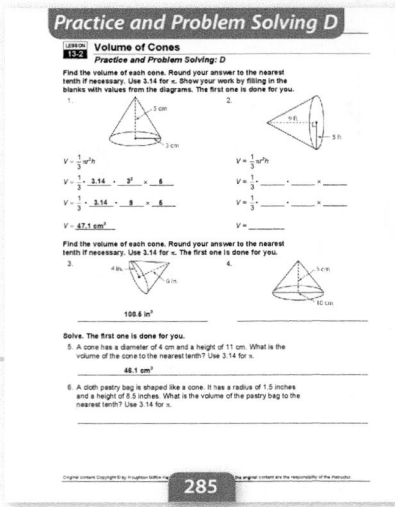
Practice and Problem Solving D — 285

Work Area

19. Alex wants to know the volume of sand in an hourglass. When all the sand is in the bottom, he stands a ruler up beside the hourglass and estimates the height of the cone of sand.

   a. What else does he need to measure to find the volume of sand?

   either the diameter or the radius
   of the base

   b. **Make a Conjecture** If the volume of sand is increasing at a constant rate, is the height increasing at a constant rate? Explain.

   No; the cone is tapered as it goes from top to bottom.
   An equal volume of sand has a smaller radius and a
   greater height as the sand rises.

20. **Problem Solving** The diameter of a cone is x cm, the height is 18 cm, and the volume is 301.44 cm³. What is x? Use 3.14 for π.

$$x = 8 \text{ cm}$$

21. **Analyze Relationships** A cone has a radius of 1 foot and a height of 2 feet. How many cones of liquid would it take to fill a cylinder with a diameter of 2 feet and a height of 2 feet? Explain.

   Since the radius and height of the cones and cylinder
   are the same, it will take 3 cones to equal the volume
   of the cylinder.

22. **Critique Reasoning** Herb knows that the volume of a cone is one third that of a cylinder with the same base and height. He reasons that a cone with the same height as a given cylinder but 3 times the radius should therefore have the same volume as the cylinder, since $\frac{1}{3} \cdot 3 = 1$. Is Herb correct? Explain.

   No; the volume of the cone will be 3 times that of the
   cylinder because the radius is squared in the formula.
   For example, for a cylinder with radius 1 and height 5,
   $V = \pi (1)^2(5) = 5\pi$. For a cone with radius 3 and height 5,
   $V = \frac{1}{3}\pi (3)^2(5) = 15\pi$, or 3 times as much.

© Houghton Mifflin Harcourt Publishing Company

DIFFERENTIATE INSTRUCTION *Extend-the-Math Activity* **PRE-AP**

Activity The activity in the previous lesson explored the cross sections formed when a plane intersects a cylinder. The three shapes that can be obtained are a rectangle, a circle, and an ellipse.

Have students explore the cross sections of a right circular cone, either by using drawings or making a cone of clay or plastic foam, and cutting it in various ways. What two cross sections of a cylinder can also be obtained from a cone? circle, ellipse What shape cannot be obtained? rectangle What is the new shape obtained if the cut is through the vertex and perpendicular to the base? triangle Students will also find that they can generate curved shapes that are either parabolas or hyperbolas. Collectively, these cross sections are known as the *conic sections*.

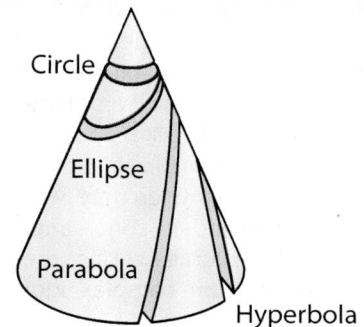

Circle

Ellipse

Parabola

Hyperbola

✔ Quick Check

13.2 Lesson Quiz

Round your answers to the nearest tenth if needed. Use 3.14 for π.

1. The volume of a cone is 20 cm³. What is the volume of a cylinder with the same base and height? 60 cm³

2. Find the volume of the cone. 78.5 in³

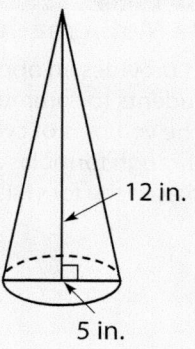

12 in.

5 in.

3. Find the volume of a cone with a radius of 20 inches and a height of 25 inches. 10,466.7 in³

4. A paper cup in the shape of a cone has a diameter of 6 centimeters and is 7 centimeters high. Ken needs to add about 264 cm³ of water to his plaster mixture. How many paper cups of water will he need to use? 4 cups

---

Differentiate Instruction

IF a student misses more than one question, THEN

Differentiate Instruction:

- 13.2 Reteach
- Personal Math Trainer

Interactive Whiteboard
Interactive Lesson quiz available online

Lesson Support

Content Objective Students will learn how to find the volume of a sphere.

Professional Development

Integrate Mathematical Processes MP.6

This lesson provides an opportunity to address this Mathematical Processes standard. It calls for students to communicate mathematics precisely. Students explore the relationship between the volumes of cylinders, cones, and spheres. Students learn to express the volumes through formulas and to explain the differences and similarities in the coefficients and variables in the formulas.

FOCUS

Building Background

Eliciting Prior Knowledge Ask students to describe a sphere in their own words. Discuss the relationship between a circle and a sphere. Elicit or point out that all cross sections of a sphere are circles and that all points on the surface of a sphere lie at the same distance, called the *radius*, from the center.

COHERENCE

Learning Progressions

In this lesson, students find the volume of a sphere. They begin the lesson by exploring the relationships among the volumes of a sphere, a cylinder, and a cone. Important understandings for students include the following:

- **Model the volume of a sphere.**
- **Find the volume of a sphere using a formula.**
- **Find the volume of a sphere in a real-world context.**

At the conclusion of this module students will have a solid foundation in the geometry of cylinders, cones, and spheres and in methods for finding their volumes, both in real-world and in numerical problem-solving situations. This will prepare students for more advanced work in solid geometry in later math courses, when they will find surface areas of cylinders, cones, and spheres, and the volumes, surface areas, and properties of more complex figures.

RIGOR

Cluster Connections

This lesson provides an excellent opportunity to connect ideas in this cluster:

Solve real-world and mathematical problems involving the volumes of cylinders, cones, and spheres.

Tell students that an ice cream shop has a model of an ice cream cone with a spherical scoop of ice cream on top of the cone. The diameter of the sphere and the cone is 6 inches. The cone is 9 inches tall. Ask students to find the volume of the ice cream cone model to the nearest tenth.

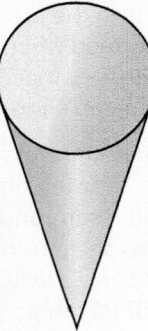

197.8 in³

Language Support ELL

Language Objective Students will demonstrate how to find the volume of a sphere.

Leveled Strategies for English Learners ELL

Emerging
Have students at this level of English proficiency work in pairs to copy the formula for the volume of a sphere and then read aloud the steps in Example 2 and calculate the volume of the soccer ball.

Expanding
Have students at this level of English proficiency work in pairs to list the steps necessary to calculate the volume of a sphere and then calculate the volume of a tennis ball and golf ball.

Bridging
Have students at this level of English proficiency work in pairs to discuss the steps necessary for calculating the volume of a sphere and then calculate the volume of a tennis ball, a baseball, and a basketball.

Write out and model for students a sentence frame to begin their answer.

The formula for the volume of a sphere with a known diameter would be written _____.

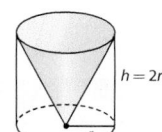 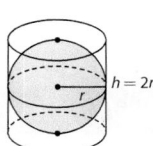

Linguistic Support ELL

Academic/Content Vocabulary
This lesson on the volume of spheres relies on students' understanding of the definition of a sphere—a three-dimensional figure with all points the same distance from the center. It might help students to remember examples of spheres, such as soccer balls and basketballs. At this point in the module it is also important that students understand how spheres, cones, and cylinders relate to each other. Discuss this with English learners and have them add these formulas to their math journals.

Building Background
Word problems can help students recognize the value of learning math by connecting it to the world they live in. All students benefit from connecting what they already know to what they are learning. Although not critical for solving the word problems in the Independent Practice, learning the words *hummingbird*, *fossilized*, and *ostrich* will expand and further develop students' English language proficiency.

Image Credits: ©PhotoDisc/Getty Images

Volume of Spheres

1 Engage

❓ ESSENTIAL QUESTION

How do you find the volume of a sphere? Sample answer: Find the product of $\frac{4}{3}$, the cube of the radius, and π.

Motivate the Lesson

Ask: What are some sports that are played with a ball? What is the mathematical name for this shape? How can you find the volume of a ball? Begin the Explore Activity to find out.

2 Explore

EXPLORE ACTIVITY

Engage with the Whiteboard

Have a student use a red marker to circle the height for each figure (to emphasize that h is the same for each). Then have a student use a blue marker to circle the three radii.

❓ ESSENTIAL QUESTION

How do you find the volume of a sphere?

EXPLORE ACTIVITY

Modeling the Volume of a Sphere

A **sphere** is a three-dimensional figure with all points the same distance from the center. The **radius** of a sphere is the distance from the center to any point on the sphere.

You have seen that a cone fills $\frac{1}{3}$ of a cylinder of the same radius and height h. If you were to do a similar experiment with a sphere of the same radius, you would find that a sphere fills $\frac{2}{3}$ of the cylinder. The cylinder's height is equal to twice the radius of the sphere.

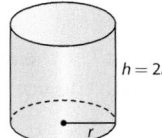 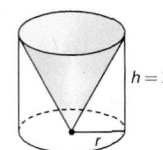 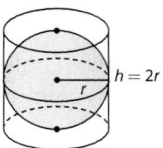

STEP 1 Write the formula $V = Bh$ for each shape. Use $B = \pi r^2$ and substitute the fractions you know for the cone and sphere.

Cylinder	Cone	Sphere
$V = \pi r^2 h$	$V = \frac{1}{3}\pi r^2 h$	$V = \frac{2}{3}\pi r^2 h$

STEP 2 Notice that a sphere always has a height equal to twice the radius. Substitute $2r$ for h.

$V = \frac{2}{3}\pi r^2(2r)$

STEP 3 Simplify this formula for the volume of a sphere. $V = \boxed{\frac{4}{3}}\pi r^3$

Reflect

1. **Analyze Relationships** A cone has a radius of r and a height of $2r$. A sphere has a radius of r. Compare the volume of the sphere and cone.

The cone's volume is $\frac{1}{3}$ of a cylinder with radius r and height

$2r$. The sphere's volume is $\frac{2}{3}$ of the volume of this cylinder.

So, the sphere's volume is twice the cone's volume.

© Houghton Mifflin Harcourt Publishing Company

DIFFERENTIATE INSTRUCTION *Leveled Questions*

	EXPLORE ACTIVITY
AL DOK 1 *Recall*	What dimensions do you need to know to find the volume of a sphere? the radius r
OL DOK 2 *Skills/Concepts*	A lab has 12 congruent cylindrical containers of a liquid. How many conical containers with the cylinder's height and diameter will the liquid fill? spherical containers with the cylinder's diameter? conical: 36; spherical: 18
BL DOK 3 *Strategic Thinking*	A cylinder contains two cones whose bases are the cylinder's top and bottom, and whose vertices meet at the cylinder's center. Compare the total volume of the two cones to the volume of the single largest cone that could fit in the cylinder. The cones take up $\frac{1}{3}$ of the total cylinder, which is the same volume taken up by the single largest cone.

LEVELED QUESTIONS: **AL** Approaching Level | **OL** On Level | **BL** Beyond Level

Math On the Spot
my.hrw.com

Finding the Volume of a Sphere Using a Formula

The Explore Activity illustrates a formula for the volume of a sphere with radius r.

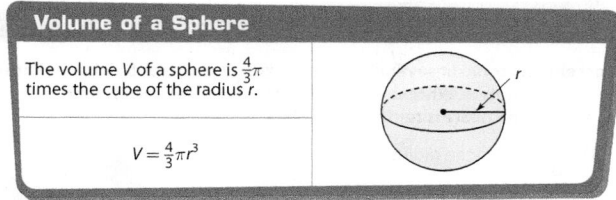

Volume of a Sphere

The volume V of a sphere is $\frac{4}{3}\pi$ times the cube of the radius r.

$$V = \frac{4}{3}\pi r^3$$

EXAMPLE 1

Find the volume of each sphere. Round your answers to the nearest tenth if necessary. Use 3.14 for π.

A

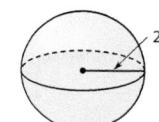

2.1 cm

$V = \frac{4}{3}\pi r^3$

$\approx \frac{4}{3} \cdot 3.14 \cdot 2.1^3$ Substitute.

$\approx \frac{4}{3} \cdot 3.14 \cdot 9.26$ Simplify.

≈ 38.8 Multiply.

The volume is about 38.8 cm³.

B

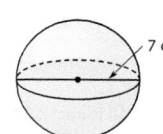

7 cm

Since the diameter is 7 cm, the radius is 3.5 cm.

$V = \frac{4}{3}\pi r^3$

$\approx \frac{4}{3} \cdot 3.14 \cdot 3.5^3$ Substitute.

$\approx \frac{4}{3} \cdot 3.14 \cdot 42.9$ Simplify.

≈ 179.6 Multiply.

The volume is about 179.6 cm³.

Math Talk
Mathematical Processes

If you know the diameter of a sphere, how would the formula for the volume of a sphere be written in terms of d?

$V = \frac{4}{3}\pi\left(\frac{d}{2}\right)^3$

YOUR TURN

Personal Math Trainer
Online Assessment and Intervention
my.hrw.com

Find the volume of each sphere. Round your answers to the nearest tenth. Use 3.14 for π.

2. A sphere has a radius of 10 centimeters. _____ 4186.7 cm³

3. A sphere has a diameter of 3.4 meters. _____ 20.6 m³

© Houghton Mifflin Harcourt Publishing Company

3 Explain

EXAMPLE 1

ADDITIONAL EXAMPLE 1
Find the volume of each sphere. Round your answers to the nearest tenth if necessary. Use 3.14 for π.

A

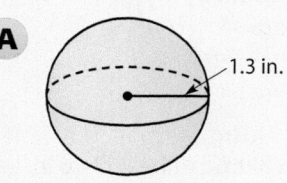

1.3 in.

9.2 in³

B

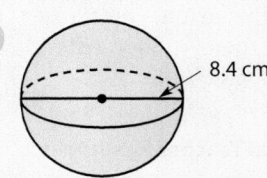

8.4 cm

310.2 cm³

 Interactive Whiteboard
Interactive example available online

YOUR TURN   MP.2

Avoid Common Errors
To avoid using the wrong value for the radius, have students circle the word *radius* or underline the word *diameter* twice in the problem before they substitute values.

TEACHER TO TEACHER

Modeling The volume of a hemisphere is exactly halfway between the volume of a cone and the volume of a cylinder, which both have the same radius r as the hemisphere and a height equal to r.

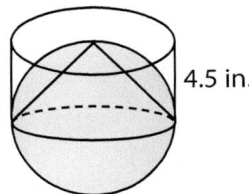

4.5 in.

The radius of a basketball is about 4.5 inches. To find the volume of a basketball, imagine the ball is sliced into two halves. Then find the volume of one half and multiply times 2.

	EXAMPLE 1
(AL) **DOK 1** *Recall*	How does Part B of the example differ from Part A? In Part B, you are given the diameter instead of the radius, so you must first find the radius.
(OL) **DOK 2** *Skills/Concepts*	Why is the "approximately equals" symbol used when calculating volume? The value for π used (3.14) is an approximation.
(BL) **DOK 3** *Strategic Thinking*	How can you rewrite the volume of a sphere formula so that the sphere's diameter is the input? Show your work. Substitute $\frac{d}{2}$ for r in the formula and then simplify to get $V = \frac{4}{3}\pi\left(\frac{d}{2}\right)^3 = \frac{4}{3}\pi\left(\frac{d^3}{8}\right) = \frac{1}{6}\pi d^3$

EXAMPLE 2

ADDITIONAL EXAMPLE 2 A steel ball bearing has a diameter of 1.6 centimeters. What is the volume of this steel ball? Round your answer to the nearest tenth if necessary. Use 3.14 for π.

2.1 cm³

Interactive Whiteboard
Interactive example available online

YOUR TURN   MP.3

Focus on Critical Thinking
One student found the volume to be 7234.6 in³ instead of the correct answer. Describe an error that might have led to this result. This answer could result from using the diameter instead of the radius to calculate the volume.

Digital Teacher Resources

Go online to access all your lesson-level resources.

Differentiated Instruction
• Reteach
• Reading Strategies
• Success for English Learners
• Practice and Problem Solving A/B, C, D

Math on the Spot Videos

my.hrw.com

Finding the Volume of a Sphere in a Real-World Context

Many sports, including golf and tennis, use a ball that is spherical in shape.

EXAMPLE 2   Real World

Soccer balls come in several different sizes. One soccer ball has a diameter of 22 centimeters. What is the volume of this soccer ball? Round your answer to the nearest tenth. Use 3.14 for π.

STEP 1 Find the radius.

$$r = \frac{d}{2} = 11 \text{ cm}$$

STEP 2 Find the volume of the soccer ball.

$$V = \frac{4}{3}\pi r^3$$
$$\approx \frac{4}{3} \cdot 3.14 \cdot 11^3 \qquad \text{Substitute.}$$
$$\approx \frac{4}{3} \cdot 3.14 \cdot 1331 \qquad \text{Simplify.}$$
$$\approx 5572.4533 \qquad \text{Multiply.}$$

The volume of the soccer ball is about 5572.5 cm³.

Reflect

4. What is the volume of the soccer ball in terms of π, to the nearest whole number multiple? Explain your answer.
   1,775π; Sample answer: I multiplied $\frac{4}{3}$ and 11^3 and rounded.

5. **Analyze Relationships** The diameter of a basketball is about 1.1 times that of a soccer ball. The diameter of a tennis ball is about 0.3 times that of a soccer ball. How do the volumes of these balls compare to that of a soccer ball? Explain.
   Basketball: about 1.3 times as big; tennis ball: about 0.03 times as big. The radius is cubed in the formula, so compared to the soccer ball, $1.1^3 \approx 1.3$, and $0.3^3 \approx 0.03$.

© Houghton Mifflin Harcourt Publishing Company • Image Credits: ©PhotoDisc/Getty Images

 **YOUR TURN**

6. Val measures the diameter of a ball as 12 inches. How many cubic inches of air does this ball hold, to the nearest tenth? Use 3.14 for π.
   904.3 in³

Personal Math Trainer
Online Assessment and Intervention
my.hrw.com

DIFFERENTIATE INSTRUCTION *Leveled Questions*

	EXAMPLE 2
(AL) DOK 1 *Recall*	What is the exact volume in this example? $\frac{4}{3}\pi(11)^3 = \frac{11^3 \cdot 4}{3}\pi = 1774\frac{2}{3}\pi$ cm³
(OL) DOK 2 *Skills/Concepts*	Official volleyballs can vary from 8.15 to 8.39 inches in diameter. What is the difference in the largest and smallest possible volumes to the nearest cubic inch? 26 in³
(BL) DOK 3 *Strategic Thinking*	Sierra accidentally used the diameter of the soccer ball when she used her calculator to work the example. What can she do to the result to find the correct volume? Explain. Divide it by 8; she used $(2r)^3 = 8r^3$ instead of r^3.

1. Vocabulary A sphere is a three-dimensional figure with all points <u>the same distance</u> from the center. (Explore Activity)

2. Vocabulary The <u>radius</u> is the distance from the center of a sphere to a point on the sphere. (Explore Activity)

Find the volume of each sphere. Round your answers to the nearest tenth if necessary. Use 3.14 for π. (Example 1)

3.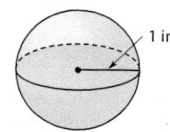
1 in.

<u>4.2 in³</u>

4.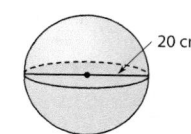
20 cm

<u>4,186.7 cm³</u>

5. A sphere has a radius of 1.5 feet. <u>14.1 ft³</u>

6. A sphere has a diameter of 2 yards. <u>4.2 yd³</u>

7. A baseball has a diameter of 2.9 inches. Find the volume of the baseball. Round your answer to the nearest tenth if necessary. Use 3.14 for π. (Example 2) <u>12.8 in³</u>

8. A basketball has a radius of 4.7 inches. What is its volume to the nearest cubic inch. Use 3.14 for π. (Example 2) <u>435 in³</u>

9. A company is deciding whether to package a ball in a cubic box or a cylindrical box. In either case, the ball will touch the bottom, top, and sides. (Explore Activity)

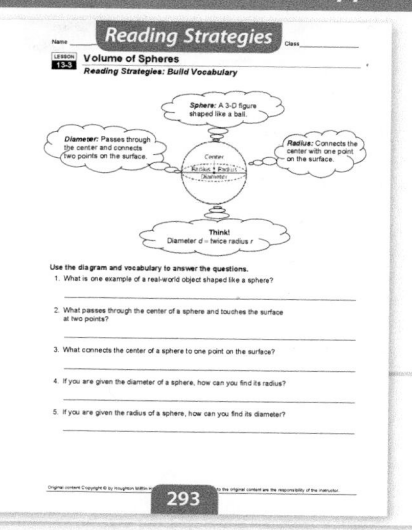 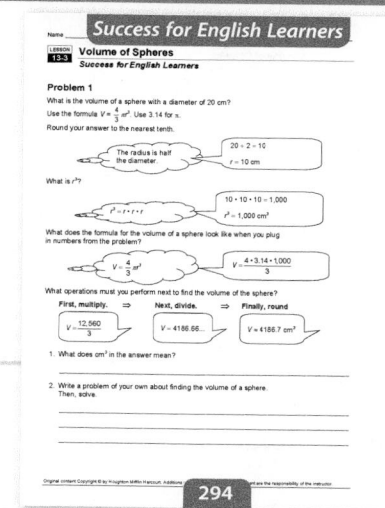

a. What portion of the space inside the cylindrical box is empty? Explain.
<u>$\frac{1}{3}$; the ball takes up $\frac{2}{3}$ of the space, so $\frac{1}{3}$ is empty.</u>

b. Find an expression for the volume of the cubic box. <u>$(2r)^3 = 8r^3$</u>

c. About what portion of the space inside the cubic box is empty? Explain.
<u>Almost $\frac{1}{2}$; the empty space is $8r^3 - \left(\frac{4}{3}\right)\pi r^3$, or about $3.81r^3$, and $\frac{3.81}{8} \approx 0.48$.</u>

? ESSENTIAL QUESTION CHECK-IN

10. Explain the steps you use to find the volume of a sphere.
<u>Find the radius. Then substitute r into the formula $V = \frac{4}{3}\pi r^3$ and simplify.</u>

© Houghton Mifflin Harcourt Publishing Company

4 Elaborate

Talk About It

Summarize the Lesson

Ask: What do you need to know about a sphere to be able to calculate its volume?
You need to know the radius or be able to determine the radius from the diameter.

Guided Practice

Engage with the Whiteboard

In **Exercises 5–8**, draw diagrams of the spheres and label the diameter or radius as appropriate.

Avoid Common Errors

Exercises 4, 6, 8 Remind students to pay attention to the measurement they are given. If they are given the diameter, they must divide it by 2 to find the radius before using the volume formula.

DIFFERENTIATE INSTRUCTION *Intervention and Additional Support*

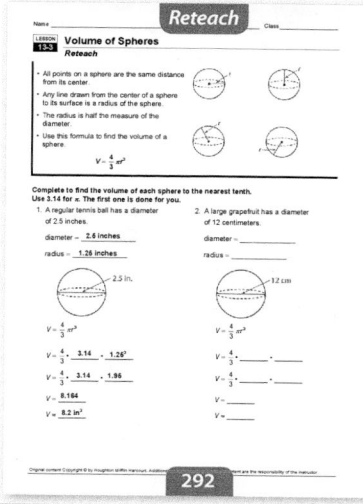

Personal Math Trainer
Daily Intervention
13.3 Homework

Pages shown are from *Differentiated Instruction.*
Also available online.

Pressed for Time

13.3 Differentiated Homework Assignments

AL Approaching Level	11–20
OL On Level	17–24
BL Beyond Level	20–27

*For **Below Level** students, assign Personal Math Trainer, Daily Intervention 13.3 Homework.*

Mathematical Processes	Exercises
MP.1 Problem Solving	20
MP.2 Reasoning	23, 26
MP.3 Logic	24, 27
MP.4 Modeling	17–19, 25
MP.5 Using Tools	11–16
MP.6 Precision	21
MP.7 Using Structure	22

Focus on Higher Order Thinking

Depth of Knowledge	Exercises
2 Skills/Concepts	11–19, 21, 23
3 Strategic Thinking **H.O.T.**	20, 22, 24–27

Name_____ Class_____ Date_____

Personal Math Trainer
Online Assessment and Intervention
my.hrw.com

13.3 Independent Practice

Find the volume of each sphere. Round your answers to the nearest tenth if necessary. Use 3.14 for π.

11. radius of 3.1 meters _____ 124.7 m³

12. diameter of 18 inches _____ 3,052.1 in³

13. $r = 6$ in. _____ 904.3 in³

14. $d = 36$ m _____ 24,416.6 m³

15.

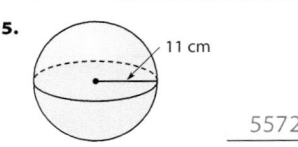
11 cm

_____ 5572.5 cm³

16.

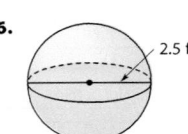
2.5 ft

_____ 8.2 ft³

The eggs of birds and other animals come in many different shapes and sizes. Eggs often have a shape that is nearly spherical. When this is true, you can use the formula for a sphere to find their volume.

17. The green turtle lays eggs that are approximately spherical with an average diameter of 4.5 centimeters. Each turtle lays an average of 113 eggs at one time. Find the total volume of these eggs, to the nearest cubic centimeter.

_____ 5389 cm³

18. Hummingbirds lay eggs that are nearly spherical and about 1 centimeter in diameter. Find the volume of an egg. Round your answer to the nearest tenth.

_____ 0.5 cm³

---

19. Fossilized spherical eggs of dinosaurs called titanosaurid sauropods were found in Patagonia. These eggs were 15 centimeters in diameter. Find the volume of an egg. Round your answer to the nearest tenth.

_____ 1766.3 cm³

20. **Persevere in Problem Solving** An ostrich egg has about the same volume as a sphere with a diameter of 5 inches. If the eggshell is about $\frac{1}{12}$ inch thick, find the volume of just the shell, not including the interior of the egg. Round your answer to the nearest tenth.

_____ 6.3 in³

21. **Multistep** Write the steps you would use to find a formula for the volume of the figure at right. Then write the formula.

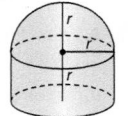

Find the volume of a sphere with radius r: $V = \frac{4}{3}\pi r^3$. Divide by 2 to find the volume of the hemisphere: $V = \frac{2}{3}\pi r^3$. Find the volume of the cylinder: $V = \pi r^2 h = \pi r^3$. Note that $h = r$. Add the volume of the hemisphere and the volume of the cylinder: $V = \frac{2}{3}\pi r^3 + \pi r^3 = \frac{5}{3}\pi r^3$.

© Houghton Mifflin Harcourt Publishing Company

DIFFERENTIATE INSTRUCTION *Leveled Homework/Practice*

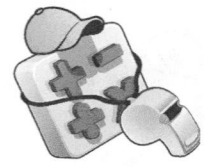

Personal Math Trainer
- 13.3 Homework

Pages shown are from *Differentiated Instruction.* **Also available online.**

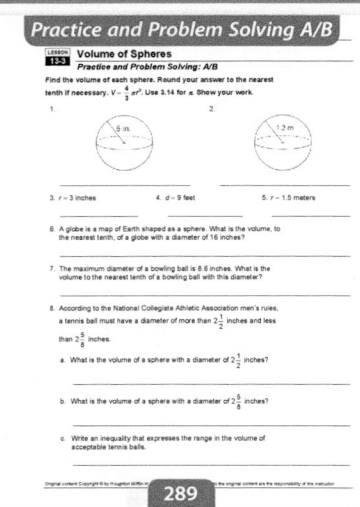

Practice and Problem Solving A/B

289

Practice and Problem Solving C

290

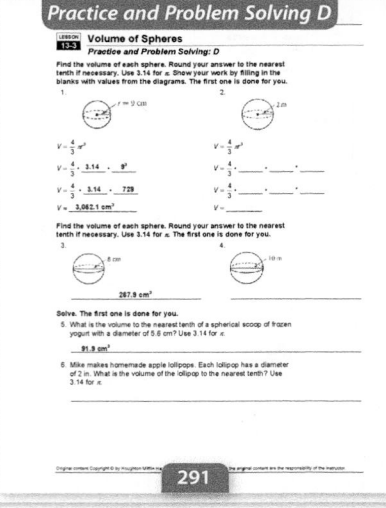

Practice and Problem Solving D

291

22. Critical Thinking Explain what happens to the volume of a sphere if you double the radius.

The volume is multiplied by 8 (or 2 cubed).

23. Multistep A cylindrical can of tennis balls holds a stack of three balls so that they touch the can at the top, bottom, and sides. The radius of each ball is 1.25 inches. Find the volume inside the can that is not taken up by the three tennis balls.

12.3 in³

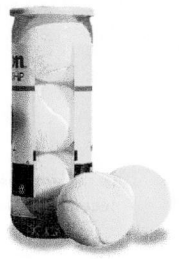

 **FOCUS ON HIGHER ORDER THINKING**

24. Critique Reasoning A sphere has a radius of 4 inches, and a cube-shaped box has an edge length of 7.5 inches. J.D. says the box has a greater volume, so the sphere will fit in the box. Is he correct? Explain.

No; the box has a greater volume, but it would need an edge length of 8 inches, the diameter of the sphere, for the sphere to fit inside the box.

25. Critical Thinking Which would hold the most water: a bowl in the shape of a hemisphere with radius r, a cylindrical glass with radius r and height r, or a cone-shaped drinking cup with radius r and height r? Explain.

The cylindrical glass; the cylinder has a volume of πr^3, while the hemisphere's volume is $\frac{2}{3}\pi r^3$, and the cone's volume is $\frac{1}{3}\pi r^3$.

26. Analyze Relationships Hari has models of a sphere, a cylinder, and a cone. The sphere's diameter and the cylinder's height are the same, $2r$. The cylinder has radius r. The cone has diameter $2r$ and height $2r$. Compare the volumes of the cone and the sphere to the volume of the cylinder.

The volume of the cone is one-sixth the volume of the cylinder. The volume of the sphere is two-thirds the volume of the cylinder.

27. A spherical helium balloon that is 8 feet in diameter can lift about 17 pounds. What does the diameter of a balloon need to be to lift a person who weighs 136 pounds? Explain.

About 16 feet; 136 is 8 times 17, so the volume must be 8 times as big. Because $2^3 = 8$, this means that the radius, and thus the diameter, must be twice as big.

Work Area

© Houghton Mifflin Harcourt Publishing Company

13.3 Lesson Quiz

Round your answers to the nearest tenth if necessary. Use 3.14 for π.

1. A ball fits exactly into a cylinder as shown in the figure. The volume of the cylinder is 30 cm³. What is the volume of the sphere? 20 cm³

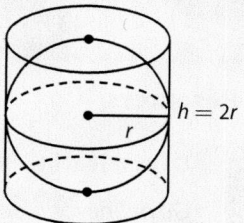

2. Find the volume of a sphere with a radius of 2.6 inches. 73.6 in³

3. Find the volume of a sphere with a diameter of 8.2 meters. 288.5 m³

4. Jen has a silver charm on her bracelet in the shape of a soccer ball with a radius of 1 centimeter. What is the volume of this charm? 4.2 cm³

5. A ball has a diameter of 12 inches. What is the volume of the ball? 904.3 in³

Differentiate Instruction

IF a student misses more than one question, THEN

Differentiate Instruction:

• 13.3 Reteach
• Personal Math Trainer

 Interactive Whiteboard
Interactive Lesson quiz available online

DIFFERENTIATE INSTRUCTION *Extend-the-Math Activity* **PRE-AP**

Activity Use a sphere of clay or plastic foam, and intersect, or cut, it with a plane passing through the center of the sphere. The cross section formed is a *great circle* of the sphere, the largest cross section for that sphere. The distance along the edge of a great circle is the shortest distance between two points on the sphere. Examine a globe. What is the name for the special great circle on Earth from which latitude is measured? equator How many different intersections are possible that result in a cross section that is a great circle? infinitely many Are all great circles of a given sphere congruent? yes Examine a flat map of the world. What is the shortest route from New York to Beijing, China? Now look at a globe. Do you see a shorter route? Help students see that the shortest route from New York to Beijing is a great circle route that passes over the Arctic regions.

Ready to Go On?

Assess Mastery

Access *Ready to Go On?* assessment online, and receive instant scoring, feedback, and customized intervention or enrichment.

Personal Math Trainer

Online Assessment and Intervention
• Module 13 Posttest

Additional Resources

Digital Teacher Resources

Go online for module-level resources.

Assessment Resources
• Module 13 Quiz: B, p.63
• Module 13 Quiz: D, p.65

my.hrw.com

Ready to Go On?

Personal Math Trainer
Online Assessment and Intervention
my.hrw.com

13.1 Volume of Cylinders

Find the volume of each cylinder. Round your answers to the nearest tenth if necessary. Use 3.14 for π.

1. 6 ft
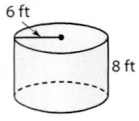
8 ft

904.3 ft³

2. A can of juice has a radius of 4 inches and a height of 7 inches. What is the volume of the can?

351.7 in³

13.2 Volume of Cones

Find the volume of each cone. Round your answers to the nearest tenth if necessary. Use 3.14 for π.

3.
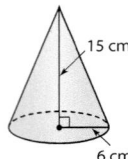
15 cm
6 cm

565.2 cm³

4.
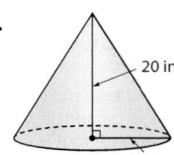
20 in.
12 in.

3014.4 in³

13.3 Volume of Spheres

Find the volume of each sphere. Round your answers to the nearest tenth if necessary. Use 3.14 for π.

5.
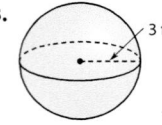
3 ft

113 ft³

6.
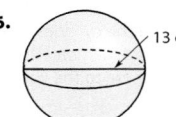
13 cm

1149.8 cm³

? ESSENTIAL QUESTION

7. What measurements do you need to know to find the volume of a cylinder? a cone? a sphere?

cylinder: radius of base and height; cone: radius of
base and height; sphere: radius

© Houghton Mifflin Harcourt Publishing Company

READY TO GO ON? *Diagnostic Assessment*

RtI Response to Intervention

Use to determine if students have mastered the concepts covered in this module.

Lesson	Exercises	Content Focus	Review with *Differentiated Instruction*
13.1	1–2	Volume of Cylinders	**13.1** Reteach **13.1** Reading Strategies **13.1** Success for English Learners
13.2	3–4	Volume of Cones	**13.2** Reteach **13.2** Reading Strategies **13.2** Success for English Learners
13.3	5–6	Volume of Spheres	**13.3** Reteach **13.3** Reading Strategies **13.3** Success for English Learners

Assessment Readiness

Personal Math Trainer

Online Assessment and Intervention

my.hrw.com

Selected Response

1. The bed of a pickup truck measures 4 feet by 8 feet. To the nearest inch, what is the length of the longest thin metal bar that will lie flat in the bed?

- (A) 11 ft 3 in.
- (C) 8 ft 11 in.
- (B) 10 ft 0 in.
- (D) 8 ft 9 in.

2. Using 3.14 for π, what is the volume of the cylinder below to the nearest tenth?

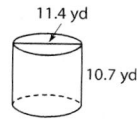

11.4 yd

10.7 yd

- (A) 102 cubic yards
- (B) 347.6 cubic yards
- (C) 1,091.6 cubic yards
- (D) 4,366.4 cubic yards

3. Rhett made mini waffle cones for a birthday party. Each waffle cone was 3.5 inches high and had a radius of 0.8 inches. What is the volume of each cone to the nearest hundredth?

- (A) 1.70 cubic inches
- (B) 2.24 cubic inches
- (C) 2.34 cubic inches
- (D) 8.79 cubic inches

4. What is the volume of a cone that has a height of 17 meters and a base with a radius of 6 meters? Use 3.14 for π and round to the nearest tenth.

- (A) 204 cubic meters
- (B) 640.6 cubic meters
- (C) 2,562.2 cubic meters
- (D) 10,249 cubic meters

418 Unit 5

5. Using 3.14 for π, what is the volume of the sphere to the nearest tenth?

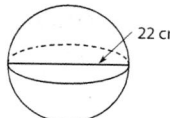

22 cm

- (A) 4180 cubic centimeters
- (B) 5572.5 cubic centimeters
- (C) 33,434.7 cubic centimeters
- (D) 44,579.6 cubic centimeters

Mini-Task

6. A diagram of a deodorant container is shown. It is made up of a cylinder and half of a sphere.

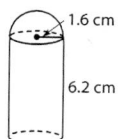

1.6 cm

6.2 cm

Use 3.14 for π and round answers to the nearest tenth.

a. What is the volume of the half sphere?

8.6 cubic centimeters

b. What is the volume of the cylinder?

49.8 cubic centimeters

c. What is the volume of the whole figure?

58.4 cubic centimeters

© Houghton Mifflin Harcourt Publishing Company

Preparing for High Stakes Tests

Assessment Readiness Tip

Students can use estimation to eliminate some of the answer choices.

- **Item 2** Students can round 11.4 down to 10, 10.7 down to 10, and 3.14 down to 3. This makes the estimate for the volume of the cylinder $3(5)^2(10) = 750$. Because all numbers were rounded down, the estimate is less than the actual volume. Answer choices A and B are less than the estimate, and D is several times larger than the estimate. C is the only reasonable answer.

- **Item 4** Students can round 17 to 20, 6 to 5, and 3.14 to 3, and then plug into the formula to find $\frac{1}{3}(3)(5)^2(20) = 500$. The only answer choice close to 500 is B, 640.6.

Avoid Common Errors

- **Item 3** Remind students that the volumes of both cylinders and cones are defined by radius and height, and they need to read the problem carefully to decide which formula to use. Some students may use the formula for the volume of a cylinder rather than the volume of a cone.

- **Item 6** Students may correctly find the volume of the sphere but forget to divide it by 2 to make it a half-sphere. Remind students to confirm that their numerical answer corresponds to the question that was asked.

Items	Grade 8 Lessons	Mathematical Processes
1*	12.1	MP.4
2	13.1	MP.4
3	13.2	MP.4
4	13.2	MP.2
5	13.3	MP.4
6	13.1, 13.3	MP.4

*Item integrates mixed review concepts from previous modules or a previous course.

DIFFERENTIATE ASSESSMENT

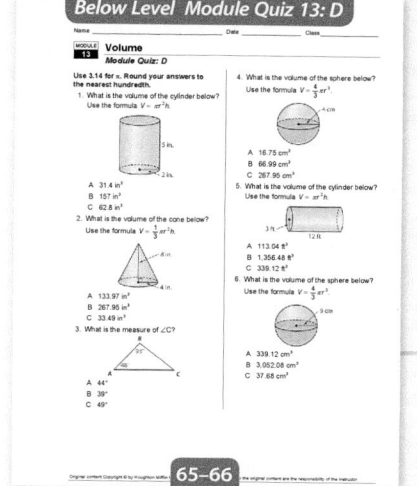

Below Level Module Quiz 13: D

65–66

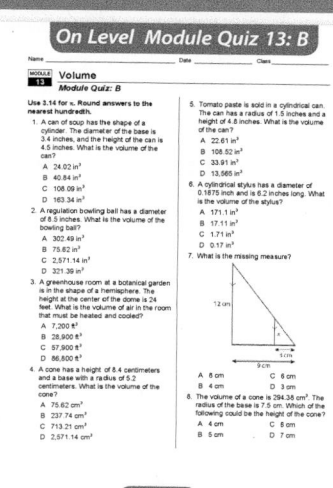

On Level Module Quiz 13: B

63–64

Personal Math Trainer

Module 13 Assessment Readiness

Pages shown are from *Assessment Resources*. **Also available online.**

Measurement Geometry

Study Guide Review

Vocabulary Development

Integrating Language Arts

Encourage students to practice using the unit vocabulary as they talk and write about mathematics. Understanding vocabulary will aid their understanding of the concepts.

MODULE 11

Angle Relationships in Parallel Lines and Triangles

Key Concepts

- The alternate interior angles formed by transversal intersecting parallel lines are congruent as are the alternate exterior angles. Same-side interior angles are supplementary. *(Lesson 11.1)*

- The sum of the interior angle measures of a triangle is 180°. *(Lesson 11.2)*

- The measure of the exterior angle of a triangle is equal to the sum of its remote interior angles. *(Lesson 11.2)*

- If two angles of one triangle are congruent to two angles of another triangle, then the triangles are similar. *(Lesson 11.3)*

MODULE 11 **Angle Relationships in Parallel Lines and Triangles**

Key Vocabulary

alternate exterior angles *(ángulos alternos externos)*

alternate interior angles *(ángulos alternos internos)*

corresponding angles *(ángulos correspondientes (para líneas))*

exterior angle *(ángulo externo)*

interior angle *(ángulos internos)*

remote interior angle *(ángulo interno remoto)*

same-side interior angles *(ángulos internos del mismo lado)*

similar *(semejantes)*

transversal *(transversal)*

❓ ESSENTIAL QUESTION

How can you solve real-world problems that involve angle relationships in parallel lines and triangles?

EXAMPLE 1

Find each angle measure when m∠6 = 81°.

A m∠5 = 180° − 81° = 99°

   5 and 6 are supplementary angles.

B m∠1 = 99°

   1 and 5 are corresponding angles.

C m∠3 = 180° − 81° = 99°

   3 and 6 are same-side interior angles.

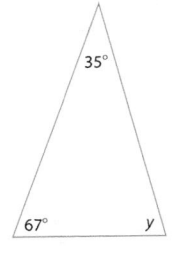

EXAMPLE 2

Are the triangles similar? Explain your answer.

$y = 180° − (67° + 35°)$

$y = 78°$

$x = 180° − (67° + 67°)$

$x = 46°$

The triangles are not similar, because they do not have 2 or more pairs of corresponding congruent angles.

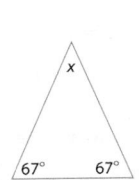

Unit 5 **419**

© Houghton Mifflin Harcourt Publishing Company

EXERCISES

1. If m∠GHA = 106°, find the measures of the given angles.
(Lesson 11.1)

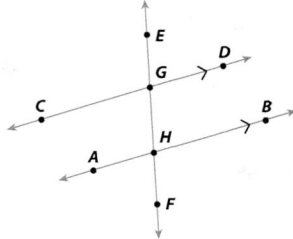

m∠EGC = __106°__

m∠EGD = __74°__

m∠BHF = __106°__

m∠HGD = __106°__

2. Find the measure of the missing angles. (Lesson 11.2)

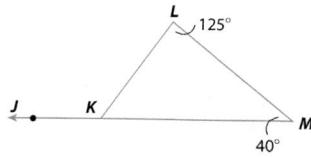

m∠JKL = __165°__

m∠LKM = __15°__

3. Is the larger triangle similar to the smaller triangle?
Explain your answer. (Lesson 11.3)

__The triangles are similar because all of__

__their angles are congruent.__

_____

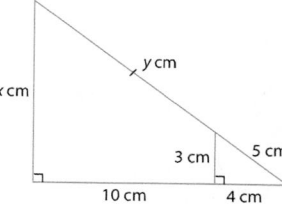

4. Find the value of x and y in the figure. (Lesson 11.3)

__x = 10.5 cm and y = 12.5 cm__

5. If m∠CJI = 132° and m∠EIH = 59°, find the measures of
the given angles. (Lesson 11.1)

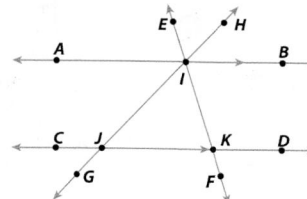

m∠IKJ = __73°__

m∠HIB = __48°__

m∠EIJ = __121°__

m∠AIK = __107°__

© Houghton Mifflin Harcourt Publishing Company

Key Concepts

- If a triangle is a right triangle, the sum of the squares of the lengths of the legs is equal to the square of the length of the hypotenuse. **(Lesson 12.1)**

- If the sum of the squares of the lengths of the legs of a triangle is equal to the square of the hypotenuse, then it is a right triangle. **(Lesson 12.2)**

- The Distance Formula states that the distance d between two points (x_1, y_1) and (x_2, y_2) is $d = \sqrt{(x_2 - x_1)^2 + (y_2 - y_1)^2}$ **(Lesson 12.3)**

MODULE 12 **The Pythagorean Theorem**

Key Vocabulary
hypotenuse *(hipotenusa)*
legs *(catetos)*
Pythagorean Theorem
   (teorema de Pitágoras)

? **ESSENTIAL QUESTION**

How can you use the Pythagorean Theorem to solve real-world problems?

EXAMPLE 1

**Find the missing side length.
Round your answer to the nearest tenth.**

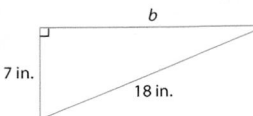

$a^2 + b^2 = c^2$

$7^2 + b^2 = 18^2$

$49 + b^2 = 324$

$b^2 = 275$

$b = \sqrt{275} \approx 16.6$

The length of the leg is about 16.6 inches.

EXAMPLE 2

Thomas drew a diagram to represent the location of his house, the school, and his friend Manuel's house. What is the distance from the school to Manuel's house? Round your answer to the nearest tenth.

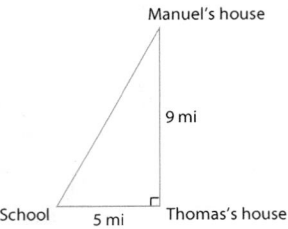

$a^2 + b^2 = c^2$

$5^2 + 9^2 = c^2$

$25 + 81 = c^2$

$c^2 = 106$

$c = \sqrt{106} \approx 10.3$

The distance from the school to Manuel's house is about 10.3 miles.

EXERCISES

Find the missing side lengths. Round your answers to the nearest hundredth. (Lesson 12.1)

1.

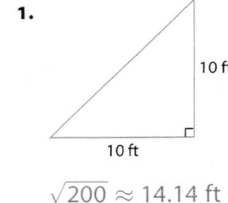

$\sqrt{200} \approx 14.14$ ft

2.

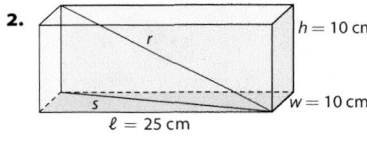

$s = \sqrt{725} \approx 26.93$ cm;

$r = \sqrt{825} \approx 28.72$ cm

© Houghton Mifflin Harcourt Publishing Company

3. Hye Sun has a modern coffee table whose top is a triangle with the following side lengths: 8 feet, 3 feet, and 5 feet. Is Hye Sun's coffee table top a right triangle? (Lesson 12.2)

No, it is not a right triangle.

4. Find the length of each side of triangle *ABC*. If necessary, round your answers to the nearest hundredth. (Lesson 12.3)

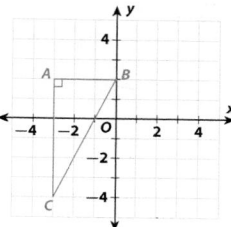

$\overline{AB}$ ___3 units___

$\overline{BC}$ ___$\sqrt{45} \approx 6.71$ units___

$\overline{AC}$ ___6 units___

 **Volume**

?⃝ **ESSENTIAL QUESTION**

How can you solve real-world problems that involve volume?

> **Key Vocabulary**
> cone *(cono)*
> cylinder *(cilindro)*
> sphere *(esfera)*

EXAMPLE 1

Find the volume of the cistern. Round your answer to the nearest hundredth.

$V = \pi r^2 h$

$\approx 3.14 \cdot 2.5^2 \cdot 7.5$

$\approx 3.14 \cdot 6.25 \cdot 7.5$

≈ 147.19

The cistern has a volume of approximately 147.19 cubic feet.

EXAMPLE 2

Find the volume of a sphere with a radius of 3.7 cm. Write your answer in terms of π and to the nearest hundredth.

$V = \frac{4}{3}\pi r^3$

$\approx \frac{4}{3} \cdot \pi \cdot 3.7^3$

$\approx \frac{4}{3} \cdot \pi \cdot 50.653$

$\approx 67.54\pi$

$V = \frac{4}{3}\pi r^3$

$\approx \frac{4}{3} \cdot 3.14 \cdot 3.7^3$

$\approx \frac{4}{3} \cdot 3.14 \cdot 50.653$

≈ 212.07

The volume of the sphere is approximately 67.54π cm³, or 212.07 cm³.

© Houghton Mifflin Harcourt Publishing Company

Volume

Key Concepts

- A cylinder is a three-dimensional figure with two congruent circular bases. To find the volume of a cylinder, use the formula $V = Bh$ or $V = \pi r^2 h$. **(Lesson 13.1)**

- A cone is a three-dimensional figure with one circular base and one vertex. To find the volume of a cone, use the formula $V = \frac{1}{3}Bh$ or $V = \frac{1}{3}\pi r^2 h$. **(Lesson 13.2)**

- A sphere is a three-dimensional figure with all points the same distance from the center. To find the volume of a cylinder, use the formula $V = \frac{4}{3}\pi r^3$. **(Lesson 13.3)**

EXERCISES

Find the volume of each figure. Round your answers to the nearest hundredth. (Lessons 13.1, 13.2, 13.3)

1.

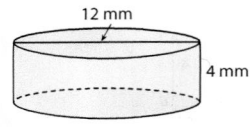
12 mm
4 mm

_____452.16 mm³_____

2.

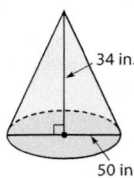
34 in.
50 in.

_____22,241.67 in³_____

3. Find the volume of a ball with a radius of 1.68 inches.

_____19.85 in³_____

4.

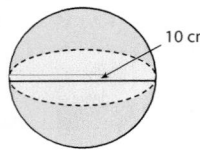
10 cm

_____523.33 cm³_____

5.

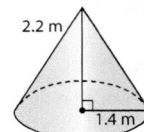
2.2 m
1.4 m

_____4.51 m³_____

6. A round above-ground swimming pool has a diameter of 15 ft and a height of 4.5 ft. What is the volume of the swimming pool?

_____794.81 ft³_____

7.

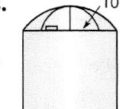
0.8 in.
11.2 in.

_____22.51 in³_____

8.

10 yd
13.3 yd

_____1,305.72 yd³_____

9. A paper cup in the shape of a cone has a height of 4.7 inches and a diameter of 3.6 inches. What is the volume of the paper cup?

_____15.94 in³_____

© Houghton Mifflin Harcourt Publishing Company

1. **CAREERS IN MATH** Hydrologist A hydrologist needs to estimate the mass of water in an underground aquifer, which is roughly cylindrical in shape. The diameter of the aquifer is 65 meters, and its depth is 8 meters. One cubic meter of water has a mass of about 1000 kilograms.

   a. The aquifer is completely filled with water. What is the total mass of the water in the aquifer? Explain how you found your answer. Use 3.14 for π and round your answer to the nearest kilogram.

   Multiply the mass of one cubic meter of water by the volume

   of the aquifer; $(3.14)(32.5^2)(8)(1000) = 26{,}533{,}000$ kg

   b. Another cylindrical aquifer has a diameter of 70 meters and a depth of 9 meters. The mass of the water in it is 27×10^7 kilograms. Is the aquifer totally filled with water? Explain your reasoning.

   No; if it were full of water, the mass would be 34,618,500 kg,

   or 3.4×10^7 kg. Since the mass of the water is less than this,

   the aquifer must not be full.

2. From his home, Myles walked his dog north 5 blocks, east 2 blocks, and then stopped at a drinking fountain. He then walked north 3 more blocks and east 4 more blocks. It started to rain so he cut through a field and walked straight home.

   a. Draw a diagram of his path.

   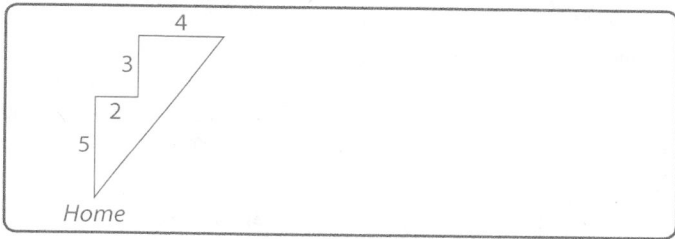

   b. How many blocks did Myles walk in all? How much longer was his walk before it started to rain than his walk home?

   24 blocks; 4 blocks longer

© Houghton Mifflin Harcourt Publishing Company

Performance Tasks

The Performance Tasks provide students with the opportunity to apply concepts from this unit in real-world problem situations.

CAREERS IN MATH

Hydrologist
In Performance Task Item 1, students can see how a hydrologist uses mathematics on the job.

Scoring Guides For Performance Tasks

1. **Mathematical Processes**
   MP.1, MP.4, MP.6

Task	Possible Points (Total: 6)
a	**1 point** for explanation: Multiply the density, 1000 kg/m³, by the volume of the cylinder, $\pi r^2 h$, to find the mass. **2 points** for correct calculation and mass: 26,533,000 kg
b	**1 point** for correct answer: no **2 points** for explanation: The volume of the aquifer is 34,618.5 m³, which is 34,618,500 kg of water. Since the answer in **a** is less, the aquifer is not completely full.

2. **Mathematical Processes**
   MP.2, MP.4, MP.6

Task	Possible Points (Total: 6)
a	**3 points** for correct diagram:

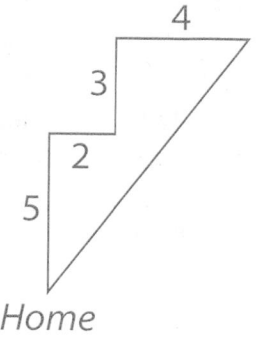

Task	
b	**2 points** for correctly calculating that the total distance was 24 blocks. **1 point** for correctly calculating that the walk before the rain was 4 blocks longer than the walk home.

Assessment Readiness

Assessment Readiness Tip

Encourage students to draw a picture or diagram to organize information from the problem.

- **Item 5** Students can draw a right triangle to represent the situation in the word problem, which will help them plug the lengths into the Pythagorean Theorem correctly.

- **Item 7** If students draw a right triangle beside the problem with the legs and hypotenuse labeled, it may help them to put the numbers into the Pythagorean Theorem correctly, with the longest side always being the hypotenuse.

Avoid Common Errors

- **Item 2** Many students find x but forget to plug x back into the original expressions to find the smallest angle. Remind students to read carefully and double-check that they have completely finished the problem before selecting an answer.

Items	Grade 8 Lessons	Mathematical Processes
1	**11.1**	MP.2
2	**11.2**	MP.2
3	**13.1**	MP.2
4*	**1.1**	MP.6
5	**12.1**	MP.4
6	**13.3**	MP.2
7	**12.2**	MP.7
8*	**8.5**	MP.6
9*	**1.1**	MP.2
10*	**8.4**	MP.2
11	**11.1**	MP.2
12	**11.3, 12.1**	MP.1
13	**13.2, 13.3**	MP.1

* Item integrates mixed review concepts from previous modules or a previous course.

Assessment Readiness

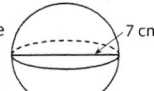

Personal Math Trainer
my.hrw.com
Online Assessment and Intervention

Selected Response

1. Which of the following angle pairs formed by a transversal that intersects two parallel lines are not congruent?

- Ⓐ alternate interior angles
- Ⓑ adjacent angles
- Ⓒ corresponding angles
- Ⓓ alternate exterior angles

2. The measures of the three angles of a triangle are given by $3x + 1$, $2x - 3$, and $9x$. What is the measure of the smallest angle?

- Ⓐ 13°
- Ⓒ 29°
- Ⓑ 23°
- Ⓓ 40°

3. Using 3.14 for π, what is the volume of the cylinder?

- Ⓐ 200 cubic yards
- Ⓑ 628 cubic yards
- Ⓒ 1256 cubic yards
- Ⓓ 2512 cubic yards

10 yd
8 yd

4. Which of the following is **not** true?

- Ⓐ $\sqrt{36} + 2 > \sqrt{16} + 5$
- Ⓑ $5\pi < 17$
- Ⓒ $\sqrt{10} + 1 < \frac{9}{2}$
- Ⓓ $5 - \sqrt{35} < 0$

5. A pole is 65 feet tall. A support wire is attached to the top of the pole and secured to the ground 33 feet from the base of the pole. Find the approximate length of the wire.

- Ⓐ 32 feet
- Ⓒ 56 feet
- Ⓑ 73 feet
- Ⓓ 60 feet

6. Using 3.14 for π, what is the volume of the sphere to the nearest tenth?

7 cm

- Ⓐ 205.1 cm³
- Ⓑ 1077 cm³
- Ⓒ 179.5 cm³
- Ⓓ 4308.1 cm³

7. Which set of lengths are **not** the side lengths of a right triangle?

- Ⓐ 28, 45, 53
- Ⓒ 36, 77, 85
- Ⓑ 13, 84, 85
- Ⓓ 16, 61, 65

8. Which statement describes the solution of a system of linear equations for two lines with different slopes and different y-intercepts?

- Ⓐ one nonzero solution
- Ⓑ infinitely many solutions
- Ⓒ no solution
- Ⓓ solution of 0

9. What is the side length of a cube that has a volume of 729 cubic inches?

- Ⓐ 7 inches
- Ⓒ 9 inches
- Ⓑ 8 inches
- Ⓓ 10 inches

10. What is the solution to the system of equations?

$$\begin{cases} x + 3y = 5 \\ 2x - y = -4 \end{cases}$$

- Ⓐ no solution
- Ⓑ infinitely many solutions
- Ⓒ (2, 1)
- Ⓓ (–1, 2)

© Houghton Mifflin Harcourt Publishing Company

DIFFERENTIATE ASSESSMENT

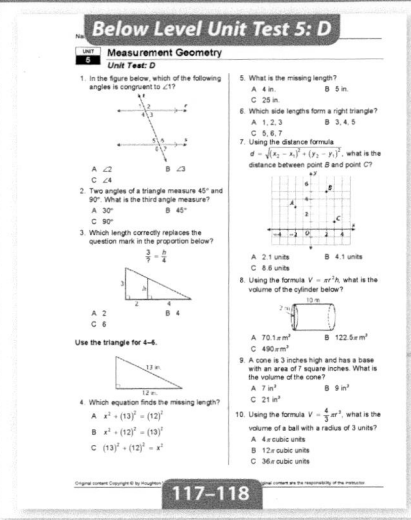

Below Level Unit Test 5: D

117–118

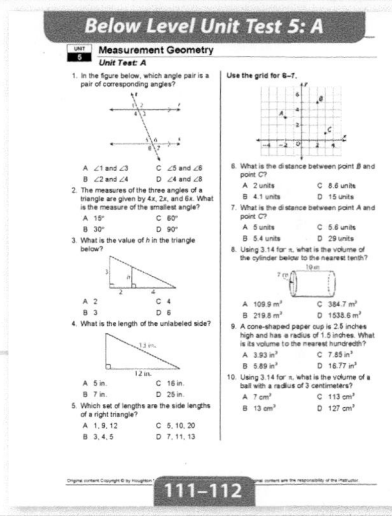

Below Level Unit Test 5: A

111–112

Mini-Tasks

11. In the figure shown, m∠AGE = (5x − 7)°
and m∠BGH = (3x + 19)°.

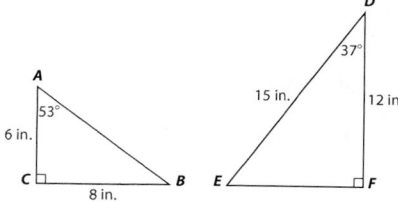

a. Find the value of x. _____ $x = 13$

b. Find m∠AGE. _____ $58°$

c. Find m∠GHD. _____ $122°$

12. Tom drew two right triangles as shown with angle measures to the nearest whole unit.

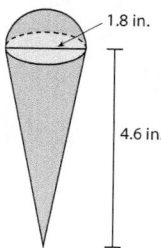

a. Find the length of $\overline{AB}$ in triangle ABC.

_____ 10 in. _____

b. Find the length of $\overline{EF}$ in triangle DEF.

_____ 9 in. _____

c. Are the triangles similar? Explain your answer.

yes; m∠B = 90° − 53° = 37°,

and m∠E = 90° − 37° = 53°,

so there are two pairs of

corresponding angles with the

same measure.

Read graphs and diagrams carefully. Look at the labels for important information.

13. In the diagram, the figure at the top of the cone is a hemisphere.

1.8 in.

4.6 in.

a. What is the volume of the cone? Round your answer to the nearest hundredth.

_____ 3.90 in³ _____

b. What is the volume of the hemisphere on the top of the cone? Round your answer to the nearest hundredth.

_____ 1.53 in³ _____

c. What would be the radius of a sphere with the same total volume as the figure? Explain how you found your answer.

About 1.09 in.; the total

volume of the figure is about

5.43 in³. You can solve the

equation $\frac{4}{3}\pi r^3 = 5.43$ to find r.

You have to estimate the cube

root of 1.30, which is about 1.09.

© Houghton Mifflin Harcourt Publishing Company

Personal Math Trainer

Online Assessment and Intervention

Additional Resources

Digital Teacher Resources

Go online for unit-level resources.

Assessment Resources
- Leveled Unit Tests: A, B, C, D
- Unit Performance Task

my.hrw.com

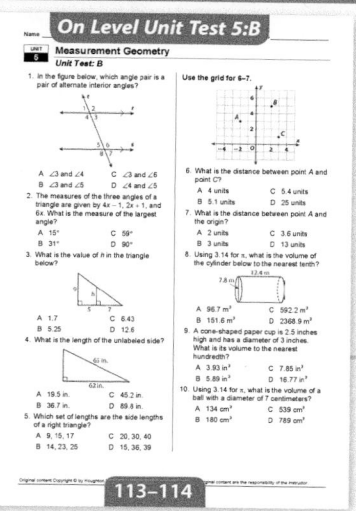

113–114

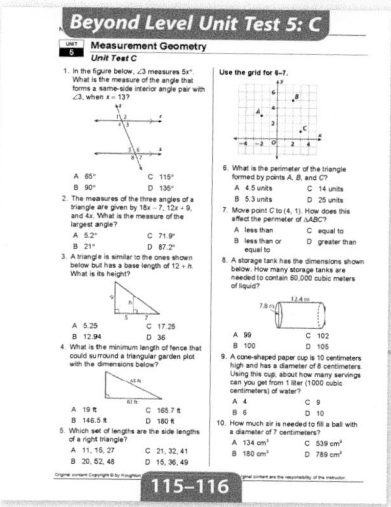

115–116

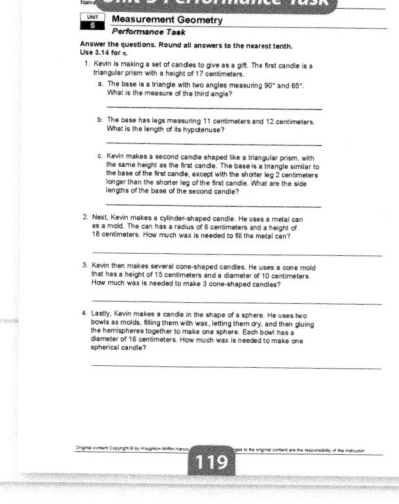

119

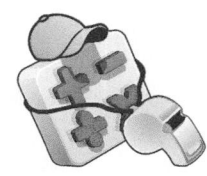

Personal Math Trainer

Unit 5 Assessment Readiness

Pages shown are from *Assessment Resources*
Also available online.

Statistics

Contents

Teacher Notes

PLANNING AND PACING GUIDE
Instructional Path

Lesson	Lesson Objectives	Pacing*
UNIT 6 | Statistics		
Progress Tracker 1 2 3 4 5 **6**		
MODULE 14 | Scatter Plots		1 day
14.1 Scatter Plots and Association	Students will construct and interpret scatter plots.	2 days
14.2 Trend Lines and Predictions **Activity 14.2** Prime Predictions	Students will use a trend line to make a prediction from a scatter plot. Students will plot a sequence of prime numbers in the coordinate plane and use a trend line to predict other prime numbers.	3 days
Ready to Go On? **Module 14 Assessment Readiness**		1 day
MODULE 15 | Two-Way Tables		1 day
15.1 Two-Way Frequency Tables	Students will construct and interpret two-way frequency tables.	1 day
15.2 Two-Way Relative Frequency Tables	Students will organize and analyze categorical data.	2 days
Ready to Go On? **Module 15 Assessment Readiness**		1 day
Study Guide Review **Unit 6 Assessment Readiness**		2 days

* Based on a 45-minute class period

Teaching for Depth

Scatter Plots and Association

A scatter plot is a graph that shows *bivariate data*; that is, data for which there are two variables for each observation, such as height and weight. One point on the scatter plot represents one data pair. Students are often tempted to connect points on a graph. It is essential that they understand that a scatter plot shows all the collected data and it is meaningless to connect all the points.

A scatter plot may suggest an association or a correlation between two variables. The terms *association* and *correlation* are mistakenly used interchangeably, but they do not mean exactly the same thing. An association can be linear or nonlinear, but a correlation always refers to a linear association. Associations and correlations may be negative or positive.

Trend Lines and Lines of Best Fit

A scatter plot may show a linear relationship between bivariate data. A line can be drawn to represent the data, called the trend line or the line of best fit. A trend line can be drawn by visualizing where a line would fall that best fits the data, usually with half the data points above the line and half below. The line of best fit is usually calculated using a statistical method of linear regression such as least squares. Least squares means the equation of the line chosen minimizes the sum of the squares of the residuals for the line. The residuals are the differences between the actual data values and the associated data values that fit the model. A graphing calculator automatically uses this method to give the line of best fit.

> *An important step toward college and career readiness is to prepare students for success on high-stakes assessments. Rigorous exercise sets in Go Math integrate problem-solving, critical thinking, and analysis to help students develop deep conceptual understandings of mathematical concepts.*

STEVE LEINWAND on Preparing for High-Stakes Assessments

Two-Way Tables

Two-way tables are used to show frequencies of data that is categorized two ways. The columns represent one categorization for the population and the rows represent a different categorization for the population. You can use relative frequencies in two-way tables to draw conclusions about whether or not there is an association between the two categories.

In real-life statistical situations, relative frequencies will often vary somewhat due to chance even when there is no association between two variables. A statistical test called a chi-squared test of independence is able to evaluate whether two variables are associated, even when the data have a great deal of variation.

Two-way frequency tables can also be used to find other types of frequencies. A two-way relative frequency table can be created from a two-way frequency table. This table shows both joint relative frequency and marginal relative frequency. You can also find a conditional relative frequency from a two-way frequency table by dividing a frequency that is not in a total row or total column by the frequency's row total or column total. Conditional relative frequency can be used to see if there is an association between two variables.

Professional Development Videos

Module 15: Two-Way Tables

UNIT 6

Statistics

CAREERS IN MATH

Psychologist

A psychologist uses math to recognize correlations and patterns in how humans behave. You will learn more about analyzing psychological data in the Performance Tasks at the end of the unit.

For more information about careers in mathematics as well as various mathematics appreciation topics, visit the American Mathematical Society at www.ams.org.

CAREERS IN MATH

Psychologist A psychologist investigates the physical, mental, emotional, and social aspects of human behavior. Psychologists use math to evaluate and interpret data about human activities and the human mind. They create and use mathematical models to predict behavior of humans, both individually and in groups.

If you are interested in a career in psychology, you should study the following mathematical subjects:
- Algebra
- Trigonometry
- Probability and Statistics
- Calculus

Research other careers that require the analysis of data and use of mathematical models.

Unit 6 Performance Task

At the end of the unit, check out how **psychologists** use math.

© Houghton Mifflin Harcourt Publishing Company • Image Credits
©Ron Levine/Getty Images

Unit 6 **427**

Vocabulary Preview

Use the puzzle to preview key vocabulary from this unit. Unscramble the circled letters within found words to answer the riddle at the bottom of the page.

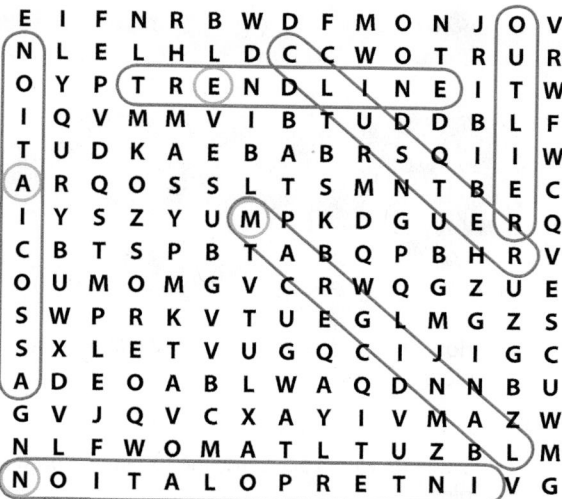

A description of how sets of data are related. (Lesson 14.1) association

A set of closely related data. (Lesson 14.1) cluster

A data point that is very different from the rest of the data in the set. (Lesson 14.1) outlier

A straight line that comes closest to the points on a scatter plot (2 words). (Lesson 14.2) trend line

Using a trend line to predict a value between data points you already know. (Lesson 14.2) interpolation

A relative frequency found by dividing a row total or a column total by the grand total. (Lesson 15.2) marginal

Q: Why doesn't Joe Average have any friends?

A: Because he's so M E A N !

© Houghton Mifflin Harcourt Publishing Company

Vocabulary Preview

Use the puzzle to give students a preview of important concepts in this unit. Students may work individually, in pairs, or in groups.

Digital Teacher Resources

Go online for unit-level resources.

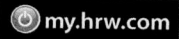

my.hrw.com

LEARNING PROGRESSIONS ACROSS THE GRADES

Before	In this Unit	After
Students understand: • how to interpret data • find the mean of a data set • solve problems using graphs of data	Students will learn about: • scatter plots and associations • trend lines and predictions • two-way frequency and relative frequency tables	Students will connect: • scatter plots and trend lines with linear equations • frequency and relative frequency

Module At A Glance

Module Essential Question: How can you use scatter plots to solve real-world problems?

MODULE 14 | Scatter Plots

Lessons at A Glance	Lesson 14.1 Scatter Plots and Association	Lesson 14.2 Trend Lines and Predictions
	Pg. T433A	Pg. T439A
Essential Question	How can you construct and interpret scatter plots?	How can you use a trend line to make a prediction from a scatter plot?
Objective	Students will construct and interpret scatter plots.	Students will use a trend line to make a prediction from a scatter plot.
Vocabulary	association, cluster, outlier, scatter plot	trend line
Go online for all your module resources my.hrw.com 	14.1 *i*Student Edition 14.1 *i*Teacher Edition 14.1 *e*Student Edition 🚲 Personal Math Trainer 📺 Math on the Spot Videos 📊 Animated Math	14.2 *i*Student Edition 14.2 *i*Teacher Edition 14.2 *e*Student Edition 🚲 Personal Math Trainer 📺 Math on the Spot Videos

Print Resources	**14.1 Student Edition:** Lesson
	Differentiated Instruction
	    14.1 Practice and Problem Solving A/B, C, and D
	    14.1 Reteach
	    14.1 Reading Strategies
	    14.1 Success for English Learners
		14.2 Student Edition: Lesson
		Differentiated Instruction
		    14.2 Practice and Problem Solving A/B, C, and D
		    14.2 Reteach
		    14.2 Reading Strategies
		    14.2 Success for English Learners

RtI — Response to Intervention

Before the Module	During the Lesson	After the Module
Are You Ready	**Guided/Independent Practice**	**Ready to Go On?**
• Prerequisite Skills Activities • Personal Math Trainer	• Reteach • Personal Math Trainer • Practice and Problem Solving D	• Reteach • Personal Math Trainer

Teacher Notes

Activity	Math on the Spot Videos	Animated Math
Prime Predictions After Lesson 14.2	One for every Example in every Lesson	During Lesson 14.1

Check It Out!

Real-World Video Viewing Guide

After students have watched the video, discuss the following:

- What does a scatter plot show? the relationship between two variables

- How can you use a scatter plot to estimate the weight of a dinosaur?

Professional Development Video

Author Juli Dixon models successful teaching practices as she explores the concept of scatter plots in an actual eighth-grade classroom.

Scatter Plots

© Houghton Mifflin Harcourt Publishing Company

? ESSENTIAL QUESTION

How can you use scatter plots to solve real-world problems?

You can use scatter plots to find the relationships between two sets of real-world data.

LESSON 14.1
Scatter Plots and Association

LESSON 14.2
Trend Lines and Predictions

Real-World Video

An anthropologist measures dinosaur bones. To estimate a dinosaur's height based on the length of a bone, he can make a scatter plot comparing bone length and height of several dinosaurs.

my.hrw.com

GO DIGITAL
my.hrw.com

my.hrw.com	Math On the Spot	Animated Math	Personal Math Trainer
Go digital with your write-in student edition, accessible on any device.	Scan with your smart phone to jump directly to the online edition, video tutor, and more.	Interactively explore key concepts to see how math works.	Get immediate feedback and help as you work through practice sets.

429

TEACHER ONLINE RESOURCES

ONLINE TEACHER EDITION Access a full suite of teaching resources online—plan, present, and manage classes and assignments.

MY SMART PLANNER Easily plan your classes and access all your resources online.

INTERACTIVE WHITEBOARDS Engage students with interactive whiteboard-ready examples and a lesson quiz for each lesson.

PERSONAL MATH TRAINER: Online Assessment and Intervention Assign automatically graded homework, quizzes, tests, and intervention activities. Prepare your students for standardized tests in short-answer and multiple-choice formats.

Reading Start-Up

Visualize Vocabulary

Use the ✔ words to complete the right column of the chart.

<table>
<tr><th colspan="2">Reviewing Slope</th></tr>
<tr><th>Mathematical Representation</th><th>Review Word</th></tr>
<tr><td>$y = mx + b$</td><td>slope-intercept form of an equation, linear equation</td></tr>
<tr><td>y</td><td>y-coordinate</td></tr>
<tr><td>m</td><td>slope</td></tr>
<tr><td>x</td><td>x-coordinate</td></tr>
<tr><td>b</td><td>y-intercept</td></tr>
</table>

Understand Vocabulary

Match the term on the left to the correct expression on the right.

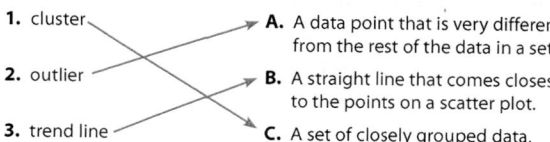

1. cluster
2. outlier
3. trend line

A. A data point that is very different from the rest of the data in a set

B. A straight line that comes closest to the points on a scatter plot.

C. A set of closely grouped data.

© Houghton Mifflin Harcourt Publishing Company

Vocabulary

Review Words
- bivariate data *(datos bivariados)*
- data *(datos)*
- ✔ linear equation *(ecuación lineal)*
- ✔ slope *(pendiente)*
- ✔ slope-intercept form of an equation *(forma pendiente-intersección)*
- ✔ *x*-coordinate *(coordenada x)*
- ✔ *y*-coordinate *(coordenada y)*
- ✔ *y*-intercept *(intersección con el eje y)*

Preview Words
- cluster *(agrupación)*
- outlier *(valor extremo)*
- scatter plot *(diagrama de dispersión)*
- trend line *(línea de tendencia)*

Active Reading

Two-Panel Flip Chart Create a two-panel flip chart, to help you understand the concepts in this module. Label each flap with the title of one of the lessons in the module. As you study each lesson, write important ideas under the appropriate flap. Include any sample problems or equations that will help you remember the concepts later when you look back at your notes.

Reading Start-Up

Visualize Vocabulary
The content chart helps students review slope to prepare them to graph trend lines. Students should write one or more review words in the cells in the right column of the chart. As a class, review the process for finding slope and define each of the terms represented in the chart.

Understand Vocabulary
Use the following explanation to help students learn the preview words.

*In data analysis, a **cluster** is a set of closely grouped data. In a scatter plot, the dots showing a cluster are grouped close together. If they cluster in a linear fashion, you can draw a **trend line** to model the data. An **outlier** is a point that is very different from the others in the data set. On the scatter plot, an outlier is far away from the other dots and not close to the trend line.*

Active Reading

Integrating Language Arts
Students can use these reading and note-taking strategies to help them organize and understand new concepts and vocabulary.

Additional Resources
Differentiated Instruction
- Reading Strategies **ELL**
- Interactive multilingual glossary

LEARNING PROGRESSIONS ACROSS THE GRADES

Before	In this Module	After
Students understand: • ways to display data • ways to solve problems using graphs of data • ways to compare two sets of data	Students learn to: • represent data in a scatter plot • describe associations in data in scatter plots • represent bivariate data in a scatter plot with a trend line • make predictions from a scatter plot or trend line	Students will connect: • scatter plots and linear and nonlinear associations • scatter plots and positive and negative associations • scatter plots and trend lines • trend lines and linear equations

Are You Ready?

Assess Readiness

Access *Are You Ready?* assessment online, and receive instant scoring, feedback, and customized intervention or enrichment.

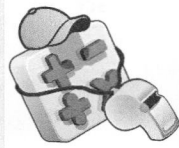

Personal Math Trainer

Online Assessment and Intervention

Additional Resources

Digital Teacher Resources

Go online for module-level resources.

my.hrw.com

Are YOU Ready?

Personal Math Trainer

Online Assessment and Intervention

my.hrw.com

Complete these exercises to review skills you will need for this module.

Evaluate Expressions

EXAMPLE   Evaluate $4x + 3$ for $x = 5$.

$4x + 3 = 4(5) + 3$ Substitute the given value for x.

$\quad\quad = 20 + 3$ Multiply.

$\quad\quad = 23$ Add.

Evaluate each expression for the given value of *x*.

1. $6x - 5$ for $x = 4$ **2.** $-2x + 7$ for $x = 2$ **3.** $5x - 6$ for $x = 3$

$\quad\quad 19$ 3 9

4. $0.5x + 8.4$ for $x = -1$ **5.** $\frac{3}{4}x - 9$ for $x = -20$ **6.** $1.4x + 3.5$ for $x = -4$

$\quad\quad 7.9$ -24 -2.1

Solve Two-Step Equations

EXAMPLE $5x + 3 = -7$

$\quad\quad \underline{-3 = -3}$ Subtract 3 from both sides.

$\quad\quad 5x = -10$

$\quad\quad \dfrac{5x}{5} = \dfrac{-10}{5}$ Divide both sides by 5.

$\quad\quad x = -2$

Solve for *x*.

7. $3x + 4 = 10$ **8.** $5x - 11 = 34$ **9.** $-2x + 5 = -9$ **10.** $8x + 13 = -11$

$\quad 2$ 9 7 -3

11. $4x - 7 = -27$ **12.** $\frac{1}{2}x + 16 = 39$ **13.** $\frac{2}{3}x - 16 = 12$ **14.** $0.5x - 1.5 = -6.5$

$\quad -5$ 46 42 -10

© Houghton Mifflin Harcourt Publishing Company

ARE YOU READY? *Diagnostic Assessment*

RtI Response to Intervention

Use to determine if students need intervention for the module's prerequisite skills.

Skill	Missed More Than . . .	Intervene With *Skills Intervention* worksheets (available online)	For Enrichment *Differentiated Instruction* (available in print and online)
Evaluate Expressions	1 question	**Skill 54** Evaluate Expressions	**Module 14 Challenge** Extend-the-Math Lesson Activities in TE
Solve Two-Step Equations	2 questions	**Skill 60** Solve Two-Step Equations	**Module 14 Challenge** Extend-the-Math Lesson Activities in TE

Are YOU Ready? *(cont'd)*

Complete these exercises to review skills you will need for this module.

Evaluate Expressions

15. Show why the expression $-1.3x - 6.5$ is neither positive nor negative when $x = -5$.

> The expression can be evaluated as follows:
> $-1.3x - 6.5 = -1.3(-5) - 6.5$ Substitute -5 for x.
> $\qquad\qquad\quad = 6.5 - 6.5$ Multiply.
> $\qquad\qquad\quad = 0$ Subtract.
> 0 is neither positive nor negative.

16. Evaluate the expression $\frac{1}{2}x + 6.8$ for $x = -2, 0, 2,$ and 4. Describe a pattern in the results.

> 5.8, 6.8, 7.8, and 8.8; as the value of x increases by 2, the value of the expression increases by 1.

Solve Two-Step Equations

17. Describe a plan using inverse operations to solve $\frac{1}{2}x + 8 = 42$. Then find the solution.

> Use the inverse of addition by subtracting 8 from both sides. Simplify both sides. Then multiply both sides by the reciprocal of $\frac{1}{2}$, or 2, and simplify again.
> The value of x is 68.

18. Caroline solved the equation below as shown. What was Caroline's error?
$$0.5x - 1.2 = 8$$
$$0.5x = 6.8$$
$$x = 13.6$$

> The first operation used to simplify $0.5x - 1.2 = 8$ should have been adding 1.2 to both sides, not subtracting 1.2 from the right side. The correct solution is $x = 18.4$.

© Houghton Mifflin Harcourt Publishing Company

Evaluate Expressions

Exercise 15 Make sure students understand integer multiplication before evaluating the expression.

Exercise 16 Encourage students to solve the problem on their own and then compare the patterns they find.

Solve Two-Step Equations

Exercise 17 Students may make errors in solving the equation if they use the incorrect inverse operations. Encourage students to check their answers in the original problem.

Exercise 18 Make sure students understand that they need to analyze each step carefully before they decide which inverse operation to choose. This will help them avoid the common error of choosing the wrong inverse operation.

Use to determine if students are able to apply the module's prerequisite skills.

Skill	Exercise	Depth of Knowledge (D.O.K.)	Mathematical Processes
Evaluate Expressions	15	**3** Strategic Thinking	**MP.2** Abstract and Quantitative Reasoning
	16	**2** Skills/Concepts	**MP.8** Generalize
Solve Two-Step Equations	17	**3** Strategic Thinking	**MP.1** Problem Solving
	18	**2** Skills/Concepts	**MP.3** Use and Evaluate Logical Reasoning

Lesson Support

Content Objective Students will learn to construct and interpret scatter plots.

Professional Development

Integrate Mathematical Processes MP.7

This lesson provides an opportunity to address this Mathematical Processes standard. It calls for students to look closely to discern a pattern or structure. Students will look for patterns in scatter plots of bivariate data. They use a scatter plot to interpret clusters of data and identify any outliers. They also use scatter plots to identify how sets of data are associated.

FOCUS

Building Background

Connecting with Everyday Life Ask: "Is there any relationship between a person's height and the number of pets that he or she has? Is there a relationship between a person's height and his or her sleeve length?" Have students discuss ways they could record and compare relevant data to investigate these questions.

COHERENCE

Learning Progressions

In this lesson, students use scatter plots to build their knowledge of patterns of association in bivariate data. Key understandings include the following:

- **A scatter plot is a graph with points plotted to show the relationship between two sets of data.**
- **A cluster is a set of closely grouped data. An outlier is a data point that is very different from the rest of the data in the set.**
- **Association describes how sets of data are related. There can be a positive association, a negative association, or no association.**

Students continue to represent and analyze bivariate data by creating scatter plots with trend lines and making predictions in Lesson 14.2. This prepares students to further study scatter plots, linear and nonlinear associations, and linear equations in higher grades.

RIGOR

Cluster Connections

This lesson provides an excellent opportunity to connect ideas in this cluster:

Investigate patterns of association in bivariate data.

Tell students: "Phil recorded his sleeve length at different ages.

Age (yr)	6	8	10	12	14
Sleeve Length (in.)	19	22	23	27	32

Make a scatter plot of Phil's data. Describe and explain the association between Phil's age and his sleeve length."

The association is positive and linear; as Phil gets older, his sleeve length increases. However, if data for increasing age were plotted, we would see that Phil's sleeve size stops increasing.

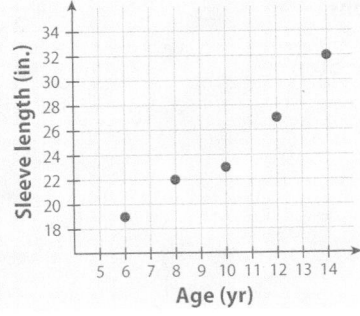

Phil's Sleeve Length

Language Support ELL

Language Objective Students will write a description of how to construct and interpret scatter plots.

Leveled Strategies for English Learners ELL

Emerging
Have students at this level of English proficiency work in pairs to recreate on graph paper the scatter plot in Explore Activity 1 using the data in the table.

Expanding
Have students at this level of English proficiency work in pairs to create a table without student names, like the one in Explore Activity 1, and then plot the data from their group.

Bridging
Have students at this level of English proficiency work in pairs to create a table without student names, like the one in Explore Activity 1, and then plot the data from their group. Then, have them identify and discuss outliers in the data.

Math Talk

Write out and model for students a sentence frame to begin their answer.

_____ (Yes/No) if the point (20,1) appeared on the scatter plot, it world _____ an oulier because _____ .

Linguistic Support ELL

Academic/Content Vocabulary
This lesson on scatter plots and association relies on students' understanding of the definition of the terms *scatter plot*, *bivariate*, *cluster*, *outlier*, and *association*. While some English learners might have encountered some of these words in other classes, the words may be new to them in mathematics. Even with the definition in the lesson, students may benefit from adding an illustration along with the word to their word journals. Also point out the benefit of using the glossary to verify their understanding of the terms.

Building Background
Explore Activity 2 introduces Yellowstone National Park, a national park located primarily in Wyoming and known for its wildlife and Old Faithful geyser, one of the most popular features in the park. A geyser is a natural hot spring that sends water into the air from time to time. Point out to students that the first syllable of the word *geyser* is pronounced like the word *guy* so they will recognize it when they hear it. Then have them add this to their word journals.

Image Credits: ©PhotoDisc/Getty Images

Scatter Plots and Association

1 Engage

ESSENTIAL QUESTION

How can you construct and interpret scatter plots?
Sample answer: Plot bivariate data on a coordinate plane, with one variable represented by each axis. Look for positive or negative association, clusters, and outliers to interpret the data.

Motivate the Lesson

Ask: Do you think the grade you get on a test is related to how long you study for the test? Take a guess. Begin the Explore Activity to find out.

2 Explore

EXPLORE ACTIVITY 1

Focus on Math Connections

Emphasize that a scatter plot is used to investigate patterns of association between two quantities. This scatter plot shows hours spent studying as the independent variable and test grades as the dependent variable. Encourage students to discuss any trends they may see in the data in terms of these variables. It is important to keep in mind that an association between data sets does not mean that one data set causes the change in the other data set.

Scatter Plots and Association

8.6.14.1
Students will construct and interpret scatter plots.

ESSENTIAL QUESTION

How can you construct and interpret scatter plots?

EXPLORE ACTIVITY 1 Real World

Making a Scatter Plot

Recall that a set of bivariate data involves two variables. Bivariate data are used to explore the relationship between two variables. You can graph bivariate data on a *scatter plot*. A **scatter plot** is a graph with points plotted to show the relationship between two sets of data.

Hours Spent Studying	Test Grade
0	75
0.5	80
1	80
1	85
1.5	85
1.5	95
2	90
3	100
4	90

The final question on a math test reads, "How many hours did you spend studying for this test?" The teacher records the number of hours each student studied and the grade the student received on the test.

A Make a prediction about the relationship between the number of hours spent studying and test grades.

Sample answer: A greater number of study hours are likely to be associated with higher test grades.

B Make a scatter plot. Graph hours spent studying as the independent variable and test grades as the dependent variable.

Reflect

1. What trend do you see in the data?
In general, test scores increase as the number of study hours increases.

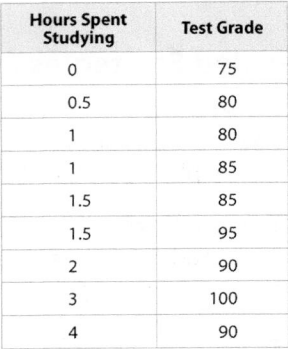

2. **Justify Reasoning** Do you think the grade associated with studying for 10 hours would follow this trend?
No; the graph shows a general upward trend, but the grade cannot exceed 100.

© Houghton Mifflin Harcourt Publishing Company

Lesson 14.1 **433**

DIFFERENTIATE INSTRUCTION *Leveled Questions*

	EXPLORE ACTIVITY 1
AL DOK 1 *Recall*	Describe the relationship shown in the table and scatter plot. As the number of hours spent studying increases, the test grade increases with it.
OL DOK 2 *Skills/Concepts*	If you used this data to decide how long to study, how long would you study in order to make a 90 on the test? Sample answer: at least 2 hours
BL DOK 3 *Strategic Thinking*	Suppose the test grades were represented on the horizontal axis and the hours spent studying were represented on the vertical axis. What relationship would the scatter plot show then? Same; it would show an increase with the hours spent studying as the grades increased.

LEVELED QUESTIONS: AL Approaching Level | OL On Level | BL Beyond Level

Interpreting Clusters and Outliers

A **cluster** is a set of closely grouped data. Data may cluster around a point or along a line. An **outlier** is a data point that is very different from the rest of the data in the set.

A scientist gathers information about the eruptions of Old Faithful, a geyser in Yellowstone National Park. She uses the data to create a scatter plot. The data show the length of time between eruptions (interval) and how long the eruption lasts (duration).

A Describe any clusters you see in the scatter plot.

There are clusters around the 50-minute and 80-minute intervals.

B What do the clusters tell you about eruptions of Old Faithful?

There are short wait times followed by short eruptions and longer wait times followed by longer eruptions.

C Describe any outliers you see in the scatter plot.

The point near (57, 3) appears to be an outlier because it does not fall into either cluster.

Math Talk Anno: Yes; because it would not fall near either cluster, it would satisfy the conditions for being an outlier.

Math Talk
Mathematical Processes

If the point (20, 1) appeared on the scatter plot, would it be an outlier? Explain.

Reflect

3. Suppose the geyser erupts for 2.2 minutes after a 75-minute interval. Would this point lie in one of the clusters? Would it be an outlier? Explain your answer.

No, the interval was too long for the first cluster, and the duration was too short for the second cluster. It might be considered an outlier because it is not very close to the rest of the data.

4. Suppose the geyser erupts after an 80-minute interval. Give a range of possible duration times for which the point on the scatter plot would not be considered an outlier. Explain your reasoning.

Sample range: 3 to 5 minutes. The duration for other data points on the scatter plot that have an interval of 80 minutes are within this range.

© Houghton Mifflin Harcourt Publishing Company • Image Credits: ©PhotoDisc/Getty Images

---

	EXPLORE ACTIVITY 2
AL) DOK 1 *Recall*	How many clusters are there in this scatter plot? Where? 2 clusters; one around 2 minutes in duration and another around 4.5 minutes in duration.
OL) DOK 2 *Skills/Concepts*	For an eruption that occurs 90 minutes after the previous one, what approximate duration might be considered an outlier? Sample answer: less than 3.25 minutes or greater than 5.5 minutes
BL) DOK 3 *Strategic Thinking*	Suppose an eruption lasting 2 minutes occurs 70 minutes after the previous eruption. In what way is this unusual? In what way is it not unusual? It has the duration you would predict for an eruption 50 minutes after the previous one, instead of 70 minutes; there are many other eruptions that are about 2 minutes in duration.

---

3 Explain

Avoid Common Errors

A common error is to try to connect the points of a scatter plot. Point out that a scatter plot shows all of the collected data, and that it is incorrect and misleading to connect the points in a jagged line.

EXPLORE ACTIVITY 2

Talk About It

Check for Understanding

Ask: How can you identify an outlier in a scatter plot? An outlier can be identified in a scatter plot as a point that is separated from all other data points. It does not fall within any cluster.

TEACHER TO TEACHER

Kinesthetic Experience Clear space on a wall and make a large first quadrant coordinate plane using chalk or long strips of paper, with height as the vertical axis and months of the year as the horizontal axis. Then ask the students to place themselves on the scatter plot according to their birth month, and mark their heights. Depending on space, you may need to divide the class into groups and have them take turns. Have students describe the type(s) of association shown in the human scatter plot.

EXAMPLE 1

ADDITIONAL EXAMPLE 1 Juan recorded the shoe size and the math test scores of several students. The scatter plot shows what he recorded. Describe the association between test score and shoe size. no association

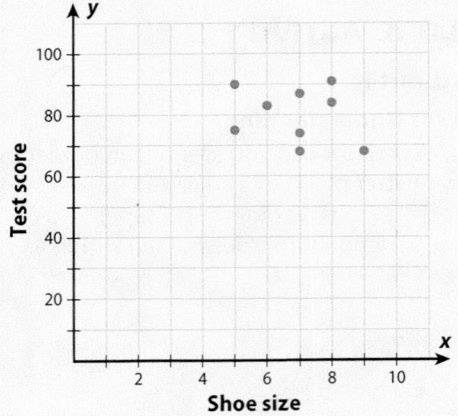

Interactive Whiteboard
Interactive example available online

Animated Math

Scatter Plots and Association
Students model real-world data by creating scatter plots; students then engage in exploring associations in the data.

my.hrw.com

YOUR TURN MP.1

Engage with the Whiteboard

 Ask students if they see any clusters or outliers, and have them come up and circle them. They could say the points are clustered along a line with positive slope in **Exercise 6**, and the point (6, 45) could be recognized as an outlier.

Digital Teacher Resources

Go online to access all your lesson-level resources.

Differentiated Instruction
• Reteach
• Reading Strategies
• Success for English Learners
• Practice and Problem Solving A/B, C, D

Math on the Spot Videos

my.hrw.com

Determining Association

Association describes how sets of data are related. A *positive* association means that both data sets increase together. A *negative* association means that as one data set increases, the other decreases. *No* association means that there is no relationship between the two data sets.

Math On the Spot
my.hrw.com

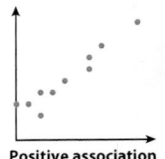
Positive association

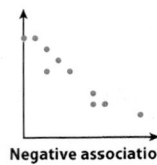
Negative association

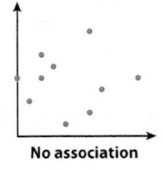
No association

Data that show a positive or negative association and lie basically along a line exhibit a *linear* association. Data that show a positive or negative association but do not lie basically along a line exhibit a *nonlinear* association.

EXAMPLE 1 (Real World)

Susan asked 20 people if they would buy a new product she developed at each of several prices. The scatter plot shows how many of the 20 said "yes" at a given price. Describe the association between price and the number of buyers.

As price increases, the number of buyers decreases. So, there is a negative association. Because the data points do not lie along a line, the association is nonlinear.

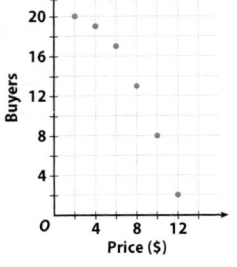

Animated Math
my.hrw.com

Reflect

5. **What If?** Based on the association shown in the scatter plot, what might happen if Susan increased the price to $14?

It is likely that no one would buy the product.

YOUR TURN

6. The plot shows the reading level and height for 16 students in a district. Describe the association and give a possible reason for it.

Positive and basically linear:

Older students would be taller

and read at a higher level.

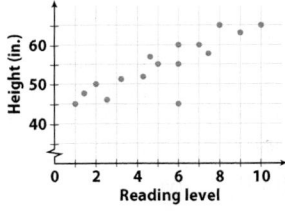

Personal Math Trainer
Online Assessment and Intervention
my.hrw.com

Lesson 14.1 **435**

© Houghton Mifflin Harcourt Publishing Company

DIFFERENTIATE INSTRUCTION *Leveled Questions*

	EXAMPLE 1
AL DOK 1 *Recall*	What is the maximum number of buyers possible in this example? Explain. 20; there are 20 people surveyed.
OL DOK 2 *Skills/Concepts*	What does it mean for bivariate data to have a nonlinear association? It means that the data show a positive or negative relationship, but the points do not fall along a line; that is, they may fall along a curve.
BL DOK 3 *Strategic Thinking*	What would be the association in the graph if the same survey data were graphed on a coordinate plane with the vertical axis recording NON-Buyers and the horizontal axis were the same? The association would be positive; as price increased, the number of people NOT buying would increase (beginning with 0 at the lowest price).

LEVELED QUESTIONS: AL Approaching Level | **OL** On Level | **BL** Beyond Level

Bob recorded his height at different ages. The table below shows his data.

Age (years)	6	8	10	12	14
Height (inches)	45	50	55	61	63

1. Make a scatter plot of Bob's data. (Explore Activity 1)

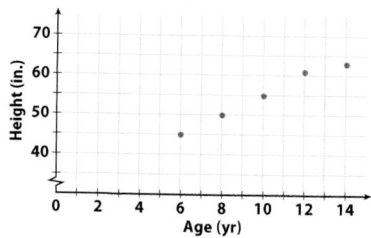

2. Describe the association between Bob's age and his height. Explain the association. (Example 1)

Positive and basically linear; as Bob gets older, his height increases. But if the data continued for increasing age, we would see that Bob's height stops increasing.

3. The scatter plot shows the basketball shooting results for 14 players. Describe any clusters you see in the scatter plot. Identify any outliers. (Explore Activity 2)

There is a cluster in the 20—23 shots attempted range, and a lesser one in the 7—14 shots attempted range. The point (35, 18) is an outlier.

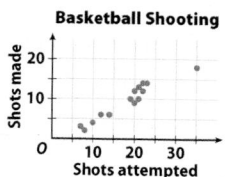

ESSENTIAL QUESTION CHECK-IN

4. Explain how you can make a scatter plot from a set of bivariate data.

Let the numbers on the x-axis represent one variable and the numbers on the y-axis represent the other variable. Then plot points (x, y) for each pair of numbers in the bivariate data set.

© Houghton Mifflin Harcourt Publishing Company

4 Elaborate

Talk About It

Summarize the Lesson

Ask: Which scatter plot shows a negative association? a positive association? no association? Label each plot with the correct type of association.

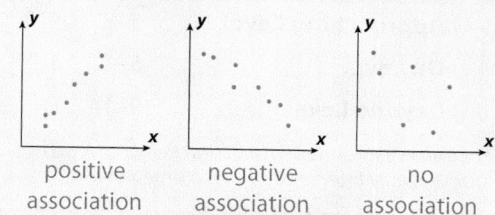

positive association   negative association   no association

Guided Practice

Engage with the Whiteboard

Ask student volunteers to complete **Exercise 1**. Discuss the type(s) of association between Bob's age in years and his height.

Avoid Common Errors

Exercise 3 Students may fail to identify the point at (35, 18) as an outlier because it fits the general trend of the data. Point out that if most of the data are clearly clustered, any point that lies outside the cluster or clusters is an outlier.

DIFFERENTIATE INSTRUCTION *Intervention and Additional Support*

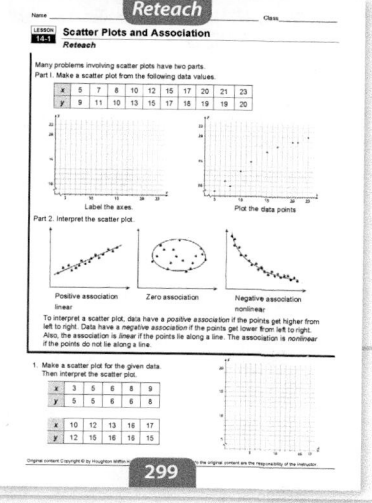

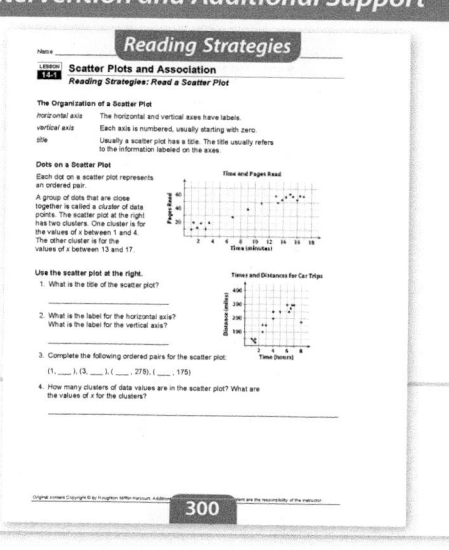

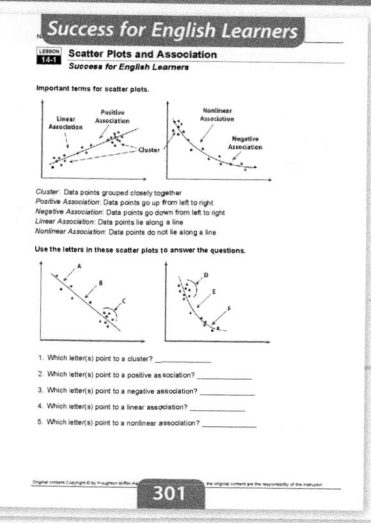

Personal Math Trainer
Daily Intervention
14.1 Homework

Pages shown are from *Differentiated Instruction.*
Also available online.

5 Evaluate

 **Pressed for Time**

14.1 Differentiated Homework Assignments

(AL)	**Approaching Level**	5–8, 10–12
(OL)	**On Level**	5–11, 13
(BL)	**Beyond Level**	9–14

*For **Below Level** students, assign Personal Math Trainer, Daily Intervention 14.1 Homework.*

Mathematical Processes	Exercises
MP.3 Logic	13–14
MP.6 Precision	10–11
MP.7 Using Structure	5–9, 12

Focus on Higher Order Thinking

Depth of Knowledge	Exercises
2 Skills/Concepts	5–11
3 Strategic Thinking H.O.T.\	12–14

14.1 Independent Practice

Personal Math Trainer
Online Assessment and Intervention
my.hrw.com

Sports Use the scatter plot for 5–8.

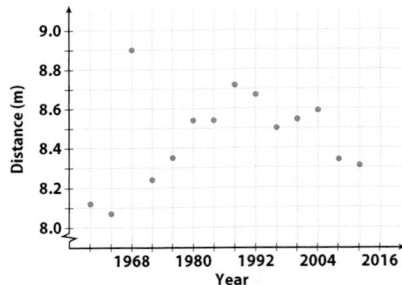

Olympic Men's Long Jump Winning Distances

5. Describe the association between the year and the distance jumped for the years 1960 to 1988.

The data generally show a positive linear association. As the years increase, so does the winning distance.

6. Describe the association between the year and the distance jumped for the years after 1988.

Overall, the data from 1988 to 2012 generally show a negative association, even though the 8 year period from 1996 to 2004 looked at by itself shows a slight rise in distance jumped over time.

7. For the entire scatter plot, is the association between the year and the distance jumped linear or nonlinear?

Nonlinear; the data points first rise as the years increased from 1960 to 1988 and then fall as the years increase from 1988 to 2012, so there is no overall linear pattern.

8. Identify the outlier and interpret its meaning.

(1968, 8.9); the outlier represents a jump of 8.9 meters in 1968, a jump that far exceeds any jump made in prior or later years.

9. **Communicate Mathematical Ideas** Compare a scatter plot that shows no association to one that shows negative association.

Sample answer: A plot with no association has randomly scattered data points. There does not appear to be any pattern in the association. On a plot with negative association, the data points fall from left to right. As one data set increases the other decreases.

Lesson 14.1 **437**

© Houghton Mifflin Harcourt Publishing Company

DIFFERENTIATE INSTRUCTION *Leveled Homework/Practice*

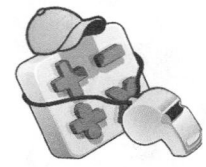

Personal Math Trainer
- 14.1 Homework

Pages shown are from *Differentiated Instruction.* **Also available online.**

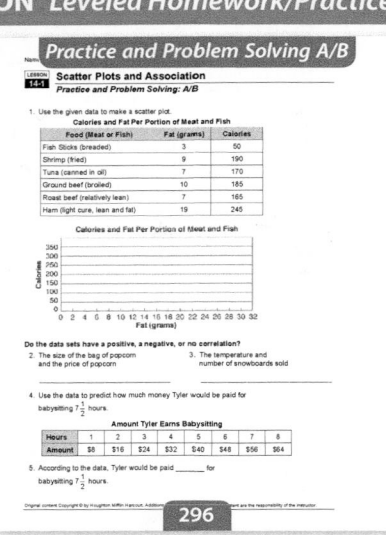

Practice and Problem Solving A/B

296

Practice and Problem Solving C

297

Practice and Problem Solving D

298

For 10–11, describe a set of real-world bivariate data that the given scatter plot could represent. Define the variable represented on each axis.

10.

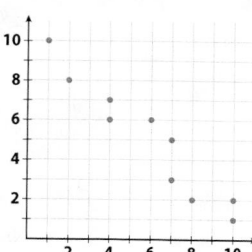

Sample answer: *x*-axis is number of people doing a job; *y*-axis is number of hours to do the job

11.

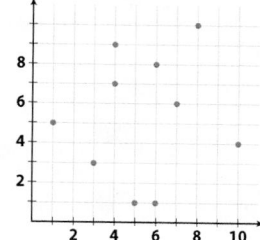

Sample answer: *x*-axis is miles student lives from school; *y*-axis is student's score on a 10-pt quiz

H.O.T. FOCUS ON HIGHER ORDER THINKING

12. Multiple Representations Describe what you might see in a table of bivariate data that would lead you to conclude that the scatter plot of the data would show a cluster.

Sample answer: You would see a number of data items with *x*-values and *y*-values that are close to one another.

13. Justify Reasoning Is it possible for a scatter plot to have a positive or negative association that is not linear? Explain.

Yes; for example, the data points may appear to lie mostly along a rising or falling curve, or may generally rise or fall, but not in a way that suggests a linear association.

14. Critical Thinking To try to increase profits, a theater owner increases the price of a ticket by $25 every month. Describe what a scatter plot might look like if *x* represents the number of months and *y* represents the profits. Explain your reasoning.

Sample answer: Initially, the number of tickets sold might decline a little, but the price increase would offset the loss in sales. So, profits would increase, showing a positive association. When the price got too high, ticket sales would decline more rapidly, so profits would fall, giving a negative association.

Work Area

© Houghton Mifflin Harcourt Publishing Company

DIFFERENTIATE INSTRUCTION *Extend-the-Math Activity* **PRE-AP**

Activity Use a graphing calculator to create a scatter plot of the height and points scored during the season for each player on the school basketball team. Then describe the type(s) of association you see between the height and number of points scored. There is no association in the data sets.

Height	Points
72, 68, 65, 73, 67, 78, 71, 72, 75, 77, 77, 78	85, 87, 62, 78, 78, 58, 24, 45, 52, 87, 79, 90

Press **STAT** and select "1: Edit" to enter the values for height and points into two lists L1 and L2. Press **2nd** **Y=** , choose "1:", select "On", then choose the scatter plot (first style), L1, and L2. Press **ZOOM** and choose "9: ZoomStat" to see the scatter plot.

✓ **Quick Check**

14.1 Lesson Quiz

Use the table for Exercises 1–2.

Height (in.)	Weight (lb)	Height (in.)	Weight (lb)
50	83	60	98
53	90	65	97
56	86	65	103
57	92	68	100

1. Make a scatter plot of the data.

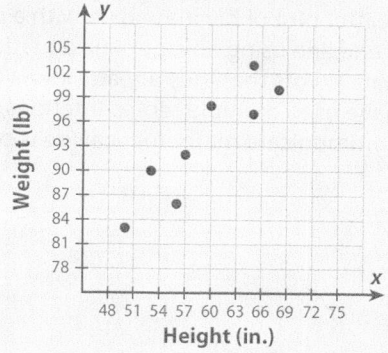

2. Describe the type(s) of association you see between the height and the weight. Explain.
Positive and linear; weight increases with height.

For Exercises 3–4, use the scatter plot.

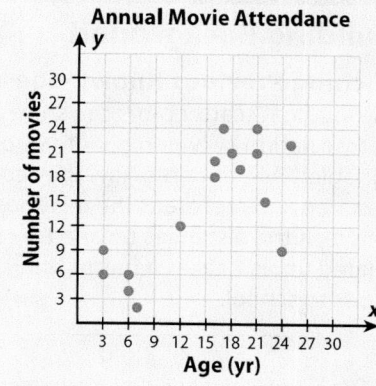

3. Describe any clusters you see. clusters around age 6 and 18

4. Describe any outliers you see. (24, 9); (12, 12)

Differentiate Instruction

IF a student misses more than one question, THEN

Differentiate Instruction:
• 14.1 Reteach
• Personal Math Trainer

Interactive Whiteboard
Interactive Lesson quiz available online

Lesson Support

Content Objective Students will learn how to use a trend line to make a prediction from a scatter plot.

Professional Development

Integrate Mathematical Processes MP.6

This lesson provides an opportunity to address this Mathematical Processes standard. It calls for students to communicate precisely to others. Students draw a trend line for a scatter plot of bivariate data with a positive linear association. Then students represent the trend line using an algebraic equation and use the equation to predict a value between data points that they already know or outside the data they know. In this way, students have used multiple representations, including symbols, graphs, and language, to communicate mathematical ideas precisely.

FOCUS

Building Background

Eliciting Previous Knowledge Review the fact that scatter plots can show patterns of association between quantities or variables. Ask students how they could describe and represent the relationship between the distances traveled and the related times it takes a bus to bring students to school.

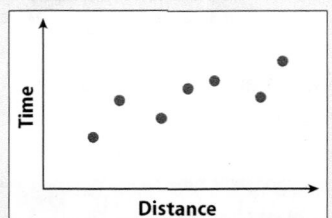

COHERENCE

Learning Progressions

In this lesson, students expand their understanding of patterns of association in bivariate data by using trend lines and related linear equations from scatter plots to make predictions. Important understandings include the following:

- **A trend line is a straight line that comes closest to the points on a scatter plot.**
- **Two points on a trend line can be used to write an equation in slope-intercept form for the trend line.**
- **A trend line or its equation can be used to interpolate, or predict, a value between already known data points.**
- **Extrapolating is making a prediction that is outside known data.**

By representing and analyzing bivariate data in scatter plots and making predictions, students prepare to further investigate patterns of association in two-way tables in Module 15.

RIGOR

Cluster Connections

This lesson provides an excellent opportunity to connect ideas in this cluster:

Investigate patterns of association in bivariate data.

Tell students that the following points are on a scatter plot that shows the relationship between x, the number of cold days in a month, and y, the number of pairs of gloves sold. Ask students to write an equation for a trend line.

(2, 2), (3, 3), (4, 2), (5, 3), (6, 5), (7, 3), (7, 6), (8, 6), (9, 8), (10,6)

Answers may vary. Sample answer: $y = \frac{3}{4}x$

Language Support **ELL**

Leveled Strategies for English Learners **ELL**

Emerging

Have students at this level of English proficiency work in pairs to copy the graph from Example 1 and the steps for writing an equation for the trend line. Have them decide whether or not the equation for this trend line is $y = 10x$.

Expanding

Have students at this level of English proficiency work in pairs to read aloud and list the steps for writing an equation for the trend line in Example 1. Have them identify the points above and below the trend line.

Bridging

Have students at this level of English proficiency work in pairs to discuss the steps for writing an equation for the trend line in Example 1. Have them try out other points to see if they fit the trend line.

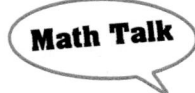

Math Talk Write out and model for students a sentence frame to begin their answer.

These two points are the best because trend lines should have about the same _____.

Linguistic Support **ELL**

Academic/Content Vocabulary

This lesson relies on students' understanding of the meaning of the terms *trend line*, *linear*, *interpolate*, and *extrapolate*. While some English learners might have encountered the word *trend* in everyday language, it is probably new to them in math. Also, point out that the word *linear* has the word *line* in it, which might help them remember what it means. For Spanish-speaking English learners, it may be helpful for them to learn that *interpolate* and *extrapolate* are English/Spanish cognates: *interpolar*, *extrapolar*.

Building Background

In this lesson students are asked to write an equation for the trend line in a scatter plot showing the relationship between the number of rainy days in a month and umbrellas sold. Adding the suffix *-y* changes the noun *rain* to the adjective *rainy*. English learners will be familiar with many other English noun-to-adjective conversions with the suffix *-y*, such as *rain/rainy*, *cloud/cloudy*, *snow/snowy*, *wind/windy*, and *sun/sunny*.

Image Credits: ©Lars Christensen/Fotolia

Trend Lines and Predictions

1 Engage

❓ ESSENTIAL QUESTION

How can you use a trend line to make a prediction from a scatter plot? Sample answer: Draw a trend line that fits the points as closely as possible. Then write an equation for that line, and use it to make predictions by substituting and solving.

Motivate the Lesson

Ask: Are you able to predict how far you can run in 5 minutes? in 30 minutes? Begin the Explore Activity to find out.

2 Explore

EXPLORE ACTIVITY 1

Focus on Patterns

Point out that trend lines should only be drawn if there is a clear linear association in the data once it is displayed in a scatter plot. Emphasize that you disregard the outliers when drawing a trend line because they do not fit the trend.

Trend Lines and Predictions

❓ ESSENTIAL QUESTION

How can you use a trend line to make a prediction from a scatter plot?

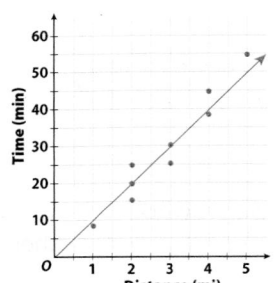

EXPLORE ACTIVITY 1 — Real World

Drawing a Trend Line

When a scatter plot shows a linear association, you can use a line to model the relationship between the variables. A **trend line** is a straight line that comes closest to the points on a scatter plot.

Joyce is training for a 10K race. For some of her training runs, she records the distance she ran and how many minutes she ran.

A Make a scatter plot of Joyce's running data.

Distance (mi)	Time (min)
4	38
2	25
1	7
2	16
3	26
5	55
2	20
4	45
3	31

B To draw a trend line, use a straight edge to draw a line that has about the same number of points above and below it. Ignore any outliers.

C Use your trend line to predict how long it would take Joyce to run 4.5 miles.

about 45 minutes

Reflect

1. How well does your trend line fit the data? Explain.

All the data points are close to the line. The data show a strong linear association, so the line should fit well.

© Houghton Mifflin Harcourt Publishing Company • Image Credits: ©Comstock Images/Getty Images

---

DIFFERENTIATE INSTRUCTION *Leveled Questions*

	EXPLORE ACTIVITY 1
AL **DOK 1** *Recall*	Using the trend line, how far would you predict that Joyce would run in 35 minutes? about 3.5 miles
OL **DOK 2** *Skills/Concepts*	How would you feel about making a prediction using a trend line if the data were scattered around and not close to the line at all? Explain. Not sure; if the data does not show a strong association, it would be difficult to trust any prediction from a trend line.
BL **DOK 3** *Strategic Thinking*	Suppose Joyce had an outlier time, such as running, say, 3 miles in 55 minutes. How would that affect the trend line? It should not affect the trend line because outliers should be ignored.

LEVELED QUESTIONS: **AL** Approaching Level | **OL** On Level | **BL** Beyond Level

2. Do you think you can use a scatter plot that shows no association to make a prediction? Explain your answer.

No; no association means that there is no relationship between the variables and the scatter plot shows no pattern.

Math On the Spot
my.hrw.com

Finding the Equation of a Trend Line

You can use two points on a trend line to write an equation in slope-intercept form for the trend line.

EXAMPLE 1 Real World

The scatter plot and trend line show the relationship between the number of chapters and the total number of pages for several books. Write an equation for the trend line.

STEP 1 Find the slope of the trend line. The line passes through points (5, 50) and (17, 170).

$m = \dfrac{y_2 - y_1}{x_2 - x_1}$ Use the slope formula.

$m = \dfrac{170 - 50}{17 - 5}$ Substitute (5, 50) for (x_1, y_1) and (17, 170) for (x_2, y_2).

$m = \dfrac{120}{12} = 10$ Simplify.

> **Math Talk**
> **Mathematical Processes**
> Why are (5, 50) and (17, 170) the best points to use to draw the trend line?

Trend lines should have about the same number of points above the line as below it. By using (5, 50) and (17, 170), you get four points above the line and four points below it.

STEP 2 Find the y-intercept of the trend line.

$y = mx + b$ Slope-intercept form

$50 = 10 \cdot 5 + b$ Substitute 50 for y, 10 for m, and 5 for x.

$50 = 50 + b$ Simplify.

$50 - 50 = 50 - 50 + b$ Subtract 50 from both sides.

$0 = b$ Simplify.

STEP 3 Use your slope and y-intercept values to write the equation.

$y = mx + b$ Slope-intercept form

$y = 10x + 0$ Substitute 10 for m and 0 for y.

The equation for the trend line is $y = 10x$.

© Houghton Mifflin Harcourt Publishing Company

---

3 Explain

EXAMPLE 1

ADDITIONAL EXAMPLE 1 The scatter plot and trend line show the relationship between the number of customers that enter an electronics store in a day and the number of TVs sold. Write an equation for the trend line. Answers may vary; sample answer: $y = 0.05x$

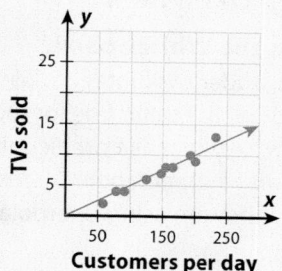

Interactive Whiteboard
Interactive example available online

Avoid Common Errors
A common error is to attempt to use the trend line to connect as many points of a scatter plot as possible. Point out that this may not be the best trend line, however, because it may make other data points too far away from the line and, therefore, not give the best fit.

	EXAMPLE 1
(AL) DOK 1 *Recall*	What two points are used to find the equation for the trend line in this example? (5, 50) and (17, 170)
(OL) DOK 2 *Skills/Concepts*	When using two points to write an equation for the trend line, should the points be data points or points on the trend line? Choose two points on the trend line to find the equation for the trend line; they may or may not be data points.
(BL) DOK 3 *Strategic Thinking*	If labels on the axes were swapped, would the association still be positive? Explain. The data shows that as the number of chapters in a book increases, the number of pages in the book also increases. If the labels were swapped, the association would still be positive, showing that as the number of pages increases, the number of chapters also increases.

TEACHER TO TEACHER

Curriculum Connection Ask students to brainstorm situations in social studies, science, or finance in which scatter plots and trend lines could be useful to show relationships or make predictions. For example, in social studies trend lines could be used to predict population growth, in biology a scatter plot could show relationships between temperature and plant growth, and businesses could use trend lines to help make decisions on future investments or products.

Avoid Common Errors

Suggest that students not pick two points that are close together to calculate the slope. Students may pick (0, 0) and (1, 1) and get a slope of 1. Point out that the line passes through (10, 9), which can be used with (0, 0) to get a more accurate value for the slope.

EXPLORE ACTIVITY 2

Engage with the Whiteboard

   Invite a student volunteer to use the equation of the trend line for the data in Your Turn Exercise 6 to make predictions using interpolation and extrapolation. Discuss how they know whether they are using interpolation or extrapolation.

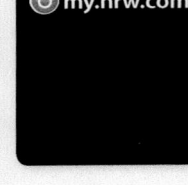

Digital Teacher Resources

Go online to access all your lesson-level resources.

Differentiated Instruction
- Reteach
- Reading Strategies
- Success for English Learners
- Practice and Problem Solving A/B, C, D

Math on the Spot Videos

my.hrw.com

Reflect

3. What type(s) of association does the scatter plot show?
   <u>positive; linear</u>

4. What is the meaning of the slope in this situation?
   <u>There is an average of 10 pages per chapter.</u>

5. What is the meaning of the *y*-intercept in this situation?
   <u>the number of pages in a book with 0 chapters (0)</u>

YOUR TURN

6. The scatter plot and trend line show the relationship between the number of rainy days in a month and the number of umbrellas sold each month. Write an equation for the trend line.
   <u>Answers may vary.</u>
   Sample answer: $y = \frac{9}{10}x$

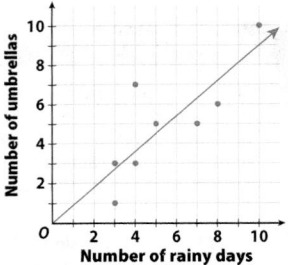

Personal Math Trainer
Online Assessment and Intervention
my.hrw.com

© Houghton Mifflin Harcourt Publishing Company

EXPLORE ACTIVITY 2 *Real World*

Making Predictions

When you use a trend line or its equation to predict a value between data points that you already know, you *interpolate* the predicted value. When you make a prediction that is outside the data that you know, you *extrapolate* the predicted value.

Use the equation of the trend line in Example 1 to predict how many pages would be in a book with 26 chapters.

Is this prediction an example of interpolation or extrapolation? <u>extrapolation</u>

$y = \boxed{10x}$ *Write the equation for your trend line.*

$y = \boxed{10(26)}$ *Substitute the number of chapters for x.*

$y = \boxed{260}$ *Simplify.*

I predict that a book with 26 chapters will have <u>260</u> pages.

DIFFERENTIATE INSTRUCTION *Leveled Questions*

	EXPLORE ACTIVITY 2
(AL) DOK 1 *Recall*	What does it mean to use interpolation? extrapolation? Interpolation is to predict points within the range of known points; extrapolation is to predict points outside the range of known points.
(OL) DOK 2 *Skills/Concepts*	Explain why predicting the number of pages in a book with 26 chapters is extrapolation. The greatest number of chapters in the data set is a 20-chapter book. A prediction about a 26-chapter book will estimate a value beyond the known values.
(BL) DOK 3 *Strategic Thinking*	Which would you expect to be less reliable: interpolation or extrapolation? Explain your reasoning. Extrapolation; interpolation predicts within the domain for which the test was performed. Extrapolation predicts outside of the domain for which the test was performed, so the trend may not continue to be true.

LEVELED QUESTIONS: (AL) Approaching Level | (OL) On Level | (BL) Beyond Level

Reflect

7. **Make a Prediction** Predict how many pages would be in a book with 14 chapters. Is this prediction an example of interpolation or extrapolation?

    140 pages; interpolation

8. Do you think that extrapolation or interpolation is more accurate? Explain.

    Sample answer: Interpolation; the predicted value fits between known points where the trend is known. There is no guarantee that a trend will continue beyond the known data points.

Guided Practice

Angela recorded the price of different weights of several bulk grains. She made a scatter plot of her data. Use the scatter plot for 1–4.

Answers for 1–4 may vary slightly.

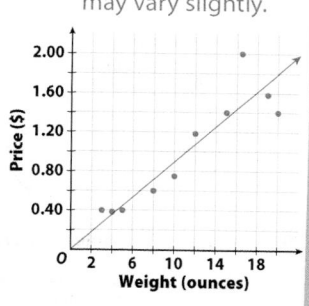

1. Draw a trend line for the scatter plot. (Explore Activity 1)

2. How do you know whether your trend line is a good fit for the data? (Explore Activity 1)

    Most of the data points are close to the trend line and there is about the same number of points above and below the line.

3. Write an equation for your trend line. (Example 1) $y = 0.09x$

4. Use the equation for your trend line to interpolate the price of 7 ounces and extrapolate the price of 50 ounces.

    (Explore Activity 2) $0.63; $4.50

? ESSENTIAL QUESTION CHECK-IN

5. A trend line passes through two points on a scatter plot. How can you use the trend line to make a prediction between or outside the given data points?

    Use the two points to write the equation of the line. Substitute in the equation the value of x for which you want to make a prediction. The value of y that you obtain is the prediction.

© Houghton Mifflin Harcourt Publishing Company

④ Elaborate

Talk About It

Summarize the Lesson

Have students fill in the blanks in the graphic organizer below to show the steps to find the equation of a trend line. Sample answers are shown.

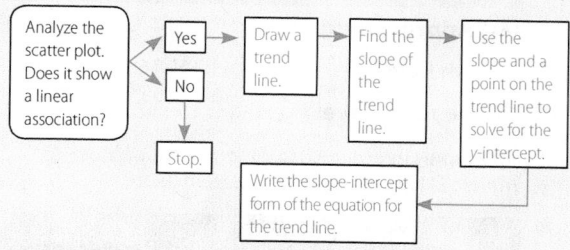

Guided Practice

Engage with the Whiteboard

Ask a student to complete **Exercise 1** at the board. Have him or her mark two points on the line and use them to calculate the slope and y-intercept for **Exercise 3**. Have a student mark a point on the line to check the reasonableness of the answer found for **Exercise 4**.

Avoid Common Errors

*   **Exercise 1** A common error is to try to connect the points of the scatter plot. Point out that this would not give a single straight line. Emphasize that they cannot find the equation of a jagged line, and therefore cannot make predictions using it.

*   **Exercise 2** A common error is to assume a good fit for the line is if the trend line goes through as many data values as possible. Point out that this may place more values farther away from the line than if equal numbers of points lie above and below the line.

DIFFERENTIATE INSTRUCTION *Intervention and Additional Support*

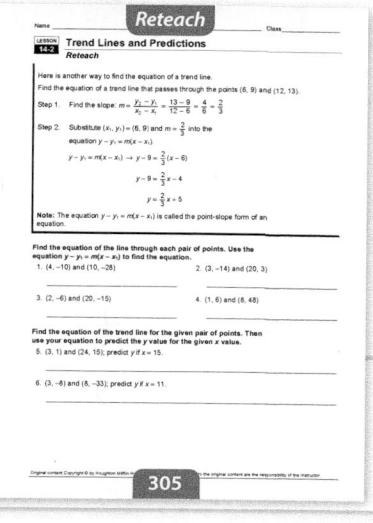

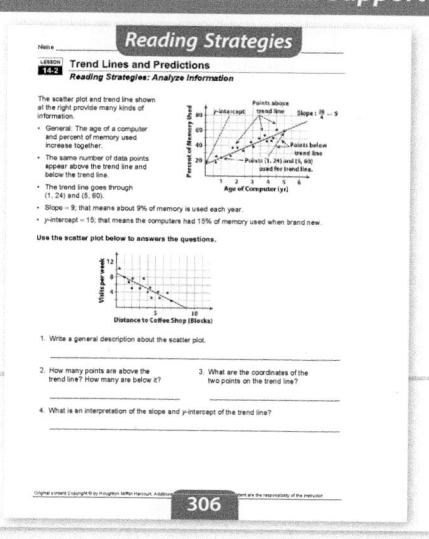

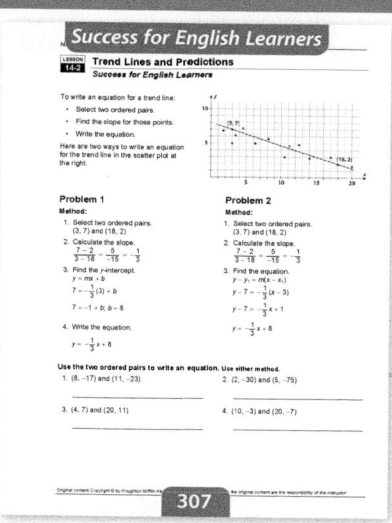

Personal Math Trainer
Daily Intervention
14.2 Homework

Pages shown are from *Differentiated Instruction*.
Also available online.

5 Evaluate

Independent Practice

Pressed for Time

14.2 Differentiated Homework Assignments

(AL) **Approaching Level**	6–14	
(OL) **On Level**	11–16	
(BL) **Beyond Level**	15–17	

*For **Below Level** students, assign Personal Math Trainer, Daily Intervention 14.2 Homework.*

Mathematical Processes	Exercises
MP.3 Logic	15–17
MP.4 Modeling	6–14

Focus on Higher Order Thinking

Depth of Knowledge	Exercises
2 Skills/Concepts	6–14
3 Strategic Thinking H.O.T.	15–17

14.2 Independent Practice

Personal Math Trainer
my.hrw.com
Online Assessment and Intervention

Answers for 6–14 may vary slightly.

Use the data in the table for Exercises 6–10.

Apparent Temperature Due to Wind at 15 °F						
Wind speed (mi/h)	10	20	30	40	50	60
Wind chill (°F)	2.7	−2.3	−5.5	−7.9	−9.8	−11.4

6. Make a scatter plot of the data and draw a trend line.

7. What type of association does the trend line show?
_____ negative; basically linear _____

8. Write an equation for your trend line. Sample answer: $y = -\frac{1}{4}x + 3$

9. **Make a Prediction** Use the trend line to predict the wind chill at these wind speeds.

  a. 36 mi/h _about −6 °F_   **b.** 100 mi/h _about −22 °F_

10. What is the meaning of the slope of the line?
The wind chill falls about 1 degree for every increase of
4 miles per hour in wind speed.

Apparent Temperature Due to Wind at 15 °F

(graph: Wind chill (°F) vs Wind speed (mi/h))

Use the data in the table for Exercises 11–14.

Apparent Temperature Due to Humidity at a Room Temperature of 72 °F						
Humidity (%)	0	20	40	60	80	100
Apparent temperature (°F)	64	67	70	72	74	76

11. Make a scatter plot of the data and draw a trend line.

12. Write an equation for your trend line.
Sample answer: $y = \frac{2}{15}x + 64$

13. **Make a Prediction** Use the trend line to predict the apparent temperature at 70% humidity. _____ about 73 °F

14. What is the meaning of the y-intercept of the line?
At 0% humidity, the apparent temperature is 64 °F.

Apparent Temperature at a Room Temperature of 72 °F

(graph: Apparent temperature (°F) vs Humidity (%))

© Houghton Mifflin Harcourt Publishing Company

DIFFERENTIATE INSTRUCTION *Leveled Homework/Practice*

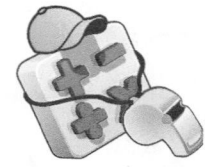

Personal Math Trainer
• 14.2 Homework

Pages shown are from
Differentiated Instruction.
Also available online.

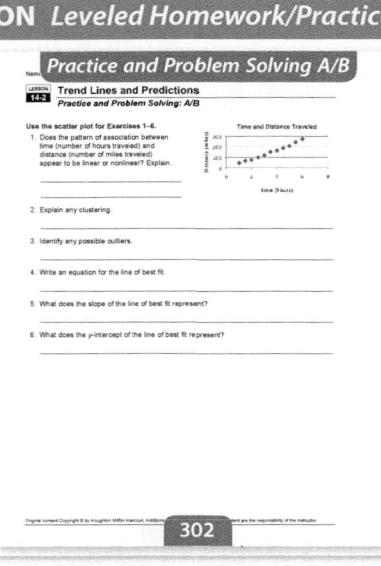

Practice and Problem Solving A/B

302

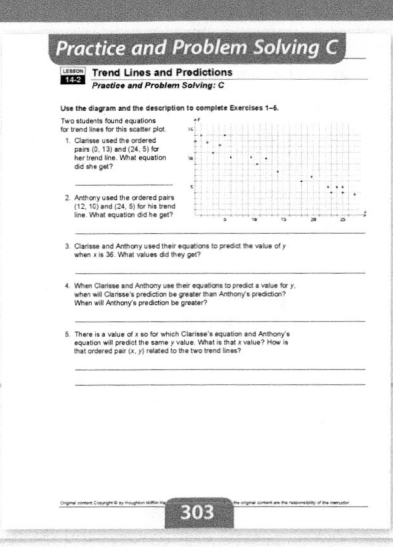

Practice and Problem Solving C

303

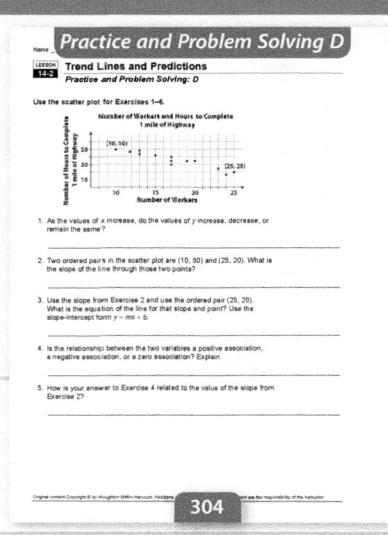

Practice and Problem Solving D

304

Work Area

15. Communicate Mathematical Ideas Is it possible to draw a trend line on a scatter plot that shows no association? Explain.

No; if the scatter plot shows no association, the data points have no relationship to one another. Unless there is a linear association you cannot draw a trend line.

16. Critique Reasoning Sam drew a trend line that had about the same number of data points above it as below it, but did not pass through any data points. He then picked two data points to write the equation for the line. Is this a correct way to write the equation? Explain.

No; although Sam drew the trend line correctly, he should use two points on the line to write the equation. Choosing two data points that are not on the line will result in an incorrect equation for the line.

17. Marlene wanted to find a relationship between the areas and populations of counties in Texas. She plotted x (area in square miles) and y (population) for two counties on a scatter plot:

Kent County (903, 808)   Edwards County (2118, 2002)

She concluded that the population of Texas counties is approximately equal to their area in square miles and drew a trend line through her points.

a. Critique Reasoning Do you agree with Marlene's method of creating a scatter plot and a trend line? Explain why or why not.

No; two points are not sufficient for creating a scatter plot or a trend line. Marlene should have plotted data points for many more counties.

b. Counterexamples Harris County has an area of 1778 square miles and a population of about 4.3 million people. Dallas County has an area of 908 square miles and a population of about 2.5 million people. What does this data show about Marlene's conjecture that the population of Texas counties is approximately equal to their area?

Sample answer: Marlene's conjecture is incorrect. Marlene chose counties whose areas are about equal to their populations. Harris and Dallas counties provide counterexamples for Marlene's original data.

© Houghton Mifflin Harcourt Publishing Company

DIFFERENTIATE INSTRUCTION *Extend-the-Math Activity* **PRE-AP**

Activity Use a graphing calculator to find the equation of a trend line for a scatter plot of the data. Then use the trend line to predict the distance traveled in 12 hours. 701 mi

Time (h)	2	4	5.5	6	7	9	10
Distance (mi)	115	250	330	340	400	540	580

Follow the instructions given in Extend the Math for Lesson 14.1 to make a scatter plot of the data. Press **STAT**, select the "CALC" menu, then select "4: LinReg (ax+b)" and press **ENTER**. Press **Y=** and then press **VARS** and choose "5: Statistics". Select the EQ menu and choose "1: RegEQ". Press **ZOOM** and choose "9: ZoomStat" to see the trend line.

✔ Quick Check

14.2 Lesson Quiz

Marni recorded the cost of different weights of apples and made a scatter plot of her data. For Exercises 1–5, use the sample trend line drawn in the scatter plot.

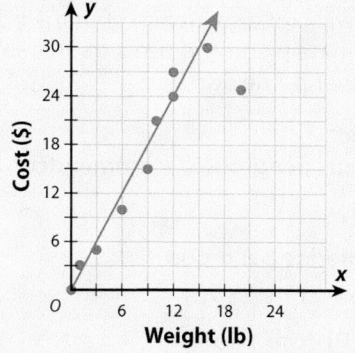

1. What type(s) of association does the scatter plot show? positive, linear

2. Find the slope of the trend line. 2

3. Find the equation of the trend line. $y = 2x$

4. What is the meaning of the slope in this situation? The average cost of the price of apples is $2 per pound.

5. a. Use the equation of the trend line to predict the cost of buying 5 pounds of apples. $10

   b. Is this prediction an example of interpolation or extrapolation? interpolation

Differentiate Instruction

IF a student misses more than one question, THEN

Differentiate Instruction:
- 14.2 Reteach
- Personal Math Trainer

 Interactive Whiteboard
Interactive Lesson quiz available online

Prime Predictions

Objective
Students will plot a sequence of prime numbers in the coordinate plane and use a trend line to predict other prime numbers.

Grouping
2–4 students per group (recommended)

Materials
- 1 straightedge per group
- grid paper

Teacher Preparation
Make sure students have the required materials.

Key Concepts
This activity provides students with practice identifying prime numbers and using trend lines to make predictions. Students will:
- identify prime numbers from 1 to 50
- plot the sequence of prime numbers on a coordinate plane
- estimate a trend line for the data in the scatter plot
- use their trend line to predict more prime numbers
- evaluate how well the trend line serves as a model for prime numbers

Encourage students to create the trend line based only on the prime numbers less than 50. Then they can see how well the model fits for prime numbers greater than 50.

Prime Predictions

Recall that a prime number is a number that is divisible by only 1 and itself. There are infinitely many prime numbers, but there is no formula to find them.

$2\,3\,5\,7\,11$

In this activity, you will find prime numbers and attempt to predict prime numbers.

INSTRUCTIONS

STEP 1 Use a Sieve of Eratosthenes to find all prime numbers less than 50.

How to Create a Sieve of Eratosthenes
- Make a list of whole numbers in order from 1 to 50 in boxes of grid paper.
- Cross off 1 because it is not prime.
- The next number, 2, is prime. Circle it. Cross off all multiples of 2 because they are not prime.
- Circle the next number on the list that is not crossed off, 3. It is prime. Cross off all multiples of 3 because they are not prime.
- Continue with the prime number 5 and its multiples.
- Repeat this process until all of the numbers are circled or crossed off. The circled numbers will all be prime numbers.

A partially completed Sieve of Eratosthenes is shown.

1	2	3	4	5	6	7	8	9	10
11	12	13	14	15	16	17	18	19	20
21	22	23	24	25	26	27	28	29	30
31	32	33	34	35	36	37	38	39	40

STEP 2 Create a scatter plot of the first 15 prime numbers.

Prime number, x	2	3	5	7	11	13	17	19	23	29	31	37	41	43	47
Position in sequence, y	1	2	3	4	5	6	7	8	9	10	11	12	13	14	15

● *Use the prime numbers as the x-coordinates and their positions as the y-coordinates.*

© Houghton Mifflin Harcourt Publishing Company

WARM-UP EXERCISES

1. **What is a prime number? What is a composite number?** A whole number with factors of only 1 and itself; any whole number that is not prime.

2. **List the first five prime numbers greater than 1.** 2, 3, 5, 7, 11

STEP 3 Estimate a trend line for your scatter plot.

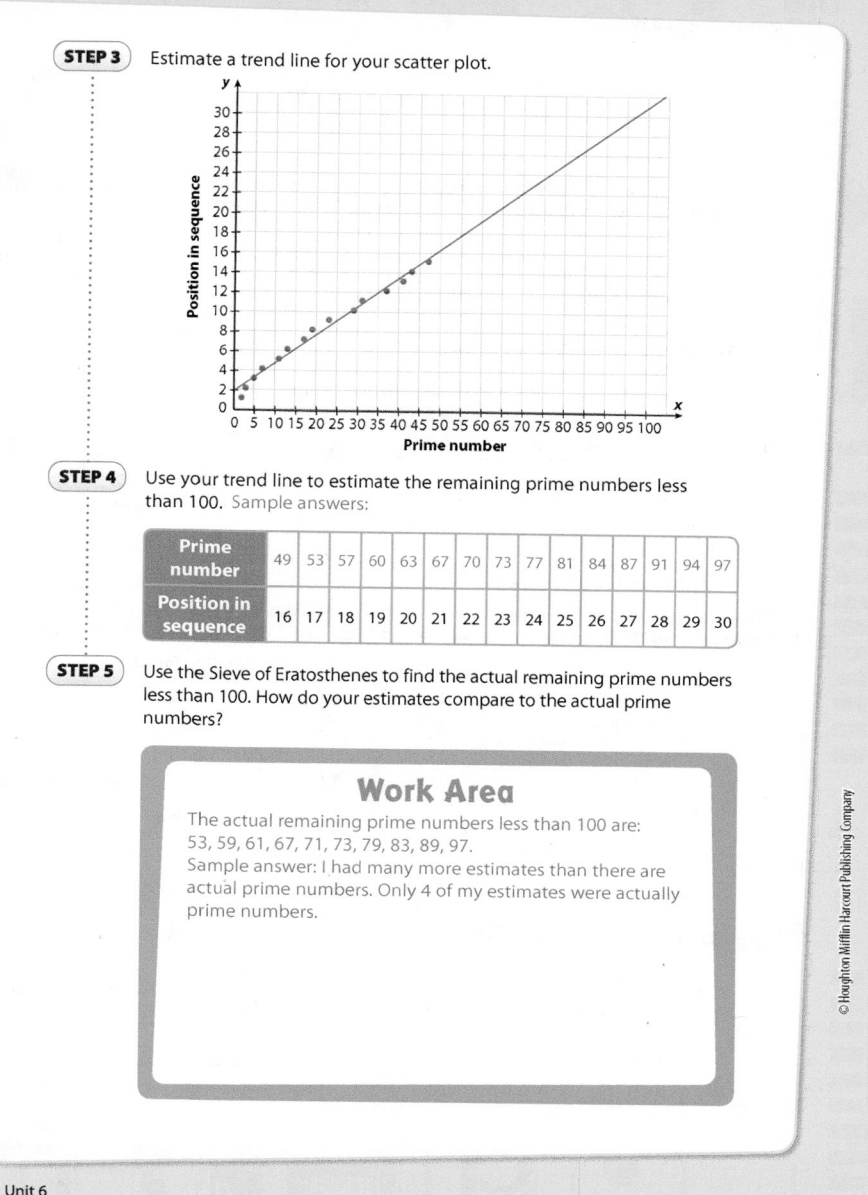

STEP 4 Use your trend line to estimate the remaining prime numbers less than 100. Sample answers:

Prime number	49	53	57	60	63	67	70	73	77	81	84	87	91	94	97
Position in sequence	16	17	18	19	20	21	22	23	24	25	26	27	28	29	30

STEP 5 Use the Sieve of Eratosthenes to find the actual remaining prime numbers less than 100. How do your estimates compare to the actual prime numbers?

Work Area

The actual remaining prime numbers less than 100 are:
53, 59, 61, 67, 71, 73, 79, 83, 89, 97.
Sample answer: I had many more estimates than there are actual prime numbers. Only 4 of my estimates were actually prime numbers.

© Houghton Mifflin Harcourt Publishing Company

Instructions

STEP 1 Students should create a Sieve of Eratosthenes using the grid paper.

STEP 2 Have students create a scatter plot of the first 15 prime numbers, using prime numbers as the *x*-coordinates and their positions in the sequence as the *y*-coordinates.

STEP 3 Students should estimate a trend line for their scatter plot.

STEP 4 Have students use their trend line to estimate the remaining prime numbers less than 100.

STEP 5 Students should use the Sieve of Eratosthenes to check their estimates from the trend line, and describe how their estimates compare to the actual prime numbers.

TEACHER NOTES

• **Discussion** Discuss with students whether they think a trend line from a scatter plot is a good way to estimate the prime numbers.

Ready to Go On?

Assess Mastery

Access *Ready to Go On?* assessment online, and receive instant scoring, feedback, and customized intervention or enrichment.

Personal Math Trainer

Online Assessment and Intervention
• Module 14 Posttest

Additional Resources

Digital Teacher Resources

Go online for module-level resources.

Assessment Resources
• Module 14 Quiz: B, p.67
• Module 14 Quiz: D, p.69

my.hrw.com

Ready to Go On?

14.1 Scatter Plots and Association

An auto store is having a sale on motor oil. The chart shows the price per quart as the number of quarts purchased increases. Use the data for Exs. 1–2.

Number of quarts	1	2	3	4	5	6
Price per quart ($)	2	1.50	1.25	1.10	1	0.95

1. Use the given data to make a scatter plot.

2. Describe the association you see between the number of quarts purchased and the price per quart. Explain.

   Negative but nonlinear; as number of
   quarts rises, price per quart decreases,
   but the data appear to lie along a curve.

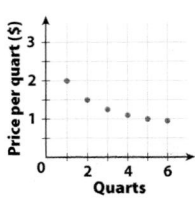

14.2 Trend Lines and Predictions

The scatter plot below shows data comparing wind speed and wind chill for an air temperature of 20°F. Use the scatter plot for Exs. 3–5. Answers may vary slightly.

3. Draw a trend line for the scatter plot.

4. Write an equation for your trend line.
   Sample ans.: $y = -\frac{1}{3}x + \frac{37}{3}$

5. Use your equation to predict the wind chill to the nearest degree for a wind speed of 60 mi/h.

   $-8°F$

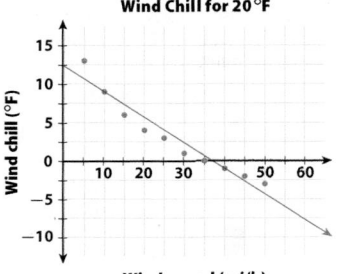

Wind Chill for 20°F

 ESSENTIAL QUESTION

6. How can you use scatter plots to solve real-world problems?

   Sample answer: You can plot data points and draw trend lines
   to make predictions.

© Houghton Mifflin Harcourt Publishing Company

READY TO GO ON? *Diagnostic Assessment*

Response to Intervention

Use to determine if students have mastered the concepts covered in this module.

Lesson	Exercises	Content Focus	Review with *Differentiated Instruction*
14.1	1–2	Scatter Plots and Association	**14.1** Reteach **14.1** Reading Strategies **14.1** Success for English Learners
14.2	3–5	Trend Lines and Predictions	**14.2** Reteach **14.2** Reading Strategies **14.2** Success for English Learners

Assessment Readiness

Personal Math Trainer

Online Assessment and Intervention

my.hrw.com

Selected Response

1. Which scatter plot could have a trend line whose equation is $y = 3x + 10$?

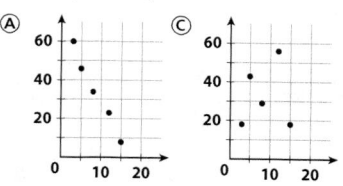

Ⓐ Ⓒ Ⓑ Ⓓ

2. What type of association would you expect between a person's age and hair length?

Ⓐ linear
Ⓑ negative
Ⓒ none
Ⓓ positive

3. Which is **not** shown on the scatter plot?

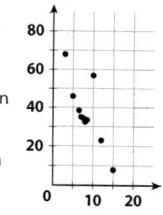

Ⓐ cluster
Ⓑ negative association
Ⓒ outlier
Ⓓ positive association

4. A restaurant claims to have served 352,000,000 hamburgers. What is this number in scientific notation?

Ⓐ 3.52×10^6
Ⓒ 35.2×10^7
Ⓑ 3.52×10^8
Ⓓ 352×10^6

5. Which equation describes the relationship between x and y in the table?

x	−8	−4	0	4	8
y	2	1	0	−1	−2

Ⓐ $y = -4x$
Ⓒ $y = 4x$
Ⓑ $y = -\frac{1}{4}x$
Ⓓ $y = \frac{1}{4}x$

Mini-Task

6. Use the data in the table.

Temp (°F)	97	94	87	92	100	90
Pool visitors	370	315	205	135	365	240

a. Make a scatterplot of the data.

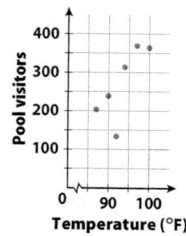

b. Which data point is an outlier?
(92, 135)

c. Predict the number of visitors on a day when the high temperature is 102°F.
about 410 visitors

© Houghton Mifflin Harcourt Publishing Company

Preparing for High Stakes Tests

Assessment Readiness Tip

Students should always be alert for the word *not*, and highlight or underline it to help them solve the problem correctly.

- **Item 3** If students overlook the word *not* in the question stem, any of the three incorrect answers will appear correct. Encourage them to read the question carefully.

Avoid Common Errors

- **Item 2** Some students are reluctant to choose an answer such as 'none' or 'not here.' Reinforce to the students that there isn't a relationship between every two quantities compared - sometimes, there might not be any relationship at all.

- **Item 6** For part c, remind students to go with the general trend, rather than simply with the last two points. If they look at only the last two points, they might believe that the graph has flattened out and will remain below 400.

Items	Grade 8 Lessons	Mathematical Processes
1	14.2	MP.4
2	14.1	MP.4
3	14.1	MP.6
4*	2.2	MP.4
5*	3.1	MP.4
6	14.1, 14.2	MP.4, MP.6

Item integrates mixed review concepts from previous modules or a previous course.

DIFFERENTIATE ASSESSMENT

Below Level *Module Quiz 14: D*

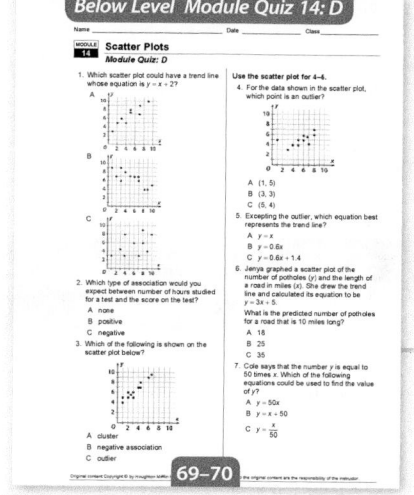

69–70

On Level *Module Quiz 14: B*

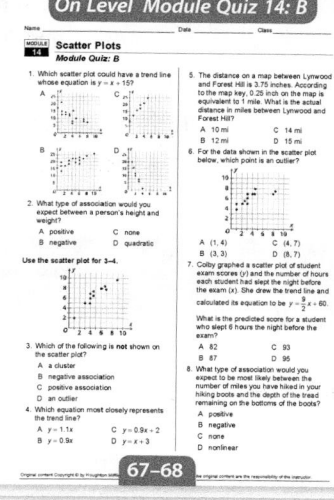

67–68

Personal Math Trainer
Module 14 Assessment Readiness

Pages shown are from *Assessment Resources.* **Also available online.**

Module At A Glance

Module Essential Question: How can you use two-way frequency tables to solve real-world problems?

MODULE 15 | Two-Way Tables

Lessons at A Glance	Lesson 15.1 Two-Way Frequency Tables	Lesson 15.2 Two-Way Relative Frequency Tables
	Pg. T451A	Pg. T457A
Essential Question	How can you construct and interpret two-way frequency tables?	How can categorical data be organized and analyzed?
Objective	Students will construct and interpret two-way frequency tables.	Students will organize and analyze categorical data.
Vocabulary	frequency, relative frequency, two-way table	conditional relative frequency, joint relative frequency, marginal relative frequency, two-way frequency table, two-way relative frequency table
Go online for all your module resources my.hrw.com	15.1 *i*Student Edition 15.1 *i*Teacher Edition 15.1 *e*Student Edition Personal Math Trainer Math on the Spot Videos Animated Math	15.2 *i*Student Edition 15.2 *i*Teacher Edition 15.2 *e*Student Edition Personal Math Trainer Math on the Spot Videos
Print Resources	**15.1 Student Edition:** Lesson *Differentiated Instruction* 15.1 Practice and Problem Solving A/B, C, and D 15.1 Reteach 15.1 Reading Strategies 15.1 Success for English Learners	**15.2 Student Edition:** Lesson *Differentiated Instruction* 15.2 Practice and Problem Solving A/B, C, and D 15.2 Reteach 15.2 Reading Strategies 15.2 Success for English Learners

RtI
Response to Intervention

Before the Module	During the Lesson	After the Module
Are You Ready	**Guided/Independent Practice**	**Ready to Go On?**
• Prerequisite Skills Activities • Personal Math Trainer	• Reteach • Personal Math Trainer • Practice and Problem Solving D	• Reteach • Personal Math Trainer

Teacher Notes

Check It Out!

Math on the Spot Videos	Animated Math
One for every Example in every Lesson	During Lesson 15.1

Two-Way Tables

Real-World Video Viewing Guide

After students have watched the video, discuss the following:

- How can you use a two-way table to record and analyze data?

- Do more men or women prefer basketball in the video? more women prefer basketball

Professional Development Video

Author Julie Dixon models successful teaching practices as she explores the concept of relative frequency in an actual eighth-grade classroom.

Two-Way Tables

MODULE **15**

? ESSENTIAL QUESTION

How can you use two-way frequency tables to solve real-world problems?

You can use two-way frequency tables to organize and analyze real-world data that are paired and categorical.

LESSON 15.1
Two-Way Frequency Tables

LESSON 15.2
Two-Way Relative Frequency Tables

Real-World Video

Two-way tables can help identify and compare probabilities for non-numerical data, such as the probability that girls will like one of two sports teams more than boys will.

my.hrw.com

© Houghton Mifflin Harcourt Publishing Company • Image Credits: ©John Rowley/Getty Images

GO DIGITAL
my.hrw.com

my.hrw.com	Math On the Spot	Animated Math	Personal Math Trainer
Go digital with your write-in student edition, accessible on any device.	Scan with your smart phone to jump directly to the online edition, video tutor, and more.	Interactively explore key concepts to see how math works.	Get immediate feedback and help as you work through practice sets.

447

TEACHER ONLINE RESOURCES

ONLINE TEACHER EDITION Access a full suite of teaching resources online—plan, present, and manage classes and assignments.

MY SMART PLANNER Easily plan your classes and access all your resources online.

INTERACTIVE WHITEBOARDS Engage students with interactive whiteboard-ready examples and a lesson quiz for each lesson.

PERSONAL MATH TRAINER: Online Assessment and Intervention Assign automatically graded homework, quizzes, tests, and intervention activities. Prepare your students for standardized tests in short-answer and multiple-choice formats.

Reading Start-Up

Visualize Vocabulary

Use the ✔ words to complete the chart.

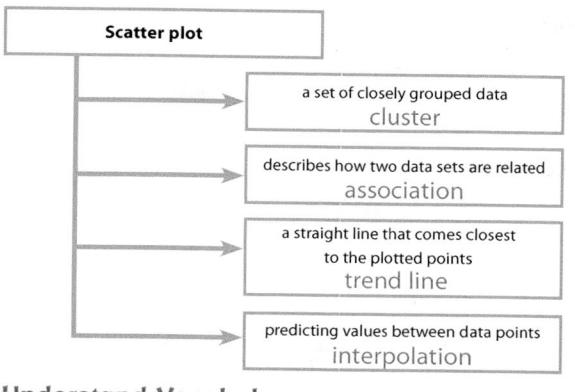

Scatter plot

- a set of closely grouped data
  cluster

- describes how two data sets are related
  association

- a straight line that comes closest to the plotted points
  trend line

- predicting values between data points
  interpolation

Understand Vocabulary

Complete the sentences using preview words.

1. The _____**frequency**_____ is the number of times an event occurs.

2. A _____**two-way table**_____ shows the frequencies of data that is categorized two ways.

3. _____**Relative frequency**_____ is the ratio of the number of times an event occurs to the total number of events.

© Houghton Mifflin Harcourt Publishing Company

Vocabulary

Review Words
- ✔ association *(asociación)*
- ✔ cluster *(grupo)*
- data *(datos)*
- ✔ interpolation *(interpolación)*
- extrapolation *(extrapolación)*
- outlier *(parte aislada)*
- scatter plot *(gráfico de dispersión)*
- ✔ trend line *(la línea de tendencia)*

Preview Words
- conditional relative frequency *(frecuencia relativa condicional)*
- frequency *(frecuencia)*
- joint relative frequency *(frecuencia relativa conjunta)*
- marginal relative frequency *(frecuencia relativa marginal)*
- relative frequency *(frecuencia relativa)*
- two-way table *(tabla de doble entrada)*
- two-way relative frequency table *(tabla de frecuencia relativa de doble entrada)*

Active Reading

Tri-Fold Before beginning the module, create a tri-fold to help you learn the concepts and vocabulary in this module. Fold the paper into three sections. Label the columns "What I Know," "What I Want to Know," and "What I Learned." Complete the first two columns before you read. After studying the module, complete the third column.

Reading Start-Up

Visualize Vocabulary

The diagram helps students review vocabulary associated with scatter plots. Students should write one review word with its definition in each of the four rectangles.

Understand Vocabulary

Use the following explanations to help students learn the preview words.

*Joint, marginal, and conditional relative frequencies all refer to different ratios between quantities found in a two-way table. A **joint relative frequency** is found by dividing the frequency of a cell in the body of the table by the grand total. A **marginal relative frequency** is the ratio of the total frequency of a row or column to the grand total. A **conditional relative frequency** is found by dividing the frequency of a cell in the body by a row or column total.*

Active Reading

Integrating Language Arts

Students can use these reading and note-taking strategies to help them organize and understand new concepts and vocabulary.

Additional Resources

Differentiated Instruction

- Reading Strategies **ELL**
- Interactive multilingual glossary

LEARNING PROGRESSIONS ACROSS THE GRADES

Before	In this Module	After
Students understand:	Students will learn how to:	Students will connect:
• how to change a fraction into a decimal or percent	• create two-way frequency and relative frequency tables for categorical data	• frequencies and relative frequencies given as decimals or percents
• how to represent and analyze quantitative data	• calculate joint, marginal, and conditional relative frequencies given a two-way relative frequency table	• frequency tables and associations between variables
	• analyze a two-way table to discover any association between the variables	

Are You Ready?

Assess Readiness

Access *Are You Ready?* assessment online, and receive instant scoring, feedback, and customized intervention or enrichment.

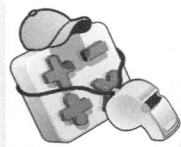

Personal Math Trainer

Online Assessment and Intervention

Additional Resources

Digital Teacher Resources

Go online for module-level resources.

my.hrw.com

Are YOU Ready?

Complete these exercises to review skills you will need for this module.

Personal Math Trainer
Online Assessment and Intervention

my.hrw.com

Simplify Fractions

EXAMPLE Simplify $\frac{18}{30}$.

$\frac{1, 2, 3, 6, 9, 18}{1, 2, 3, 5, 6, 10, 30}$

$\frac{18 \div 6}{30 \div 6} = \frac{3}{5}$

List all the factors of the numerator and denominator.

Find the greatest common factor (GCF). Divide the numerator and denominator by the GCF.

Write each fraction in simplest form.

1. $\frac{25}{30}$ ___ $\frac{5}{6}$
2. $\frac{27}{36}$ ___ $\frac{3}{4}$
3. $\frac{14}{16}$ ___ $\frac{7}{8}$
4. $\frac{15}{45}$ ___ $\frac{1}{3}$

5. $\frac{27}{63}$ ___ $\frac{3}{7}$
6. $\frac{45}{75}$ ___ $\frac{3}{5}$
7. $\frac{8}{27}$ ___ $\frac{8}{27}$
8. $\frac{16}{28}$ ___ $\frac{4}{7}$

Fractions, Decimals, Percents

EXAMPLE Write $\frac{13}{20}$ as a decimal and a percent.

$$20\overline{)13.00} \quad \begin{array}{r} 0.65 \\ \underline{12\ 0} \\ 100 \\ \underline{-100} \\ 0 \end{array}$$

Write the fraction as a division problem. Write a decimal point and zeros in the dividend.

Place a decimal point in the quotient.

$0.65 = 65\%$ Write the decimal as a percent.

Write each fraction as a decimal and a percent.

9. $\frac{7}{8}$ ___ 0.875; 87.5%
10. $\frac{4}{5}$ ___ 0.8; 80%
11. $\frac{5}{4}$ ___ 1.25; 125%

12. $\frac{3}{10}$ ___ 0.30; 30%
13. $\frac{19}{20}$ ___ 0.95; 95%
14. $\frac{7}{25}$ ___ 0.28; 28%

Find the Percent of a Number

EXAMPLE 6.5% of 24 = ?

$6.5\% = 0.065$ Write the percent as a decimal.

$$\begin{array}{r} 24 \\ \times\ 0.065 \\ \hline 1.56 \end{array}$$ Multiply.

Find each percent of a number.

15. 4% of 40 ___ 1.6
16. 7% of 300 ___ 21
17. 4.3% of 1,200 ___ 51.6

18. 2.9% of 780 ___ 22.62
19. 1.6% of 75.20 ___ 1.2032
20. 3.56% of 3,200 ___ 113.92

© Houghton Mifflin Harcourt Publishing Company

ARE YOU READY? *Diagnostic Assessment*

RtI Response to Intervention

Use to determine if students need intervention for the module's prerequisite skills.

Skill	Missed More Than . . .	Intervene With *Skills Intervention* worksheets (available online)	For Enrichment *Differentiated Instruction* (available in print and online)
Simplify Fractions	2 questions	**Skill 19** Simplify Fractions	**Module 15 Challenge** Extend-the-Math Lesson Activities in TE
Fractions, Decimals, Percents	2 questions	**Skill 31** Fractions, Decimals, Percents	**Module 15 Challenge** Extend-the-Math Lesson Activities in TE
Find the Percent of a Number	1 question	**Skill 46** Find the Percent of a Number	**Module 15 Challenge** Extend-the-Math Lesson Activities in TE

Complete these exercises to review skills you will need for this module.

Simplify Fractions

21. Explain how to write $\frac{45}{70}$ in simplest form.

> List all the factors of the numerator and denominator.
> Factors of 45: 1, 3, 5, 9, 15, 45;
> Factors of 70: 1, 2, 5, 7, 10, 14, 35, 70
> Find the greatest common factor (GCF): 5
> Divide the numerator and denominator by the GCF: $\frac{45 \div 5}{70 \div 5} = \frac{9}{14}$

Fractions, Decimals, Percents

22. Dina wrote $\frac{18}{15}$ as 1.2 and as 120%. Justify her answers.

> To convert $\frac{18}{15}$ to a decimal, write $\frac{18}{15}$ as a division problem: $15\overline{)18}$. Write a decimal point and zeros in the dividend: $15\overline{)18.0}$.
> Find the quotient by long division and place the decimal point in the quotient
> $$15\overline{)18.0}$$
> $$\begin{array}{r} 1.2 \\ \underline{15} \\ 30 \\ \underline{-30} \\ 0 \end{array}$$
> Write the decimal 1.2 as a percent by moving the decimal point two places to the right: 120%.

Find the Percent of a Number

23. To find 3.5% of 1,050, Enrique wrote $1{,}050 \times 3.5 = 3{,}675$. Find and correct Enrique's error.

> Enrique should have converted 3.5% to the decimal 0.035 before multiplying.
> $1{,}050 \times 0.035 = 36.75$.

24. Soccer cleats cost $85. The sales tax is 7%. If Lori has $90, does she have enough money to buy the soccer cleats? Explain.

> No.
> Sales tax: $85 \times 7\% = 85 \times 0.07 = 5.95$
> $\$85 + \$5.95 = \$90.95$
> Because $90.95 is greater than $90, Lori does not have enough money.

© Houghton Mifflin Harcourt Publishing Company

Simplify Fractions

Exercise 21 Remind students that a fraction is in simplest form when the only common factor of the numerator and denominator is 1. Check whether students understand the difference between a common factor and the greatest common factor.

Fractions, Decimals, Percents

Exercise 22 Make sure students understand how to find equivalent fractions and decimals and how to write equivalent percents. Some students may find it easier to simplify the improper fraction first, and then find the equivalent decimal using mental math, $\frac{18}{15} = \frac{6}{5} = 1\frac{1}{5} = 1.2$.

Find the Percent of a Number

Exercise 23 Check whether students understand how to move the decimal point to change a percent to a decimal.

Exercise 24 Encourage students to use estimation to help them understand the problem. Explain that 1% = $0.85 or about $0.90, and $7 \times \$0.90$ is about $6, and $\$85 + \$6 > \$90$.

Use to determine if students are able to apply the module's prerequisite skills.

Skill	Exercise	Depth of Knowledge (D.O.K.)	Mathematical Processes
Simplify Fractions	21	**2** Skills/Concepts	**MP.2** Abstract and Quantitative Reasoning
Fractions, Decimals, Percents	22	**2** Skills/Concepts	**MP.6** Use Precise Mathematical Language
Find the Percent of a Number	23	**3** Strategic Thinking	**MP.3** Use and Evaluate Logical Reasoning
	24	**2** Skills/Concepts	**MP.1** Problem Solving

Lesson Support

Content Objective Students will learn to construct and interpret two-way frequency tables.

Professional Development

Integrate Mathematical Processes MP.6

This lesson provides an opportunity to address this Mathematical Processes standard, which calls for students to attend to precision. When constructing two-way tables, students need to be accurate with their computations and precise in their recording of the data. The row elements and column elements must be correctly placed in order for the totals to be calculated correctly. Relative frequencies will often not be whole percents, so students must choose to represent them with an appropriate degree of precision.

FOCUS

Building Background

Connecting with Everyday Life Have students discuss how they could display and interpret the preferences of male and female students in their class for watching films or reading books. Have the class discuss different ways they could represent and compare the frequency of the data sets they collect.

COHERENCE

Learning Progressions

In this lesson, students increase their understanding of patterns in bivariate data by using two-way tables to compare frequencies to judge if an association exists between two categories of a population. Some key understandings include the following:

- **The frequency is the number of times an event occurs.**
- **A two-way table shows the frequencies of data that are categorized two ways: by the rows and by the columns.**
- **Relative frequency is the ratio of the number of times an event occurs to the total number of events.**

Representing and analyzing bivariate data in two-way frequency tables gets students ready for exploring relative frequencies given as decimals or percents and associations between variables in Lesson 15.2.

RIGOR

Cluster Connections

This lesson provides an excellent opportunity to connect ideas in this cluster:

Investigate patterns of association in bivariate data.

Tell students: "A poll of 100 middle school students found that 20% own a bike. Of those who own a bike, 15% are often late to school. Of those who do not own a bike, 70% are usually on time. Make a two-way frequency table and determine whether there is an association between the events."

	On Time	Late	TOTAL
Bike	17	3	20
No Bike	56	24	80
TOTAL	73	27	100

The relative frequency of being on time is 73%. The relative frequency of being on time among those that own a bike is 85%. Comparing the relative frequencies shows that having a bike makes it more likely that a person will be on time.

Language Support ELL

Leveled Strategies for English Learners ELL

Emerging

Provide scaffolding by asking students to point to examples of *rows* and *columns* to make sure they understand the concept. Use the following sentence frame:

> In a two-way table, _____ indicate one categorization and _____ indicate another.

Expanding

Have students at this level of English proficiency work in pairs and complete the following sentence frame:

> In a two-way table, rows _____ and columns _____.

Bridging

Have students at this level of English proficiency work in pairs to discuss what two-way tables show, how the data are displayed, and what the rows and columns indicate.

Math Talk

Write out and model for students a sentence frame to begin their answer.

> The difference between frequency and relative frequency is _____.

	Farmer's Market	No Farmer's Market	TOTAL
Bike	36	12	48
No Bike	18	54	72
TOTAL	54	66	120

Linguistic Support ELL

Academic/Content Vocabulary

This lesson on two-way frequency tables relies on students' understanding of the meanings of the terms *frequency*, *relative frequency*, and *two-way table*. Have students brainstorm these words to find out what they already know, and have them work in pairs to check the glossary for additional information. All three of these terms are English/Spanish cognates: *frecuencia*, *frecuencia relativa*, and *tabla de doble entrada*.

Building Background

Example 1 refers to domestic flights and international flights. Point out that domestic flights are *within* the United States. Example 1 also polls students on their chores and their curfews. Explain to English learners that the word *chores* means "work that family members do around the house," and *curfew* is the time when someone is required to be home. Have students add these words to their word journals.

Image Credits: ©best images/Shutterstock

Two-Way Frequency Tables

1 Engage

❓ ESSENTIAL QUESTION

How can you construct and interpret two-way frequency tables? Sample answer: Make a table in which columns represent one set of categories for a population and the rows represent a different set of categories for the same population. You can compare the relative frequency of one event in a subpopulation to the frequency in the whole population to see if there is an association between categories.

Motivate the Lesson

Ask: How can you display and interpret data that is categorized in two ways? Begin the Explore Activity to find out.

2 Explore

EXPLORE ACTIVITY

Engage with the Whiteboard

Invite volunteers to complete the table and Parts A–E of the activity. Have them demonstrate the math used to arrive at their answers.

LESSON
15.1 **Two-Way Frequency Tables**

8.6.15.1
Students will construct and interpret two-way frequency tables.

❓ ESSENTIAL QUESTION
How can you construct and interpret two-way frequency tables?

EXPLORE ACTIVITY *Real World*

Making a Two-Way Table

The **frequency** is the number of times an event occurs. A **two-way table** shows the frequencies of data that is categorized two ways. The rows indicate one categorization and the columns indicate another.

A poll of 120 town residents found that 40% own a bike. Of those who own a bike, 75% shop at the farmer's market. Of those who do not own a bike, 25% shop at the farmer's market.

	Farmer's Market	No Farmer's Market	TOTAL
Bike	36	12	48
No Bike	18	54	72
TOTAL	54	66	120

A Start in the bottom right cell of the table. Enter the total number of people polled.

B **Fill in the right column.** 40% of 120 people polled own a bike.

The remaining people polled do not own a bike.

C **Fill in the top row.** 75% of those who own a bike also shop at the market.

The remaining bike owners do not shop at the market.

D **Fill in the second row.** 25% of those who do not own a bike shop at the market.

The remaining people without bikes do not shop at the market.

E **Fill in the last row.** In each column, add the numbers in the first two rows to find the total number of people who shop at the farmer's market and who do not shop at the farmer's market.

Lesson 15.1 **451**

© Houghton Mifflin Harcourt Publishing Company • Image Credits: ©Chuck Pefley/Alamy Images

---

DIFFERENTIATE INSTRUCTION *Leveled Questions*

	EXPLORE ACTIVITY
(AL) DOK 1 *Recall*	The table places 120 town residents into what four categories? (1) own bike and shop farmer's market, (2) own bike and do not shop farmer's market, (3) do not own bike and shop farmer's market, (4) do not own bike and do not shop farmer's market
(OL) DOK 2 *Skills/Concepts*	Can you complete the table with the farmer's market information before the completing it with the bike information? Explain. No; famer's market information is given relative to bike ownership.
(BL) DOK 3 *Strategic Thinking*	Based on this data, is it more likely for a bike owner to shop at the farmer's market or not? Explain. Bike owners are more likely to shop at the farmer's market; according to this data, 75% of bike owners shop at the farmer's market, but only 25% of non-bike-owners shop at the farmer's market.

LEVELED QUESTIONS: (AL) Approaching Level | (OL) On Level | (BL) Beyond Level

Reflect

1. How can you check that your table is completed correctly?

The last number in each row or column should be the

sum of the other numbers in that row or column.

Math On the Spot
my.hrw.com

Animated Math
my.hrw.com

Deciding Whether There Is an Association

Relative frequency is the ratio of the number of times an event occurs to the total number of events. In the Explore Activity, the relative frequency of bike owners who shop at the farmer's market is $\frac{36}{120} = 0.30 = 30\%$. You can use relative frequencies to decide if there is an association between two variables or events.

EXAMPLE 1

Determine whether there is an association between the events.

A One hundred teens were polled about whether they are required to do chores and whether they have a curfew. Is there an association between having a curfew and having to do chores?

	Curfew	No Curfew	TOTAL
Chores	16	4	20
No Chores	16	64	80
TOTAL	32	68	100

STEP 1 Find the relative frequency of having to do chores.

Total who have to do chores → $\frac{20}{100} = 0.20 = 20\%$
Total number of teens polled →

STEP 2 Find the relative frequency of having to do chores among those who have a curfew.

Number with a curfew who have chores → $\frac{16}{32} = 0.50 = 50\%$
Total number with a curfew →

STEP 3 **Compare the relative frequencies.** Students who have a curfew are more likely to have to do chores than the general population. There is an association. The relative frequencies show that students who have a curfew are more likely to have to do chores than the general population of teens polled in the survey.

Math Talk
Mathematical Processes
What is the difference between frequency and relative frequency?

Frequency is the number of times an event occurs. Relative frequency is the ratio of the frequency to the total number of events.

© Houghton Mifflin Harcourt Publishing Company

3 Explain

Connect to Vocabulary ELL

Compare *frequency* and *relative frequency*. Explain that frequency is the number of times an event occurs. Relative frequency is the *ratio* of the frequency of an event to the total number of events.

EXAMPLE 1

ADDITIONAL EXAMPLE 1
Determine whether there is an association between the events.

A Is there an association between having a car and having voted in the last election?

	Voted	Not Voted	TOTAL
Car	50	10	60
No Car	20	20	40
TOTAL	70	30	100

The relative frequency of having voted is 70%. The relative frequency of having voted among those that own a car is about 83%. The relative frequencies show that those who have a car were more likely to have voted than the general population.

(continued on page 453)

Animated Math

Create a Two-Way Frequency Table
Students create a two-way frequency table from a set of data and interpret the meaning of the results.

my.hrw.com

	EXAMPLE 1
AL DOK 1 *Recall*	Of all those polled, what percent are required to do chores and what percent have a curfew? 20%; 32%
OL DOK 2 *Skills/Concepts*	How do you use relative frequency to determine whether there is an association between two events? Find the total relative frequency of one of the events, independent of the other event, and compare it with the relative frequency of that event among those who also have the second event. If they are close, there's likely no association. If not close, there may be association.
BL DOK 3 *Strategic Thinking*	Compare the association between curfew students with chores (Part A) with chore students with a curfew. Which association is stronger? Explain. The latter association is stronger. In Part A, 50% of curfew students have chores, but 80% of chore students have a curfew.

TEACHER TO TEACHER

Home Connection Collect data from students in your class on whether they have a curfew on school nights (Curfew/No Curfew) and whether they have regular chores at home (Chores/No Chores). Record the data for the students to see in a two-way table. Compare the relative frequencies of your class data to determine if there is an association between having a curfew and having to do chores. Compare your results to the data in Example 1 Part A.

EXAMPLE 1   (continued)

ADDITIONAL EXAMPLE 1 *continued*
Determine whether there is an association between the events.

B Is there an association between a student not owning a cell phone and being late for school?

	Late	Not Late	TOTAL
Phone	22	198	220
No Phone	8	72	80
TOTAL	30	270	300

The relative frequency of being late is 10%. The relative frequency of being late among those that do not own a cell phone is 10%. There is no association.

 Interactive Whiteboard
Interactive example available online

YOUR TURN   MP.4

Focus on Reasoning
Discuss with students the different possible combinations of relative frequencies that could be found for this table. Two relative frequencies can be calculated for each column and for each row.

 **Digital Teacher Resources**

Go online to access all your lesson-level resources.

Differentiated Instruction
• Reteach
• Reading Strategies
• Success for English Learners
• Practice and Problem Solving A/B, C, D

Math on the Spot Videos

my.hrw.com

B Data from 200 flights were collected. The flights were categorized as domestic or international and late or not late. Is there an association between international flights and a flight being late?

	Late	Not Late	TOTAL
Domestic	30	120	150
International	10	40	50
TOTAL	40	160	200

STEP 1 Find the relative frequency of a flight being late.

Total flights that are late → $\dfrac{40}{200} = 0.20 = 20\%$
Total number of flights →

STEP 2 Find the relative frequency of a flight being late among international flights.

Number of international flights that are late → $\dfrac{10}{50} = 0.20 = 20\%$
Total number of international flights →

STEP 3 **Compare the relative frequencies.** International flights are no more likely to be late than flights in general. There is no association. The relative frequencies show that international flights are just as likely to be late as any other flight.

YOUR TURN

2. Data from 200 middle school and high school students were collected. Students were asked whether or not they had visited at least one national park. Is there an association between being a high school student and visiting a national park? Explain.

	Have Visited a National Park	Have NOT Visited a National Park	TOTAL
Middle School	25	55	80
High School	80	40	120
TOTAL	105	95	200

Yes; relative frequency of visiting a park $= \dfrac{105}{200} =$ 0.525 = 52.5%; relative frequency of visiting a park among high school students $= \dfrac{80}{120} \approx 0.667 = 66.7\%$; 66.7% > 52.5%, so high school students are more likely to have visited a national park than is the general population of students polled.

 **Personal Math Trainer**
Online Assessment and Intervention
my.hrw.com

Lesson 15.1 **453**

© Houghton Mifflin Harcourt Publishing Company • Image Credits: ©Photodisc/ Getty Images

1. In a survey of 50 students, 60% said that they have a cat. Of the students who have a cat, 70% also have a dog. Of the students who do not have a cat, 75% have a dog. Complete the two-way table. (Explore Activity)

	Dog	No Dog	TOTAL
Cat	21	9	30
No Cat	15	5	20
TOTAL	36	14	50

   a. Enter the total number of students surveyed in the bottom right cell of the table.

   b. Fill in right column.

   c. Fill in top row.

   d. Fill in second row.

   e. Fill in last row.

2. The results of a survey at a school are shown. Is there an association between being a boy and being left-handed? Explain. (Example 1)

	Left-handed	Right-handed	TOTAL
Boys	14	126	140
Girls	10	90	100
TOTAL	24	216	240

No; the relative frequency of being left-handed ($\frac{24}{240} = 10\%$) is the same as the relative frequency of being left-handed among boys ($\frac{14}{140} = 10\%$).

? ESSENTIAL QUESTION CHECK-IN

3. Voters were polled to see whether they supported Smith or Jones. Can you construct a two-way table of the results? Why or why not?

No; the poll collected data on only one variable, voters. A two-way table requires data on two variables, such as men and women.

© Houghton Mifflin Harcourt Publishing Company

④ Elaborate

Talk About It

Summarize the Lesson

Ask: How are relative frequencies determined, and how do you know when there is an association between two variables? Relative frequency is found by writing a ratio comparing the frequency of an event to the total number of events. When the relative frequency of a variable within a subpopulation is significantly different than the relative frequency of the variable overall, there is an association between the variables.

Guided Practice

Engage with the Whiteboard

For **Exercise 1**, have volunteers take turns completing the table. Have volunteers explain how to determine the value to write in each cell and have them show their arithmetic where necessary.

Avoid Common Errors

Exercise 2 Caution students to be careful in choosing the relative frequencies to calculate. For example, if they compare the relative frequency of being a boy with the relative frequency of being left-handed among those who are boys, they will arrive at the wrong answer. Note, however, that the correct conclusion can also be found by observing that the relative frequency of being a boy ($\frac{140}{240} \approx 58\%$) is the same as the relative frequency of being a boy among those students who are left-handed ($\frac{14}{24} \approx 58\%$).

DIFFERENTIATE INSTRUCTION *Intervention and Additional Support*

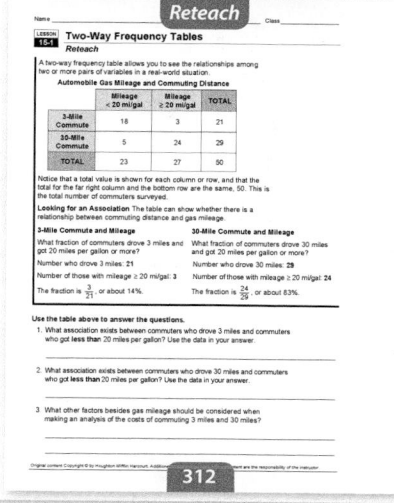

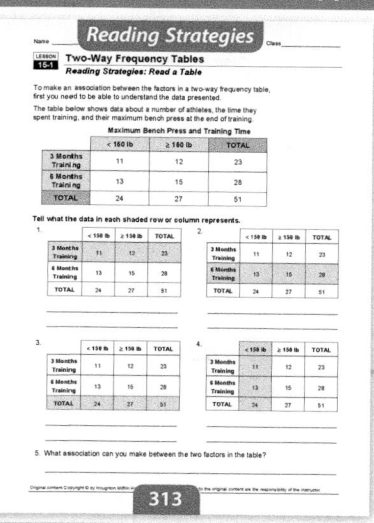

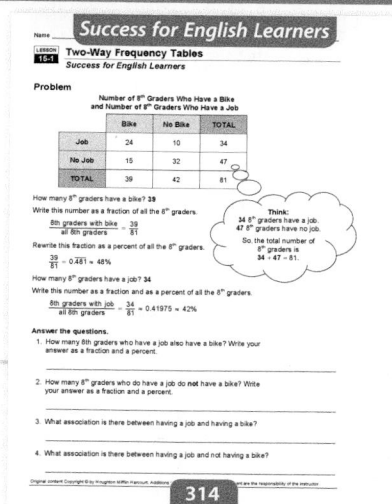

Personal Math Trainer
Daily Intervention
15.1 Homework

Pages shown are from *Differentiated Instruction*.
Also available online.

Pressed for Time

15.1 Differentiated Homework Assignments

(AL) **Approaching Level**	4–6
(OL) **On Level**	5–7
(BL) **Beyond Level**	4, 7

*For **Below Level** students, assign Personal Math Trainer, Daily Intervention 15.1 Homework.*

Mathematical Processes	Exercises
MP.1 Problem Solving	6
MP.2 Reasoning	7
MP.4 Modeling	4–5

Focus on Higher Order Thinking

Depth of Knowledge	Exercises
2 Skills/Concepts	4
3 Strategic Thinking H.O.T.	5–7

Name_____ Class_____ Date_____

Personal Math Trainer
Online Assessment and Intervention
my.hrw.com

15.1 Independent Practice

4. Represent Real-World Problems One hundred forty students were asked about their language classes. Out of 111 who take French, only 31 do not take Spanish. Twelve take neither French nor Spanish. Use this information to make a two-way table.

	Take French	Do NOT Take French	TOTAL
Take Spanish	80	17	97
Do NOT Take Spanish	31	12	43
TOTAL	111	29	140

5. Represent Real-World Problems Seventh- and eighth-grade students were asked whether they preferred science or math.

a. Complete the two-way table.

	Prefer Science	Prefer Math	TOTAL
Seventh Grade	24	72	96
Eighth Grade	32	48	80
TOTAL	56	120	176

b. Is there an association between being in eighth grade and preferring math? Explain.

No; the relative frequency of preferring math is $\frac{120}{176}$ ≈ 68%, and the relative frequency of preferring math among eighth graders is $\frac{48}{80}$ = 60%, so eighth graders are slightly less likely to prefer math than the general population of students polled.

6. Persevere in Problem Solving The table gives partial information on the number of men and women who play in the four sections of the Metro Orchestra.

a. Complete the table.

	Strings	Brass	Woodwinds	Percussion	TOTAL
Men	13	7	8	5	33
Women	42	9	10	4	65
TOTAL	55	16	18	9	98

Lesson 15.1 **455**

© Houghton Mifflin Harcourt Publishing Company

DIFFERENTIATE INSTRUCTION *Leveled Homework/Practice*

Personal Math Trainer
• 15.1 Homework

Pages shown are from *Differentiated Instruction.*
Also available online.

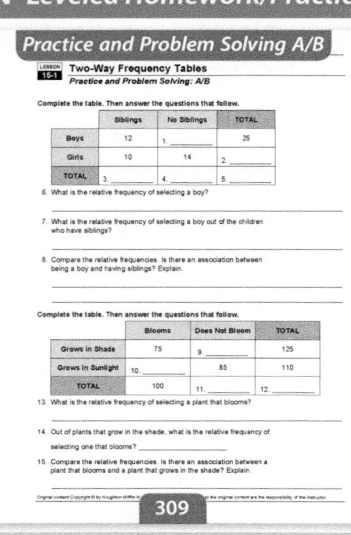
Practice and Problem Solving A/B
309

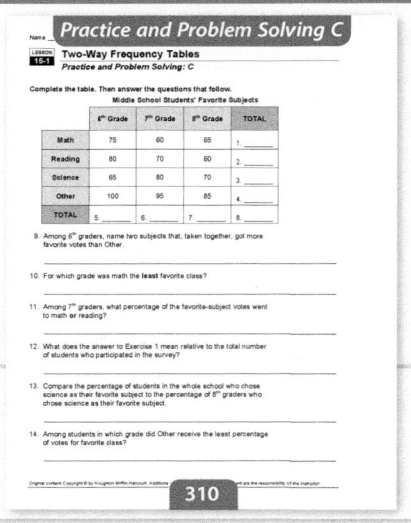
Practice and Problem Solving C
310

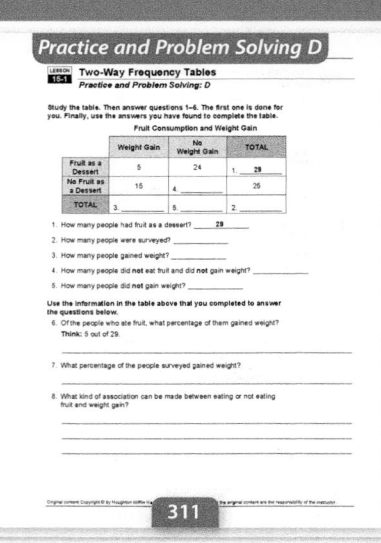
Practice and Problem Solving D
311

b. Is there an association between being a woman and playing strings? Explain.

Yes; the relative frequency of strings players is $\frac{55}{98} \approx 56\%$, and the relative frequency of strings players among women is $\frac{42}{55} \approx 76\%$, so women are more likely to play strings than the general orchestra population.

 **FOCUS ON HIGHER ORDER THINKING**

7. Multi-Step The two-way table below shows the results of a survey of Florida teenagers who were asked whether they preferred surfing or snorkeling.

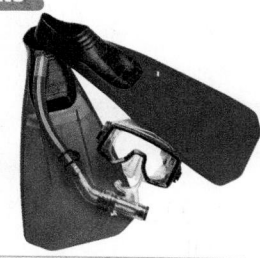

a. To the right of the number in each cell, write the relative frequency of the number compared to the total for the *row* the number is in. Round to the nearest percent.

	Prefer Surfing	Prefer Snorkeling	TOTAL
Ages 13–15	52 _40%_ ; _50%_	78 _60%_ ; _74%_	130 _100%_
Ages 16–18	52 _65%_ ; _50%_	28 _35%_ ; _26%_	80 _100%_
TOTAL	104 _50%_ ; _100%_	106 _50%_ ; _100%_	210 _100%_

b. Explain the meaning of the relative frequency you wrote beside 28.

It is the relative frequency of teenagers who are 16 to 18 years old and who prefer snorkeling to all 16- to 18-year-olds who were surveyed.

c. To the right of each number you wrote in part a, write the relative frequency of each number compared to the total for the *column* the number is in. Are the relative frequencies the same? Why or why not?

No; the total numbers in the last column (ages) are not the same as the total numbers in the last row (preferences), so the relative frequencies are different.

d. Explain the meaning of the relative frequency you wrote beside 28.

It is the relative frequency of teenagers who are 16 to 18 years old and who prefer snorkeling to all of those surveyed who prefer snorkeling.

© Houghton Mifflin Harcourt Publishing Company • Image Credits: ©Comstock/Getty Images

Work Area

✔ Quick Check

15.1 Lesson Quiz

1. In a survey of 50 students, 40% said they mow lawns on Saturday. Of the students who mow lawns, 25% sleep until noon. Of the students who do not mow lawns, 70% sleep until noon. Complete the two-way table.

	Sleeps Until Noon	Does Not Sleep Until Noon	TOTAL
Mows	5	15	20
Does Not Mow	21	9	30
TOTAL	26	24	50

2. For the data in Exercise 1, is there an association between mowing lawns and sleeping until noon? The relative frequency of mowing lawns is 40%. The relative frequency of mowing lawns among those who sleep until noon is about 19%. Yes, students who sleep until noon are less likely to mow lawns.

3. The results of a survey at a preschool are shown. Is there an association between being a boy and wearing a red shirt?

	Red	Not Red	TOTAL
Boys	10	15	25
Girls	5	15	20
TOTAL	15	30	45

The relative frequency of wearing a red shirt is about 33%. The relative frequency of being a boy wearing a red shirt is 40%. Yes, boys are more likely to wear red shirts.

Differentiate Instruction

IF a student misses more than one question, THEN

Differentiate Instruction:
• 15.1 Reteach
• Personal Math Trainer

 Interactive Whiteboard
Interactive Lesson quiz available online

DIFFERENTIATE INSTRUCTION *Extend-the-Math Activity* [PRE-AP]

Activity What could be concluded if the relative frequency of an event is equal to 1? What could be concluded if the relative frequency of an event is equal to 0?

In a two-way table, if there is one event in a column with a relative frequency of 1, what must the relative frequency be for the other event in that same column? Justify your answer.

A relative frequency of 1 or 100% means that all the observations had that outcome. A relative frequency of 0 or 0% means that none of the observations had that outcome.

The other event must have a relative frequency of 0. The sum of the two relative frequencies must be 1 or 100%.

Lesson Support

Content Objective Students will learn how categorical data can be organized and analyzed.

Professional Development

Integrate Mathematical Processes MP.8

This lesson provides an opportunity to address this Mathematical Processes standard, which calls for students to look for and express regularity in repeated reasoning. As students repeat calculations for each cell in a two-way relative frequency table, they become increasingly proficient in the process of calculating relative frequency. In addition, they generalize the process so they can apply the same calculations and reasoning to any categorical data set organized in a two-way frequency table.

FOCUS

Building Background

Eliciting Prior Knowledge Ask students: "How do two-way tables show frequencies that are categorized in two ways?" Have students discuss how two-way tables can help them find whether an association exists between the two categories. Explain that comparing relative frequencies in two-way tables can help students draw conclusions about whether or not an association exists between the two categories.

COHERENCE

Learning Progressions

In this lesson, students use two-way relative frequency tables to continue investigating patterns of association in bivariate data. They learn to calculate joint, marginal, and conditional relative frequencies. Some key understandings include the following:

- **Relative frequencies (joint and marginal) can be obtained from a two-way frequency table.**
- **Relative frequency tables show what part of the whole data set each category or category pair represents.**
- **A conditional relative frequency can be used to find whether an association exists between two variables.**

Representing and analyzing data in two-way relative frequency tables lays a foundation for understanding how to summarize, represent, and interpret categorical and quantitative data in later mathematics courses.

RIGOR

Cluster Connections

This lesson provides an excellent opportunity to connect ideas in this cluster:

Investigate patterns of association in bivariate data.

Display the frequency table. Tell students: "The table gives data on preferred juice flavors. Find the conditional frequency that a student prefers apple juice, given that the student is a girl. Then find the conditional frequency that a student surveyed is a boy, given that the student prefers orange juice."

Gender ⇓ Preferred Flavor ⇒	Orange	Apple	Other	TOTAL
Girl	18	6	4	28
Boy	16	4	2	22
TOTAL	34	10	6	50

$\frac{6}{28} \approx 0.21$ or 21%; $\frac{16}{34} \approx 0.47$ or 47%

Language Support **ELL**

Leveled Strategies for English Learners **ELL**

Emerging
Have students at this level of English proficiency work in pairs to review the lesson for examples of frequency and two-way frequency tables. Have them label their examples.

Expanding
Have students at this level of English proficiency work in pairs to identify and list the types of tables used to organize and analyze categorical data.

Bridging
Form small groups to discuss and provide examples of the types of tables that can be used to organize and analyze categorical data.

Write out and model for students a sentence frame to begin their answer.

The relationship between joint relative frequency and marginal relative frequency is _____.

Image Credits: ©Pavel Chernobrivets/Fotolia

Linguistic Support **ELL**

Building Background
All students benefit when you connect what they already know to what they are learning. An exercise in the Guided Practice asks students about their favorite vacation *spot* or *destination*. Point out to students that these words are sometimes used interchangeably. Although not critical for solving the word problems in this lesson, learning the words *spot* and *destination* in this context may benefit English learners in other classes. Have students add these words to their word journals.

Academic/Content Vocabulary
This lesson on two-way relative frequency tables builds on students' understanding of the previous lesson concepts as well as the meanings of several new terms. Point out that the following terms are English/Spanish cognates:

English	Spanish
two-way frequency table	tabla de frecuencia relativa de doble entrada
joint relative frequency	frecuencia relativa conjunta
marginal relative frequency	frecuencia relativa marginal
conditional	frecuencia relativa condicional

Two-Way Relative Frequency Tables

1 Engage

❓ ESSENTIAL QUESTION

How can categorical data be organized and analyzed? Sample answer: You can use frequency tables and two-way frequency tables to show the frequency for each category or category pair. You can use relative frequency tables and two-way relative frequency tables to show what part of the whole data set is represented by each category or category pair. From these tables you can obtain joint relative frequencies, marginal relative frequencies, and conditional relative frequencies.

Motivate the Lesson

Ask: What is the sum of the relative frequencies in a frequency table? Begin the Explore Activity to find out.

2 Explore

EXPLORE ACTIVITY 1

Connect Vocabulary ELL

Remind students that the *frequencies* in a frequency table are the number of times events occur. The *relative frequency* table shows the ratio of frequency of an event to the total number of events. These ratios are most often written as decimals or percents.

LESSON 15.2 Two-Way Relative Frequency Tables

8.6.15.2
Students will organize and analyze categorical data.

❓ ESSENTIAL QUESTION

How can categorical data be organized and analyzed?

EXPLORE ACTIVITY 1 · Real World

Creating a Relative Frequency Table

The frequency table below shows the results of a survey that Maria took at her school. She asked 50 randomly selected students whether they preferred dogs, cats, or other pets. Convert this table to a *relative frequency* table that uses decimals as well as one that uses percents.

Preferred Pet	Dog	Cat	Other	TOTAL
Frequency	22	15	13	50

A Divide the numbers in the frequency table by the total to obtain relative frequencies as decimals. Record the results in the table below.

Preferred Pet	Dog	Cat	Other	TOTAL
Relative Frequency	$\frac{22}{50} = 0.44$	$\frac{15}{50} = 0.3$	$\frac{13}{50} = 0.26$	$\frac{50}{50} = 1$

B Write the decimals as percents in the table below.

Preferred Pet	Dog	Cat	Other	TOTAL
Relative Frequency	44%	30%	26%	100%

Reflect

1. How can you check that you have correctly converted frequencies to relative frequencies?

The sum of the relative frequencies as decimals should be 1; the sum of the relative frequencies as percents should be 100%.

2. Explain why the number in the Total column of a relative frequency table is always 1 or 100%.

To obtain a relative frequency from a frequency, you divide the frequency by the total. The total divided by itself will always equal 1 or 100%.

© Houghton Mifflin Harcourt Publishing Company

DIFFERENTIATE INSTRUCTION *Leveled Questions*

	EXPLORE ACTIVITY 1
(AL) DOK 1 *Recall*	What is the difference between a frequency table and a relative frequency table? A frequency table gives the amounts in each cell; a relative frequency table gives the percentage of the total (as a percent or decimal) in each cell.
(OL) DOK 2 *Skills/Concepts*	What is the relative frequency of students who preferred a pet that is not a cat? not a dog? 70%; 56%
(BL) DOK 3 *Strategic Thinking*	What is the relative frequency of students who preferred a fish? Explain. You cannot tell. The answer is not simply the "Other" relative frequency because that could be a combination of students who answered any animal that is not a cat or dog.

LEVELED QUESTIONS: (AL) Approaching Level | (OL) On Level | (BL) Beyond Level

Creating a Two-Way Frequency Table

In the previous Explore Activity, the categorical variable was pet preference, and the variable had three possible data values: dog, cat, and other. The frequency table listed the frequency for each value of that single variable. If you have two categorical variables whose values have been paired, you list the frequencies of the paired values in a **two-way frequency table**.

For her survey, Maria also recorded the gender of each student. The results are shown in the two-way frequency table below. Each entry is the frequency of students who prefer a certain pet *and* are a certain gender. For instance, 10 girls prefer dogs as pets. Complete the table.

Preferred Pet Gender	Dog	Cat	Other	TOTAL
Girl	10	9	3	22
Boy	12	6	10	28
TOTAL	22	15	13	50

A Find the total for each gender by adding the frequencies in each row.

B Find the total for each pet by adding the frequencies in each column.

C Find the grand total, which is the sum of the row totals as well as the sum of the column totals. Write this in the lower-right corner.

Reflect

3. Where have you seen the numbers in the Total row before?

They are from the frequency table in the previous activity.

4. In terms of Maria's survey, what does the grand total represent?

The number of students surveyed

Creating a Two-Way Relative Frequency Table

You can obtain *relative* frequencies from a two-way frequency table:

---

3 Explain

EXPLORE ACTIVITY 2

Focus on Critical Thinking

Make sure students understand the difference between categorical and quantitative data. Categorical data refers to data that is defined by words or has a limited number of answer options, such as "What is the color of your backpack?" Quantitative data refers to data that numerically measures a particular characteristic, such as "How much does your backpack weigh?"

© Houghton Mifflin Harcourt Publishing Company

TEACHER TO TEACHER

Modeling The results of Maria's survey from Explore Activity 2 are also used in Explore Activity 3, Example 1, and Example 2. Have students copy the completed frequency table of data from Explore Activity 2 on one side of an index card. On the other side of the index card, have students copy the relative frequency table for Maria's data. They can then refer to their index cards when they need to extract data to answer questions.

	EXPLORE ACTIVITY 2
(AL) DOK 1 *Recall*	Could the two-way frequency table also be created using the columns for genders and the rows for pets? Explain. Yes, the rows and columns can be swapped.
(OL) DOK 2 *Skills/Concepts*	In a two-way frequency table, what is the relationship between the sum of the row totals and the sum of the column totals? They are equal.
(BL) DOK 3 *Strategic Thinking*	Based on this data, do you think it is more likely for a girl or a boy to prefer a cat? Explain your reasoning. More likely for girls to prefer cats; only 6 out of 28 (about 21%) of the boys prefer cats and only 15 out of 50 (30%) out of all students prefer cats, but of all the 22 girls surveyed, 9 of them (about 41%) prefer cats.

Avoid Common Errors

Some students may confuse joint relative frequency with marginal relative frequency. It may help them to think of the row and column totals as located in the margins of the table, and therefore the starting points for finding marginal relative frequency.

- A **joint relative frequency** is found by dividing a frequency that is not in the Total row or the Total column by the grand total.
- A **marginal relative frequency** is found by dividing a row total or a column total by the grand total.

A **two-way relative frequency table** displays both joint relative frequencies and marginal relative frequencies.

> **Math Talk**
> Mathematical Processes
>
> What is the relationship between joint relative frequency and marginal relative frequency?

Create a two-way relative frequency table for Maria's data.

A Divide each number in the two-way frequency table from the previous Explore Activity by the grand total. Write the quotients as decimals.

Preferred Pet / Gender	Dog	Cat	Other	TOTAL
Girl	$\frac{10}{50} = 0.2$	$\frac{9}{50} = 0.18$	$\frac{3}{50} = 0.06$	$\frac{22}{50} = 0.44$
Boy	$\frac{12}{50} = 0.24$	$\frac{6}{50} = 0.12$	$\frac{10}{50} = 0.2$	$\frac{28}{50} = 0.56$
TOTAL	$\frac{22}{50} = 0.44$	$\frac{15}{50} = 0.3$	$\frac{13}{50} = 0.26$	$\frac{50}{50} = 1$

The sum of the joint relative frequencies in each row or column of a two-way relative frequency table must equal that row's or that column's marginal relative frequency.

B Check by adding the joint relative frequencies in a row or column to see if the sum equals that row's or column's marginal relative frequency.

Girl row: $0.2 + \underline{\ 0.18\ } + \underline{\ 0.06\ } = \underline{\ 0.44\ }$

Boy row: $\underline{\ 0.24\ } + \underline{\ 0.12\ } + \underline{\ 0.2\ } = \underline{\ 0.56\ }$

Dog column: $0.2 + \underline{\ 0.24\ } = \underline{\ 0.44\ }$

Cat column: $\underline{\ 0.18\ } + \underline{\ 0.12\ } = \underline{\ 0.3\ }$

Other column: $\underline{\ 0.06\ } + \underline{\ 0.2\ } = \underline{\ 0.26\ }$

Reflect

5. A joint relative frequency in a two-way relative frequency table tells you what portion of the entire data set falls into the intersection of a particular value of one variable and a particular value of the other variable. What is the joint relative frequency of students surveyed who are boys and prefer cats as pets?

0.12, or 12%

6. A marginal relative frequency in a two-way relative frequency table tells you what portion of the entire data set represents a particular value of just one of the variables. What is the marginal relative frequency of students surveyed who are boys?

0.56, or 56%

© Houghton Mifflin Harcourt Publishing Company

Lesson 15.2 **459**

DIFFERENTIATE INSTRUCTION *Leveled Questions*

	EXPLORE ACTIVITY 3
(AL) DOK 1 *Recall*	What are the relative frequencies of row totals or column totals called? What are the relative frequencies of the paired data values (not row totals or column totals) called? marginal relative frequencies; joint relative frequencies
(OL) DOK 2 *Skills/Concepts*	How do the sums of the row totals and of the column totals in a two-way relative frequency table differ from these sums in a two-way frequency table? In the relative frequency table the sums are 1 (or 100%), while in the frequency table the sums are the total number of data values.
(BL) DOK 3 *Strategic Thinking*	Can you use a two-way relative frequency table to recreate the two-way frequency table on which it was based? **Explain.** No; the values in a relative frequency table are percents. If, however, you know the total number of data values, then you can recreate the frequency table.

LEVELED QUESTIONS: (AL) Approaching Level | (OL) On Level | (BL) Beyond Level

Math On the Spot
my.hrw.com

Calculating Conditional Relative Frequencies

One other type of relative frequency that you can obtain from a two-way frequency table is a *conditional relative frequency*. A **conditional relative frequency** is found by dividing a frequency that is not in the Total row or the Total column by the frequency's row total or column total.

EXAMPLE 1

From Maria's two-way frequency table you know that 22 students are girls and 15 students prefer cats. You also know that 9 students are girls who prefer cats. Use this to find each conditional relative frequency.

A Find the conditional relative frequency that a student surveyed prefers cats as pets, given that the student is a girl.

Divide the number of girls who prefer cats by the number of girls. Express your answer as a decimal and as a percent.

$\frac{9}{22} = 0.409$, or 40.9%

B Find the conditional relative frequency that a student surveyed is a girl, given that the student prefers cats as pets.

Divide the number of girls who prefer cats by the number of students who prefer cats. Express your answer as a decimal and as a percent.

$\frac{9}{15} = 0.6$, or 60%

Reflect

7. When calculating a conditional relative frequency, why do you divide by a row total or a column total and not by the grand total?

The "given" in a conditional relative frequency restricts the discussion to a single row or column of a two-way frequency table. A conditional relative frequency is the portion of the data in just that row or column (not the portion of all data) that meets a certain criterion.

© Houghton Mifflin Harcourt Publishing Company

Personal Math Trainer
Online Assessment and Intervention
my.hrw.com

YOUR TURN

8. You can obtain conditional relative frequencies from a two-way relative frequency table. Find the conditional relative frequency that a student prefers cats as pets, given that the student is a girl.

$\frac{0.18}{0.44} \approx 0.409$, or 40.9%

	EXAMPLE 1
AL DOK 1 *Recall*	When finding a conditional relative frequency, what word or words signal that a particular row total or column total should go in the denominator of the fraction? given that
OL DOK 2 *Skills/Concepts*	What is a conditional relative frequency that is not asked for in this example? Give the frequency also. Sample answer: What is the conditional relative frequency that a student surveyed is a boy given that the student prefers "other" as pets? $\frac{10}{13} \approx 77\%$
BL DOK 3 *Strategic Thinking*	Which conditional relative frequency is higher—that a student prefers dogs given that the student is a boy, or that a student is a boy given that the student prefers dogs? that a student is a boy given that the student prefers dogs (about 55% versus 43%)

EXAMPLE 1

ADDITIONAL EXAMPLE 1

Use the frequency table shown below about preferred flavors of frozen yogurt. Express each answer as a decimal and as a percent.

Gender \ Preferred Flavor	Vanilla	Chocolate	Other	TOTAL
Boy	1	6	4	11
Girl	3	4	2	9
TOTAL	4	10	6	20

A Find the conditional relative frequency that a student prefers vanilla yogurt, given that the student is a boy.

$\frac{1}{11} \approx 0.09$ or 9%

B Find the conditional relative frequency that a student surveyed is a boy, given that the student prefers vanilla frozen yogurt.

$\frac{1}{4} \approx 0.25$ or 25%

Interactive Whiteboard
Interactive example available online

YOUR TURN   MP.4

Avoid Common Errors
To avoid errors in calculations with decimals within a fraction, suggest that students clear the decimals first by multiplying the numerator and denominator by the same power of 10. In **Exercise 8**, 0.18 and 0.44 can each be multiplied by 100 to arrive at the fraction $\frac{18}{44}$.

TEACHER TO TEACHER

Visual Cues To help students recall each type of frequency, have them copy a simple relative frequency table, and then color coordinate the fractions below with the cells in the table.

	Dog	Cat	TOTAL
Girl	Frequency	Frequency	Frequency total
Boy	Frequency	Frequency	Frequency total
TOTAL	Frequency total	Frequency total	Grand total

- Marginal relative frequency = $\frac{\text{frequency total}}{\text{grand total}}$
- Joint relative frequency = $\frac{\text{frequency}}{\text{grand total}}$
- Conditional relative frequency = $\frac{\text{frequency}}{\text{frequency total}}$

EXAMPLE 2

ADDITIONAL EXAMPLE 2 Use the two-way frequency table from Additional Example 1 to investigate a possible gender-specific difference in frozen yogurt flavor preference.

Step 1. Identify the percent of all students surveyed who are boys. 55%

Step 2. Determine each conditional relative frequency: percent who are boys, given a preference for vanilla frozen yogurt; percent who are boys, given a preference for chocolate frozen yogurt; and percent who are boys, given a preference for other flavors of frozen yogurt. 25%; 60%; 67%

Step 3. Interpret the results by comparing each conditional relative frequency to the percent of all students surveyed who are boys. The percent of boys who prefer vanilla is much less than 55%, so boys are less likely to prefer vanilla than girls are. The percent of boys who prefer chocolate is a little more than 55%, so boys are more likely to prefer chocolate than girls are. The percent of boys who prefer other flavors is greater than 55%, so boys are more likely to prefer other flavors of frozen yogurt than girls are.

 Interactive Whiteboard
Interactive example available online

YOUR TURN   MP.3

Engage with the Whiteboard

 For **Exercise 9** have volunteers calculate the percents and then explain how to analyze the data.

Digital Teacher Resources

Go online to access all your lesson-level resources.

Differentiated Instruction
• Reteach
• Reading Strategies
• Success for English Learners
• Practice and Problem Solving A/B, C, D

Math on the Spot Videos

Finding Possible Associations Between Variables

You can use conditional relative frequency to see if there is an association between two variables.

EXAMPLE 2

Maria conducted her survey because she was interested in the question "Does gender influence what type of pet people prefer?" If there is no influence, then the distribution of gender within each subgroup of pet preference should roughly equal the distribution of gender within the whole group. Use the results of Maria's survey to investigate possible influences of gender on pet preference.

STEP 1 Identify the percent of all students surveyed who are girls: 44%

STEP 2 Determine each conditional relative frequency.

Of the 22 students who prefer dogs as pets, 10 are girls. Percent who are girls, given a preference for dogs as pets: 45%

Of the 15 students who prefer cats as pets, 9 are girls. Percent who are girls, given a preference for cats as pets: 60%

Of the 13 students who prefer other pets. 3 are girls. Percent who are girls, given a preference for other pets: 23%

STEP 3 Interpret the results by comparing each conditional relative frequency to the percent of all students surveyed who are girls.

The percent of girls among students who prefer dogs is close to 44%, so gender does not appear to influence preference for dogs.

The percent of girls among students who prefer cats is much greater than 44%, so girls are more likely than boys to prefer cats.

The percent of girls among students who prefer other pets is much less than 44%, so girls are less likely than boys to prefer other pets.

YOUR TURN

9. Suppose you analyzed the data by focusing on boys rather than girls. How would the percent in Step 1 change? How would the percents in Step 2 change? How would the conclusions in Step 3 change?

Step 1: 44% becomes 56%; Step 2: 45% becomes 55%, 60% becomes 40%, and 23% becomes 77%; Step 3: conclusions would not change.

Personal Math Trainer
Online Assessment and Intervention
my.hrw.com

My Notes

© Houghton Mifflin Harcourt Publishing Company

DIFFERENTIATE INSTRUCTION *Leveled Questions*

	EXAMPLE 2
AL DOK 1 *Recall*	For there to be no significant association between gender and pet preference, how would these percents relate to those of boys and girls in the survey who prefer each pet? The percentages would be about the same (56% boys vs. 44% girls among students who prefer each pet).
OL DOK 2 *Skills/Concepts*	If you know that a student prefers cats as pets, what prediction can you make about the student's gender given the conditional relative frequencies? What about if you know that a student prefers other pets? The student is more likely to be a girl; more likely to be a boy.
BL DOK 3 *Strategic Thinking*	How can the results of this survey be used in advertising and marketing? Sample answer: Advertisers can better understand to which gender they might sell more dog treats, cat toys, or live snake food.

LEVELED QUESTIONS: **AL** Approaching Level | **OL** On Level | **BL** Beyond Level

1. In a class survey, students were asked to choose their favorite vacation destination. The results are displayed by gender in the two-way frequency table. (Explore Activities 1–3)

Preferred Pet / Gender	Seashore	Mountains	Other	TOTAL
Girl	7	3	2	12
Boy	5	2	6	13
TOTAL	12	5	8	25

a. Find the total for each gender by adding the frequencies in each row. Write the row totals in the Total column.

b. Find the total for each preferred vacation spot by adding the frequencies in each column. Write the column totals in the Total row.

c. Write the grand total (the sum of the row totals and the column totals) in the lower-right corner of the table.

d. Create a two-way relative frequency table by dividing each number in the above table by the grand total. Write the quotients as decimals.

Preferred Pet / Gender	Seashore	Mountains	Other	TOTAL
Girl	0.28	0.12	0.08	0.48
Boy	0.2	0.08	0.24	0.52
TOTAL	0.48	0.2	0.32	1.00

e. Use the table to find the joint relative frequency of students surveyed who are boys and who prefer vacationing in the mountains.

0.08, or 8%

f. Use the table to find the marginal relative frequency of students surveyed who prefer vacationing at the seashore.

0.48, or 48%

g. Find the conditional relative frequency that a student surveyed prefers vacationing in the mountains, given that the student is a girl. Interpret this result. (Examples 1–2)

0.25, or 25%; girls are more likely than boys to prefer the mountains.

ESSENTIAL QUESTION CHECK-IN

2. How can you use a two-way frequency table to learn more about its data?

You can find joint relative frequencies, marginal relative frequencies, conditional relative frequencies, and possible associations.

© Houghton Mifflin Harcourt Publishing Company

④ Elaborate

Talk About It

Summarize the Lesson

Ask: What does it mean when all of the conditional relative frequencies for the rows of a table are similar or the same? It means that the variables are not highly associated with each other.

Guided Practice

Engage with the Whiteboard

For **Exercise 1**, have volunteers explain the process of arriving at the correct value as they complete the table.

Avoid Common Errors

Exercise 1d Remind students that the data they used to complete the table in Exercises 1a–c will be needed to complete this table. Suggest students check their values by making sure the sum of the column totals and the sum of the row totals are the same.

DIFFERENTIATE INSTRUCTION *Intervention and Additional Support*

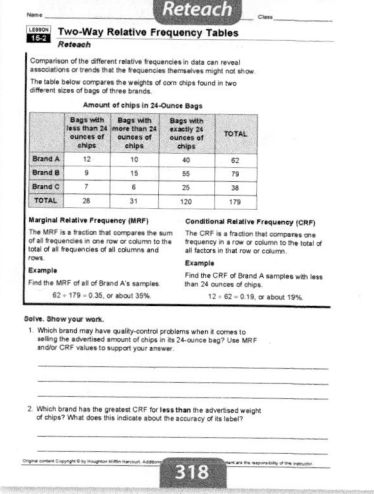

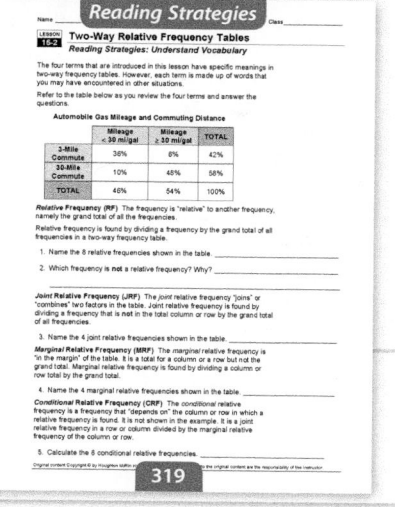

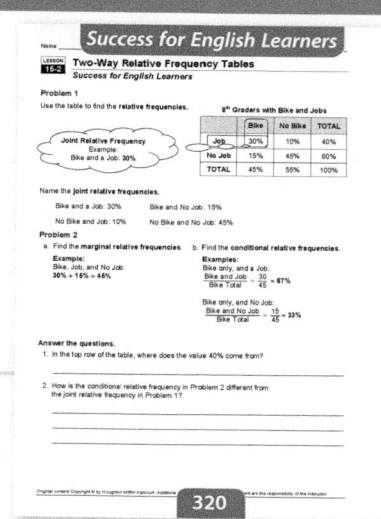

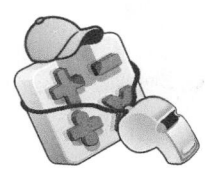

Personal Math Trainer
Daily Intervention
15.2 Homework

Pages shown are from *Differentiated Instruction.*
Also available online.

Pressed for Time

15.2 Differentiated Homework Assignments

(AL) **Approaching Level**	3–5	
(OL) **On Level**	4–6	
(BL) **Beyond Level**	4, 7–8	

*For **Below Level** students, assign Personal Math Trainer, Daily Intervention 15.2 Homework.*

Mathematical Processes	Exercises
MP.1 Problem Solving	4
MP.2 Reasoning	7
MP.3 Logic	6
MP.4 Modeling	5
MP.6 Precision	8
MP.7 Using Structure	3

Focus on Higher Order Thinking

Depth of Knowledge	Exercises
2 Skills/Concepts	4–5
3 Strategic Thinking H.O.T.\	3, 6–8

Name_____ Class_____ Date_____

15.2 Independent Practice

Personal Math Trainer
Online Assessment and Intervention
my.hrw.com

Stefan surveyed 75 of his classmates about their participation in school activities as well as whether they have a part-time job. The results are shown in the two-way frequency table. Use the table for Exercises 3–6.

Activity / Job	Clubs Only	Sports Only	Both	Neither	TOTAL
Yes	10	12	20	9	51
No	5	6	10	3	24
TOTAL	15	18	30	12	75

3. a. Complete the table.

b. Explain how you found the correct data to enter in the table.

Sample answer: I worked backward from the given data, using the fact that the sum of the entries in each row and each column must equal the total for that row or column.

4. Create a two-way relative frequency table using decimals. Round to the nearest hundredth.

Activity / Job	Clubs Only	Sports Only	Both	Neither	TOTAL
Yes	0.13	0.16	0.27	0.12	0.68
No	0.07	0.08	0.13	0.04	0.32
TOTAL	0.2	0.24	0.4	0.16	1.00

5. Give each relative frequency as a percent.

a. the joint relative frequency of students surveyed who participate in school clubs only and have part-time jobs _____13%_____

b. the marginal frequency of students surveyed who do not have a part-time job _____32%_____

c. the conditional relative frequency that a student surveyed participates in both school clubs and sports, given that the student has a part-time job _____about 40%_____

© Houghton Mifflin Harcourt Publishing Company · Image Credits: ©H. Mark Weidman Photography/Alamy Images

---

DIFFERENTIATE INSTRUCTION *Leveled Homework/Practice*

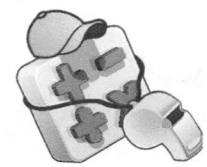

Personal Math Trainer
• 15.2 Homework

Pages shown are from *Differentiated Instruction.*
Also available online.

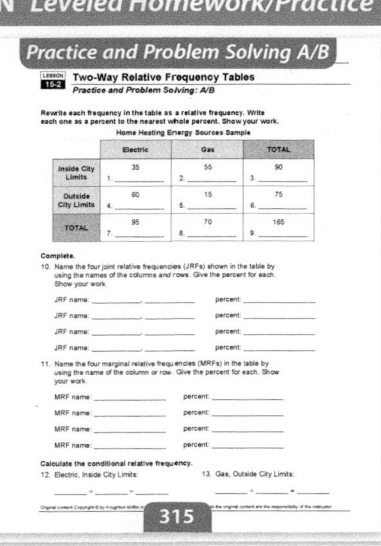

Practice and Problem Solving A/B

LESSON 15-2 **Two-Way Relative Frequency Tables**
Practice and Problem Solving: A/B

Rewrite each frequency in the table as a relative frequency. Write each one as a percent to the nearest whole percent. Show your work.

Home Heating Energy Sources Sample

	Electric	Gas	TOTAL
Inside City Limits	35 (1.)	55 (2.)	90 (3.)
Outside City Limits	60 (4.)	15 (5.)	75 (6.)
TOTAL	95 (7.)	70 (8.)	165 (9.)

Complete.

10. Name the four joint relative frequencies (JRFs) shown in the table by using the names of the columns and rows. Give the percent for each. Show your work.

JRF name: _____ percent: _____
JRF name: _____ percent: _____
JRF name: _____ percent: _____
JRF name: _____ percent: _____

11. Name the four marginal relative frequencies (MRFs) in the table by using the name of the column or row. Give the percent for each. Show your work.

MRF name: _____ percent: _____
MRF name: _____ percent: _____
MRF name: _____ percent: _____
MRF name: _____ percent: _____

Calculate the conditional relative frequency.

12. Electric, Inside City Limits: _____ 13. Gas, Outside City Limits: _____

315

Practice and Problem Solving C

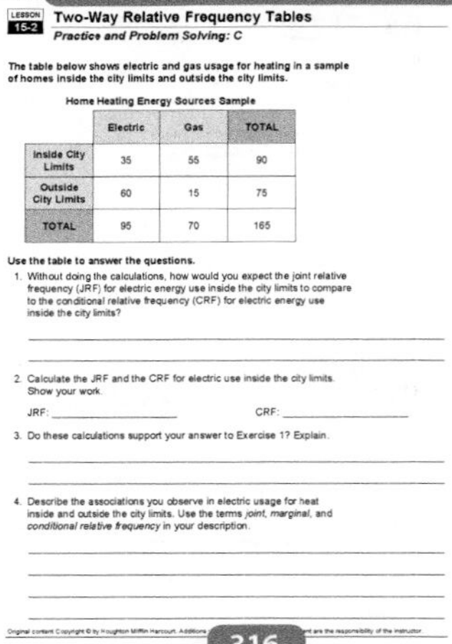

Name_____
LESSON 15-2 **Two-Way Relative Frequency Tables**
Practice and Problem Solving: C

The table below shows electric and gas usage for heating in a sample of homes inside the city limits and outside the city limits.

Home Heating Energy Sources Sample

	Electric	Gas	TOTAL
Inside City Limits	35	55	90
Outside City Limits	60	15	75
TOTAL	95	70	165

Use the table to answer the questions.

1. Without doing the calculations, how would you expect the joint relative frequency (JRF) for electric energy use inside the city limits to compare to the conditional relative frequency (CRF) for electric energy use inside the city limits?

2. Calculate the JRF and the CRF for electric use inside the city limits. Show your work.

JRF: _____ CRF: _____

3. Do these calculations support your answer to Exercise 17 Explain.

4. Describe the associations you observe in electric usage for heat inside and outside the city limits. Use the terms *joint*, *marginal*, and *conditional relative frequency* in your description.

316

Practice and Problem Solving D

LESSON 15-2 **Two-Way Relative Frequency Tables**
Practice and Problem Solving: D
Bowling Averages and Bowling Ball Ownership

	Average > 160	Average ≤ 160	TOTAL
Owns a Bowling Ball	21	17	38
Does Not Own a Bowling Ball	16	23	39
TOTAL	37	40	77

Find the relative frequencies for the data shown in the table above. The first one of each type has been done for you.

1. the joint relative frequency of averaging more than 160 and owning a bowling ball

21 ÷ 77 = 0.27 = 27 %

2. the joint relative frequency of averaging 160 or less and owning a bowling ball

3. the marginal relative frequency of owning a bowling ball

21 + 17 = 38 ÷ 77 = 0.49 = 49 %

4. the marginal relative frequency of not owning a bowling ball

____ + ____ = ____ ÷ ____ = ____ %

5. the conditional relative frequency of averaging more than 160 and owning a bowling ball

21 ÷ 38 = 0.55 = 55 %

6. the conditional relative frequency of averaging 160 or less and owning a bowling ball

____ ÷ ____ = ____ = ____ %

317

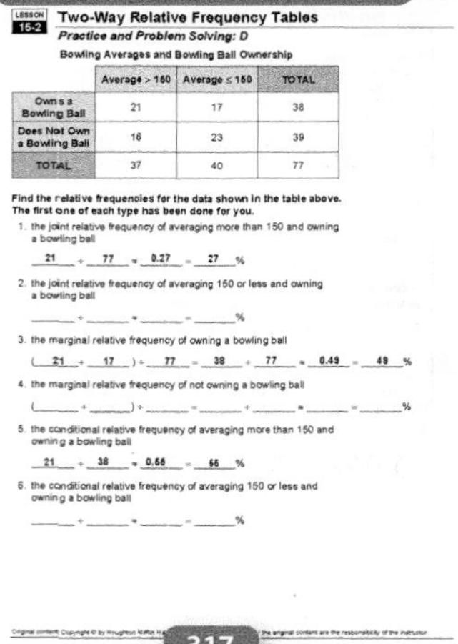

6. Discuss possible influences of having a part-time job on participation in school activities. Support your response with an analysis of the data.

Sample answer: There does not appear to be any influence. Within each category of school activity, the percent of students who have a part-time job is fairly close to 68%, the percent for the whole group.

H.O.T. FOCUS ON HIGHER ORDER THINKING

7. The head of quality control for a chair manufacturer collected data on the quality of two types of wood that the company grows on its tree farm. The table shows the acceptance and rejection data.

Accept/Reject Wood	Accepted	Rejected	TOTAL
White Oak	245	105	350
Redwood	140	110	250
TOTAL	385	215	600

a. Critique Reasoning To create a two-way relative frequency table for this data, the head of quality control divided each number in each row by the row total. Is this correct? Explain.

No; each data value should have been divided by the grand total, 600, not by the row total.

b. Draw Conclusions Are any of the data the head of quality control entered into the two-way relative frequency table correct? If so, which is and which isn't? Explain.

Yes; the data in the Total row and Total column are correct. These entries were created by dividing each entry by 600, the grand total, which results in the correct marginal relative frequency. The joint relative frequencies are incorrect.

8. Analyze Relationships What is the difference between relative frequency and conditional relative frequency?

Relative frequency is the quotient of a frequency and the grand total. Conditional relative frequency is the quotient of a frequency and a column total or row total.

Work Area

© Houghton Mifflin Harcourt Publishing Company • Image Credits: ©Jim West/Alamy Images

---

DIFFERENTIATE INSTRUCTION *Extend-the-Math Activity* **PRE-AP**

Activity Conduct your own survey using gender and a three-category variable of your choice. Organize your data in two-way frequency and relative frequency tables. Next, find conditional relative frequencies based on your calculations. Finally, use the conditional relative frequencies to analyze the data to investigate any possible association between gender and the variable you have chosen.

✔ **Quick Check**

15.2 Lesson Quiz

1. In a survey, 5 students prefer red, 9 prefer green, and 6 prefer blue. Create a relative frequency table of this data.

Preferred Color	Red	Green	Blue	TOTAL
Relative Frequency	25%	45%	30%	100%

2. In the survey from Exercise 1, 2 boys prefer red, 5 girls prefer green, and 3 girls prefer blue. Use this information to complete the two-way frequency table below.

Preferred Color / Gender	Red	Green	Blue	TOTAL
Boy	2	4	3	9
Girl	3	5	3	11
TOTAL	5	9	6	20

3. Create a two-way relative frequency table for the data in Exercise 2. Write the relative frequencies as decimals.

Preferred Color / Gender	Red	Green	Blue	TOTAL
Boy	0.1	0.2	0.15	0.45
Girl	0.15	0.25	0.15	0.55
TOTAL	0.25	0.45	0.30	1

4. Find the conditional relative frequency that a student prefers the color red, given that the student is a boy. $\frac{2}{9} \approx 0.22$ or about 22%

5. Use the two-way frequency table from Exercise 2 to investigate the possible association between gender and color preference. Sample answer: Boys appear somewhat less likely to prefer red than girls and somewhat more likely to prefer blue.

Differentiate Instruction

IF a student misses more than one question, THEN

Differentiate Instruction:

• 15.2 Reteach

• Personal Math Trainer

 Interactive Whiteboard
Interactive Lesson quiz available online

Ready to Go On?

Assess Mastery

Access *Ready to Go On?* assessment online, and receive instant scoring, feedback, and customized intervention or enrichment.

Personal Math Trainer

Online Assessment and Intervention
• Module 15 Posttest

Additional Resources

Digital Teacher Resources

Go online for module-level resources.

Assessment Resources
• Module 15 Quiz: B, p.71
• Module 15 Quiz: D, p.73

my.hrw.com

Ready to Go On?

Personal Math Trainer
Online Assessment and Intervention
my.hrw.com

15.1 Two-Way Frequency Tables

Martin collected data from students about whether they played a musical instrument. The table shows his results. Use the table for Exercises 1–4.

	Instrument	No Instrument	TOTAL
Boys	42	70	112
Girls	48		88
Total	90	110	200

1. Of the students surveyed, how many played an instrument? _____ 90

2. How many girls surveyed did NOT play an instrument? _____ 40

3. What is the relative frequency of a student playing an instrument? Write the answer as a percent. _____ 45%

4. What is the relative frequency of playing an instrument among boys? Write the answer as a decimal. _____ 0.375

15.2 Two-Way Relative Frequency Tables

Students were asked how they traveled to school. The two-way relative frequency table shows the results. Use the table for Exercises 5–7. Write answers as decimals rounded to the nearest hundredth.

	Method			
School	Car	Bus	Other	TOTAL
Middle School	0.18	0.14	0.10	0.42
High School	0.38	0.12	0.08	0.58
TOTAL	0.56	0.26	0.18	1.00

5. What is the joint relative frequency of high school students who ride the bus? _____ 0.12

6. What is the marginal relative frequency of students surveyed who are in middle school? _____ 0.42

7. What is the conditional relative frequency that a student rides the bus, given that the student is in middle school? _____ 0.33

 ESSENTIAL QUESTION

8. How can you use two-way tables to solve real-world problems?
   You can use two-way tables to find frequencies, various types of relative frequencies, and possible associations.

© Houghton Mifflin Harcourt Publishing Company

READY TO GO ON? *Diagnostic Assessment*

RtI Response to Intervention

Use to determine if students have mastered the concepts covered in this module.

Lesson	Exercises	Content Focus	Review with *Differentiated Instruction*
15.1	1–4	Two-Way Frequency Tables	**15.1** Reteach **15.1** Reading Strategies **15.1** Success for English Learners
15.2	5–7	Two-Way Relative Frequency Tables	**15.2** Reteach **15.2** Reading Strategies **15.2** Success for English Learners

Assessment Readiness

Personal Math Trainer
Online Assessment and Intervention
my.hrw.com

Preparing for High Stakes Tests

Selected Response

The table gives data on the length of time that teachers at Tenth Avenue School have taught. Use the table for Exercises 1–5.

	Fewer than 10 years	10 or more years	TOTAL
Male	9	6	15
Female	?	4	25
TOTAL	30	10	40

1. How many female teachers have taught for fewer than 10 years?
- Ⓐ 4
- Ⓒ 21
- Ⓑ 9
- Ⓓ 30

2. What is the relative frequency of teachers who have taught for 10 or more years?
- Ⓐ 10%
- Ⓒ 30%
- Ⓑ 25%
- Ⓓ 60%

3. What is the relative frequency of having taught for fewer than 10 years among male teachers?
- Ⓐ 0.09
- Ⓒ 0.6
- Ⓑ 0.225
- Ⓓ 1.50

4. What is the joint relative frequency of female teachers who have taught for more than 10 years?
- Ⓐ 4%
- Ⓒ 16%
- Ⓑ 10%
- Ⓓ 25%

5. What is the marginal relative frequency of teachers who are female?
- Ⓐ 0.16
- Ⓒ 0.4
- Ⓑ 0.25
- Ⓓ 0.625

6. A triangle has an exterior angle of $x°$. Which of the following represents the measure of the interior angle next to it?
- Ⓐ $(180 - x)°$
- Ⓒ $(90 - x)°$
- Ⓑ $(x - 180)°$
- Ⓓ $(x - 90)°$

7. What is the volume of a cone that has a diameter of 12 cm and a height of 4 cm? Use 3.14 for π and round to the nearest tenth.
- Ⓐ 25.12 cm^3
- Ⓒ 150.72 cm^3
- Ⓑ 602.88 cm^3
- Ⓓ $1,808.64 \text{ cm}^3$

Mini-Task

8. The table gives data on books read by members of the Summer Reading Club.

	Fewer than 25 books	25 or more books	TOTAL
Boys	7	21	28
Girls	9	27	36
TOTAL	16	48	64

a. Find the relative frequency of a club member reading fewer than 25 books.

$\frac{16}{64} = 0.25 = 25\%$

b. Find the relative frequency of reading fewer than 25 books among girl club members.

$\frac{9}{36} = 0.25 = 25\%$

c. Is there an association between being a girl and reading fewer than 25 books? Explain.

No; the relative frequencies show that girls are equally as likely to read fewer than 25 books as are members in general.

© Houghton Mifflin Harcourt Publishing Company

Assessment Readiness Tip

Even if students do not remember the precise meaning of a vocabulary term, they can often use logic to arrive at the correct answer.

- **Item 2** If students do not immediately remember the difference between frequency and relative frequency, encourage them to look at the answer choices. The fact that the answers are all percents should lead them in the right direction.

- **Item 5** Students may not recall the meaning of the term *marginal relative frequency*. However, if they read the item carefully, they may note that only a single characteristic from the chart is mentioned—being female. Given this, the only relative frequency that could make sense is the frequency of female teachers to total teachers.

Avoid Common Errors

- **Item 3** If students choose answer B, point out that they found the joint relative frequency of male teachers who have taught for fewer than 10 years. For the relative frequency, they should ignore the female teachers.

- **Item 7** Remind students that to find the volume of a cone, they need to know the radius of the base.

Items	Grade 8 Lessons	Mathematical Processes
1	15.1	MP.4
2	15.2	MP.4
3	15.2	MP.4
4	15.2	MP.4
5	15.2	MP.4
6*	11.2	MP.7
7*	13.2	MP.4
8	15.2	MP.3, MP.4

* Item integrates mixed review concepts from previous modules or a previous course.

DIFFERENTIATE ASSESSMENT

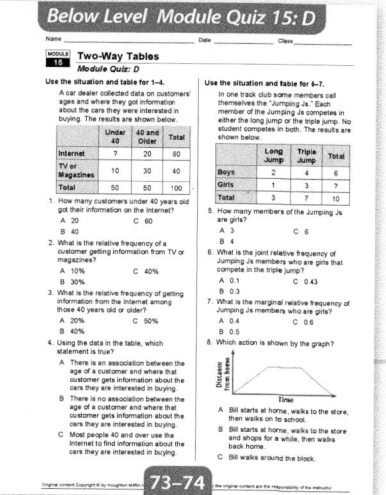

Below Level Module Quiz 15: D

73–74

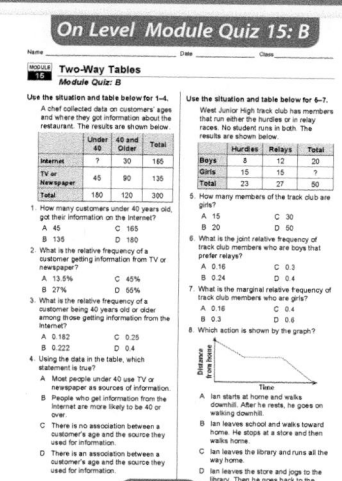

On Level Module Quiz 15: B

71–72

Personal Math Trainer

Module 15 Assessment Readiness

Pages shown are from *Assessment Resources*. **Also available online.**

UNIT 6

Statistics

Study Guide Review

Vocabulary Development

Integrating Language Arts

Encourage students to practice using the unit vocabulary as they talk and write about mathematics. Understanding vocabulary will aid their understanding of the concepts.

MODULE 14

Scatter Plots

Key Concepts

- A scatter plot is a graph with points plotted to show the relationship between two sets of data. *(Lesson 14.1)*

- If two sets of data increase together, they show a positive association. If one set increases while the other decreases, they have a negative association. If changes in one data set have no effect on the other, they have no association. *(Lesson 14.1)*

- Data that have a linear association cluster along a line and can be modeled by a trend line. *(Lessons 14.1, 14.2)*

MODULE 14 Scatter Plots

? ESSENTIAL QUESTION

How can you use scatter plots to solve real-world problems?

Key Vocabulary
cluster (*agrupación*)
outlier (*valor extremo*)
scatter plot (*diagrama de dispersión*)
trend line (*línea de tendencia*)

EXAMPLE 1

As part of a research project, a researcher made a table of test scores and the number of hours of sleep a person got the night before the test. Make a scatter plot of the data. Does the data show a positive association, negative association, or no association?

Sleep (hours)	Test score
4	30
5	40
6	50
6	70
8	100
9	90
10	100

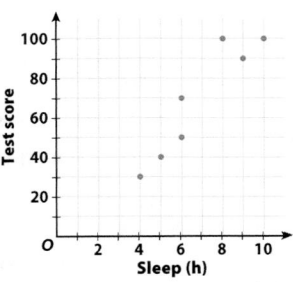

The data show a positive association. Generally, as the number of hours of sleep increases, so do the test scores.

EXAMPLE 2

Write an equation for a trend line of the data shown on the graph.

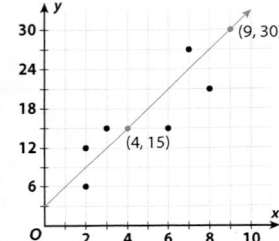

$m = \frac{30 - 15}{9 - 4} = 3$ Find the slope.

$15 = 3(4) + b$ Find the y-intercept.

$b = 3$

$y = 3x + 3$ Use the slope and y-intercept to write the equation.

Unit 6 **467**

EXERCISES

1. The table shows the income of 8 households, in thousands of dollars, and the number of televisions in each household. (Lesson 14.1)

Income ($1000)	20	20	30	30	40	60	70	90
Number of televisions	4	0	1	2	2	3	3	4

a. Make a scatter plot of the data.

b. Describe the association between income and number of televisions. Are any of the values outliers?

<u>The data generally shows a positive</u>

<u>association between income and</u>

<u>number of televisions. As income</u>

<u>increases, so does the number of</u>

<u>televisions. There is an outlier at (20, 4).</u>

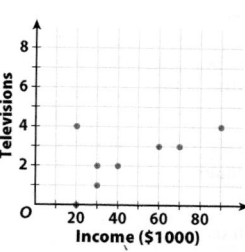

2. The scatter plot shows the relationship between the price of a product and the number of potential buyers. (Lesson 14.2)

a. Draw a trend line for the scatter plot.

b. Write an equation for your trend line.

<u>Sample answer: $y = -2x + 24$</u>

c. When the price of the product is $3.50, the number of potential buyers will be

about ____<u>Sample answer: 17</u>____.

d. When the price of the product is $5.50, the number of potential buyers will be

about ____<u>Sample answer: 13</u>____.

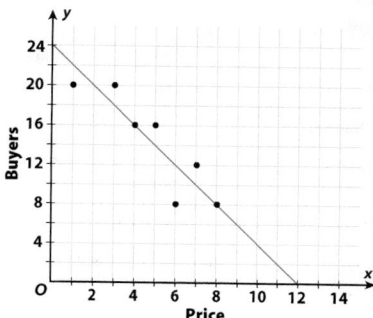

© Houghton Mifflin Harcourt Publishing Company

Two-Way Tables

Key Concepts

• Two-way tables are used to display two types of categorical data for a single population at the same time. **(Lesson 15.1)**

• Frequency and relative frequency tables can be used to decide if there is an association between two variables. **(Lessons 15.1, 15.2)**

MODULE **15** **Two-Way Tables**

? ESSENTIAL QUESTION

How can you use two-way tables to solve real-world problems?

EXAMPLE

A movie theater kept a record of patrons who bought tickets for a particular movie for two different times. The results are shown in the two-way frequency table. Create a two-way relative frequency table of these data.

	5:00 P.M. Showing	8:00 P.M. Showing	Total
Adults	22	39	61
Children	40	25	65
Total	62	64	126

Step 1: Divide each entry by the total number of patrons. Round to the nearest hundredth.

	5:00 P.M. Showing	8:00 P.M. Showing	Total
Adults	$\frac{22}{126} \approx 0.17$	$\frac{39}{126} \approx 0.31$	$\frac{61}{126} \approx 0.48$
Children	$\frac{40}{126} \approx 0.32$	$\frac{25}{126} \approx 0.20$	$\frac{65}{126} \approx 0.52$
Total	$\frac{62}{126} \approx 0.49$	$\frac{64}{126} \approx 0.51$	$\frac{126}{126} \approx 1.00$

Step 2: Convert decimals to percents.

	5:00 P.M. Showing	8:00 P.M. Showing	Total
Adults	17%	31%	48%
Children	32%	20%	52%
Total	49%	51%	100%

EXERCISES

Use the tables in the Example to answer each question.

1. What is the joint relative frequency of patrons who are adults and attended the 8:00 P.M. showing?

_0.31, or 31%_

2. What is the marginal relative frequency of patrons who went to the 8:00 P.M. showing?

_0.51, or 51%_

3. What is the conditional relative frequency that a patron is an adult, given that the patron attends the 8:00 P.M. showing?

_0.61, or 61%_

© Houghton Mifflin Harcourt Publishing Company

Key Vocabulary

conditional relative frequency *(frecuencia relativa condicional)*

frequency *(frecuencia)*

joint relative frequency *(frecuencia relativa común)*

marginal relative frequency *(frecuencia relativa marginal)*

relative frequency *(frecuencia relativa)*

two-way frequency table *(tabla de frecuencia de doble entrada)*

two-way relative frequency table *(tabla de frecuencia relativa de doble entrada)*

two-way table *(tabla de doble entrada)*

1. **CAREERS IN MATH** Psychologist A psychologist gave a test to 15 women of different ages to measure their short-term memory. The test score scale goes from 0 to 24, and a higher score means that the participant has a better short-term memory. The scatter plot shows the results of this study.

a. Describe the pattern in the data. Is there a positive or negative correlation?

The graph exhibits a roughly linear association and shows a negative correlation.

b. Draw a line of best fit on the scatter plot and estimate its slope. Interpret the slope in the context of the problem.

The slope is around -0.4; it means short-term memory test scores decrease by about 0.4 points per year.

c. In another test, a 70-year-old woman scored 8. Does your line of best fit predict a higher or lower score? What may have happened?

The line of best fit predicts a lower score. Sample answer: The score for this woman is an outlier, or short-term memory tends to level off after 65.

2. Kalila has developed two different varieties of tomatoes, called Big Red and Sweet Summer, which she grows in her garden. When she harvests the tomatoes, she measures the diameters of each variety. The results are shown in the table.

	Diameter ≤ 2 in.	Diameter > 2 in.
Big Red	36	45
Sweet Summer	28	39

a. Use the data to create a two-way frequency table.

	Diameter ≤ 2 in.	Diameter > 2 in.	Total
Big Red	36	45	81
Sweet Summer	28	39	67
Total	64	84	148

b. What is the relative frequency of a tomato having a diameter that is greater than two inches? Round to the nearest percent.   57%

c. What is the relative frequency of having a diameter that is greater than two inches among Big Red tomatoes? Round to the nearest percent.   56%

d. Is there an association between Big Red tomatoes and diameters that are greater than two inches? Explain.

No; the relative frequencies show that Big Red tomatoes are just as likely to have diameters greater than two inches as any other tomato.

© Houghton Mifflin Harcourt Publishing Company

Performance Tasks

The Performance Tasks provide students with the opportunity to apply concepts from this unit in real-world problem situations.

CAREERS IN MATH

Psychologist

In Performance Task Item 1, students can see how a psychologist uses mathematics on the job.

Scoring Guides For Performance Tasks

1. **Mathematical Processes**

MP.4, MP.6, MP.7

Task	Possible Points (Total: 6)
a	**1 point** for correctly describing the graph as exhibiting a roughly linear association, or another correct description, and **1 point** for the correct answer of negative association.
b	**1 point** for a reasonable line, such as the line shown in the answer on the student page, and **1 point** for finding a reasonable slope of around −0.4 and explaining that it means test scores decrease by about 0.4 points per year of age.
c	**1 point** for noting that the line of best fit predicts a lower score, and **1 point** for any reasonable explanation, for example: the score for this woman was an outlier, or short-term memory tends to level off at ages after 65.

2. **Mathematical Processes**

MP.1, MP.2, MP.4, MP.7

Task	Possible Points (Total: 6)
a	**2 points** for correctly filling in the frequency table: from top to bottom, total column should 81, 67, 148; from left to right, total row should be 64, 84, 148
b	**1 point** for correctly finding the solution 57%
c	**1 point** for correctly finding the solution 56%
d	**1 point** for correctly answering no; and 1 point for a correct explanation, for example: The relative frequencies show that Big Red tomatoes are no more likely to have diameters greater than two inches than any of the tomatoes Kalila grew.

Assessment Readiness

Avoid Common Errors

- **Item 1** Students may calculate the percentage of only female voters that were between 18 and 62 years of age, rather than calculating the percentage of all voters that were female and between 18 and 62 years. Encourage students to double-check the question to see if they are supposed to find a percentage of a part, or a percentage of the whole.

- **Item 3** The formula for the volume of a sphere uses the radius, and this problem gives the diameter. Remind students to check to see if they have the correct values before substituting into the formula and solving.

Items	Grade 8 Lessons	Mathematical Processes
1	**15.1**	MP.1
2	**14.1**	MP.6
3*	**13.3**	MP.2
4	**14.2**	MP.6
5	**15.2**	MP.1
6*	**9.4**	MP.2
7	**14.1**	MP.2
8	**14.2**	MP.4

* Item integrates mixed review concepts from previous modules or a previous course.

Assessment Readiness

Personal Math Trainer
Online Assessment and Intervention
my.hrw.com

Selected Response

> **Read graphs and diagrams carefully. Look at the labels for important information.**

1. A local election conducted an exit poll of the age and gender of its voters. The results are shown in the two-way frequency table.

	18–62 years old	63 years and older	Total
Female	142	22	164
Male	126	15	141
Total	268	37	305

What percent of the voters were female and 18 to 62 years old?

- (A) 6.5%
- (B) 47%
- (C) 53%
- (D) 87%

2. What type of association is there between the speed of a car and the distance the car travels in a given time at that speed?

- (A) cluster
- (B) negative association
- (C) no association
- (D) positive association

3. Using 3.14 for π, what is the volume of the sphere to the nearest tenth?

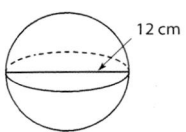

12 cm

- (A) 508.7 cubic centimeters
- (B) 678.2 cubic centimeters
- (C) 904.3 cubic centimeters
- (D) 2713 cubic centimeters

4. Which scatter plot could have a trend line given by the equation $y = -4x + 70$?

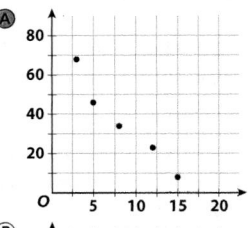

(A)

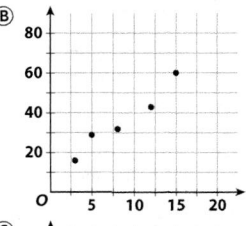

(B)

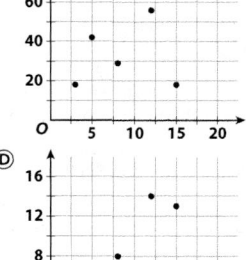

(C)

(D)

© Houghton Mifflin Harcourt Publishing Company

DIFFERENTIATE ASSESSMENT

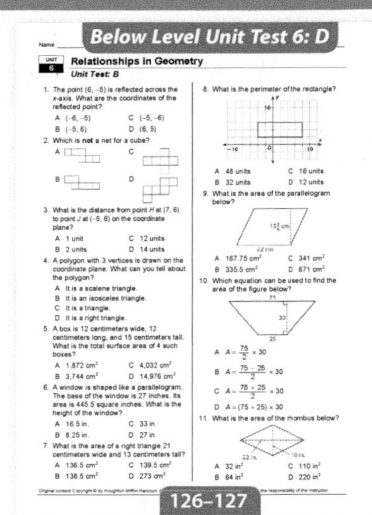

Below Level Unit Test 6: D

126–127

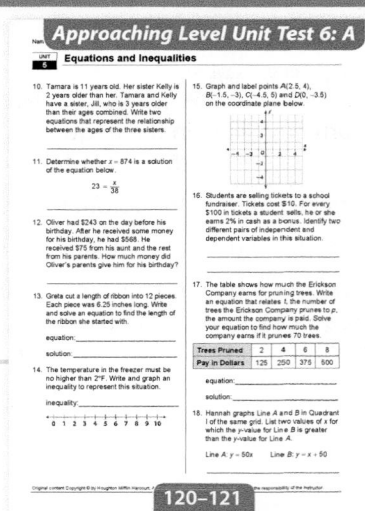

Approaching Level Unit Test 6: A

120–121

5. A group of middle school students were asked whether they prefer communicating with their friends by text message or email. The results are shown in the two-way frequency table.

	Text Message	Email	Total
Female	28	16	44
Male	31	18	49
Total	59	34	93

What is the conditional relative frequency that a student prefers email, given that the student is female?

Ⓐ 17%   Ⓒ 47%

Ⓑ 36%   Ⓓ 64%

6. The vertices of a triangle are (11, 9), (7, 4), and (1, 11). What are the vertices after the triangle has been reflected over the *y*-axis?

Ⓐ (9, 11), (4, 7), (11, 1)

Ⓑ (11, −9), (7, −4), (1, −11)

Ⓒ (9, 11), (4, 7), (11, 1)

Ⓓ (−11, 9), (−7, −4), (−1, 11)

7. Which of the following is **not** shown on the scatter plot below?

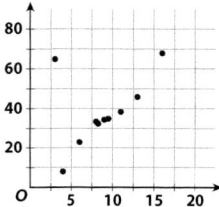

Ⓐ cluster

Ⓑ negative association

Ⓒ outlier

Ⓓ positive association

Mini-Task

8. A scatter plot and trend line of the weight of a Chihuahua puppy versus age is shown.

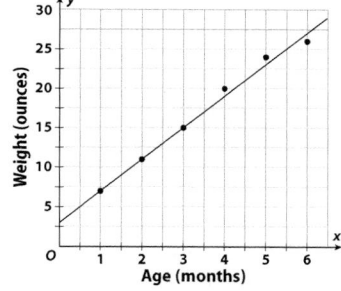

a. The trend line for these data is given by $y = 4x + 3$. What does the 3 represent in this context?

the weight of the puppy when

it is 0 months old

b. If you use the trend line to predict the weight of the puppy after 60 months, the result is 243 ounces, or about 15 pounds. Is this a reasonable weight for the Chihuahua at 5 years old? Explain.

No, because the Chihuahua will

stop growing at a certain point

and its weight will level off.

© Houghton Mifflin Harcourt Publishing Company

Assessment Readiness Tip

Students should underline or highlight the word *not* when it appears in problem situations.

- **Item 7** Remind students to highlight the word *not* every time they see it, and it will tell them to find the opposite of what they would normally look for. In this problem, if they miss the word *not*, any of the three incorrect answers will appear to be correct.

Personal Math Trainer

Online Assessment and Intervention

Additional Resources

Digital Teacher Resources

Go online for unit-level resources.

Assessment Resources
- Leveled Unit Tests: A, B, C, D
- Unit Performance Task

my.hrw.com

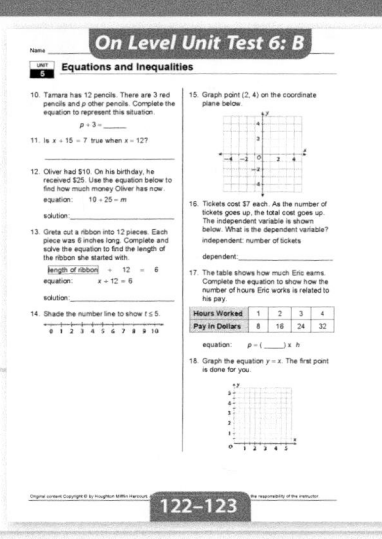

On Level Unit Test 6: B

122–123

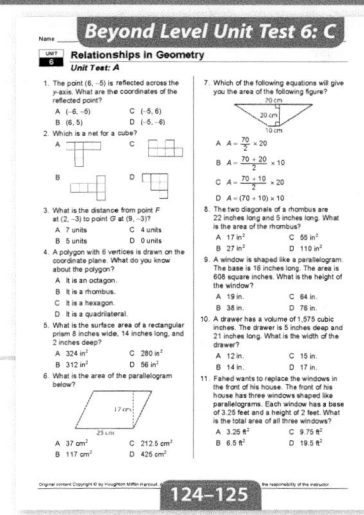

Beyond Level Unit Test 6: C

124–125

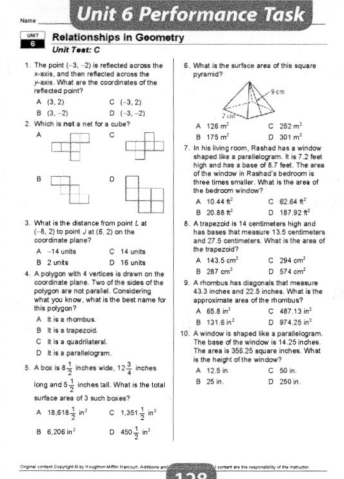

Unit 6 Performance Task

128

Personal Math Trainer

Unit 6 Assessment Readiness

Pages shown are from *Assessment Resources*. **Also available online.**

Glossary/Glosario

A

ENGLISH	SPANISH	EXAMPLES
absolute value The distance of a number from zero on a number line; shown by | |.	**valor absoluto** Distancia a la que está un número de 0 en una recta numérica. El símbolo del valor absoluto es | |.	$\|-5\| = 5$
accuracy The closeness of a given measurement or value to the actual measurement or value.	**exactitud** Cercanía de una medida o un valor a la medida o el valor real.	
acute angle An angle that measures greater than 0° and less than 90°.	**ángulo agudo** Ángulo que mide mas de 0° y menos de 90°.	
acute triangle A triangle with all angles measuring less than 90°.	**triángulo acutángulo** Triángulo en el que todos los ángulos miden menos de 90°.	
Addition Property of Equality The property that states that if you add the same number to both sides of an equation, the new equation will have the same solution.	**Propiedad de igualdad de la suma** Propiedad que establece que puedes sumar el mismo número a ambos lados de una ecuación y la nueva ecuación tendrá la misma solución.	$14 - 6 = \quad 8$ $\underline{+6 \quad +6}$ $14 \quad = \quad 14$
Addition Property of Opposites The property that states that the sum of a number and its opposite equals zero.	**Propiedad de la suma de los opuestos** Propiedad que establece que la suma de un número y su opuesto es cero.	$12 + (-12) = 0$
additive inverse The opposite of a number.	**inverso aditivo** El opuesto de un número.	The additive inverse of 5 is -5.
adjacent angles Angles in the same plane that have a common vertex and a common side.	**ángulos adyacentes** Ángulos en el mismo plano que comparten un vértice y un lado.	
algebraic expression An expression that contains at least one variable.	**expresión algebraica** Expresión que contiene al menos una variable.	$x + 8$ $4(m - b)$
algebraic inequality An inequality that contains at least one variable.	**desigualdad algebraica** Desigualdad que contiene al menos una variable.	$x + 3 > 10$ $5a > b + 3$

© Houghton Mifflin Harcourt Publishing Company

ENGLISH	SPANISH	EXAMPLES
alternate exterior angles For two lines intersected by a transversal, a pair of angles that lie on opposite sides of the transversal and outside the other two lines.	**ángulos alternos externos** Dadas dos rectas cortadas por una transversal, par de ángulos no adyacentes ubicados en los lados opuestos de la transversal y fuera de las otras dos rectas.	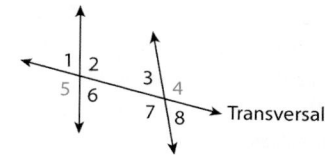 ∠4 and ∠5 are alternate exterior angles.
alternate interior angles For two lines intersected by a transversal, a pair of nonadjacent angles that lie on opposite sides of the transversal and between the other two lines.	**ángulos alternos internos** Dadas dos rectas cortadas por una transversal, par de ángulos no adyacentes ubicados en los lados opuestos de la transversal y entre de las otras dos rectas.	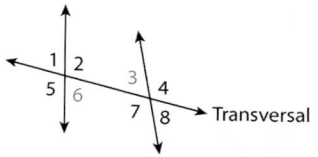 ∠3 and ∠6 are alternate interior angles.
angle A figure formed by two rays with a common endpoint called the vertex.	**ángulo** Figura formada por dos rayos con un extremo común llamado vértice.	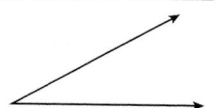
angle bisector A line, segment, or ray that divides an angle into two congruent angles.	**bisectriz de un ángulo** Línea, segmento o rayo que divide un ángulo en dos ángulos congruentes.	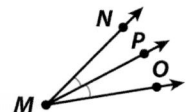 $\overrightarrow{MP}$ is an angle bisector.
arc An unbroken part of a circle.	**arco** Parte continua de un círculo.	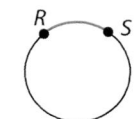
area The number of square units needed to cover a given surface.	**área** El número de unidades cuadradas que se necesitan para cubrir una superficie dada.	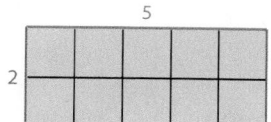
arithmetic sequence An ordered list of numbers in which the difference between consecutive terms is always the same.	**sucesión aritmética** Lista ordenada de números en la que la diferencia entre términos consecutivos es siempre la misma.	The sequence 2, 5, 8, 11, 14 ... is an arithmetic sequence.
association A description of how data sets are related.	**asociación** Descripción de cómo se relaciona un conjunto de datos.	
Associative Property (of Addition) The property that states that for all real numbers a, b, and c, the sum is always the same, regardless of their grouping.	**Propiedad asociativa (de la suma)** Propiedad que establece que para todos los números reales a, b y c, la suma siempre es la misma sin importar cómo se agrupen.	$a + b + c = (a + b) + c = a + (b + c)$

© Houghton Mifflin Harcourt Publishing Company

Glossary/Glosario

ENGLISH	SPANISH	EXAMPLES
Associative Property (of Multiplication) The property that states that for all real numbers *a, b,* and *c,* their product is always the same, regardless of their grouping.	**Propiedad asociativa (de la multiplicación)** Propiedad que establece que para todos los números reales *a, b* y *c,* el producto siempre es el mismo, sin importar cómo se agrupen.	$a \cdot b \cdot c = (a \cdot b) \cdot c = a \cdot (b \cdot c)$
average The sum of a set of data divided by the number of items in the data set; also called *mean.*	**promedio** La suma de los elementos de un conjunto de datos dividida entre el número de elementos del conjunto. También se llama media.	Data set: 4, 6, 7, 8, 10 Average: $\frac{4+6+7+8+10}{5}$ $= \frac{35}{5} = 7$

B

ENGLISH	SPANISH	EXAMPLES
back-to-back stem-and-leaf plot A stem-and-leaf plot that compares two sets of data by displaying one set of data to the left of the stem and the other to the right.	**diagrama doble de tallo y hojas** Diagrama de tallo y hojas que compara dos conjuntos de datos presentando uno de ellos a la izquierda del tallo y el otro a la derecha.	Data set A: 9, 12, 14, 16, 23, 27 Data set B: 6, 8, 10, 13, 15, 16, 21 Set A | | Set B 9 | 0 | 6 8 6 4 2 | 1 | 0 3 5 6 7 3 | 2 | 1 *Key*: |2| 1 means 21 7 |2| means 27
bar graph A graph that uses vertical or horizontal bars to display data.	**gráfica de barras** Gráfica en la que se usan barras verticales u horizontales para presentar datos.	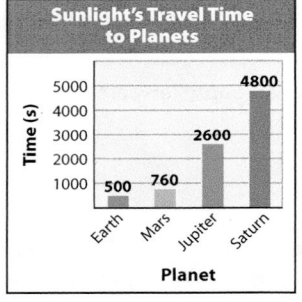
base When a number is raised to a power, the number that is used as a factor is the base.	**base** Cuando un número es elevado a una potencia, el número que se usa como factor es la base.	$3^5 = 3 \cdot 3 \cdot 3 \cdot 3 \cdot 3$; 3 is the base.
base (of a polygon or three-dimensional figure) A side of a polygon; a face of a three-dimensional figure by which the figure is measured or classified.	**base (de un polígono o figura tridimensional)** Lado de un polígono; cara de una figura tridimensional según la cual se mide o se clasifica la figura.	 Bases of a cylinder Bases of a prism 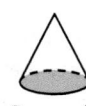  Base of a cone Base of a pyramid

© Houghton Mifflin Harcourt Publishing Company

Glossary/Glosario

biased question A question that leads people to give a certain answer.

pregunta tendenciosa pregunta que lleva a las personas a dar una respuesta determinada

---

biased sample A sample that does not fairly represent the population.

muestra no representativa Muestra que no representa adecuadamente la población.

---

binomial A polynomial with two terms.

binomio Polinomio con dos términos.

$x + y$
$2a^2 - 3$
$4m^3n^2 + 6mn^4$

---

bisect To divide into two congruent parts.

trazar una bisectriz Dividir en dos partes congruentes.

$\overrightarrow{JK}$ bisects $\angle LJM$.

---

bivariate data A set of data that is made of two paired variables.

datos bivariados Conjunto de datos compuesto de dos variables apareadas.

---

boundary line The set of points where the two sides of a two-variable linear inequality are equal.

línea de límite Conjunto de puntos donde los dos lados de una desigualdad lineal con dos variables son iguales.

Boundary line

---

box-and-whisker plot A graph that shows how data are distributed by using the median, quartiles, least value, and greatest value; also called a *box plot*.

gráfica de mediana y rango Gráfica para demostrar la distribución de datos utilizando la mediana, los cuartiles y los valores menos y más grande; también llamado gráfica de caja.

First quartile   Third quartile
Minimum   Median   Maximum
0 2 4 6 8 10 12 14

---

break (graph) A zigzag on a horizontal or vertical scale of a graph that indicates that some of the numbers on the scale have been omitted.

discontinuidad (gráfica) Zig-zag en la escala horizontal o vertical de una gráfica que indica la omisión de algunos de los números de la escala.

100
90
80
70
60
50
0
2 4 6 8 10 12 14 16 18 20

C

capacity The amount a container can hold when filled.

capacidad Cantidad que cabe en un recipiente cuando se llena.

A large milk container has a capacity of 1 gallon.

Celsius A metric scale for measuring temperature in which 0 °C is the freezing point of water and 100 °C is the boiling point of water; also called *centigrade*.

Celsius Escala métrica para medir la temperatura, en la que 0 °C es el punto de congelación del agua y 100 °C es el punto de ebullición. También se llama *centígrado*.

© Houghton Mifflin Harcourt Publishing Company

Glossary/Glosario

center (of a circle) The point inside a circle that is the same distance from all the points on the circle.

centro (de un círculo) Punto interior de un círculo que se encuentra a la misma distancia de todos los puntos de la circunferencia.

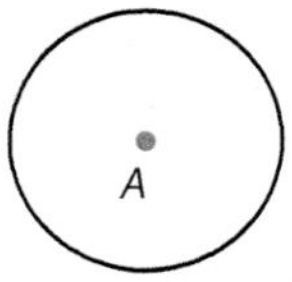

center of dilation The point of intersection of lines through each pair of corresponding vertices in a dilation.

centro de una dilatación Punto de intersección de las líneas que pasan a través de cada par de vértices correspondientes en una dilatación.

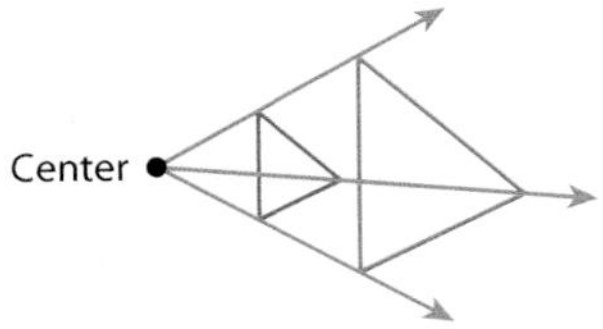

center of rotation The point about which a figure is rotated.

centro de una rotación Punto alrededor del cual se hace girar una figura.

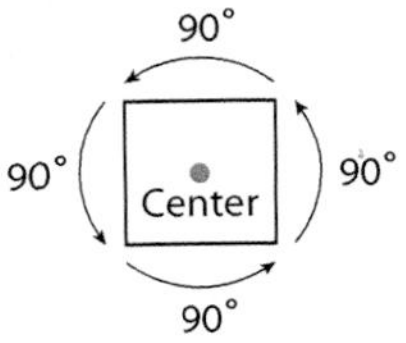

central angle An angle formed by two radii with its vertex at the center of a circle.

ángulo central de un círculo Ángulo formado por dos radios cuyo vértice se encuentra en el centro de un círculo.

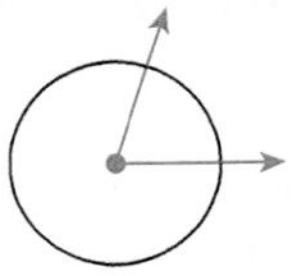

chord A segment with its endpoints on a circle.

cuerda Segmento de recta cuyos extremos forman parte de un círculo.

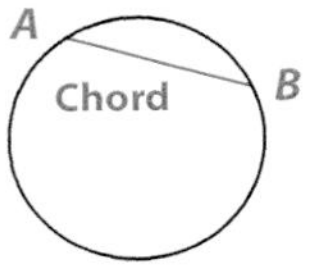

circle The set of all points in a plane that are the same distance from a given point called the center.

círculo Conjunto de todos los puntos en un plano que se encuentran a la misma distancia de un punto dado llamado centro.

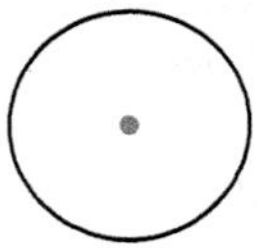

circle graph A graph that uses sectors of a circle to compare parts to the whole and parts to other parts.

gráfica circular Gráfica que usa secciones de un círculo para comparar partes con el todo y con otras partes.

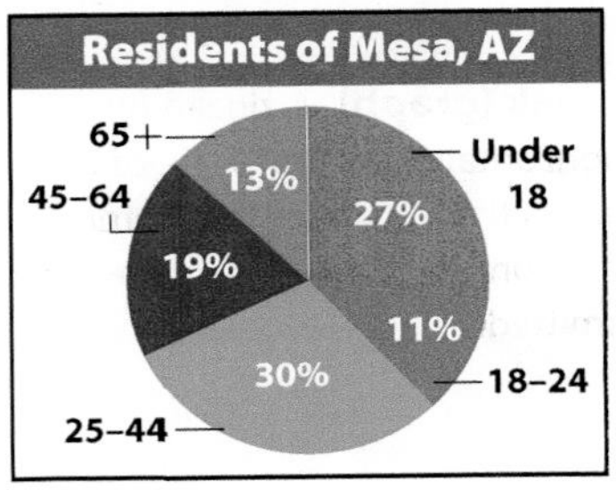

Residents of Mesa, AZ

circuit A path in a graph that begins and ends at the same vertex.

circuito Una trayectoria en una gráfica que empieza y termina en el mismo vértice.

circumference The distance around a circle.

circunferencia Distancia alrededor de un círculo.

© Houghton Mifflin Harcourt Publishing Company

Glossary/Glosario

clockwise A circular movement in the direction shown.

en el sentido de las manecillas del reloj Movimiento circular en la dirección que se indica.

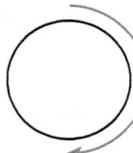

---

cluster A set of closely grouped data.

agrupación Conjunto de datos bien agrupados.

---

clustering A condition that occurs when data points in a scatter plot are grouped more in one part of the graph than another.

arracimando Una condición que ocurre cuando los datos están apiñando en una parte de una diagrama de dispersión mas que en otras partes.

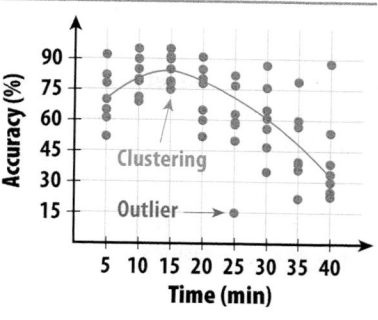

---

coefficient The number that is multiplied by the variable in an algebraic expression.

coeficiente Número que se multiplica por la variable en una expresión algebraica.

5 is the coefficient in 5*b*.

---

combination An arrangement of items or events in which order does not matter.

combinación Agrupación de objetos o sucesos en la que el orden no es importante.

For objects *A*, *B*, *C*, and *D*, there are 6 different combinations of 2 objects: *AB, AC, AD, BC, BD, CD.*

---

commission A fee paid to a person for making a sale.

comisión Pago que recibe una persona por realizar una venta.

---

commission rate The fee paid to a person who makes a sale expressed as a percent of the selling price.

tasa de comisión Pago que recibe una persona por hacer una venta, expresado como un porcentaje del precio de venta.

A commission rate of 5% on a sale of $10,000 results in a commission of $500.

---

common denominator A denominator that is the same in two or more fractions.

denominador común Denominador que es común a dos o más fracciones.

The common denominator of $\frac{5}{8}$ and $\frac{2}{8}$ is 8.

---

common factor A number that is a factor of two or more numbers.

factor común Número que es factor de dos o más números.

8 is a common factor of 16 and 40.

---

common multiple A number that is a multiple of each of two or more numbers.

múltiplo común Número que es múltiplo de dos o más números.

15 is a common multiple of 3 and 5.

---

common ratio The ratio each term is multiplied by to produce the next term in a geometric sequence.

razón común Razón por la que se multiplica cada término para obtener el siguiente término de una sucesión geométrica.

In the geometric sequence 32, 16, 8, 4, 2, …, the common ratio is $\frac{1}{2}$.

Commutative Property (of Addition) The property that states that two or more numbers can be added in any order without changing the sum.

Propiedad conmutativa (de la suma) Propiedad que establece que sumar dos o más números en cualquier orden no altera la suma.

$8 + 20 = 20 + 8; a + b = b + a$

© Houghton Mifflin Harcourt Publishing Company

ENGLISH	SPANISH	EXAMPLES
Commutative Property (of Multiplication) The property that states that two or more numbers can be multiplied in any order without changing the product.	**Propiedad conmutativa (de la multiplicación)** Propiedad que establece que multiplicar dos o más números en cualquier orden no altera el producto.	$6 \cdot 12 = 12 \cdot 6; a \cdot b = b \cdot a$
compatible numbers Numbers that are close to the given numbers that make estimation or mental calculation easier.	**números compatibles** Números que están cerca de los números dados y hacen más fácil la estimación o el cálculo mental.	To estimate $7{,}957 + 5{,}009$, use the compatible numbers 8,000 and 5,000: $8{,}000 + 5{,}000 = 13{,}000$
complement The set of all outcomes in the sample space that are not the event.	**complemento** La serie de resultados que no están en el suceso.	Experiment: rolling a number cube Sample space: {1, 2, 3, 4, 5, 6} Event: rolling a 1, 3, 4, or 6 Complement: rolling a 2 or 5
complementary angles Two angles whose measures add to 90°.	**ángulos complementarios** Dos ángulos cuyas medidas suman 90°.	37° B A 53° The complement of a 53° angle is a 37° angle.
composite figure A figure made up of simple geometric shapes.	**figura compuesta** Figura formada por figuras geométricas simples.	2 cm 5 cm 4 cm 4 cm 4 cm 5 cm 3 cm
composite number A number greater than 1 that has more than two whole-number factors.	**número compuesto** Número mayor que 1 que tiene más de dos factores que son números cabales.	4, 6, 8, and 9 are composite numbers.
compound interest Interest earned or paid on principal and previously earned or paid interest.	**interés compuesto** Interés que se gana o se paga sobre el capital y los intereses previamente ganados o pagados.	If $100 is put into an account with an interest rate of 5% compounded monthly, then after 2 years, the account will have $100\left(1 + \frac{0.05}{12}\right)^{12 \cdot 2} =$ $110.49
conditional relative frequency The ratio of a joint relative frequency to a related marginal relative frequency in a two-way table.	**frecuencia relativa condicional** Razón de una frecuencia relativa conjunta a una frecuencia relativa marginal en una tabla de doble entrada.	
cone A three-dimensional figure with one vertex and one circular base.	**cono** Figura tridimensional con un vértice y una base circular.	
congruence transformation A transformation that results in an image that is the same shape and the same size as the original figure.	**transformación de congruencia** Una transformación que resulta en una imagen que tiene la misma forma y el mismo tamaño como la figura original.	J M K L J' M' K' L'

© Houghton Mifflin Harcourt Publishing Company

ENGLISH	SPANISH	EXAMPLES

congruent Having the same size and shape; the symbol for congruent is ≅.

congruentes Que tienen la misma forma y el mismo tamaño expresado por ≅.

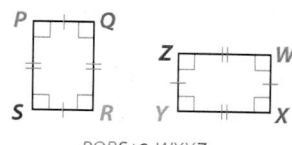

PQRS ≅ WXYZ

---

congruent angles Angles that have the same measure.

ángulos congruentes Ángulos que tienen la misma medida.

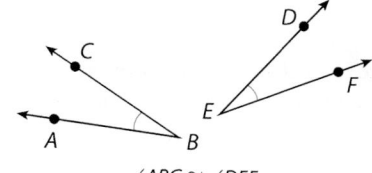

∠ABC ≅ ∠DEF

---

congruent figures See *congruent*.

figuras congruentes Vea *congruentes*.

---

congruent segments Segments that have the same length.

segmentos congruentes Segmentos que tienen la misma longitud.

$\overline{PQ} \cong \overline{SR}$

---

conjecture A statement believed to be true.

conjetura Enunciado que se supone verdadero.

---

constant A value that does not change.

constante Valor que no cambia.

3, 0, π

---

constant of variation The constant *k* in direct and inverse variation equations.

constante de variación La constante *k* en ecuaciones de variación directa e inversa.

$y = 5x$
↑
Constant of variation

---

continuous graph A graph made up of connected lines or curves.

gráfica continua Gráfica compuesta por líneas rectas o curvas conectadas.

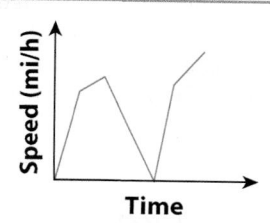

---

convenience sample A sample based on members of the population that are readily available.

muestra de conveniencia Una muestra basada en miembros de la población que están fácilmente disponibles.

---

conversion factor A fraction whose numerator and denominator represent the same quantity but use different units; the fraction is equal to 1 because the numerator and denominator are equal.

factor de conversión Fracción cuyo numerador y denominador representan la misma cantidad pero con unidades distintas; la fracción es igual a 1 porque el numerador y el denominador son iguales.

$\frac{24 \text{ hours}}{1 \text{ day}}$ and $\frac{1 \text{ day}}{24 \text{ hours}}$

---

coordinate One of the numbers of an ordered pair that locate a point on a coordinate graph.

coordenada Uno de los números de un par ordenado que ubica un punto en una gráfica de coordenadas.

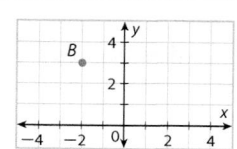

The coordinates of *B* are (−2, 3).

© Houghton Mifflin Harcourt Publishing Company

Glossary/Glosario

ENGLISH	SPANISH	EXAMPLES
coordinate plane A plane formed by the intersection of a horizontal number line called the *x*-axis and a vertical number line called the *y*-axis.	**plano cartesiano** Plano formado por la intersección de una recta numérica horizontal llamada eje *x* y otra vertical llamada eje *y*.	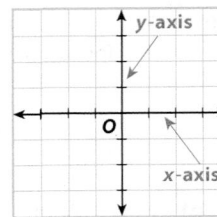
correlation The description of the relationship between two data sets.	**correlación** Descripción de la relación entre dos conjuntos de datos.	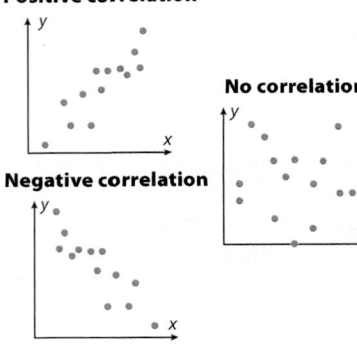
correspondence The relationship between two or more objects that are matched.	**correspondencia** La relación entre dos o más objetos que coinciden.	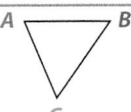 ∠*A* and ∠*D* are corresponding angles. 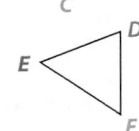 $\overline{AB}$ and $\overline{DE}$ are corresponding sides.
corresponding angles (for lines) For two lines intersected by a transversal, a pair of angles that lie on the same side of the transversal and on the same sides of the other two lines.	**ángulos correspondientes (en líneas)** Dadas dos rectas cortadas por una transversal, el par de ángulos ubicados en el mismo lado de la transversal y en los mismos lados de las otras dos rectas.	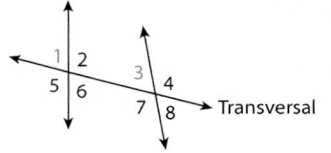 ∠1 and ∠3 are corresponding angles.
corresponding angles (of polygons) Angles in the same relative position in polygons with an equal number of sides.	**ángulos correspondientes (en polígonos)** Ángulos en la misma posición formaron cuando una tercera línea interseca dos líneas.	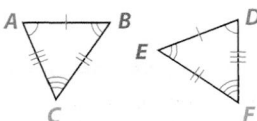 ∠*A* and ∠*D* are corresponding angles.
corresponding sides Matching sides of two or more polygons.	**lados correspondientes** Lados que se ubican en la misma posición relativa en dos o más polígonos.	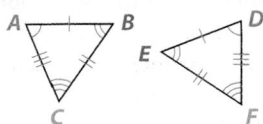 $\overline{AB}$ and $\overline{DE}$ are corresponding sides.
counterclockwise A circular movement in the direction shown.	**en sentido contrario a las manecillas del reloj** Movimiento circular en la dirección que se indica.	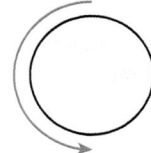

© Houghton Mifflin Harcourt Publishing Company

Glossary/Glosario

ENGLISH	SPANISH	EXAMPLES
counterexample An example that proves that a conjecture or statement is false.	**contraejemplo** Ejemplo que demuestra que una conjetura o enunciado es falso.	
cube (geometric figure) A rectangular prism with six congruent square faces.	**cubo (figura geométrica)** Prisma rectangular con seis caras cuadradas congruentes.	
cube (in numeration) A number raised to the third power.	**cubo (en numeración)** Número elevado a la tercera potencia.	$2^3 = 2 \cdot 2 \cdot 2 = 8$ 8 is the cube of 2.
cube root A number, written as $\sqrt[3]{x}$, whose cube is x.	**raíz cúbica** Número, expresado como $\sqrt[3]{x}$, cuyo cubo es x.	$\sqrt[3]{8} = \sqrt[3]{2 \cdot 2 \cdot 2} = 2$ 2 is the cube root of 8.
cumulative frequency The sum of successive data items.	**frecuencia acumulativa** La suma de datos sucesivos.	
customary system of measurement The measurement system often used in the United States.	**sistema usual de medidas** El sistema de medidas que se usa comúnmente en Estados Unidos.	inches, feet, miles, ounces, pounds, tons, cups, quarts, gallons
cylinder A three-dimensional figure with two parallel, congruent circular bases connected by a curved lateral surface.	**cilindro** Figura tridimensional con dos bases circulares paralelas y congruentes, unidas por una superficie lateral curva.	

D

decagon A polygon with ten sides.	**decágono** Polígono de diez lados.	
degree The unit of measure for angles or temperature.	**grado** Unidad de medida para ángulos y temperaturas.	
degree of a polynomial The highest power of the variable in a polynomial.	**grado de un polinomio** La potencia más alta de la variable en un polinomio.	The polynomial $4x^5 - 6x^2 + 7$ has degree 5.
denominator The bottom number of a fraction that tells how many equal parts are in the whole.	**denominador** Número que está abajo en una fracción y que indica en cuántas partes iguales se divide el entero.	In the fraction $\frac{2}{5}$, 5 is the denominator.
Density Property The property that states that between any two real numbers there is always another real number.	**Propiedad de densidad** Propiedad según la cual entre dos números reales cualesquiera siempre hay otro número real.	

© Houghton Mifflin Harcourt Publishing Company

dependent events Events for which the outcome of one event affects the probability of the other.

sucesos dependientes Dos sucesos son dependientes si el resultado de uno afecta la probabilidad del otro.

A bag contains 3 red marbles and 2 blue marbles. Drawing a red marble and then drawing a blue marble without replacing the first marble is an example of dependent events.

---

dependent variable The output of a function; a variable whose value depends on the value of the input, or independent variable.

variable dependiente Salida de una función; variable cuyo valor depende del valor de la entrada, o variable independiente.

For $y = 2x + 1$, y is the dependent variable.
input: x output: y

---

diagonal A line segment that connects two nonadjacent vertices of a polygon.

diagonal Segmento de recta que une dos vértices no adyacentes de un polígono.

---

diameter A line segment that passes through the center of a circle and has endpoints on the circle, or the length of that segment.

diámetro Segmento de recta que pasa por el centro de un círculo y tiene sus extremos en la circunferencia, o bien la longitud de ese segmento.

---

dilation A transformation that enlarges or reduces a figure.

dilatación Transformación que agranda o reduce una figura.

---

dimensions (geometry) The length, width, or height of a figure.

dimensiones (geometría) Longitud, ancho o altura de una figura.

---

dimensions (of a matrix) The number of horizontal rows and vertical columns in a matrix.

dimensiones (de una matriz) Número de filas y columnas que hay en una matriz.

---

direct variation A linear relationship between two variables, x and y, that can be written in the form $y = kx$, where k is a nonzero constant.

variación directa Relación lineal entre dos variables, x e y, que puede expresarse en la forma $y = kx$, donde k es una constante distinta de cero.

$y = 2x$

---

discount The amount by which the original price is reduced.

descuento Cantidad que se resta del precio original de un artículo.

---

discrete graph A graph made up of unconnected points.

gráfica discreta Gráfica compuesta de puntos no conectados.

Cost of Photo Printing

Cost ($)

Number of photos

© Houghton Mifflin Harcourt Publishing Company

Glossary/Glosario

ENGLISH	SPANISH	EXAMPLES
disjoint events See *mutually exclusive*.	**sucesos disjuntos** Vea *mutuamente excluyentes*.	
Distributive Property For all real numbers a, b, and c, $a(b + c) = ab + ac$, and $a(b - c) = ab - ac$.	**Propiedad distributiva** Dados los números reales a, b, y c, $a(b + c) = ab + ac$, y $a(b - c) = ab - ac$.	$5 \cdot 21 = 5(20 + 1) = (5 \cdot 20) + (5 \cdot 1)$
dividend The number to be divided in a division problem.	**dividendo** Número que se divide en un problema de división.	In $8 \div 4 = 2$, 8 is the dividend.
divisible Can be divided by a number without leaving a remainder.	**divisible** Que se puede dividir entre un número sin dejar residuo.	18 is divisible by 3.
Division Property of Equality The property that states that if you divide both sides of an equation by the same nonzero number, the new equation will have the same solution.	**Propiedad de igualdad de la división** Propiedad que establece que puedes dividir ambos lados de una ecuación entre el mismo número distinto de cero, y la nueva ecuación tendrá la misma solución.	
divisor The number you are dividing by in a division problem.	**divisor** El número entre el que se divide en un problema de división.	In $8 \div 4 = 2$, 4 is the divisor.
dodecahedron A polyhedron with 12 faces.	**dodecaedro** Poliedro de 12 caras.	
domain The set of all possible input values of a function.	**dominio** Conjunto de todos los posibles valores de entrada de una función.	The domain of the function $y = x^2 + 1$ is all real numbers.
double-bar graph A bar graph that compares two related sets of data.	**gráfica de doble barra** Gráfica de barras que compara dos conjuntos de datos relacionados.	

© Houghton Mifflin Harcourt Publishing Company

ENGLISH	SPANISH	EXAMPLES

double-line graph A line graph that shows how two related sets of data change over time.

gráfica de doble línea Gráfica lineal que muestra cómo cambian con el tiempo dos conjuntos de datos relacionados.

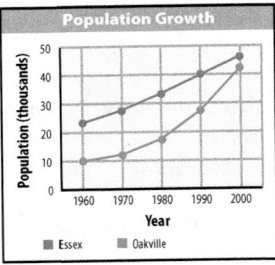

edge The line segment along which two faces of a polyhedron intersect.

arista Segmento de recta donde se intersecan dos caras de un poliedro.

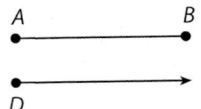
Edge

endpoint A point at the end of a line segment or ray.

extremo Un punto ubicado al final de un segmento de recta o rayo.

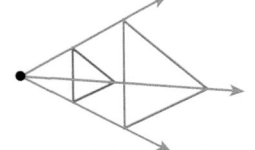

enlargement An increase in size of all dimensions in the same proportions.

agrandamiento Aumento de tamaño de todas las dimensiones en las mismas proporciones.

entries (of a matrix) Individual entries in a matrix.

elementos (de una matriz) Entradas individuales de una matriz.

equally likely Outcomes that have the same probability.

resultados igualmente probables Resultados que tienen la misma probabilidad de ocurrir.

When tossing a coin, the outcomes "heads" and "tails" are equally likely.

equation A mathematical sentence that shows that two expressions are equivalent.

ecuación Enunciado matemático que indica que dos expresiones son equivalentes.

$x + 4 = 7$
$6 + 1 = 10 - 3$

equilateral triangle A triangle with three congruent sides.

triángulo equilátero Triángulo con tres lados congruentes.

equivalent Having the same value.

equivalentes Que tienen el mismo valor.

equivalent expressions Expressions that have the same value for all values of the variables.

expresiones equivalentes Las expresiones equivalentes tienen el mismo valor para todos los valores de las variables.

$4x + 5x$ and $9x$ are equivalent expressions.

equivalent fractions Fractions that name the same amount or part.

fracciones equivalentes Fracciones que representan la misma cantidad o parte.

$\frac{1}{2}$ and $\frac{2}{4}$ are equivalent fractions.

© Houghton Mifflin Harcourt Publishing Company

equivalent ratios Ratios that name the same comparison.

razones equivalentes Razones que representan la misma comparación.

$\frac{1}{2}$ and $\frac{2}{4}$ are equivalent ratios.

---

estimate (**n**) An answer that is close to the exact answer and is found by rounding or other methods. (**v**) To find such an answer.

estimación Una solución aproximada a la respuesta exacta que se halla mediante el redondeo u otros métodos.
estimar Hallar una solución aproximada a la respuesta exacta.

500 is an estimate for the sum $98 + 287 + 104$.

---

evaluate To find the value of a numerical or algebraic expression.

evaluar Hallar el valor de una expresión numérica o algebraica.

Evaluate $2x + 7$ for $x = 3$.
$2x + 7$
$2(3) + 7$
$6 + 7$
13

---

event An outcome or set of outcomes of an experiment or situation.

suceso Un resultado o una serie de resultados de un experimento o una situación.

When rolling a number cube, the event "an odd number" consists of the outcomes 1, 3, and 5.

---

expanded form A number written as the sum of the values of its digits.

forma desarrollada Número escrito como suma de los valores de sus dígitos.

236,536 written in expanded form is $200,000 + 30,000 + 6,000 + 500 + 30 + 6$.

---

experiment (probability) In probability, any activity based on chance (such as tossing a coin).

experimento (probabilidad) En probabilidad, cualquier actividad basada en la posibilidad, como lanzar una moneda.

Tossing a coin 10 times and noting the number of "heads"

---

experimental probability The ratio of the number of times an event occurs to the total number of trials, or times that the activity is performed.

probabilidad experimental Razón del número de veces que ocurre un suceso al número total de pruebas o al número de que se realiza el experimento.

Kendra attempted 27 free throws and made 16 of them. Her experimental probability of making a free throw is
$$\frac{\text{number made}}{\text{number attempted}} = \frac{16}{27} \approx 0.59.$$

---

exponent The number that indicates how many times the base is used as a factor.

exponente Número que indica cuántas veces se usa la base como factor.

$2^3 = 2 \times 2 \times 2 = 8$;
3 is the exponent.

---

exponential decay An exponential function of the form $f(x) = a \cdot r^x$ in which $0 < r < 1$.

decremento exponencial Función exponencial del tipo $f(x) = a \cdot r^x$ en la cual $0 < r < 1$.

---

exponential form A number written with a base and an exponent.

forma exponencial Se dice que un número está en forma exponencial cuando se escribe con una base y un exponente.

4^2 is the exponential form for $4 \cdot 4$.

---

exponential function A nonlinear function in which the variable is in the exponent.

función exponencial Función no lineal en la que la variable está en el exponente.

$f(x) = 4^x$

---

exponential growth An exponential function of the form $f(x) = a \cdot r^x$ in which $r > 1$.

crecimiento exponencial Función exponencial del tipo $f(x) = a \cdot r^x$ en la cual $r > 1$.

© Houghton Mifflin Harcourt Publishing Company

Glossary/Glosario

ENGLISH	SPANISH	EXAMPLES
expression A mathematical phrase that contains operations, numbers, and/or variables.	**expresión** Enunciado matemático que contiene operaciones, números y/o variables.	$6x + 1$
exterior angle (of a polygon) An angle formed by one side of a polygon and the extension of an adjacent side.	**ángulo extreno de un polígono** Ángulo formado por un lado de un polígono y la prolongación del lado adyacente.	

F

ENGLISH	SPANISH	EXAMPLES
face A flat surface of a polyhedron.	**cara** Superficie plana de un poliedro.	
factor A number that is multiplied by another number to get a product.	**factor** Número que se multiplica por otro para hallar un producto.	7 is a factor of 21 since $7 \cdot 3 = 21$.
factorial The product of all whole numbers except zero that are less than or equal to a number.	**factorial** El producto de todos los números cabales, excepto cero, que son menores que o iguales a un número.	4 factorial $= 4! = 4 \cdot 3 \cdot 2 \cdot 1$
Fahrenheit A temperature scale in which 32 °F is the freezing point of water and 212 °F is the boiling point of water.	**Fahrenheit** Escala de temperatura en la que 32° F es el punto de congelación del agua y 212° F es el punto de ebullición.	
fair When all outcomes of an experiment are equally likely, the experiment is said to be fair.	**justo** Se dice de un experimento donde todos los resultados posibles son igualmente probables.	When tossing a coin, heads and tails are equally likely, so it is a fair experiment.
Fibonacci sequence The infinite sequence of numbers (1, 1, 2, 3, 5, 8, 13,…); starting with the third term, each number is the sum of the two previous numbers; it is named after the thirteenth-century mathematician Leonardo Fibonacci.	**sucesión de Fibonacci** La sucesión infinita de números (1, 1, 2, 3, 5, 8, 13…); a partir del tercer término, cada número es la suma de los dos anteriores. Esta sucesión lleva el nombre de Leonardo Fibonacci, un matemático del siglo XIII.	1, 1, 2, 3, 5, 8, 13, . . .
first differences A sequence formed by subtracting each term of a sequence from the next term.	**primeras diferencias** Sucesión que se forma al restar cada término de una sucesión del término siguiente.	For the sequence 4, 7, 10, 13, 16, . . ., the first differences are all 3.
first quartile The median of the lower half of a set of data; also called *lower quartile*.	**primer cuartil** La mediana de la mitad inferior de un conjunto de datos. También se llama *cuartil inferior*.	

© Houghton Mifflin Harcourt Publishing Company

ENGLISH	SPANISH	EXAMPLES

FOIL An acronym for the terms used when multiplying two binomials: the First, Outer, Inner, and Last terms.

FOIL Sigla en inglés de los términos que se usan al multiplicar dos binomios: los primeros, los externos, los internos y los últimos (First, Outer, Inner, Last).

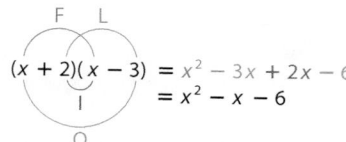

$$(x + 2)(x - 3) = x^2 - 3x + 2x - 6$$
$$= x^2 - x - 6$$

---

formula A rule showing relationships among quantities.

fórmula Regla que muestra relaciones entre cantidades.

$A = \ell w$ is the formula for the area of a rectangle.

---

fractal A structure with repeating patterns containing shapes that are like the whole but are of different sizes throughout.

fractal Estructura con patrones repetidos que contiene figuras similares al patrón general pero de diferente tamaño.

---

fraction A number in the form $\frac{a}{b}$, where $b \neq 0$.

fracción Número escrito en la forma $\frac{a}{b}$, donde $b \neq 0$.

$\frac{2}{3}$

---

frequency The number of times the value appears in the data set.

frecuencia Cantidad de veces que aparece el valor en un conjunto de datos.

Data set: 5, 6, 6, 7, 8, 9
The data value 6 has a frequency of 2.

---

frequency table A table that lists items together according to the number of times, or frequency, that the items occur.

tabla de frecuencia Una tabla en la que se organizan los datos de acuerdo con el número de veces que aparece cada valor (o la frecuencia).

Data set: 1, 1, 2, 2, 3, 5, 5, 5
Frequency table:

Data	Frequency
1	2
2	2
3	1

---

function An input-output relationship that has exactly one output for each input.

función Regla que relaciona dos candidates de forma que a cada valor de entrada corresponde exactamente un valor de salida.

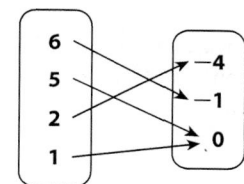

---

function notation The notation used to describe a function.

notación de función Notación que se usa para describir una función.

Equation: $y = 2x$
Function notation: $f(x) = 2x$

---

function table A table of ordered pairs that represent solutions of a function.

tabla de función Tabla de pares ordenados que representan soluciones de una función.

x	3	4	5	6
y	7	9	11	13

Fundamental Counting Principle If one event has m possible outcomes and a second event has n possible outcomes after the first event has occurred, then there are $m \cdot n$ total possible outcomes for the two events.

Principio fundamental de conteo Si un suceso tiene m resultados posibles y otro suceso tiene n resultados posibles después de ocurrido el primer suceso, entonces hay $m \cdot n$ resultados posibles en total para los dos sucesos.

There are 4 colors of shirts and 3 colors of pants. There are $4 \cdot 3 = 12$ possible outfits.

© Houghton Mifflin Harcourt Publishing Company

Glossary/Glosario

Glossary/Glosario

geometric probability A form of theoretical probability determined by a ratio of geometric measures such as lengths, areas, or volumes.

probabilidad geométrica Método para calcular probabilidades basado en una medida geométrica como la longitud o el área.

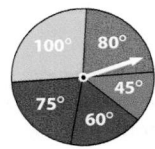

The probability of the pointer landing on red is $\frac{80}{360}$, or $\frac{2}{9}$.

geometric sequence An ordered list of numbers that has a common ratio between consecutive terms.

sucesión geométrica Lista ordenada de números que tiene una razón común entre términos consecutivos.

The sequence 2, 4, 8, 16 . . . is a geometric sequence.

graph of an equation A graph of the set of ordered pairs that are solutions of the equation.

gráfica de una ecuación Gráfica del conjunto de pares ordenados que son soluciones de la ecuación.

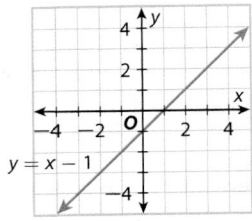

$y = x - 1$

great circle A circle on a sphere such that the plane containing the circle passes through the center of the sphere.

círculo máximo Círculo de una esfera tal que el plano que contiene el círculo pasa por el centro de la esfera.

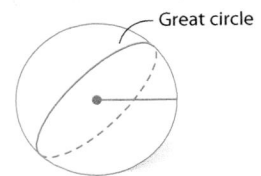

Great circle

greatest common factor (GCF) The largest common factor of two or more given numbers.

máximo común divisor (MCD) El mayor de los factores comunes compartidos por dos o más números dados.

The GCF of 27 and 45 is 9.

height In a pyramid or cone, the perpendicular distance from the base to the opposite vertex.

altura En una pirámide o cono, la distancia perpendicular desde la base al vértice opuesto.

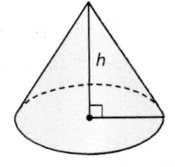

In a triangle or quadrilateral, the perpendicular distance from the base to the opposite vertex or side.

En un triángulo o cuadrilátero, la distancia perpendicular desde la base de la figura al vértice o lado opuesto.

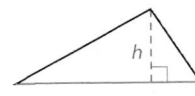

In a prism or cylinder, the perpendicular distance between the bases.

En un prisma o cilindro, la distancia perpendicular entre las bases.

© Houghton Mifflin Harcourt Publishing Company

ENGLISH	SPANISH	EXAMPLES

hemisphere A half of a sphere.

hemisferio La mitad de una esfera.

---

heptagon A seven-sided polygon.

heptágono Polígono de siete lados.

---

hexagon A six-sided polygon.

hexágono Polígono de seis lados.

---

histogram A bar graph that shows the frequency of data within equal intervals.

histograma Gráfica de barras que muestra la frecuencia de los datos en intervalos iguales.

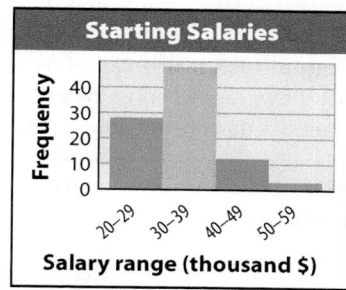

---

hypotenuse In a right triangle, the side opposite the right angle.

hipotenusa En un triángulo rectángulo, el lado opuesto al ángulo recto.

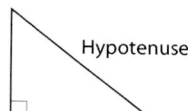

Identity Property Addition The property that states the sum of zero and any number is that number.

Propiedad de identidad de la suma Propiedad que establece que la suma de cero y cualquier número es ese número.

$4 + 0 = 4$
$-3 + 0 = -3$

Identity Property Multiplication The property that states that the product of 1 and any number is that number.

Propiedad de identidad de la multiplicación Propiedad que establece que el producto de 1 y cualquier número es ese número.

$4 \cdot 1 = 4$
$-3 \cdot 1 = -3$

---

image A figure resulting from a transformation.

imagen Figura que resulta de una transformación.

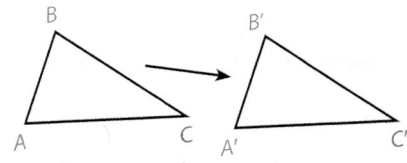

A'B'C' is the image of ABC.

---

improper fraction A fraction in which the numerator is greater than or equal to the denominator.

fracción impropia Fracción cuyo numerador es mayor que o igual al denominador.

$\frac{17}{5}, \frac{3}{3}$

© Houghton Mifflin Harcourt Publishing Company

Glossary/Glosario

ENGLISH	SPANISH	EXAMPLES
independent events Events for which the outcome of one event does not affect the probability of the other.	**sucesos independientes** Dos sucesos son independientes si el resultado de uno no afecta la probabilidad del otro.	A bag contains 3 red marbles and 2 blue marbles. Drawing a red marble, replacing it, and then drawing a blue marble is an example of independent events.
independent variable The input of a function; a variable whose value determines the value of the output, or dependent variable.	**variable independiente** Entrada de una función; variable cuyo valor determina el valor de la salida, o variable dependiente.	For $y = 2x + 1$, x is the independent variable. input: x output: y
indirect measurement The technique of using similar figures and proportions to find a measure.	**medición indirecta** La técnica de usar figuras semejantes y proporciones para hallar una medida.	
inductive reasoning Using a pattern to make a conclusion.	**razonamiento inductivo** Uso de un patrón para sacar una conclusión.	
inequality A mathematical sentence that shows the relationship between quantities that are not equivalent.	**desigualdad** Enunciado matemático que muestra una relación entre cantidades que no son equivalentes.	$5 < 8$ $5x + 2 \geq 12$
input The value substituted into an expression or function.	**valor de entrada** Valor que se usa para sustituir una variable en una expresión o función.	For the function $y = 6x$, the input 4 produces an output of 24.
inscribed angle An angle formed by two chords with its vertex on a circle.	**ángulo inscrito** Ángulo formado por dos cuerdas cuyo vértice está en un círculo.	
integers The set of whole numbers and their opposites.	**enteros** Conjunto de todos los números cabales y sus opuestos.	$\ldots -3, -2, -1, 0, 1, 2, 3, \ldots$
interest The amount of money charged for borrowing or using money.	**interés** Cantidad de dinero que se cobra por el préstamo o uso del dinero.	
interior angles Angles on the inner sides of two lines cut by a transversal.	**ángulos internos** Ángulos en los lados internos de dos líneas intersecadas por una transversal.	∠1 is an interior angle.
interquartile range (IQR) The difference of the third (upper) and first (lower) quartiles in a data set, representing the middle half of the data.	**rango intercuartil (RIC)** Diferencia entre el tercer cuartil (superior) y el primer cuartil (inferior) de un conjunto de datos, que representa la mitad central de los datos.	Lower half / Upper half 18, (23,) 28, 29, (36,) 42 First quartile / Third quartile Interquartile range: $36 - 23 = 13$
intersecting lines Lines that cross at exactly one point.	**líneas secantes** Líneas que se cruzan en un solo punto.	

© Houghton Mifflin Harcourt Publishing Company

Glossary/Glosario

ENGLISH	SPANISH	EXAMPLES
interval The space between marked values on a number line or the scale of a graph.	**intervalo** El espacio entre los valores marcados en una recta numérica o en la escala de una gráfica.	
inverse operations Operations that undo each other: addition and subtraction, or multiplication and division.	**operaciones inversas** Operaciones que se cancelan mutuamente: suma y resta, o multiplicación y división.	Addition and subtraction are inverse operations: $5 + 3 = 8; 8 - 3 = 5$ Multiplication and division are inverse operations: $2 \cdot 3 = 6; 6 \div 3 = 2$
inverse variation A relationship in which one variable quantity increases as another variable quantity decreases; the product of the variables is a constant.	**variación inversa** Relación en la que una cantidad variable aumenta a medida que otra cantidad variable disminuye; el producto de las variables es una constante.	$xy = 7, y = \frac{7}{x}$
irrational number A number that cannot be expressed as a ratio of two integers or as a repeating or terminating decimal.	**número irracional** Número que no se puede expresar como una razón de dos enteros ni como un decimal periódico o finito.	$\sqrt{2}, \pi$
isolate the variable To get a variable alone on one side of an equation or inequality in order to solve the equation or inequality.	**despejar la variable** Dejar sola la variable en un lado de una ecuación o desigualdad para resolverla.	$x + 7 = 22$ $\frac{12}{3} = \frac{3x}{3}$ $\underline{-7 \quad -7}$ $4 = x$ $x \quad = 15$
isometric drawing A representation of a three-dimensional figure that is drawn on a grid of equilateral triangles.	**dibujo isométrico** Representación de una figura tridimensional que se dibuja sobre una cuadrícula de triángulos equiláteros.	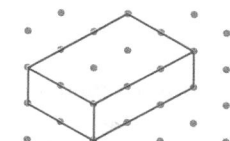
isosceles triangle A triangle with at least two congruent sides.	**triángulo isósceles** Triángulo que tiene al menos dos lados congruentes.	

joint relative frequency The ratio of the frequency in a particular category divided by the total number of data values.	**frecuencia relativa conjunta** La razón de la frecuencia en una determinada categoría dividida entre el número total de valores.	

lateral area The sum of the areas of the lateral faces of a prism or pyramid, or the area of the lateral surface of a cylinder or cone.	**área lateral** Suma de las áreas de las caras laterales de un prisma o pirámide, o área de la superficie lateral de un cilindro o cono.	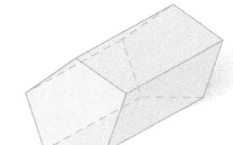

Lateral area = area of the 5 rectangular faces

© Houghton Mifflin Harcourt Publishing Company

Glossary/Glosario

lateral face In a prism or a pyramid, a face that is not a base.

cara lateral En un prisma o pirámide, una cara que no es la base.

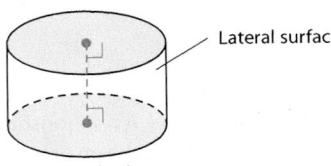

Bases — Lateral face

Right prism

---

lateral surface In a cylinder, the curved surface connecting the circular bases; in a cone, the curved surface that is not a base.

superficie lateral En un cilindro, superficie curva que une las bases circulares; en un cono, la superficie curva que no es la base.

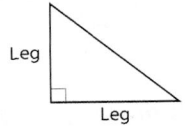

Lateral surface

Right cylinder

---

least common denominator (LCD) The least common multiple of two or more denominators.

mínimo común denominador (mcd) El mínimo común múltiplo más pequeño de dos o más denominadores.

The LCD of $\frac{3}{4}$ and $\frac{5}{6}$ is 12.

---

least common multiple (LCM) The smallest whole number, other than zero, that is a multiple of two or more given numbers.

mínimo común múltiplo (mcm) El menor de los números cabales, distinto de cero, que es múltiplo de dos o más números dados.

The LCM of 6 and 10 is 30.

---

legs In a right triangle, the sides that include the right angle; in an isosceles triangle, the pair of congruent sides.

catetos En un triángulo rectángulo, los lados adyacentes al ángulo recto. En un triángulo isósceles, el par de lados congruentes.

Leg

Leg

---

like fractions Fractions that have the same denominator.

fracciones semejantes Fracciones que tienen el mismo denominador.

$\frac{5}{12}$ and $\frac{7}{12}$ are like fractions.

---

like terms Terms that have the same variable raised to the same exponents.

términos semejantes Términos que contienen las mismas variables elevada a las mismas exponentes.

In the expression $3a^2 + 5b + 12a^2$, $3a^2$ and $12a^2$ are like terms.

---

line A straight path that has no thickness and extends forever.

línea Un trazo recto que no tiene grosor y se extiende infinitamente.

---

line graph A graph that uses line segments to show how data changes.

gráfica lineal Gráfica que muestra cómo cambian los datos mediante segmentos de recta.

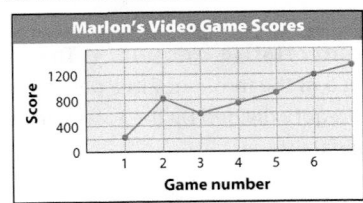

Marlon's Video Game Scores

---

line of best fit A straight line that comes closest to the points on a scatter plot.

línea de mejor ajuste La línea recta que más se aproxima a los puntos de un diagrama de dispersión.

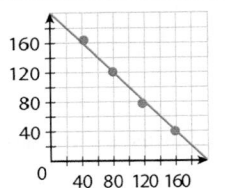

© Houghton Mifflin Harcourt Publishing Company

ENGLISH	SPANISH	EXAMPLES
line of reflection A line that a figure is flipped across to create a mirror image of the original figure.	**línea de reflexión** Línea sobre la cual se invierte una figura para crear una imagen reflejada de la figura original.	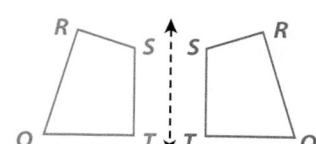
line of symmetry A line that divides a figure into two congruent reflected halves.	**eje de simetría** Línea que divide una figura en dos mitades reflejas.	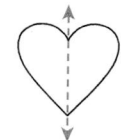
line plot A number line with marks or dots that show frequency.	**diagrama de acumulación** Recta numérica con marcas o puntos que indican la frecuencia.	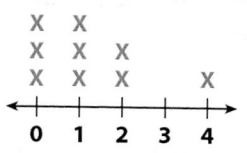 **Number of Pets**
line segment A part of a line consisting of two endpoints and all points between them.	**segmento de recta** Parte de una línea que consiste en dos extremos y todos los puntos entre éstos.	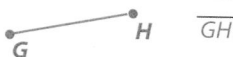
line symmetry A figure has line symmetry if one half is a mirror image of the other half.	**simetría axial** Una figura tiene simetría axial si una de sus mitades es la imagen reflejada de la otra.	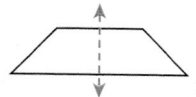
linear equation An equation whose solutions form a straight line on a coordinate plane.	**ecuación lineal** Ecuación cuyas soluciones forman una línea recta en un plano cartesiano.	$y = 2x + 1$
linear function A function whose graph is a straight line.	**función lineal** Función cuya gráfica es una línea recta.	$y = x - 1$ 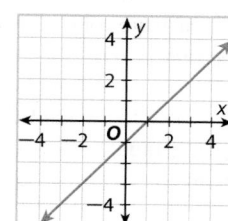
linear inequality A mathematical sentence using $<$, $>$, $\leq$, or $\geq$ whose graph is a region with a straight-line boundary.	**desigualdad lineal** Enunciado matemático en que se usan los símbolos $<$, $>$, $\leq$, o $\geq$ y cuya gráfica es una región con una línea de límite recta.	
literal equation An equation that contains two or more variables.	**ecuación literal** Ecuación que contiene dos o más variables.	$d = rt$ $A = bh$

© Houghton Mifflin Harcourt Publishing Company

Glossary/Glosario

major arc An arc that is more than half of a circle.	**arco mayor** Arco que es más de la mitad de un círculo.	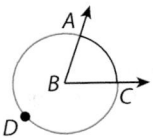 $\overarc{ADC}$ is a major arc of the circle.
marginal relative frequency The sum of the joint relative frequencies in a row or column of a two-way table.	**frecuencia relativa marginal** La suma de las frecuencias relativas conjuntas en una fila o columna de una tabla de doble entrada.	
matrix A rectangular arrangement of data enclosed in brackets.	**matriz** Arreglo rectangular de datos encerrado entre corchetes.	$\begin{bmatrix} 1 & 0 & 3 \\ -2 & 2 & -5 \\ 7 & -6 & 3 \end{bmatrix}$
mean The sum of a set of data divided by the number of items in the data set; also called *average*.	**media** La suma de todos los elementos de un conjunto de datos dividida entre el número de elementos del conjunto. También se llama promedio.	Data set: 4, 6, 7, 8, 10 Mean: $\frac{4+6+7+8+10}{5} = \frac{35}{5} = 7$
mean absolute deviation (MAD) The mean distance between each data value and the mean of the data set.	**desviación absoluta media (DAM)** Distancia media entre cada dato y la media del conjunto de datos.	
measure of center A measure used to describe the middle of a data set; the mean, median, and mode are measures of center. Also called *measure of central tendency*.	**medida de tendencia dominante** Medida que describe la parte media de un conjunto de datos; la media, la mediana y la moda son medidas de tendencia dominante.	
median The middle number, or the mean (average) of the two middle numbers, in an ordered set of data.	**mediana** El número intermedio o la media (el promedio) de los dos números intermedios en un conjunto ordenado de datos.	Data set: 4, 6, 7, 8, 10 Median: 7
metric system of measurement A decimal system of weights and measures that is used universally in science and commonly throughout the world.	**sistema métrico de medición** Sistema decimal de pesos y medidas empleado universalmente en las ciencias y de uso común en todo el mundo.	centimeters, meters, kilometers, grams, kilograms, milliliters, liters
midpoint The point that divides a line segment into two congruent line segments.	**punto medio** El punto que divide un segmento de recta en dos segmentos de recta congruentes.	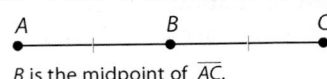 B is the midpoint of $\overline{AC}$.
minor arc An arc that is less than half of a circle.	**arco menor** Arco que es menor que la mitad de un círculo.	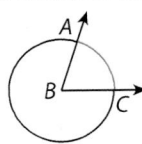 $\overarc{AC}$ is the minor arc of the circle.

© Houghton Mifflin Harcourt Publishing Company

mixed number A number made up of a whole number that is not zero and a fraction.	**número mixto** Número compuesto por un número cabal distinto de cero y una fracción.	$4\frac{1}{8}$
mode The number or numbers that occur most frequently in a set of data; when all numbers occur with the same frequency, we say there is no mode.	**moda** Número o números más frecuentes en un conjunto de datos; si todos los números aparecen con la misma frecuencia, no hay moda.	Data set: 3, 5, 8, 8, 10 Mode: 8
monomial A number or a product of numbers and variables with exponents that are whole numbers.	**monomio** Un número o un producto de números y variables con exponentes que son números cabales.	$3x^2y^4$
Multiplication Property of Equality The property that states that if you multiply both sides of an equation by the same number, the new equation will have the same solution.	**Propiedad de igualdad de la multiplicación** Propiedad que establece que puedes multiplicar ambos lados de una ecuación por el mismo número y la nueva ecuación tendrá la misma solución.	$3 \cdot 4 = 12$ $3 \cdot 4 \cdot 2 = 12 \cdot 2$ $24 = 24$
Multiplication Property of Zero The property that states that for all real numbers a, $a \cdot 0 = 0$ and $0 \cdot a = 0$.	**Propiedad de multiplicación del cero** Propiedad que establece que para todos los números reales a, $a \cdot 0 = 0$ y $0 \cdot a = 0$.	
multiplicative inverse A number times its multiplicative inverse is equal to 1; also called *reciprocal*.	**inverso multiplicativo** Un número multiplicado por su inverso multiplicativo es igual a 1. También se llama *recíproco*.	The multiplicative inverse of $\frac{4}{5}$ is $\frac{5}{4}$.
multiple The product of any number and a nonzero whole number is a multiple of that number.	**múltiplo** El producto de cualquier número y un número cabal distinto de cero es un múltiplo de ese número.	
mutually exclusive Two events are mutually exclusive if they cannot occur in the same trial of an experiment.	**mutuamente excluyentes** Dos sucesos son mutuamente excluyentes cuando no pueden ocurrir en la misma prueba de un experimento.	When rolling a number cube once, rolling a 3 and rolling an even number are mutually exclusive events.

N

negative correlation Two data sets have a negative correlation if one set of data values increases while the other decreases.	**correlación negativa** Dos conjuntos de datos tienen correlación negativa si los valores de un conjunto aumentan a medida que los valores del otro conjunto disminuyen.	
negative integer An integer less than zero.	**entero negativo** Entero menor que cero.	-2 is a negative integer.

© Houghton Mifflin Harcourt Publishing Company

Glossary/Glosario

Glossary/Glosario

net An arrangement of two-dimensional figures that can be folded to form a polyhedron.

plantilla Arreglo de figuras bidimensionales que se doblan para formar un poliedro.

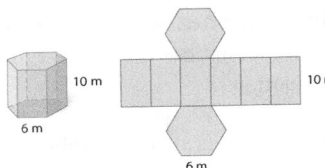

---

network A set of points and the line segments or arcs that connect the points.

red Conjunto de puntos y los segmentos de recta o arcos que los conectan.

---

no correlation Two data sets have no correlation when there is no relationship between their data values.

sin correlación Caso en que los valores de dos conjuntos no muestran ninguna relación.

---

nonlinear function A function whose graph is not a straight line.

función no lineal Función cuya gráfica no es una línea recta.

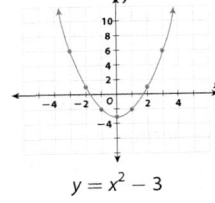

$y = x^2 - 3$

---

nonlinear relationship
A relationship between two variables in which the data do not increase or decrease together at the same rate.

relación no lineal Relación entre dos variables en la cual los datos no aumentan o disminuyen al mismo tiempo a una tasa constante.

---

nonterminating decimal
A decimal that never ends.

decimal infinito Decimal que nunca termina.

$0.\overline{3}$

---

numerator The top number of a fraction that tells how many parts of a whole are being considered.

numerador El número de arriba de una fracción; indica cuántas partes de un entero se consideran.

$\frac{4}{5}$ ← numerator

---

numerical expression An expression that contains only numbers and operations.

expresión numérica Expresión que incluye sólo números y operaciones.

$(2 \cdot 3) + 1$

obtuse angle An angle whose measure is greater than 90° but less than 180°.

ángulo obtuso Ángulo que mide más de 90° y menos de 180°.

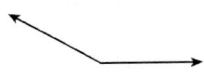

---

obtuse triangle A triangle containing one obtuse angle.

triángulo obtusángulo Triángulo que tiene un ángulo obtuso.

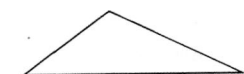

---

octagon An eight-sided polygon.

octágono Polígono de ocho lados.

© Houghton Mifflin Harcourt Publishing Company

ENGLISH	SPANISH	EXAMPLES
odds A comparison of the number of ways an event can occur and the number of ways an event can *not* occur.	**probabilidades** Comparación del número de las maneras que puede ocurrir un suceso y el número de maneras que no puede ocurrir el suceso.	
odds against The ratio of the number of unfavorable outcomes to the number of favorable outcomes.	**probabilidades en contra** Razón del número de resultados no favorables al número de resultados favorables.	The odds against rolling a 3 on a number cube are 5:1.
odds in favor The ratio of the number of favorable outcomes to the number of unfavorable outcomes.	**probabilidades a favor** Razón del número de resultados favorables al número de resultados no favorables.	The odds in favor of rolling a 3 on a number cube are 1:5.

opposites Two numbers that are an equal distance from zero on a number line; also called *additive inverse*.

opuestos Dos números que están a la misma distancia de cero en una recta numérica. También se llaman *inversos aditivos*.

5 and −5 are opposites.

5 units   5 units
−6 −5 −4 −3 −2 −1 0 1 2 3 4 5 6

order of operations A rule for evaluating expressions: First perform the operations in parentheses, then compute powers and roots, then perform all multiplication and division from left to right, and then perform all addition and subtraction from left to right.

orden de las operaciones Regla para evaluar expresiones: primero se hacen las operaciones entre paréntesis, luego se hallan las potencias y raíces, después todas las multiplicaciones y divisiones de izquierda a derecha, y por último, todas las sumas y restas de izquierda a derecha.

$4^2 + 8 \div 2$	Evaluate the power.
$16 + 8 \div 2$	Divide.
$16 + 4$	Add.
20	

ordered pair A pair of numbers that can be used to locate a point on a coordinate plane.

par ordenado Par de números que sirven para ubicar un punto en un plano cartesiano.

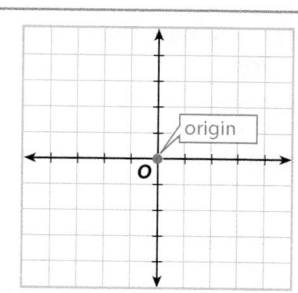

The coordinates of *B* are (−2, 3).

origin The point where the *x*-axis and *y*-axis intersect on the coordinate plane; (0, 0).

origen Punto de intersección entre el eje *x* y el eje *y* en un plano cartesiano: (0, 0).

orthogonal views A drawing that shows the top, bottom, front, back, and side views of a three-dimensional object.

vista ortogonal Un dibujo que muestra la vista superior, inferior, frontal, posterior y lateral de un objeto de tres dimensiones.

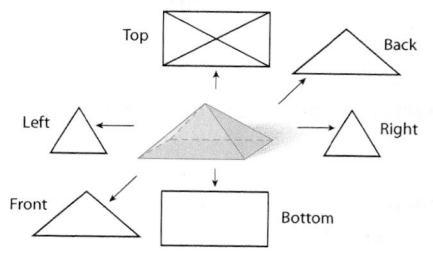

outcome (probability) A possible result of a probability experiment.

resultado (en probabilidad) Posible resultado de un experimento de probabilidad.

When rolling a number cube, the possible outcomes are 1, 2, 3, 4, 5, and 6.

© Houghton Mifflin Harcourt Publishing Company

outlier A value much greater or much less than the others in a data set. | **valor extremo** Un valor mucho mayor o menor que los demás valores de un conjunto de datos. |

output The value that results from the substitution of a given input into an expression or function. | **valor de salida** Valor que resulta después de sustituir una variable por un valor de entrada determinado en una expresión o función. | For the function $y = 6x$, the input 4 produces an output of 24.

P

parabola The graph of a quadratic function. | **parábola** Gráfica de una función cuadrática. |

parallel lines Lines in a plane that do not intersect. | **líneas paralelas** Líneas que se encuentran en el mismo plano pero que nunca se intersecan. |

parallelogram A quadrilateral with two pairs of parallel sides. | **paralelogramo** Cuadrilátero con dos pares de lados paralelos. |

pentagon A five-sided polygon. | **pentágono** Polígono de cinco lados. |

percent A ratio comparing a number to 100. | **porcentaje** Razón que compara un número con el número 100. | $45\% = \frac{45}{100}$

percent change The amount stated as a percent that a number increases or decreases. | **porcentaje de cambio** Cantidad en que un número aumenta o disminuye, expresada como un porcentaje. |

percent decrease A percent change describing a decrease in a quantity. | **porcentaje de disminución** Porcentaje de cambio en que una cantidad disminuye. | An item that costs \$8 is marked down to \$6. The amount of the decrease is \$2, and the percent decrease is $\frac{2}{8} = 0.25 = 25\%$.

percent increase A percent change describing an increase in a quantity. | **porcentaje de incremento** Porcentaje de cambio en que una cantidad aumenta. | The price of an item increases from \$8 to \$12. The amount of the increase is \$4, and the percent increase is $\frac{4}{8} = 0.5 = 50\%$.

perfect cube A cube of a whole number. | **cubo perfecto** El cubo de un número cabal. | $2^3 = 8$, so 8 is a perfect cube.

perfect square A square of a whole number. | **cuadrado perfecto** El cuadrado de un número cabal. | $5^2 = 25$, so 25 is a perfect square.

perimeter The distance around a polygon. | **perímetro** Distancia alrededor de un polígono. |
perimeter $= 18 + 6 + 18 + 6 = 48$ ft

© Houghton Mifflin Harcourt Publishing Company

Glossary/Glosario

permutation An arrangement of items or events in which order is important.

permutación Arreglo de objetos o sucesos en el que el orden es importante.

For objects *A*, *B*, and *C*, there are 6 different permutations: *ABC*, *ACB*, *BAC*, *BCA*, *CAB*, *CBA*.

---

perpendicular bisector A line that intersects a segment at its midpoint and is perpendicular to the segment.

mediatriz Línea que cruza un segmento en su punto medio y es perpendicular al segmento.

---

perpendicular lines Lines that intersect to form right angles.

líneas perpendiculares Líneas que al intersecarse forman ángulos rectos.

---

pi (π) The ratio of the circumference of a circle to the length of its diameter; $\pi \approx 3.14$ or $\frac{22}{7}$.

pi (π) Razón de la circunferencia de un círculo a la longitud de su diámetro; $\pi \approx 3.14$ ó $\frac{22}{7}$.

---

plane A flat surface that has no thickness and extends forever.

plano Superficie plana que no tiene ningún grueso y que se extiende por siempre.

---

point An exact location that has no size.

punto Ubicación exacta que no tiene ningún tamaño.

---

point-slope form The equation of a line in the form of $y - y_1 = m(x - x_1)$, where *m* is the slope and (x_1, y_1) is a specific point on the line.

forma de punto y pendiente Ecuación lineal del tipo $y - y_1 = m(x - x_1)$, donde *m* es la pendiente y (x_1, y_1) es un punto específico de la línea.

$y - 3 = 2(x - 3)$

---

polygon A closed plane figure formed by three or more line segments that intersect only at their endpoints (vertices).

polígono Figura plana cerrada, formada por tres o más segmentos de recta que se intersecan sólo en sus extremos (vértices).

---

polyhedron A three-dimensional figure in which all the surfaces or faces are polygons.

poliedro Figura tridimensional cuyas superficies o caras tiene forma de polígonos.

---

polynomial One monomial or the sum or difference of monomials.

polinomio Un monomio o la suma o la diferencia de monomios.

$2x^2 + 3xy - 7y^2$

---

population The entire group of objects or individuals considered for a survey.

población Grupo completo de objetos o individuos que se desea estudiar.

In a survey about study habits of middle school students, the population is all middle school students.

© Houghton Mifflin Harcourt Publishing Company

Glossary/Glosario

positive correlation Two data sets have a positive correlation when their data values increase or decrease together.

correlación positiva Dos conjuntos de datos tienen una correlación positiva cuando los valores de ambos conjuntos aumentan o disminuyen al mismo tiempo.

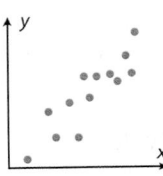

---

positive integer An integer greater than zero.

entero positivo Entero mayor que cero.

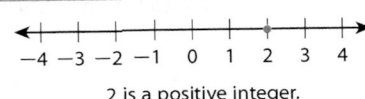

2 is a positive integer.

---

power A number produced by raising a base to an exponent.

potencia Número que resulta al elevar una base a un exponente.

$2^3 = 8$, so 2 to the 3rd power is 8.

---

preimage The original figure in a transformation.

imagen original Figura original en una transformación.

---

prime factorization A number written as the product of its prime factors.

factorización prima Un número escrito como el producto de sus factores primos.

$10 = 2 \cdot 5,$
$24 = 2^3 \cdot 3$

---

prime number A whole number greater than 1 that has exactly two factors, itself and 1.

número primo Número cabal mayor que 1 que sólo es divisible entre 1 y él mismo.

5 is prime because its only factors are 5 and 1.

---

principal The initial amount of money borrowed or saved.

principal Cantidad inicial de dinero depositada o recibida en préstamo.

---

principal square root The nonnegative square root of a number.

raíz cuadrada principal Raíz cuadrada no negativa de un número.

$\sqrt{25} = 5$; the principal square root of 25 is 5.

---

prism A polyhedron that has two congruent, polygon-shaped bases and other faces that are all parallelograms.

prisma Poliedro con dos bases congruentes con forma de polígono y caras con forma de paralelogramo.

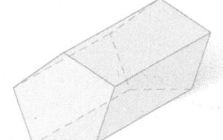

---

probability A number from 0 to 1 (or 0% to 100%) that describes how likely an event is to occur.

probabilidad Un número entre 0 y 1 (ó 0% y 100%) que describe qué tan probable es un suceso.

A bag contains 3 red marbles and 4 blue marbles. The probability of randomly choosing a red marble is $\frac{3}{7}$.

---

proper fraction A fraction in which the numerator is less than the denominator.

fracción propia Fracción en la que el numerador es menor que el denominador.

$\frac{3}{4}, \frac{1}{12}, \frac{7}{8}$

---

proportion An equation that states that two ratios are equivalent.

proporción Ecuación que establece que dos razones son equivalentes.

$\frac{2}{3} = \frac{4}{6}$

---

proportional relationship A relationship between two quantities in which the ratio of one quantity to the other quantity is constant.

relación proporcional Relación entre dos cantidades en que la razón de una cantidad a la otra es constante.

© Houghton Mifflin Harcourt Publishing Company

protractor A tool for measuring angles.

transportador Instrumento para medir ángulos.

---

pyramid A polyhedron with a polygon base and triangular sides that all meet at a common vertex.

pirámide Poliedro cuya base es un polígono; tiene caras triangulares que se juntan en un vértice común.

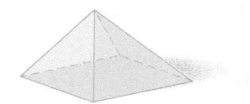

Pythagorean Theorem In a right triangle, the square of the length of the hypotenuse is equal to the sum of the squares of the lengths of the legs.

Teorema de Pitágoras En un triángulo rectángulo, la suma de los cuadrados de los catetos es igual al cuadrado de la hipotenusa.

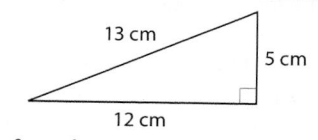

$$5^2 + 12^2 = 13^2$$
$$25 + 144 = 169$$

Pythagorean triple A set of three positive integers a, b, and c such that $a^2 + b^2 = c^2$.

Tripleta de Pitágoras Conjunto de tres números enteros positivos de cero a, b y c tal que $a^2 + b^2 = c^2$.

3, 4, 5 because $3^2 + 4^2 = 5^2$

quadrant The x- and y-axes divide the coordinate plane into four regions. Each region is called a quadrant.

cuadrante El eje x y el eje y dividen el plano cartesiano en cuatro regiones. Cada región recibe el nombre de cuadrante.

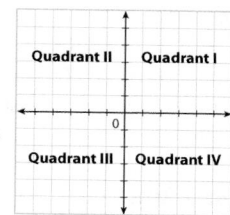

---

quadratic function A function of the form $y = ax^2 + bx + c$, where $a \neq 0$.

función cuadrática Función del tipo $y = ax^2 + bx + c$, donde $a \neq 0$.

$y = x^2 - 6x + 8$

---

quadrilateral A four-sided polygon.

cuadrilátero Polígono de cuatro lados.

---

quarterly Four times a year.

trimestral Cuatro veces al año.

---

quartile Three values, one of which is the median, that divide a data set into fourths.

cuartil Cada uno de tres valores, uno de los cuales es la mediana, que dividen en cuartos un conjunto de datos.

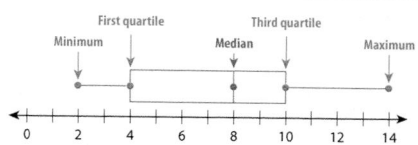

---

quotient The result when one number is divided by another.

cociente Resultado de dividir un número entre otro.

In $8 \div 4 = 2$, 2 is the quotient.

© Houghton Mifflin Harcourt Publishing Company

radical symbol The symbol $\sqrt{}$ used to represent the nonnegative square root of a number.

símbolo de radical El símbolo $\sqrt{}$ con que se representa la raíz cuadrada no negativa de un número.

---

radius A line segment with one endpoint at the center of the circle and the other endpoint on the circle, or the length of that segment.

radio Segmento de recta con un extremo en el centro de un círculo y el otro en la circunferencia, o bien se llama radio a la longitud de ese segmento.

---

random numbers In a set of random numbers, each number has an equal chance of appearing.

muestra aleatoria Muestra en la que cada individuo u objeto de la población tiene la misma posibilidad de ser elegido.

---

random sample A sample in which each individual or object in the entire population has an equal chance of being selected.

números aleatorios En un conjunto de números aleatorios, todos los números tienen la misma probabilidad de ser seleccionados.

---

range (in statistics) The difference between the greatest and least values in a data set.

rango (en estadística) Diferencia entre los valores máximo y mínimo de un conjunto de datos.

Data set: 3, 5, 7, 7, 12
Range: $12 - 3 = 9$

---

range (of a function) The set of all possible output values of a function.

rango (en una función) El conjunto de todos los valores posibles de una función.

The range of $y = |x|$ is $y \geq 0$.

---

rate A ratio that compares two quantities measured in different units.

tasa Una razón que compara dos cantidades medidas en diferentes unidades.

The speed limit is 55 miles per hour or 55 mi/h.

---

rate of change A ratio that compares the amount of change in a dependent variable to the amount of change in an independent variable.

tasa de cambio Razón que compara la cantidad de cambio de la variable dependiente con la cantidad de cambio de la variable independiente.

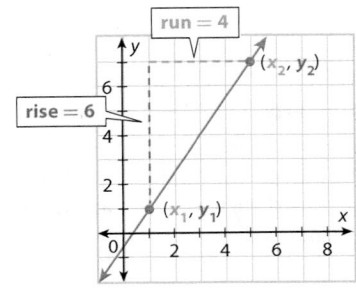

Rate of change $= \dfrac{\text{change in } y}{\text{change in } x} = \dfrac{6}{4} = \dfrac{3}{2}$

---

rate of interest The percent charged or earned on an amount of money; see *simple interest*.

tasa de interés Porcentaje que se cobra por una cantidad de dinero prestada o que se gana por una cantidad de dinero ahorrada; ver *interés simple*.

© Houghton Mifflin Harcourt Publishing Company

Glossary/Glosario

ENGLISH	SPANISH	EXAMPLES
ratio A comparison of two quantities by division.	**razón** Comparación de dos cantidades mediante una división.	12 to 25, 12:25, $\frac{12}{25}$
rational number Any number that can be expressed as a ratio of two integers.	**número racional** Número que se puede escribir como una razón de dos enteros.	6 can be expressed as $\frac{6}{1}$. 0.5 can be expressed as $\frac{1}{2}$.
ray A part of a line that starts at one endpoint and extends forever in one direction.	**rayo** Parte de una línea que comienza en un extremo y se extiende de manera infinitamente en una dirección.	
real number A rational or irrational number.	**número real** Número racional o irracional.	
reciprocal One of two numbers whose product is 1; also called *multiplicative inverse*.	**recíproco** Uno de dos números cuyo producto es igual a 1. También se llama *inverso multiplicativo*.	The reciprocal of $\frac{2}{3}$ is $\frac{3}{2}$.
rectangle A parallelogram with four right angles.	**rectángulo** Paralelogramo con cuatro ángulos rectos.	
rectangular prism A polyhedron whose bases are rectangles and whose other faces are parallelograms.	**prisma rectangular** Poliedro cuyas bases son rectángulos y cuyas caras tienen forma de paralelogramo.	
reduction A decrease in the size of all dimensions.	**reducción** Disminución de tamaño en todas las dimensiones de una figura.	
reflection A transformation of a figure that flips the figure across a line.	**reflexión** Transformación que ocurre cuando se invierte una figura sobre una línea.	
regular polygon A polygon with congruent sides and angles.	**polígono regular** Polígono con lados y ángulos congruentes.	
regular pyramid A pyramid whose base is a regular polygon and whose lateral faces are all congruent.	**pirámide regular** Pirámide que tiene un polígono regular como base y caras laterales congruentes.	
relation A set of ordered pairs.	**relación** Conjunto de pares ordenados.	(0, 5), (0, 4), (2, 3), (4, 0)
relative frequency The frequency of a specific data value divided by the total number of data values in the set.	**frecuencia relativa** La frecuencia de un valor dividido por el número total de los valores en el conjunto.	

© Houghton Mifflin Harcourt Publishing Company

Glossary/Glosario

Glossary/Glosario

ENGLISH	SPANISH	EXAMPLES
relatively prime Two numbers are relatively prime if their greatest common factor (GCF) is 1.	**primo relativo** Dos números son primos relativos si su máximo común divisor (MCD) es 1.	8 and 15 are relatively prime.
remote interior angle An interior angle of a polygon that is not adjacent to the exterior angle.	**ángulo interno remoto** Ángulo interno de un polígono que no es adyacente al ángulo externo.	
repeating decimal A decimal in which one or more digits repeat infinitely.	**decimal periódico** Decimal en el que uno o más dígitos se repiten infinitamente.	$0.757575\ldots = 0.\overline{75}$
rhombus A parallelogram with all sides congruent.	**rombo** Paralelogramo en el que todos los lados son congruentes.	
right angle An angle that measures 90°.	**ángulo recto** Ángulo que mide exactamente 90°.	
right cone A cone in which a perpendicular line drawn from the base to the tip (vertex) passes through the center of the base.	**cono regular** Cono en el que una línea perpendicular trazada de la base a la punta (vértice) pasa por el centro de la base.	Right cone
right triangle A triangle containing a right angle.	**triángulo rectángulo** Triángulo que tiene un ángulo recto.	
rise The vertical change when the slope of a line is expressed as the ratio $\frac{\text{rise}}{\text{run}}$, or "rise over run."	**distancia vertical** El cambio vertical cuando la pendiente de una línea se expresa como la razón $\frac{\text{distancia vertical}}{\text{distancia horizontal}}$, o "distancia vertical sobre distancia horizontal".	For the points $(3, -1)$ and $(6, 5)$, the rise is $5 - (-1) = 6$.
rotation A transformation in which a figure is turned around a point.	**rotación** Transformación que ocurre cuando una figura gira alrededor de un punto.	
rotational symmetry A figure has rotational symmetry if it can be rotated less than 360° around a central point and coincide with the original figure.	**simetría de rotación** Ocurre cuando una figura gira menos de 360° alrededor de un punto central sin dejar de ser congruente con la figura original.	90° 90° 90° 90°

© Houghton Mifflin Harcourt Publishing Company

run The horizontal change when the slope of a line is expressed as the ratio $\frac{\text{rise}}{\text{run}}$, or "rise over run."

distancia horizontal El cambio horizontal cuando la pendiente de una línea se expresa como la razón $\frac{\text{distancia vertical}}{\text{distancia horizontal}}$, o "distancia vertical sobre distancia horizontal".

For the points (3, −1) and (6, 5), the run is 6 − 3 = 3.

sales tax A percent of the cost of an item that is charged by governments to raise money.

impuesto sobre la venta Porcentaje del costo de un artículo que los gobiernos cobran para recaudar fondos.

---

same-side interior angles A pair of angles on the same side of a transversal and between two lines intersected by the transversal.

ángulo internos del mismo lado Dadas dos rectas cortadas por una transversal, par de ángulos ubicados en el mismo lado de la transversal y entre las dos rectas.

---

sample A part of the population.

muestra Una parte de la población.

---

sample space All possible outcomes of an experiment.

espacio muestral Conjunto de todos los resultados posibles de un experimento.

When rolling a number cube, the sample space is 1, 2, 3, 4, 5, 6.

---

scale The ratio between two sets of measurements.

escala La razón entre dos conjuntos de medidas.

1 cm : 5 mi

---

scale drawing A drawing that uses a scale to make an object smaller than (a reduction) or larger than (an enlargement) the real object.

dibujo a escala Dibujo en el que se usa una escala para que un objeto se vea menor (reducción) o mayor (agrandamiento) que el objeto real al que representa.

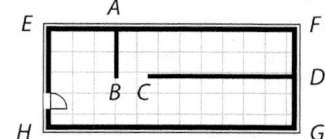

A blueprint is an example of a scale drawing.

---

scale factor The ratio used to enlarge or reduce similar figures.

factor de escala Razón empleada para agrandar o reducir figuras semejantes.

---

scale model A proportional model of a three-dimensional object.

modelo a escala Modelo proporcional de un objeto tridimensional.

---

scalene triangle A triangle with no congruent sides.

triángulo escaleno Triángulo que no tiene lados congruentes.

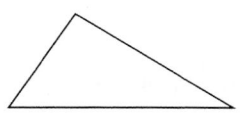

---

scatter plot A graph with points plotted to show a possible relationship between two sets of data.

diagrama de dispersión Gráfica de puntos que muestra una posible relación entre dos conjuntos de datos.

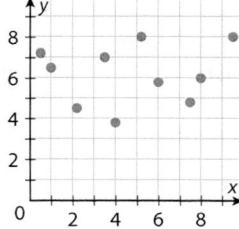

© Houghton Mifflin Harcourt Publishing Company

Glossary/Glosario

ENGLISH	SPANISH	EXAMPLES
scientific notation A method of writing very large or very small numbers by using powers of 10.	**notación científica** Método que se usa para escribir números muy grandes o muy pequeños mediante potencias de 10.	$12{,}560{,}000{,}000{,}000 = 1.256 \times 10^{13}$
second quartile The median of a set of data.	**segundo cuartil** Mediana de un conjunto de datos.	Data set: 4, 6, 7, 8, 10 Second quartile: 7
segment A part of a line between two endpoints.	**segmento** Parte de una línea entre dos extremos.	
self-selected sample A sample in which members choose to be in the sample.	**muestra auto-seleccionada** Una muestra en la que los miembros eligen participar.	A store provides survey cards for customers who choose to fill them out.
sequence An ordered list of numbers.	**sucesión** Lista ordenada de números.	2, 4, 6, 8, 10, …
side A line bounding a geometric figure; one of the faces forming the outside of an object.	**lado** Línea que delimita las figuras geométricas; una de las caras que forman la parte exterior de un objeto.	
similar Figures with the same shape but not necessarily the same size.	**semejantes** Figuras que tienen la misma forma, pero no necesariamente el mismo tamaño.	
similarity transformation A transformation that results in an image that is the same shape, but not necessarily the same size, as the original figure.	**transformación de semejanza** Una transformación que resulta en una imagen que tiene la misma forma, pero no necesariamente el mismo tamaño como la figura original.	
simple interest A fixed percent of the principal. It is found using the formula $I = Prt$, where P represents the principal, r the rate of interest, and t the time.	**interés simple** Un porcentaje fijo del capital. Se calcula con la fórmula $I = Cit$, donde C representa el capital, i, la tasa de interés y t, el tiempo.	$100 is put into an account with a simple interest rate of 5%. After 2 years, the account will have earned $I = 100 \cdot 0.05 \cdot 2 = \$10$.
simplest form A fraction in which the numerator and denominator have no common factors other than 1.	**mínima expresión** Una fracción está en su mínima expresión cuando el numerador y el denominador no tienen más factor común que 1.	Fraction: $\frac{8}{12}$ Simplest form: $\frac{2}{3}$
simplify To write a fraction or expression in simplest form.	**simplificar** Escribir una fracción o expresión numérica en su mínima expresión.	
simulation A model of an experiment, often one that would be too difficult or too time-consuming to actually perform.	**simulación** Representación de un experimento, por lo general, de uno cuya realización sería demasiado difícil o llevaría mucho tiempo.	

© Houghton Mifflin Harcourt Publishing Company

	ENGLISH	SPANISH	EXAMPLES

slant height (of a regular pyramid) The distance from the vertex of a regular pyramid to the midpoint of an edge of the base.

altura inclinada (de una pirámide) Distancia desde el vértice de una pirámide hasta el punto medio de una arista de la base.

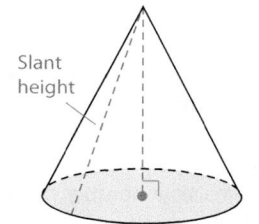

Regular pyramid

---

slant height (of a right cone) The distance from the vertex of a right cone to a point on the edge of the base.

altura inclinada (de un cono recto) Distancia desde el vértice de un cono recto hasta un punto en el borde de la base.

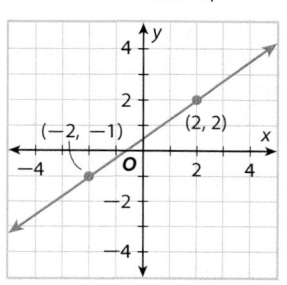

Slant height

---

slope A measure of the steepness of a line on a graph; the rise divided by the run.

pendiente Medida de la inclinación de una línea en una gráfica. Razón de la distancia vertical a la distancia horizontal.

$\text{Slope} = \frac{\text{rise}}{\text{run}} = \frac{3}{4}$

$(-2, -1)$ $(2, 2)$

---

slope-intercept form A linear equation written in the form $y = mx + b$, where m represents slope and b represents the y-intercept.

forma de pendiente-intersección Ecuación lineal escrita en la forma $y = mx + b$, donde m es la pendiente y b es la intersección con el eje y.

$y = 6x - 3$

---

solution of an equation A value or values that make an equation true.

solución de una ecuación Valor o valores que hacen verdadera una ecuación.

Equation: $x + 2 = 6$
Solution: $x = 4$

---

solution of an inequality A value or values that make an inequality true.

solución de una desigualdad Valor o valores que hacen verdadera una desigualdad.

Inequality: $x + 3 \geq 10$
Solution: $x \geq 7$

---

solution of a system of equations A set of values that make all equations in a system true.

solución de un sistema de ecuaciones Conjunto de valores que hacen verdaderas todas las ecuaciones de un sistema.

System: $\begin{cases} x + y = -1 \\ -x + y = -3 \end{cases}$
Solution: $(1, -2)$

---

solution set The set of values that make a statement true.

conjunto solución Conjunto de valores que hacen verdadero un enunciado.

Inequality: $x + 3 \geq 5$
Solution set: $x \geq 2$

$-4 \ -3 \ -2 \ -1 \ 0 \ 1 \ 2 \ 3 \ 4 \ 5 \ 6$

---

solve To find an answer or a solution.

resolver Hallar una respuesta o solución.

© Houghton Mifflin Harcourt Publishing Company

Glossary/Glosario

ENGLISH	SPANISH	EXAMPLES
sphere A three-dimensional figure with all points the same distance from the center.	**esfera** Figura tridimensional en la que todos los puntos están a la misma distancia del centro.	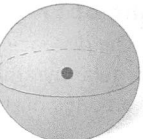
square A rectangle with four congruent sides.	**cuadrado** Rectángulo con cuatro lados congruentes.	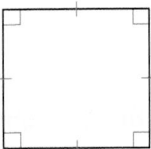
square (numeration) A number raised to the second power.	**cuadrado (en numeración)** Número elevado a la segunda potencia.	In 5^2, the number 5 is squared.
square root A number that is multiplied by itself to form a product is called a square root of that product.	**raíz cuadrada** El número que se multiplica por sí mismo para formar un producto se denomina la raíz cuadrada de ese producto.	A square root of 16 is 4, because $4^2 = 4 \cdot 4 = 16$. Another square root of 16 is -4 because $(-4)^2 = (-4)(-4) = 16$.
stem-and-leaf plot A graph used to organize and display data so that the frequencies can be compared.	**diagrama de tallo y hojas** Gráfica que muestra y ordena los datos, y que sirve para comparar las frecuencias.	Stem | Leaves 3 | 2 3 4 4 7 9 4 | 0 1 5 7 7 7 8 5 | 1 2 2 3 *Key: 3|2 means 3.2*
straight angle An angle that measures 180°.	**ángulo llano** Ángulo que mide exactamente 180°.	← • →
substitute To replace a variable with a number or another expression in an algebraic expression.	**sustituir** Reemplazar una variable por un número u otra expresión en una expresión algebraica.	Substituting 3 for m in the expression $5m - 2$ gives $5(3) - 2 = 15 - 2 = 13$.
Subtraction Property of Equality The property that states that if you subtract the same number from both sides of an equation, the new equation will have the same solution.	**Propiedad de igualdad de la resta** Propiedad que establece que puedes restar el mismo número de ambos lados de una ecuación y la nueva ecuación tendrá la misma solución.	$14 - 6 = 8$ $\underline{-6 = -6}$ $14 - 12 = 2$
supplementary angles Two angles whose measures have a sum of 180°.	**ángulos suplementarios** Dos ángulos cuyas medidas suman 180°.	30° \\ 150°
surface area The sum of the areas of the faces, or surfaces, of a three-dimensional figure.	**área total** Suma de las áreas de las caras, o superficies, de una figura tridimensional.	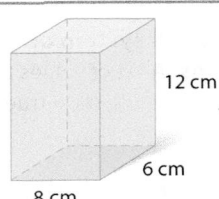 12 cm 6 cm 8 cm Surface area = 2(8)(12) + 2(8)(6) + 2(12)(6) = 432 cm²

© Houghton Mifflin Harcourt Publishing Company

ENGLISH	SPANISH	EXAMPLES
system of equations A set of two or more equations that contain two or more variables.	**sistema de ecuaciones** Conjunto de dos o más ecuaciones que contienen dos o más variables.	$\begin{cases} x + y = -1 \\ -x + y = -3 \end{cases}$
systematic sample A sample of a population that has been selected using a pattern.	**muestra sistemática** Muestra de una población, que ha sido elegida mediante un patrón.	To conduct a phone survey, every tenth name is chosen from the phone book.

T

ENGLISH	SPANISH	EXAMPLES
term (in an expression) A part of an expression that is added or subtracted.	**término (en una expresión)** Las partes de una expresión que se suman o se restan.	$3x^2 \quad + \quad 6x \quad - \quad 8$ Term Term Term
term (in a sequence) An element or number in a sequence.	**término (en una sucesión)** Elemento o número de una sucesión.	5 is the third term in the sequence 1, 3, 5, 7, 9, …
terminating decimal A decimal number that ends, or terminates.	**decimal finito** Decimal con un número determinado de posiciones decimales.	6.75
tessellation A repeating pattern of plane figures that completely cover a plane with no gaps or overlaps.	**teselado** Patrón repetido de figuras planas que cubren totalmente un plano sin superponerse ni dejar huecos.	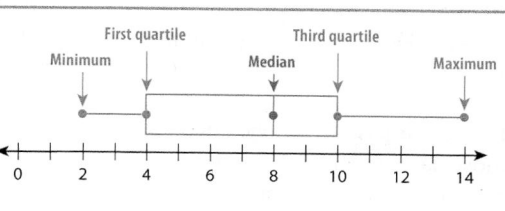
theoretical probability The ratio of the number of ways an event can occur to the number of equally likely outcomes.	**probabilidad teórica** Razón del número de las maneras que puede ocurrir un suceso al numero total de resultados igualmente probables.	When rolling a number cube, the theoretical probability of rolling a 4 is $\frac{1}{6}$.
third quartile The median of the upper half of a set of data; also called *upper quartile*.	**tercer cuartil** La mediana de la mitad superior de un conjunto de datos. También se llama *cuartil superior*.	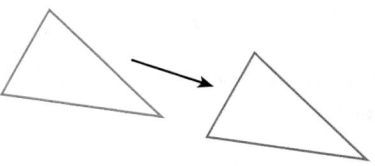
transformation A change in the size or position of a figure.	**transformación** Cambio en el tamaño o la posición de una figura.	
translation A movement (slide) of a figure along a straight line.	**traslación** Desplazamiento de una figura a lo largo de una línea recta.	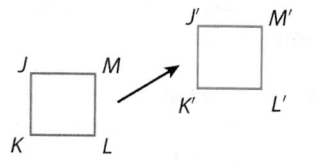

© Houghton Mifflin Harcourt Publishing Company

Glossary/Glosario

transversal A line that intersects two or more lines.

transversal Línea que cruza dos o más líneas.

---

trapezoid A quadrilateral with at least one pair of parallel sides.

trapecio Cuadrilátero con al menos un par de lados paralelos.

---

tree diagram A branching diagram that shows all possible combinations or outcomes of an event.

diagrama de árbol Diagrama ramificado que muestra todas las posibles combinaciones o resultados de un suceso.

H   T

1 2 3 4 5 6   1 2 3 4 5 6

---

trend line A line on a scatter plot that helps show the correlation between data sets more clearly.

línea de tendencia Línea en un diagrama de dispersión que sirve para mostrar la correlación entre conjuntos de datos más claramente. *ver también* línea de mejor ajuste.

---

trial Each repetition or observation of an experiment.

prueba Una sola repetición u observación de un experimento.

When rolling a number cube, each roll is one trial.

Triangle Inequality Theorem The theorem that states that the sum of the lengths of any two sides of a triangle is greater than the length of the third side.

Teorema de desigualdad de triángulos El teorema dice que la suma de cualquier dos lados de un triangulo es mayor que la longitud del lado tercero.

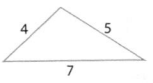

Can form a triangle

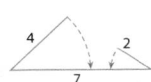

Cannot form a triangle

Triangle Sum Theorem The theorem that states that the measures of the angles in a triangle add up to 180°.

Teorema de la suma del triángulo Teorema que establece que las medidas de los ángulos de un triángulo suman 180°.

---

triangular prism A polyhedron whose bases are triangles and whose other faces are parallelograms.

prisma triangular Poliedro cuyas bases son triángulos y cuyas demás caras tienen forma de paralelogramo.

---

trinomial A polynomial with three terms.

trinomio Polinomio con tres términos.

$4x^2 + 3xy - 5y^2$

---

two-way relative frequency table A two-way table that displays relative frequencies.

tabla de frecuencia relativa de doble entrada Una tabla de doble entrada que muestran las frecuencias relativas.

---

two-way table A table that displays two-variable data by organizing it into rows and columns.

tabla de doble entrada Una tabla que muestran los datos de dos variables por organizándolos en columnas y filas.

	Preference		
Pet	**Inside**	**Outside**	*Total*
Cats	35	15	50
Dogs	20	30	50
Total	55	45	100

© Houghton Mifflin Harcourt Publishing Company

unit conversion The process of changing one unit of measure to another.

conversión de unidades Proceso que consiste en cambiar una unidad de medida por otra.

---

unit conversion factor A fraction used in unit conversion in which the numerator and denominator represent the same amount but are in different units.

factor de conversión de unidades Fracción que se usa para la conversión de unidades, donde el numerador y el denominador representan la misma cantidad pero están en unidades distintas.

$\frac{60 \text{ min}}{1 \text{ h}}$ or $\frac{1 \text{ h}}{60 \text{ min}}$

---

unit price A unit rate used to compare prices.

precio unitario Tasa unitaria que sirve para comparar precios.

Cereal costs $0.23 per ounce.

---

unit rate A rate in which the second quantity in the comparison is one unit.

tasa unitaria Una tasa en la que la segunda cantidad de la comparación es la unidad.

10 cm per minute

variability The spread of values in a set of data.

variabilidad Amplitud de los valores de un conjunto de datos.

The data set {1, 5, 7, 10, 25} has greater variability than the data set {8, 8, 9, 9, 9}.

---

variable A symbol used to represent a quantity that can change.

variable Símbolo que representa una cantidad que puede cambiar.

In the expression $2x + 3$, x is the variable.

Venn diagram A diagram that is used to show relationships between sets.

diagrama de Venn Diagrama que muestra las relaciones entre conjuntos.

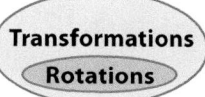

---

vertex On an angle or polygon, the point where two sides intersect; on a polyhedron, the intersection of three or more faces; on a cone or pyramid, the top point.

vértice En un ángulo o polígono, el punto de intersección de dos lados; en un poliedro, el punto de intersección de tres o más caras; en un cono o pirámide, la punta.

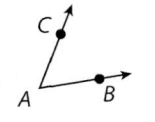

A is the vertex of $\angle CAB$.

---

vertical angles A pair of opposite congruent angles formed by intersecting lines.

ángulos opuestos por el vértice Par de ángulos opuestos congruentes formados por líneas secantes.

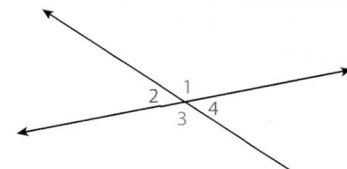

$\angle 1$ and $\angle 3$ are vertical angles.

© Houghton Mifflin Harcourt Publishing Company

Glossary/Glosario

vertical line test A test used to determine whether a relation is a function. If any vertical line crosses the graph of a relation more than once, the relation is not a function.

prueba de la línea vertical Prueba utilizada para determinar si una relación es una función. Si una línea vertical corta la gráfica de una relación más de una vez, la relación no es una función.

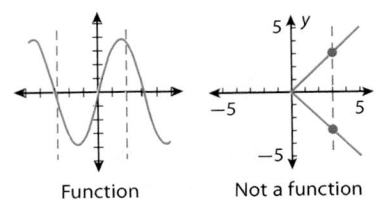

Function   Not a function

volume The number of cubic units needed to fill a given space.

volumen Número de unidades cúbicas que se necesitan para llenar un espacio.

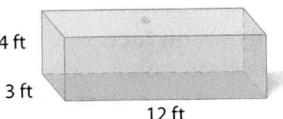

4 ft

3 ft

12 ft

Volume = $3 \cdot 4 \cdot 12 = 144$ ft^3

weighted average A mean that is calculated by multiplying each data value by a weight, and dividing the sum of these products by the sum of the weights.

promedio ponderado Promedio que se calcula por multiplicando cada valor de datos por un peso, y dividiendo la suma de estos productos por la suma de los pesos.

If the data values 0, 5, and 10 are assigned the weights 0.1, 0.2, and 0.7, respectively, the weighted average is:

$$\frac{0(0.1) + 5(0.2) + 10(0.7)}{0.1 + 0.2 + 0.7} = \frac{8}{1}$$

x-axis The horizontal axis on a coordinate plane.

eje x El eje horizontal del plano cartesiano.

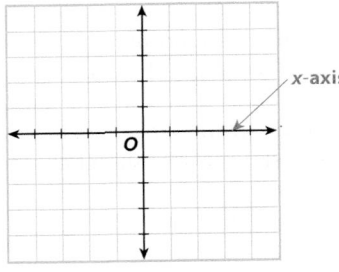

x-axis

O

x-coordinate The first number in an ordered pair; it tells the distance to move right or left from the origin (0, 0).

coordenada x El primer número de un par ordenado; indica la distancia que debes moverte hacia la izquierda o la derecha desde el origen, (0, 0).

5 is the x-coordinate in (5, 3).

x-intercept The x-coordinate of the point where the graph of a line crosses the x-axis.

intersección con el eje x Coordenada x del punto donde la gráfica de una línea cruza el eje x.

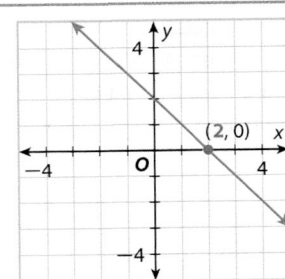

(2, 0)

The x-intercept is 2.

© Houghton Mifflin Harcourt Publishing Company

Y

y-axis The vertical axis on a coordinate plane.

eje y El eje vertical del plano cartesiano.

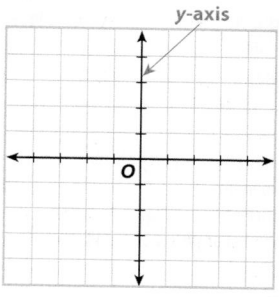

y-coordinate The second number in an ordered pair; it tells the distance to move up or down from the origin (0, 0).

coordenada y El segundo número de un par ordenado; indica la distancia que debes avanzar hacia arriba o hacia abajo desde el origen, (0, 0).

3 is the y-coordinate in (5, 3).

y-intercept The y-coordinate of the point where the graph of a line crosses the y-axis.

intersección con el eje y Coordenada y del punto donde la gráfica de una línea cruza el eje y.

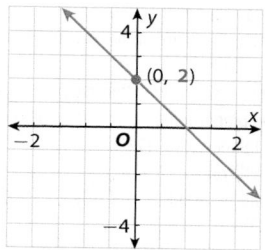

The y-intercept is 2.

Z

zero pair A number and its opposite, which add to 0.

par nulo Un número y su opuesto, cuya suma es 0.

18 and -18

© Houghton Mifflin Harcourt Publishing Company

Glossary/Glosario

Index

© Houghton Mifflin Harcourt Publishing Company

Commutative Property, 308

compare
- costs, 198–199
- functions, 167–172
- graphs and descriptions, 169–170
- irrational numbers, 21, 24
- proportional and nonproportional relationships, 116–117
- tables and equations, 167–168
- unit rates, 85

conditional relative frequency, 450, 460, 462–464

cones
- defined, 342, 398
- volume of, 405–410

congruence, 304
- algebraic representations of transformations, 297–302
- of reflections, 285–290, 303
- of rotations, 291–296, 303–308
- of translations, 279–284, 304–306

congruent angles, 361, 362

congruent figures, 303–308
- combining transformations, 303
- defined, 304
- sequences of transformations for, 304–305

constant of proportionality, 72, 73, 84

constants, 261

coordinate plane, 374
- dilations on, 316–317
- Distance Formula in, 388–390
- Pythagorean Theorem in, 387–388
- rectangles and parallelograms on, 81
- translations in, 281–282

corresponding angles, 280, 347, 348, 363

costs
- comparing, 171, 198–199
- total, 153, 198–199

Counterexamples, 308, 444

Critical Thinking, 20, 46, 88, 103, 112, 213, 234, 284, 290, 302, 320, 325, 351, 360, 368, 406, 438

Critique Reasoning, 20, 26, 37, 38, 50, 82, 100, 106, 146, 208, 220, 326, 352, 368, 386, 406, 410, 444, 464

cube, perfect, 9

cube root, 9

cubic units, 399

cycling, 88

cylinders, 342, 398–404

D
---

data
- association in sets of, 435–438
- bivariate, 66, 126, 142–143, 433
- categorizing frequencies of. *See* two-way tables
- linear and nonlinear, 142–143
- on scatter plots, 433–438

decimal coefficient, 192

decimals
- approximating irrational numbers as, 21
- equations with variables on both sides involving, 204–205

expressed as rational numbers, 8–9, 12
- rational numbers expressed as, 7–8, 12
- repeating, 2, 7
  - bar indicating, 7
  - defined, 7
  - expressed as rational numbers, 8
- in scientific notation, 39–41, 45–48
- terminating, 7
  - defined, 7
  - expressed as rational numbers, 8
- writing fractions as, 7–8
- written as fractions, 8–9

depth, volume and, 401

diameter
- in scientific notation, 45, 47, 49
- and volume, 400, 401, 413

dilations, 274, 315–320
- algebraic representations of, 321–326
- center of dilation, 315
- in creating animations, 327–332
- in creating similar figures, 327–329
- of quadrilaterals, 316
- of rectangles, 318
- of triangles, 315–316, 331

distance
- Distance Formula, 388–390
- from Earth to Moon and Neptune, 37
- estimating, 23, 25
- leagues, 71–72
- miles, 71–72
- ordering, 23
- Pythagorean Theorem for, 387–392
- rate of change, 78, 80
- in scientific notation, 40
- unit rate and slope, 84
- written as decimals, 13

Distributive Property, 209–214
- on both sides of equations, 210
- in solving equations, 209
- in solving real-world problems, 211

division
- with scientific notation, 52–54
- of two powers with the same base, 34

Draw Conclusions, 14, 19, 20, 38, 44, 49, 88, 108, 159, 166, 202, 208, 258, 263, 264, 332, 352, 360, 382, 386, 464

duration, 434

E

Earth, 37, 40, 73

elimination method
- defined, 243
- solving systems by, 243–250, 261
  - with addition, 243–252
  - with multiplication, 251–258
  - with subtraction, 245–250, 253–254

enlargements, 274, 317, 321–322

entomology, 43

equations
- comparing tables and, 167–168
- defined, 192

to distinguish between proportional vs. nonproportional relationships, 114
- linear. *See* linear equations
- with many solutions or no solutions, 215–220, 259–264
  - determining number of solutions, 215–216, 263
  - infinitely many, 218–220, 259–264
  - writing, with a given number of solutions, 216–217
- for proportional relationships, 72, 73, 85
- simplifying, 215–216
- slope-intercept form of, 101–112, 127–130, 230
- solving with Distributive Property, 209–214
- systems of, 228–231, 235–264
  - solved by elimination, 243–250, 261
  - solved by elimination with multiplication, 251–258
  - solved by substitution, 235–242, 260
  - special systems, 259–264
- of a trend line, 440–441
- with variables on both sides, 197–202
  - inverse operations for, 198–199, 203, 205
  - involving decimals, 204–205
  - involving fractions, 203–204
  - modeling, 197–198
  - with rational numbers, 203–208
  - solving, 198–199
  - using Distributive Property for, 210
  - writing real-world situations from, 199–200, 205–206

equilateral triangles, 367

equivalent expressions, 36

Error Analysis, 166

Essential Question. *Essential Question appears in every lesson. See, for example,* 7, 15, 21, 27, 39, 45, 71, 77, 89

estimation
- distance, 23, 25
- of irrational numbers, 10–11
- length, 25
- of solution of systems, 237–238, 240

Euler's number, 26

Europe, 53

Explain the Error, 20, 44, 56, 112, 146, 202, 208, 214, 250, 257

exponents
- addition of, 37
- defined, 32
- equivalent expressions using properties of, 36
- integer, 33–38
  - applying properties of, 35, 36
  - exploring properties of, 34–35
  - using patterns of, 33
- negative, 45–47
- positive, 39–41

expressions
- comparing costs, 198–199
- Distance Formula, 388–390
- equivalent, using properties of exponents, 36
- functions, 158

© Houghton Mifflin Harcourt Publishing Company

© Houghton Mifflin Harcourt Publishing Company

© Houghton Mifflin Harcourt Publishing Company

Index

© Houghton Mifflin Harcourt Publishing Company

Index

© Houghton Mifflin Harcourt Publishing Company

Index

© Houghton Mifflin Harcourt Publishing Company

ASSESSMENT REFERENCE SHEET

TABLE OF MEASURES

Length

1 inch = 2.54 centimeters

1 meter ≈ 39.37 inches

1 mile = 5,280 feet

1 mile = 1,760 yards

1 mile ≈ 1.609 kilometers

1 kilometer ≈ 0.62 mile

Mass/Weight

1 pound = 16 ounces

1 pound ≈ 0.454 kilogram

1 kilogram ≈ 2.2 pounds

1 ton = 2,000 pounds

Capacity

1 cup = 8 fluid ounces

1 pint = 2 cups

1 quart = 2 pints

1 gallon = 4 quarts

1 gallon ≈ 3.785 liters

1 liter ≈ 0.264 gallon

1 liter = 1000 cubic centimeters

FORMULAS

Area

Parallelogram	$A = bh$
Circle	$A = \pi r^2$
Triangle	$A = \frac{1}{2} bh$

Circumference

Circle	$C = \pi d$ or $C = 2\pi r$

Volume

General Prisms	$V = Bh$
Cylinder	$V = \pi r^2 h$
Sphere	$V = \frac{4}{3} \pi r^3$
Cone	$V = \frac{1}{3} \pi r^2 h$

Other

Pythagorean Theorem	$a^2 + b^2 = c^2$

© Houghton Mifflin Harcourt Publishing Company